# Living Things

# Living Things

Biology is about our whole being—our very existence. Yet most people assume it is a subject only for the experts. The great advances in our knowledge during the 19th and 20th Centuries have, until now, meant relatively little to the layman. Now he is asking questions in a new and more acute way—and is demanding answers.

This book attempts to convey in an authoritative yet straightforward manner at least part—if not all—of those answers.

Here is a unique guide to an enthralling subject. It explains simply, yet graphically, how life has developed since the very beginnings. The book also deals with other living things. It explains how animals conduct themselves as individuals and social groups. It describes in detail the essential role played by the plant world in sustaining life.

Here is biology brought into perspective for everyone. All the main areas are covered in a compulsive and easily followed way. The book serves as an indispensable background to new developments and gives the layman a chance to assess their significance.

Marshall Cavendish, London

*Published by Marshall Cavendish Publications Ltd,*
*58 Old Compton Street,*
*London, W1V 5PA.*



*This material was first published by*
*Marshall Cavendish Ltd, in the partwork* Mind Alive

*This volume first printed 1973*

*Printed by Henri Proost, Turnhout, Belgium.*

*ISBN 0 85685 009 8*

# Picture Credits

Robert G. Milne, Virus Laboratory, University of California, Berkeley
UK Atomic Energy Authority
Ken Moreman
Mansell
Bayerische Staatsbibliothek, Munich
Barnaby's Picture Library
U.S. Information Service
Gordon Leedale
Photo Researchers
South African Government Tourist Office
Brian Ford
R. W. Horne
*Virology*
British Museum
R. B. Fleming
Technische Hogeschool, Delft
*British Medical Journal*
Dr. T. F. Anderson
Institute of Biophysics
University of Geneva
Dr. Kenneth W. Fisher
French Government Tourist Office
Mount Wilson and Palomar Observatories
Picturepoint
Dr. M. N. Bramlette
Novosti Press
*Radio Times* Hulton Picture Library
Popperfoto
Dr. E. H. Mercer, University of California
*Time Life* Incorporated
Stephen Dalton
Des Bartlett
W. Warwick James
Mullard
W. Grant
Margiocci
George Hyde
Valerie Finnis
Malayan Rubber Board
H. Smith
Jane Burton
Charles Ott
A. C. Moore
Neville Clayton
South African Embassy
Sally Anne Thompson
Press Association
Alginate Industries
Heather Angel
Colin Doeg
Church Missionary Society
H. M. Stationery Office
Geological Survey
Frank Lane
Linnaean Society
John Freeman
Natural History Photographic Agency
Dr. C. Mer
ARC Unit of Plant Physiology
Mrs. H. Stevenson-Hamilton
Treat Davidson
Bill Ratcliffe
Arthur Christiansen
Russ Kinne
Hawker Siddeley Aviation
San Diego Zoo

R. van Nostrand
Ronald Austin
H. V. Lacey

Richard L. Cassell
Rossi Adolf
Paul Lemmons
Merlyn Severn
Philip Yaffe
Dr. B. M. G. Jones
A. D. Webb
Ampleforth College Natural History Society
Hugh Newman
D. L. Ebbels
Hugh Spencer
John C. Pitkin
Fritz Siedel
Lynwood M. Chace
Sistine Chapel, Rome
Geological Museum, London
R. B. Fleming
Brooklyn National Laboratory, New York
Plant Breeding Institute, Cambridge
C. G. Vosa, Botany School, Oxford
B. S. Cox, Oxford University
Rentokil Laboratories
Heinz Schrempp
E. V. Watson
Clive Jermy
Shell
Rijksmuseum, Amsterdam
Forestry Commission
Maurice Nimmo
J. K. Burras
Douglas P. Wilson
Geoffrey Kinns
Marineland of Florida
Stephanie Manchipp
David Attenborough
Edwin Way Teale
Walter Rohdich
Roy A. Harris
K. R. Duff
Arthur Hayward
Fox Photos
Transworld Features
Eric Hosking
Parke Davis
Natural Science Photos
Leonard Lee Rue III
V-DIA Verlag
A. K. Kleinschmidt
Walter Jarchow, Banting and Best Dept. of Medical Research, University of Toronto
L. C. Luckwill
Peter Hinchliffe
D. C. Honsowetz
Hugh B. Cott
Methuen
Institute of Ophthalmology
Lennart Nilsson
Bruce Coleman, Ltd
Armand Denis Productions
Ludwig Harren
Norman Myers
B. H. Reed
Ron Garrison
S. C. Bisserot
Russ E. Hutchins

Wisconsin Regional Primate Research Centre
Graham Pizzey
Dr. R. Bott
Ronald Thompson
Masood Quarishy
B. D. Wyke
British Aircraft Corporation
Micro Colour (International)
Geoffrey Chamberlain
Miss V. J. Bailey
F. D. Roosevelt School, London
Andrew Lanyon
William Vandivert
Dr. J. A. L. Cooke
Dr. D. P. Wilson
P. H. Ward
Tierbilder Okapia
Professor E. W. Knight-Jones
S. R. Pelling
John Gooders
Jack van Coevering
John Armitage, FRPS
H. Hoflinger
Dr. R. J. Muller
Fish and Wildlife Service, US Dept of the Interior
Gerhard Gronefeld
S. C. Porter
Jacana
Pierre Auradon
W. Sands
Colin Butter
C. G. Butler
Phillipa Scott
M. P. Harris
Norman Myers
P. H. Ward
James Simon
Simon Trevor
Robert S. Bailey
Philip A. Du Mont
P. Scoones
E. Lodge
D. J. Shillcock
S. C. Bisserot
C. M. Dixon
National Vegetable Research Station, Wellesbourne
K. Oldroyd
*Farmer and Stockbreeder*
Museum of English Rural Life, Reading
Food and Agriculture Organisation
Ministry of Agriculture, Fisheries and Food
Fitzwilliam Museum, Cambridge
U.S. Department of Agriculture
Central Electricity Generating Board
Kodak
Polaroid
Professor Henry Harris
Australian Atomic Energy Commission
Fisons
Shandon-Elliott
R. Harvey
National Institute for Medical Research
British Food Manufacturers
Industrial Research Association
Ian Yeomans
Sue Gooders
Horniman Museum

Peter David
M. Alison Wilson
H. Lou Gibson
Lawrence Perkins
Robert C. Hermes
Alan Root
Australian Information Service
Glasshouse Crops Research Institute
J. Taylor
South West Optical Instruments
Gene Cox
Cavendish Laboratory, Cambridge
Michael Holford
Wellcome Trustees
*Radio Times* Hulton Picture Library
Mary Evans Picture Library
J. Allan Cash
John Markham
Ronan Picture Library
Keystone
Rex Features
Ordnance Survey
W. J. Garnett
*Daily Telegraph*
Vu Picture Agency
Mondadoripress
Anton Last
Spectrum
Eric Jewell Associates
Barratts

# Contents

# How did life begin?

**Spontaneous generation – perhaps a sudden act of divine intervention – or a development over millions of years of ever more complex molecules? Today's biologists may be close to the answer.**

FOR THOUSANDS of years men have been trying to discover the secret of living things and find out how life began. What is it that makes one collection of atoms and molecules into a living organism, such as a flea or a man, and another collection of atoms and molecules into an inanimate object like a rock or a bridge? The complete answer to this question has yet to be found, although scientific evidence has steadily accumulated over the centuries, so that today the theories about the origin of life are more informed than ever before. But they are still only theories.

The puzzle of life is enormous. As the physicist J. D. Bernal has pointed out, even stating this problem is beyond the reach of any one scientist. For such a scientist would have to be a competent mathematician, physicist and organic chemist, all at the same time. He would also need an extensive knowledge of geology, geophysics and geochemistry and be completely at home in all the biological sciences. Bernal suggests that, sooner or later, this problem will have to be given to groups of scientists representing all these disciplines working closely together on experiments and theories.

## Did life arise spontaneously?

One of the earliest theories of the origin of life, the Theory of Spontaneous Generation, was proposed by the early Greek philosopher Aristotle. It was based on the evidence of the senses. Do not maggots come from decaying meat, mice from corn, and worms from mud? Then is not all life created spontaneously?

This theory was held universally until the seventeenth century, when Francesco Redi showed that the maggots in decaying flesh are grubs from the eggs of flies. But the theory was again favoured when the Dutchman Anton van Leeuwenhoek saw bacteria for the first time with the aid of his primitive microscope. Where did these bacteria come from except from decaying matter itself? Biologists disputed for nearly 200 years about the true nature of bacteria. Then, in a series of brilliant experiments, Louis Pasteur demonstrated that bacteria live on other organisms and so cannot be an original form of life.

Charles Darwin was the first scientist to trace life back systematically to an 'original' source. According to Darwin, the higher forms of life have evolved from lower forms. He found evidence for this theory, now generally accepted, in fossils, which show that the oldest forms of living matter that have left traces may date back as much as 700 million years.

Not long after Darwin proposed his theory of the origin of species, the physicist John Tyndall postulated that every part of a living organism can be reduced to inorganic matter. There may be a great difference between a man and a rock, but the conventional division between living things and non-living things is artificial and there is no chemical difference between the two. Tyndall believed that it is the special arrangements of the elements of a living body that produce the phenomenon of life.

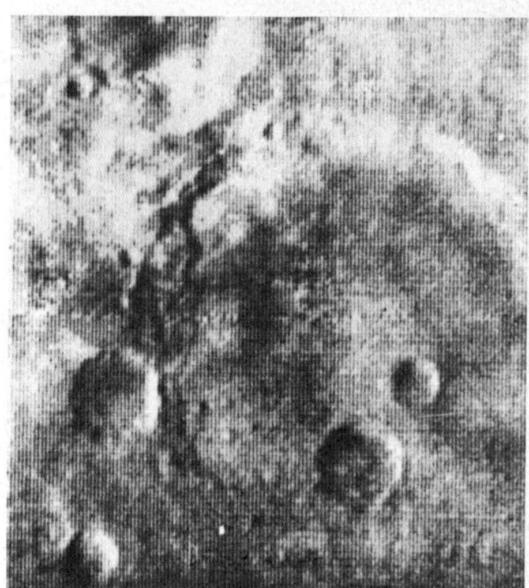

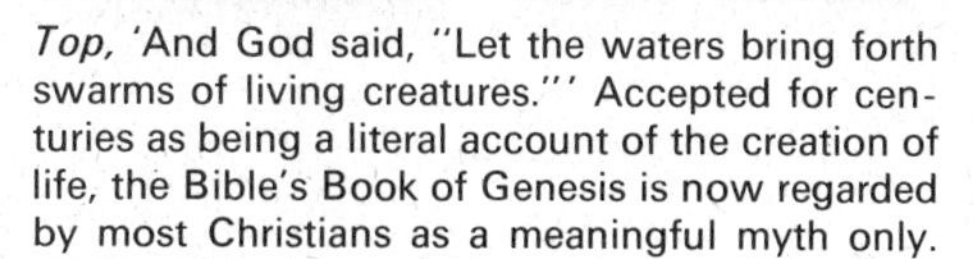

*Top,* 'And God said, "Let the waters bring forth swarms of living creatures."' Accepted for centuries as being a literal account of the creation of life, the Bible's Book of Genesis is now regarded by most Christians as a meaningful myth only.

*Left,* the Milky Way contains millions of planets, and one of science's most tantalizing questions has been whether any have forms of life similar to our own. As far as we know, only Mars, *above,* can support even the most primitive vegetation.

A.I. Oparin, the Russian biochemist, developed Tyndall's ideas in the twentieth century and sought scientific proof that there is no fundamental difference between a living organism and dead matter. J.B.S. Haldane, the British biologist, held similar views. He suggested that the synthesis of organic compounds into living things resulted from the action of ultraviolet light from the sun on the Earth's primitive atmosphere. These organic compounds then accumulated until they gained a 'life force'. Experiments by the present-day American scientist, Professor Stanley Lloyd Miller (and by scientists all over the world, subsequently), confirm these views.

To understand properly these recent theories, it is necessary to know something about the structure of the primitive world in which life first appeared. Most scientists agree that at one time the Earth was a great ball of fire, a mass of hot cosmic gases. In the coldness of space it cooled comparatively rapidly and developed a crust. After many upheavals, the crust settled into continents and seas, which were formed by the condensation of steam surrounding the still hot planet. This development took place over millions of years. When the Earth's crust was cooled by torrential downpours from the vapour surrounding it, it was also eroded, and fertile mud accumulated on the sea beds. But the Earth's atmosphere was very different from that of today. There was little or no oxygen, and instead methane, ammonia, carbon dioxide and water vapour formed the atmosphere. Constant and heavy thunderstorms were also a feature of this time in the Earth's history.

The composition of this early atmosphere is generally accepted, but Professor Miller was the first scientist to re-create these conditions. He placed a mixture of the gases in a large flask and bombarded them with electric charges similar to those which might be expected during thunderstorms. If the theory was correct, he reasoned that the basic materials of living substances, amino acids, would form. And within a week they did.

These and other similar experiments led to a number of conclusions. Millions of years ago amino acids formed in the atmosphere and rained down on both land and sea, where their transformation into protein compounds took place. This was the first purely chemical synthesis of organic material. But millions more years passed before even the most primitive kinds of life were formed. Under favourable circumstances, which have also been simulated in laboratories, collections of proteins joined to form larger constructions. Again, millions of years went by and then something new happened: the constructions divided and *reproduction* began, this early reproduction being a multiplication of molecules.

The multiplication process almost certainly came about as a result of the action

*Left,* this violently erupting volcano, showering great fragments of flaming lava into the night, gives us some idea of what the Earth must have looked like 4,000 million years ago. For a long time the Earth was uninhabitable – little more than a surging, heaving furnace. Gradually, it cooled in space and formed a crust, but its tremendous heat had caused vapour to condense. Torrential rains came, pouring down steadily day after day – the crust cooled further and settled slowly into the seas and the continents. From the gases surrounding the Earth the first primitive organic compounds were formed. Violent electrical charges, such as are causing the flash of lightning, *below left,* to fill the sky with its brilliance were vital in forming amino acids, the basic materials of life. Another agent in the synthesis of organic compounds into living things was the ultraviolet light in the sun's rays, which then fell upon the Earth unfiltered by the dense layer of ozone in the atmosphere that protects us from its effects today.

of *catalysts,* which are substances that speed up a chemical reaction. The catalysts may have arisen by the absorption of minerals deposited on the Earth by the constant heavy thunderstorms. Particularly important were *autocatalysts,* catalysts that are able to stimulate their own further production. So, as Dr Heinz Woltereck has pointed out, it was the catalysed end-product which contributed to its own creation.

Professor Oparin has suggested a mechanism by which those organic compounds, which included electrically active groups, would arrange and line-up water molecules around them. When droplets of opposite charges mix, they precipitate a complex colloidal aggregate, called a *coacervate,* which is capable of absorbing water on to its surface. This aggregate might have provided a basis for a primitive sort of membrane and a development of an individual unit of potentially living matter.

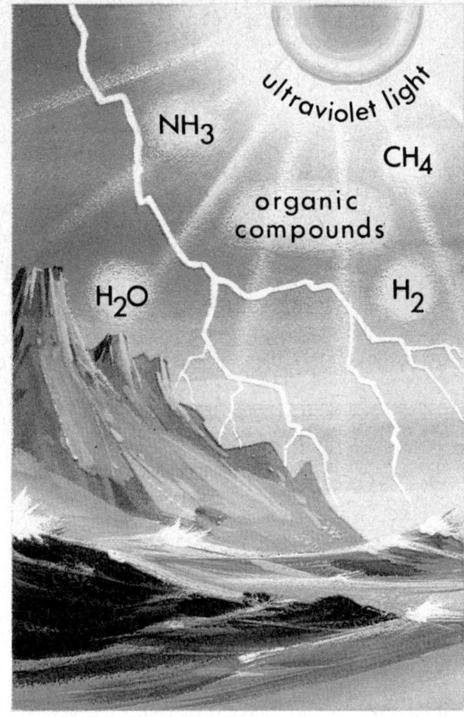


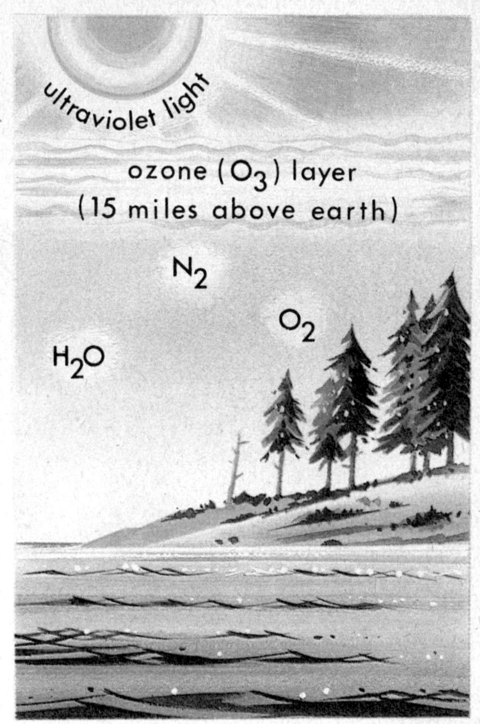


*Left,* at one stage the Earth's atmosphere made it impossible for life to survive. The undiluted ultraviolet light in the sun's rays was vital in forming the first organic compounds from such gases as methane, carbon dioxide and ammonia. *Right,* today the atmosphere is very different. A layer of ozone filters the ultraviolet rays; oxygen, so necessary to us, is now present in quantity.

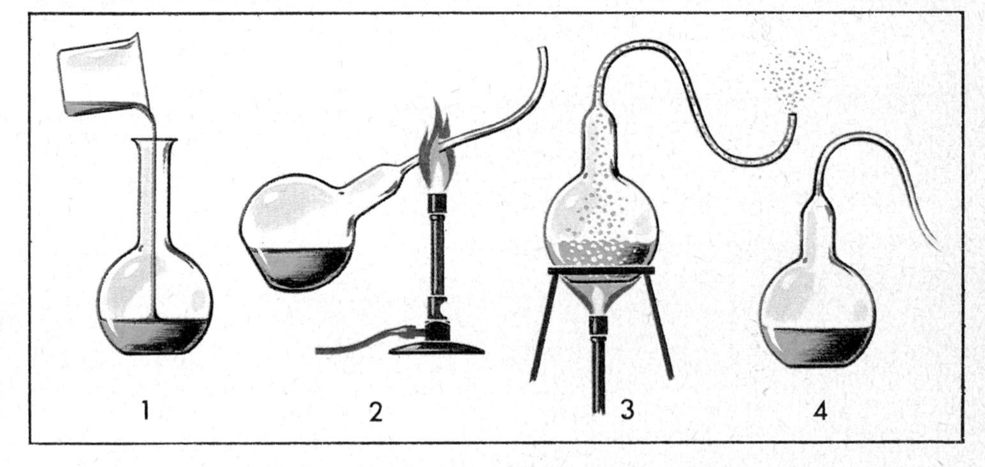


Pasteur's theory refuted the theory of spontaneous generation. A nutrient solution is placed in a flask (1); the neck bent into an S-shape (2); the solution sterilized by boiling (3), slowly cooled (4). Bacteria-laden air sticks to the side of the tube and therefore cannot reach the solution, which remains pure. Thus Pasteur proved that it is bacteria that contaminate a solution, not air.

## A chance experiment in nature?

Over the course of millions of years, these molecular aggregates could have become organized in their structure and hence genuinely living matter. Initially, this matter would have fed on the organic compounds from which it was made up. In time this 'food supply' would be exhausted and, in order to survive, the aggregates would need the new capacity of being able to synthesize organic products from inorganic sources. This would lead to the development of *photosynthesis,* which is the ability, common in plants, to form organic compounds from water and carbon dioxide in the presence of sunlight.

The key to photosynthesis is the substance *chlorophyll,* and so this development was only possible if these first organisms had chlorophyll available. Here again scientists have, with considerable difficulty, reproduced the conditions believed to have existed millions of years ago on Earth. When ammonia, carbon dioxide and water vapour are passed over heated silica (which is thought to resemble primeval rock), an organic compound called porphyrin, which is similar to chlorophyll, is formed. This experiment proves that, providing the conditions of the primeval Earth were accurately simulated, the formation of chlorophyll was possible millions of years ago and could have provided a means of nourishment for the first cells. It is impossible in our present state of knowledge to pinpoint exactly when and how inorganic matter became organic, although the theories briefly outlined here are now substantially accepted by many of our leading scientists.

Once 'living molecules' were established they could have 'reproduced' at a great rate. But their initial formation appears to have been a lucky coincidence of many favourable factors. The specific formation of a protein molecule capable of autocatalysis appears to require so many conditions which must be exactly right, that many people reject a natural explanation of the origin of life as so improbable as to be almost impossible. It should be appreciated, however, that opportunities for an 'improbability' to occur are enormous when we consider the time-scale involved.

It is generally believed that the Earth is between 4,000 and 5,000 million years old, and the conditions thought to be suitable for the establishment of molecular life could have come about at any time during a period of 2,000 million years. (Fossil records show comparatively complicated organisms existed 700 million years ago.) Apart from the time factor, there were (and are) countless atoms on the Earth in which the vital change could occur.

From the points of view of time and material, therefore, there were endless possibilities for natural experimentation. Undoubtedly numberless crude beginnings of the living substance disappeared because they were not up to standard and only the best adapted and survived. In the long history of the Earth, there has been more than enough time for trial and error.

As Man's knowledge has increased, it is interesting to note that he has had to work *down* the scale of evolutionary development to find his answers to the mystery of life. At one time most thinkers in the West believed that Man was directly created, in the form that he now has, by God; in the nineteenth century Charles Darwin went to the amoeba for his starting point. This century, increasing knowledge has sent us back to molecules and atoms, and in the future the science of nuclear physics is likely to extend considerably our knowledge of the absolute beginnings of life.

## Life on other worlds?

It is also worth noting that if we accept that the action of autocatalysts caused the regular division of protein molecules, which is an action of spontaneous fermentation, we are back to a theory of spontaneous generation as the prime source of life. Admittedly our theories are far more sophisticated than those of our forefathers, who thought mice were generated by dirty linen, but the underlying

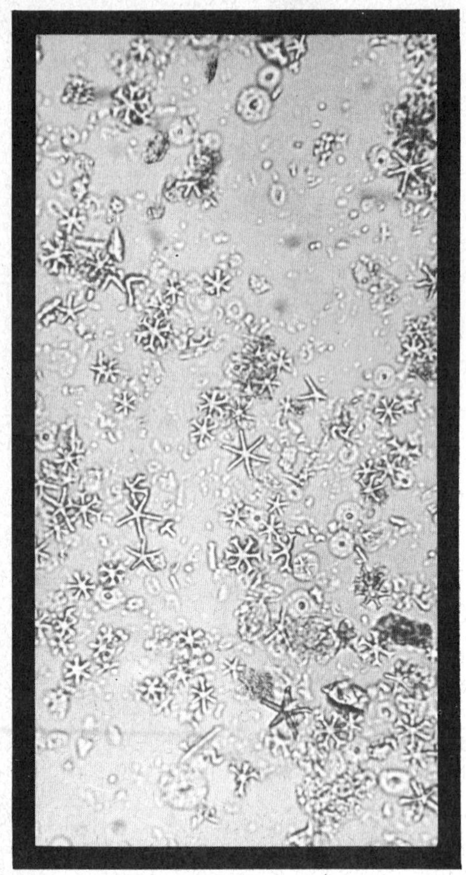

Miocene plankton fossils of 25 million years ago. Simple organic compounds possibly formed similar clusters from which more complex ones arose.

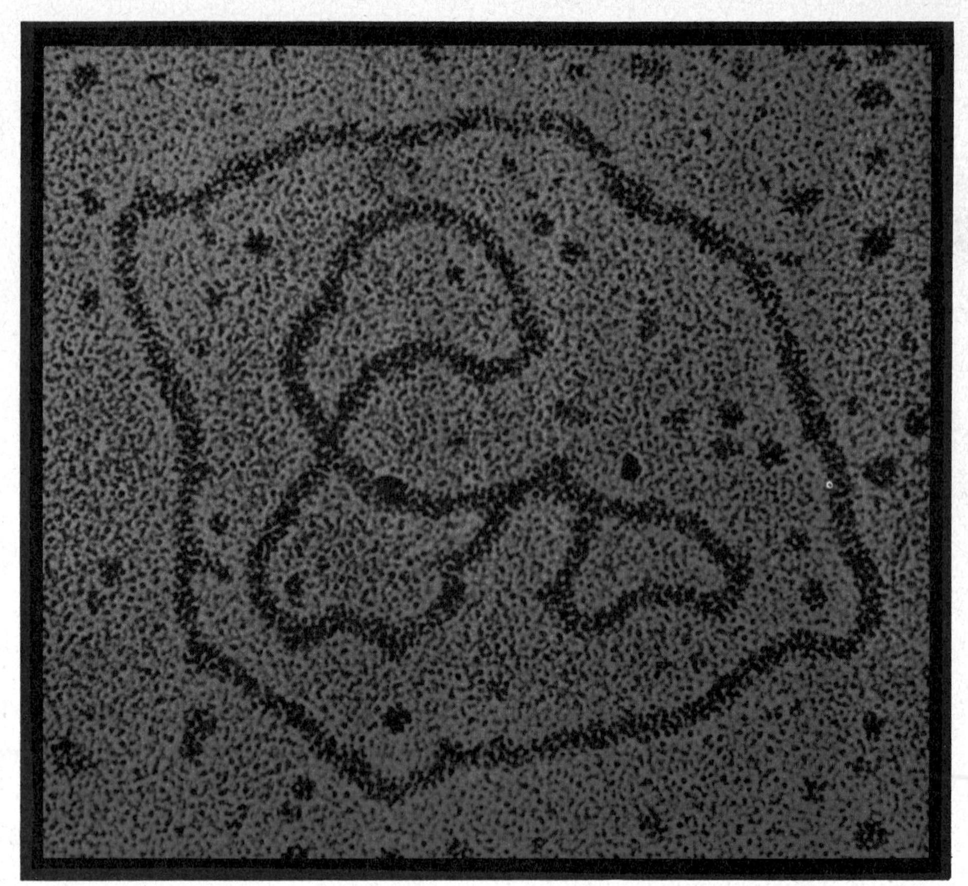

The electron micrograph of double viral DNA rings is of tremendous significance, for it represents Man's first successful attempt at creating life in a test-tube. This was the achievement of a team of American scientists who, in 1967, synthesized a simple Phi X virus able to reproduce itself.

principles are not really so dissimilar.

The question, 'Is there life on other worlds?' has exercised the minds of men almost as long as they have inquired about the origins of life. Today we can give an answer in the light of our latest knowledge, not only about the nature of life but also about the composition of the Universe. Within our solar system, it is almost certain that the Earth is the only planet likely to be able to support any forms of higher life. But in the whole of the vast Universe, with its innumerable planets, it is unlikely that the Earth is unique in producing recognizable life-forms.

## Martians are ruled out

For centuries men have cherished dreams that the other planets in our solar system might be capable of producing creatures similar to or dissimilar from ourselves. We now know more about the conditions necessary for life. The first essential is a temperature range of between 0 and 104 °F. So the sun and the stars could not give birth to even the most primitive life-forms, such as bacteria, for their surfaces have temperatures of several thousand degrees. This leaves the planets and their satellites.

The moon is not hospitable to life. It has no atmosphere and the temperature conditions, ranging between −302 and 212 °F., are definitely unfavourable. The sun shines uncomfortably brightly on the moon and bombards it with cosmic radiation of dangerous strengths. It is possible that low forms of plant life, such as algae, may exist, but certainly no higher forms of life.

Mars almost certainly has some primitive vegetation, but nothing more. It has a thin dry atmosphere, very little water, and temperatures which range between −210 and 86 °F. during a Martian day.

Venus is somewhat more of a mystery because it is perpetually obscured by dense cloud. It is subjected to intense solar radiation resulting in very high temperatures. The atmosphere appears to be mainly carbon dioxide, and the midday temperature is thought to be around 600 °F.

All the remainder of our planets can be dismissed. Jupiter, Uranus, Saturn and Neptune are so far from the sun that they are much too cold for any form of life. Their atmospheres contain only poisonous gases. Mercury, nearest the sun, has no atmosphere at all.

Alexander Oparin, the Russian biochemist who sought scientific proof for Tyndall's theory that all life could be reduced to inorganic matter.

But although the Earth may be unique in its solar system because it has conditions favourable to life, it is unlikely that it is unique in the whole of the Universe. Our solar system is only a tiny scrap in an enormous cosmic configuration. Our own galaxy, the Milky Way, has a diameter of about 600 million billion miles. And there are many more galaxies, possibly of similar size.

Within the Milky Way there are millions of planets and, according to astronomers, at least one million of these could have physical and chemical conditions similar to those of the Earth. Everything indicates that the Universe is built on a single principle and there is no reason to suppose that the conditions necessary for life should differ from place to place in the Universe. It is therefore possible to reason that many other planets may have the conditions to support life as we understand it.

Some astronomers also suggest that there may be at least 100 million other planets that could support different types of life. The manufacture of proteins through the presence of essential chemical elements might vary to produce life quite different from that which we know on Earth.

For centuries man has thought himself lord of creation, king of the Universe. This idea may be justifiable in our own solar system. But in the infinities of space, we are almost certainly not alone.

# Where does life begin?

Since Man first wondered about his relationship with the world around him, he has tried to distinguish between living things and inanimate objects. Is a final answer possible today?

EARLY MAN ENDOWED all things – mountains, trees and animals – with supernatural spirits. But as he began to make greater use of natural objects he found that some things grow while others do not. This may once have been a useful, if crude way of separating the living from the non-living, but the more Man has probed the world of the extremely small the more difficult it has become to decide where the line dividing the biological from the physical world should be drawn. Viruses, some of which are crystallizable like minerals, have in recent years made the problem a much more difficult one.

## A crystal can move and grow

There are immediately obvious differences between a rock and an animal. An animal generally moves while a rock does not. But equally, a tree remains rooted to one spot throughout its life. Since it does not move are we then to exclude it from the world of the living? Although many living creatures and some simpler plants, like one-celled algae move, clearly movement is not a reliable criterion.

Lay a pot-plant on its side and the shoot will turn to grow upwards in defiance of gravity. Shine a light on a blowfly larva and it will inch away from the light-source. These are examples of a response to a stimulus – of behaviour. Living things are sensitive to light and heat, to touch and sound, as well as to various chemical substances. This characteristic of sensitivity is even possessed by a single-celled organism like an amoeba, which has no visible sense organs. A boulder, on the other hand, may roll down a hillside, if it is dislodged – but its rolling is simply an effect of gravity and not a response to it.

Plants and animals grow, increasing their size and sometimes altering their shape. Though a stone may weather and decrease in size it will never grow. A copper-sulphate crystal immersed in a solution of copper sulphate may increase in size retaining the same overall shape of the original crystal. But this kind of growth is quite different in character from the growth of a living thing, in which a mass of different materials are collected from the environment and incorporated into a body.

## Living things need energy

To obtain these different materials from its surroundings, the living thing must take them into its body and into the cells of which its body is composed. Some bacteria – among the smallest of living things – can take simple chemical substances, like nitrogen salts, from their surroundings and use them to make the protein required to build new cells. Plants take water from the soil and carbon dioxide from the air to manufacture sugars which they also need

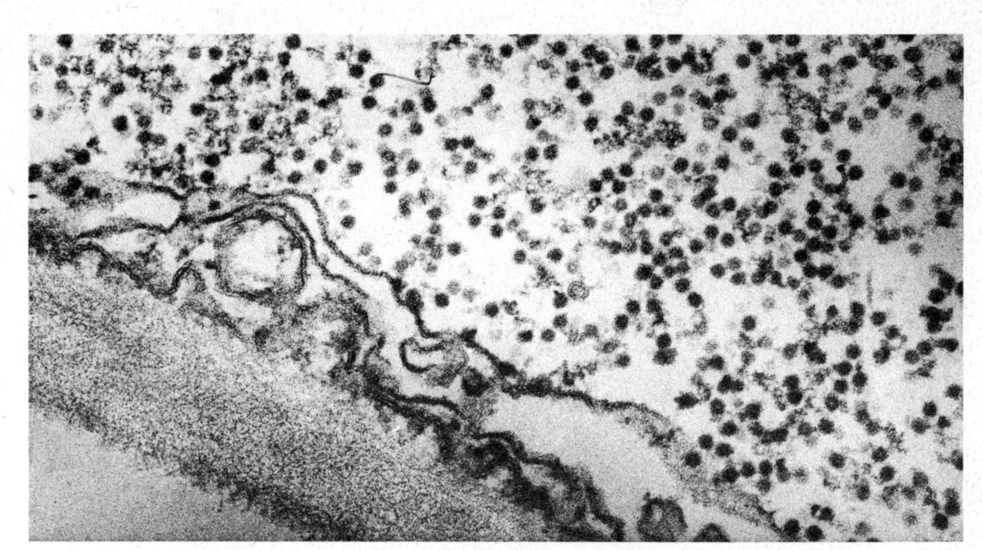

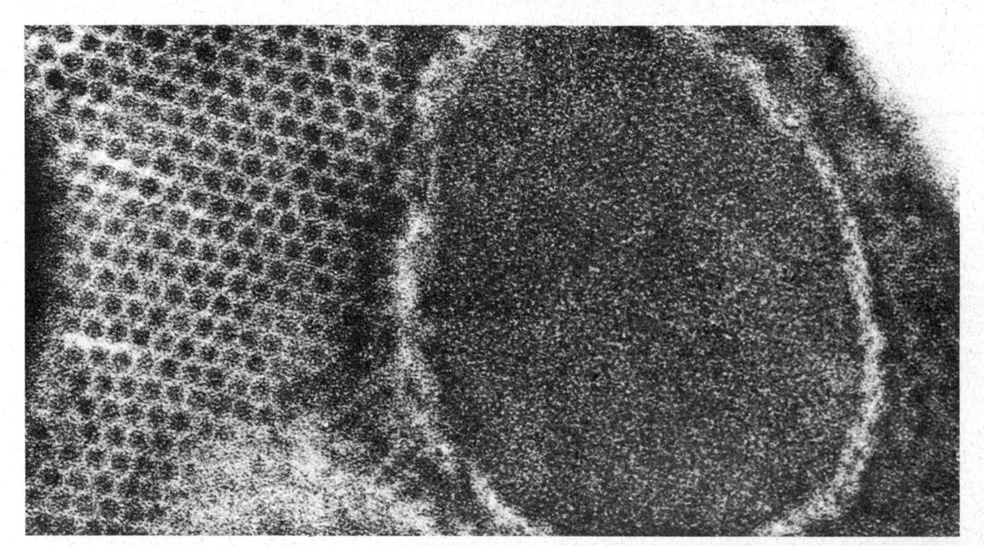

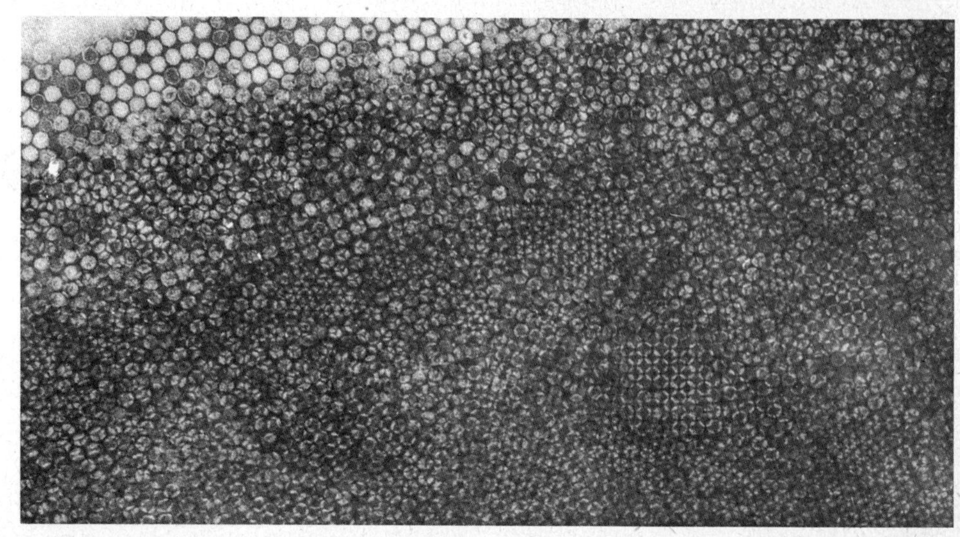

*Top,* a sowbane mosaic virus invades a section of a leaf cell. The virus particles appear as dark blobs within the cytoplasm, clearly revealing signs of life. The photograph has been enlarged 80,000 times. *Centre,* the same virus seen within a cell, having now adopted crystalline form (see honeycomb structure). Enlargement: 144,000:1.

*Below,* showing the same virus again, but now as a concentrated droplet containing the particles in their dried and crystallized form, apparently quite inanimate. This virus therefore shows the blurring of the dividing line between living and non-living things: here a seemingly lifeless particle has come alive, once inside a host cell.

in constructing the materials of their bodies. The great majority of animals do not have the plant's power to synthesize their food and must feed upon the proteins, carbohydrates and fats of other living things to meet their bodily needs.

A sign that chemical processes are taking place in a living body is the production of various excretory products. These are residual products of life-supporting reactions and are of no further use to the organism – they may even be positively poisonous to it. Neither carbon dioxide and the various nitrogenous products excreted or exhaled by an animal, nor the oxygen given out by a plant originally entered in that form. Being produced in the bodies of living things these excretory products are proof of the breakdown reactions inseparable from life as we know it.

Not only do living things feed and grow, they also reproduce almost exact copies of themselves. To do this they must pass on information which can be used to direct the building of the copies; this is the process of genetical inheritance, the information being contained and passed on in a genetic code. The copies will be built from materials in the environment that are absorbed and reformed into the materials of the living body.

Some of the excretory products, such as carbon dioxide, are produced in the process of respiration or breathing – an important way of obtaining energy from substances originally in the environment. This energy is needed to enable muscles to work and to facilitate the synthesis of new tissues and cells. Ultimately derived from the sun, it is locked within the complex molecules of the food substances and can only be released in a controlled way and utilized by the body after the complex chemical processes of respiration and digestion have occurred. Under natural conditions only living things can accommodate these processes, for they are processes depending on *enzymes*, substances which speed up biochemical reactions and are not produced anywhere but in living organisms. The energy must be released step by step. Burning, for example, releases energy from sugar, but dissipates it as heat. Sugar in the cell gives up its energy in stages, enabling it to be stored in the adenosine triphosphate (ATP) of the cell for later use.

For a living thing to grow and reproduce successfully it must organize material from the environment into a special pattern. All living things are organized, even if, like a virus, they consist of little more than protein and nucleic acids. Whether thousands or trillions of molecules are involved they are invariably in an ordered three-dimensional pattern. This organization is a highly improbable state for matter to be in. All inanimate matter – *and* dead matter – tends to become more and more disordered and randomly scattered. To a physicist, this is known as the tendency to increase entropy, for entropy is simply a measure of disorder. To counter this probable tendency, energy is required, so living things can only retain their organized state – of low entropy – by respiration and the production of energy. When the supply of energy ceases on the death of an organism, dissolution and decay set in.

### In a sea of disorder . . .

Let us view this organization through the eyes of the physicist. He has to do with two main kinds of law. The first deals with the conservation of matter and energy. It applies throughout the known world, and living things obey it along with the rest. Living things cannot create energy or make matter out of nothing: they can only convert energy which is already there in the substances of their environment or, in the case of plants, energy radiating from the sun. But the second kind of physical law is concerned with the statistics of events – not with what an individual atom does but with the most probable outcome of the activity of a mass of atoms. The laws which gases obey are good examples.

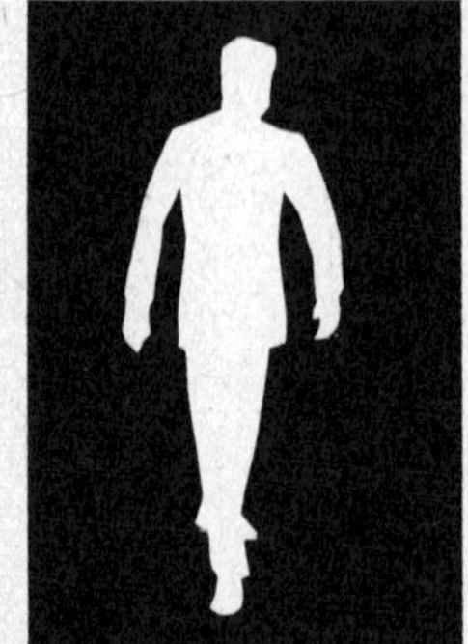

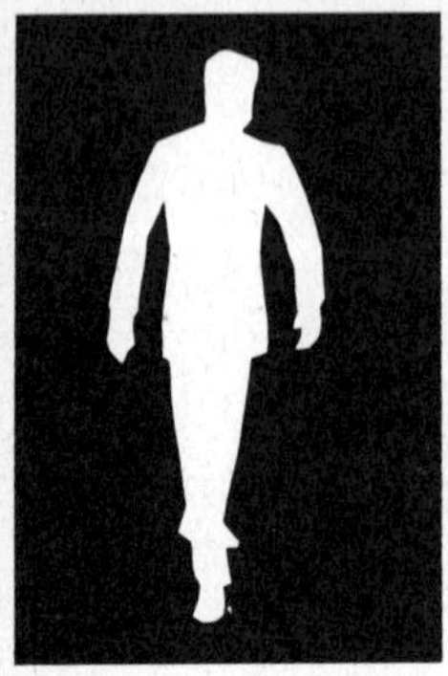

The double sequence, *above,* illustrates one of the chief differences between living things and inanimate objects. If a man is pushed over, he can usually return to his former position by standing up. But if a wall is knocked down, it stays that way until perhaps another external force is applied. Living things have an internal organization which enables them – while they live – to resist environmental forces and preserve their integrity as organisms. Inanimate objects, on the other hand, are perpetually at the mercy of these forces and as time passes the elements of which they are composed tend to become increasingly disordered. Entropy is simply a measure of disorder. Hence inanimate objects exhibit a high and living things a low degree of entropy. The self-preserving organization of a living thing is largely due to the properties of the carbon atom, *top.*

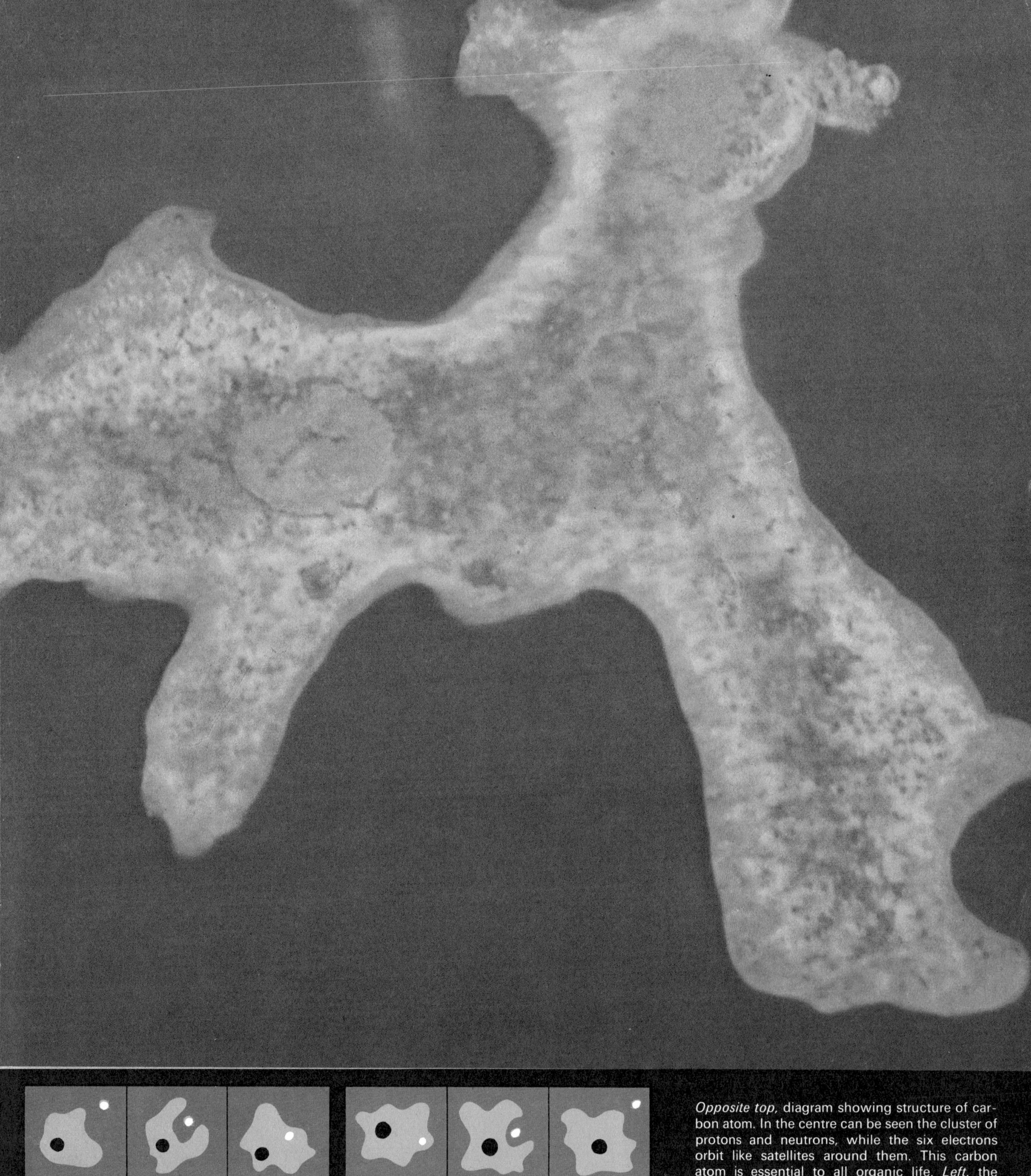

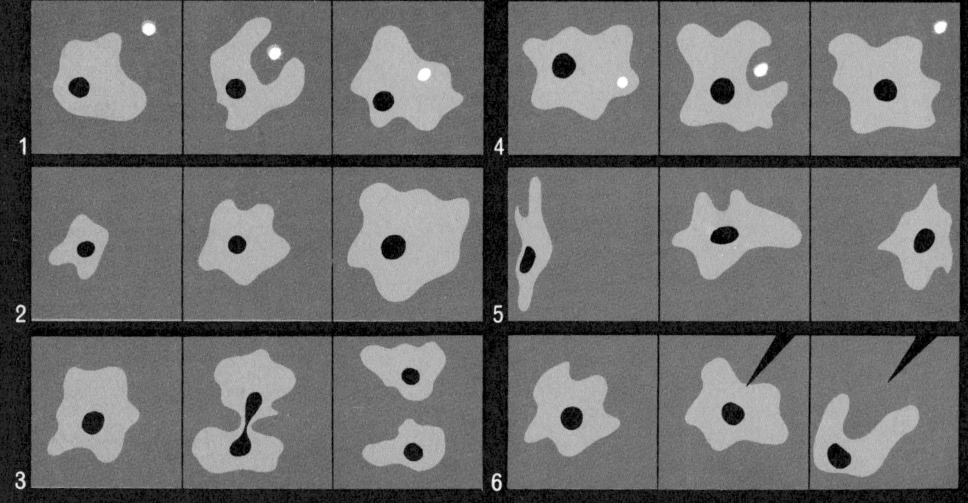


*Opposite top,* diagram showing structure of carbon atom. In the centre can be seen the cluster of protons and neutrons, while the six electrons orbit like satellites around them. This carbon atom is essential to all organic life. *Left,* the single-celled amoeba embodies all the criteria of life. **1** *Digestion:* organisms are absorbed by being surrounded. **2** *Growth:* after cell division, new growth cycle begins. **3** *Reproduction:* unicellular or asexual division occurs when cell becomes too large. Two nuclei are formed at opposite ends of cell, which splits. **4** *Excretion:* this is done by isolating and leaving behind waste particles. **5** *Movement:* matter in the cell glides forward irregularly. **6** *Irritability:* most cells are sensitive to light or touch and shrink away from stimulus. *Above,* amoeba in action – note its changing shape. The colours are due to interference microscopy.

They do not describe what an individual atom in a gas does as it jigs to and fro, but what the thousands and millions of atoms are doing collectively. It is this kind of law, typified by the *Second Law of Thermodynamics*, which living things seem to avoid with impunity. The Second Law predicts that any spontaneous change in a closed system will tend to move towards greater probability. This simply means that a hot poker removed from a fire will cool until it assumes the temperature of its surroundings. That it will cool is indeed highly probable. The poker is a closed system because it cannot of itself replenish the energy it loses as it cools – it cannot feed or breathe and it cannot excrete. The remarkable thing about a living organism is that it can persist as a highly improbable arrangement of matter even though changes are taking place within it.

### . . . Islands of organization

Living things, however, only *appear* to be exceptions for they are really open systems in which energy and matter enter and leave, the energy being used to decrease their entropy, that is, maintain and increase their organization by feeding and breathing. Living things are islands of organization in a sea of disorder; they are the most ordered, unstable and improbable things known. They are able to maintain their organization only by virtue of certain internal control mechanisms. In the short term, these are so-called *homeostatic* devices. Essentially they involve a process which tends to increase, say, the production of a substance which is the effect of the substance itself on the process. This is called 'feed-back' – a term borrowed from engineering. If only a little of the substance is required, the feed-back from the accumulating substance reduces the manufacture as the concentration rises, just as a governor on a steam engine rises as the speed increases and shuts off steam so preventing the engine from over-running. This is an example of negative feed-back. Negative feed-back cuts down production; positive feed-back boosts it. The great majority of the controls in the living body are of the negative feed-back type; and on the simplest level, they tell us when we have had enough to eat.

### Carbon: the key of life

The system does not work for ever. If it did we would be immortal. Disorder catches up with all living things in the end, and this is what death entails. As a result, individuals must pass on a formula for making copies of themselves. One way is by division in two, but at each division only one new organism is formed. The most effective way to make copies is by passing on a detailed code, a plan of organization which will serve as a pattern for numerous offspring. This is what happens in all living things. They all contain some substance, usually deoxyribose nucleic acid (DNA) upon which the genetic code is based. The plan must be a protected stabilized form of code in order that it can survive the effects of the environment which cause the death of the adult. DNA makes such a code. It is a large complex molecule made up of very many sub-units. These are interchangeable and so a great number of re-combinations can be derived giving a vocabulary large enough to encode all the instructions needed to form the organism and to maintain it. In addition it is a *co-valently* bonded molecule, and co-valent bonds are the strongest we know; indeed we can say that only linkages of this sort could persist for millions of years.

The firmness of the co-valent bond stresses the importance of the versatile atom of carbon in living systems. Carbon is found by itself in the ground in the form of diamonds or graphite, but in its compounds it is found today mainly in living organisms or their remains.

Most elements form compounds by losing or gaining electrons from other elements. Unique among the simpler elements, carbon can *share* its electrons with other elements, or with other carbon atoms. In this way, long and strong chains of carbon atoms can be formed – and all manner of other configurations can be attached to the chain in the process. Carbon's ability to share electrons – to form co-valent bonds – makes this element the basis of all living structures. Its long-chain compounds are found only in living or dead organisms – hence they are called organic compounds.

A chain of carbon atoms may close at its ends to form a ring. The most familiar of these is probably the '6-carbon benzene ring', a most important building brick for the materials of life. Combined with chains and rings of the same or different numbers, carbon atoms can form a large number of different numbers of different configurations, or molecular skeletons. These can be bodied out with a range of side chains utilizing mainly other carbon atoms, hydrogen atoms and nitrogen atoms, to produce what is potentially a vast array of substances. Yet the materials of living things consist in the main of proteins, sugars and fats, with the addition of nucleic acids and adenosine phosphates.

### Is the virus alive?

The discovery of very small particles which would pass through a filter holding back bacteria and which were yet able to reproduce meant that a reconsideration of the definition of life became necessary. Crystallizable like an inorganic compound viruses seemed inadmissible for inclusion among living things. They reproduce it is true, but only in the environment of a living cell. Left to themselves they seem unable to mobilize the materials in the environment for this purpose. Nevertheless, they do possess a genetic code; the new viruses are like their parent. By means of an electron microscope we can see that viruses have quite characteristic shapes; their molecules are arranged in an organized way determined by the genetic information.

In the last analysis, organization and coded instructions for reproduction seem to be the criteria of life, even where none of the other qualifications – moving, sensitivity, growth, excretion, feeding and respiration – hold good.

A High voltage cable
B Electron gun
C Electron beam
D Specimen holder
E Specimen chamber
F Lenses
G Magnets
H Viewing chamber
I Viewing screen

Although similar in purpose to the optical microscope, the electron microscope has much greater *resolving power* – it can produce separate images of objects very close together and makes detail clearer than ever before. This has had important consequences in biology. For example, until viruses were made visible by the electron microscope, their existence had only been inferred. Instead of using a beam of light to illuminate the object, a parallel beam of electrons is used. The object – in the form of a very thin film of material – allows the electron beam to pass through it, and an image of the object is carried forward in the electron beam. This beam passes through a magnetic or electrostatic focusing system rather like the optical lens system in the ordinary microscope. The image is then received on a fluorescent screen, like that in a TV or radar set, and recorded on a photographic plate.

# Life's history in stone

**Forms of life many millions of years old lie locked in the layers of the Earth's crust. This vast specimen case of petrified remains shows how life developed in the aeons before Man.**

PALAEONTOLOGISTS ARE SCIENTISTS who study the living things that dwelt on this planet in its distant youth. And, from a few fragmentary remains they have been able to piece together the crowded story of living things on Earth and their evolution. Most of these remains take the form of fossils, and to be able to date them and place them on the evolutionary tree of life, we must know something about the rocks in which they are found. For instance, layers of *sedimentary* rocks laid down under the sea contain characteristic groups of fossils which differ in some respects from those found in layers of older rocks below, and in more recent layers above.

The major rock groups or *systems* distinguished by the fossils they contain, and the time intervals or *periods* during which they were laid down, are generally illustrated by a diagram called the *Geological Column*. Palaeontology also has a second equally vital role. Study of the fossils of plants and animals in rocks shows that some groups increase in number and variety in the layers of younger rocks above, whereas others die out. Some forms became extinct in rocks millions of years old, while in the case of others, the line along which they have evolved can be traced right through to their modern descendants.

## Carbon dating of rocks

Today, scientists have available improved techniques for measuring the ages of rocks. Some rocks contain radioactive elements which gradually decay as atoms lose electrons and particles from their nuclei. In the decay process, some of the original 'parent' material is lost, leaving a new 'daughter' substance. The rates at which these changes take place follow a known physical law and are characteristic for a given radioactive element. As a result, from a knowledge of the proportions of parent and daughter elements in a sample of rock, scientists can calculate its age. Fossils themselves can also be dated by similar methods. We can now therefore view evolution in terms of actual numbers of years.

How life began still remains much of a mystery. Experiments have shown that electric sparks passed through a mixture of gases such as methane, ammonia and water vapour – the same gases as are thought to have existed in the Earth's early 'atmosphere' – produce several kinds of amino acids. These are the 'building bricks' from which proteins are constructed. Lightning flashes passing through this mixture may have produced the earliest organic compounds which, aided by clay minerals acting as catalysts in the mud of a primeval shore, became the first living things. Another theory is that the change from inorganic to living matter was brought about by radiation from space penetrating a less protective atmosphere than that of today.

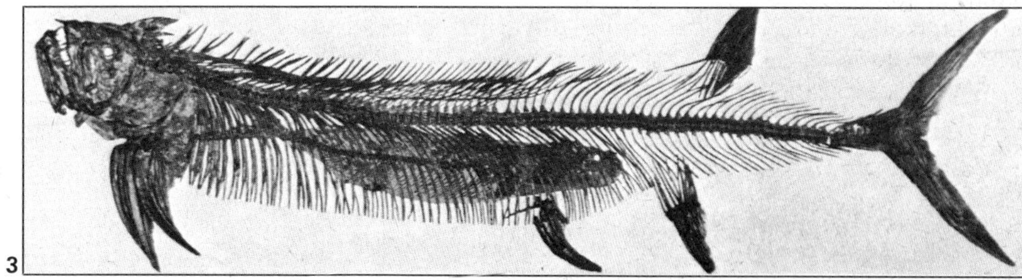

**1** Fossilized graptolite colonies, occurring in many parts of the world, provide a means of correlating the age of rocks in different geographical locations.
**2** Trilobites possessed a pair of compound eyes and had the ability to roll themselves into a ball to conserve moisture. They were the dominant form of life for more than 100 million years.
**3** This fossil of *Portheus molossus* shows another fish in its stomach. Apparently the predator died before digestion was complete.

Among the earliest organisms were probably simple single-celled plants living in water without needing free oxygen but producing it through their life processes. The development of photosynthesis by plants could have produced the oxygen in the atmosphere necessary for the development of animal life, and experiments have shown that substances resembling chlorophyll – necessary for photosynthesis – can be formed from simple starting materials.

The point at which life originated may never be known, but evidence from Pre-Cambrian rocks, such as limestone from Rhodesia over 2,800 million years old, indicates that simple organisms existed in very early times. This Rhodesian limestone and other ancient limestones contain lumpy structures known as *stromatolites,* which are made up of thin layers of calcium carbonate similar to those secreted today by blue-green algae. Almost certainly stromatolites are also traces of similar marine plants. In Ontario a rock known as *chert,* some 2,000 million years old, has yielded fossils of primitive fungi, algae and bacteria.

The record of life from these very early times until the beginning of the Cambrian period 570 million years ago is obscure. Cambrian animal fossils are plentiful and varied, with life forms so complex that highly organized ancestors must have existed well back into the Pre-Cambrian era.

## Fossils of soft organisms

Fossil remains are lacking because these creatures were soft bodied, and so left few traces. In recent years, however, geologists in South Australia have found the impressions in sandstone of a group of late Pre-Cambrian fossils. These resemble jelly-fish, annelid worms, and frond-like objects, possibly sea-pens. Frond- and disc-like impressions also occur in rocks aged about 1,000 million years from the Charnwood Forest area of Leicestershire. All Pre-Cambrian fossils found so far have been in rocks laid down in shallow water.

When the Cambrian period began, almost seven-eighths of Earth's existence (up to the present) had already elapsed. Suddenly the record of life was transformed. Within the deposits from Cambrian sea-floors, fossils of nearly all the invertebrate phyla have been found. The reason for this transformation appears to be that animals began to develop hard parts, usually of calcium carbonate (chalk), but sometimes of horny chitin. The chances of fossilization were thus greatly increased. Most highly organized and certainly the most striking in appearance of the Cambrian animals were the *trilobites*. Crawling over the sea-floor, burrowing into the mud, or swimming near the bottom, these creatures were the dominant life forms for at least 100 million years. Their importance continued through the succeeding Ordovician and Silurian periods, and their final extinction was not until Permian times, less than 280 million years ago.

*Brachiopods*, mostly with horny shells, were fairly common, but although bivalves (two-shelled animals resembling cockles) and gastropods (single-shelled animals resembling snails) existed, they were rather rare. Early forms of corals and *graptolites* (colonial animals similar to coral) were already in existence.

Existing through 90 million years of Ordovician and Silurian times, the graptolites provide the most useful fossils for geologists. These were tiny individual creatures inhabiting branching colonies resembling fretsaw blades which drifted at the mercy of waves and currents over deep oceans and shallow seas. New shapes with different arrangements of branches rapidly evolved and their remains, entombed in the bottom sediments, enable detailed correlations to be made between rocks in widely separated parts of the world.

*Jamoytius* – a primitive fish-like creature with a skeleton of cartilage, found in Silurian shales – may perhaps illustrate the form taken by the earliest chordates.

Coal forests developed during the Carboniferous period. These were mainly giant club mosses, up to 100 feet high, in an undergrowth of horsetail trees and seed ferns.

The date at which the earliest vertebrate animals branched from the same stock as the echinoderms is still unknown, but must have been much earlier. The teeming life of the warm shallow Silurian seas is wonderfully illustrated after 410 million years on weathered slabs of Wenlock limestone crowded with fossils such as bryozoa, crinoids, brachiopods and trilobites.

## The Earth dries out

Late Silurian and early Devonian times – about 400 million years ago – were periods of dramatic advance in the story of life. Plants with well-developed sap-conducting systems and spores dispersed by the wind began to spread on to the land, and the first air-breathing insects and spiders appeared. In lakes, rivers and estuaries, heavily armoured, jawless fish – the *ostracoderms* – became abundant while true fish of many varieties soon followed.

Sedimentary rocks were laid down in the sea or in a lake, and show distinct stratification. The strata, or layers, are particularly noticeable in sea cliffs such as this.

Dry conditions were widespread during the Devonian period and some fishes developed lungs and limb-like pairs of fins and were able to crawl from drying pools to more permanent water. These were the ancestors of the amphibians which came into existence by the early Carboniferous period, which began 345 million years ago.

Carboniferous times began with the British area largely submerged by shallow tropical seas, abounding with corals, crinoids, brachiopods and some coiled cephalopods – squid-like creatures called *goniatites*. River deltas were built up, converting the seas into swamps on which the coal forests grew in the steamy heat. Giant club mosses growing up to 100 feet tall towered above the profuse smaller growth of horsetail trees, seed ferns and primitive gymnosperms. Thin-shelled freshwater mussels flourished in delta channels and estuaries. Fishes were common and salamander-like amphibians – the *labyrinthodonts* – sprawled on the mud-flats.

At this time Europe, North America and much of Asia formed a single continent lying far to the south of their present latitudes – a fact which explains the tropical nature of the vegetation. Africa, Australia, South America and Antarctica, together with much of India, comprised a continent called Gondwana centred close to the South Pole and suffering repeated glaciation. From Permian times onwards, as the ancient land masses were split and shifted to their present positions by the processes of continental drift, climatic changes, together with the isolation of some areas in the southern hemisphere, had a profound effect on the development

| Era | Evolutionary Time Scale | Geological Time Scale |
|---|---|---|
| Cryptozoic | **Pre-Cambrian** Primitive life – algae, fungi, soft-bodied marine animals – appears on earth. | **4,550,000,000 years ago** Formation of the earth's crust, and the appearance of the seas and continental land masses. |
| Palaeozoic | **Cambrian** Appearance of primitive arthropods, plus a few molluscs, worms and sponges. | **570,000,000 years ago** Large areas of Europe covered by shallow seas. Sinking of Norway and parts of England. |
| Palaeozoic | **Ordovician** Clams, starfish, coral and other marine invertebrates join arthropods in sea. First fish appear. | **500,000,000 years ago** North-west European troughs built up from the Caledonian Mountains. |
| Palaeozoic | **Silurian** Beginning of plant and animal life on land. | **440,000,000 years ago** Formation of the Caledonian Mountains from the old red North Continent. |
| Palaeozoic | **Devonian** First appearance of large, tree-like plants on land. Rise of the amphibians. | **395,000,000 years ago** Elevation of the Varistic Mountains. Shallow seas of Scandinavia displaced by elevations. |
| Palaeozoic | **Carboniferous** Fish abound in seas. Appearance of first reptiles. Giant insects dominate forests. | **345,000,000 years ago** Filling up of Central Europe by Varistic Mountains. Swamps and forest which become coal. |
| Palaeozoic | **Permian** Rise of modern insects and increased expansion of vertebrates, i.e. amphibians and reptiles. | **280,000,000 years ago** Varistic Mountains buried under own debris. Period marked by violent volcanic activity. |
| Mesozoic | **Triassic** Rise of the dinosaurs. Vertebrates begin replacing invertebrates as dominant life form. | **225,000,000 years ago** Continued levelling of the earth. |
| Mesozoic | **Jurassic** First appearance of mammals and birds. Dinosaurs reach their peak. | **195,000,000 years ago** Spreading of the seas over extensive areas of Europe and Asia. Gentle warping of the earth. |
| Mesozoic | **Cretaceous** Extinction of the dinosaurs. Sharp increase in mammals. Modern trees appear. | **136,000,000 years ago** Mild climates nearly everywhere. Further expansion of the seas. |
| Cenozoic | **Tertiary** Mammals dominate the earth and bony fish dominate the seas. | **65,000,000 years ago** Violent volcanic activity. Rising of large fold-mountains of Pyrenees, Alps and Carpathians. |
| Cenozoic | **Quaternary** Mammal dominance continues. Man appears. | **1,500,000 years ago** Movement of glaciers from Scandinavia into German uplands and Alpine glaciers into foreland. |

**Biological Time Scale**

Seaweed and invertebrates
Fish
Land plants
Amphibians
Reptiles
Mammals
Birds
Man

The relation between the geological and biological time scales is clearly shown in this diagram. Carbon dating plays a large part in determining the ages of fossils and rocks.

of plant and animal life.

Earth movements, beginning in the late Carboniferous period, produced high mountain chains. Large areas of the northern hemisphere, formerly clothed by the coal forests, became deserts. Ice Ages continued to afflict the Southern Continent. The disappearance of the last trilobites typified the dying out of many forms of life that had existed since the Cambrian period. The Palaeozoic era ('the time of early life') was over, but new groups of animals and plants that were to dominate the Mesozoic era ('the time of middle life') began to emerge. Early reptiles which had evolved from the Carboniferous amphibians increased in variety and number. Ammonites and belemnites appeared in the seas, while land vegetation included the first conifers.

The 165 million years of the Triassic, Jurassic and Cretaceous periods have been called the 'Age of Reptiles'. This developing group, unlike the amphibians, was not confined to water for breeding, and varieties such as the dinosaurs which appeared in the Triassic period rapidly spread over the land, even to hostile desert areas. The streamlined ichthyosaurs and plesiosaurs were adapted to life in the open sea, while by the Jurassic period the light-boned pterosaurs had taken to the air. The ancestors of the dinosaurs were the small and agile Triassic thecodonts, from whom many different varieties descended. The 80-foot-long, four-legged Diplodocus waded through the Jurassic

1 The fossil of a sea lily, which is a relative of the starfishes, was found in Wenlock limestone, and is about 430 million years old. Each 'head' is about $4\frac{1}{2}$ inches long.

2 This model of a jawless fish was reconstructed from a fossil about 410 million years old. The creature, known as *Cephalaspis,* was well protected by heavy armour plating.

swamps, a contemporary of the ten-ton Stegosaurus with its three-ounce brain; both were harmless herbivores. By contrast Tyrannosaurus (20 feet in height and living in the Cretaceous period) was probably the most formidable predator ever to walk the Earth's surface. The ankylosaurs developed heavy defensive armour whilst Triceratops, with its three horns and head armour, typified another prominent group. Small light dinosaurs, including the ostrich-like Struthiomimus, relied on their speed for safety.

Fossil teeth and jaws about the size of a shrew's found in Triassic debris filling cracks in older rock are the earliest evidence of the mammals. Through most of Mesozoic time these were insignificant creatures inconspicuously coexisting with the dinosaurs.

Archaeopteryx, the first known bird, still possessing teeth and many reptilian features, was excavated from fine-grained Jurassic limestone in southern Germany. The Mesozoic seas swarmed with ammonites. Hundreds of species with subtle differences in their coiled shells rapidly evolved and spread far and wide. These fossils are of the greatest value in correlating Jurassic and Cretaceous rocks throughout the world. Among the other marine invertebrates belemnites, bivalves, gastropods, echinoids and corals also flourished.

From the character of the plant life, the Triassic and Jurassic periods have been termed the 'Age of Gymnosperms'. Conifers and their more primitive allies, the cycads, together with ferns, dominated the vegetation. In the Cretaceous period, however, flowering plants – the angiosperms – appeared, and increasingly trees familiar in the modern world entered the scene.

One of geology's greatest mysteries is the wholesale extinction, at the close of the Mesozoic era, of flourishing groups of animals and the drastic reduction in the importance of others. The dinosaurs, ichthyosaurs, plesiosaurs, flying reptiles, ammonites and belemnites disappeared before the earliest Cenozoic ('the time of recent life') rocks were laid down. Some forms had become so specialized that they failed to adapt to geographic and climatic changes. A recent attractive theory suggests that changes in the Earth's magnetic field may have reduced protection from radiation from space, which might have accelerated genetic changes.

Although subdivided into seven epochs – the Palaeocene, Eocene, Oligocene, Miocene, Pliocene, Pleistocene, and Holocene – the entire Cenozoic era covers only 70 million years. By Eocene times vegetation had a generally modern appearance. Deciduous trees and other flowering plants were more important than conifers and ferns. Grasses, developing later in the Oligocene period, spread widely in drier areas. Generally warmer climates in the earlier part of the Cenozoic era accounted for tropical flora as far north as Britain and temperate plants in the Arctic.

Ultimately dependent on the new vegetation, the mammals rapidly increased in early Tertiary times to dominate life on land. Despite the incoming of snakes, reptiles and amphibians were of relatively minor importance. Among the new animals were the creodonts, ancestors of the carnivores, and condylarths, predecessors of the hoofed herbivores. Other strange forms now extinct include the lumbering Uintatherium with six bony projections on its head, and Baluchitherium, a rhinoceros 18 feet high at the shoulder.

## The ascendancy of the mammals

Mammals as a group probably reached their acme in the Miocene period, for although most families alive at that time have persisted to the present day, some of the larger forms, including Moropus 'the clawed horse' have become extinct.

A trend towards cooler, drier climates continuing through the Pliocene period was accompanied by the extension of grasslands and shrinking of forests, thus favouring fast-running hoofed animals such as the horse, antelope and gazelle. These were the prey of carnivores like the sabre-toothed cat. Cenozoic marine life was similar in many respects to that of today. Gastropods and bivalves were abundant. Early whales had developed in the Eocene period and the teeth of 60-foot-long sharks are found in Pliocene marine rocks. As on land, the distribution of marine life changed with climatic conditions.

Since the Miocene period, apes had become abundant and the fossils of some showing certain man-like characteristics have been found in the Pliocene rocks of Africa. Almost three million years ago in Kenya, Australopithecus chipped stones to form the first edged tools. Modern man has evolved against the fluctuating climatic background of the Pleistocene Ice Age. Today, three million years after the earliest stone axes, he operates the mass spectrometer to probe the history of the Earth.

And it is with such advanced scientific tools as the mass spectrometer that biologists are able to read and understand the story of the fossils, which form an exact and detailed calendar of the Earth and the plant and animal life which grew, flourished and died in its forests and seas.

# Putting living things in their place

**Teeming varieties of plants and animals, diverse yet interrelated. How do biologists classify this apparent chaos? And how has the study of biology benefited from their efforts?**

THROUGHOUT HIS RECORDED HISTORY, Man has sought to classify the objects which he sees about him. He saw such classification as a necessary step in increasing his understanding of the world, by creating an ordered system out of the apparently chaotic profusion.

In fact, one of the major contributions which Greek philosophy made to the advance of science was a system of classification devised by Aristotle. Aristotle's method was to classify objects by defining differences between them. In Aristotle's view, it did not matter very much which particular differences were used – the result would be the same, an ordered system. An example which springs to mind is that the bee is 'useful' and the fly is 'not useful'. This is a crude criterion, but it serves to divide the animal kingdom into two classes. This process can be carried out as far as necessary, using more and more subtle distinctions, until the necessary stage of subdivision is reached.

If all known things were classified according to a universally acceptable system, and were named in accordance with the categories to which they belonged, scientists would be able to deduce certain facts about an animal or plant merely from its name, and would also be able to allot categories and names to newly discovered types. Such an ordered classification would be of immense value to botanists and zoologists in particular, who were faced with the immense task of mastering information about a bewildering array of living things that abound in the world.

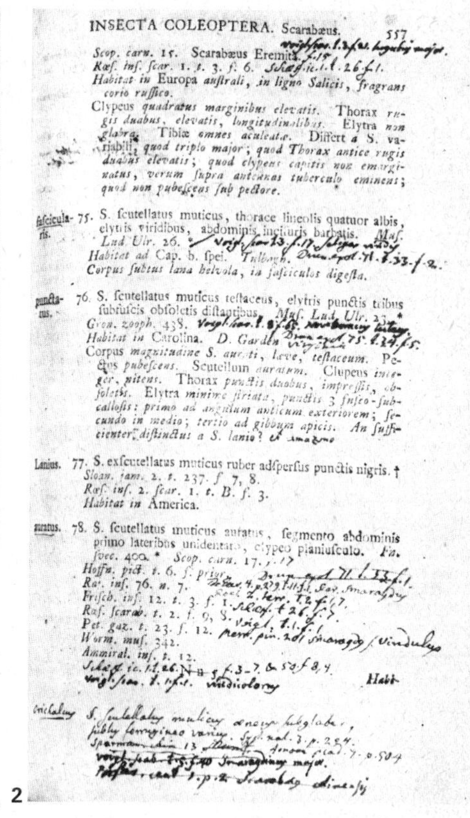

INSECTA COLEOPTERA. Scarabæus. 557

*Scop. carn.* 15. Scarabæus Eremita.
*Ræſ. inſ. ſcar.* 1. *t.* 3. *f.* 6.
*Habitat in* Europa *auſtrali*, *in ligno Salicis*, *fragrans corio ruſſico.*
Clypeus *quadratus marginibus elevatis.* Thorax *rugis duabus*, *elevatis*, *longitudinalibus.* Elytra *non glabra.* Tibiæ *omnes aculeatæ.* Differt *a* S. variabili, *quod triplo major*; *quod Thorax antice rugis duabus elevatis*; *quod clypeus capitis non emarginatus*, *verum ſupra antennas tuberculo eminens*; *quod non pubeſcens ſub pectore.*

fasciculatus. 75. S. ſcutellatus muticus, thorace lineolis quatuor albis, elytris viridibus, abdominis inciſuris barbatis. *Muſ. Lud. Ulr.* 26.
*Habitat ad* Cap. b. ſpei. *Tulbagh.*
*Corpus ſubtus lana helvola*, *in faſciculos digeſta.*

punctatus. 76. S. ſcutellatus muticus teſtaceus, elytris punctis tribus ſubfuſcis obſoletis diſtantibus. *Muſ. Lud. Ulr.* 23.*
*Gron. zooph.* 438.
*Habitat in* Carolina. *D. Garden.*
Corpus *magnitudine S. aurati*, *læve*, *teſtaceum.* Pectus *pubeſcens.* Scutellum *auratum.* Clypeus *integer*, *nitens.* Thorax *punctis duobus*, *impreſſis*, *obſoletis.* Elytra *minime ſtriata*, *punctis* 3 *fuſco-ſubcalloſis*: *primo ad angulum anticum exteriorem*; *ſecundo in medio*; *tertio ad gibbum apicis.* *An ſufficienter diſtinctus a S. lanio?*

Lanius. 77. S. exſcutellatus muticus ruber adſperſus punctis nigris. †
*Sloan. jam.* 2. *t.* 237. *f.* 7, 8.
*Ræſ. inſ.* 2. *ſcar.* 1. *t. B. f.* 3.
*Habitat in* America.

auratus. 78. S. ſcutellatus muticus auratus, ſegmento abdominis primo lateribus unidentato, clypeo planiuſculo. *Fn. ſvec.* 400.* *Scop. carn.* 17.
*Hoffn. pict. t.* 6. *f. prior.*
*Rai. inſ.* 76. *n.* 7.
*Friſch. inſ.* 12. *t.* 3. *f.* 1.
*Ræſ. ſcarab. t.* 2. *f.* 9, 8.
*Pet. gaz. t.* 23. *f.* 12.
*Worm. muſ.* 342.
*Ammiral. inſ. t.* 12.

**1** Carl von Linné (1707–78), the Swedish naturalist who did pioneer work on an ordered system of classifying living things.

**2** This is a facsimile of a page from *Systema Naturae*, the book Linné (also called Linnaeus) wrote to describe his classification system.

It was, in fact, a Swedish botanist, Carl von Linné (better known by his family name of Carolus Linnaeus), who in the eighteenth century, developed a system of classification which formed the basis for the terms used today. Linnaeus proposed that organisms should be classified according to general structure and shape, physiology, distribution and mode of life. An incidental advantage of this system is that it has often helped scientists seeking the origins of various species.

As a first step, Linnaeus divided the Universe into animal, vegetable and mineral kingdoms. It is easy to see the yardsticks which he applied in this division, although in recent years scientists have established that the divisions are by no means as clear-cut as they might at first appear. While retaining the three kingdoms, modern classification takes into account many more classifications and divisions than Linnaeus did, not only because of the vast number of new plants and animals discovered in the last two centuries, but also to allow scientists to define organisms with a much higher degree of exactness.

Interbreeding among animals of the same species produces offspring which show characteristics of both parents. This dog appears to be the offspring of a St Bernard and a beagle.

## Major subdivisions

The extremely detailed study of organisms necessitated by this more detailed system of classification has led biologists to uncover a number of unexpected points of resemblance between apparently dissimilar organisms, particularly in the animal kingdom. In many cases, anatomical studies have shown common features which have been disguised, over the generations, by environmental development. Hence, classification has provided much evidence to support evolutionary theory, even to suggesting possible characteristics of 'missing links'.

In his hierarchical classification Man, a member of the animal kingdom, falls into the *sub-kingdom Metazoa,* which includes all animals (except sponges) which have more than one cell. His possession of a backbone places him in the *phylum Chordata,* and within this phylum he is allotted the *subphylum Gnasthostomata* (animals with true jaws).

At each stage of this differentiation, the subdivision into which Man falls contains fewer and fewer creatures, until, eventually, Man is the only one left and is uniquely described as belonging to the *species sapiens* within the *genus Homo.*

Every organism, almost without exception, can be uniquely classified in this way by the accumulation of more and more specific characteristics which distinguish it from other organisms. The final classification is the species, which can be regarded as a biologically closed set. The individuals within a species are able to breed to produce offspring similar to the parents, but are unable to breed with individuals of another species.

The number of species within a single genus, and in general the number of subdivisions of any stage varies widely. For example there is only one species (Man) within the family Hominidae, whereas there are more than 22,000 species of daisy and over 930,000 species of insects. When biologists have classified a species, it must be named. Linnaeus first used what is called the *binomial system* of naming, and animals (but not plants) are named according to the system published in his *Systema Naturae* (1758). In this system, each animal is designated by two words, the first indicating the genus to which it belongs and the second the species. For example, both the wolf and the dog are placed in the genus *Canis,* the wolf being *Canis lupus* and the dog *Canis familiaris.* From these names it can be seen that the wolf and the dog are closely related animals, but very unlikely to interbreed, at least under natural conditions.

The wolf and the dog illustrate how deceptive physical appearance can be when determining species. Wolves and Alsatians are very similar to each other, and in fact at a distance one can easily be mistaken for the other. On the other hand, there seems very little resemblance between an Alsatian and a Cairn terrier, but both these dogs are of the same species and can interbreed freely.

## Naming system

It is usual to write the generic name with a capital letter and the specific name with a small letter. Under the International Rules of Nomenclature, no two genera shall have the same name but a genus of plants may have the same name as a genus of animals, as confusion between the two is rather unlikely. Species belonging to different genera may have the same specific name, however, the specific name usually indicating a similar habitat or perhaps a similarity in colour. For example, the white wagtail (*Motacilla alba*) and the fairy tern (*Gygis alba*) share the same specific name. This similarity of names indicates that both kinds of birds are largely white in colour (*alba* is the Latin word for white).

1

2

**1** Classification is a means of picking out one species from the confusing variety within the plant or animal kingdoms. Each organism can be conveniently classified and defined.
**2** Male birds often have bright, colourful plumage to attract a female for mating. The female's feathers are usually dull and drab to camouflage her while she hatches her eggs.

Most modern taxonomists (specialists in classification) accept the idea that all newly discovered species should have a *type specimen,* which is used to designate the particular characteristics of that species. In this way, the type specimen serves as a basis for identification of other specimens and to carry the name of that particular species. If, as in the cases of many well-known species, the original specimen is lost (for instance the first dog or horse to be classified), a new one called a *lectotype* is selected.

When a species is first described and named, the reason for the name must be given and usually the first name proposed is given preference. For instance, when Professor J.L.B. Smith described the first modern coelacanth fish caught in 1938, he named it *Latimeria chalumnae* after his assistant Miss Latimer. This became the type specimen of this species. The second coelacanth, caught in 1953, he named *Malania anjouanae* in honour of Dr Malan who was then Prime Minister of South Africa. However, the species may be transferred to another genus under a revised

**1** Species within the class Mammalia range from Man, to the bat, to the extraordinary duck-billed platypus. Although these species are so very different in habitat and physiology, anatomical studies show how they could have developed from common ancestors. Each species has developed characteristics which are advantageous to it within its environment.

**2** Physical appearance is not always a reliable guide in identifying a species. All dogs belong to the same species (*Canis familiaris*) despite their marked physical differences. On the other hand the fox, although it resembles a dog, cannot interbreed with dogs under normal circumstances to produce offspring, and so is of a different species.

classification. In complete naming, the author's name and the date the species was first 'described' (studied carefully) follows the specific name. The author's name may be abbreviated if it is well known, thus Linnaeus is usually abbreviated to 'Linn' or 'L'. The full name given to man is therefore Homo *sapiens* Linnaeus 1758.

In many of the vertebrate (back-boned) animals which are found in different parts of the world, there may be considerable variation in individuals of the species. Such a species is divided into a number of geographically defined *subspecies*. Characteristically, members of one subspecies must occupy a distinct geographical area and must show distinctive structural features.

When a subspecies is first described and named, a third name (the subspecific name) follows the binomial name of the species and so the subspecies has a *trinomial* nomenclature. One of the first subspecies to be described usually takes the species name as its subspecific name, but this does not necessarily mean that it shows specially typical characteristics. For example, the mallard duck found in Great Britain is *Anas platyrhynchos*, whereas the Greenland mallard is *Anas platyrhynchos conboschas*, and the Florida duck *Anas platyrhynchos fulvigula*. Most geographical subspecies occur in birds because they are best adapted to cover a large geographical range. The tiny bird which is known in Britain by the tiny word *wren*

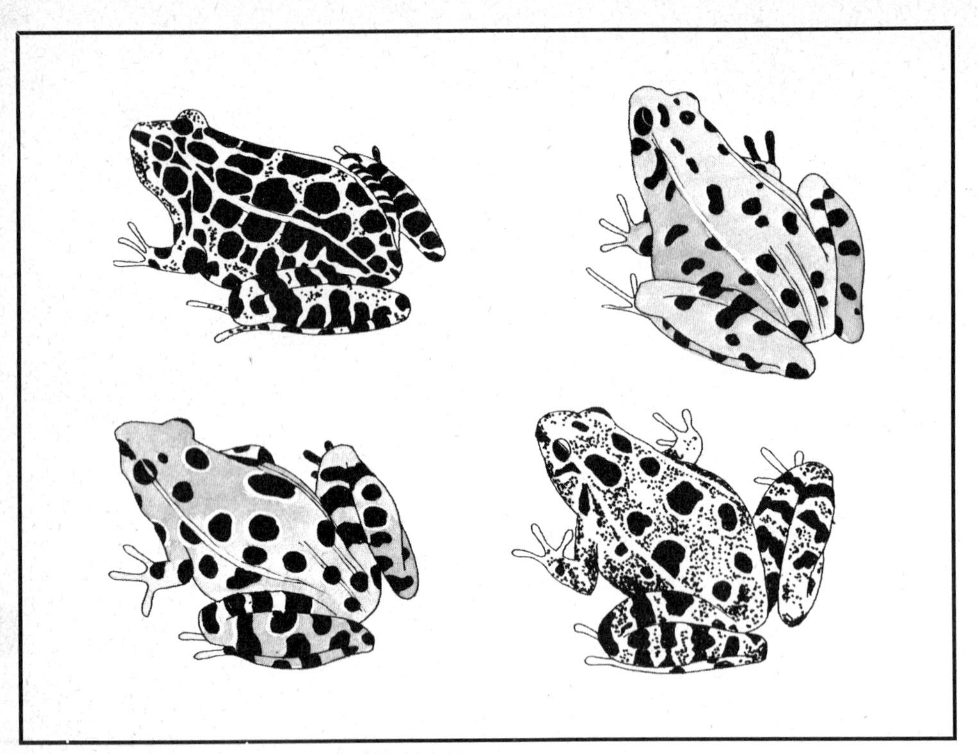

Geographical variations are often very marked. These frogs are of the species *Rana pipiens*. *Top*, Florida and New Jersey varieties; *bottom*, Colorado and Texas varieties.

rejoices in the scientific name of *Troglodytes troglodytes troglodytes*.

Characteristics of different subspecies may be relatively constant, with only minor differences, or there may be more variation. The great tit (*Parus major*) occurs over most of Europe and Asia but its characteristics stay more or less constant throughout the whole of the northern part of its range. However, there is more variation in plumage in the southern part of its range. Until 1960, subspecies were further subdivided into *varieties*, and in horticulture these were even further subdivided into *strains*. But all divisions and subspecies are now taxonomically obsolete.

## Variations within species

A species, as a unit, is reproductively isolated and it generally breeds true, so that the new generation will closely resemble the old. Exceptions do occur, however, and such variants are referred to as *mutants*. The chances of a new mutation being successful are very low, and such an organism is unlikely to survive in the wild, especially if it differs greatly from the normal type. Some species produce mutations more than others do, and species with such a high variability are better equipped to tolerate sudden changes in climate or vegetation, or even invasion by competing species.

The taxonomist therefore has the problem of deciding when a mutation has become a new, distinct species. He also must face the difficulties which arise from variations within species, as well as from cross-breeding and marked differences between the sexes of one species. He may then have to find a place in his classification system for these 'new' creatures.

Variations less drastic than mutations occur in all species of animals and plants, and the variations become most obvious in the 'highest' (most advanced) groups. Variations become more conspicuous still in the vertebrate group of animals, and especially in the primates (the group of mammals of which Man is a member).

Variations in both physique and intellectual capacity in Man are obvious, and to us, no two people are alike. However, such variations are insignificant in taxonomy and cannot form the basis for the breakdown into separate species, as all 'races' of Man are able to interbreed.

There are similar variations within other groups of animals (for example in monkeys), but variations in some characteristics usually seem less obvious to us. Variations within a species occur in other mammals too and are especially conspicuous in the mouse and the guinea-pig, where a wide range of colour patterns can occur. Variations within a species are much less frequent in the invertebrate animals.

In some groups of invertebrate animals, not only is there little variation within a species but there may be little variation *between* separate species. Examples can be found among the insects, where sometimes two species have apparently the same forms at all stages in their life history (for example, in two species of the fruit fly *Drosophilae*). There are similar instances among the vertebrates, but here there are also frequently differences in behaviour or distribution which help in distinguishing different species.

Variations within a species often occur due to differences in sex (called *sexual dimorphism*) and these differences are especially obvious in birds. The males of a species are often adorned with brightly coloured feathers to attract the female, while the female herself may be drably coloured so that she is camouflaged while incubating her eggs; the difference in colour between a cock and a hen pheasant is a good example.

Variations within a species occur in plants, too, and such differences are most obvious in flowering plants where there may be variations in flowering time, stem length and seed size.

Occasionally in nature, and more often under controlled conditions, it is found that two distinct species *will* interbreed. Such interbreeding produces a *hybrid* which generally has a form which is a combination of those of the two parents. Cases of cross-breeding do occur most frequently in animals kept isolated and under confined conditions, and the two parents are usually of closely related species – almost always of the same genus. For instance, the mule is a hybrid of a male ass and a female horse. In plants, the range of hybrids may be enormous and the taxonomist usually lumps them all together as species *hybrida* – for instance, all cultivated garden roses are *Rosa hybrida*.

Hybrids are sometimes bred to bring together desirable characteristics of two species. For example canaries, *Serinus canarius*, are often crossed with goldfinches, *Carduelis carduelis*, to produce a hybrid (a so-called canary 'mule') which has a fine song. However, such 'mules' are generally unable to interbreed.

Hybrids do occur occasionally in the wild. Such cross-breeding between species is rare in nature, as by definition the species should be distinct in its physiology and habitat as well as in structure, and if such species were not isolated genetically they would eventually merge and become a single species.

## Modern developments

Taxonomy is not a static science, and changes are continually being made as new evidence is accumulated. This evidence may come from fossil finds which supply the 'missing links' for a chain of reasoning which enables a taxonomist to classify an organism in terms of its evolution from earlier extinct species. In addition, the science of genetics, by looking inside the cell at the genes and chromosomes which determine just what the outward characteristics of a creature shall be, provides another way of establishing classifications.

Future advances in this most important branch of science will depend to a very great extent on the outcome of current research to link anatomical and physical characteristics with variations in genetic patterns within the cell. The day may not be too far distant when classification is done purely on the basis of microscopic investigation of the cells. Results of work already completed show that in most cases these studies have confirmed the work of men like Linnaeus, who worked without the benefit of modern cytology and palaeontology. Regardless of the form which the science of taxonomy may take in the future, science will always be indebted to these men whose overwhelming curiosity about the world around them, and determination to build an ordered system, has done so much to increase our understanding of the plant and animal kingdoms in all their marvellous diversity.

# Sorting the living millions

A million and a half known species inhabit our globe, yet biologists have found similarities which place them into definite family groupings. Some creatures have rather surprising relatives.

THERE ARE many different kinds of living things, many more than any one person could ever hope to see in his lifetime. At the last count, there were about one and a half million distinct species of animals and plants. The array of different forms and modes of living is staggering.

But despite their obvious differences, all living things have seven basic characteristics in common. The way in which these characteristics vary from species to species affects the shape and structure of the organism and so leads to the great diversity of life forms. These basic characteristics are locomotion (movement), nutrition, growth, respiration, excretion, sensitivity (irritability) and reproduction.

For convenience, and to make their study easier, biologists divide forms of life into a number of groups of various sizes. The major division is into animals and plants, generally called the Animal Kingdom and the Plant Kingdom. This division rests on five features in which the two main groups differ.

### Animal and plant growth

Firstly, the patterns of growth are different. An animal generally grows to a certain size and shape – and then stops. Furthermore, growth occurs 'all over', although sometimes not all growth takes place at the same rate. For instance, the size of a newborn baby's head is much larger in proportion to the rest of his body than it is in an adult. In contrast to this, a plant usually grows continuously and the growth tends to be restricted to a certain part of the plant, such as a root or shoot.

Secondly, animals and plants differ in their numbers of organs. Most animals have organs (such as the liver or kidney) in definite numbers, whereas plants show an indefinite repetition of similar organs – they have lots of leaves, lots of flowers and lots of seeds.

Thirdly, one of the most important differences between members of the two kingdoms is that of nutrition, and this is perhaps the most fundamental difference of all. Plants obtain all their food using *simple* raw materials (carbon dioxide and water) and sunlight. This process is called *phototrophic* nutrition because it depends on the presence of light (photosynthesis). Animals do not contain the essential substance for this process – chlorophyll – and must rely on taking in ready-made *complex* foodstuffs. This is called *heterotrophic* nutrition. Plants such as fungi and mistletoe, which lack chlorophyll, also take in complex foodstuffs and are heterotrophic, violating the general rule.

The fourth feature in which animals and plants differ is that of movement. In general, animals are free-moving and plants are static.

Despite their extreme and obvious differences, the calf and the Japanese Sunshade (*Coprinus plicatus*) are both examples of heterotrophic organisms. These take in their food in complex form, while most plants use sunlight and simple chemicals to manufacture their food.

Finally, the fundamental difference is carried right down to the cell level. Plant cells are generally surrounded by a definite cell wall, whereas those of animals are not, having only a thin membrane separating the inside of the cell from its external environment.

These, then, are the gross differences between animals and plants. By and large they enable a biologist to decide to which kingdom a certain organism belongs. For instance, no one would have difficulty assigning an oak tree or a horse to its appropriate kingdom. But it is by no means so easy for all organisms, especially some of the single-celled organisms (such as bacteria) or flagellate organisms (such as the euglena). Furthermore, certain species of flagellates possess the ability to change their form of nutrition depending on the conditions around them. In one stage, they may feed like plants, and at the next stage, after losing their chlorophyll, they may absorb ready-made food in much the same way as an animal does.

Because so many of these single-celled creatures appear to be on the border-line between animals and plants, and cannot dogmatically be called either, many scientists have suggested creating a third kingdom called the *Protists* into which all these forms can be lumped. As a result, the Protists tend to be a mixed group sharing only one common characteristic – that of consisting of a single cell.

There are nearly one and a half million living species in the world, but how many living creatures? Nobody has ever really tried to figure this out, and even if this were possible, the result would be so huge as to be almost meaningless. All that can be done is to give some idea of the numbers of a single representative kind of animal or plant. For example, it has been estimated that in the Gulf of Maine off the north-east coast of the United States there are about 8,000 million single-celled plants called *diatoms* in every square metre of sea water. In the same gulf, in about 36,000 square miles of sea, there are something like four million tons of small marine crustaceans called *copepods*. Another example is the huge number of roundworms (*nematodes*) taken from a single rotting apple – 90,600 of three different species!

More useful perhaps than total numbers of individuals is the number of different species known in each group. Of the one and a half million known species, more than a million are animals – and 97 per cent of these are invertebrates.

Biologists divide the animals into 13 main subdivisions called *phyla*. The members of the first phylum, the *Protozoans,* occur practically everywhere. They are classified into four main groups according to the ways they move. The *Flagellata* possess long whip-like threads called flagella which they lash in order to move through the water in which they live. The *Rhizopods,* typified by the amoeba, do not possess flagella but move by producing a lobe at one side of the body and 'flowing' the rest of the body into this extension. The third group move by beating short hairs called cilia and so are called *Ciliates.* Most of the members of these three groups are free-living and are found in soils, lakes, streams, the sea, and so on. They also vary in their methods of nutrition: some are *heterotrophic* (food-eating) and some, being able to synthesize their own food, are *autotrophic*. But the fourth group, the *Sporozoa,* are all characterized by being parasitic. They either do not move at all (except when their host moves) or they show amoeboid movement like the Rhizopods. A good example is *Plasmodium,* the parasitic organism which causes malaria.

## Feeding habits

The Protozoans are mainly microscopic, only one or two being just visible to the naked eye. The members of other phyla of the Animal Kingdom are generally larger. Most people have seen a sponge, which is an animal of the next phylum, the *Porifera.* Many of these animals are brightly coloured, and there is a great variation in size and shape. But whatever their size, they all feed in the same way. They draw in a current of water through many small pores over their surface and trap suspended food particles in *collar-cells* which ingest the food. The water leaves via fewer, larger holes.

The next phylum has a greater number of species and includes corals, sea-anemones and jelly-fish. These, called the *Coelenterates,* also show a much greater variety of forms, of which the two basic ones are the *polyp* (like coral) and the *medusa* (like a jelly-fish). A polyp resembles a small anchored jelly-like tube with a

**Protists:** one-celled organisms with simple structures. Some heterotrophs (food-eating); some autotrophs (food-making); some both.

**Flagellates** (Phylum Mastigophora): one-celled; movement by long, hair-like flagella.

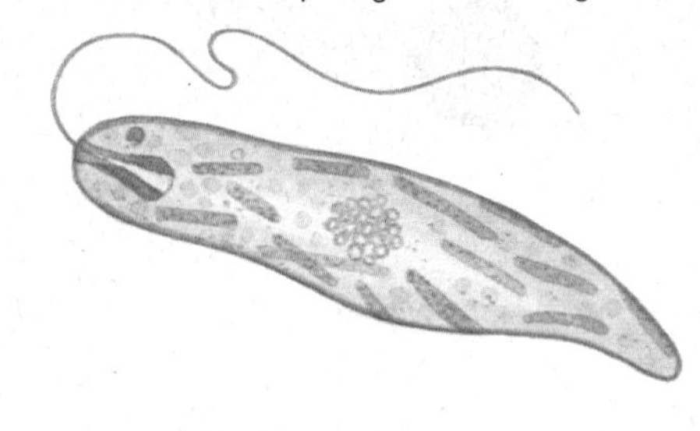

Euglena

**Ciliates** (Phylum Ciliophora): one-celled; many tiny hairs called cilia for motion.

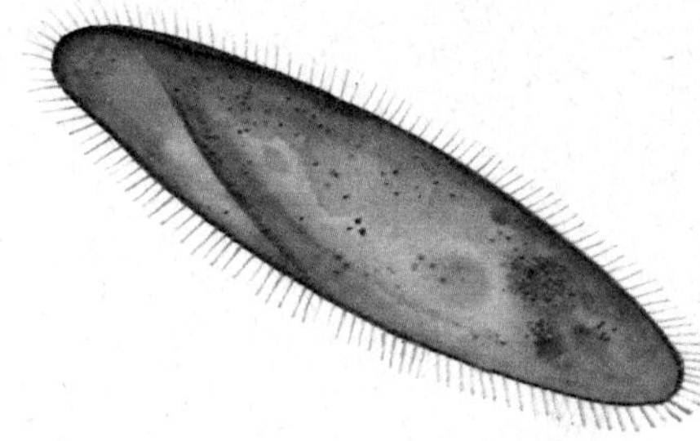

Paramecium

**Rhizopods** (Phylum Sarcodina): one-celled; movement by pseudopods ('false feet').

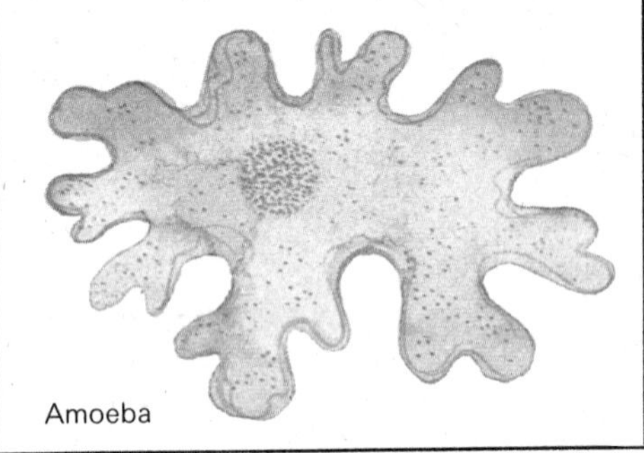

Amoeba

**Sporozoans** (Phylum Sporozoa): one-celled parasites; no adaptation for motion.

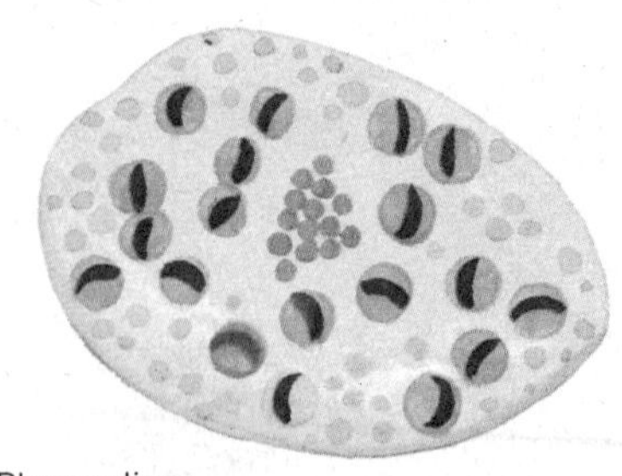

Plasmodium

**Plants:** autotrophic (produce their own food); chlorophyll in chloroplasts for use in photosynthesis; multi-celled (many cells) in complex organization.

**Thallophytes** (Phylum Thallophyta): single-celled or multi-celled; capable of sexual and/or asexual reproduction; sometimes classified as protists because they lack chlorophyll.

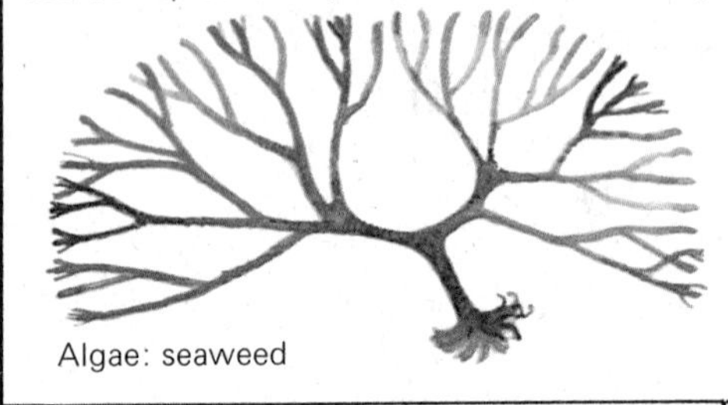

Algae: seaweed

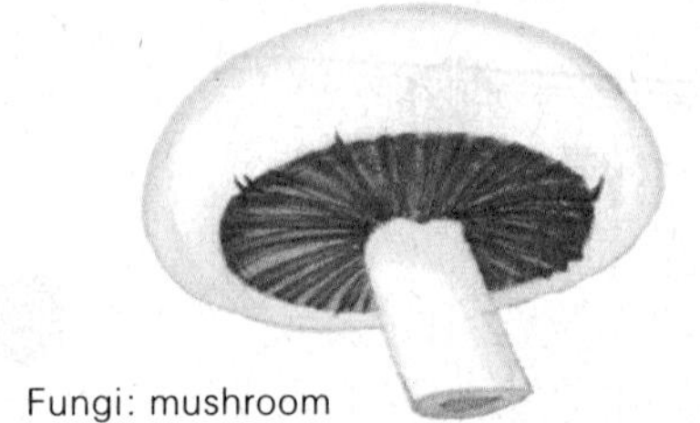

Fungi: mushroom

**Bryophytes** (Phylum Bryophyta): mosses and ferns; generally live in moist areas; usually small.

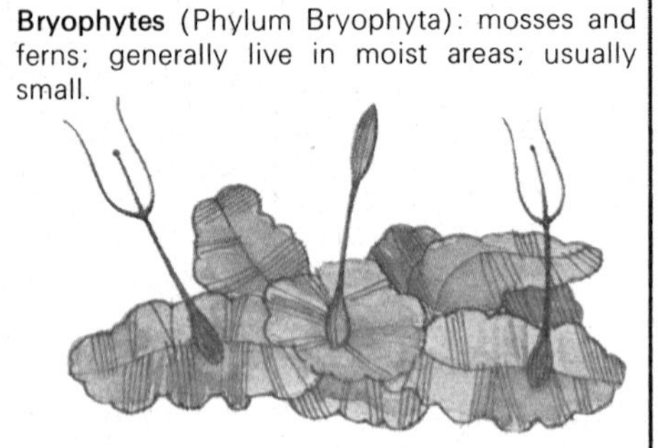

Horned liverwort

**Ferns** (Phylum Tracheophyta, Class Filicineae): no seeds; conducting tubes inside.

Lady fern

**Conifers** (Phylum Tracheophyta, Class Gymnospermae): produce seeds in cones.

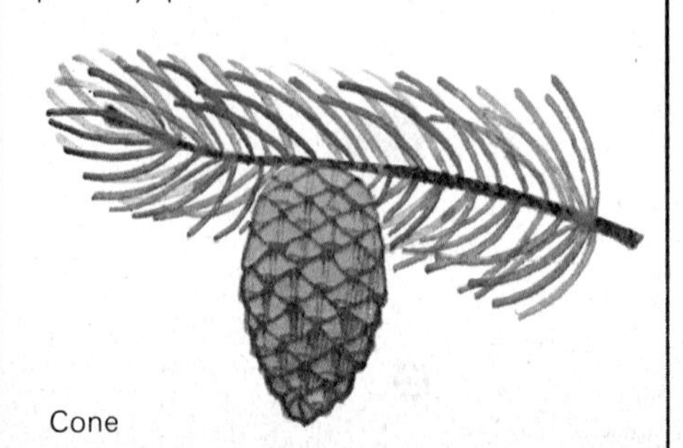

Cone

**Flowers** (Phylum Tracheophyta, Class Angiospermae): seeds within fruits; conducting tubes.

Rose

Protists, plants and animals are the three main divisions of living things. Examples taken from each phylum within these groups show the diversity which occurs. Even within an individual phylum, there are extremely wide variations in appearance, habitat and physiology.

**Animals:** all heterotrophic (food-eating) and composed of more than one cell (multi-cellular); most are capable of some form of motion; nerve cells control the body, except in sponges.

**Sponges** (Phylum Porifera): no movement; fibrous skeleton or mineral skeleton.

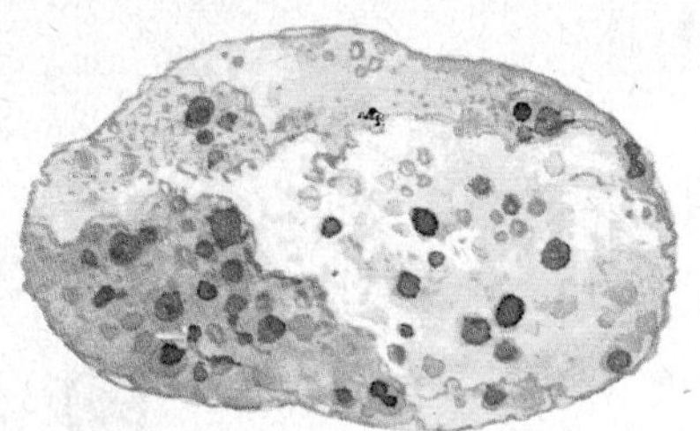

Bath sponge

**Coelenterates** (Phylum Coelenterata): have only two layers of cells (diploblastic); basic forms are polyp (like coral) and medusa (like jelly-fish); tentacles with stinging cells.

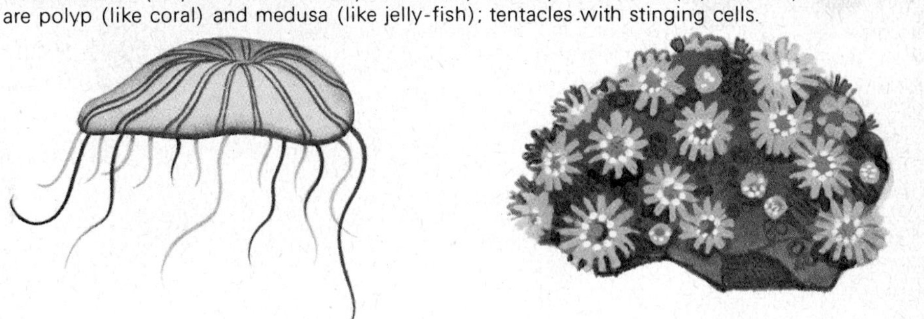

Jelly-fish

Coral

**Flatworms** (Phylum Platyhelminthes): flat-bodied worms, many parasitic.

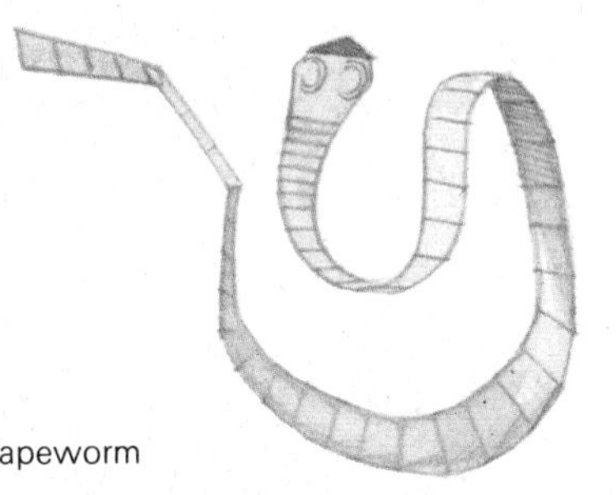

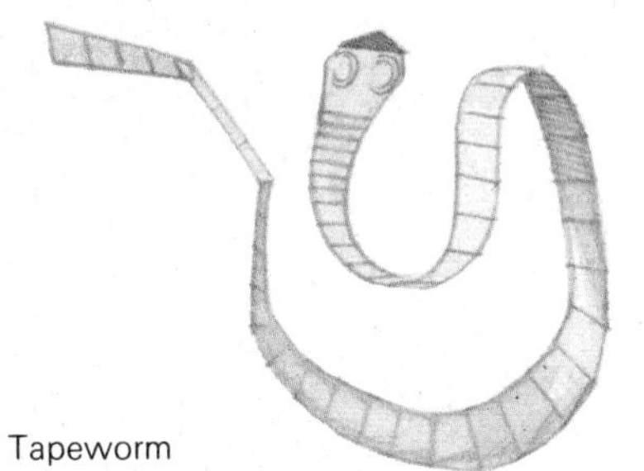

Tapeworm

**Segmented Worms** (Phylum Annelida): body composed of similar segments.

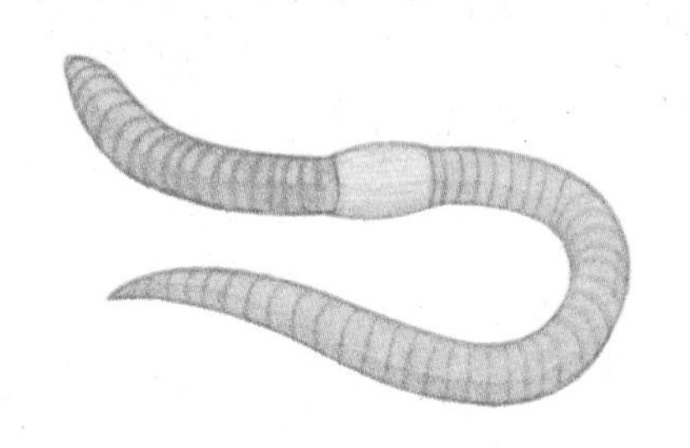

Earthworm

**Insects** (Phylum Arthropoda, Class Insecta): external skeleton; three pairs of legs.

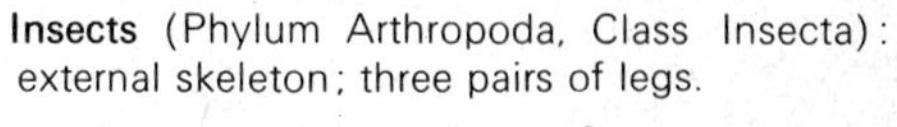

Butterfly

**Crustaceans** (Phylum Arthropoda, Class Crustacea): jointed legs; external skeleton.

Crab

**Arachnids** (Phylum Arthropoda, Class Arachnida): eight jointed legs in pairs.

Tarantula

**Molluscs** (Phylum Mollusca): often possess a shell; internal fluid circulation.

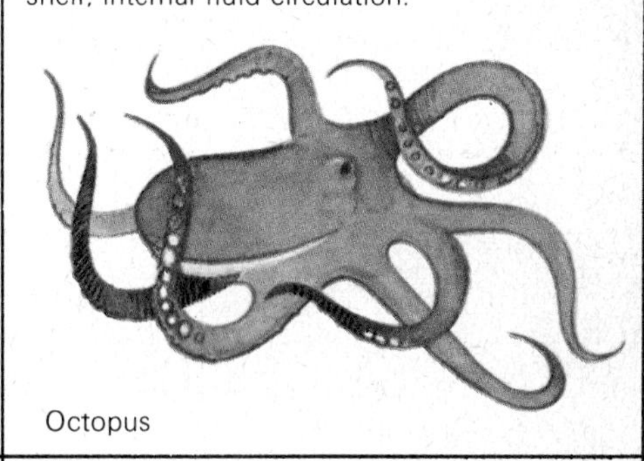

Octopus

**Echinoderms** (Phylum Echinodermata): spiny body; marine (live in water).

Starfish

**Fishes** (Phylum Chordata, Class Pisces): breathe with gills; internal skeleton; often fins.

Trout

**Amphibians** (Phylum Chordata, Class Amphibia): live in land and water; lungs in adults.

Newt

**Reptiles** (Phylum Chordata, Class Reptilia): dry skin; scale-covered body.

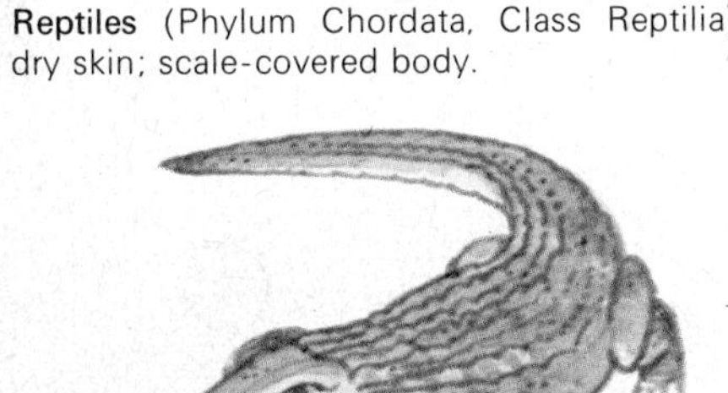

Alligator

**Birds** (Phylum Chordata, Class Aves): feathers on body; constant temperature; many fly.

Seagull

**Mammals** (Phylum Chordata, Class Mammalia): constant temperature; produce milk for young.

Horse

fringe of tentacles at the open end with which it catches food. A medusa is a free-swimming creature, also with tentacles.

Some Coelenterates, such as the *Hydrazoa*, can exist in both polyp and medusa forms in alternation. In the sea-anemones (*Anthazoa*) the medusal stage is reduced and the polyp is much developed. On the other hand the true jelly-fish (*Scyphozoa*) have the polyp stage reduced so that the animals spend all their life floating or gently pulsating in the surface waters of the oceans.

The Coelenterates are characterized by having only two layers of cells making up their bodies (called the *diploblastic* condition). All the rest of the animals can be considered as having a third layer between the two (the *tripoblastic* condition).

This latter condition is seen in its simplest form in the next phylum, which contains worm-like creatures called *Platyhelminths*. Most important of these are the parasitic flukes (*trematodes*) and tapeworms (*cestodes*) which account for diseases which affect 90 per cent of the population in some tropical areas of the world.

## Worms and insects

The next large phylum also consists of worms, the *Annelids*. Perhaps more familiar, but again presenting a bewildering array of forms, these include the earthworm and marine worms such as the ragworm and lugworm. All these worms share the dubious distinction of being used as bait by fishermen. There are also worms which live in tubes, such as *Pomatoceros*, which lives in a chalky triangular tube, and the fanworm, which lives in a tube of mucus studded with grains of sand. The Annelids also include the leeches, of which only a few species, despite their reputation, are blood-suckers.

The next phylum contains the *Arthropods*. This is the largest and most varied group of all, and 850,000 of the 930,000 known species are insects. These mostly highly successful animals are the only invertebrates to colonize all the land and also to master flight. The insects include the dragonflies, mayflies, cockroaches, grasshoppers, locusts, lice, bugs, bees, wasps, beetles, weevils, flies, termites, earwigs, ants, butterflies, moths and many other smaller and lesser-known groups. Apart from the insects, there are two other main groups, the *Crustaceans* and the *Arachnids*, as well as six other minor groups (including the *Myriapods* – the centipedes and millipedes). The Crustaceans are mostly marine forms and include shrimps, prawns, lobsters, crayfish, squat lobsters, hermit crabs and true crabs, as well as the copepods (probably the largest group in terms of numbers of individuals). The Arachnids, like the insects, are mainly terrestrial forms and include the scorpions and the spiders.

The next phylum, the *Molluscs*, are very much fewer than the Arthropods in terms of numbers, but rival them in the diversity of forms they present. The three main types are *gastropods* (snails, winkles, and so on), *bivalves* (mussels, cockles, scallops, and so on) and the *cephalopods* (squids, octopuses and cuttle-fish). Although the cephalopods are invertebrate, they are the only forms to rival the Chordates in terms of skill and intelligence. Octopuses are frequently used in psychological experiments on learning.

Plants like this water-lily live almost completely in water, while their roots are embedded in the mud beneath.

The spiny-skinned *Echinoderms* which make up the next phylum have a relatively small number of species, but are of especial interest to biologists because of the possible connection between their ancestors and those of Chordate stock. Again this phylum is entirely marine and contains such creatures as the brittle-stars, sea urchins and starfish.

Finally come the *Chordates*, the phylum that includes all the higher animals. Again there are a great variety of forms which represent the ultimate in animal evolution. The main groups are the fishes, the amphibians, the reptiles, the birds and the mammals. Into this last group, biologists put Man himself.

The Plant Kingdom contains far fewer known species. Nevertheless, their importance should not be underrated, for without plants there would be no animal life. The distinction between the principal groups of plants is perhaps less obvious, but most botanists acknowledge five main groups, often called divisions rather than phyla.

The *Thallophytes* are the simplest kinds of plants and include the algae and the fungi. Algae range from single-celled diatoms to giant-fronded seaweeds. The fungi constitute a variety of plants which range from microscopic moulds which grow on stale food to toadstools and mushrooms, some of which are edible. Closely related to fungi are the large group of plant-like creatures called bacteria; all of these are microscopic in size and many are important as the causes of various diseases.

The *Bryophytes* contain the mosses and liverworts. These plants have more complicated forms than do the Thallophytes, but share with them the characteristic of being non-vascular – that is, they do not produce specialized tissues for conveying materials from one part of the plant to another. The Bryophytes and Thallophytes together represent 130,000 of the 300,000 species of plants. The ferns and horsetails make up the *Pteridophytes*. There are 10,000 species, representing a further increase in complexity, because they have a definite root, stem and leaf structure. Like the preceding groups, they reproduce by means of a simple unit, the *spore*.

## Reproduction by seed

The reproductive unit of the next two groups is the much more complex *seed*. The group of tree-like forms, such as pines, spruces and larches, are called *Gymnosperms*. The seeds of these plants are naked, not enclosed in a protective case like those of the next group, the *Angiosperms*.

About half the known species of plants are Angiosperms. They include the well-known flowering plants, such as the oak, daffodil, dandelion, cabbage and grasses.

These are the main taxonomic groups of the Plant Kingdom, based on distinguishing physical characteristics. It is possible, however, to divide plants into groups based on their structures and habitats. One such scheme depends on the position of the buds in relation to the soil surface while they 'rest' during adverse conditions. For instance, tall perennial plants which have resting buds well clear of the soil are called *Phanerophytes* ('phaneros' means visible), and include most trees. On the other hand, *Geophytes* ('geo' means earth) have their resting buds well below the soil to protect them during adverse conditions. This group includes all plants with tubers (such as potatoes), bulbs (tulips) and corms (crocuses).

As regards habitat, the various forms living in a given set of specialized conditions can be grouped together. For instance, the *Hydrophytes* live submerged in water where they are protected from extremes of temperature and so on. Plants which can survive in soils with a high concentration of minerals such as salt are *Halophytes*.

This great variety of forms of animals and plants results from the process of evolution. Why should such variation occur? Most environments present an organism with an ever-changing set of conditions. Physical factors (temperature, pressure, light, viscosity, and so on) may vary, chemical factors (salinity, acidity, and so on) may change, and so might biological factors such as numbers and kinds of associated organisms, predators, competitors and parasites.

To allow for these various changes, an animal or plant species in the course of its race history may do one of a number of things. It may simply tolerate the conditions and continue to exist unchanged. Or it can avoid the conditions by moving or by growing a 'thick skin'. Or it can adjust to the conditions so that any changes are taken 'in its stride'. The different ways animals and plants have become adapted to their own particular sets of conditions have resulted in the diverse variations which are seen today.

# The cellular units of life

All plants and animals are composed of cells – each cell an incredibly complex living unit. While all cells have much in common, plant and animal cells differ in a number of striking ways.

ONE DAY houses will be built of bricks almost as complex as the cells which make up our bodies. No longer will the common brick be a static, solid lump. It will be a mixture of different materials – ceramics, plastics and metals – interwoven with tiny electrical circuits to control the functions which will then be taken for granted in living-room walls.

These bricks will be sensitive to sound, light and touch! Even so, they will be no more than crude models of *some* aspects of a living cell. Unlike cells, they will not be able to breed or, if damaged, heal themselves.

The way in which an organism – a plant or an animal – is related to the cells of which it is composed is also in some ways like the relationship of a community to its members. Like the members of a community, cells have their own individual characters and special tasks and together determine the nature and activity of the organism – the whole of which they are the parts.

Whether plant or animal, all organisms visible to the naked eye (macrocosmic organisms) are made up of cells comprising a *nucleus* – an inner controlling region – surrounded by a jelly-like substance, the *cytoplasm*.

## Animal and vegetable

The cell as a whole is usually isolated from its environment by a flexible, elastic membrane, the *cell membrane*. Within the cell, the nucleus is separated from the cytoplasm by a similar sort of structure, composed of lipoprotein, the *nuclear membrane*. Both of these membranes are visible in the living cell viewed through an optical microscope, and it is not difficult to take hold of them with fine needles and forceps. The cell membrane is a single membrane, but the nuclear membrane is a double structure. It has two parts equivalent to the cell membrane on either side of a space like the space inside an envelope. Accordingly the margin separating nucleus and cytoplasm is nowadays called *the nuclear envelope*.

Plant and animal cells are basically similar in all macroscopic organisms. However, we all know that plants and animals differ in important ways: animals eat other animals and plants, move from place to place and utter sounds, while plants cannot do any of these things; on the other hand, plants have leaves containing chlorophyll enabling them to make starch and sugar from water, air, sunlight and a small quantity of inorganic salts – which animals are quite unable to do.

These differences mean that plant cells have machinery or *cell organelles* inside them which are not found in animal cells and that animals are composed of types of

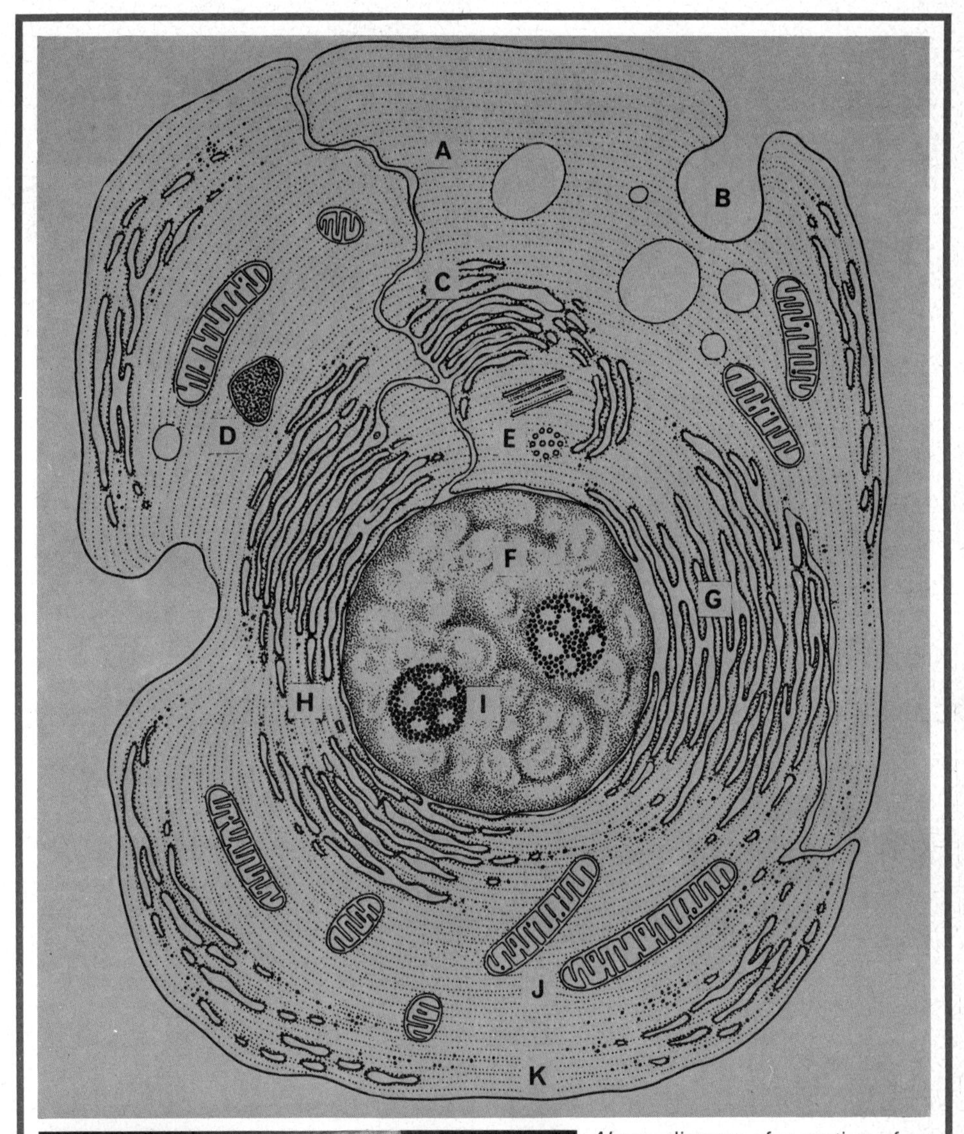


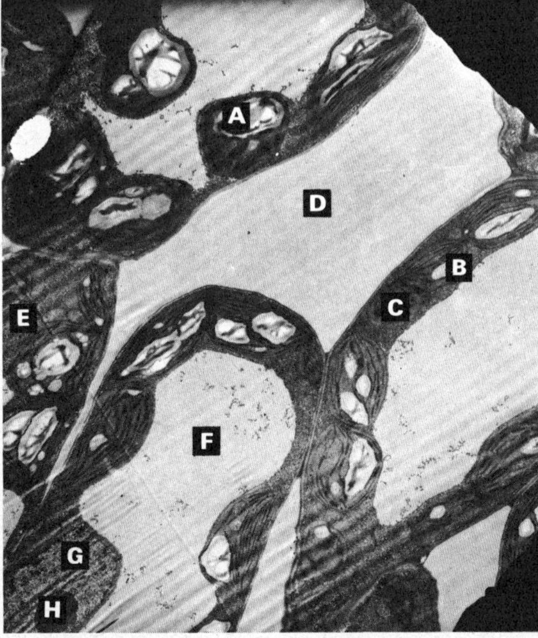


*Above,* diagram of a section of an animal cell as it appears when viewed through an electron microscope. **A** – Cytoplasm. **B** – Pinocytic vesicle. **C** – Golgi body. **D** – Lysosome. **E** – Centrosomes. **F** – Nucleus. **G** – Endoplasmic Reticulum. **H** – Nuclear membrane. **I** – Nucleolus. **J** – Mitochondria. **K** – Cell membrane. *Left,* a chenopodium leaf cell magnified approximately 4,000 times. **A** – Chloroplast. **B** – Starch. **C** – Cell wall. **D** – Air space. **E** – Mitochondria. **F** – Cell vacuole. **G** – Nucleus. **H** – Nucleolus. Here the features which distinguish the plant cell from the animal cell are clearly visible – the chloroplasts, the cell vacuole and the cell wall. The chloroplasts contain the chlorophyll without which the plant would be unable to manufacture carbohydrates. The cell vacuole contains the plant sap, while the cell wall supports plant tissue, and gives it comparative inflexibility. Cell walls are mainly cellulose – wood is the cellulose skeleton of a tree.

cells not found in plants. The fundamental similarity, but remarkable diversity, of cells within a single animal is astonishing, and when different animals in the animal kingdom are compared, or when plants are compared with animals, the diversity of cell structure is seen to be even greater. Apparently evolution operates on the Kipling principle that of 'nine and sixty ways . . . every single one of them is right' – provided that the organism survives within its environment, and breeds successfully. Principles of biological organization such as competition and natural selection, appear to operate at all levels, from the level of interaction between organisms, down to the level of interaction between cells and molecules.

Hence there are always points of resemblance as well as difference between organisms and between cells. Nowadays the points of resemblance between plant cells and animal cells are as striking as the points of difference which originally led to the recognition of separate plant and animal kingdoms. Most biologists today would agree that there is one biological kingdom of organisms – some plants, some animals, some micro-organisms, neither or both, and some, the viruses, which are in many ways more like chemicals than organisms.

## Redwood and Blue Whale

Nevertheless, the plant cell differs in three significant ways from the animal cell: it possesses *chloroplasts,* a cell wall and a *cell vacuole.* The chloroplasts (also called *plastids*) are green particles within the cytoplasm. They are green because they contain chlorophyll. When, in a living chloroplast, chlorophyll is activated by energy in sunlight, a complicated series of chemical reactions occurs in which carbon dioxide is converted into much-needed carbohydrates such as sugar, starch and cellulose. This process is called *photosynthesis.* Animal cells, which do not contain chloroplasts, are unable to get their own carbohydrate in this way.

The second feature of plant cells, the possession of a distinctive *cell wall,* depends on this ability to manufacture carbohydrates in large quantities. The plant cell walls are composed of material – mainly cellulose – produced by the cells themselves. It is photosynthesis that enables the chloroplasts to make the glucose molecules which link to form the cellulose walls. Like cement in a building the walls bind the cells into a larger organism, the plant, and support its weight. And since the chloroplasts need little more than sunlight, the carbon dioxide in the air, and water to function efficiently, plants tend to keep on growing to a remarkable extent. From cells and the supporting substances made by cells come the giant Californian redwoods.

Animal cells also produce intercellular substances and supporting materials – usually a fibrous protein like collagen – strong enough to support the bulk of an African elephant or a blue whale. However, plant cells are usually surrounded and separated by much greater quantities of intercellular substance. Cellulose is present as fairly thick walls between the cells and these cell walls are left behind when plant cells die, just as the skeleton is left behind when an animal dies. This is what wood and cork are. Cells shut up within walls are naturally capable of much less activity than the more flexibly organized cells found in animals. Plants are therefore ill adapted to move and react like animals or to eat like them.

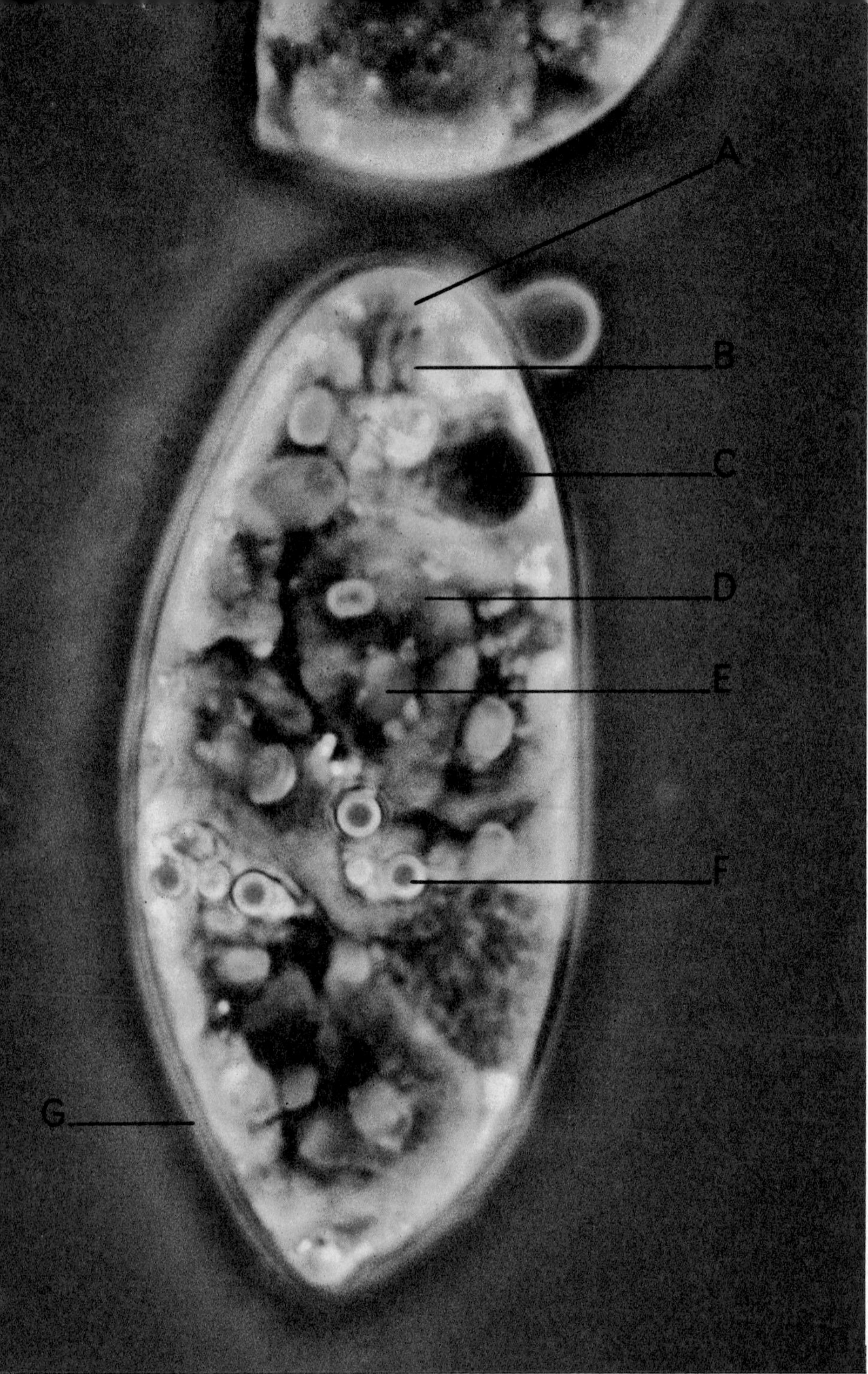


The euglena. **A** – Mouth. **B** – Gullet. **C** – Contractile vacuole. **D** – Nucleus. **E** – Endosome. **F** – Storage granules. **G** – Pellicle. Botanists and zoologists are still arguing about how this single-celled organism should be classified. For while exhibiting traits peculiar to the unicellular animals, it is also capable of developing chlorophyll, and can manufacture its own food like a plant.

Cells were first seen early in the seventeenth century with simple optical microscopes. In 1663 Robert Hooke found that thin sections of cork showed 'pores' or 'cells', and that in green vegetables these cells were filled with juices. It took nearly two centuries for scientists to realize fully that it was the juices inside the cells that were the important units of construction and *not* their walls. During this long time the word 'cell' gradually came to mean what it does today.

This meaning was worked out by the German biologists Theodor Schwann (1810–82) and Matthias Schleiden (1804–81) and other scientists, such as Rudolph Virchow (1821–1902) and Johannes Purkinje (1787–1869), as the essential propositions of the *cell theory*: (i) plants and animals are composed of similar living units – cells; (ii) all cells are derived from other cells; (iii) all tissues are composed of cells or cellular derivatives; and (iv) tissues although often differing in function, develop according to the same laws.

Although enclosed by cell walls, plant cells still need food and oxygen; and the more cells there are, the bigger the problem of providing for them. In a way, therefore, a tree is rather like a city – it has to

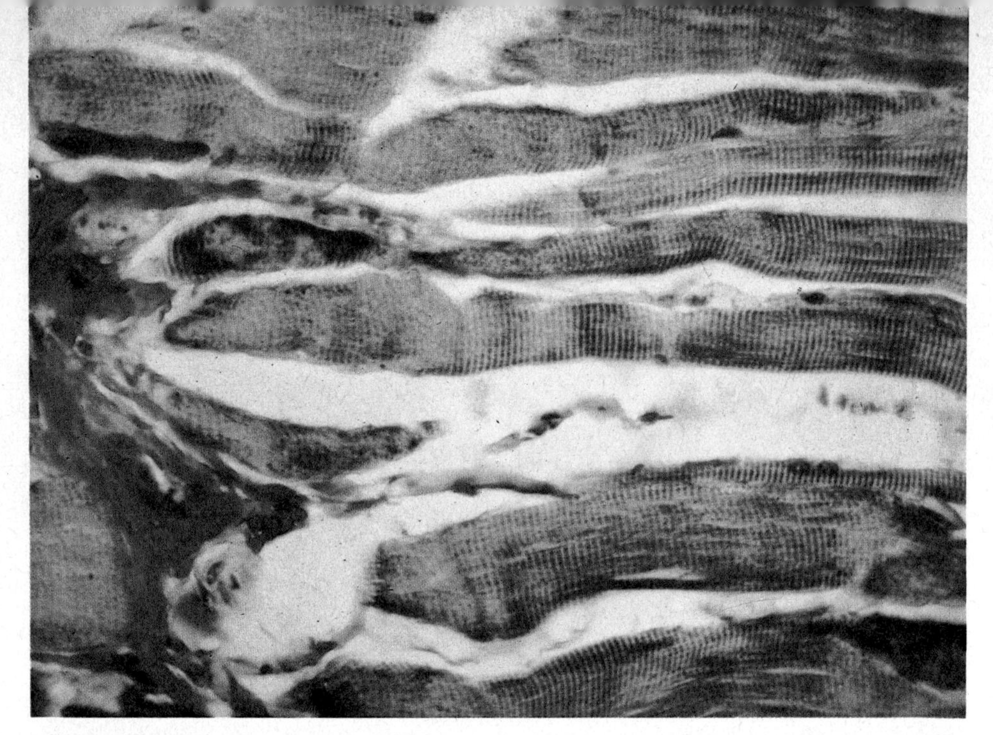

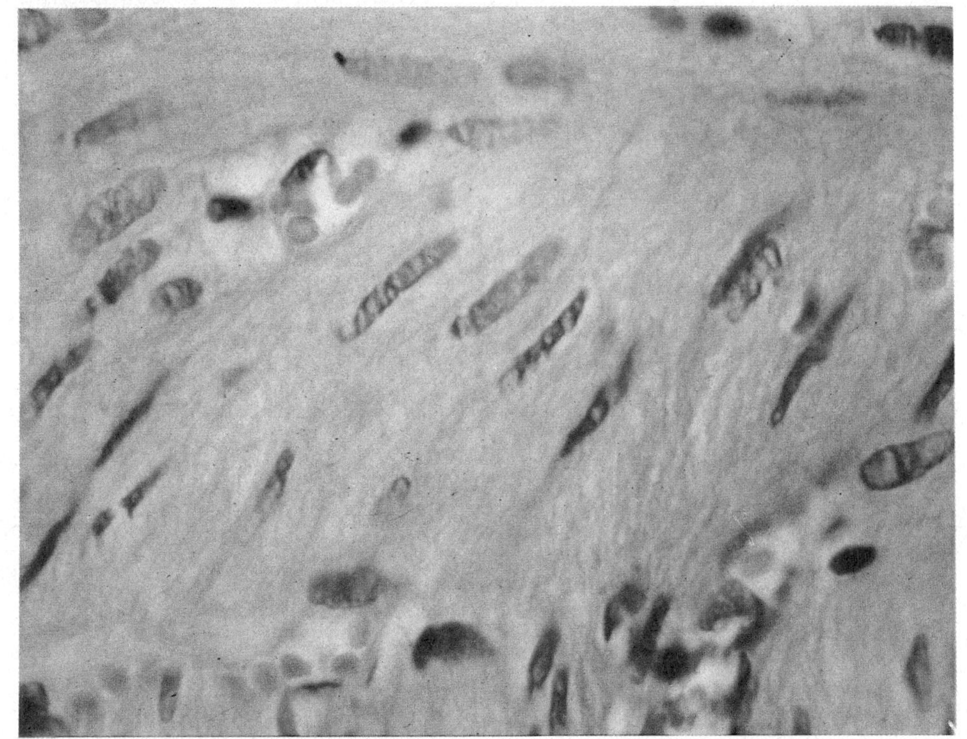

Section from the human tongue shows the large elongated cells crossed by parallel bands (transverse striations) typical of striped, or 'striated' muscle. It is used primarily to move the limbs.

Smooth muscle tissue, *bottom*, is to be found in sheets surrounding hollow organs such as the blood vessels and the gut. It has no transverse striations and cannot contract as rapidly.

develop avenues of communication and supply and exits and entrances into all its cells. It does this by developing pores or channels through each cell wall, and by developing a special tubular-shaped cell inside which there is a water space or channel, known as the *cell vacuole*. These cells, or *sieve tubes*, conduct food materials throughout the plant. Water transport is carried out by *vessels*, which are originally made up of rows of cells but, when mature, consist mainly of wide cylinders of cell-wall material.

Once a plant cell has developed a large internal vacuole, and a surrounding thick cell wall, it has little capacity for movement. Similarly, in animals, bone or cartilage cells are surrounded by hard intercellular tissue effectively preventing movement or contraction. Animals are, however, mainly composed of soft, flexible tissues.

## How muscle contracts

All cells are capable of some form of contraction, and animals have developed remarkable cells which are highly specialized for this activity, the muscle cells. Muscle cells have within their cytoplasm quantities of proteins, known as *actomyosins*. These form bundles of fine fibrils with a built-in contractile mechanism. This mechanism is not yet fully understood and is accordingly the subject of intensive research today.

A striped or striated muscle fibre – and most of the big voluntary muscles in the body are composed of cross-striped or banded fibres – contracts because one set of fibrils slides over another. The muscle tissue looks striped under a high-powered optical microscope because the fibrils in the cytoplasm of the muscle cells are arranged in overlapping bundles, and the more the fibril bundles overlap the more the muscle contracts and shortens. The fibrils themselves and the reason for their patterned arrangement along striped muscle fibre could not be seen and understood until after the invention of the electron microscope. It was then soon realized that the stripes are caused by two basic elements: thick *myosin* filaments and thin *actin* filaments.

## Cell or animal?

As scientists investigate more of the organisms around us, from the minutest to the largest, it increasingly appears that all muscular contraction and movement is related to the activity of actin- and myosin-like proteins interacting in some sort of sliding process. The myosin-like proteins are also enzymes, which is rather like saying that one has a car built of petrol. They are structural elements but at the same time chemically active. This is probably true of many of the proteins found in cells.

Large animals like elephants and dinosaurs contain vast quantities of contractile proteins (the prize steak of the gourmet is largely actomyosin) produced in all but some of the smallest animals by the activity of groups of cells. However, if you have ever looked through an optical microscope at a drop of water from a bird bath or a stagnant pond you will know that there is a whole new world of small microscopic animals actively swimming, growing and eating. In this tiny world, the

*Below*, seventeenth-century microscope, believed to be the one through which Robert Hooke first saw 'little boxes' in living things. Because of the resemblance he named them cells.

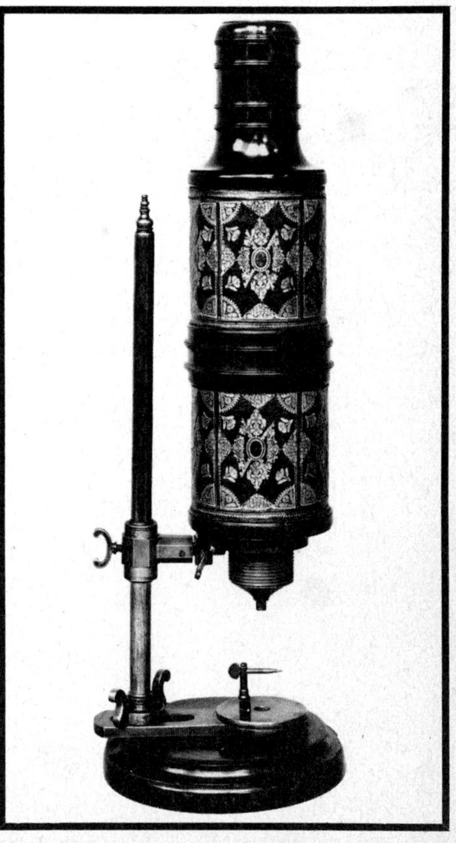

largest animals, for example the *Stentor* and the *Paramecium*, are just visible to the naked eye as fine dots in a test-tube full of clean water held up to the light. Are these animals composed of cells like the bigger animals?

The answer is a rather surprising *No*. These animals, collectively known as *Protozoa*, are in fact each roughly the equivalent of only one cell of the bigger multicellular animals. They can be called *unicellular* animals, to indicate this rough equivalence, or they can be called *acellular*, to indicate that the equivalence is only rough, and that each acellular organism can live, move and reproduce independently of the cell complex of a larger animal. For the last 40 years it has been possible to grow and maintain small pieces of multicellular tissue in the laboratory in what is called 'tissue culture', but this is much more difficult than maintaining a colony of acellular animals, which can be done quite easily at home with a few jam-jars on the window sill. A tissue culture requires sterilized surroundings and special food substances. Protozoa will often multiply happily in rainwater to which one has added a few small pieces of carrot.

These giant redwood trees in California are basically no different from the smallest plant, for they are made up of similar microscopic cells fused together by intercellular substances.

Even the elephant's great bulk can virtually be reduced to the two elements of myosin and actin, since together these form the fibre cells of the principal body tissue, striped muscle.

## Big and small nuclei

Like the cells of larger animals, protozoa are also divided into nucleus and cytoplasm, and possess within the cytoplasm the same fundamental organelles – mitochondria, ribosomes, contractile protein, and lipoprotein membrane systems. But the protozoön often possesses many tiny, more complicated structures than are seen in single cells, enabling it to move and eat as a separate organism. Members of one group of Protozoa, the *Ciliates*, have developed thousands of fine whip-like structures called *cilia*, all over the surface of their bodies. These cilia can be lashed rhythmically so enabling the animals to swim rapidly. As in the Paramecium, they can be arranged into a funnel-shaped gullet region, which acts as a kind of mouth, down which the food is swept.

The Ciliates have evolved to their present size – large for microscopic organisms – without dividing into separate cells. When any organization or structure becomes large, problems of control and communication between different parts become acute. Hence the large Ciliates have developed two kinds of nucleus, and often have many nuclei. One sort of nucleus, the *micronucleus*, is small and single, and is active mainly in reproduction. The other, the *meganucleus*, is large and there are often several of them. These meganuclei are the 'managing directors' of the organism, and are responsible for 'day-to-day running' of the animal's activities, but do not play a part at reproduction. Both sorts of nucleus, like those in the cells of all living tissues, contain the fundamental nucleic acid DNA.

In this small world, the distinction between plants and animals which seems fairly obvious when one is talking about multicellular organisms, becomes blurred. The most important feature in plants, the possession of chloroplasts, still helps us, and the primitive rule: 'that which is green is a plant', generally holds. But the distinction is complicated by the fact that some organisms can be both Protozoa (first animals) *and Protophyta* (first plants), depending on the circumstances, and can gain or lose chloroplasts according to the conditions under which they are grown, like some species of *Euglena*.

## More and less than cells

When chloroplasts are gained or lost, the food and respiratory functions of the organism also change. Here again is an aspect of cell structure and activity which is today under close investigation.

In considering the Protozoa and Protophyta we have been discussing organisms which are not quite cells, but something slightly more than cells. On the other hand, bacteria and viruses are examples of entities which are not quite organisms and are slightly less than cells. Viruses are the smallest micro-organisms of all – virtually biological molecules.

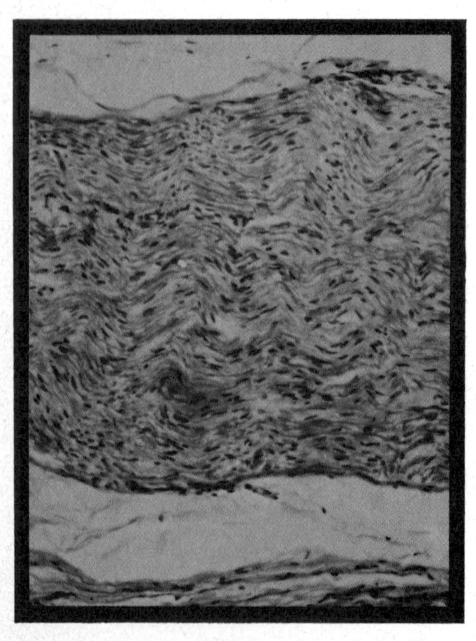

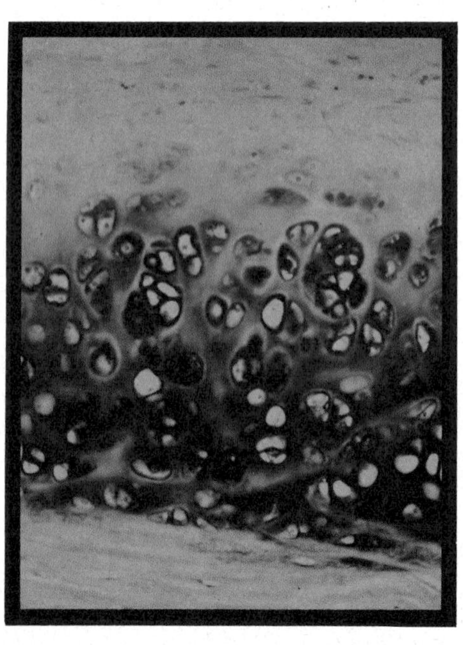

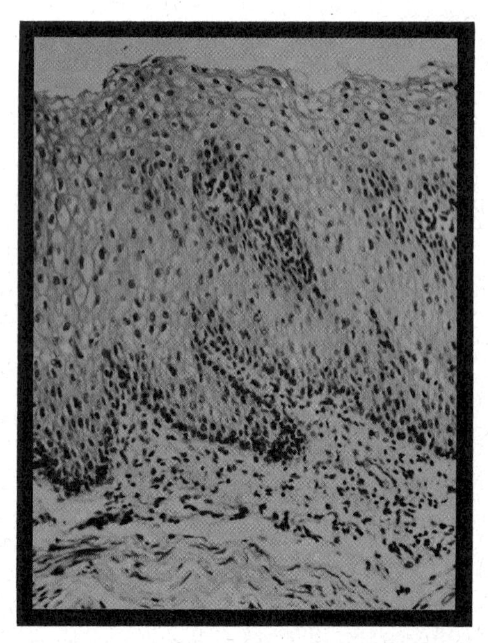

Although the cells within any one organism are all similar in composition, there is a tremendous variety of appearance according to their function and location. This is clearly illustrated by these cells taken from different parts of the human body. *Left*, longitudinal section of a nerve bundle. *Centre*, cartilage cells from the wall of the trachea (wind-pipe). *Right*, view of the epithelium cells lining the oesophagus (throat).

# Architect and builder in the living cell

**Every animal and plant cell consists of thousands of different chemical substances, each with a special task. Among them are the cell's 'architect' and 'builder' – nucleic acid and protein.**

IN 1839 a German scientist, Theodor Schwann, suggested that life could be explained in terms of ordinary chemical and physical forces. This revolutionary suggestion upset a great many people. For more than a hundred years men argued – but the evidence gradually accumulated in Schwann's favour.

Biochemists began to isolate and identify many of the organic compounds present in cells. Important among these were *enzymes*, protein molecules capable of stimulating or speeding up chemical reactions within living cells. At the same time, biologists studied the internal organization of cells.

They slowly unravelled the complex changes that take place during a cell's lifetime, particularly during cell division. They also found a clue to the chemical nature of cell structures by showing that different dyes would stain different parts of a cell. But it was not until 1940 that they began to pool their ideas and form a picture of the ceaseless chemical changes that constitute life.

After 1940, many new techniques in cell research were developed. Cells were torn open and their parts separated by powerful high-speed centrifuges. Biochemists used this technique to work out the chemical composition of *ribosomes* and *mitochondria*, tiny structures found in living cells.

Later, biologists learned to prise open cells more gently, so that delicate parts would not be damaged. They were then able to study the cell components in isolation and find out what function they performed. The invention of the electron microscope, an invaluable research tool, enabled scientists to see almost to the molecular level of cell architecture. A stage has now been reached when all this information can be fitted together to provide an explanation of life at the cellular level, solely on the basis of chemical and physical laws.

## The linchpins of life

First claim for importance among the chemicals of life must rest jointly with huge molecules called *nucleic acids* and *proteins*, because at least one of them occurs in all things considered to be 'living'. Compounds such as carbohydrates and organic acids are not universal in living cells and can be considered of secondary importance.

Nucleic acids are the compounds responsible for storing inherited information. They keep it in the form of a 'code' which is 'translated' when required. Proteins are the only compounds made directly from the instructions of this coded information, but once synthesized, proteins are responsible for running the cell. All other compounds present in cells are there either because they were synthesized by an enzymic protein, or because the protein of the cell membrane let them in.

Nucleic acids and proteins are accordingly the linchpins of life. Both are giant molecules built up from thousands of smaller simpler units. They are able to perform their special tasks solely because of their enormous size. Yet their behaviour is governed by exactly the same chemical and physical laws that apply to the smaller units from which they are built.

Fig. 1. This diagram shows how a variety of amino-acid groups link in a chain to form a simple polypeptide molecule. The importance of the peptide bond can be seen at once. (C=carbon atom. H=hydrogen. N=nitrogen. O=oxygen. S=sulphur.)

Phenylalanine | Alanine | Valine | Glycine | Leucine | Cysteine | Tyrosine (or p-hydroxyphenyl alanine) | Serine | Aspartic acid | Glutamic acid | Asparagine | Glutamine | Arginine

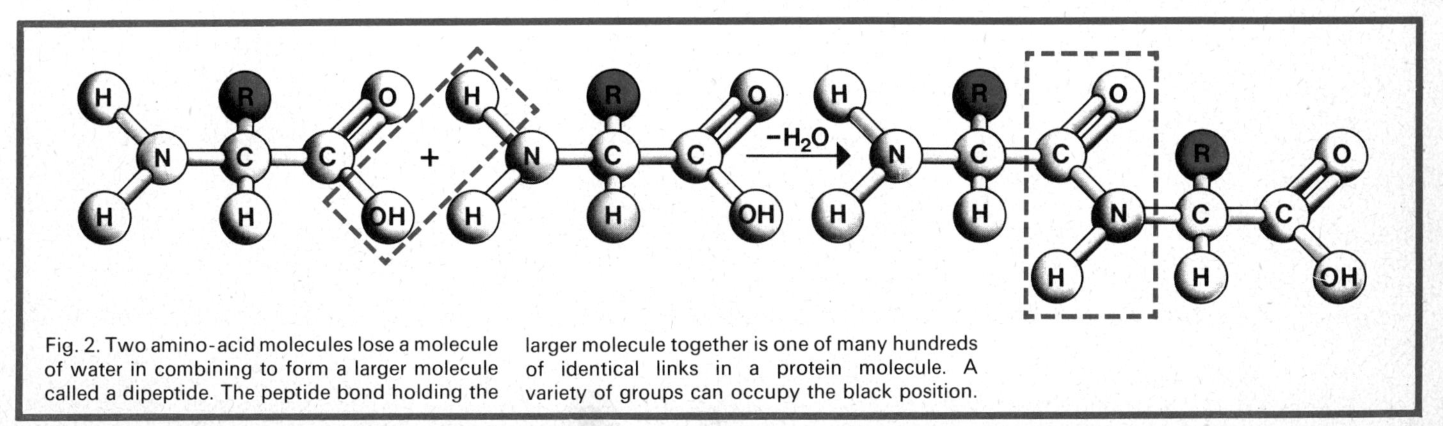


Fig. 2. Two amino-acid molecules lose a molecule of water in combining to form a larger molecule called a dipeptide. The peptide bond holding the larger molecule together is one of many hundreds of identical links in a protein molecule. A variety of groups can occupy the black position.

It was only after scientists finally worked out the ordered, yet stunningly complex, structures of these two master molecules that man's attention could be turned to how these molecules performed their functions.

Proteins are very large molecules made up of basic units called *amino acids*. An amino acid has the general formula shown in Fig. 2. About 20 kinds of amino acids are found in proteins. The acids are joined to each other to form a long, unbranched chain. The amino group ($NH_2$) of one amino acid links to the carboxyl group (COOH) of the next to form a *peptide bond* (Fig. 2).

The sequence in which the amino acids are joined is known as its *primary* structure. The primary structure of one kind of protein is different from that of any other kind. An example of a simple polypeptide chain is shown in Fig. 1. This illustration also shows the variety of amino acids found in proteins.

If a protein molecule has a molecular weight of more than 10,000, it is a true protein. However, if it is less than 10,000, it is more properly called a *polypeptide*. The chain lengths of polypeptides and proteins found in nature vary enormously.

A protein molecule may be not just one chain, but often a combination of two or more chains held together by weak chemical bonds. It may even be linked with a variety of metal atoms, or molecules such as carbohydrates, nucleic acids, or *lipids* (fats). For example, the hormone *insulin* is made up of two chains.

Though the sequence of amino acids in a protein – the primary structure – is very important, it by no means explains all of a protein's remarkable properties. Most proteins are three-dimensional, and in describing them we often use the terms *secondary* and *tertiary* protein structures.

Examples of secondary structure are fibrous protein such as *collagen* and *keratin*. These have their amino-acid chains wound in a long *helix* (coil), a portion of which is illustrated in Fig. 5. Globular proteins show this helical secondary structure over certain portions of their length. In addition, however, their molecules are folded and bent in a particular way, giving rise to a *tertiary structure* (Fig. 4).

Once nature has evolved a suitably tailored molecule, it is loath to change it. Minor variations in the amino-acid sequence of a protein *can* occur provided that the same *functional centres* (the 'engine rooms' of the molecule) occur in the same places in the molecule. For example, variations in the primary structure of insulin from different sources occur only in positions 8, 9, 10 of the *A* chain and at position 30 of the *B* chain. This is presumably because changes in the other amino acids would alter the molecule drastically and destroy its activity. An active or functional centre of a protein molecule is not just a sequence of amino acids along one chain. It is a region where various amino-acids distant in the chain are brought close together by the tertiary structure.

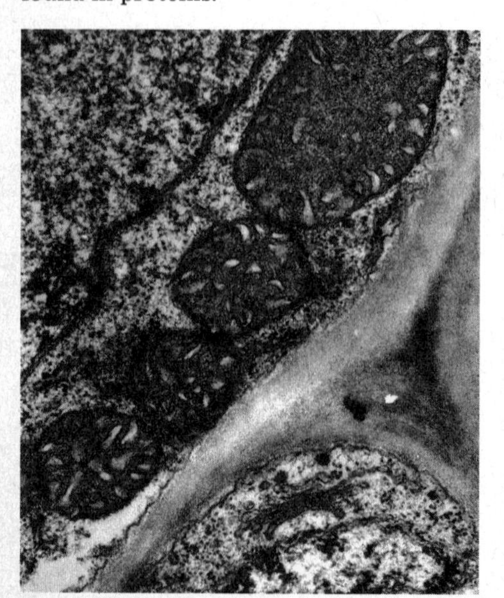

Fig. 3. Electron micrograph of part of a leaf cell showing cell organelles. The circular objects are 'mitochondria', the cell's energy centres.

Fig. 4. Model of a protein (myoglobin). The balls show the positions of the 2,500 atoms in the molecule. The bar shows the lie of the chain.

## How enzymes work

In a living cell, proteins either form part of fairly permanent structures, such as *organelles* (cell components with specialized functions), or they occur in solution. Proteins that form part of organelles, the so-called *structural proteins*, have active centres that induce identical molecules to fit together to produce organized structures (Fig. 3). These structures can be assembled from molecules synthesized elsewhere in the cell. They are built on a repeating pattern and allow for growth by the addition or insertion of new molecules. Both two-dimensional and solid structures can be built up. In feather, horn and hair, the *A* helices of keratin molecules are themselves twisted together to form rope-like *super helices*. On the other hand, cell organelles, such as plasma membrane, chloroplast lamellae, and mito-

chondrial membranes, or the coat proteins of viruses are examples of two-dimensional surface crystals. Structural proteins in organelles are often associated with a *phospholipid* (fat-like substance containing phosphorus) layer but the precise bonding arrangement is not known. In chloroplasts and mitochondria, enzymic protein molecules are inserted among the structural protein of the membranes, but just how the various proteins are slotted together is still a mystery.

Proteins which do not form part of an organized structure lie free in the cytoplasm and are retained by semipermeable membranes that surround cells. The vast majority of these proteins are enzymes, that is, protein molecules which accelerate chemical reactions. Enzymes are sophisticated catalysts because they will usually accelerate only one type of chemical reaction. They work by lowering the *activation energy* needed for a particular reaction to take place. Thus, under ordinary conditions, they make reactions occur at a greatly increased rate. We still do not know all their secrets. We know that the substrate molecule forms a temporary complex with the enzyme molecule (although the complex has never actually been isolated). The complex rapidly breaks to yield the products of the reaction – and the intact enzyme molecule – ready to react again. The *specificity* of an enzyme for its substrate has been likened to a lock and a key. At the molecular level biochemists believe that groups in the active centres of the enzyme bind or attract the substrate molecule and induce it to react. Once it has reacted, the products then look so different that they are no longer

Fig. 5. *Above,* the most important nucleic acid of all – the key to life itself. Model of part of a DNA molecule showing the arrangement of its molecular chains in a helix or extended coil. *Below,* a diagrammatic representation of the double-helix structure of the DNA molecule. A, T, G and C represent adenine, thymine, guanine, and cytosine. P stands for phosphate and DR for deoxyribose.

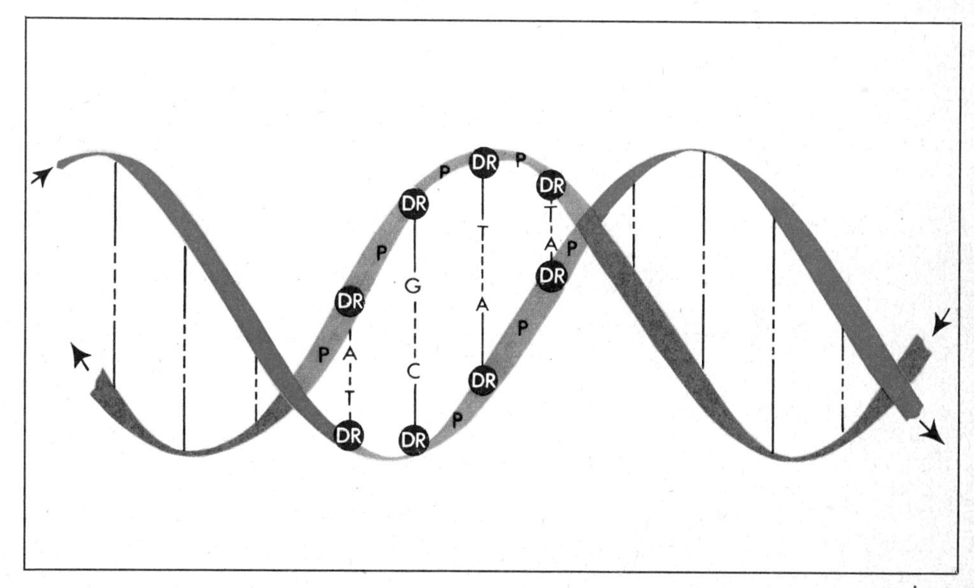


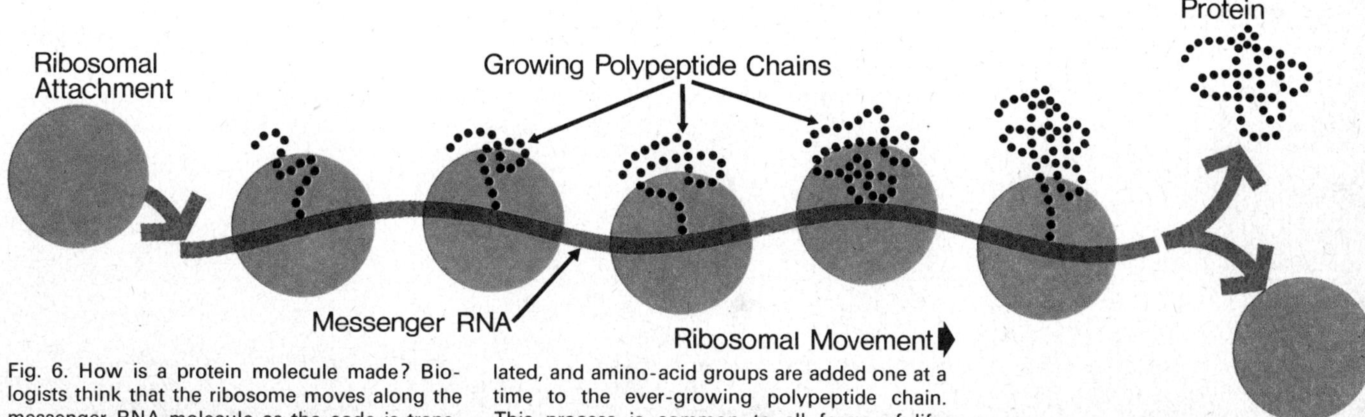


Fig. 6. How is a protein molecule made? Biologists think that the ribosome moves along the messenger-RNA molecule as the code is translated, and amino-acid groups are added one at a time to the ever-growing polypeptide chain. This process is common to all forms of life.

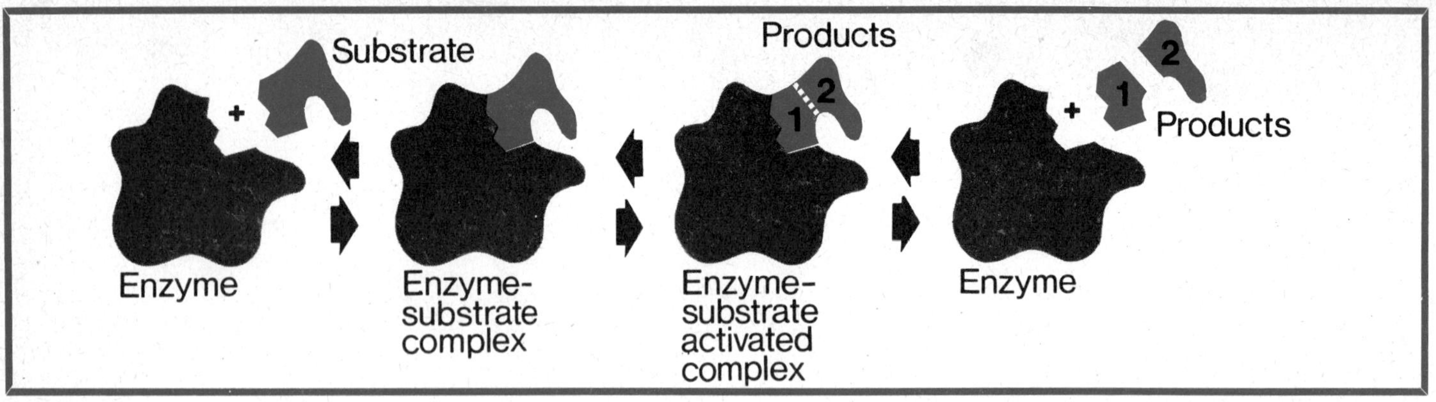


'recognized' by the enzyme and are released (Fig. 7).

Some organelles, such as mitochondria and chloroplasts, can perform complete chemical processes on their own. These processes are composed of several reactions, each catalysed in turn by a different enzyme. Enzymes found free in the cytoplasm are responsible for the reactions of all other metabolic processes such as the initial stages of glucose breakdown, nitrogen metabolism and carbohydrate conversions.

Proteins formed from two pairs of identical amino-acid chains are called *antibody molecules,* and are synthesized by mammals as a defence against *antigens,* organisms that cause disease. Each antibody molecule has two functional centres which bind to parts of invading antigens. Antibody molecules vary only in their functional centres. They are synthesized in response to different diseases and the functional centre is fashioned to attack the cause of that disease and no other. Just how the amino-acid sequence in the functional part of an antibody molecule is arranged to defeat the antigen is unknown.

## The architect is the plan

*Nucleic acids* are long-chain, giant molecules made of sugar units linked together through phosphate groups. Attached to each sugar molecule is a nitrogenous, purine or pyramidine base (Fig. 8). All nucleic acids contain four kinds of base. Two types of nucleic acids occur in cells: *deoxyribonucleic acid* (DNA), which occurs mainly in the chromosomes in the nucleus, and *ribonucleic acid* (RNA), which occurs mainly in the cytoplasm. In RNA the sugar is ribose, in DNA it is deoxyribose. The bases *adenine* (*A*) *guanine* (*G*) and *cytosine* (*C*) are common to both DNA and RNA. In RNA the fourth base is *uracil* (*U*) but in DNA it is *thymine* (*T*). The sequence of bases along the sugar phosphate 'backbone' does not form any simple, repeating pattern. However, the bases do lie in a very precise order and in this sequence is written all the coded information which an organism receives from its parents.

DNA is usually found as a double-stranded structure in which two long chain-like molecules are intertwined to form a double helix. In this configuration each base faces inwards and links with another base on the opposite chain through hydrogen bonds. Certain rules govern the formation of these *base pairs. A* will pair only with *T* (or *U* in the case of RNA) and *G* will pair only with *C* (Fig. 5). The result is that the sequence of bases in one chain dictates the sequence of bases in the other, and vice versa. If the two chains are separated, each chain (in the presence of the necessary enzymes) can direct the synthesis of a new chain. The newly formed chains will be replicas of the original double chain, and in this manner the special base sequence is transferred from one molecule to another.

From studies of mutant organisms, geneticists have known for a long time that specific regions of the nucleic-acid molecule contain the information necessary to build certain protein molecules. Somehow the sequence of bases on DNA must determine the sequence of amino acids along a protein. It is now known that this base sequence is in the form of a *triplet code.* That is, three adjacent bases along a nucleic-acid chain determine one amino acid in the corresponding protein molecule. For example, the base triplet *GAG* means glutamic acid, the base sequence *GGA* means glycine, and so on. The code is read in one direction only. It has a fixed starting point for the first amino acid in a protein, and it is non-overlapping. Already, a tentative code 'dictionary' has been worked out, though the task has been made even more difficult because any three out of four bases, put in all possible orders, makes 64 combinations. As there are only 23 amino acids for which codes are required, each amino acid may have two or three *codons* (base triplets). The actual synthesis of a protein from this coded information is divided into two events: *transcription* and *translation.*

Transcription of the DNA in a chromosome can take place at any time when the nucleus is not dividing. Part of the DNA helix uncoils and a molecule of RNA is synthesized along one of the DNA strands. This RNA molecule is called *messenger RNA* (mRNA), because having copied the information from the master memory store in the DNA, it migrates (with its message) to the ribosome in the cytoplasm where the information is put to use. The code is translated by smaller RNA molecules called *soluble* or *transfer RNA* (sRNA). On one part of the sRNA molecule is an 'anticodon', a sequence of three bases which will 'recognize' and join up with a three-base codon on the mRNA. At another part are specific groups capable of binding with one molecule of a particular kind of amino acid. The temporary addition of an amino acid to the sRNA molecule to form an active complex needs energy and an enzyme.

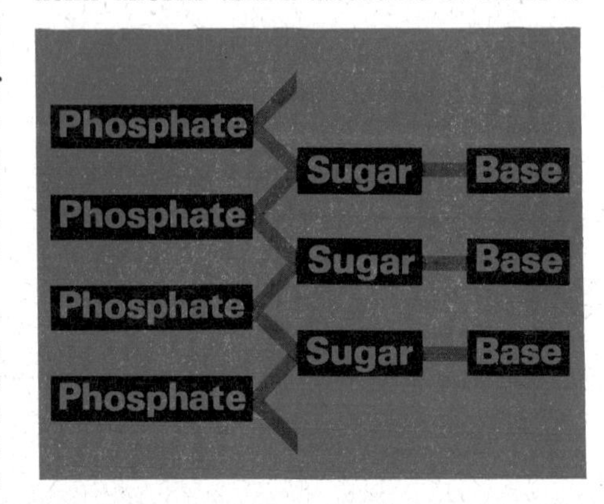


Fig. 8. The basic formula of a nucleic acid. Sugar units are linked together by means of phosphate groups. Attached to each sugar molecule is a nitrogenous, purine or pyramidine base.

Fig. 7. Acting as a catalyst, the enzyme attracts a substrate molecule and combines with it. The nature of the bond is such that the substrate molecule is put under a stress sufficient to cause it to break. The enzyme then rejects it.

## DNA: basis of all life

Amino acids are thus brought to the mRNA on the ribosome and are linked together by an enzyme capable of making them form peptide bonds. The sRNA molecule is then released. Scientists think that the ribosome moves along the mRNA molecule as the code is translated, and amino acids are added, one at a time, to the ever-growing polypeptide chain (Fig. 6). There is also some evidence that at least in a few cases up to five ribosomes can move along a mRNA strand at one time, with a growing polypeptide chain attached to each one, thus increasing the efficiency of the system.

Perhaps the most astonishing fact of this incredible story is that the process of protein synthesis occurs in all forms of life that have been investigated. The DNA code appears to be a universal language. Research workers have recently synthesized biologically active nucleic-acid molecules using a nucleic-acid molecule from a virus as a primer. These molecules are capable of acting as messenger RNA, and can direct the synthesis of virus coat protein in a test-tube. The viral nucleic acid and coat protein can even be assembled to produce a complete virus – identical in all respects to that produced within living cells! Thus scientists are now able to mimic the two reactions basic to life: (*a*) copying inherited information, and (*b*) translating the information into a protein. Today, we can even synthesize some nucleic acids artificially.

# Cracking open the cell

**Much of biology is concerned with the workings of the living cell. To crack open cells and separate the individual components from each other has therefore become an important part of a biologist's research.**

RADIOACTIVE ISOTOPES have proved a most powerful weapon in the biologists' armoury only because biologists have had at hand other sophisticated tools. The overriding problem has always been how to separate cells, sub-cellular machinery, and even individual molecules. The biologist needs to be able to extract one or a few of the thousands of components in every living organism.

Living organisms are infinitely more complicated than inorganic non-living matter. Chemists and physicists are used to thinking about processes in which only a few changes take place at any one time. The biologist, however, trying to understand living things, has to make experiments with systems in which hundreds or thousands of co-ordinated reactions are taking place at the same time.

## Pieces of a puzzle

Faced with this complexity the biologist can do one of two things. He can decide to study whole animals or plants, such as the way they behave and interact with each other and their surroundings, or he can study parts of animals or plants. Thus he may look at the way a particular organ or type of cell functions or, making things even simpler for himself, he can study just one or a few of the hundreds of chemical reactions going on all the time in every cell. Eventually every biologist hopes all the information from these two approaches will fit together like pieces of a jig-saw puzzle to give a complete picture of the processes that make life.

Until recently the tools the biologist used most were the scalpel, microscope and his two eyes. But the comparatively new science of the chemistry of life has suddenly mushroomed with the production of isotopes and tools for cracking open cells and isolating their component molecules. The technical problem of this new biology is how to separate cell components without destroying their activity. To achieve this separation modern biologists use such techniques as centrifugation, electrophoresis, chromatography, immunodiffusion, and growing cells in tissue culture.

The *centrifuge,* which works on precisely the same principle as the spin drier in the laundry, is used to separate the fragmented cell components from each other. When something is spun quickly around a fixed central point, forces, known as *centrifugal forces,* develop which tend to thrust the spinning object away from the central point. Familiar examples of the effect of centrifugal forces are the forces which drive the water out of washing in a spin drier and keep people against the walls of rotating drums at a fair.

The scientist has harnessed these forces in the centrifuge which, in its simplest form, consists of two, four or six metal test-tube holders at the end of a rotor which is spun by an electric motor or by hand. If tubes of muddy water or a suspension of a precipitate are spun in such simple centrifuges, the particulate matter is forced to the bottom of the tubes, where it sediments into a compact pellet leaving the clear water or solution above.

Biologists need far more sophisticated centrifuges for some of their work because the cellular particles – the nuclei, the mitochondria, the chloroplasts and even molecules – which they are trying to separate are very light and buoyant. This means very high centrifugal forces have to be generated to make them sediment out of solution. To obtain these a wide range of centrifuges has been developed and some, the ultra-centrifuges, have rotors which rotate at up to 70,000 times a minute and generate forces up to 300,000 times that of gravity.

Very high-speed centrifuges have to be refrigerated, otherwise the friction between the rotors (which have to be very carefully machined and made of hard metals) and molecules of gas in air would burn up the rotors. For the same reason the rotor chambers are evacuated with vacuum pumps to reduce frictional heating.

Ultra-centrifuges are very expensive, but despite their cost and fearsome characters they have become commonplace in biological laboratories. They enable the biologist to extract the particular structures or molecules he is interested in from the soup produced when cells are cracked open in presses or literally shaken to pieces with ultrasonic vibrations.

Biologists have also developed some very clever tricks to let them fully exploit centrifugation. Centrifuges have been designed so that the suspension to be sedimented can be fed in continuously at one end, the sedimented material collects in

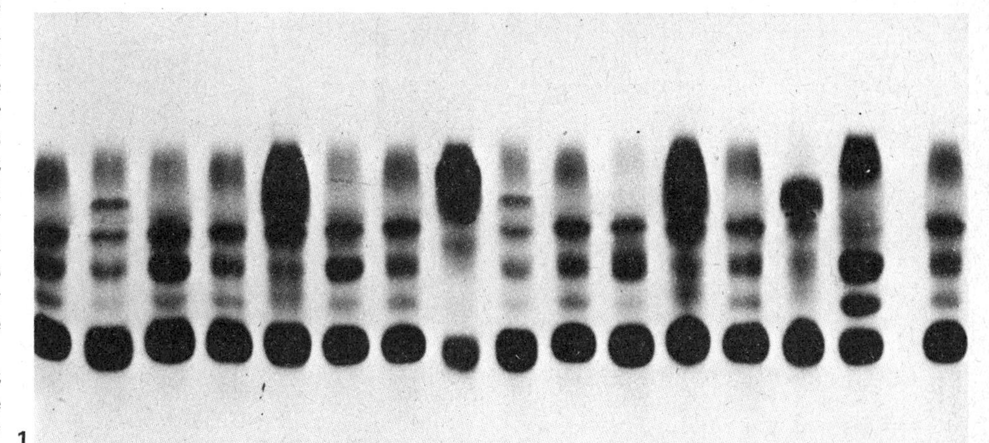

1 When blood serum is electrophoresed, the various component proteins are separated into compact bands. Diseases cause changes in certain proteins which can be picked up by this method.

2 Most biological molecules carry some electric charge. The basis of electrophoresis is to separate these molecules by making them migrate in strong electric fields.

the rotor and the clarified solution flows out at the other end. This type of *continuous centrifugation* is particularly useful for recovering cells grown in fermentation plants containing many gallons of cell suspension. Another clever technique has been invented to overcome the problems of separating molecules or particles which sediment at very similar rates. In these circumstances the pellet at the end of a centrifugation 'run' is a mixture of the components. Normal sedimentation will only separate a mixture if the components sediment at very different rates so that one can be removed at low speed, another at a higher speed and another at yet higher speed. To improve separation biologists add inert chemicals, such as sugar or metallic salts, to raise the density of the solution. This tends to make molecules float. By carefully balancing the speed of the centrifuge and the density of the solution it is possible to make molecules reach an equilibrium in which the two opposing sets of forces, centrifugal and buoyancy, are balanced. When this happens all the molecules of the same density form a band at some position in the centrifuge tube clearly separated from molecules of only a slightly different density.

## Weighing molecules

As well as being used to isolate fractions of cells centrifuges are increasingly used now to measure some of the physical properties of the large biological molecules. The density of a protein or nucleic acid, for example, can be calculated from the position to which the molecules sediment in a solution of sucrose or metal salts, the density of which is known. More importantly, the ultra-centrifuge can be used to measure the *molecular weight* of large molecules; that is the number of times heavier the molecule is than an atom of hydrogen. To do this, biologists measure the rate at which a molecule sediments under a given centrifugal force, at a known temperature in a solution of known viscosity. By substituting this rate in a complex equation and doing a great deal of arithmetic, the molecular weight can be calculated.

Not all the techniques for the separation of biological molecules require such large and costly apparatus as centrifuges; some, including *electrophoresis*, are simple and cheap. Electrophoresis is the separation of molecules by virtue of their electrical charge. Most biological molecules, including proteins and nucleic acids, have a net electric charge because the total number of acidic, or electrically negative, groups and basic, or electrically positive, groups do not balance. This means the molecule can have either a net positive or negative charge and, as a result, it will move in an

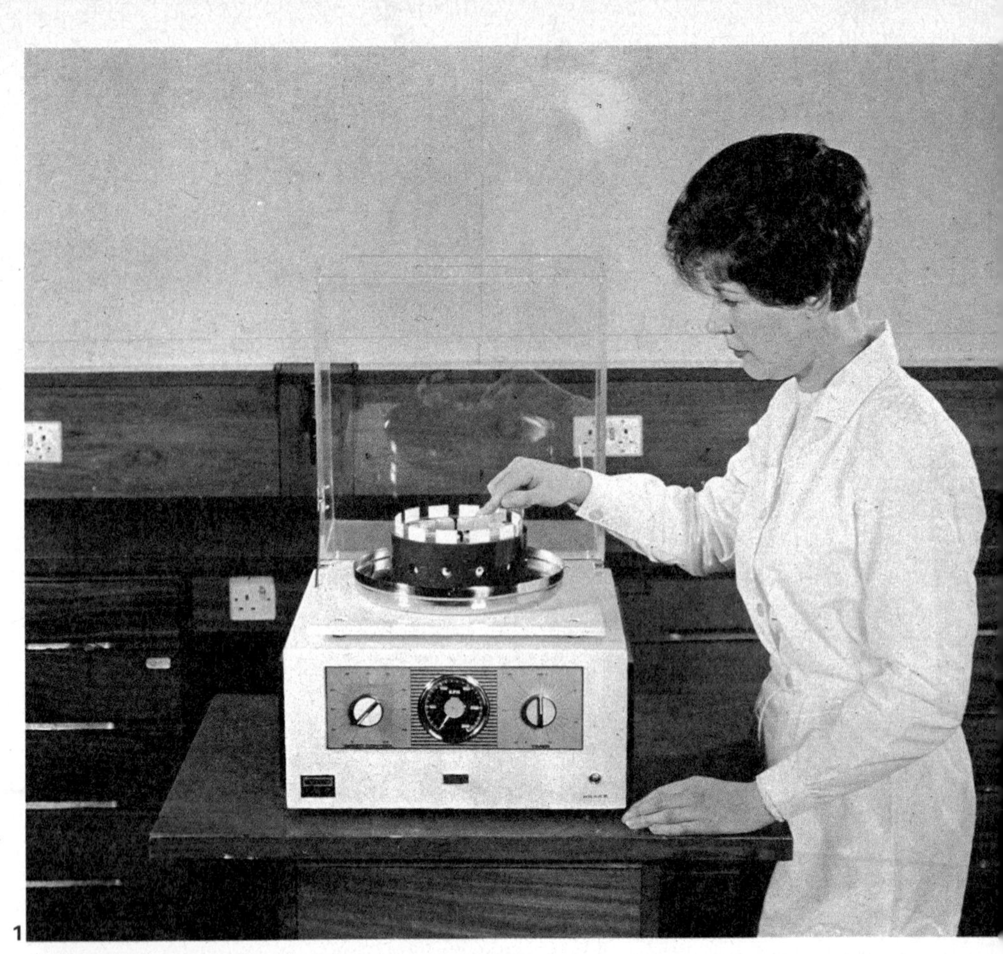

**1** Tissue culture methods are becoming increasingly important. The cells are usually very delicate and special techniques of handling them, like this cyto-centrifuge, have to be used.

**2** Chromatography is one very useful way of separating out DNA – the genetic component of cells – from any other particulate matter. The pure DNA is then used in genetic experiments.

electric field. Positively charged molecules move to a negative electrode or cathode and negatively charged molecules move to a positive anode.

In any given field the molecules will move at a characteristic rate depending chiefly on the size of the molecule's net charge, but the size and shape of the molecule are also important. Some molecules are more compact and streamlined than others, and so have less resistance to movement.

## Solution to a snag

The structure of the medium through which the molecules move has changed dramatically. When electrophoresis was first introduced the molecules were electrophoresed in aqueous solutions – with one great disadvantage: the molecules tended to diffuse throughout the solution almost as fast as they moved towards one or other electrode. This snag was soon overcome by what is known as *zone electrophoresis*. Instead of using solutions the molecules are electrophoresed through wet filter paper or through a jelly-like medium. Gelled starch with the consistency of thick custard used to be the favourite support medium but now a synthetic plastic gel, polyacrylamide, is often used. The gel is made up in a solution of constant acidity or alkalinity, a buffer solution, and is cast in glass cylinders or flat dishes with an anode at one end and a cathode at the other. The mixture of molecules is put in the centre and when the direct current is switched on, the molecules begin to migrate at characteristic rates which depend, not only on their charge and shape, but also on the porosity of the gels, which produces a sieving effect and helps increase the separation.

Electrophoresis has proved of enormous value in analytical work because very closely related compounds can be separated. The now classic example of this is the discovery of the first molecular disease, sickle cell anaemia. This disease is common in West Africa and can be diagnosed because the red blood cells of the victims have an unusual sickle shape. In 1949 four American scientists showed that the haemoglobin from sickle cells migrates in the opposite direction to normal haemoglobin on electrophoresis. Later research revealed that the only difference between the two haemoglobins was that one charged amino acid in the normal had been replaced, by mutation, with a neutral amino acid in the sickle cell haemoglobin. There are about 300 amino acids in the protein and by electrophoresis a change of just one of these was detected.

Such a powerful technique is widely used but it has its snags. The chief is that it is difficult to separate large amounts of material by electrophoresis; no one has

**1** The progress of these molecules across a thin-layer chromatographic plate is being observed under ultra-violet light. This shows up certain substances such as DNA.

**2** In modern electrophoresis work, different types of gel are used depending on the type of molecule to be separated. The molecules thus concentrate into tight 'clean' bands.

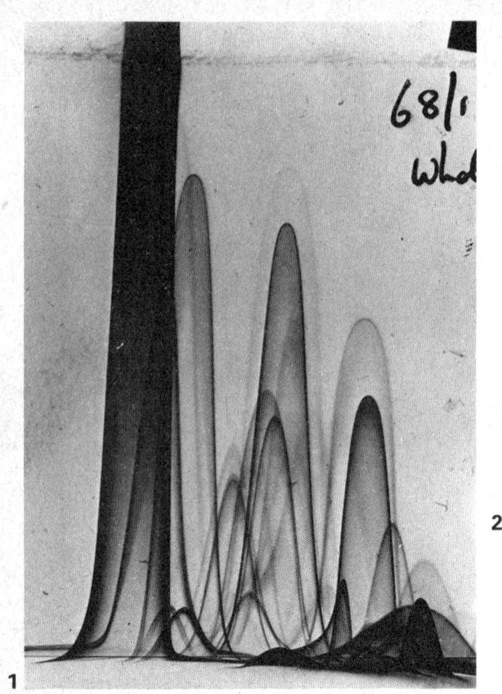

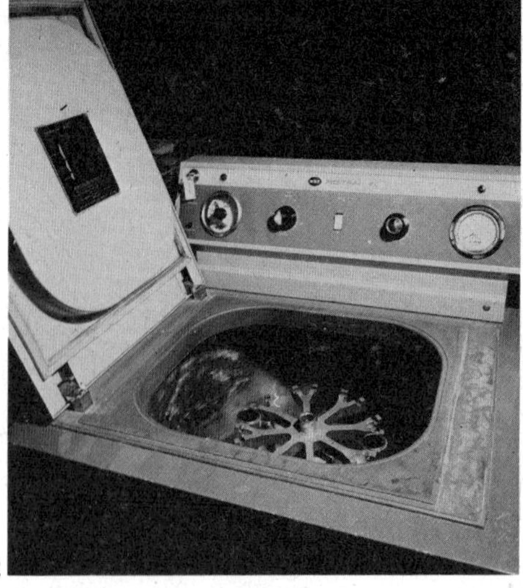

**1** By electrophoresing blood serum, first in one direction then in another at 90 degrees to the first, it is possible to get the blood protein components to form distinctive bands.

**2** By rotating at very high speeds the centrifuge causes particles – sometimes even molecules – to separate out from the solution in which they are suspended.

**3** Iodinated insulin, when added to the top of a chromatography column, passes slowly down at its own particular rate. Any impurities thus become separated out.

yet devised a large-scale apparatus so, although invaluable for work with a few millionths of a gram of material, it is no use for separating a few grams. But another technique, *chromatography,* which also involves gels, has many of the advantages of electrophoresis and can be used on a large scale.

Chromatography relies solely on differences in molecular size and shape. A familiar example is what happens, when a spot of ink falls on blotting paper. It spreads out and often ends up looking like concentric rings of different colours.

As this example shows, the tool for obtaining separation is the chromatographic bed which provides a network of chemically inert, minute particles with spaces between them. In practice the material of the bed can range from sheets of filter or blotting paper to columns packed with specially prepared gels but, irrespective of the material, separation is achieved by the flow of a solvent through the bed under the actions of gravity, capillarity or both. The compounds being separated flow to a varying extent, depending on the size and shape of the molecules and the spaces in the bed.

It might seem obvious that small molecules in a mixture will always travel fastest. Yet this need not be the case: all depends on the porosity of the bed material. Some cellulose gels, for example, have minute pores through the gel particles as well as spaces between the particles. Molecules too large to enter the pores flow quickly through the spaces, which collectively are called the *void volume,* while molecules small enough to enter the pores do so and as a result are slowed down and emerge behind the large molecules.

There are now numerous materials available that have been specially designed as substrates for chromatography, including cellulose, special papers, polyacrylamides, agar derivatives and even the silica skeletons of unicellular organisms, diatoms. This rapid development in the art of chromatography – which for the most part has taken place since the early 1960s – reflects the importance the technique has assumed because of its outstanding advantages. It is easy to do, cheap, because the bed material can be re-used, and remarkably insensitive to changes in the temperature or the solvents used. Equally important, it is a very mild technique and seldom inactivates the fragile molecules that biologists have to fractionate. It can also be scaled up so that columns taller than a man and several inches, even feet, in diameter can be used if large quantities of material have to be separated. And by varying the size of the spaces between and the pores in the bed material molecules with molecular weights ranging from less than 1,000 to several millions can be fractionated.

## Harnessing immunity

*Immunodiffusion* is another tool which employs gels, usually agar gels. Essentially it is a laboratory exploitation of the immunity system. When a foreign substance, known in immunology as an *antigen,* enters an animal's body it stimulates the body to synthesize a protein, called an *antibody,* which has the specific function of reacting with the antigen and neutralizing it.

Immunodiffusion is simply a way of harnessing immunity to the analysis of mixtures of molecules. If a biologist needs to know if a mixture of compounds contains some particular component he can prepare an antibody against that component by injecting it into a rabbit or some other animal in which it will act as an antigen. Having purified the antibody from the blood of the rabbit, by methods such as chromatography and centrifugation, he can use it to challenge the mixture he wants to analyse. If it contains even traces of antigen, the antibody will react with them. In practice the biologist usually casts a thin sheet of wet agar and cuts a pattern of small holes or 'wells' into the agar. If, for example, the antibody solution is put in a central well and the mixtures to be analysed in a ring of wells surrounding it, the molecules in each well diffuse out in all directions through the agar. Whenever an antibody diffuses into its antigen, a precipitate forms as the two interact. This precipitate builds up in the agar gel and it can be visualized as an arc of protein by staining with protein stains. Because the antibody-antigen reaction is so specific several reactions can be analysed at the same time without interfering with each other. Moreover, the method can be adapted to give approximate measures of the diffusion rates of different antigenic molecules.

By using cells grown in tissue culture biologists can study in particular the way cancer cells grow and multiply; the action of viruses on cells and the genetics of cells. This method is restricted, at present, to only a few types of cell and attempts to culture whole organs are still in their infancy. The problems are keeping the cells alive and multiplying, which means strictly controlling supplies of food and air as well as the temperature and the acidity or alkalinity of the growth solution, without allowing bacteria to enter and multiply at the same time. These technical difficulties have been overcome for a few cell types from mammals, such as Man, mice and hamsters.

By manipulating the growth medium or by feeding the cells isotopes, the rate of growth and the metabolism of the cells can be controlled and the chemical reactions involved followed. The technique not only gives the biologist a continual source of material but it also removes uncontrollable variations in the cell's environment so that the researcher can be sure that every cell receives exactly the same treatment. Because of these advantages, a great deal of effort is being devoted to improving tissue culture.

# The cell's fixtures and fittings

**Apart from nucleic acids and proteins, other essential substances are found in living cells. These include sugars and starches, fats, oils and waxes, and two remarkable colouring agents.**

THE FUNDAMENTAL chemicals of life are the nucleic acids and proteins. But it would be wrong to assume that these are the only vital chemicals in the cell. We might think of nucleic acids as architects and proteins as builders; between them they can produce a house, but it will not be ready to live in, until its 'extras' – the fixtures and fittings – are added.

These 'extras' in the chemistry of the cell include a wide variety of chemical compounds, some of which are quite as important as nucleic acids and proteins in making a cell a viable unit. They include such well-known substances as starch, waxes and oils. Many of them have been known far longer than nucleic acids and proteins, and have been studied in greater detail because of their usefulness in everyday life. Despite this, it is only since the 1930s that we have been fully able to understand their roles in the living cell.

For simplicity, we shall introduce these compounds in an order based largely on their chemical structures. Remember that compounds which are chemically very similar may often play widely differing roles within the cell and vice versa. Not all of the compounds we will mention necessarily occur *within* cells. Some, like cellulose and chitin, form a protective layer on the outside.

All biological compounds contain at least three elements: carbon (C), hydrogen (H), and oxygen (O). For simplicity, we shall examine first those compounds which contain only these three elements. Compounds which contain additional elements will be discussed later.

## Energy sources and cell walls

The name *carbohydrate* suggests a substance formed from atoms of carbon (C) and elements of water ($H_2O$) in a one-to-one ratio, and this is in fact what it is. The general formula for a carbohydrate is $(CH_2O)_n$, where $n$ is commonly 6 or some multiple of 6. For example a carbohydrate with six carbon atoms would have the formula $C_6H_{12}O_6$. The most common carbohydrates are those which have three, four, five, six, or multiples of six, carbon atoms.

Carbohydrates with only three or four carbon atoms are not typical of the group and we shall tackle them later when we come to talk about energy release in cells. For present purposes we shall restrict ourselves to an investigation of carbohydrates having six carbon atoms, called *hexoses*, or multiples of six carbon atoms.

Hexose molecules can exist as straight chains or as a variety of other shapes. The most common shape is the ring and tail structure illustrated in Fig. 1. This figure illustrates the ring structures of the sugars glucose and fructose respectively. Notice that glucose and fructose both have the same formula, $C_6H_{12}O_6$. They differ only in the way that their atoms are arranged in the molecule. Ring structures are significant, because by the removal of a molecule of water, two rings can join together. One molecule contributes the hydroxyl group ($OH^-$) and the other a proton ($H^+$). Granulated sugar, cane sugar, or sucrose, is formed from a fructose molecule linked to a glucose molecule by just such a system.

By removing molecules of water between a number of hexoses, a chain of these

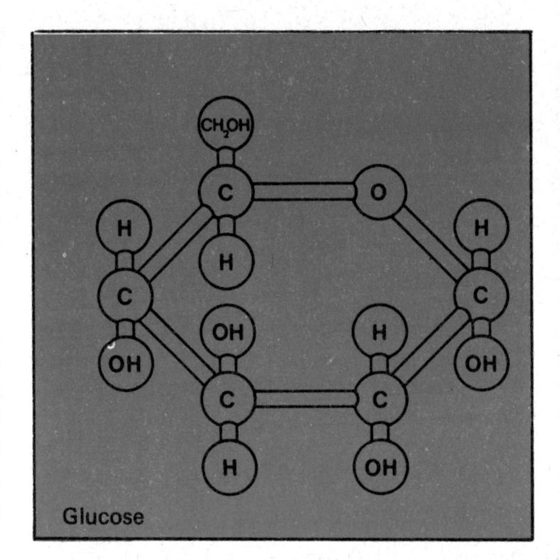


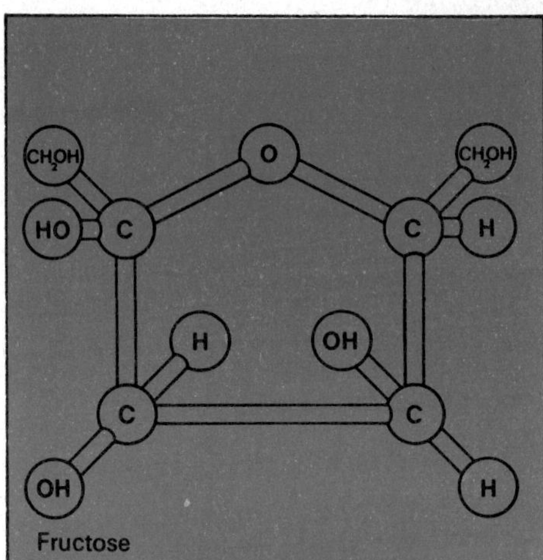


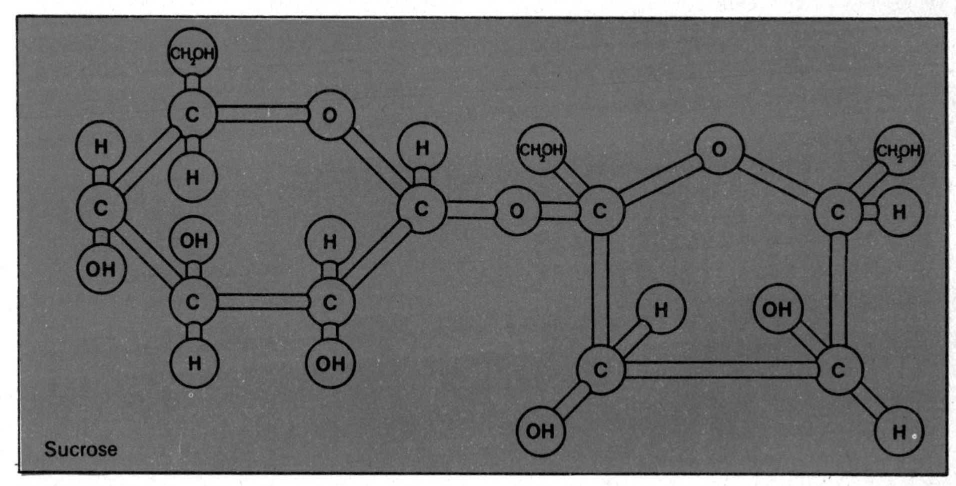


Fig. 1. What is sugar? Two important ring-shaped hexose molecules, glucose, *top left*, and fructose, *top right*. Notice that glucose and fructose both have exactly the same number of carbon, hydrogen and oxygen atoms and that their difference lies only in the way in which the atoms are arranged. At the expense of a molecule of water, ring-shaped molecules can join together. *Above*, glucose and fructose have joined to form the disaccharide, sucrose (granulated or cane sugar).

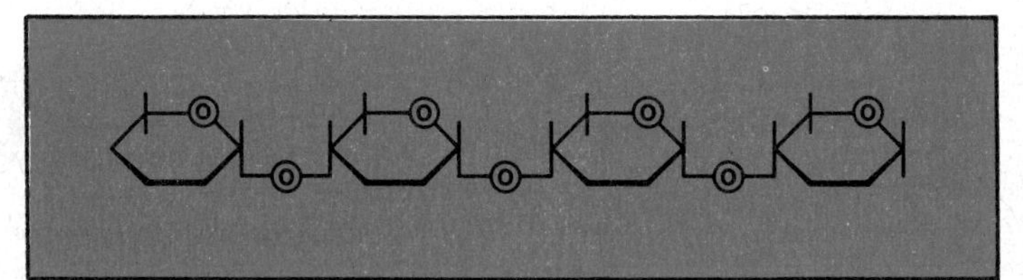

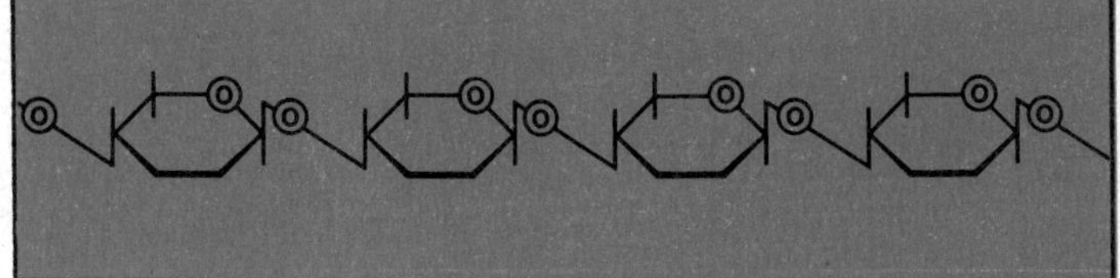

Fig. 2. Long chains of hexose units are called polysaccharides. Animals store their carbohydrate reserves as a polysaccharide called glycogen; plants as the polysaccharide, starch. *Above left*, an unbranched chain of glucose molecules as found in starch and glycogen. *Above right*, an unbranched chain of glucose molecules as found in cellulose. Cellulose is a substance forming a protective wall round all plant cells.

sugars can be built. Hexoses are therefore the building blocks from which larger molecules can be made. Longer molecules consisting of three or four hexoses linked in a row are known, but they are not common. Instead, long chains of hexose units (called *polysaccharides*) are more frequent in nature.

Whereas individual hexose molecules are soluble in water or tissue fluids, polysaccharides are not. This difference in solubility is an important feature of these two types of related molecules, and it adapts them for their separate roles. In the cell, hexoses are used as energy sources. They have to be mobile so that they can be shifted from place to place and this can only be done if the sugars are soluble.

Animals store their carbohydrate reserves as a polysaccharide called *glycogen*. Most plants store their reserves as starch. Glycogen and starch are similar in many ways. Both contain chains of glucose units linked in the same way. Indeed, glycogen is sometimes called animal starch. However, starch has a slightly more complex overall structure. In most animals, glycogen is stored in the liver, but plants have developed a variety of specialized storage organs.

Not all plants store their carbohydrate reserves in the form of starch. Many of them use units of fructose, which they join end to end to make a polysaccharide called *inulin*. Inulin occurs in the roots of plants of the Compositae family such as dahlias and Jerusalem artichokes. The molecule is about 30 units long and has a sucrose molecule at one end. Many grasses and bacteria contain slightly different fructose polymers called *levans*. Levans contain only fructose, are generally not as long as inulin molecules, and are often branched.

As only the hexoses or smaller carbohydrates can be used directly to produce energy, the reserve polysaccharides must be broken down into their constituent hexose units before the cell can use them. The enzymes responsible for this breakdown are found in such places as the saliva, where polysaccharides are broken down as the first step in digestion; in the liver, where glucose is released from the glycogen store when the body needs energy; and in germinating seeds, where food reserves need to be tapped to provide energy for growth.

Cellulose is another important plant polysaccharide. It is chemically similar to glycogen and starch, but has a completely different function. Cellulose is the compound which surrounds all plant cells, forming a protective wall. Cellulose is made from repeating glucose units in unbranched chains. But the bonds between the units differ slightly from those in starch and cellulose. Also, because the long chains of glucose molecules in cellulose lie side by side, cross links form between adjacent chains to produce a stronger structure (Fig. 2).

Although some micro-organisms and invertebrate animals can manufacture the enzymes necessary to break down cellulose, vertebrate animals are unable to do so. Herbivorous animals have to rely on the micro-organisms present in their gut to perform this task, before they are able to absorb and make use of their food.

In addition to the pure carbohydrates, derivatives of them also occur in which a hydrogen atom (H) or a hydroxyl group (OH) has been replaced by a phosphate ($PO_4$), sulphate ($SO_4$) or amino ($NH_2$) group. For example, glucose-6-phosphate is the 'activated' form of glucose which is actually employed for the release of energy. In fact, the polysaccharides formed from these derivatives fit more widespread roles than those formed from the pure carbohydrates.

The *exoskeleton* (skeleton in the skin, or covering the surface of creatures) of arthropods, called *chitin*, is a polymer of *glucosamine* (the amine derivative of glucose). Similarly, mammalian skin, corneas, cartilage and artery walls all contain polysaccharides made from different derivatives of the hexose *galactose*. By varying the substituted group or the type of bond used to make long chains, the simple hexose molecule is used in a variety of ways.

water soluble head (glycerol)

water repellent hydrocarbon tails, 12 to 24 carbon atoms long

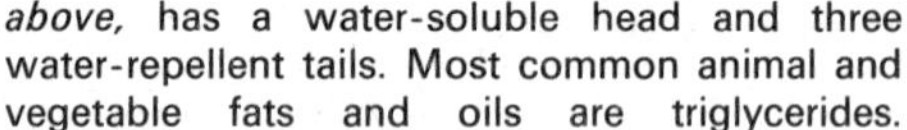

Fig. 3. Fatty acids usually form part of a larger molecule by addition to an alcohol molecule such as glycerol. The result, a triglyceride, *above*, has a water-soluble head and three water-repellent tails. Most common animal and vegetable fats and oils are triglycerides.

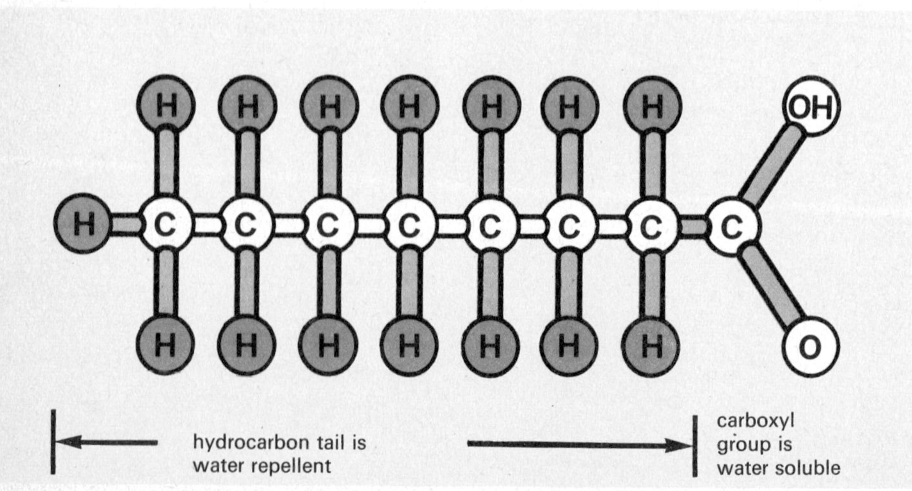


Fig. 4. Fatty acids are molecules with a chain of carbon atoms to which hydrogen atoms are attached. At one end of the molecule is a carboxyl group (COOH), which is acidic and soluble in water. At the other end is a methyl group forming a water-repellent tail of variable length.

## Fatty food stores

No one has yet found a really satisfactory definition of a lipid. Older, inexact terms, such as waxes, oils and fats, were used originally to specify whether a substance was (normally) liquid or solid at room temperature. But these terms have no precise chemical meaning. What we can say is that lipids are compounds that are insoluble in water, but which can be extracted from biological materials by organic solvents such as acetone, alcohol, ether or petroleum. These compounds can then be roughly subdivided into three categories: *simple lipids, compound lipids and steroids,* but they are not grouped according to their possession of a particular structure.

A simple lipid is either a *fatty acid* or a combination of a fatty acid with an alcohol such as *glycerol*. Acid-alcohol combinations are properly called *esters*. Fatty acids are molecules with a chain of carbon atoms to which hydrogen atoms are attached. At one end of the molecule is a *carboxyl group* (COOH), and at the other end is a methyl group (Fig. 4).

The carboxyl group is acidic and is soluble in water, but the carbon and hydrogen chain which forms a kind of tail is not. The length of the carbon tail can vary. Acids with only short tails, such as acetic acid, are soluble in water. Those with long tails, such as palmitic acids, are completely insoluble. In nature, the most widespread fatty acids have from 12 to 24 carbon atoms in their tails, and are, therefore, not soluble in water. However, the fact that the carboxyl group possesses such different characteristics from the hydrocarbon tail confers some unusual properties on the whole molecule, as we shall see later.

Fatty acids rarely occur in biological materials as such. More often they form part of a larger molecule by addition to an alcohol, such as glycerol, through their carboxyl groups. The compound thus produced is called a *triglyceride*. It has a water-soluble head and three water-repellent tails (Fig. 3). It is the triglycerides which comprise the bulk of the common animal and vegetable fats and oils. In the cell, triglycerides occur predominantly as small droplets which act as food stores.

Animals often develop special cells solely for fat storage. In this role, the lipids are a highly concentrated energy source. They can provide more than twice as many calories as an equivalent weight of carbohydrate or protein. Outside the cell they are often used as waterproofing, as in the case, for example, of the waxy cuticle found on the leaves of some plants.

Compound lipids resemble simple lipids except that when they are broken down they yield other compounds in addition to fatty acids. These additional compounds frequently contain nitrogen (N) and phosphorus (P). Most common among the compound lipids are the *lecithins*. Lecithins are *phospholipids* (lipid molecules containing phosphorus) and occur in cell membranes because of the dual characteristics of their molecules. If a phospholipid is mixed with water, it will form a film on the surface in which all the molecules are pointing in the same direction. The hydrocarbon tails will project into the air and water-soluble heads will stick into the water (Fig. 5, *top*).

Biological membranes are somewhat similar, but they involve two layers of molecules. The water-repellent tails face each other, and the water-soluble heads lie to the outside, associated with protein (Fig. 5, *middle*). In cell bodies such as mitochondria, phospholid molecules are associated with the enzymes which produce energy from the breakdown of pyruvic acid. In the chloroplasts found in plant cells, phospholipids are associated with the light-trapping pigments, the chlorophylls and carotenoids (Fig. 5, *bottom*).

Steroids are compounds formed from carbon atoms joined together to produce ring-like structures rather than long chains. All steroids have the basic polycyclic structure known (rather frighteningly) as the *cyclopentanoper hydrophenanthrene* skeleton. Various steroids differ in the nature of the side groups which

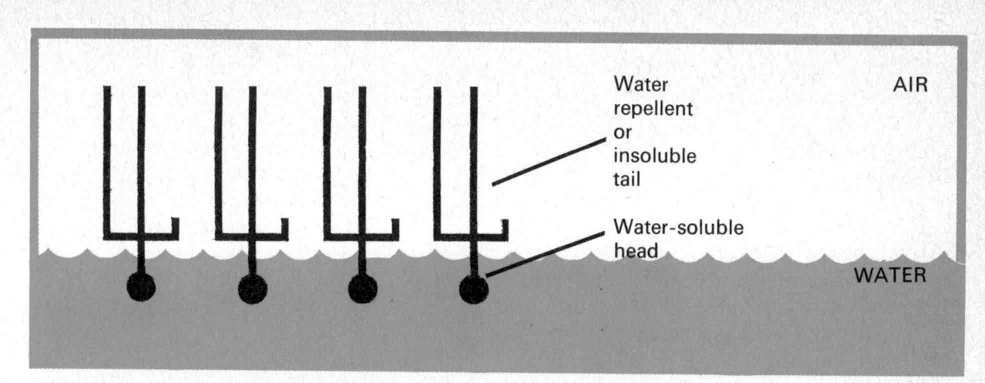


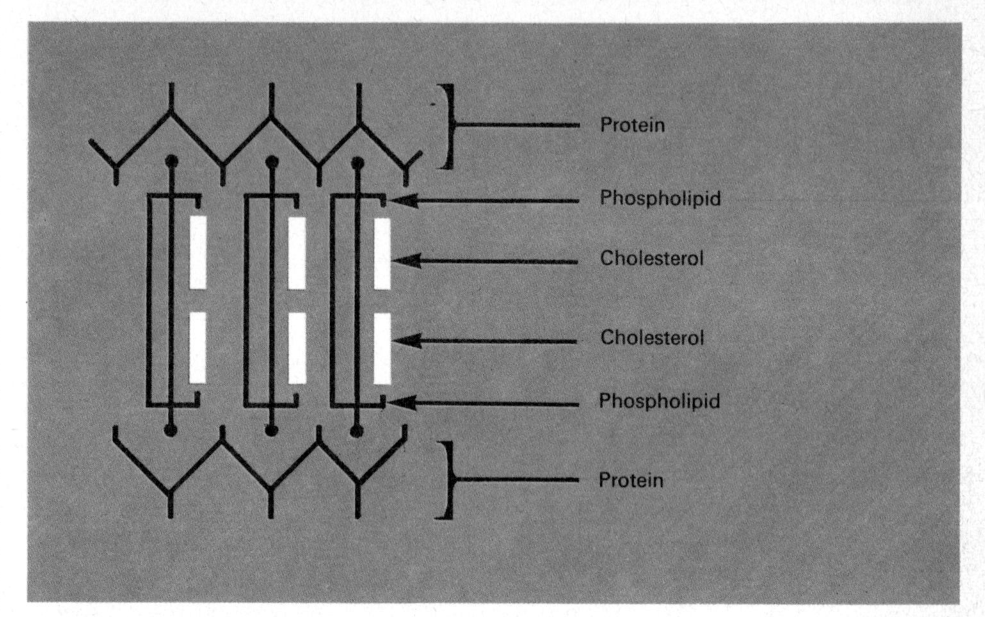


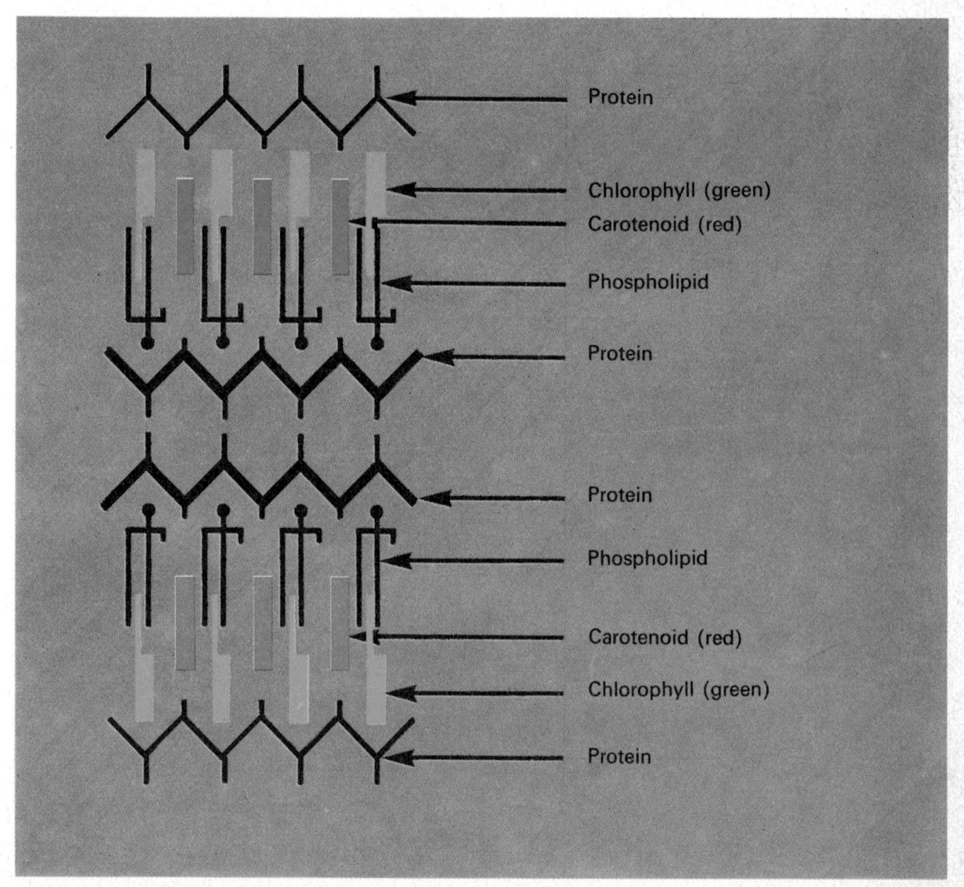


Fig. 5. *Top,* if a phospholipid is mixed with water, it forms a thin film on the surface in which all the molecules are pointing in the same direction. The hydrocarbon tails project into the air while the water-soluble heads stick into the water. *Middle,* membranes found in living things are rather similar, only they consist of two layers of molecules. The water-repellent tails face each other, while the water-soluble heads lie to the outside, associating with protein chains. Structure of a lipoprotein membrane is shown schematically. *Bottom,* structure of compound phospholipid membranes of a chloroplast, the chlorophyll container in plant cells.

are attached to this skeleton. Large numbers of steroids are known, but probably the most abundant is *cholesterol,* which occurs in many membranes alongside lecithin.

Cholesterol is biologically important because it is the key intermediate from which other steroids are synthesized. Recently, interest in the steroids has centred around those which act as mammalian hormones. One of these, *cortisone,* is produced by the adrenal cortex. It controls the balance of electrolytes in the body, and the rates of carbohydrate and nitrogen metabolism. Other steroids, such as *estrone, testosterone,* and *androsterone,* are hormones which control the development of the secondary sex characteristics.

## Sources of muscle power

Another very important group of compounds, the energy-transferring compounds, are concerned with the oxidation of substances within the cell, and with the production of chemical energy. Energy is needed to drive processes such as muscle contraction and the synthesis of new cells.

When carbohydrates or fatty acids are used for energy production, the molecules are whittled down by enzymes into carbon dioxide and hydrogen. The hydrogen atoms are not released as a gas, but are removed by compounds which work in conjunction with the breakdown enzymes. These 'hydrogen dustmen' are called *coenzymes.* Two major coenzymes occur in cells. They are *nicotinamide adenine dinucleotide* (NAD) and *nicotinamide adenine dinucleotide phosphate* (NADP). Both have the ability to receive or donate hydrogen atoms.

During carbohydrate or fatty acid oxidation, the coenzymes become reduced – that is, they accept hydrogen atoms. It is the reduced form of these compounds which can then be used in the cell to drive synthetic reactions, which often require the addition of hydrogen atoms to particular compounds. Alternatively, in the presence of an enzyme, coenzymes can cause hydrogen atoms to react with a variety of *acceptors.* Millions of years ago, when there was little oxygen in the atmosphere, living things used compounds such as sulphates and nitrates as hydrogen acceptors. But as the amount of oxygen in the atmosphere increased, oxygen gradually became the preferred hydrogen acceptor.

Hydrogen plus oxygen makes water – which sounds very simple. But the involved process we have just outlined seems a very complicated way of making one of our most abundant commodities. Why is this so? The explanation lies in the fact that the reaction which, in the laboratory, produces energy in the form of heat can, in the controlled environment of the living cell, be used to produce chemical energy.

The energy released in the cell is used to convert a substance called *adenosine diphosphate* (ADP) to its close relative *adenosine triphosphate* (ATP) by the addition of a third phosphate ($PO_3$ ) group (Fig. 6). The two substances can be compared to an accumulator, in which case ADP would represent the uncharged and ATP the charged states. The phosphate groups are bound to each other by what may be called high-energy phosphate bonds. It is the energy stored in these bonds which is later used to drive all of the work processes in the cell.

The apparatus by which the transfer of hydrogen from the reduced coenzyme to oxygen is coupled to the production of ATP from ADP is found mainly in the mitochondria. Indeed, the mitochondria are often called the 'powerhouses' of the cell.

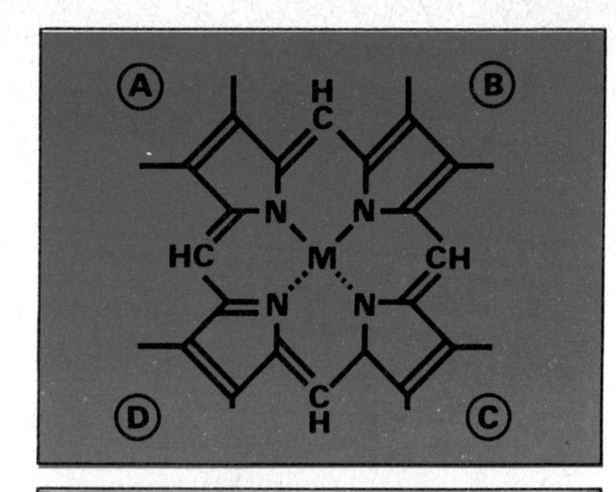


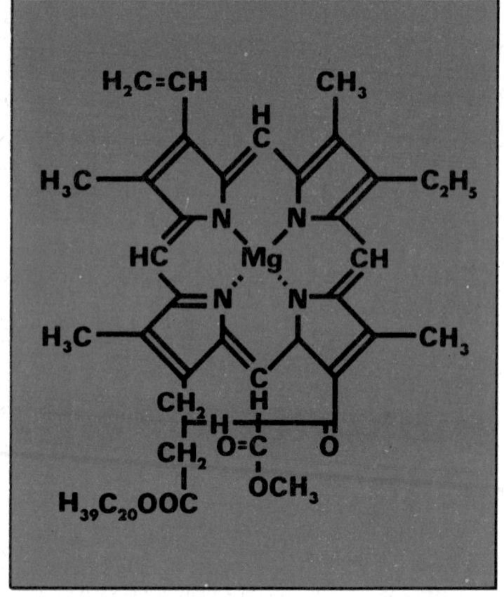


Fig. 7. *Top,* basic porphyrin skeleton. Four pyrrole groups (*A, B, C, D*) are linked by CH groups to form a ring. A metal atom *M* is held in the ring by bonds from the nitrogen atoms in the pyrrole groups. *Bottom,* structure of a chlorophyll molecule showing its porphyrin nucleus.

## Blood red and grass green

It is remarkable that two pigments vital to higher plants and animals have a basic chemical skeleton that is almost identical – despite the fact that the two molecules do quite different jobs. The red pigment in blood cells, *haemoglobin,* and the green pigment in plant cells, *chlorophyll,* are both based on an astonishingly similar chemical unit called a *porphyrin nucleus* (Fig. 7). The porphyrin nucleus is actually built up from four similar sub-units called *pyrroles* which are linked to form a ring. A metal atom is held inside the ring by linkages from the nitrogen atoms on the pyrrole groups. In haemoglobin the metal is iron, and in chlorophyll it is magnesium.

The porphyrin part of haemoglobin occurs in cells linked to a protein, and only functions in this conjugated form. Haemoglobin is able to capture, carry and release oxygen in higher animals. In plants, chlorophyll can absorb the sun's energy and convert it into the chemical energy which will be required to split water during photosynthesis.

This brief look at cell chemistry will probably be enough to warn you against talking about the '..nportant' and 'less important' chemicals of life. The fixtures and fittings, in fact, are vital to the house. It is safe to say that no cell could live for long without a steady supply of carbohydrates. And a higher plant without chlorophyll would be in a very bad way indeed!

The chemistry of a cell is a highly organised and complex pattern of reaction chains and cycles which are interwoven into one chemical process. Every chemical has its place in this microcosmic laboratory, and each one is as important to the cell as any other.

Fig. 6. Structural formula of adenosine triphosphate (ATP). Energy released in the cell is used to convert a substance called adenosine diphosphate (ADP) into adenosine triphosphate by the addition of a third phosphate group. Together ADP and ATP can be compared to an accumulator or battery in which case ADP would represent the uncharged and ATP the charged states. The phosphate groups are bound to each other by what may called *high-energy* phosphate bonds. It is the energy stored in these bonds that is later used to drive all the work processes in the cell.

# Controlling the cell system

Many of the basic activities of the animal's cells are controlled by tiny chemical messengers released in small amounts from the glands. These hormones provide an extremely effective cellular control.

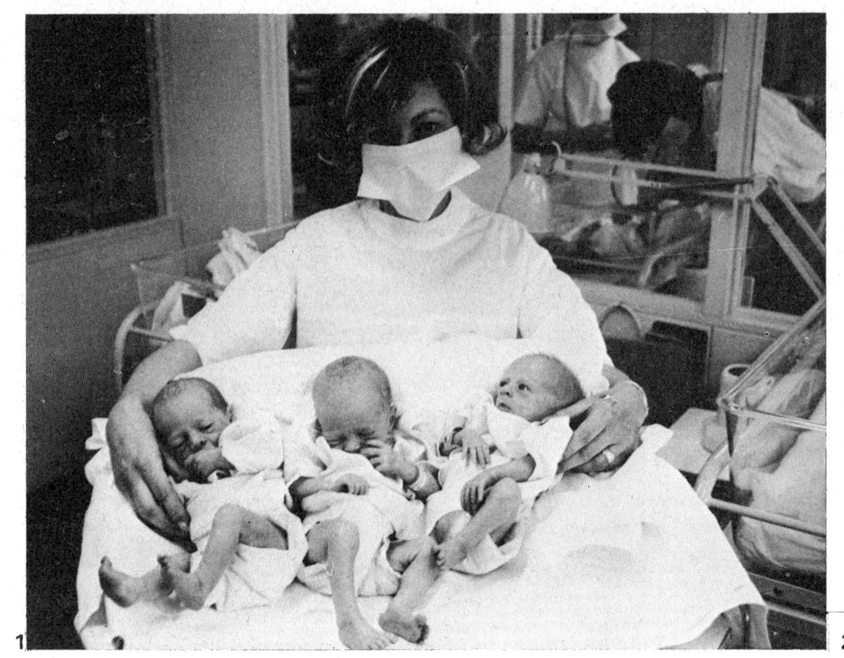

1

2

THE BODIES of higher plants and animals consist of millions of individual cells, each of which have certain specialized tasks to contribute to the overall metabolism of the body. Naturally, like any other complex system, the body will only function effectively if the activities of each cell can be subordinated to the requirements of the body as a whole. This presupposes some central control over the activities of the cells, and a system of communication between them. The body contains various means of carrying out these functions, but the most important is the system of hormones – the humoral system.

The word hormone is derived from the Greek word meaning to excite or set in motion. They are so named because they are chemical substances which influence the activities of the body. Hormones are produced by specialised organs called *glands*. They pass directly from the gland into the bloodstream which carries them to the organ which they then activate. Because the glands producing hormones put them directly into the blood, they are referred to as 'ductless' glands, in contrast to glands like the salivary gland, which secrete via ducts into the gut or to the external surface of the body.

By analogy, the word hormone is also applied somewhat loosely to a group of substances which regulate the growth of plants. Some of these substances, like gibberellic acid, can be added to the soil to produce a marked increase in the rate of growth of the plant. The growth substances are effective in very small concentrations, a few parts per million being enough to produce very marked changes in the size of the plant. The properties of substances like gibberellic acid, indoleacetic acid and phenoxyacetic acids are now applied widely in agriculture. Selective weedkillers, substances designed to produce seedless fruit and to prevent fruit drop, and many other chemical analogues of the growth-promoting substances are now in production on a commercial scale. But despite considerable research on plant-growth substances over the past few years, there is still no clear interpretation of their effects, nor of the way in which they interact.

3

**1** These triplets, born early in 1969 to Mrs Tucker of Somerset, show the effects of the fertility hormone gonadotrophin. This pituitary hormone stimulates the ovary to ovulation.
**2** Androgenic hormones are responsible for the magnificent wattles, comb and tail feathers of the cock. By contrast, the plumage of the hen is much less showy.
**3** Dr Banting and Dr Best, the Toronto research workers who isolated insulin and first used it to treat diabetes, are shown here with one of the first diabetic dogs to be kept alive on insulin.

Some sort of hormonal system appears to have arisen very early in the evolution of animals, and substantially the same hormones and glands are found in most of the higher animals, with minor variations. Thus, our own hormones are very little different from those of pigs or even of whales, and are identical with hormones found in frogs.

The ductless glands are scattered about the body in an apparently haphazard way, but as we shall see, their activities are in fact carefully co-ordinated so that they fit together to form a complete system.

## Hormone synthesis

A great deal of research in the last 100 years has succeeded in isolating the organs which produce the major hormones and in many cases it has been possible to artificially manufacture or synthesize the hormones produced by the various glands. One example of this synthesis which has had considerable impact over recent years is the synthesis of the hormones which control the sexual cycle in women. These hormones, together with artificial imitations produced in chemical factories, form the basis for the contraceptive pill. In other cases, the hormones can be extracted in bulk from the glands of animals and used to treat deficiency of hormones in human beings. The classic example of this is the hormone *insulin*, produced by the pancreas. Lack of insulin causes the

disease *diabetes mellitus*, and thousands of sufferers can now be restored to health with the aid of injections of insulin derived from cattle or pigs.

The actions of the hormones have been investigated exhaustively in animals by classical experimental procedures which involve removing the organ and noting the effects on the animal, and then grafting back the same organ from another animal to see if previous symptoms are reversed. Again, hormone extracts from glands can be injected into experimental animals to see what the effects are. Other research has concentrated on the chemistry of the hormones, attempting to synthesize the hormones in the laboratory. A recent major success in this field was the synthesis of insulin by a team of scientists in Peking.

## The controlling gland

Probably the most important ductless gland is the *pituitary body*. This is a small organ about the size of a pea which is attached by a stalk to the base of the part of the brain known as the hypothalamus. The pituitary body is really two glands, one of which is derived from the nerve tissue of the hypothalamus and the other from the tissue which makes up the roof of the embryo's mouth. The nervous part of the gland *(pars nervosa)* lies behind the other part of the gland *(pars anterior)*. The nervosa tissue is closely linked to the brain and provides a means by which the brain can exercise control over the hormonal system.

The pars nervosa of the pituitary produces only two hormones: *oxytocin* and *antidiuretic hormone* (ADH). The first hormone acts on the breasts and the uterus. It causes ejection of milk while the mother is breast feeding her child, and is responsible for the contraction of the uterine muscles which precedes birth. As far as is known, oxytocin, if it is produced at all, has no role in the male animal. ADH, on the other hand, is essential in both sexes. In the absence of this hormone, a disease called *diabetes insipidus*, characterized by intense thirst and excessive production of urine, results. In Man this disease can be relieved rapidly and completely by having patients inhale a preparation of ADH.

**1** A fallow buck in velvet. The fine spread of the buck's antlers is due to an abundance of androgens. These hormones are essential to the development of secondary sexual characteristics.
**2** These toads have just undergone metamorphosis and have left the pond where they were tadpoles. Metamorphosis in amphibians is brought on by the thyroid hormone thyroxine.
**3** Plant hormones in action. These dwarf pea plants were treated with varying amounts of gibberellic acid. The smallest plant was untreated; the largest was given 10 micrograms of the acid.

The anterior part of the pituitary produces a number of hormones, many of which are responsible for controlling the function of other ductless glands. These hormones, whose main effects are on the production of other hormones by other ductless glands, are called *trophic hormones*. Among those produced by the anterior pituitary is thyroid-stimulating hormone, which influences the thyroid gland to begin secreting its own hormone. Another important trophic pituitary hormone is *adrenocorticotrophin*, so called because it stimulates the adrenal cortex to produce hormones. Other hormones from the anterior pituitary are the so-called *gonadotrophins*, which affect the activity of the gonads. Thus, hormones from the anterior pituitary stimulate the production of Graffian follicles in women and exercise overall control over the menstrual cycle, while in men they affect the activity of the interstitial cells of the testis. The pituitary control over the gonads involves a complex system of 'feed-back' interactions in which the amount of hormone secreted by the pituitary is controlled by the amount of circulating hormone from the gonads, with the result that the system works to keep the amount of gonadal hormone in the blood within closely defined limits. This type of *'servo-mechanism'* plays a large part in the overall control of hormone levels in the blood.

The other important pituitary hormone is growth hormone which is also produced

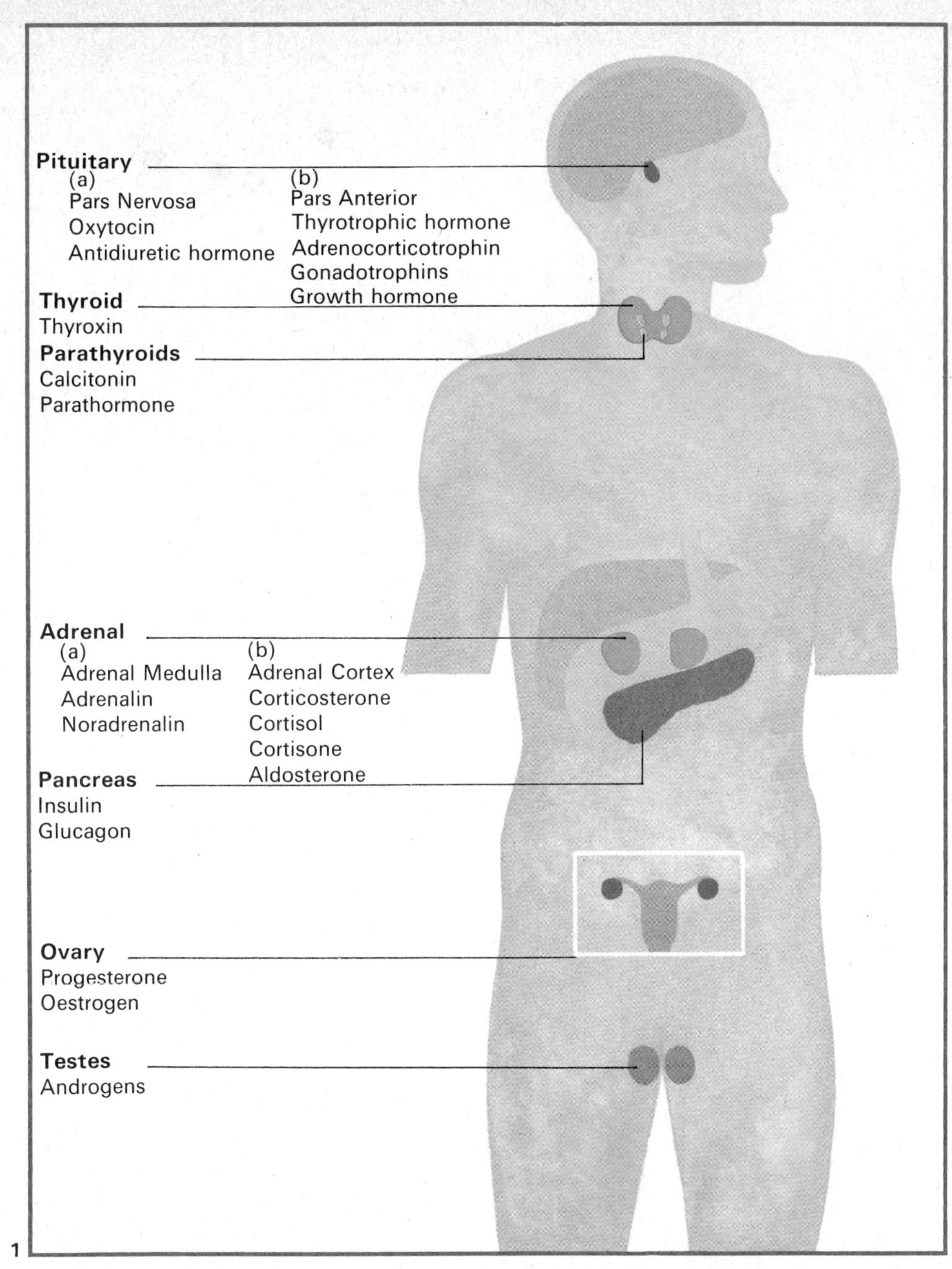


by the anterior pituitary, and stimulates the growth of tissues. Excess of this hormone in children produces giants, while if the hormone excess occurs in adulthood a syndrome known as *acromegaly* is produced. Acromegaly is characterized by the uneven growth and thickening of the bones and skin, and gives rise to a highly characteristic facial appearance.

## Thyroid and parathyroid

The thyroid and parathyroid glands, situated in the neck, are in fact separate glands with different purposes, although the parathyroids are buried in the tissue of the thyroid. The thyroid is a butterfly-shaped gland overlying the windpipe. Its chief product is the hormone *thyroxin,* formed by combining iodine with an amino acid. Thyroxin plays an important part in regulating the rate at which cells use up energy. In its absence, young animals develop a condition called in human beings *cretinism,* involving dull mental capacities, lack of energy, dry skin and thick, dry hair. Too much thyroid hormone, on the other hand, leads to over activity, with nervous manner and clammy skin. Thyroid trouble can also be brought about by a lack of iodine in the diet. Such a lack used to be common in limestone areas of Britain, where the soil contains little or none of the element. In such cases, the thyroid intensifies its efforts to trap iodine and becomes greatly enlarged, leading to a condition known as *goitre.* This has now virtually disappeared, in Britain at least, because iodine is now added in small amounts to table salt. In lower animals, the thyroid is closely concerned with the process of metamorphosis. In tadpoles, for example, removal of the thyroid means that the tadpole stays permanently immature, although addition of thyroxin to the water brings about metamorphosis to frogs. The metamorphosis of intact tadpoles can be hastened

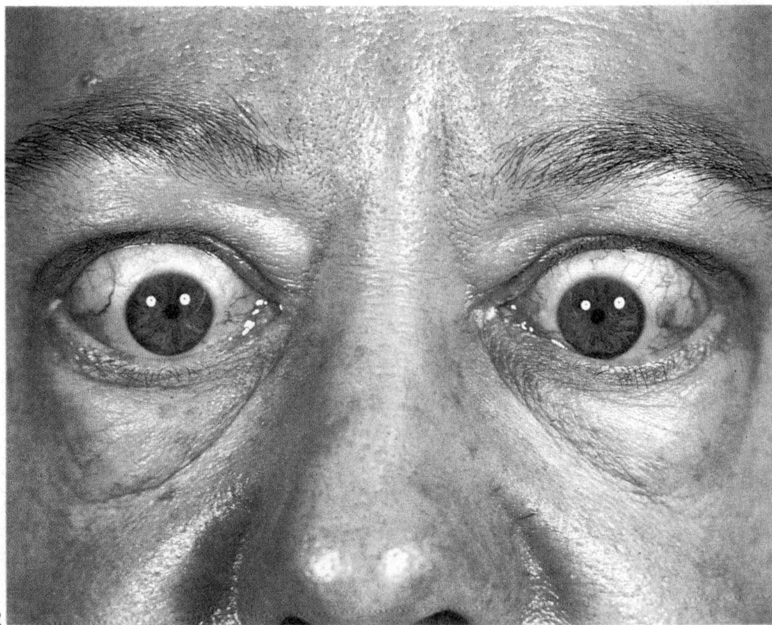


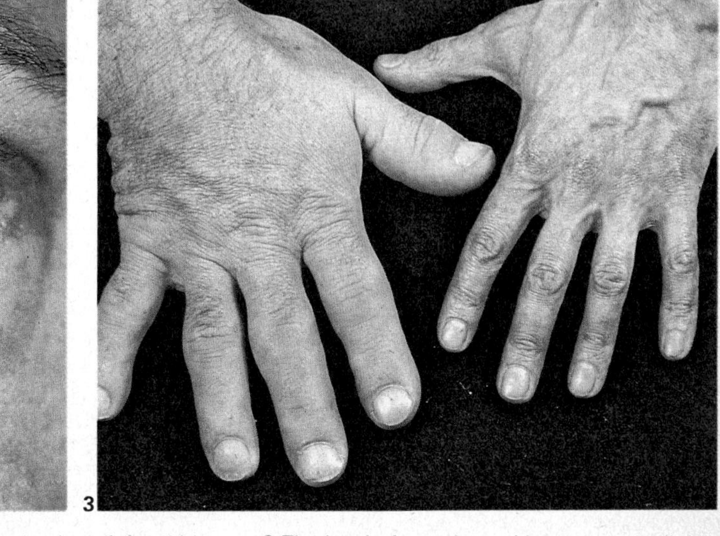


**1** Sites of the main ductless glands shown on a diagram of the human body. Note how closely most of the glands are sited to the course of the gut. Most of them arise as gut outgrowths.

**2** A woman with overproduction of thyroid hormone. Note how the eyes protrude from their sockets. This symptom, exophthalmos, is very characteristic of advanced thyroid overactivity.

**3** The hand of a patient with acromegaly (left), compared with a normal hand. Growth hormone overproduction has thickened the bones and skin and greatly increased the hand's overall size.

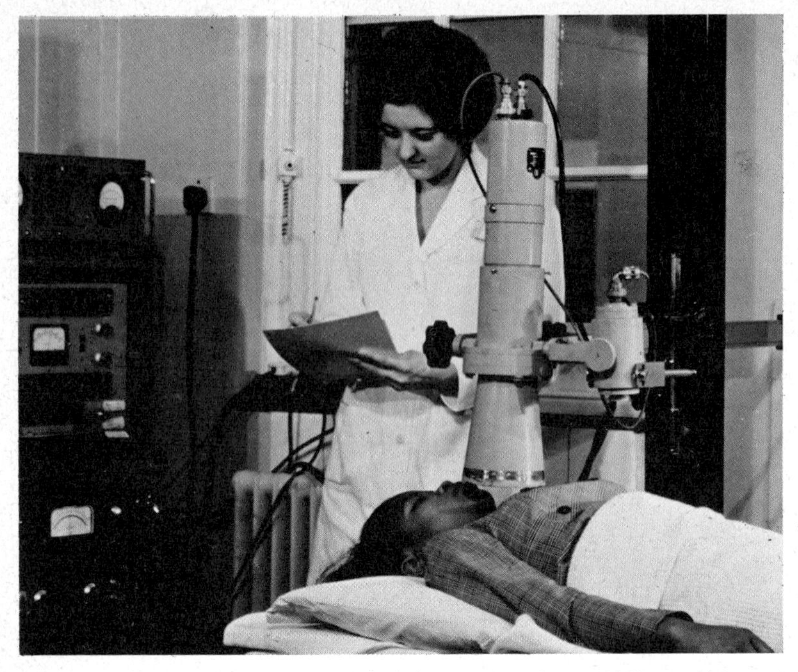

A Geiger counter is here being used to monitor the activity of the thyroid gland. Radioactive iodine is injected and the amount taken up by the thyroid is registered on the counter.

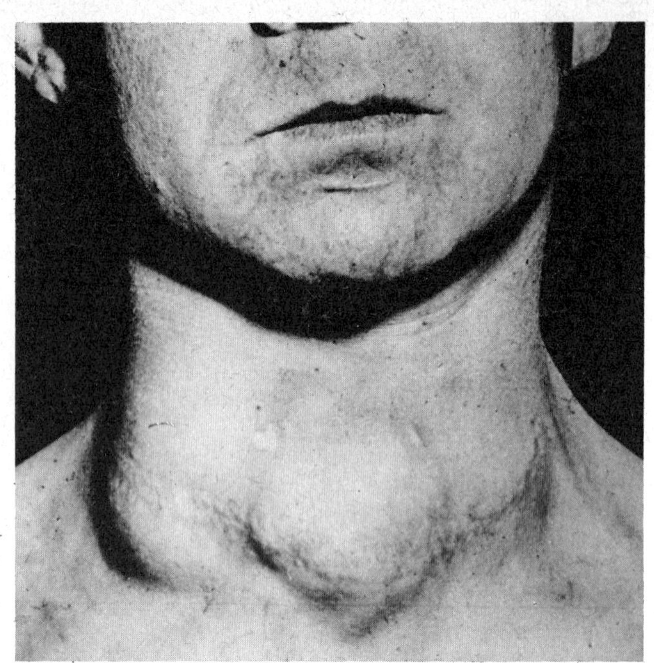

Adenoma of the thyroid gland. The growth of the gland in the neck has swollen the gland, showing its position over the trachea – the windpipe. Goitre has a similar effect.

by adding thyroxin or even iodine salts to the water.

The parathyroids, so called because they lie alongside the thyroid in the neck, produce two hormones, *calcitonin* and *parathormone*. These hormones are responsible, along with vitamin-D, for regulating the level of calcium in the blood. Without an adequate amount of calcium in the blood, a condition called *tetany* occurs in which the muscles go into spasms and the animal dies if not treated.

The next important ductless glands are the two *suprarenal* glands, which lie at the upper poles of the kidneys in males. These glands, like the pituitary, are not really single glands, but are formed by the fusion of at least two glands which were originally in different sites in the body. They play two quite distinct parts in the life of the animal. The outer part of the gland, the *adrenal medulla,* is closely related to the sympathetic nervous system and produces two hormones which are also formed by the sympathetic nerves. These are *adrenalin* and *noradrenalin.* They resemble each other chemically and in their effects on the tissues of the body.

Adrenalin is produced in large quantities whenever any unusual effort is required, for example during athletic contests or fist-fights. Its effects have been called preparations for 'flight or fight'. It raises the blood pressure, increases the output of the heart and thus brings more blood to the muscles. Like noradrenalin, it raises the blood sugar level by bringing glucose out of storage in the tissues. It causes the symptoms of anxiety and dilates the pupils of the eyes. Noradrenalin constricts the arteries and small blood vessels by causing the muscles in their walls to contract. At the same time, it causes the 'tone' or tension of the muscles to increase. These two hormones thus play an important part in situations requiring special efforts.

The use of adrenalin by athletes to improve their performance was recently banned by the Olympic authorities as an unfair use of drugs, although it is hard to see how such use could be detected. There have also been cases of racehorses with natural ability to produce very large amounts of adrenalin. This has given a distinct advantage to the horse in races and often led to charges of doping.

## Steroid hormones

The inner part of the adrenal gland, called the *cortex,* produces a number of hormones and substances involved in the synthesis of hormones. Not all these hormones, however, are normally released into the blood. The adrenal cortex hormones are not proteins, like most of the hormones discussed so far, but belong to a group of chemical compounds called *steroids.* Steroids generally have a number of six-sided carbon compounds linked together to form a network. The steroid hormones produced by the adrenal include *corticosterone, cortisol* and *cortisone.* These three hormones, in varying degrees, raise the level of glucose in the blood, though not as spectacularly as insulin lowers it. They also have an effect on the storage of sugars in the tissues. In common with other corticosteroids, they play a part in controlling the salt content of the blood, chiefly by influencing the amount of salt excreted in the urine by the kidneys. Other corticosterones, like *aldosterone*, also secreted by the adrenal, have a more marked effect on the kidneys. Aldosterone acts on the kidney to encourage it to hold on to sodium, thus preventing too much loss of salt. Other hormones from the adrenal assist the kidney to retain potassium.

The adrenal hormones, in varying degrees also have the characteristic property that they cause the development of male secondary sexual characteristics, although their effects in this respect are not as marked as those of the steroid hormones produced by the gonads themselves.

The overall effects of the corticosteroids are complex, but the gland is clearly essential to life. If it is removed surgically from animals, the animals die. In human beings, deficiency of adrenal hormones produces Addison's disease, in which the body becomes unable to cope with stress. Changes in external temperature, wounds, infections and prolonged exercise are badly tolerated by Addisonian patients.

Like insulin, *glucagon* regulates sugar levels in the blood and tissues. But unlike insulin, it acts to raise the level of blood sugar. In fact, insulin is the only hormone which lowers the blood sugar level, whereas all the other hormones which act on the blood sugar tend to raise it.

Of all the ductless glands, however, perhaps the sex glands are the most interesting. The range of their activity in women is remarkable, as variations in the level of sex hormones in blood are almost entirely responsible for the changes that accompany menstruation and child-birth.

In the male, the only parts of the gonads producing hormones are the testes, which secrete a number of steroid hormones similar to those produced by the adrenal. These hormones are the *androgens,* and they are responsible for the changes that take place at puberty, the maturation of the male secondary sexual characteristics such as antlers in stags, beards in men and wattles and spurs in poultry. These hormones also stimulate the production of sperms by the testis.

In the female, hormones produced in the ovary, chiefly *progesterone* and *oestrogen,* regulate the menstrual cycle and ovulation, thus preparing the conditions in the womb for the reception of the fertilized egg.

These are the main ductless glands of Man and the higher animals. The surprising aspect of a comparative study of the humoral systems of widely different animals is that almost all of them conform to the same basic pattern.

# A closer look at life

**The compound microscope, phase contrast, interference and electron microscope are now part of the biologist's armoury. With these tools he can probe deep into the inner mysteries of life.**

EVER SINCE the Dutchman Anton van Leeuwenhoek invented the simple microscope in the seventeenth century, the microscope has become the trade-mark of biology. The popular image of the biologist poring over a microscope has more than a grain of truth in it, and the microscope is one of the few pieces of equipment found in every biological laboratory. The microscope revolutionized biology, because most whole organisms and all cells are too small to be studied with the naked eye. But a microscope is not just a magnifier; it must also increase the amount of fine detail that can be seen – its ability to do this is its *resolving power*.

The average human eye unaided is just able to resolve, or see as separate objects, two objects which produce an angle of one minute of arc at the position of the eye. That is the same as saying that two objects 25 cm away from the eye must be separated by at least 0·07 mm in order to be seen as two objects. If they are closer than 0·07 mm they appear as one continuous object; if the detail on any one object is finer than 0·07 mm it is not seen.

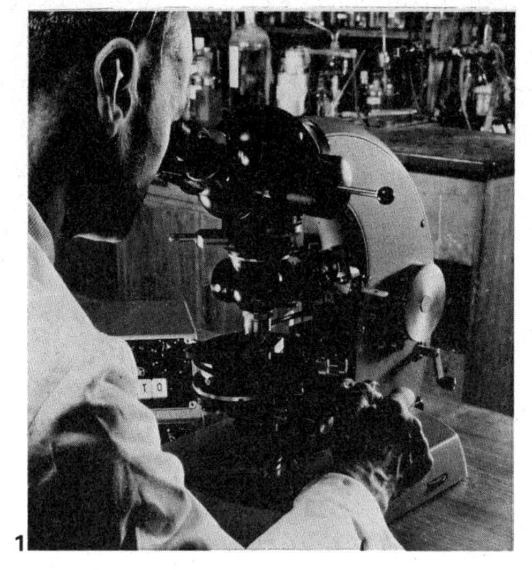

1 The modern compound microscope consists of a complicated objective and eye lens, and a condenser set under the stage. It also has its own special light source.
2 Under the light microscope a pollen grain appears as circles containing ill-defined bodies.
3 Using the electron microscope at fairly low magnification these bodies can be seen to be individual cells.
4 At high magnification, yet with good resolution, a chloroplast with its spiral of membranes is clearly seen within one of the cells.

## Distortion

If we are to see objects smaller than 0·07 mm in diameter or separated by a distance smaller than this, they must be magnified with a magnifying glass or microscope. Some of the lenses made by van Leeuwenhoek in the seventeenth century had a magnifying power of up to 250 times but it was impossible to use them to see objects only 1/250th of 0·07 mm because, like all simple lenses, they suffered from aberrations and astigmatism. Because lenses have to be made of glass or quartz, and because they cannot be perfectly machined, they suffer from defects such as *barrel* or *pin-cushion distortion – chromatic aberration, spherical aberration,* and *astigmatism*. Barrel or pin distortion causes the image of a square to appear either barrel or pin-cushion shaped; chromatic aberration causes light of different colours to be focused at different positions, and spherical aberration causes light of the same colour to be focused in different positions. Astigmatism from which the human eye often suffers stems from light from an object being more in focus in one direction than in another at right angles.

The only way to overcome these aberrations is to use a combination of lenses so that the defects of one oppose and cancel out those of the others. But even with the several lenses of a compound microscope the magnification of an object cannot be increased indefinitely.

There is a limit to a microscope's resolving power because beams of light do not really move in straight lines when they pass through an aperture, or a specimen under the microscope, they are bent by a process of diffraction. In practice some of the light emerging from any part of a specimen viewed under a microscope is so bent that it falls outside the cone of light that can be collected by the objective lens of the microscope. This light is therefore totally lost from the viewer as is the information it contains about the structure being examined. To calculate a microscope's resolving power the biologist must divide half the wavelength of the light used by the numerical aperture. The numerical aperture is simply an arithmetical description of the size of the cone of light the microscope lens can collect. In other words it describes that portion of the light bent by diffraction which does not escape the lens.

In practice light microscopes used for research have a numerical aperture of between 1·2 and 1·4. By using green light and a good instrument, it is possible to resolve objects separated by about 0·00025 of a millimetre; that is about a quarter of the length of some bacteria. The electron microscope, because it uses beams of electrons which have very small wavelengths, can resolve separations as fine as five ten-millionths of a millimetre.

Most microscopes consist of variations of the same basic optical arrangement. Below the stage which carries the slides or specimen, there is a condenser lens – a concave mirror which illuminates the specimen by focusing light on to it. The light emerging from the specimen, the cone of diffracted light, is collected by the objective lens immediately above the specimen. The numerical aperture of this lens determines the resolution of the microscope. The objective lens focuses the light to form an image in the tube of the microscope at a position called the *first image plane*. A projection lens, called the *eye piece* in the light microscope, projects a magnified second image of this first image either on a screen or on to the

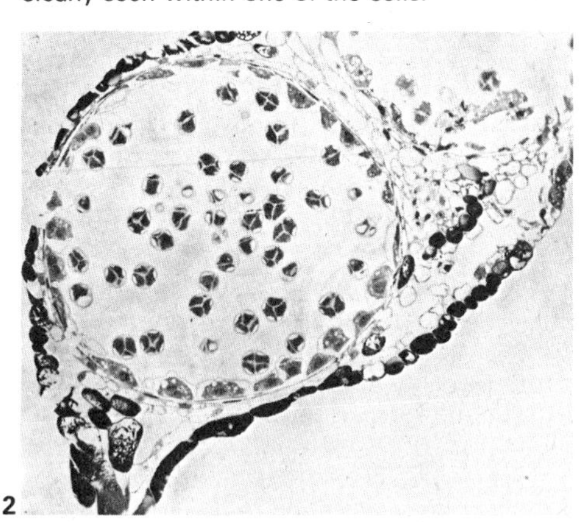

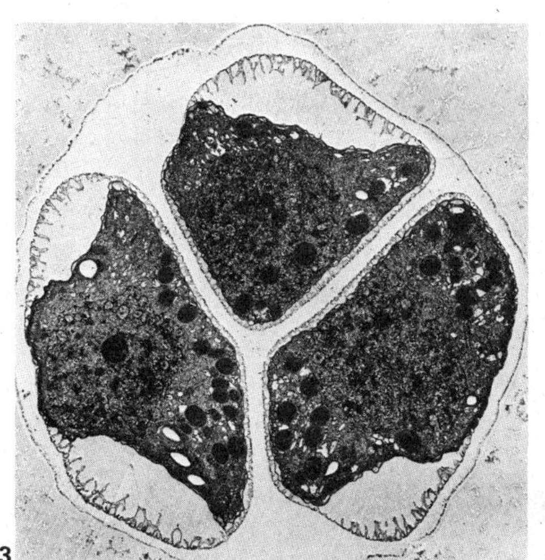

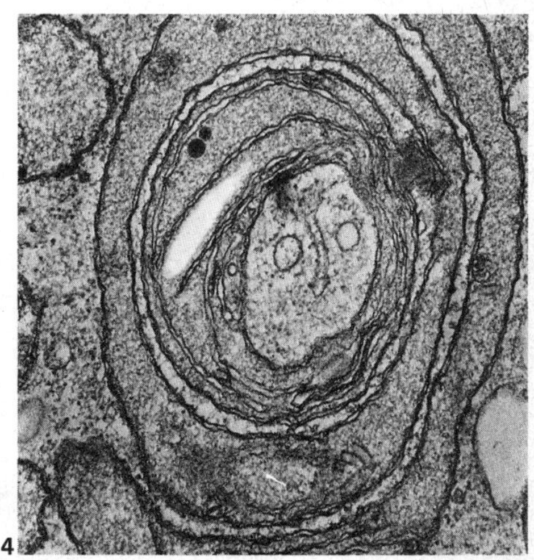

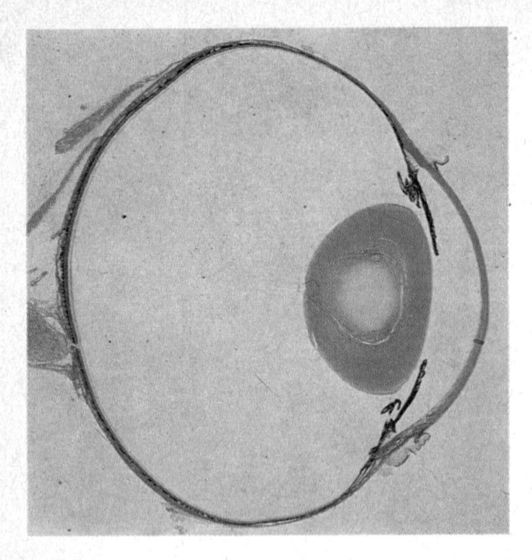

The basic shape of a ground squirel's eye and its larger components, including the cornea, the lens and iris can be easily made out in this two times magnification.

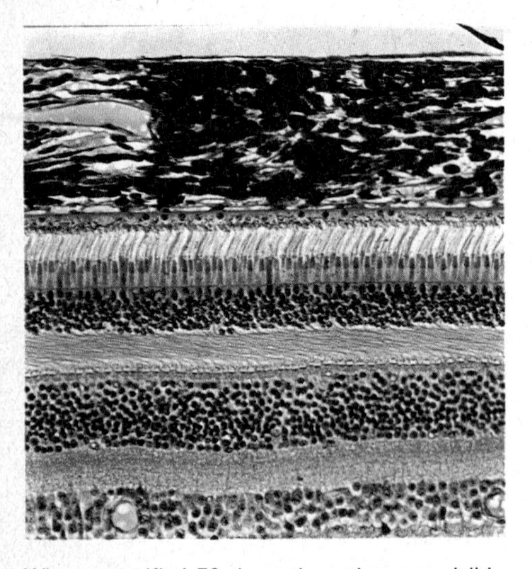

When magnified 50 times the retina, not visible at low magnifications, begins to show up clearly. A dense mass of nerve cells can thus be seen overlying the pigment cells.

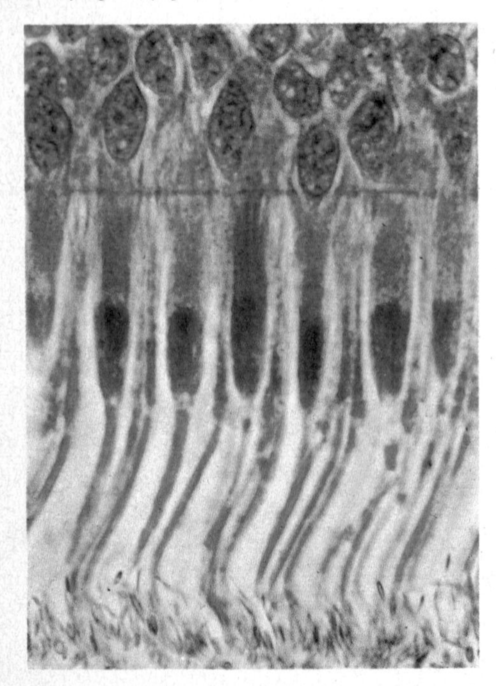

Under oil immersion the same retina is magnified 640 times, and a particular part, the light-sensory rods and cones, can be seen to be composed of individual cells with nerve fibres.

retina of the eye.

The objective lens is often made up of half a dozen or more concave and convex lenses, all mounted together in such a way as to reduce the various aberrations to a minimum. It is also essential for high resolution microscopy to put a spot of oil on the cover slip on top of the specimen and then screw the objective lens until it touches the oil. This *oil immersion procedure,* which requires a special objective lens, increases the amount of diffracted light from the specimen which can be collected and so increases resolution.

To be seen an object must stand out from its background or else any amount of magnification and resolution will not make the object distinguishable. Most cells are colourless and something has to be done to give them *contrast.* The most common method, which has yielded much information about the structure of cells, is to stain different parts of the cell with differently coloured dyes or stains. Thus the art of *histochemistry* – the chemistry of staining cells – came into being.

Over the past 100 years much research has been devoted to developing stains which will colour specific components in the cell; some stains, for example, will only dye the acid components, others only the alkaline or basic components and some stains only one sort of molecule. The Feulgen stain, for example, specifically stains DNA, the hereditary material of cells; moreover, the extent of staining is proportional to the amount of DNA present.

Even more ingenious techniques, called *cytochemistry,* have been developed for locating molecules of particular enzymes in cells. This process depends on a coloured dye or a metallic compound becoming coupled to the products of an enzyme reaction. For example, enzymes, called phosphates, can split phosphate residues from substances in cells that contain them. By adding a solution of a lead salt, the phosphate precipitates as lead phosphate. When converted to black lead sulphide in an additional reaction, a visible precipitate of black granules forms. The location of these granules shows where the phosphates enzymes reside in a cell.

Dead biological material decays and to prevent this microscopists have devised ways of fixing their material. The specimen is immersed in a fixative, such as absolute alcohol, solutions of heavy metals, or various organic compounds including formaldehyde or glutaraldehyde. Fixation has one inevitable and unfortunate consequence; after it is fixed a cell is totally dead and no longer in its natural living state. For this reason, biologists have had to accept that they are always looking at and interpreting an artefact – something which is close to the living state but not identical to it.

Biologists also face the difficult problem that whole cells, all tissues and organs are too large to be examined intact. They have to be cut into extremely thin sections. It is sometimes possible to cut sections by hand, especially of relatively rigid material like a plant shoot, but it is impossible to cut sections a few thousandths of a millimetre

The early microscopes may have looked beautiful but their lenses suffered from all kinds of aberration. They also lacked condenser lenses and their resolving power was poor.

thick by hand. To do this the specimen has first to be embedded in some supporting material. Light microscopists usually embed their material in paraffin wax but to get sections thin enough for the electron microscope – a few hundred thousandths of a millimetre thick – the material has to be embedded in a hard-setting plastic.

Once embedded in either plastic or wax the specimen block is sectioned on a machine known as a *microtome.* In essence this consists of a metal, glass or even diamond knife edge firmly clamped and arranged so that the block of specimen falls on to the knife and is advanced by a few thousandths or hundred thousandths of a millimetre between each cut.

## Using light

In recent times biologists have been able to get round the problem of contrast without resorting to staining techniques by using *phase contrast, interference* and *polarization microscopes.* These three types of microscope make transparent cells visible by exploiting a physical property of light known as interference. The phase contrast microscope is by far the most useful of the three. It produces a good contrast image of a specimen although this appears transparent in the ordinary microscope. Thus intact living cells can be studied without fixation and staining.

Interference is the process by which two beams of light either amplify each other or cancel each other out. Light is a wave motion and if two waves meet with their peaks and troughs exactly in phase, the result is one wave with peaks and troughs equal to the sum of those of the original two waves. In other words, the amplitude of the light wave, or its brightness, will be the sum of the amplitudes of the two waves. If two waves meet when they are out of

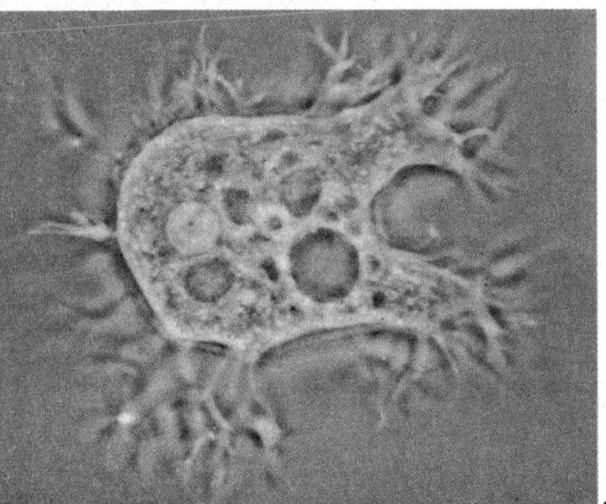

1 The exquisite beauty of the shells of the minute unicellular diatoms is brought to light in the microscope through a special technique known as dark ground illumination. In this technique light is reflected on to the slide rather than being transmitted through it.
2 Ordinary transmitted light gives a much duller effect than dark ground illumination.
3 With the phase contrast microscope it became possible for the first time to study the behaviour of living material, like this amoeba magnified some 250 times.
4 *Spirogyra,* a simple plant found in ponds, is made up of a chain of cells. At 200 times magnification the spiral cytoplasmic chain of green chloroplasts becomes visible.

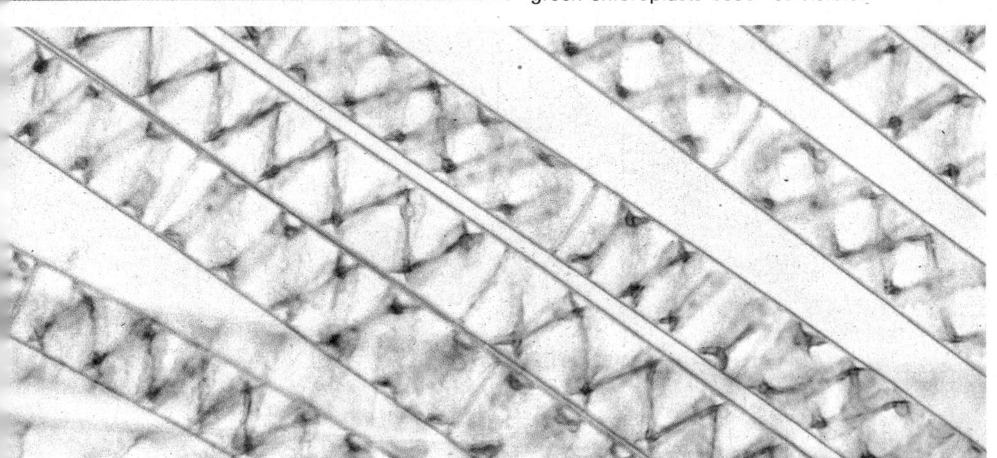

phase the trough of one cancels the peak of the other – the eye light will appear very dim.

The phase contrast and interference microscopes exploit this interference interaction. Some of the light passing through an object is diffracted but some passes through undeviated. The extent of the *diffraction,* or bending, will depend on the amount and quality of material in the specimen. If the direct beam and the diffracted beam come from the same source, the diffracted beam has to travel further than the direct beam because it is bent. There is an optical path difference between the two beams which amounts to saying thay get out of phase. The eye cannot detect phase differences but it can detect amplitude differences. The trick of the phase contrast microscope is to arrange things so that the diffracted and direct beams, necessarily out of phase, can interfere. When this happens, depending on how much the two beams are out of phase, they produce either brightness or darkness. A transparent object – so long as there are diffracting substances present – appears black, white and all shades of grey.

The interference microscope works on the same general principle but it produces an image by the interference between *all* the light going through the specimen and an independent reference beam. In effect, the interference microscope is two microscopes in one.

Its one advantage over the phase contrast microscope is that it can be used as a cell balance to measure the amount of dry matter in any volume of cell. By using the interference microscope a biologist can measure the *optical path difference* (OPD) introduced into the specimen beam. The size of the OPD depends on the refractive index of the specimen which, in turn, depends on the amount of matter in a unit volume. Both the thickness of the specimen and the area being viewed can be measured. Knowing the volume of the specimen as well as the OPD, the biologist can calculate the dry mass of matter in the cell.

The polarization microscope relies on both interference and light polarization. Although not widely used, the polarization microscope is useful for measuring the extent to which molecules are aligned with respect to each other in a cell. It was used, for example, to show that DNA in sperm cell neuclei is so regularly packed that it is virtually crystalline.

A few cells naturally contain coloured substances. When they are illuminated with white light, only those colours of the spectrum which are not absorbed pass through the specimen. This in effect acts as a natural colour filter and appears to be the colour of the transmitted light.

The principle has been extended in the ultra-violet microscope. Many cellular molecules strongly absorb ultra-violet light which, although it occurs in sunlight, is not seen by the human eye. But if microscopes are made with quartz lenses (quartz does not absorb ultra-violet light while glass does) and illuminated by mercury or xenon arc lamps, which emit much ultra-violet light, it is possible to observe the absorption of the ultra-violet light by the cell components.

Improvements in the design of light microscopes and, in particular, the invention of the phase contrast microscope are important. But it is the electron microscope that, since 1945, has completely revolutionized the study of cells. The electron microscope (EM) has shown that cytoplasm and nucleoplasm are not simply colloidal protein 'soups' but unbelievably ordered structures divided into compartments specialized for particular functions.

The EM is built on the same design principles as the light microscope. It has a condenser, objective and projector lens, but these are not glass; they are electromagnetic because only an electromagnetic field can bend and focus beams of electrons. And because gas molecules scatter electrons the microscope has to be evacuated. The image in the electron microscope must be projected by the projector lens on to a fluorescent screen which converts the energy of the electrons into visible light. The operator views the screen with a pair of binoculars, looking through a lead-glass window, which shields him from the X rays that are produced. The electron beam itself is produced by heating to white heat a tungsten filament at the top of the microscope.

The specimen is mounted on a tiny perforated copper grid covered by a layer of plastic or carbon a few molecules thick. To produce contrast, which is as much of a problem as it is in light microscopy, stains have been developed and most of them are solutions of salts of heavy metals, such as uranium, lead or tungsten. The atoms of these metals are large and since they scatter the electrons, instead of absorbing them, the contrast in the electron microscope is produced by the scattering not the absorption, of the electrons outside the collecting aperture of the lenses. The stained region thus appears darker than the background. This *positive staining* involves floating the specimen mounted on a grid on a drop of stain.

*Negative staining,* on the other hand, is a particularly valuable technique for looking at the structure of molecules or virus particles isolated from cells by centrifugation and chromatography. The solution of molecules is sprayed on to a carbon-coated grid and, when the molecules have dried down on to the support, the grid is floated on a solution of the stain. As a result more stain is deposited on the spaces between the molecules than on the molecules themselves so when the specimen is examined in the EM a dark background, heavily stained, with the less stained, and therefore lighter, molecules thrown into relief is seen.

The image produced by the conventional electron microscope is two dimensional, flat like a picture without perspective. But an electron microscope which produces a three-dimensional image, the *stereoscan microscope,* has been developed in Britain and is now available commercially. The stereoscan microscope sacrifices some of the resolution of the conventional electron microscope in order to get a picture in depth, but for some types of research the sacrifice is well worthwhile because the surface structure of the specimen can be seen in great detail.

**1** The electron microscope has revealed an entirely new world to biologists. They can now see that instead of a 'soup' the contents of cells are highly structured and complex.

**2** The surface of skin, seen at nearly 1,000 times magnification with the stereoscan microscope, appears as a complicated mesh of cells and fibres.

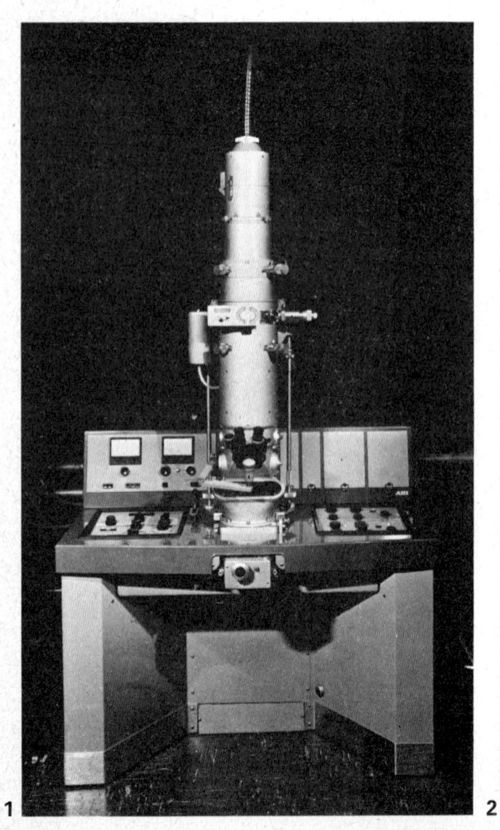

1

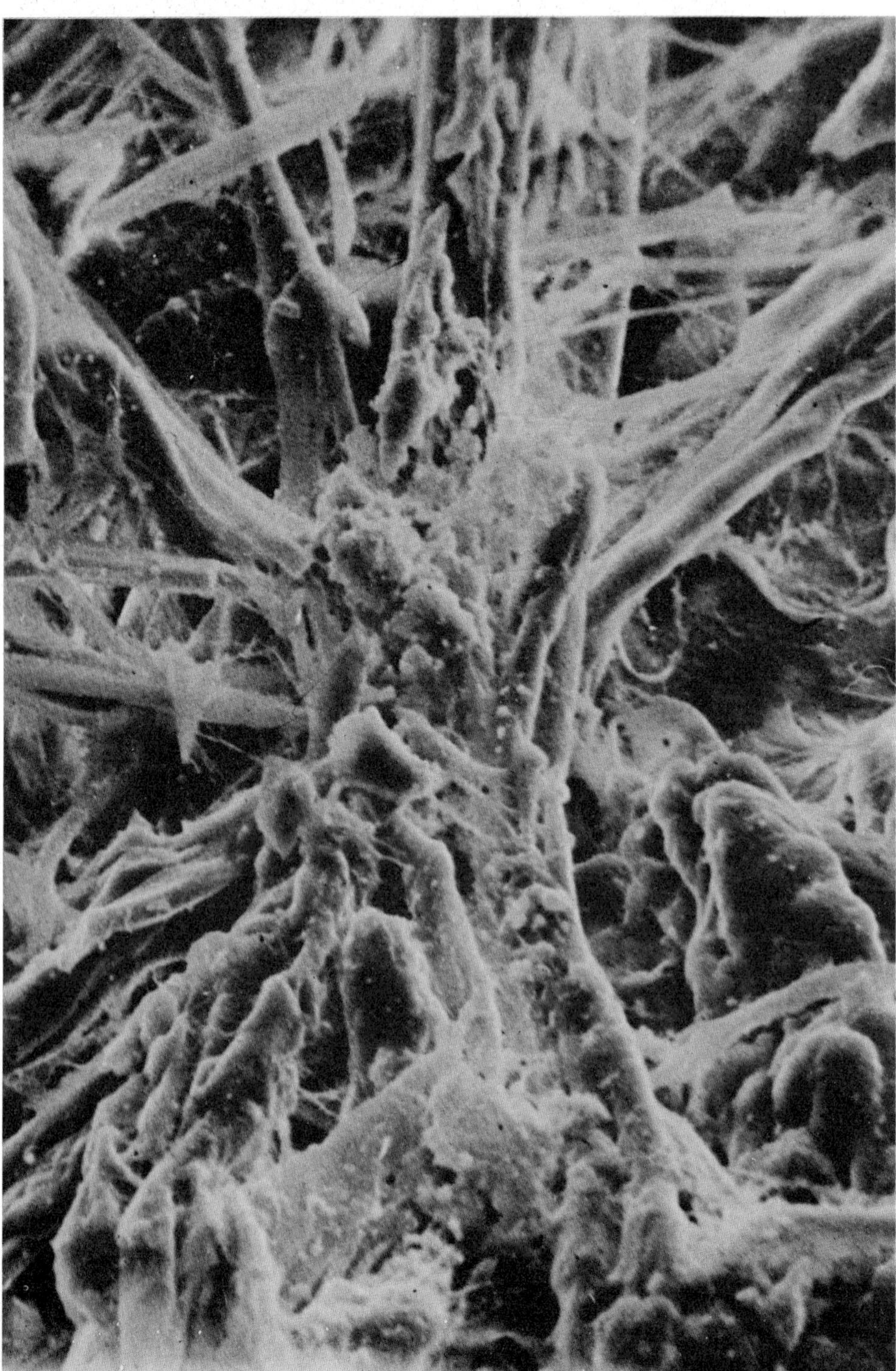

2

# The flame of life

**Energy for the processes of life comes mainly through the oxidation of fats and carbohydrates. In the test-tube, oxidation occurs by combustion. In the cell the reaction must be more controlled.**

WHEN A MAN lifts a heavy weight, his muscles contract and he does biological work with the expenditure of energy. In the world of biology, creatures are constantly using energy in this way. And even on a fine scale right down at the cell level, energy changes take place. In order to maintain their very existence, individual cells must constantly use up energy on processes such as salt uptake and the making of new materials.

The energy needed to drive all these processes is obtained mainly from the breakdown of carbon-containing compounds by oxidation. Commonly carbohydrates (such as glucose) and fatty acids are the energy-providing substances, though under certain circumstances proteins can also be used. In a test-tube, the oxidation of fats or carbohydrates generally takes the form of combustion with the release of energy as heat. But in the cell the reaction proceeds in a more controlled manner. Oxygen is not allowed to combine directly with the atoms of carbon and hydrogen, but instead atoms of hydrogen are removed by substances called coenzymes working in conjunction with enzymes. Only later are the atoms of hydrogen allowed to react with oxygen from the air, in a process which is associated with the formation of a substance called adenosine triphosphate (ATP). ATP is rich in energy; it is the common energy 'currency' of the cell.

## Why animals depend on plants

Not all cells or organisms are capable of producing their own carbon-containing energy sources from inorganic raw materials in the environment. Those that do so are called *autotrophs,* and include the higher plants, algae, photosynthetic bacteria and photosynthetic protozoa. The vast majority of animals, fungi and non-photosynthetic bacteria cannot do so and are called *chemotrophs.* At some stage in its food chain, therefore, a chemotroph must rely on an autotroph to provide these compounds. For example, man (a chemotroph) eats meat in the form of lamb (another chemotroph) which eats grass (an autotroph).

Autotrophs contain a pigment, such as chlorophyll, which can absorb light. Normally the light energy comes from the sun so that, on the Earth at least, the sun can be considered to be the primary source of energy. After the pigment has absorbed light, its energy is not dissipated as heat or lost by fluorescence, but is converted to chemical energy. In green plants, the chemical energy is used to change molecules of a coenzyme into a form that can be used in conjunction with an enzyme to 'fix' atmospheric carbon dioxide. This is the start of a series of reactions by which autotrophs produce carbohydrates. Chemotrophs are unable to trap and use light energy in this way, even though they may have enzyme systems capable of 'fixing' carbon dioxide and converting it to carbohydrates.

A champion weight-lifter, his muscles straining, gathers energy in preparation for a last great effort to heave the bar bells above his head. Because muscle tissues are so important in the production of energy, they must necessarily contain many more mitochondria than do other tissues.

Whatever the source of the substance used for energy production, there are many basic reactions which are common to all living cells. The whole process of substrate breakdown and energy release is called *respiration,* and can be divided into two parts. The first part, called *glycolysis,* can take place in the absence of oxygen or in what are called *anaerobic* conditions. It involves the splitting of a compound having six carbon atoms (a *hexose*) into two molecules, each of which contains three carbon atoms (a *triose*). The second part of respiration involves the release of carbon dioxide from the trioses by a process known as the *citric acid cycle* or *Kreb's cycle,* which can only operate in the presence of oxygen (in *aerobic* conditions). As a result, the two parts of respiration can operate together only under aerobic conditions, although glycolysis can operate alone if necessary under anaerobic conditions.

The starting material for the glycolytic pathway is glucose, which is frequently obtained from the breakdown of stored carbohydrates such as starch and glycogen. The end-product is pyruvic acid, which also serves as the starting point for the citric acid cycle. By examining these two processes, it is possible to discover how the energy stored in the chemical bonds of a molecule such as glucose can be transformed into the common energy currency of the cell – the high-energy phosphate bonds of ATP.

To make coal or petrol burn to release its energy, it must be *activated* by expending a small amount of energy in the form of heat. A match (using a small amount of energy) can set fire to thousands of gallons of petrol (releasing the heat energy in the petrol). In much the same way, glucose must be activated before it

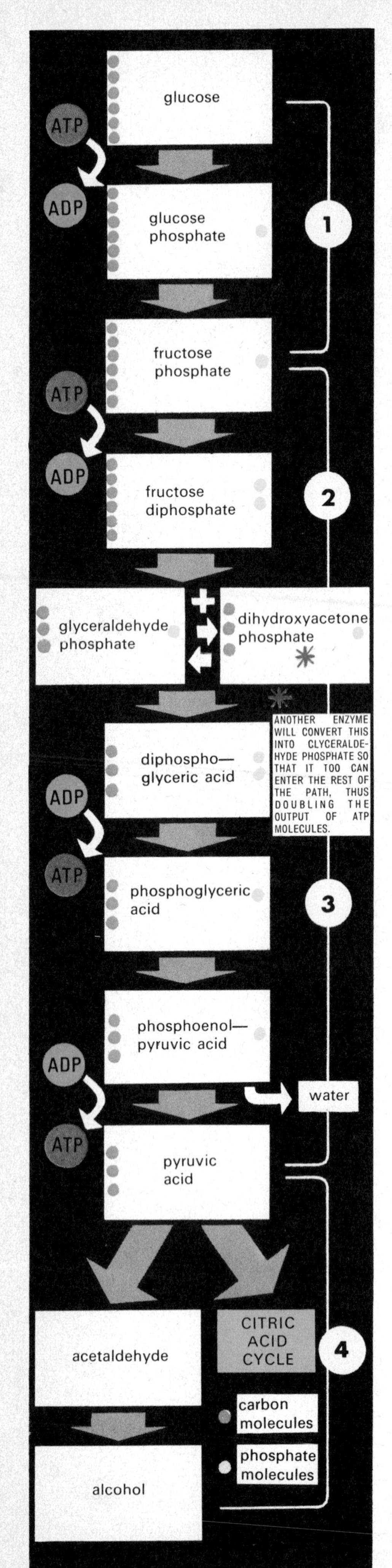


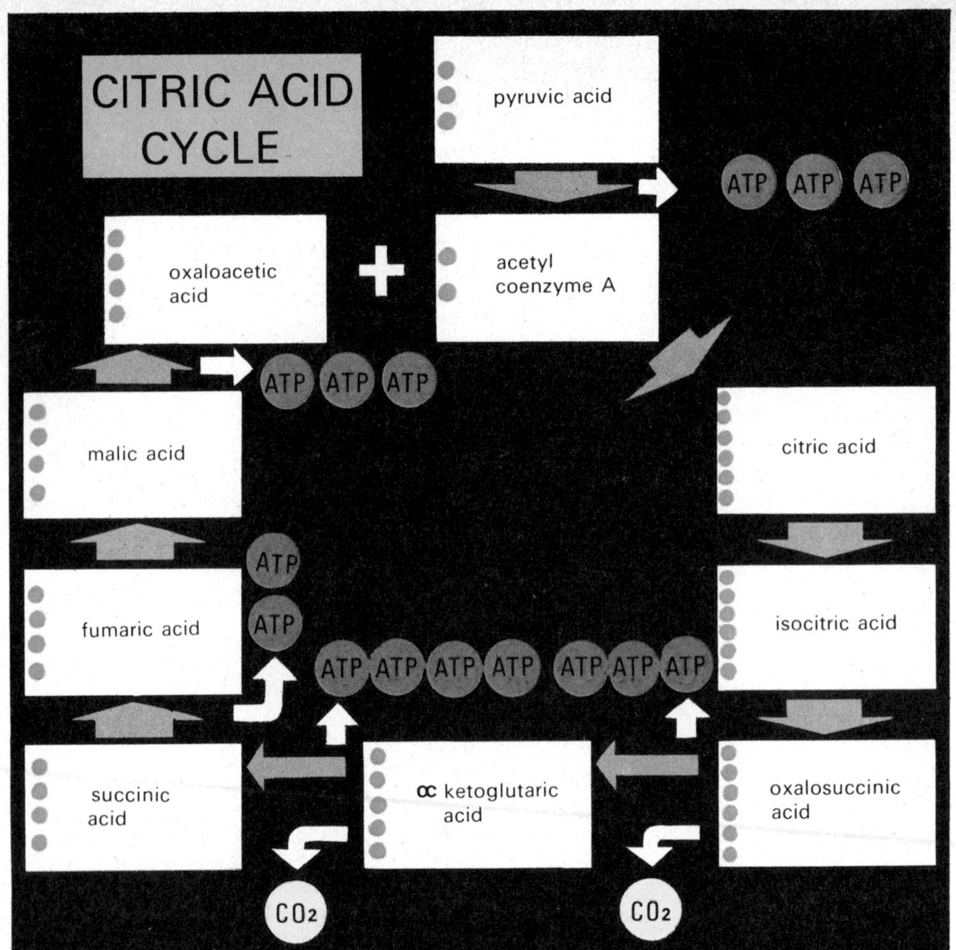


*Left,* respiration as it occurs in alcoholic fermentation. Stages one to three show glycolysis, involving substrate breakdown followed by energy release. Glycolysis is when a compound with six carbon atoms splits into two molecules, or *trioses.*

*Above,* to make the cycle a continuous one, two atoms must be jettisoned as waste carbon dioxide. Together these processes show how the energy in chemical bonds of a molecule can be turned into ATP bonds, the cell's standard energy currency.

can be made to release its energy. It is activated, in the biological sense, by the addition of a phosphate group from ATP to one of the carbon atoms of the glucose molecule. The reaction, which is catalysed by the enzyme *hexokinase,* involves the expenditure of one high-energy phosphate bond of a molecule of ATP to form the compounds glucose phosphate and adenosine diphosphate (ADP).

## How energy is produced

Subsequent reactions may be considered to be the step-wise conversion of glucose phosphate into other compounds, better suited to release their energy. In the first of these steps, glucose phosphate is changed to fructose phosphate by the enzyme *phosphohexoisomerase.* This reaction does not involve the expenditure of energy, it merely prepares the hexose molecule for the addition of a second phosphate group. This addition of phosphate, catalysed by another enzyme, again takes place at the expense of one molecule of ATP.

The compound formed, fructose diphosphate, is sufficiently activated to be split, by the enzyme *aldolase,* into two separate compounds. The two new compounds each contain three carbon atoms (dihydroxyacetone phosphate and glyceraldehyde phosphate). Only the second of these can take part in the subsequent reactions of the glycolytic pathway, but there is an enzyme which will convert dihydroxyacetone phosphate into glyceraldehyde phosphate. As a result, both of the triose molecules are eventually used.

The reactions so far have brought the hexose molecule only to a form from which its energy can be released gradually. It is in the following steps that the energy in the molecule is recovered. Glyceraldehyde phosphate is, at the same time, oxidized and induced to form a second phosphate bond. The compound formed, diphosphoglyceric acid, has one energy-rich phosphate bond and can react with a molecule of ADP to give a molecule of ATP and phosphoglyceric acid.

Before further ATP-producing steps can occur, the phosphoglyceric acid molecule must be re-arranged. This process is catalysed by two enzymes and results in the production of phosphoenolpyruvic acid. Phosphoenolpyruvic acid is also a compound which possesses a high-energy phosphate bond that can be used to form ATP from ADP, again in the presence of an enzyme. The product of the reaction is unstable and changes spontaneously into pyruvic acid.

The energy balance sheet so far is that two ATP molecules have been expended to activate a glucose molecule, and two ATP molecules have been recovered for each triose molecule which has passed through the sequence (or four ATP molecules for the whole glucose molecule).

Changes between coenzymes generate a further six ATP molecules. As a result there is a total of eight molecules of ATP so far.

Under anaerobic conditions, the pyruvic acid formed must be removed or its accumulation will slow down the reactions and eventually poison them. In yeasts and in some plants, its removal is associated with the formation of alcohol and carbon dioxide – the reaction which forms the basis for the brewing industry. In animals, pyruvic acid is removed directly with the production of lactic acid, which is carried away by the blood-stream and oxidized elsewhere.

Inside the cell, the enzymes of the glycolytic pathway occur free in the cytoplasm and the whole process works by random collisions between enzymes and substrate molecules. The product of the first enzyme reaction becomes the substrate for the second, and so on. In contrast to this, the enzymes which catalyse the reactions of the citric acid cycle occur in specialized microscopic bodies called *mitochondria*. Mitochondria are generally rod-shaped structures bounded on the outside by a double membrane. Inside they are partly divided into compartments by inward folds of the membrane called *cristae*. The space inside the mitochondrion is called the *matrix*, and it is here that the enzymes of the citric acid cycle are found. Since all the necessary enzymes are confined in such a small space, substrate molecules have to travel only a small distance before they meet the appropriate enzyme. This, in turn, improves the efficiency of the process.

## The citric acid cycle

Pyruvic acid produced in the cytoplasm by glycolysis enters the mitochondria by diffusion and immediately undergoes a rather complex reaction to prepare it for the citric acid cycle. This change can be considered to be three separate reactions, all of which occur simultaneously: the loss of one molecule of carbon dioxide, the removal of a hydrogen atom, and the coupling of the product to a substance called coenzyme A. The final product, acetyl coenzyme A, is the substance which is oxidized in the reactions of the citric acid cycle.

The oxidation of acetyl coenzyme A in the citric acid cycle is also a step-wise process. It is first condensed with a compound which contains four carbon atoms to form citric acid (a compound with six carbon atoms) and to release the molecule of coenzyme A. The subsequent steps appear rather complicated and involve a further six enzymes, but their overall effect is gradually to remove carbon and hydrogen atoms until a compound which

*Top,* all the plants in this Kenyan landscape are capable of synthesizing their food. They are termed autotrophs because they contain pigment such as chlorophyll which can absorb light energy and convert it into chemical energy. Zebras, *centre,* cannot produce energy from inorganic materials – they must rely on plants for their energy and are thus classified as chemotrophs. *Below,* although the lion eats only meat, it too must ultimately depend on autotrophs for its vital energy source.

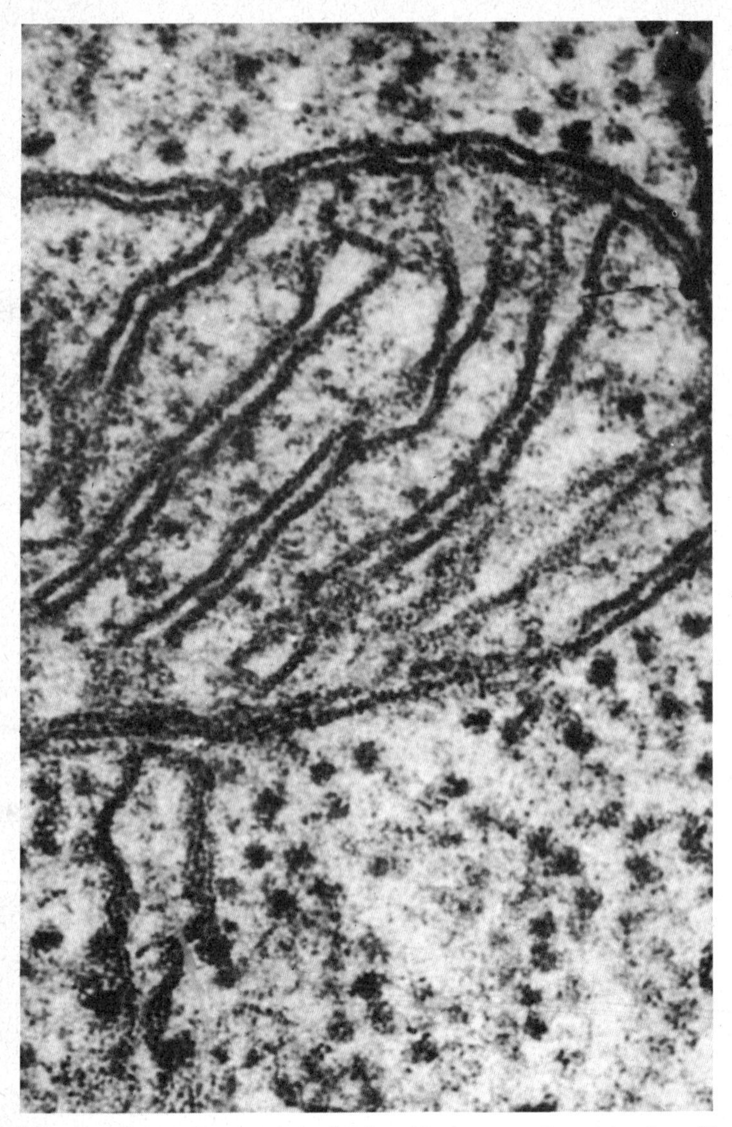

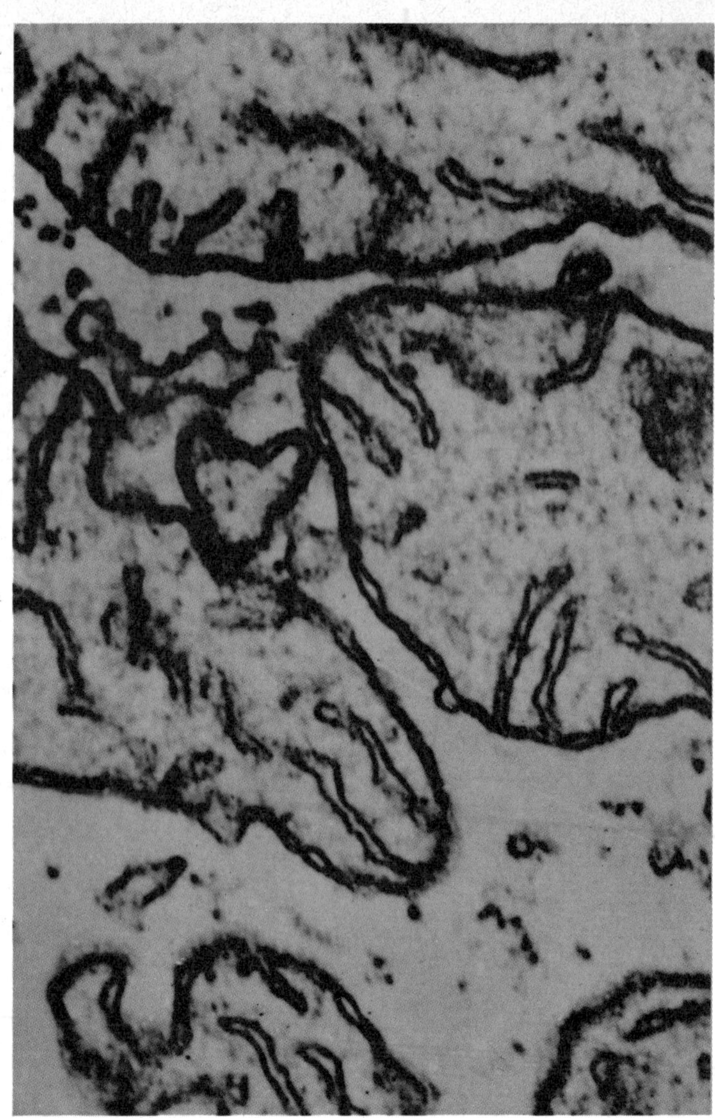

Mitochondria are microscopic bodies found in the cell cytoplasm. They are rightly termed the 'powerhouse' of the cell, for inside them ATP synthesis reactions take place. The scattered threads in the mitochondria, *left*, taken from the white blood cell of a sheep are cristae, which divide the interior of mitochondria into compartments. *Right*, they usually lie at right angles to the long axis of the mitochondria as in the larva of a liver fluke.

contains four carbon atoms remains. At the same time that the carbon atoms are being released as carbon dioxide, four molecules of hydrogen are also removed by coenzyme carriers. It is the reoxidation of these reduced coenzymes by a process known as *oxidative phosphorylation* which generates ATP. Only at one stage in the citric acid cycle is there a direct production of ATP, and the bulk of the ATP produced by mitochondria comes from oxidative phosphorylation.

## Energy for heavy work

We can calculate the total energy yield from the oxidation of pyruvic acid by the citric acid cycle as 15 molecules of ATP. Since one glucose molecule yields two pyruvate molecules, the overall ATP production is 30 molecules from the citric acid cycle plus eight molecules from glycolysis. The energy in the phosphate bond of ATP is approximately eight calories per *mole* (molecular weight expressed in grammes) and the complete combustion of glucose yields about 686 calories per mole. This means that the biological process has an efficiency of 44 per cent, which is no small achievement even by engineering standards. For this reason, the mitochondrion is sometimes called the powerhouse' of the cell.

Tissues in which energy production is important, such as muscles, often contain far more mitochondria than do other tissues. During heavy muscle exertion there may not be sufficient oxygen available and lactic acid is formed. The lactic acid is transported by the blood to the liver, where some of it is converted to pyruvate and is oxidized by the liver mitochondria. The remainder of the lactic acid is converted back to glucose by a reversal of the glycolytic reactions, a process which paradoxically is driven in the reverse direction by ATP produced in the mitochondria. The glucose is then re-circulated in the blood-stream or converted to glycogen and stored temporarily in the liver.

When animals take in a surplus of carbohydrates, they tend to be converted into fats and deposited in specialized storage tissues. Then when fat is required for use as an energy source, it is transported to the liver to be broken down. A fat is a compound – called an *ester* – of a fatty acid and glycerol. The first reaction it undergoes in the liver is the splitting of the ester bonds between the fatty-acid chains and the glycerol part. Glycerol can then be phosphorylated and used directly in glycolysis, but the long-chain fatty acids must be processed further before they can be used. They are broken down by a mechanism known as beta-oxidation in which fragments, each containing two carbon atoms, are released step-wise from the end of the chain. By means of this beta-oxidation process, the original molecule becomes shorter and shorter until all of its carbon atoms have been released. The process is similar to glycolysis in two respects: firstly, it must be activated by the expenditure of ATP; and secondly, the fragments that are released are acetyl coenzyme A, which can immediately be used in the citric acid cycle.

## Energy from proteins

Under adverse conditions, proteins can also be a source of energy, though usually only as a last resort. Before a protein can be used, it must first be hydrolysed to release its constituent amino acids. Then the amino groups are removed and disposed of in the urine as the harmless compound urea. The remaining carbon skeletons are acids which, depending on their sizes, can either enter the beta-oxidation process or the citric acid cycle. A certain amount of energy is derived from the natural turnover of body proteins at all times, but under the normal circumstances of everyday life the oxidation of glucose is the main method by which cells produce energy in the form of ATP.

# How living things use energy

Energy stored in the cell still has to be converted into light, heat, movement. This article takes as its primary examples the glow of the glow-worm and the contraction of striped muscle.

IN BIOLOGY as in the rest of science, energy is the capacity to do work. It exists in two forms – *potential* and *kinetic*. Potential energy is the energy of position, it is unused energy. When a body moves, part of its energy is kinetic and kinetic energy is the energy of movement. The total energy of matter may be given the symbol $E$, and is made up of kinetic energy, $K$, and potential energy, $P$. Therefore $E=K+P$. In this article, we are concerned primarily with the inter-conversion in biology of the two types of energy, potential and kinetic.

Green plants are the primary converters of energy. In photosynthesis they use the kinetic energy of the sun to convert the potential energy of carbon dioxide and water to more potential energy, in the form of glucose and oxygen, and some kinetic energy (heat). Animals cannot photosynthesize, so they turn the reaction round in the process known as tissue oxidation.

None of the energy in compounds such as glucose is of direct use to living things. It must first be converted into some usable form, such as an energy-rich phosphate. Probably the most important high-energy phosphate is *adenosine triphosphate* (ATP). Living things convert the potential energy of compounds such as glucose to useful energy in the form of ATP. In practice, 38 molecules of ATP can be produced from a single molecule of glucose.

## The burning of a match

One of the reasons why compounds such as ATP are rich in energy is the instability of the phosphate part. This instability is created by a 'warping' of the chemical bonds which bind phosphate to other molecules. This form of energy release in living things is analogous to the burning of a match. The active chemical in the head of a match is a phosphorus compound. The small amount of heat generated by friction when the match head is rubbed is enough to break the unstable bonds of the phosphorus compound, releasing energy in the form of heat, which causes the rest of the match to burn. The difference between the match and the biological example lies mainly in the degree of control of the energy release exhibited by living things. And the 'controllers' are enzymes.

Two of the three phosphates of ATP are connected by high-energy bonds. The energy in these bonds can be transferred to large molecules by *hydrolysis* (splitting apart by the addition of water), a mechanism which is known as the hydrolytic transfer of energy. Enzymes, which are large reactive proteins, accomplish this hydrolysis of ATP. The enzymes attract large numbers of water molecules, which form *hydration shells* around them. Many of the water molecules are made unstable by the reactivity of the enzyme. When a molecule of ATP comes close to such an enzyme, its bonds will be similarly *excited*.

## A glow-worm's light

Since some of the bonds in ATP are already unstable, a little additional instability may be enough to break a chemical bond. The ATP splits, forming adenosine *di*-phosphate (ADP) and phosphoric acid, and a large amount of energy is released. Energy released by striking a match mainly takes the form of heat. Energy released by ATP hydrolysis yields little heat; it is transferred to the enzyme molecule, where it can be made available to do useful biological work.

In cells of living things, all processes that require energy use ATP and other phosphate compounds. Two interesting activities of cells which depend upon ATP for their energy are *bioluminescence* and *muscle contraction*.

Bioluminescence is the production of light by living things. The North American firefly, for example, has a flashing luminescent organ on the underside of its abdomen. There are various insect larvae, known as 'glow-worms', which emit a continuous light. Many bacteria, and many animals that live deep in the sea, also emit light.

The uses of bioluminescence are not entirely clear. In some creatures, such as fireflies and deep-sea animals, the light may be used to attract food or mates. In others, such as glow-worms, there is no obvious purpose. Some biologists think that the light may be produced as a result of inefficient metabolism, and that part of the metabolic energy is wasted as light. But whatever the reasons, bioluminescence is essentially the conversion of potential energy in the form of ATP to kinetic energy in the form of light.

Whenever we increase the energy of molecules, they become *excited* and give off energy. Some of this extra energy may be emitted as light. For example, if we use electricity to raise the temperature and so increase the energy of molecules in the tungsten-wire filament of an electric lamp, the molecules emit light.

The important substances involved in bioluminescence are a light-emitting substance called *luciferin*, an energy-transferring enzyme, *luciferase*, and ATP. It is thought that luciferin becomes bonded to luciferase and that the enzyme then causes the hydrolysis of ATP to ADP. The energy released is transferred via the enzyme to the luciferin, exciting it and causing the emission of light.

The colour of the light emitted by any molecule is an indication of the amount of energy which excited the molecule. The energy of the light emitted by luciferin in

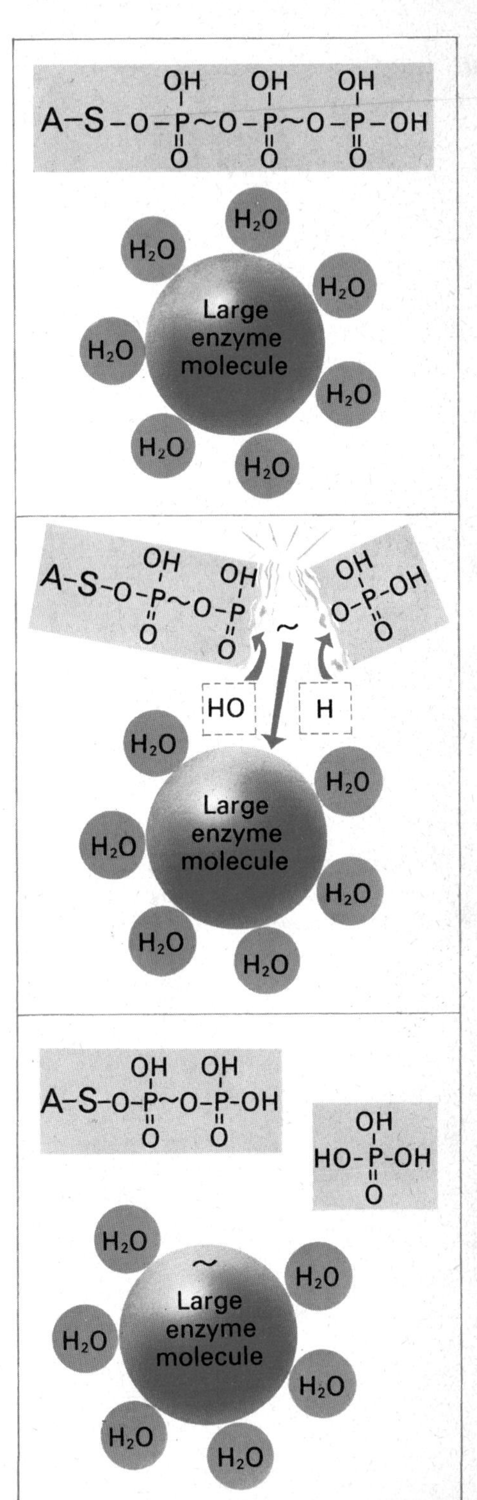


*Above,* ATP hydrolysis. Without energy, no cell reactions could take place, muscle contract, or protein be made. Cells would be unable to multiply, move, or grow. Source of this energy is ATP, adenosine triphosphate. Two of its three phosphates are connected by high-energy bonds, and hydrolysis – splitting by addition of water – is the mechanism that breaks this chemical bond. The end phosphate atom is ejected, and the released energy transferred to the enzyme molecule (which initially triggered off the splitting) where it can be now made available for biological work.

bioluminescence is quite high, between four and six times the amount of energy present in the ATP molecule. How living things can generate such large amounts of energy is not understood.

Muscles are used by higher animals to move their bodies or parts of their bodies. There are various kinds of muscles, and the type whose structure and function has been most studied is *striped* or *voluntary* muscle. (This is the kind of muscle used for walking, talking and eating; it is muscle which can be controlled at will, as opposed to *involuntary* muscle.)

## The contraction of muscle

If we look at striped muscle under an optical microscope, we can see at once where it gets its name. It is composed of bundles of small fibres called *myofibrils* which consist of alternate dark and light bands. These bands give the impression of stripes. The light bands are called *I* bands and the dark bands *A* bands.

Using an electron microscope, we can study the fine structural elements in myofibrils. Thin sections of muscle, cut parallel to the long axis, can be seen in much greater detail. The *I* bands are broken by a dense line running across the long axis of the myofibril (this is called the *Z* line). And the *A* bands are also broken, by a clear band running across the long axis (the *H* band). Thin sections of muscle cut across the long axis of the myofibril show the *I* bands to be made up of strands of thin filaments and the *A* bands to be composed of strands of thick and thin filaments. The *H* band has thick-filament strands only. Each set of repeating cross-bands along a myofibril is called a sarcomere. Under very high magnification, filamentous cross-bridges can be seen joining the thick and thin strands.

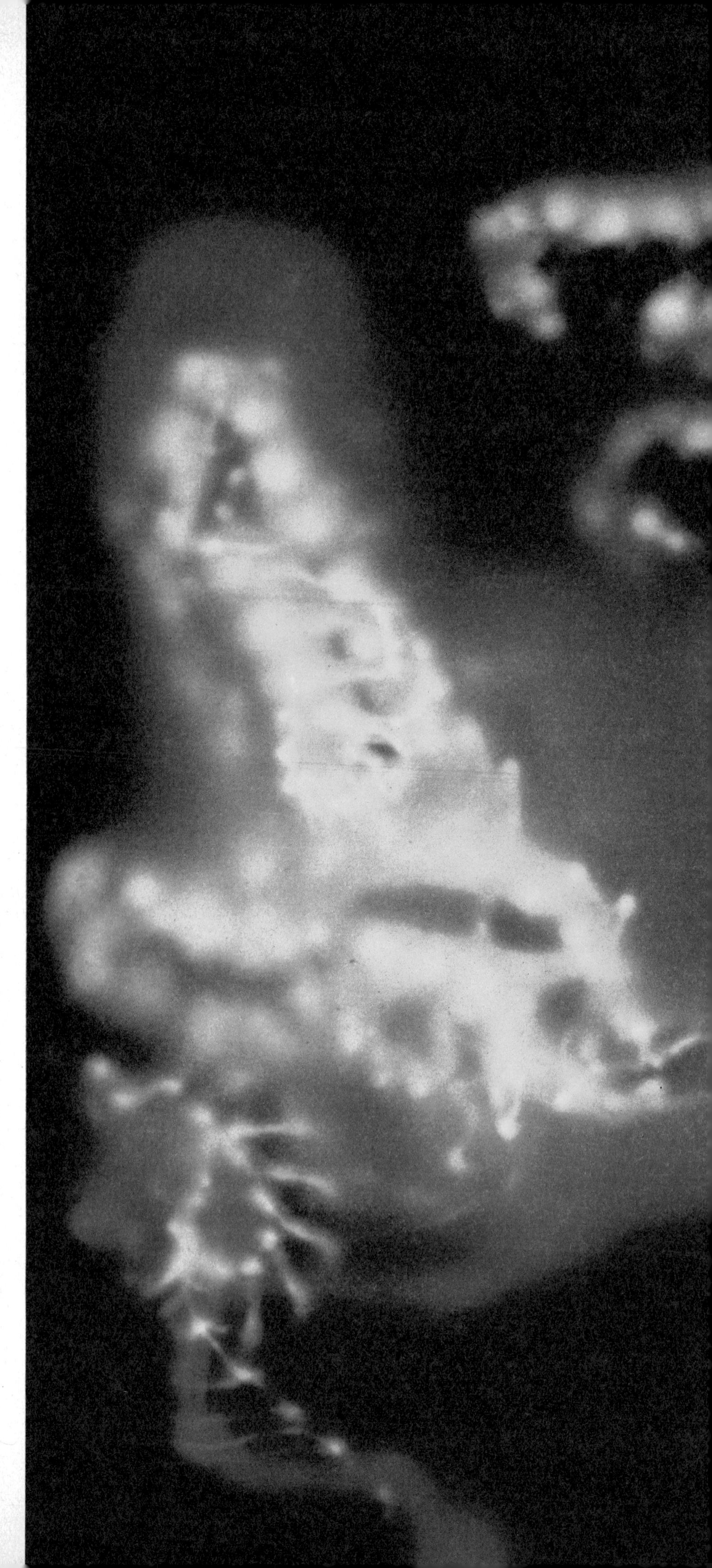

*Above,* sending out great billows of smoke and flame, this blazing oil is releasing massive quantities of uncontrolled energy in the form of heat. *Right,* bioluminescence. By daylight, the larvae of the *Phrixothrix* beetle have little to distinguish them, but when disturbed at night, they suddenly become brilliantly luminescent. The energy for their light comes directly from ATP molecules.

For a long time, biologists have known that the actual material in muscle which does the contracting is a protein. This protein is composed of two units, *actin* and *myosin,* which under certain circumstances unite to form *actomyosin.* By chemically extracting actin and myosin alternately from striped muscle, and viewing the remaining tissue under an electron microscope to see what is missing, scientists found that the thin strands are actin and the thick strands myosin.

From this structural evidence and other information, H.E. Huxley and his co-workers elaborated the sliding-filament theory of muscle contraction. According to this theory, the contraction of striped muscle takes place by the sliding of actin (thin) and myosin (thick) filaments over each other. The bridges linking the myosin and actin filaments are permanently attached to the myosin filaments. As the muscle contracts, the bridges bend and become temporarily attached to 'active' sites on the actin filaments. The bridges then straighten, moving the actin strand over to the myosin strand. This action is repeated, shortening the myofibril and the muscle. The sliding-filament theory is not accepted by all physiologists, but it does provide a simple explanation for the contraction of striped muscle. The theory does not explain contraction in other kinds of muscles less organized in structure.

## The buzzing bee

ATP is bonded to the myosin filaments in muscle. Presumably it transfers its energy to the myosin, which then moves the actin via the cross-bridges. Energy transfer from ATP to myosin is probably direct, myosin acting much as an enzyme does.

The amount of ATP in muscle is not great enough to permit prolonged contraction. Many animals have an additional phosphate compound in their muscles and other tissues, called *creatine phosphate.* This is able to donate its phosphate group to ADP to produce more ATP. Usually the amount of creatine phosphate is also insufficient for prolonged contraction, and phosphate must be freshly made by the metabolism of muscle cells.

A reserve carbohydrate called *glycogen* (animal 'starch') is also stored within the cells of striped muscle. Glycogen is first hydrolysed to its basic sugar, glucose, and the glucose then oxidized to form molecules of ATP. If sufficient oxygen is present, the glucose is oxidized completely to carbon dioxide and water. But there is generally insufficient oxygen to support prolonged movement of the muscle and the glucose is partially oxidized to lactic acid, which is then transported by the bloodstream to the liver. In the liver, most of the lactic acid is converted back to glycogen.

The contraction of muscle produces very large amounts of heat and this fact is used to advantage by most animals. Some animals (mammals and birds), which normally maintain a relatively constant body temperature, are called *homoiotherms.* Animals other than mammals and birds are known as *poikilotherms* ('cold-blooded'); they do not maintain a constant body temperature.

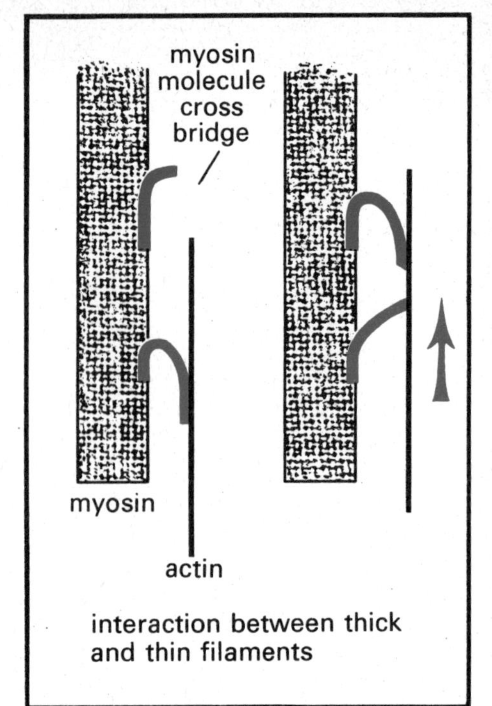

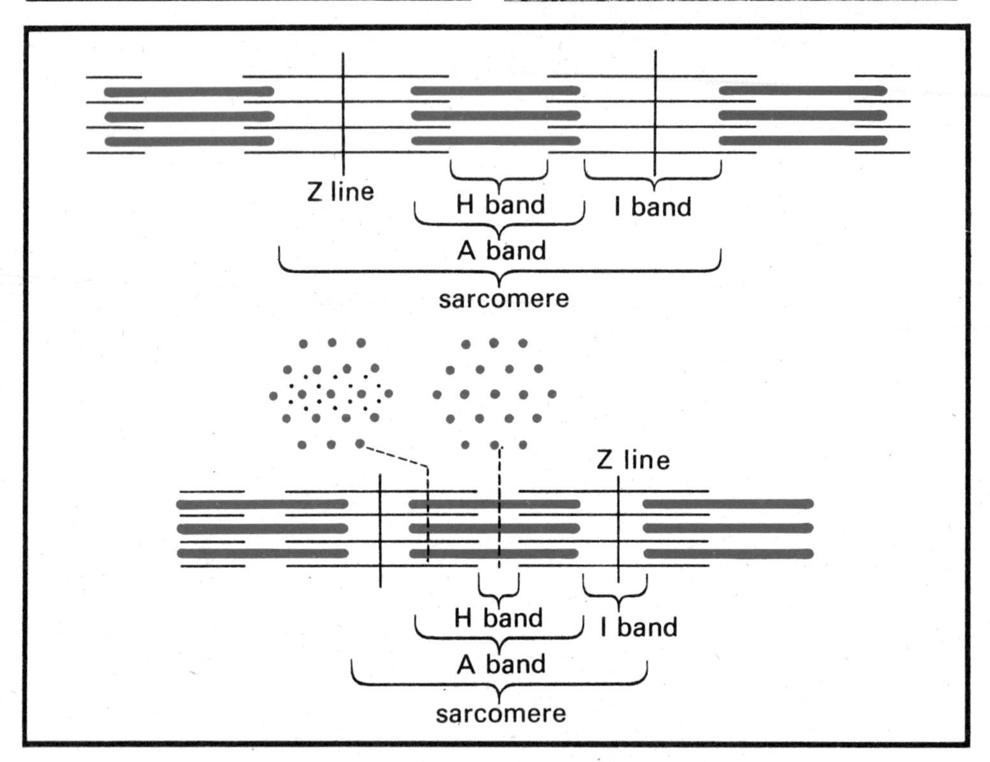


*Top left,* this diagram illustrates the sliding filament theory of striped muscle contraction. A special crossbridge molecule attached to a myosin filament swings down, grabs hold of the actin filament, then straightens, pulling the actin up with it and so on. *Top right,* cross-section of flight muscle in a blowfly, and a longitudinal view of the same below it, show the muscle fibre represented, *above.* At top, relaxed muscle fibres are shown; centre, a cross-section view of thick and thin fibres slotted together; below, we see how they are arranged when they contract.

A good example of a homoiotherm is Man. He has a high rate of metabolism, which generates quite a lot of heat. This heat is kept in the body by a reduction of heat loss from his skin and by good insulation (body fat, hair, clothes). When Man's body temperature begins to fall even a slight amount, heat-generating processes come into action and one of the chief of these is muscle contraction. When the surface of the body is cooled, we shiver. Shivering is muscle tremor produced by rapid contraction and relaxation of the muscles. Shivering may increase to a totally uncontrollable shaking of all the voluntary muscles of the body. But if a person is not too cold, his muscle activity will soon cause the body-heat to rise to normal levels and shivering will cease.

Many cold-blooded animals also use muscle tremor to warm up. For example, bees have an interesting form of 'central heating'. Whenever the temperature of the hive falls below a certain level, all the bees beat their wings, and the heat generated warms the hive. It is said that the temperature of the air around a hive can be estimated fairly accurately by timing the frequency of the wing-beating or the buzzing that accompanies it.

# Life's vital membranes

Vital to cell architecture are fine membranes. Biologists do not yet fully understand where they come from, how they grow. But without them there could be no cell, no cell activity, no life.

FOR ABOUT 300 years, optical microscopes have allowed biologists to study cells in action. But in the late 1930s, the far more powerful electron microscope unlocked the door on the world of activity *inside* the cell. In fine detail, pictures emerged of fascinating and complex structures. For the first time, men were able to study the molecular architecture of the living cell itself.

Vital to cell architecture are fine membranes. Without them there could be no cell, and no cell activity. Naked cell material, from which the membrane has been stripped, is rather like a modern jelly paint outside its tin: it has a certain stability but it can easily be disturbed. Without protection, the contents of the cell (called cytoplasm) would flow and ooze out of place. One membrane, the *plasmalemma*, encloses the cell itself. Others, including two membranes which make up the nuclear envelope, isolate certain parts of the cell from other parts. All membranes appear to have a similar basic composition and structure. They are composed largely of *lipoproteins*, with the lipid (fat) and the protein distributed in two main layers composed of molecular units called *micelles*. A unit membrane is one membrane composed of two layers. All the membranes in a cell can be treated in such a way that this double layering is revealed.

## Specialized membranes

Biologists do not fully understand where membrane comes from and how it grows. But techniques exist which prove that membranes are real objects, not just boundary lines between liquids that will not mix (like the boundary between oil and water). For example, we can break up cells and separate the bits and pieces by spinning them in a centrifuge. From a mass of tissue such as a lump of liver, the surface membranes can be separated from everything else. A biochemist can then collect membrane material in sufficient quantities to find out its composition. He can also use the same technique for other parts of the cell, such as the mitochondria, the ribosomes and the nuclei.

The cell's membranes, in addition to keeping the materials in various cell compartments separate, play an active role too. They allow and aid selected materials to pass through them and for this reason are called *semi-permeable*. They ensure not only that the materials inside the nucleus are different from those in the cytoplasm, but that these differences are actively maintained.

Inside the nuclei of all cells in plants and animals there is a high proportion of nucleic acid (DNA, deoxyribose nucleic acid). DNA gives the nucleus special properties during the life of the cell, and its presence aids the scientist studying the cell after its death. Chemical preservation called *fixation* is a first step in many methods of scientific study using microscopes. Because of the nucleic acid, we can dye the nucleus of a cell a different colour from most of its other parts. Histology, the study of tissues composed of cells, relies largely on this technique of dyeing or staining the nuclei of cells.

When a cell divides into two daughter

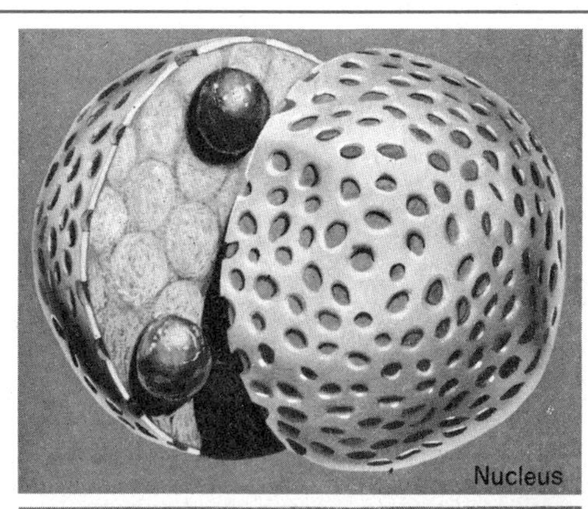


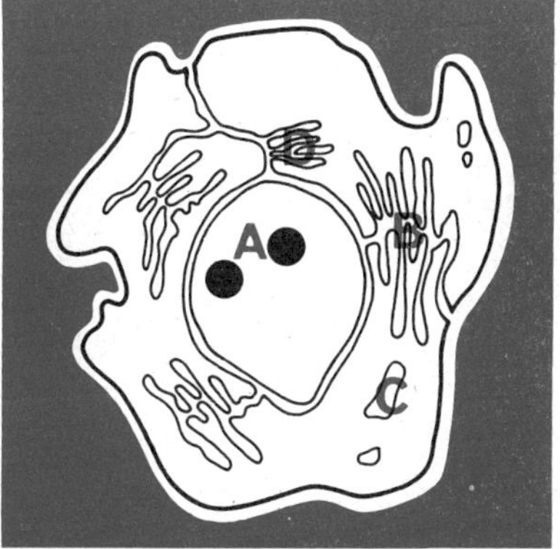


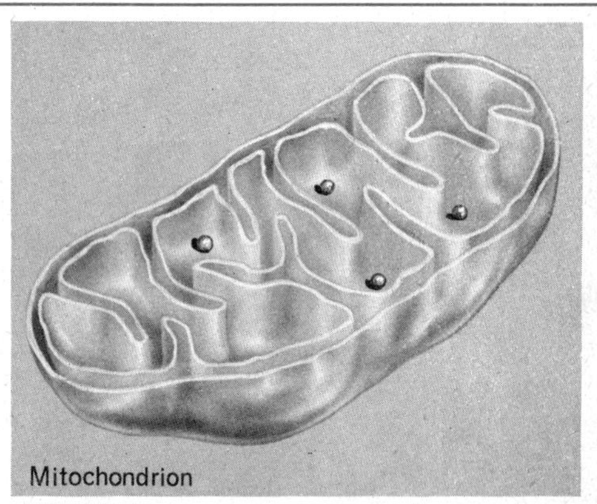


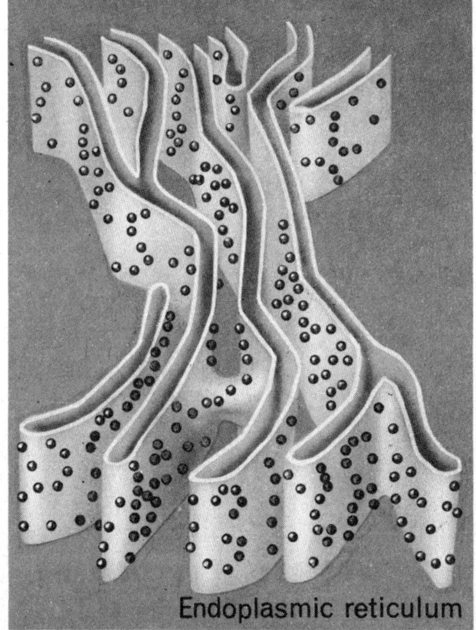


Four of the organelles most vital to the growth and organization of the cell. A – The **nucleus**, control-centre of the cell, and without which it is unable to survive. Surrounded by a pitted membrane, it contains one or more nucleoli – dense gatherings of particles rich in RNA and possibly a main source of nuclear protein. B – **Endoplasmic reticulum** (ER). Plant and animal cells both contain a complex system of membranes spread throughout the cytoplasm in a network of hollow sheets. Attached to the ER are scattered pellets – ribosomes – which contain RNA and produce protein, one of the most important building materials of the cell. C – A **mitochondrion**, the cell's energy source, is made up of two membranes, an outer, and an inner which falls in folds across the interior. Here food is converted into energy with the aid of the small, calcium-containing granules. D – **Golgi body.** The cell membrane forms stacked piles of protein-filled sacs. The perforated outer edges will break away as free-floating packets of protein.

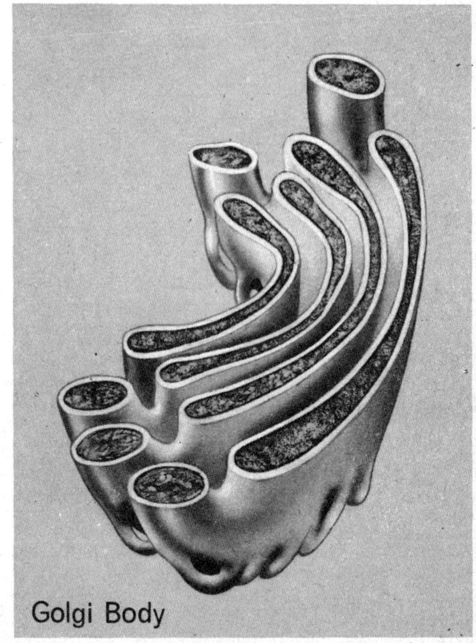

cells, the nucleic acid within the nucleus first condenses to form chromosomes. These also take up dyes and can be studied by staining dividing cells. Chromosomes are the visible record of the fact that the nucleic acid acts as the information code of the cell, repeated and divided equally between the two identical daughter cells. When a change occurs in the functional properties of the daughter cells, we can usually also detect a change in the appearance of the chromosomes and their patterned activity during cell division.

Plant and animal cells are alike in many important ways. Both types contain a nucleus (rich in DNA) and cytoplasm (rich in RNA, ribose nucleic acid). Both kinds of cells contain mitochondria, which are bodies that carry out the processes of cell respiration, and both have a complex system of membranes in the cytoplasm, called the *endoplasmic reticulum* (ER).

Parts of this membrane system become specialized for particular purposes. For example, the so-called rough endoplasmic reticulum is a special part, studded with ribosomes, which secretes cell proteins. Ribosomes are themselves granules of RNA and protein. In nerve cells, the rough ER develops a striking arrangement which can also be seen under an optical microscope. The arrays of rough membrane become large enough to show up in the cytoplasm as patches of substance called Nissl material, after the German neurologist Franz Nissl (1860–1919).

## The nuclear envelope

Smooth endoplasmic reticulum is composed of membranes that do not have ribosomes studded along them, and it shows a variety of patterns of organization. In one of these patterns, which occurs in all cell types, the membrane forms closed flattened sacs or vesicles which lie in the cytoplasm in orderly stacks. These groupings of membrane may be large enough to be seen with an optical microscope, and are called the *Golgi apparatus* after Camillo Golgi (1844–1926), the Italian physician who first described them. Another significant pattern of smooth ER, called *annulate lamellae*, consists of arrays of flattened sacs perforated by ring-shaped pores. This pattern is common in developing egg cells.

But why is there a variety of membrane patterns? It seems likely that each pattern is related functionally to the activity of the cell in synthesizing materials. Rough ER, for example, develops abundantly in pancreatic cells which are actively secreting proteins.

The simplest kinds of cells are found in tissue cultures or in early embryos. In many such cells, the membranes of the cytoplasm are rather unorganized and consist of dozens of small circular vesicles. There is not much rough ER, and most of the ribosomes lie free in the cytoplasm and not studded on the membrane. The ribosomes may be gathered into small groups, called *polysomes*, in which they are held together by a strand of a special form of nucleic acid made in the nucleus. This strand is called messenger RNA and carries a coded message from the nucleus, the control centre of the cell, to the ribosome system which manufactures protein. The length of the messenger RNA strand determines the number of ribosomes brought together into a polysome and the type of protein they synthesize.

The membrane between the nucleus and the cytoplasm is called the nuclear envelope. Its structure permits several possible lines of communication between the nucleus and the cytoplasm, probably operating in both directions. In some cases, a set of channels enclosed in membrane link the nuclear envelope directly to all parts of the cytoplasm, and even to the outer cell membrane. In many cells, the nuclear envelope has circular pores which pass through both membranes.

The surface membrane of the cell consists of a single unit membrane. But the surface of the cell can also develop a variety of special features which are important in building tissues and in transporting materials in and out of the cell. The surface may be either thrown up into numerous fine finger-like processes, called *microvilli,* or developed inwards into the cytoplasm as an extensive series of fissures and hollows into which other cell processes may fit. When a cell attaches itself to a glass surface, it throws out many fine microvilli, which act as anchors.

Cells can be held together in tissues merely by the interlocking of cell processes and microvilli in a sort of hook-and-eye fashion. Cells can also be held together

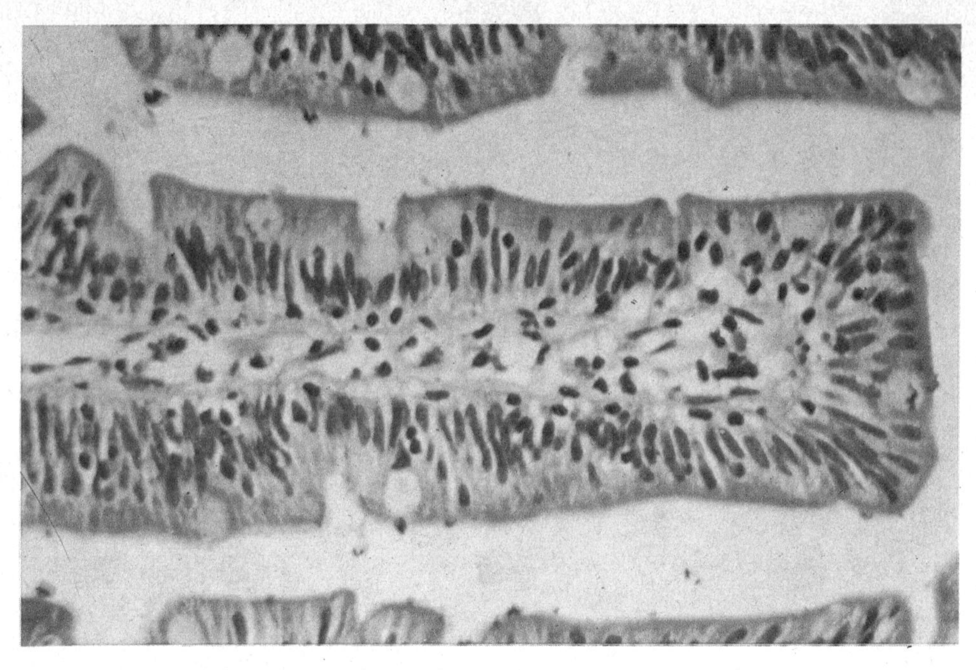

*Brush border.* Because cells facing the kidney and gut tubes need a very large available surface area to carry materials, they throw up tightly packed microvilli forming this brush-like array.

**Chromosomes - visible proof that DNA is the cell's information code.**

Chromosomes, consisting largely of DNA and protein are thread-like bodies present within the nucleus of all cells. They usually occur in pairs, the two members of each pair being identical. Only during cell division do they become visible when they contract to form short thick rods. Before every division of the nucleus each chromosome doubles, the two new chromosomes separating to the two daughter nuclei. This essentially involves replication of the DNA, which is repeated and divided between the two daughter cells. *Right,* three stages of chromosome division in the pollen grains of a lily anther, by *meiosis.* This occurs when the chromosomes are only duplicated once, halving the number present in the daughter cells. *Left,* Prophase – the starting point in cell division when the chromosomes first appear in the nucleus. *Centre,* Metaphase. The chromosomes become arranged on the 'equator' of the spindle, a body which forms in the cell at nuclear division and is involved in the distribution *Far right,* Anaphase. Daughter chromosomes go to opposite poles of the spindle.

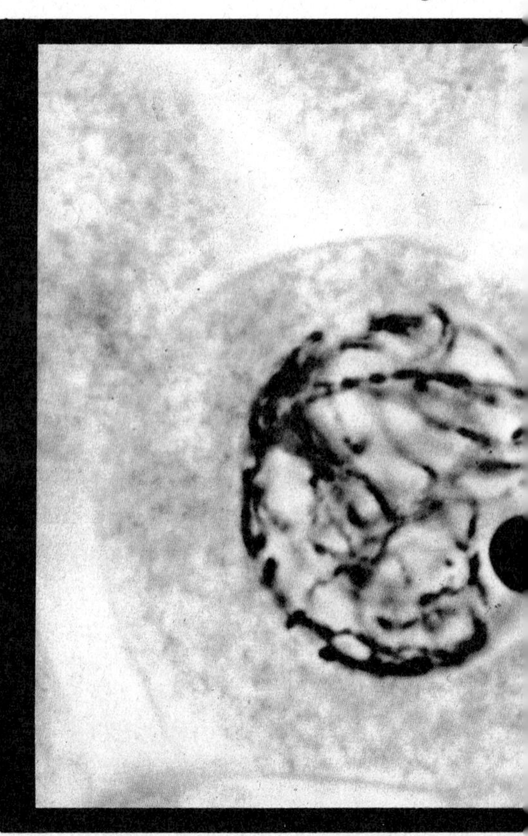

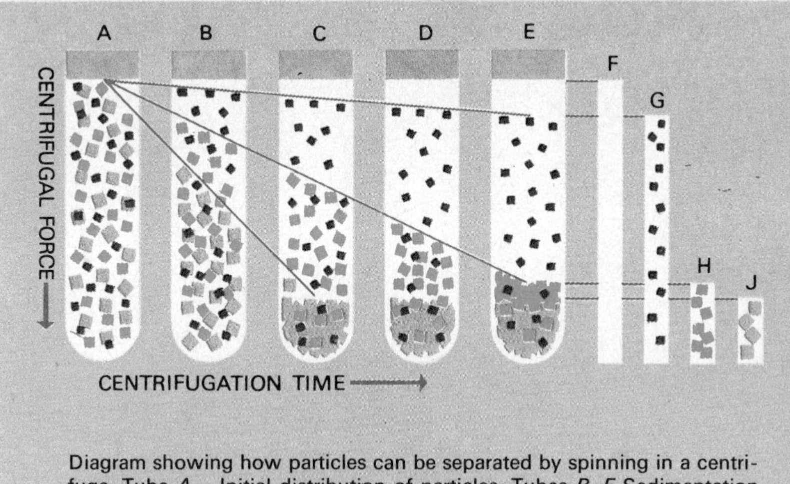


Diagram showing how particles can be separated by spinning in a centrifuge. Tube *A* – Initial distribution of particles. Tubes *B–E* Sedimentation during centrifugation. The lines indicate sedimentation rates; the bars show the distribution of solvent and particles in the last tube. *F* – Solvent. *G* – Small particles. *H* – Medium particles. *J* – Large particles. *Right,* Endoplasmic reticulum particles can be isolated from the cell similarly.

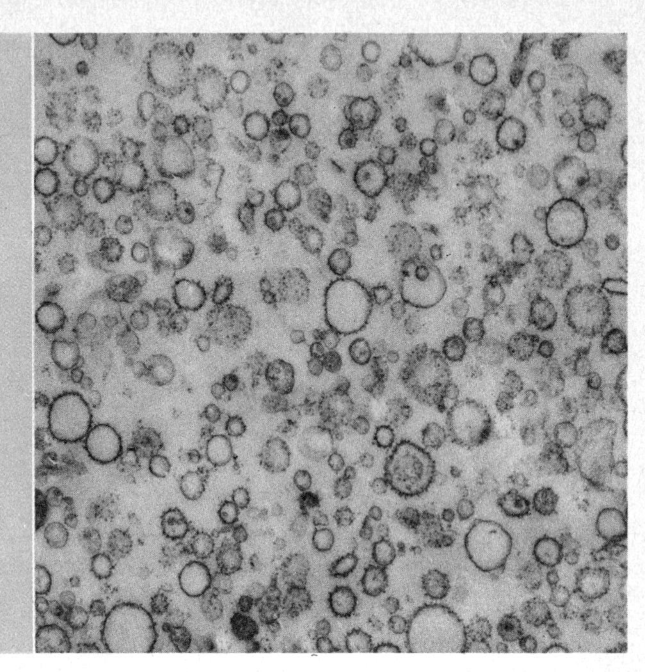

rather like a jig-saw puzzle. They have regions of very firm attachment, called *desmosomes,* where the cell membranes have become thickened by adhesive structural proteins and strongly stuck together. All epithelial tissues, which are composed of sheets or layers of cells, have many desmosomes.

## Remarkable cell-surfaces

In an organ such as the kidney or the intestine, there can be a great elaboration of the microvilli. They become highly ordered into a tightly packed brush-like array on the cell surface that faces the space of the tubes in the kidney or the gut. The development of these processes into such a brush border results in a great increase in the surface area of the cell available for the active transport of materials.

On the surfaces of cells there are often numerous thread-like lashes called cilia which act in fluids as oars to beat and produce currents. They may help to move an animal along or sweep material past the cell layer, as in the fine tubes (bronchioles) in the lungs. Within each cilium, there is a remarkable pattern of fine structure which has been found in every type of cilium in all organisms that have been examined. It is known that the '9-plus-2' pattern of fibres and its widespread occurrence suggests a common single origin for nearly all organisms.

Inside the cilium there is an outer ring of nine double fibres with little side arms attached, and an inner central pair of fibres. Like the fibres in muscle, these tubular fibres seem to be made of two sorts of contractile protein. They slide over each other and produce a rapid bending of the cilium. The central fibres and the little side arms possess enzyme activity similar to that of the myosin in muscle.

The capacity to grow cilia is a very ancient characteristic of cells, and strange uses for cilia have evolved. Many sense organs have some form of modified cilia in their highly developed sense cells. For example, cells in the retina of the eye have a ciliary stalk which joins the outer segment of the rod cell to the inner segment. This stalk has the outer nine fibres of a normal cilium but lacks the central pair. Many sense cells also develop extremely long and complicated microvilli, as in cells of the taste buds of the tongue.

Many of the structures found in the cytoplasm of the cell depend on membranes for their architecture. For example, chlorophyll-containing bodies called *chloroplasts,* which characterize plant

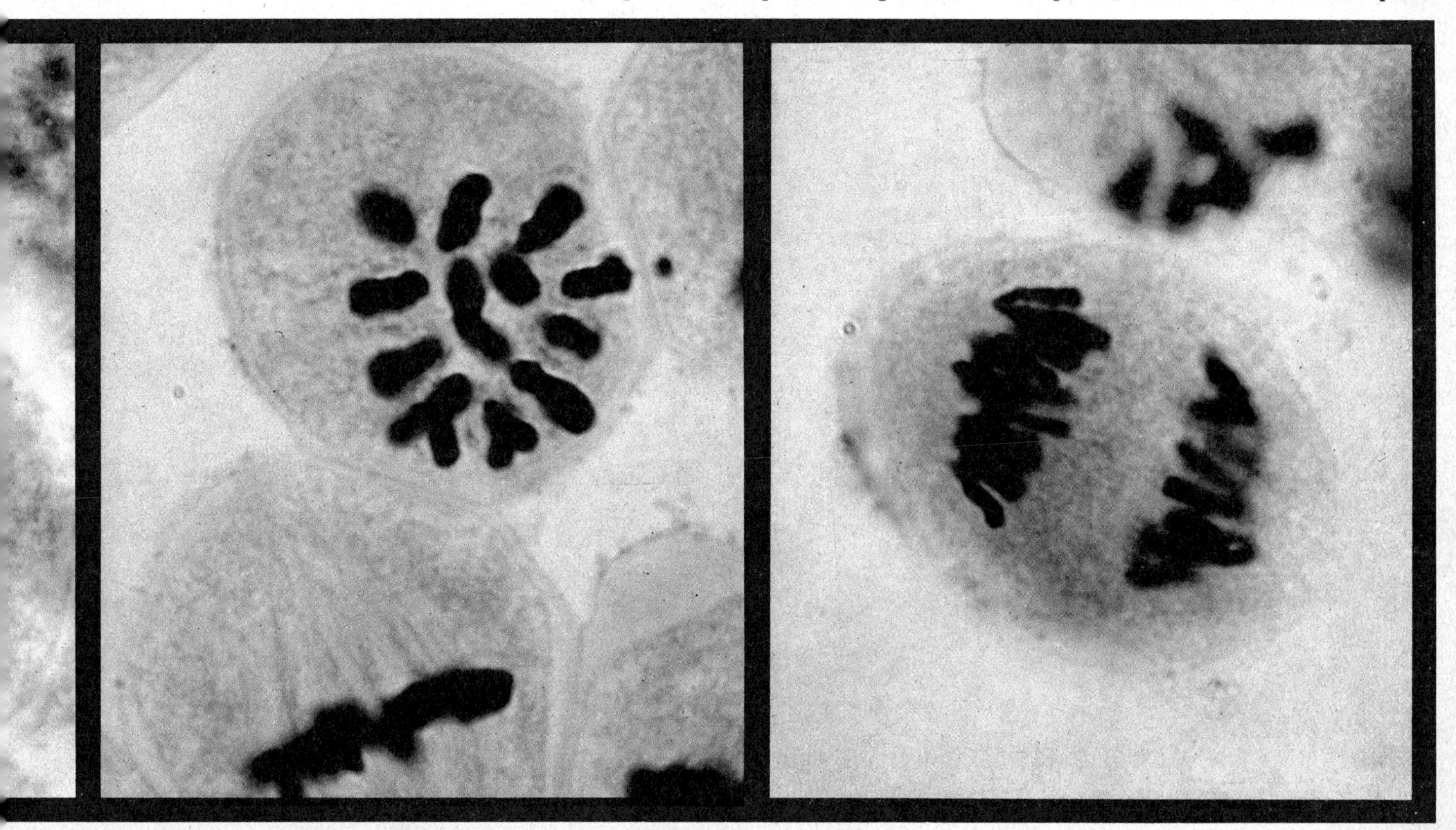

cells, are each enclosed in a skin composed of two membranes. So are mitochondria, the bodies concerned with respiration.

## The most elaborate architecture

Inside the skin of such bodies there are organized arrays of membranes where enzymes and active molecules reside. In chloroplasts, these active molecules are necessary for photosynthesis; in mitochondria, they are concerned with cell respiration. Under an optical microscope, the arrays of membranes inside chloroplasts appear like dark dots and are called *grana* (little grains). They are connected in places to the inner of the two membranes of the skin. The arrays of membrane in mitochondria are called *cristae,* and cannot be seen with an optical microscope. Cristae may be tubular or shelf-like extensions of the inner membrane of the skin, and can apparently be withdrawn when the mitochondrion swells.

With an electron microscope, grana are seen to be stacks of closed membranous sacs, connected here and there to the inner membrane of the skin. Between the different stacks, there may be narrower walled extensions of some of the sacs which link the various grana together into a continuous membrane system. The flattened sacs within grana, called thylakoids, have thicker walls containing chlorophyll molecules. Chlorophyll must be built into this complex membranous system as an integral part for it to work in photosynthesis. Surrounding the grana, enclosed within the two outer membranes, there is a space filled with material called *stroma,* which probably consists largely of soluble proteins. Biologists are still trying to determine the precise relationship between the complex structure of the chloroplast and its equally complex activity in photosynthesis. This is also true for the relationship between the structure and the respiratory function in mitochondria.

Even when the surface of the cell does not develop extensive structures like cilia and microvilli, it is still a highly active zone. The cell's outer membrane is flexible, and can become 'sticky' in places so that small patches of foreign proteins become attached to it. These areas of the surface membrane then become pouched inwards into the cytoplasm and cut off as little vesicles, called *acanthosomes.* The cell membrane can enclose small quantities of fluid by budding small liquid-filled vesicles inwards in a similar process called *pinocytosis.*

In many cells, the engulfed liquid is used by the cell itself. But in the endothelial cells that line blood vessels there is a constant traffic of small engulfed droplets across the cell from one surface to the other. In this way, food materials and large molecules which are carried in the blood can pass through the cellular walls of the blood vessels into the surrounding tissue spaces or into other cells.

But it is in the cytoplasm of a cell that the molecules produce the most elaborate architecture. Inside the nucleus, the molecules of protein and nucleic acid form collections of particles that have a much less complicated structure than the multiple-layered systems of the cytoplasm. In the ordinary nucleus of a cell, the most prominent object is the *nucleolus,* which is a dense accumulation of RNA-rich particles.

Despite its less elaborate visible fine structure, the nucleus is the most important part of the cell. Without a nucleus, cytoplasm can survive for a surprisingly long time but it eventually breaks down unless a nucleus is re-inserted. The nucleus enables the cytoplasm to divide and grow. It is the molecular control centre, a sort of information library for the cell. Through cytology (the study of cells), genetics (the study of heredity), and molecular biology (the study of biological molecules), scientists are beginning to be able to read in that library.

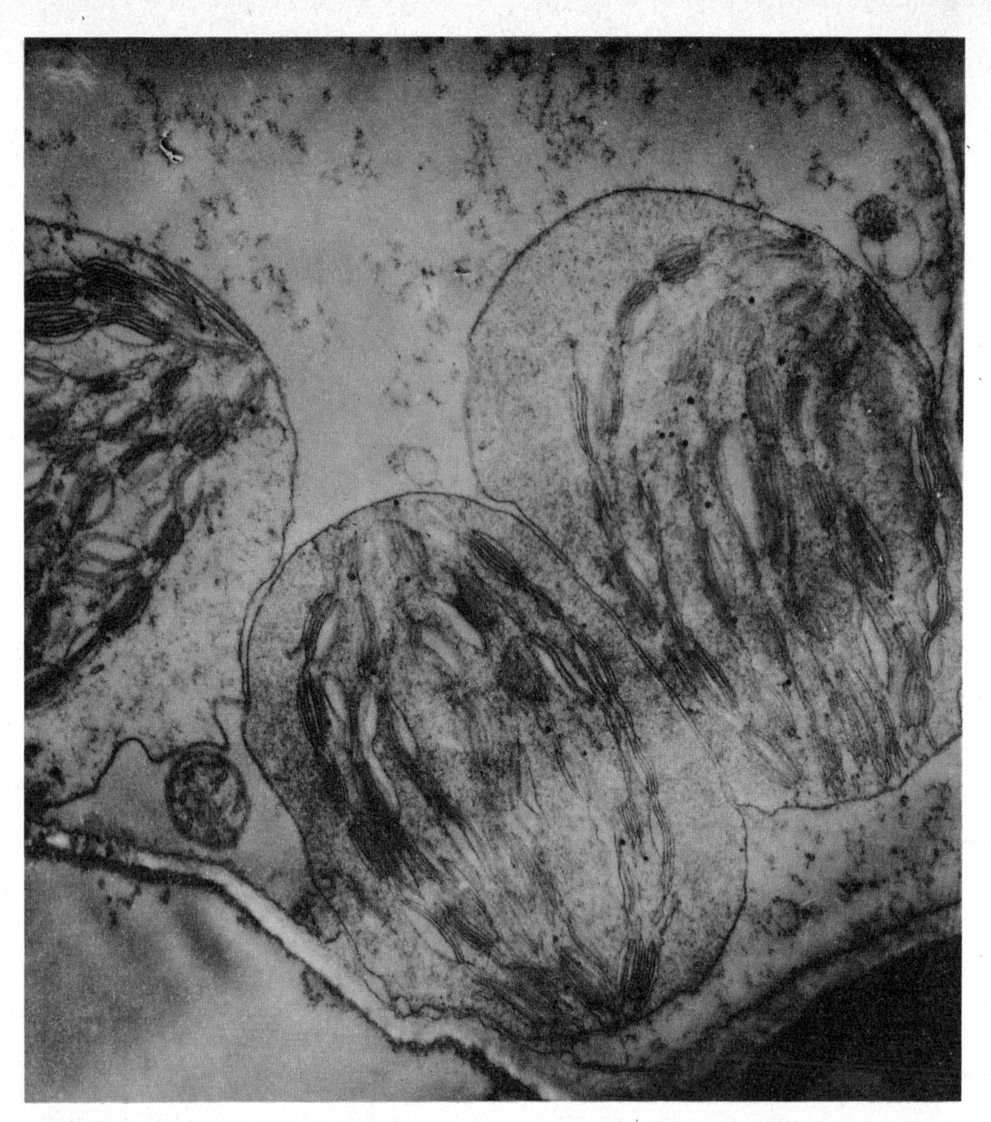

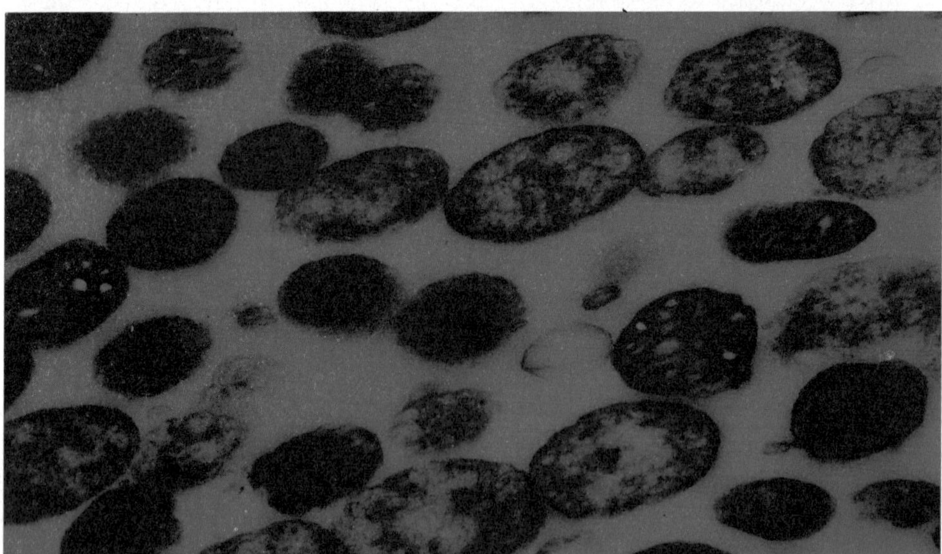

*Top,* inside the plant chloroplast are minute dark spots – *grana* – which are, in fact, highly organized arrays of membranes containing enzymes and active molecules for photo-synthesis.

*Above,* isolated mitochondria removed from the cell by a centrifuge. Now the different cell parts can at last be collected in sufficient quantity for biochemists to discover their composition.

# Molecules on the move

**Cells would die in their own wastes, or starve, without constantly renewed food supplies. But how do vital substances pass through cell membranes and from one part of a cell to another?**

THE CHIEF chemical constituent of the cell and its environment is water. Without water, a cell can survive only by taking special precautions. To avoid drying-up completely, it must enclose itself inside a protective coat rather like the coat of a plant seed. In this way, a single-celled creature like an amoeba can form a cyst and survive for a long time in a dry inactive state. The cyst germinates and hatches when water is again available, just like the seed of a plant.

Life probably originated in the sea between 500 million and 3,000 million years ago. The sea then contained, as it does now, a variety of salts in solution. The composition of this primeval sea was probably not the same as it is today because the whole surface of the Earth, both land and sea, has since been greatly affected by the waste products and remains of living things. But a chemical analysis of the cells of living tissues shows that the same salts are present there as in the sea. This similarity is more striking if one analyses blood, which is the most important tissue fluid in large organisms.

In blood, in tissues and in cells, the important salts are the phosphates, carbonates, bicarbonates and chlorides of sodium, potassium, calcium and magnesium. In solution, all these salts dissociate – that is, split up into ions. Ions are extremely small charged particles about the same size as atoms. The cations ($Na^+$, $K^+$, $Ca^{++}$, $Mg^{++}$) carry positive electrical charges, and the anions ($PO_4^{---}$, $CO_3^{--}$, $HCO_3^-$, $Cl^-$) carry negative electrical charges.

Organisms also contain large biological molecules of proteins, nucleic acids, carbohydrates and lipids. These molecules may also carry electrical charges, according to the nature of the groups along their length, and like salts they may be soluble in water. But when they dissolve they do not split up into tiny particles like ions, but remain large. This difference is important, as we shall see.

## A portable sea

The most delicate and watery organisms are generally found in an aquatic environment, particularly in the sea. For example, the grey matter of the brain has a water content of about 80 per cent, which is quite high. But as much as 96 per cent of a jellyfish may consist of water. The human body is about 66 per cent water. It is as if a land animal has to carry its own sea around with it for the sake of its cells. Some of this 'sea' is inside the cells themselves, and some of it surrounds the cells and constitutes the tissue fluids. For the sake of economy and efficiency, neither liquid is quite the same as the real sea.

In a large animal like a man, there is a constant circulation of tissue fluid round the body. And there is a constant exchange of fluid between cells and the spaces around cells, which accompanies their nutrition and respiration. Cells can easily kill themselves with their own wastes, or starve, in the absence of continually renewed food supplies. Waste removal and food supply are two of the main functions for tissue fluids and blood. So an animal can only become large by developing a circulatory system.

The membrane around a cell is a kind of barrier separating the protoplasm of the cell from the environment. It is, however, a permeable membrane – some substances can pass through it, while others cannot. Water molecules and small ions pass through easily, but the large biological molecules inside the cell membrane cannot pass out, and protein molecules in solution outside cannot pass in.

Cells are active systems, and can pump out certain ions. For example, sodium, calcium and chloride ions tend to be excluded from the red blood corpuscles in human blood, and potassium and magnesium ions concentrated inside them. The red blood corpuscle contains a large

Experiment showing how a partially permeable membrane discriminates between salt in a solution and gelatin. In the second diagram, it can be seen that the membrane has allowed the salt in the solution to pass through it, but not the gelatin. *Below right,* living things and sea water contain the same salts, but this cannot be held to support any theories of a causal relationship between the emergence of life itself and the sea, since, when life originated, the sea was already twice as salty as body fluids, and today the amount is three times as great.

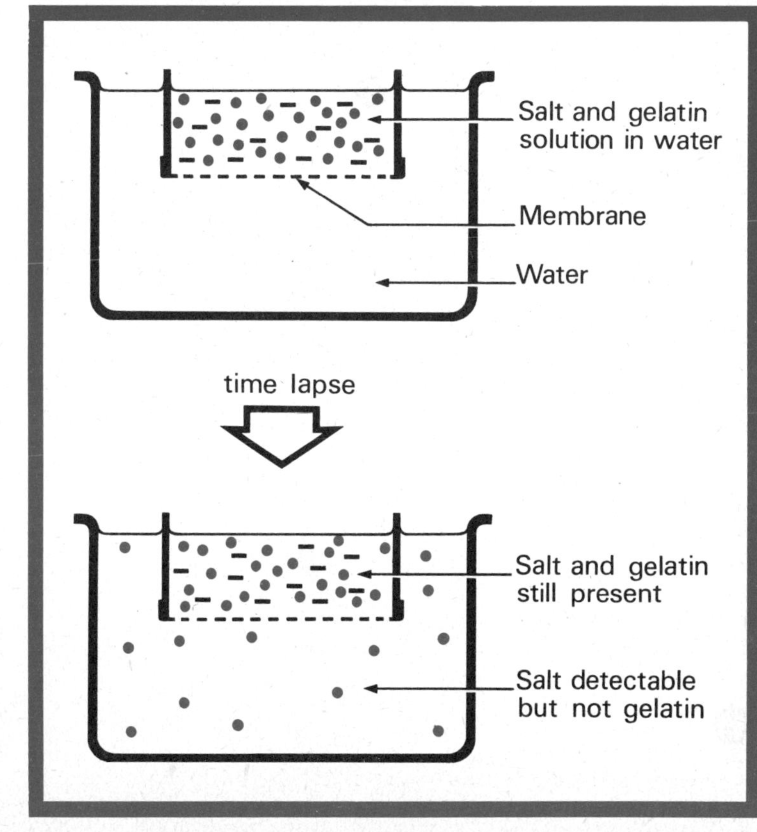


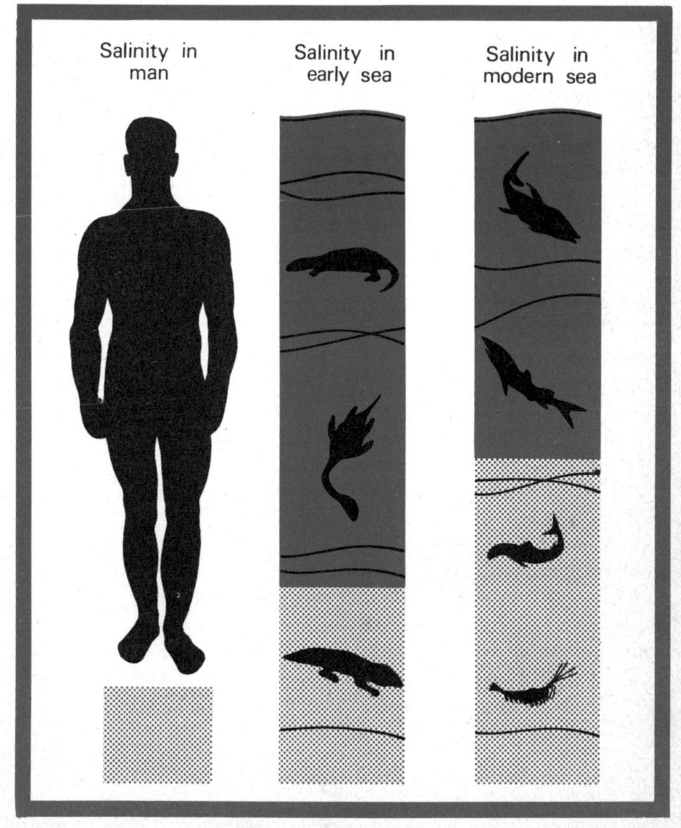

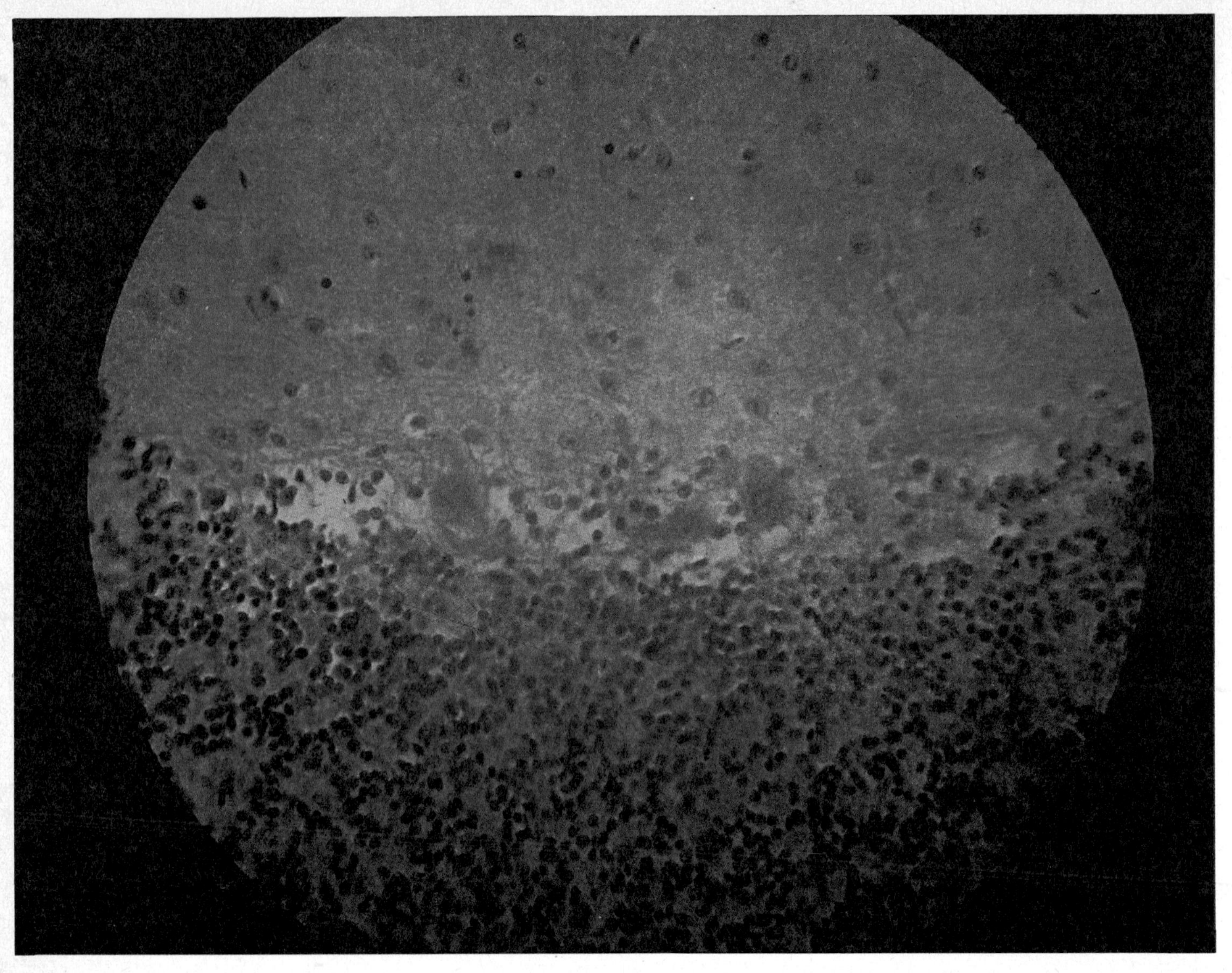

*Above,* section across the human brain. The body is 66 per cent water, but the actual water content of the grey matter in the brain is about 80 per cent. This water is found either inside cells, or surrounding them, making up the tissue fluids.

quantity of the protein haemoglobin. A red blood cell from a mammal has no nucleus, but it does have a cell membrane. It also has a uniform size, which makes swelling or shrinking easy to detect. It swells in distilled water, and shrinks and loses water in a strong salt solution.

The movement of water molecules from one place to another is an extremely important process called *osmosis*. Osmosis is the diffusion of water molecules from a solution of low concentration to a solution of high concentration, and occurs because of random movements of the water molecules. This migration of water produces a noticeable increase in the volume of the stronger aqueous solution, and a reduction in its concentration.

Sodium chloride is the commonest salt in the sea, and dissolves easily in water. Water is the *solvent,* and sodium chloride the *solute*. The molecules or ions of the solute also move randomly, but their migration makes very little change in the volume of the solution. We distinguish between *solvent diffusion* (which, when the solvent is water, is osmosis) and *solute diffusion*.

A membrane may be permeable to the movement of both solvent and solute. For example, if two solutions of glucose of different concentrations are placed on the opposite sides of such a membrane, osmosis is the most obvious process. After a time, the concentrations will become the same on both sides of the membrane, mainly by the movement of water from the dilute side to the concentrated side.

Some membranes are permeable to solvent but not to solute. In living cells, membranes may be permeable to some solute molecules but not others. Some living cells even have membranes that are impermeable to the universal solvent, water. For example, water does not penetrate the eggs of a trout. These eggs are adapted to survive in fresh water, which is a very dilute salt solution, and are highly resistant to changes in salt concentration.

## Osmosis and ultrafiltration

A living cell membrane may be both semi-permeable (letting through solvent molecules but not solute molecules) and selectively permeable (letting through solvent molecules and *some* solute molecules, but not all). Two things determine whether or not ions can pass through a membrane – their size and the electrical charge on them.

Non-living semi-permeable membranes are generally sheets of impermeable membrane with tiny holes through them. The

*Below,* fat cells: these, and bone cells, collect the materials they need for their tasks from their surroundings by a process of accumulation. They obtain what they require by osmosis through special, selectively permeable membranes.

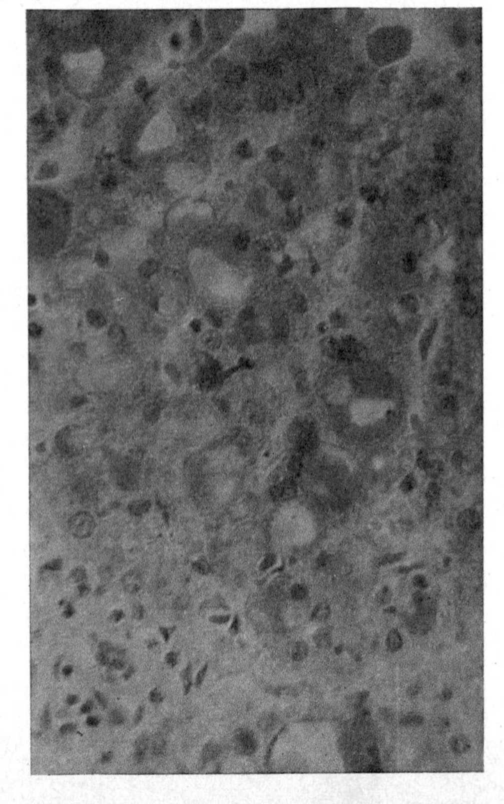

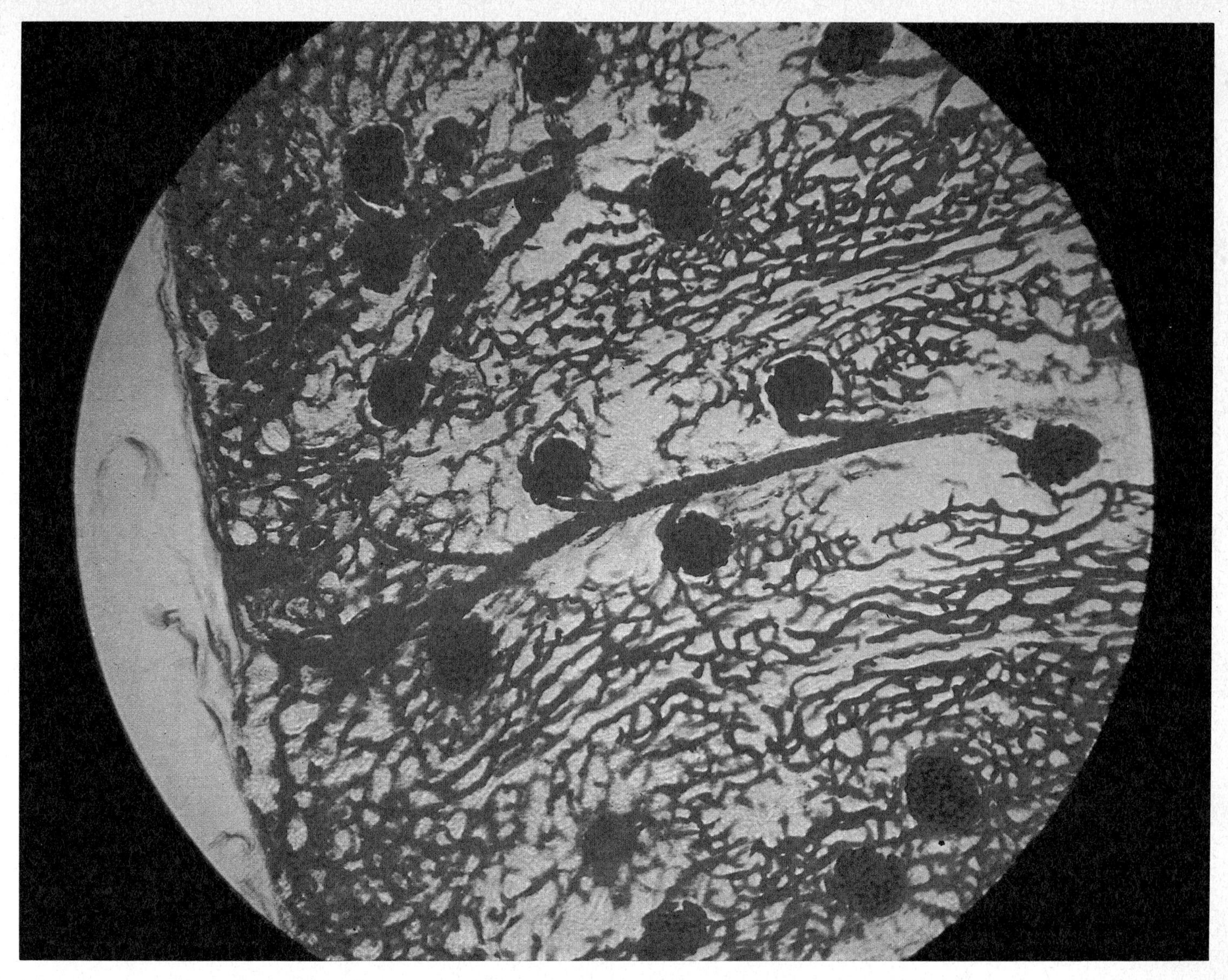

holes may be so small that they allow molecules of only a certain size through. These membranes work like a sort of filter. An important recent technical advance has been the development of manmade membranes of this kind, with precisely formed molecular pores of exactly known sizes. They are used as 'sieves' to select certain molecules.

Suppose that two solutions of glucose of different concentrations are separated by a semi-permeable membrane. The membrane is a sort of piston which allows water molecules to pass through freely, although glucose molecules cannot pass through. If initially the solutions on each side of the piston have the same volume, during the course of mixing (which can take place only by the movement of water molecules) their respective volumes will change. The strong solution will gain water and increase in volume and the piston will move.

But suppose the piston is firmly attached and cannot move, so that the compartments cannot change in volume. Osmosis and mixing are prevented, but there is still a strong tendency for it to occur. A pressure gauge attached to the strong solution compartment will measure the pressure tending to drive water in. This is the *osmotic pressure*. An opposite force prevents the movement of the water molecules. If it is sufficiently great, it can even push them in the opposite direction. This reverse movement is called *ultrafiltration* and is the direct opposite of osmosis, which is a mixing process; ultrafiltration is a separating or filtering process.

For example, in our bodies the strong pulsations of our hearts drive an ultrafiltration process in our kidneys. Through ultrafiltration, osmosis, and fluid circulation, our cells are maintained in a remarkably constant environment. Cells such as fat cells and bone cells can carry out a process of *accumulation* from the environment through their active selectively-permeable membranes. In this way, they concentrate materials necessary for particular jobs.

## Tissue fluid

Tissue fluid is more complicated than a simple solution of glucose. Many cells are more complicated than red blood corpuscles. In the interaction between tissue fluids and live cells, ordinary diffusion processes do not account for what happens. Accumulation and secretion cannot occur in simple solutions only through diffusion. But even in a non-living system, an unequal distribution of different ions (which is comparable to accumulation) can be achieved because of the existence of ions or molecules that cannot diffuse.

Many proteins of living cells are sodium salts (sodium proteinates), which are indiffusable because of their large size. So that even if the sodium chloride concentration is identical on each side of a membrane, if one side has sodium proteinate there will be an excess of sodium ions on that side and the osmotic pressure will be higher. Such a system is in equilibrium only if there is an additional restraint or force which keeps the volumes on each side of the membrane constant. Such a situation is called a Gibbs-Donnan equilibrium.

Ultrafiltration in the human kidney. Osmosis is a mixing process – its direct opposite, ultrafiltration, is a separating, or filtering process, and the one by which the kidneys extract waste materials and excess water from the blood.

In the absence of the constraint, both water and sodium and chloride ions can diffuse through the membrane because of the imbalance between the two sides. And they will diffuse continuously until either no water or sodium chloride is left outside the membrane, or until a constraint develops. If a pressure is exerted on the sodium proteinate compartment the process will be halted, and an unequal equilibrium will be attained. This will also happen with undissociated protein molecules that are not sodium salts. The pressure necessary to halt the process is a measure of the osmotic activity of the indiffusible molecule and is called the *colloid osmotic pressure*. Most substances

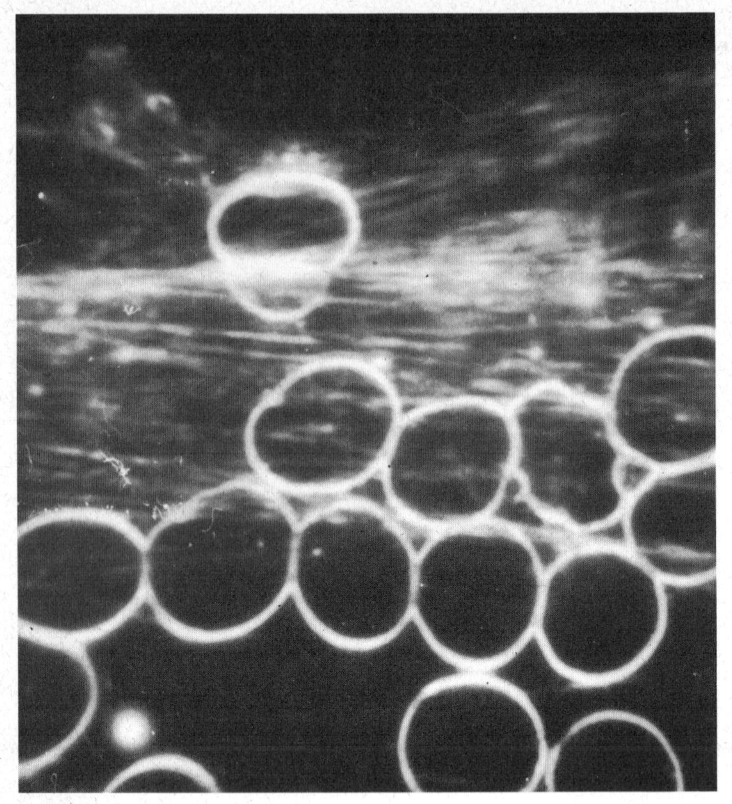

Human blood cells (erythrocytes) in a sample of freshly drawn blood. The fine threads visible are composed of fibrin, the protein which causes blood to coagulate. Because they are taken from a mammal, the cells contain no nucleus, but are surrounded by a clearly defined cell membrane.

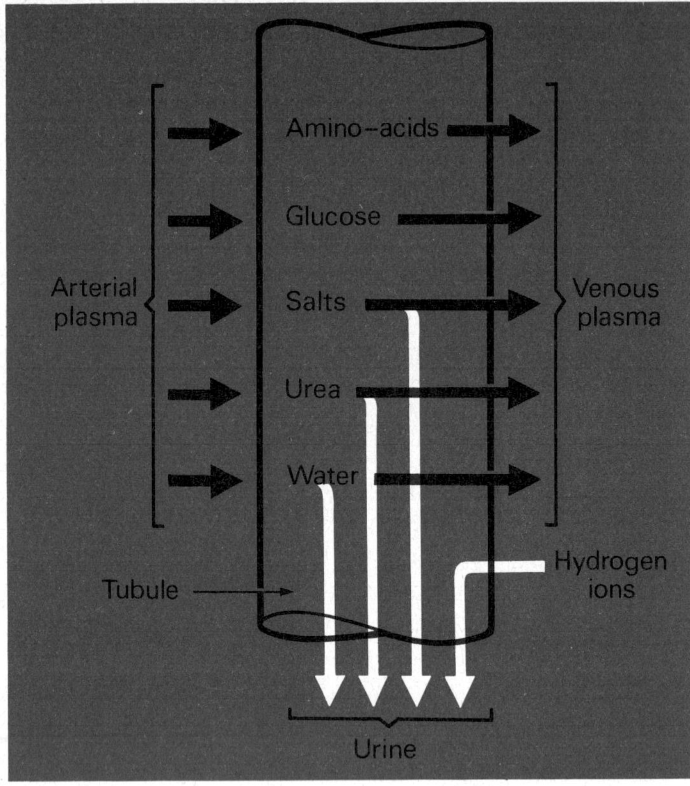


*Above right,* diagram illustrating the formation of urine in the kidneys. This shows clearly which materials are allowed to pass through, and which are the waste materials extracted from the blood as it flows through the tubules in the kidneys at high pressure to ensure complete filtration.

The substances which the kidneys convert into urine, and which are not reabsorbed at all into the blood, include excess sodium chloride, sulphate, urea, creatinine, phosphate, and a number of the final products of metabolism, as well as substances in the plasma which are foreign to the body.

are either colloids or crystalloids. The distinction between them, which is not clear cut, is one of particle size. Much of the material in the cytoplasm of cells is in the colloidal state.

The plasma left when all blood cells are centrifuged off from blood contains about ten per cent of dissolved substances, including the proteins albumen, globulin and a fibrinogen. These proteins produce a colloid osmotic pressure of about 30 to 40 mm of mercury. Haemoglobin is present in abundance in red blood cells and contributes to a Donnan equilibrium which maintains a high concentration of potassium ions within the cells and keeps sodium ions outside. The red blood corpuscle has an unusual shape. It is technically a concavo-convex disc. This shape is positively maintained by a special protein built into the coat which acts as a constraint against the inward osmosis of water. When this 'anti-sphering factor' is removed, the cell can change into a sphere, increasing its volume greatly with no change in surface area, and absorb water.

## Blood capillaries

In a circulatory system, blood plasma is separated from tissue fluid by the walls of the blood capillaries. The wall contains at least two significant layers: a layer of endothelial cells and a layer of amorphous material around them, a basement membrane called the *basal lamina*. Both layers act as filters and selectively-permeable barriers. The heart creates a high hydrostatic pressure inside the capillary. This often causes ultrafiltration on the side of a capillary network nearest the heart and drives water and all constituents except proteins out into the tissue spaces. It does this against the osmotic gradient and overcomes the resistance of the tissue to deformation.

On the side farthest from the heart, the hydrostatic pressure has dropped because of the resistance of the narrow-bore capillaries, and the plasma is slightly more concentrated. The venous end of a capillary bed re-absorbs tissue fluid. Tissue fluid (lymph) must resemble blood, because it is in constant balance with it. The *lymph system* is an extra system of vessels. It acts as an overflow collecting system and drains excess tissue fluid, sending it back eventually into large veins. In the kidney, selective permeability and hydrostatic pressure, and the processes of osmosis, diffusion and ultrafiltration, work to eliminate waste materials and excess water from the blood.

By unequal accumulation of ions within a membrane, an eletrical charge can be built up on it. Electrical charges can make things stick together or fly apart. Similarly changes in the distribution of ions in the environment of cells can make stick together or fall apart. Charged proteins can also make cells do this. For example, virus proteins can make red blood cells stick together because the virus protein is captured on the surface of one cell and tends to join it to another.

This process is a sensitive method of detecting proteins. It can also be a method purifying virus particles, by absorbing them on to red cells. Two important ions for cell stickiness and cell activity are calcium ions and magnesium ions. Many tissues can be made to fall apart into separate cells by treating them with a chemical called a *chelating* agent which preferentially 'mops-up' calcium ions.

Electrically charged membranes are significant in the functioning of nerve cells. These are cells which are specialized for the conduction of messages in the form of nerve impulses associated with electrical activity. The inside of a nerve fibre or muscle cell has a negative charge with respect to the outside and the tissue fluid, because of internal accumulation of potassium ions through a Donnan equilibrium. The difference in charge creates the *membrane potential,* and depends upon impermeability of the membrance to sodium ions. This potential is discharged when a nerve impulse passes. There is an inrush of sodium ions and an outrush of potassium ions giving a reversal of charge, so that the inside becomes positively charged. The sodium ions are then pumped out again by a process involving physiological work and the expenditure of metabolic energy.

## Balanced cell activity

In comparison with sea water, tissue fluids and cell fluids of mammals are low in sodium ions, and it may be that this 'sodium pump' mechanism evolved in all cells because the early chemical environment was over-rich in sodium ions. Magnesium and calcium are also important in both muscle contraction and in nerve conduction.

Both within and around cells, living organisms have special ways of controlling the distribution of ions through the activity of specialized membranes which permit balanced cell activity.

# Bacteria – agents of decay

While bacteria are popularly associated with disease, comparatively few species are harmful to Man. Indeed, without bacteria to decompose dead organisms, human life would be impossible.

BACTERIA – POPULARLY known as bacilli, microbes, micro-organisms and germs – are so small that they cannot be seen by the naked eye. The largest are smaller than 1/1850 inch and some are as small as 1/85000 inch. They are very simple living organisms which have not yet evolved into plants or animals and which may resemble the earliest living organisms on Earth. Today four main groups of bacteria are recognized.

The first group, *eubacteriales*, contains the lower and more numerous forms of bacteria and is divided into four sub-groups – (1) *bacteriineae*, which are unicellular bacteria with flagella (tails) enabling them to move about quite freely; (2) *caulobacteriineae*, which are rod-like bacteria; (3) *spirochaetineae*, which are curved or spiral-shaped with axial filaments; and (4) *bacillineae*, which are spherical.

The second group, *actinomycetales*, consists of slender rod-like bacteria which throw out branches. It is divided into two sub-groups – *actinomycetineae*, which have filaments made up of long cells, and *mycobacteriineae*, which have short filaments made up of very small cells.

The third group, *streptomycetales*, consists of mould-like bacteria.

The fourth group, *flexibacteriales*, comprises bacteria with a thick 'muscular' cell wall and is divided into two sub-groups: *myxobacteriineae*, which are unicellular, stubby bacteria; and *trichobacteriineae*, multicellular and slender.

## The bacterial cell

Bacteria are often, more simply, arranged into three main groups according to their shape – *bacilli*, rod-shaped; *cocci*, spherical; and *spirelli*, spiral forms.

Another popular division is into two main groups: bacteria that are *autotrophic* and obtain their carbon from the carbon dioxide in the air and their energy supply from the oxidation of inorganic substances, including inorganic compounds of nitrogen, carbon, sulphur, iron and hydrogen; and bacteria that are *heterotrophic* and require organic substances as sources of carbon and energy. Although outnumbered in the soil by heterotrophic types, autotrophic bacteria are responsible for some of the most important biochemical processes, such as the oxidation of ammonia to nitrite, nitrite to nitrate, and sulphur compounds and sulphur to sulphates.

Most bacteria have a rigid cell wall. Although they have no nucleus like that of typical plant and animal cells, there is nuclear material scattered throughout the cell. Like other living cells they are largely composed of water and contain varying amounts of proteins, lipids and carbohydrates. Examined under a microscope, bacteria are usually colourless, and

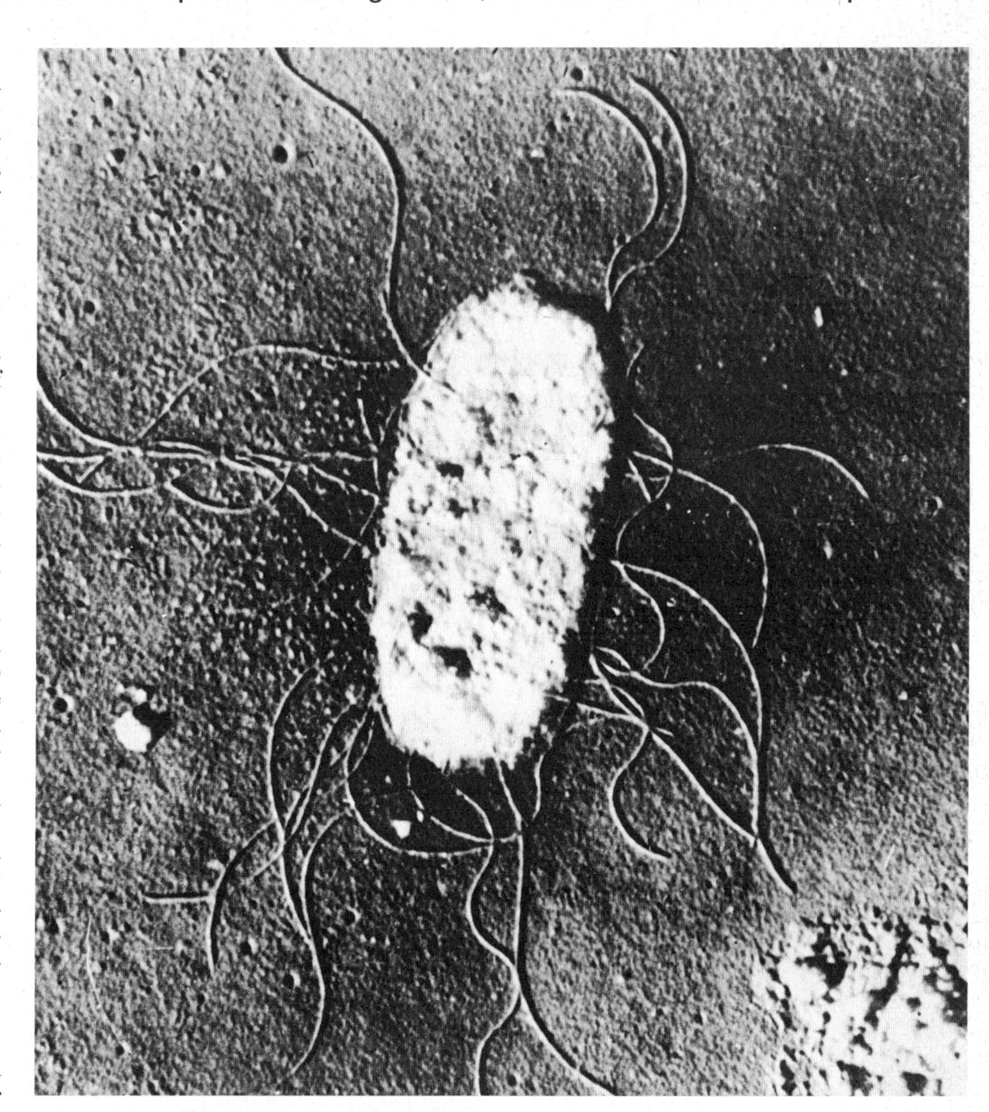

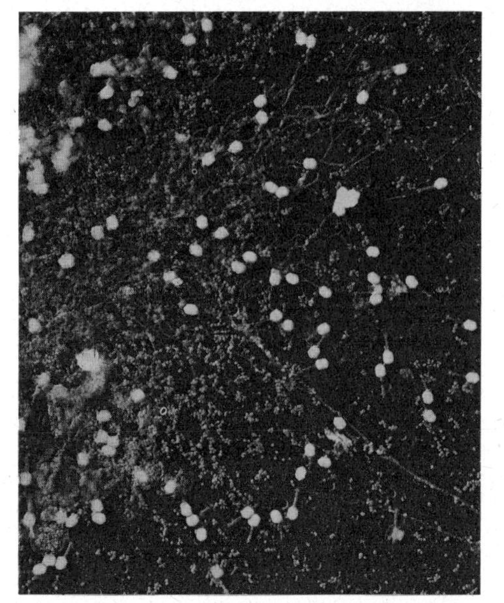

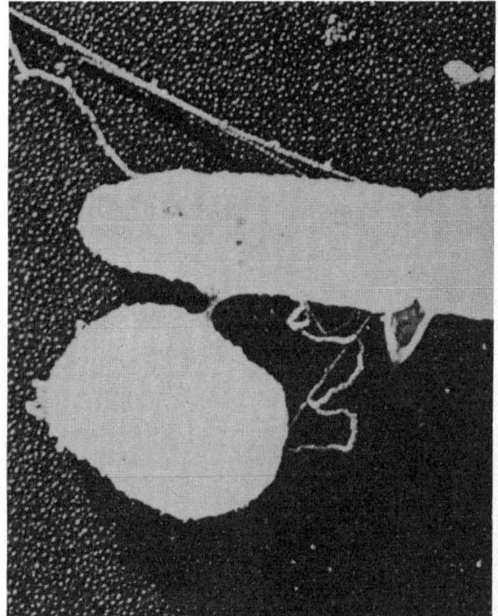

*Top*, a greatly magnified bacterium. *Above left*, part of a lysed cell – the cell membrane has ruptured and the contents dispersed. Immature and completed phages, ribosomes and DNA fibres can all be distinguished. Now, with the development of a 'shadowing' process, bacteria can be seen more clearly than ever before. *Above right*, bacteria are the most primitive form of life capable, in some forms, of reproducing sexually. Here, the (upper) male bacterium unites with a female.

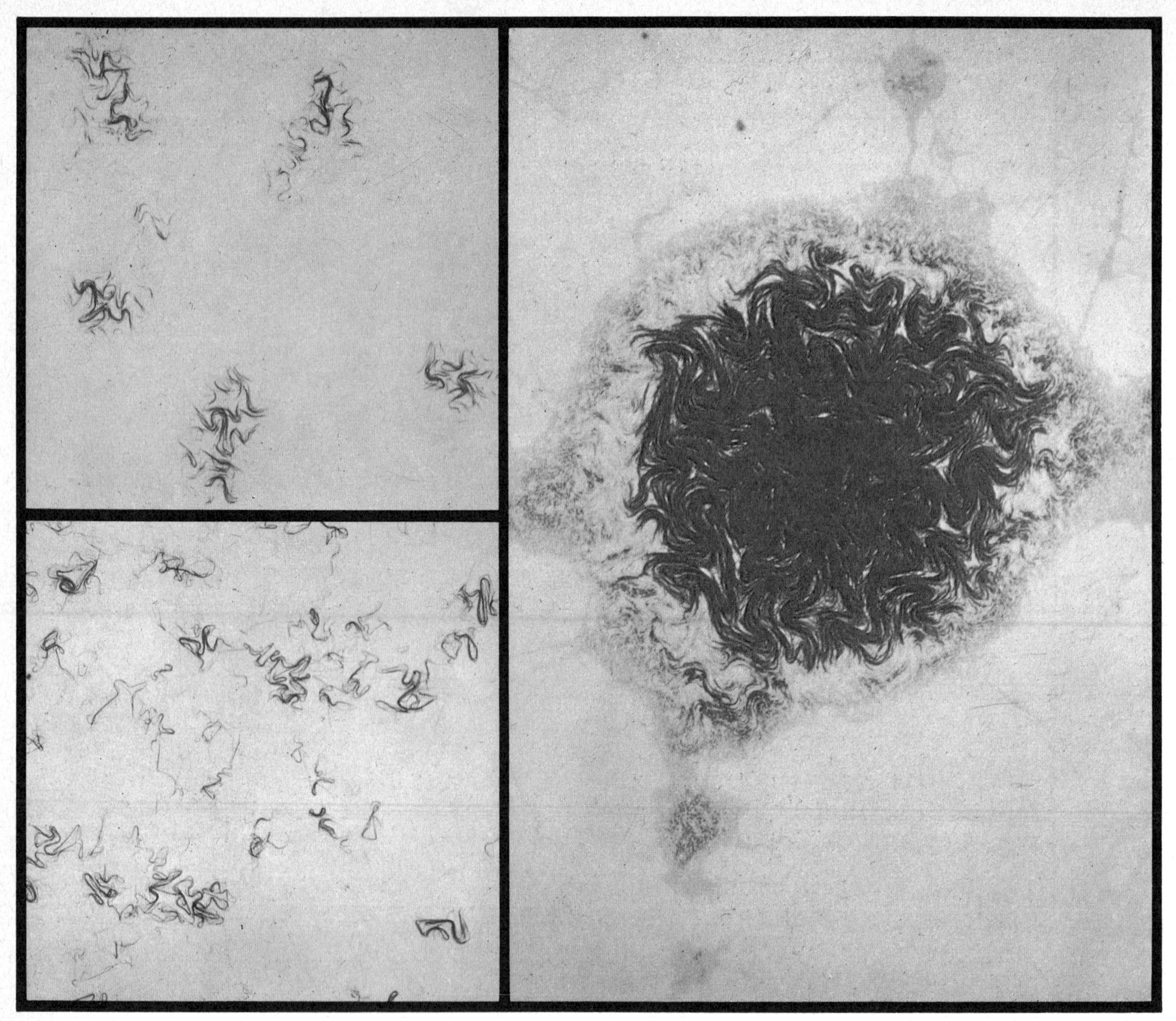

The bacillus *anthracis*, pictured here at various stages of colony division, causes anthrax, one of the oldest recorded bacterial diseases, mentioned as far back as the Old Testament. It used to attack both animals and men in epidemic proportions until Louis Pasteur discovered an effective vaccine against it in 1881. These photographs show how rapidly it multiplies. *Top left,* bacteria *anthracis* colonies at four hours after start of multiplication. *Above left, anthracis* colonies at six hours and, *above right,* at nine hours – now millions of bacteria.

surrounding the cell wall there is often a gelatinous covering which causes them to stick together and form a slimy mass, such as is found on the surface of stagnant water and round flower stalks that have begun to rot.

Bacteria are among the most widespread of living organisms. They occur in air, soil, in fresh water, on the surface and in the depths of the sea, and on and within the bodies of larger creatures of all kinds. Rain water and the higher reaches of the atmosphere contain comparatively few, but the air of a city or the water of a river immediately below a settlement of any size contains large numbers. A gramme of normal fertile soil contains some 3,000 to 5,000 million bacterial cells.

Animals, including the human animal, are very hospitable to bacteria. Large numbers of many different varieties live on the skin, in the nasal tract and in the mouth, the gut and the genital orifices. They are constantly being discharged into the air or the local environment. For example, the greater part of the dry weight of human faeces consists of living or dead micro-organisms.

## Darkness is preferred

Some species of bacteria are able to remain alive at very high or very low temperatures fatal to most other forms of life. However, as for all other organisms, there is a temperature range which is most favourable to their growth. While for most bacteria the lower limit is 12°C and the upper limit about 40°C, a few will grow at 5°C and those which decompose straw and dung grow well at about 60°C. Some bacteria have been found which survive temperatures required to liquefy hydrogen, while the sulphur bacteria flourish in hot springs at a temperature of nearly 80°C. As a rule bacteria are destroyed very quickly in bright sunlight, and all seem to grow and multiply quickly in a total absence of light.

Although most organisms can live for only a very short time without oxygen, some bacteria can live in its absence. The bacteria causing tetanus, botulism (meat poisoning) and gangrene all flourish without oxygen and are termed *anaerobes*. They are active in deep wounds (gas gangrene) and tinned food (botulism) and are destroyed by hydrogen peroxide, which liberates oxygen. Other bacteria can only live where oxygen is present, but many of the disease-producing (pathogenic) bacteria are able to live equally well with or without oxygen.

Certain types of bacteria are usually found in specific situations. For example, the *pseudomonadacae,* short rod-like bacteria, many of which produce fluorescent pigments, are typically aquatic and when they appear on land exhibit considerable preference for a fluid environment, such as sewage and decomposing organic materials. *Bacteriaceae* are best known as parasites of the bowel in land vertebrates, and include *salmonella,* which cause vomiting and diarrhoea, and *shigella,* the dysentery bacteria.

*Staphylococci* frequently dwell on the skin, where they are normally harmless, but can cause boils, abscesses and dermatitis when they invade the tissues through a hair follicle. In the human mouth, *lactobacilli* are the commonest bacteria. The acid which they produce by the fermentation of food remnants plays an important part in the decalcification of dental enamel. The main habitat of *streptomyces* is the soil, and they are largely responsible for the characteristic smell of wet earth.

Bacteria usually reproduce by splitting into two across the middle, after an initial elongation of the cell. The nuclear matter in the protoplasm divides so that there are two masses within the cell membrane; in the rigid bacteria a new cell wall grows inwards at the division and the spores of the cell separate.

Sometimes the separation is incomplete and a 'double bacterium' is formed, such as the bacillus that causes diphtheria, or even a 'double-double bacterium', which forms a four-celled bacteria such as the *tetracoccus*.

## 16 million descendants in a day

Binary fission is not the only method of reproduction and in a few species of the *eubacteriales* it appears that a form of mating takes place. In *escherichia coli,* for example, which is often found in the human gut, the individual cells appear to exhibit a primitive form of sexuality. Multiplication among bacteria can occur so rapidly that a single bacterium can produce more than 16 million new cells in a day.

Like all other living creatures, bacteria have been subject to evolutionary processes. Many authorities believe that their development runs parallel to the development of other forms of life – that they are descended from primitive organisms adapted to an aquatic environment.

On the other hand, some experts point out that while heterotrophic bacteria would have been capable of life in association with the simple organic materials which were among the first forms of life appearing on Earth, autotrophic bacteria are highly organized, in both structure and chemistry, and thus it is more reasonable to assume they were preceded by very simple heterotrophs which found sources of food and energy in organic molecules.

The most primitive bacteria are probably the spiral water bacteria, which propel themselves through liquids by means of polar flagella.

The most sophisticated terrestrial species have developed, in the same way as plants, a system of aerial distribution of reproductive cells. Many have also achieved the ability to move on land; others have adopted a plant-like habit of growth.

The *streptomyces* are among the most highly developed bacteria living on land. They are static and resemble the moulds with branched feeding tubes and this similarity has often led to their comparison with some of the higher fungi.

While bacteria are popularly associated with disease and illness, only a relatively few species are harmful to man or animals, and life as we know it today could not exist if there were no bacteria.

Most disease-producing bacteria are parasitic – they live on their hosts and are carried and spread by healthy animals which have become immune, or by dead matter. Some pathogenic bacteria are selective in their attack. For example, gonorrhoeal infections are confined to man, but the bovine tubercle bacteria is capable of infecting cattle, man, monkeys, pigs and cats alike.

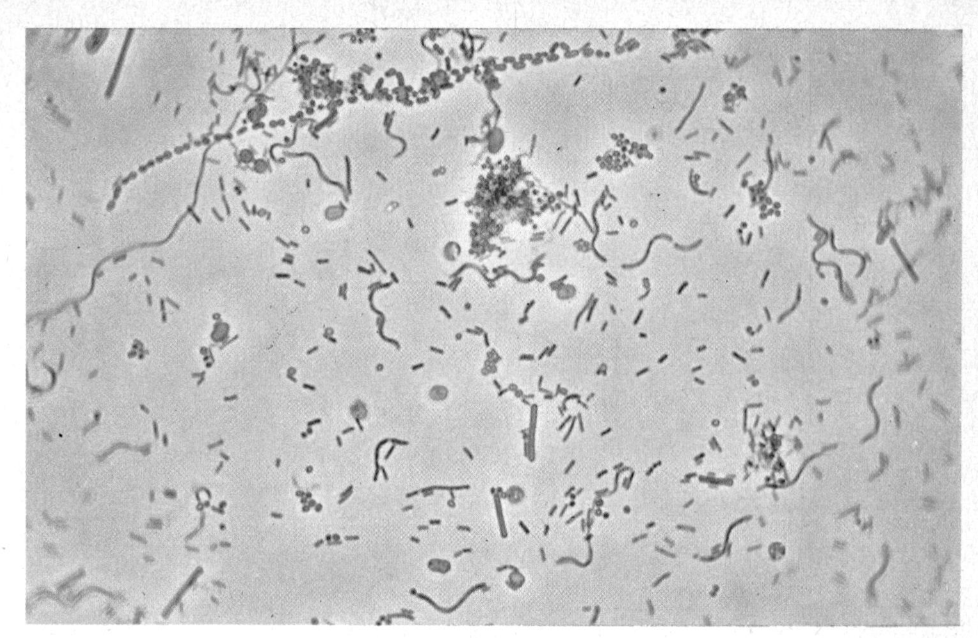

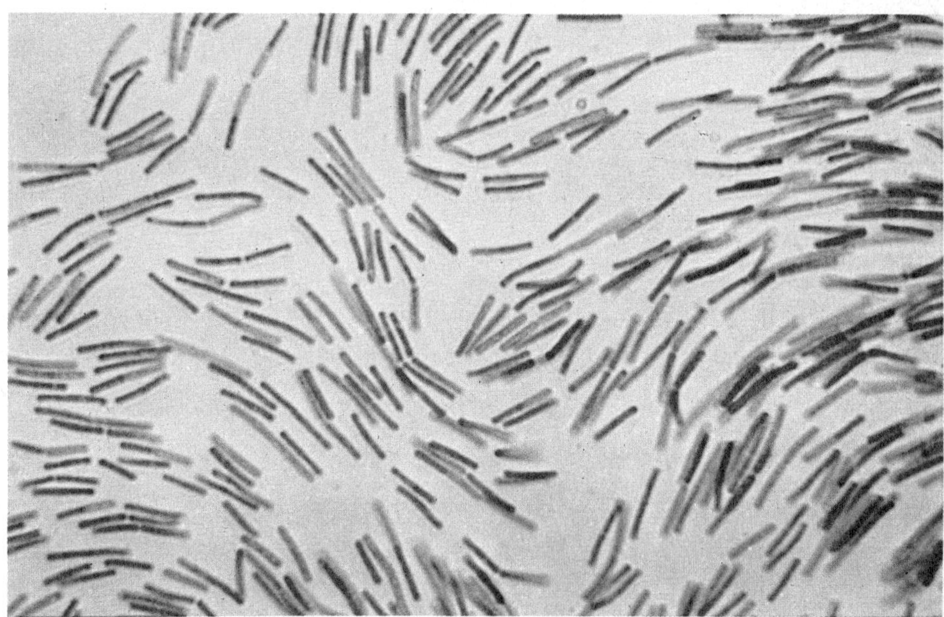

*Top,* mixed bacteria showing differing shapes. There are four main forms, spiral, spherical, rod-shaped, and a long filamentous type. But modifications can be caused by different environments.

*Above,* bacteria *anthracis.* This type of bacteria is termed a bacillus. Correctly, a bacillus is a rod-shaped bacterium which forms spores, but the term is usually applied to all rod-shaped bacteria.

## The fertility of soil

Three kinds of bacteria of considerable importance in human and veterinary medicine, each comprising a small number of closely related species, are *pasteurella, brucella* and *pfeifferella.*

The best-known species of *pasteurella* is that which causes bubonic plague among rodents and man. The disease is transmitted by the rat-flea, which occasionally attacks human beings. The lymph glands are infected, a swelling – the *bubo* – occurs and if this breaks down into the bloodstream, septicaemia and death result. (This was the Great Plague of 1666.) Pneumonic plague, which infects the lungs, is also caused by *pasteurella.*

*Brucella* causes feverish conditions in cattle, goats and pigs and can be passed to man in the form of the so-called 'Malta fever', which arises from drinking infected milk. *Pfeifferella* causes contagious abortion and sterility in domestic animals.

For well over a century it has been known that the suppuration of wounds is due to the presence of bacteria, and in 1867 the importance of antiseptics in controlling infection was established by Lord Lister. In 1876 Robert Koch isolated the bacterium which causes anthrax, and further discoveries quickly followed.

Today it has been established that bacterial infections cause blood poisoning, bubonic plague, cholera, diphtheria, enteric fever, erysipelas, gonorrhoea, leprosy, meningitis, pneumonia, rheumatic fever, whooping cough, scarlet fever, syphilis, tetanus and tuberculosis.

Disease-producing bacteria cause damage to the human or animal body in two ways: some spread rapidly through the tissues they infect, causing so much

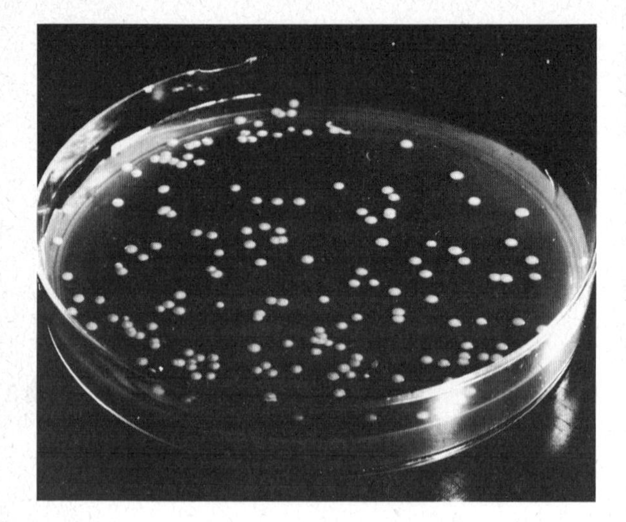

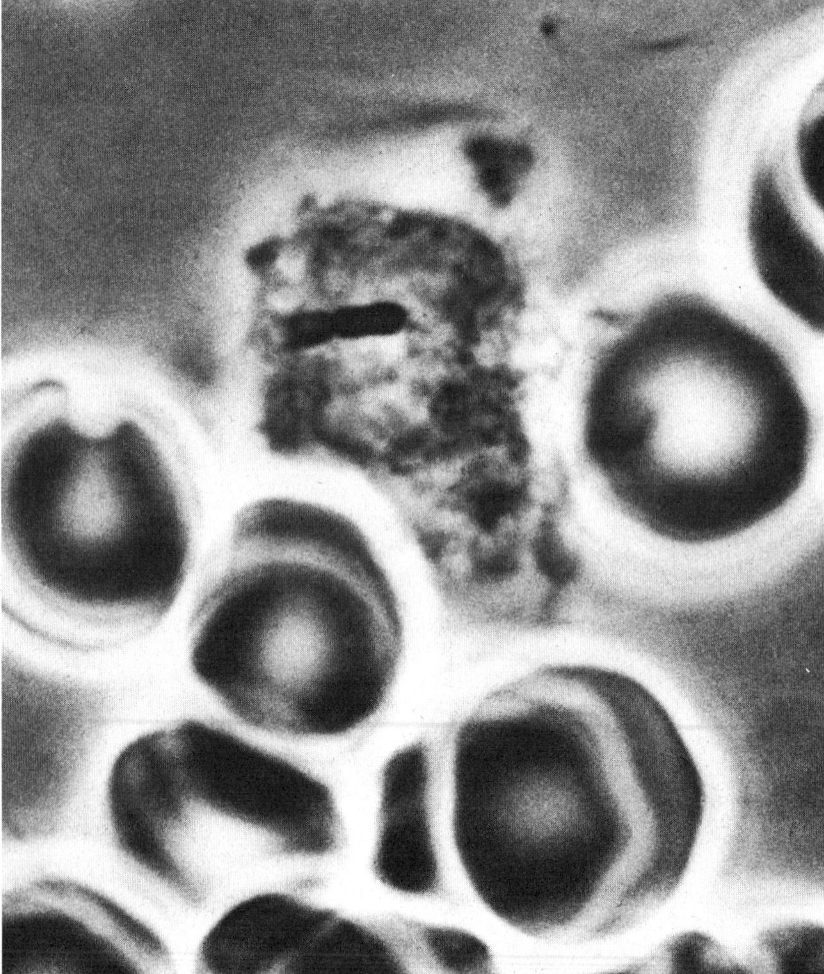

*Top,* colonies of the bacteria *escherichia coli.* How these bacteria reproduce is not fully understood; it is a sexual process, with, probably, chromosomes being transferred from one to the other.

*Above left,* although bacteria can cause so much disease, not all are harmful. In fact many are useful positively to man, such as the bacteria which are causing wine in these vats to ferment.

*Above,* a white blood corpuscle photographed in the very act of encircling and swallowing a harmful bacterium (the small, dark rod-shaped body). The other cells are the red blood corpuscles.

disorder that these are no longer able to function properly. Others are unable to spread themselves but produce bacterial toxins, which they release into the body.

Faced with the onslaught of bacteria or bacterial poisons, the body defends itself by producing antibodies. These help the white blood corpuscles to surround and destroy the bacteria, while anti-toxic substances neutralize the toxic releases.

Many bacteria which live in human and animal bodies are beneficial to their hosts. While *lactobacilli* in the mouth cause dental decay, in the vagina they produce acids which inhibit the growth of more harmful bacteria. *Veillonella* play an important part in the digestion of ruminants. Others assist in the synthesis of vitamins.

Numbers of other parasitic bacteria are neutral in effect and live in man and animals with neither beneficial nor harmful results.

One of the most important functions of bacteria lies in their contribution to what is known as *the nitrogen cycle* – the method by which nitrogen in the atmosphere is made available to animals and plants. The higher plants cannot use atmospheric nitrogen until it has been converted into nitrates by bacteria. Leguminous plants are particularly well served by bacteria – so much so that they leave the soil richer in nitrogen than before they were sown. Usually the bacteria live in the roots of the plants and by their presence they give rise to nodules on the roots.

## Fermentation and decomposition

In effect, bacteria of this type provide plants with food and energy. By their action, nitrogen is converted into ammonium compounds and then into nitrites and nitrates, which the plant builds up into proteins. After the crop is finished, the roots decay and the proteins and nitrates pass into the soil, where other species of bacteria break them down into ammonium compounds, and sometimes liberate free oxygen. By the activities of these nitrifying and de-nitrifying bacteria, the amount of oxygen in the atmosphere is kept constant, and depletion of any one form is prevented.

The action of organisms in obtaining energy by the oxidation of inorganic compounds is known as *chemotrophism.* In addition to the nitrogen cycle, bacteria initiate similar essential cycles for sulphur, carbon, iron and phosphorus. In the sulphur cycle, hydrogen sulphide is released from decomposing organic matter and is converted by various species of bacteria into sulphur and then sulphates, which are also essential to plants in forming their protein.

*Lactobacilli* are the main agents in the fermentation of silage, in which the carbohydrates of vegetable material are fermented to produce lactic acid and carbon dioxide.

Cellulose decomposition is another important activity of bacteria. Leaf and straw materials may contain between 35 and 60 per cent cellulose, and bacteria can break this down completely.

Because of their power to secrete fermenting agents, bacteria are of great economic importance, *Lactobacilli* and *streptococci* are used in the manufacture of milk products, where their action is similar to that of the fermentation of silage. Bacteria also play their part in the curing of tobacco and the manufacture of vinegar. Citric acid is produced by a mould activated by bacteria, and bacteria-activated yeast produces alcohol and glycerine. Ginger-beer is also made by fermenting sugar with yeast and introducing a bacterium.

Bacteria are also used in many industrial processes besides the production of food. They facilitate the separation of flax fibres by decomposing the connecting tissues, and jute and hemp are separated in a similar way. A bacterium known as *clostriolrum* is employed in the chemical production of acetone and butyl alcohol.

Although about 1,500 different species of bacteria have so far been discovered, only very few have been thoroughly studied; in the future it is likely that they will increasingly be employed in industrial processes concerned with organic materials.

# The virus – scourge of the cell

Outside a host cell, a virus particle is as inert as any other molecule of protein or nucleic acid. But once inside a cell, it can multiply to such an extent that the cell bursts and dies.

TOWARDS THE END of the last century, largely through the work of Louis Pasteur (1822–95) and Robert Koch (1843–1910), bacteria were identified as the agents causing many diseases in plants and animals. But all attempts to isolate the agents for some other common diseases failed. Bacteriologists could not isolate the agents that cause yellow fever, smallpox, mumps, measles or chickenpox.

Then in 1892, the Russian biologist, D. Ivanovsky, discovered that the agent causing tobacco mosaic disease passes through a filter that retains bacteria and other known disease-producing organisms. The agents causing this disease were clearly much smaller than bacteria. Other biologists found that the agents responsible for foot-and-mouth disease were also 'filterable'.

## What is a virus?

For a while there was a controversy over whether such diseases were caused by tiny agents smaller than bacteria (which were named *viruses*) or by the filtered fluid itself. Then in 1935, W. M. Stanley in the United States isolated and purified tobacco mosaic virus, and demonstrated that it consisted of particles that could be crystallized. Nearly all virus particles are much too small to be seen with an optical microscope, although they can be studied using an electron microscope, and so they were named and classified in terms of the diseases they caused. (Bacteria, which can be studied with an optical microscope, are classified according to their shapes.) It was later found that a virus is a large complex molecule formed from a protein and a nucleic acid, called a nucleoprotein. In the case of tobacco mosaic virus, the nucleic acid is a single strand of ribonucleic acid (RNA).

Although viruses have biological activity – for example, they can reproduce – they are not composed of cells and can even be crystallized like a chemical substance. They are therefore not true living things and are not totally inanimate. They may be considered to be half way between large inanimate molecules (such as proteins) and the simplest living organisms (such as the single-celled amoeba).

Viruses form a unique group with characteristics that are rather difficult to define. As we have said, only the largest viruses (such as that of cowpox) can be seen under an optical microscope, so the majority must be less than 20 millionths of a centimetre across. The smallest units of living matter, cells, are nearly three times as large.

A virus particle (called a *virion*) consists of a protein coat and nucleic acid. Living organisms contain both types of nucleic acid (DNA and RNA), but viruses have only one type. Plant viruses contain only RNA, and animal viruses contain either RNA or DNA. Although viruses can be crystallized, they cannot be described merely in terms of a chemical formula because such a definition neglects their biological properties, particularly their ability to cause disease. Outside the host cell, a virion is as inert as any other molecule of protein or nucleic acid. But once inside a cell, it can exhibit its biological properties. It does not grow or divide in the host cell, in the way that an organism grows or divides, but it does multiply to form many more identical virus particles. It is this multiplication process, resulting in the formation of new virus particles at the expense of the host cell, which is the main cause of the effects that we call a virus disease.

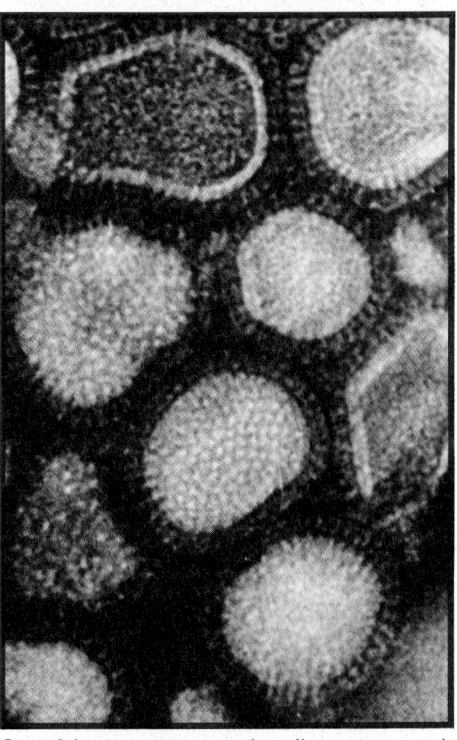

One of the most common virus diseases we catch is influenza. *Top,* influenza virus attached to the surfaces of red blood cells taken from a chicken is causing these cells to clump together in a reaction known as haemogglutination. *Above,* the face of an enemy. Isolated influenza virus particles magnified some 250,000 times.

In addition to the viruses that affect plants and animals, biologists now know of viruses which cause infections in single-celled micro-organisms such as bacteria and blue-green algae. Bacterial viruses are called *bacteriophages,* or phages for short. At one time, it was thought that they might provide a way of combating the bacteria which themselves cause disease. But no success was achieved along these lines and the introduction of antibiotics made this type of research unnecessary. Because of the ease with which bacteria can be grown in the laboratory, the bacteriophage system has continued to be used by virologists for investigating many of the puzzles of the virus-host relationship, particularly the way in which a virus takes over the direction of the host cell's metabolism.

## How virus diseases spread

Familiar virus diseases of the higher animals include psittacosis and fowl pest in birds, cowpox and foot-and-mouth disease in cattle, rabies and distemper in dogs, myxomatosis in rabbits, and poliomyelitis, influenza, warts and the common cold in man. Viruses are also known which affect lower animals such as fish, amphibians and insects. Many virus diseases flourish in the higher plants, particularly where there is intensive cultivation. Once a virus is established in a few plants of a seasonal or perennial crop (such as fruit trees), the disease will spread rapidly throughout the remainder of the crop and may cause substantial losses.

Viruses generally spread in natural populations by one of three methods. They can be passed from host to host by actual contact, as is the mosaic virus infection of tomato crops and children's diseases such as chickenpox. Or they may be taken into the body with drinking water or food, which seems to be the case with poliomyelitis and many of the so-called polyhedrosis diseases of insects. Or in certain cases, a carrier species may be involved which takes the virus from one host to another, as in the transmission of yellow fever by mosquitoes or of potato leaf-roll virus by aphids.

A few viruses, especially those which cause diseases of plants, are also able to multiply both in the cells of their insect carriers and in the cells of the plants they infect. The ability of such viruses to multiply in the cells of both animals and plants emphasizes the similarity of the life processes at the cell level, but at the same time poses problems for the virologist.

## How a virus infects a cell

What happens when a virus particle is introduced into a healthy cell? The answer began to be found in 1915 when an English microbiologist named Twort noticed some clear areas developing on the surface of a bacterial colony which he had grown on a jelly culture. He examined the clear areas with an optical microscope and found that they were regions of dead bacterial cells. When he transferred some material from the clear areas to healthy cells, he found that more clear areas (or *plaques*) were formed. The infectious material was filterable, and the number of plaques which it caused was related to its concentration. In this way, Twort established a technique for assessing the amount of infectious viral material in a preparation which is still used today.

Soon after a phage suspension has been added to a healthy bacterial culture, there is an *eclipse* phase during which no infectious particles can be recovered. Immediately after the eclipse phase, there is a period in which the amount of infectious material that can be recovered increases steadily with time. Finally the infectious bacterial cells burst and release their contents (including the newly synthesized phage particles) into the surrounding medium. Once the mature phages have been released from the dead cell, they are free to infect more healthy bacterial cells and so the process goes on. In a culture, the plaque gradually increases in size as more and more cells are infected and killed.

It has recently been established that, at the start of infection, the phage attaches itself to the wall of the bacterial cell. It then injects its nucleic acid into the cell while the protein coat remains outside. During the eclipse phase, the phage nucleic acid controls the synthesis of more phage nucleic acid and protein, which is later assembled into mature phage particles. By the time the cell bursts, as many as 200 new phage particles have been synthesized at the direction of the original particle which entered the cell.

All parts of this process do not take place in the life cycles of all viruses, but it is a useful model for the study of infection. Other types known as *temperate* phages have a special relationship with the bacterial cells they infect. They exist in the cell for many generations without infecting it and without multiplying; only after a considerable time are they stimulated into virulence and cause the bac-

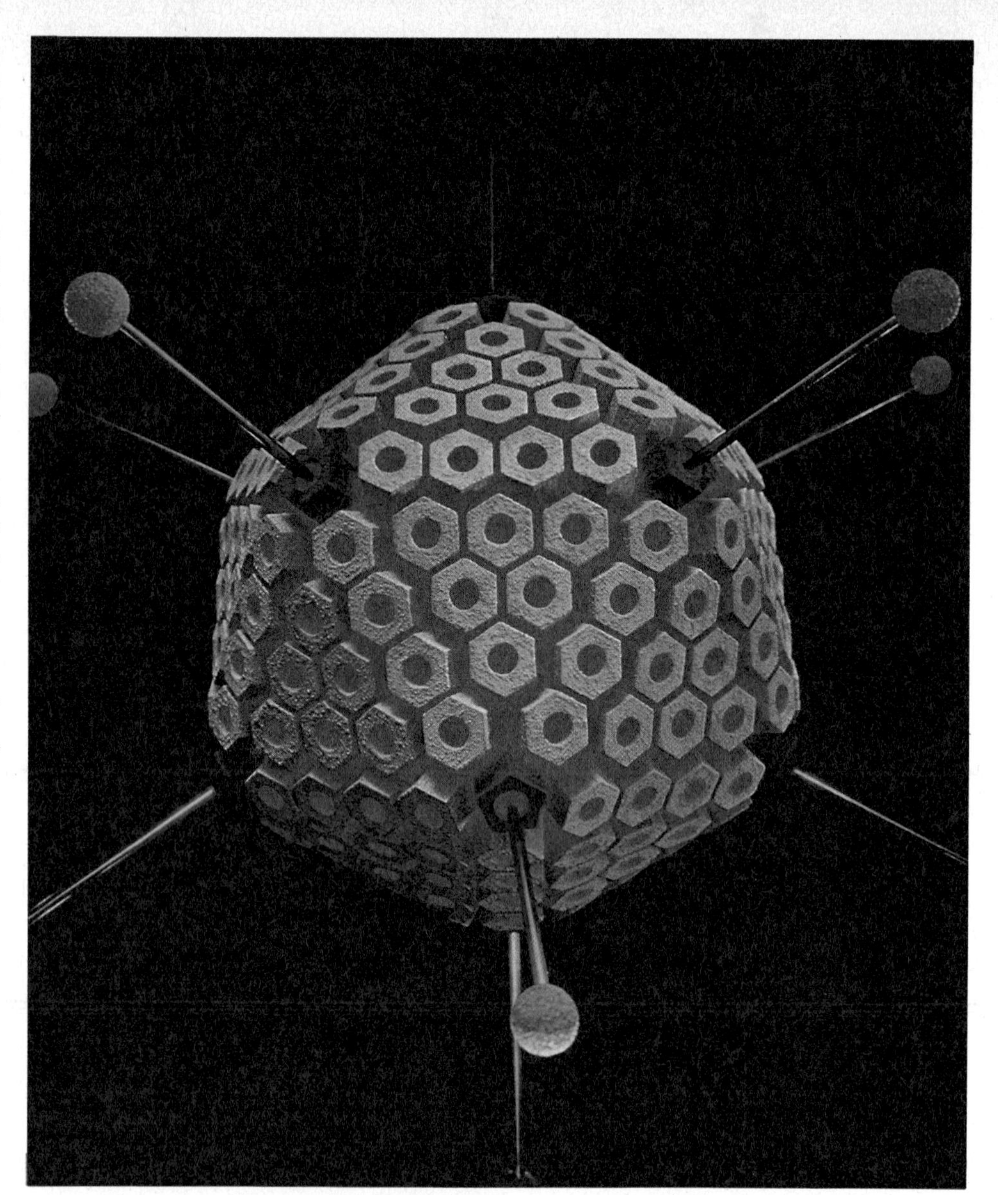

*Top,* model showing what the adenovirus would look like if enlarged 180,000 times. The protein knobs on the 'antennae' are thought to aid the virus attach itself to the tissues it infects.

*Above,* virus particles have three basic shapes, rod-like, spherical, and more complex. But spherical viruses are, in fact, icosahedral (20-faced) solids. Above is a model of a spherical virus particle.

terial cell to undergo the process just described. Animal and plant viruses differ in two important respects from the phage system. Firstly, the whole virion enters the host cell before releasing its nucleic acid, although it is the nucleic acid alone that causes infection. And secondly, these viruses pass from cell to cell without necessarily causing the cells to burst. The degenerative changes which bring about the death of infected animal or plant cells generally occur much later in the course of the disease.

## Protection against viruses

Much was learnt about the chemical and biological properties of viruses in the 50 years following Ivanovsky's discovery. But real advances came only after 1940, when the electron microscope was sufficiently well developed to enable scientists to see viruses and to compare their structures with that deduced from X-ray studies. Electron micrographs show that virus particles have three basic shapes: rod-like, spherical, or more complex, often with tadpole-like or bullet-shaped profiles.

The first virus structure to be determined in detail was that of tobacco mosaic virus, which has a rod-like shape. It is actually a cylinder made from a symmetrical coil of more than 2,000 identical protein molecules. A single strand of RNA about 6,000 molecule units long is embedded inside the cylinder. The protein molecules make up about 95 per cent of the weight of the particle and the nucleic acid molecule makes up the remaining five per cent. Other rod-shaped viruses are known which have different dimensions and more flexibility than tobacco mosaic virus, but there is no reason to suppose that their structures will be much different. There are many examples of plant viruses with rod-like shapes, including potato virus X, tobacco rattle virus, sugar beet yellows, and the soil-borne wheat mosaic. Among rod-shaped animal viruses, the nuclear polyhedroses and granuloses of insects are the best-known examples.

The so-called spherical viruses are not true spheres but are solids with icosahedral symmetry. Once again the protein coat is made up of many identical protein molecules. In the case of turnip yellow mosaic virus, there are 180 chemically identical protein molecules grouped in fives and sixes to produce a particle which has 32 'lumps' on its surface when seen under the electron microscope. The virus which causes cold sores has 162 such lumps, adenovirus (which causes a respiratory disease in man) has 252, and tipula iridescent virus (which causes a disease in the crane fly) has 812. In none of these cases do we know how many protein molecules make up the lumps. The nucleic acid of these viruses must occur within the protein coat, but its exact location is not known.

The third type of structure found for virus particles, the complex, has more variations than do the previous two types. For instance, certain phages have definite head and tail structures. The head is polyhedral with a hexagonal outline, and the tail is cylindrical with protein subunits coiled in a sheath round it. The extreme end of the tail has a plate structure for attachment to the bacterial cell wall and several fibres. Particles of a virus which causes a disease in cattle similar to foot-and-mouth disease, called vesicular stomatitis, are bullet-shaped with one rounded and one square end, containing a central coiled core. The pox viruses, such as cowpox, are brick-shaped, of various sizes, with a dense outer membrane and an inner nucleoprotein core.

In all viruses, the protein coat gives the particle its shape, and surrounds and protects the nucleic acid which contains the genetic code of the virus. The mature virion can be considered to be the extracellular form of the virus in which the delicate nucleic acid is packaged for safe transmission to a new host.

During the course of infection, the virus uses the nucleotides of the host cells to build its own nucleic acid and the protein synthesis system of the host cell to build its own proteins. As a result, the cell becomes depleted of these substances for its own use and serves mainly as an assembly line for the production of new virus particles, up to a million of which may be synthesized per cell. At the present

One of the most fatal and dreaded of virus diseases up to the nineteenth century was smallpox. Then, in 1796, Edward Jenner proved people inoculated with cowpox-infected material would fail to develop smallpox even when directly exposed to it. A contemporary cartoon lampooned the idea.

All viruses are named and classified in terms of the diseases they cause, and what they affect. Thus, the stripes and flecks on the tulip petals *above*, known as flower-breaking, are not natural, but have been produced by the tulip-breaking virus. *Right*, the flower heads of the white clover have turned into bunches of densely clustered leaves – an effect caused by the clover phyllody virus.

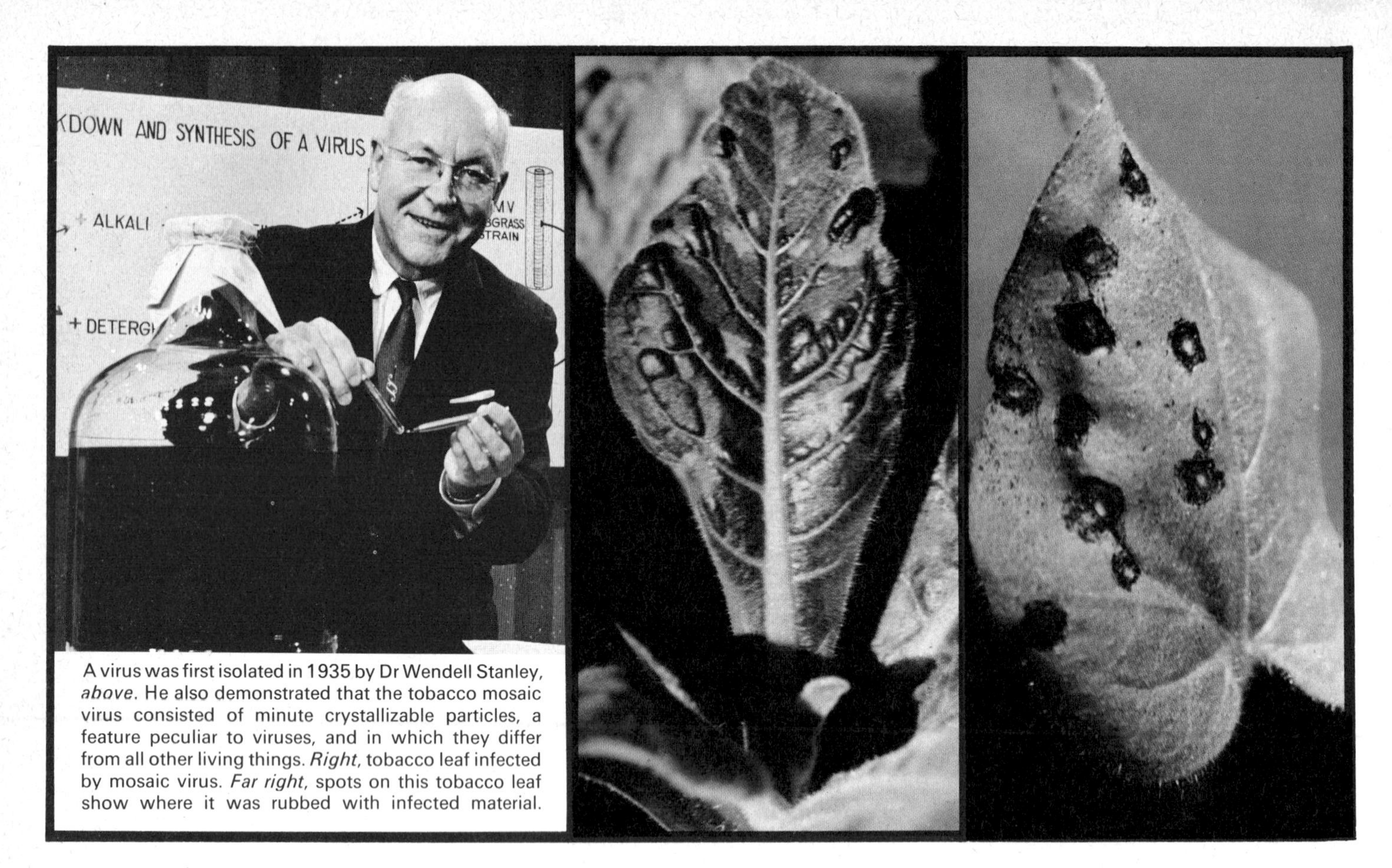


A virus was first isolated in 1935 by Dr Wendell Stanley, *above*. He also demonstrated that the tobacco mosaic virus consisted of minute crystallizable particles, a feature peculiar to viruses, and in which they differ from all other living things. *Right*, tobacco leaf infected by mosaic virus. *Far right*, spots on this tobacco leaf show where it was rubbed with infected material.

time, we know very little of the mechanisms which permit certain viruses to multiply in some organisms but not in others. Nor do we know much about the preferences which viruses have for certain tissues within the organism they infect. For example, the virus which causes poliomyelitis will multiply in the tissue of the alimentary canal in man quite harmlessly; it is only when it multiplies in the spinal-cord tissue that it produces the paralytic disease. The symptoms of a virus disease, therefore, vary according to which tissues have been infected. Chemicals are known which inhibit the synthesis of virus components in the cell, but they are not as selective as antibiotics and they also inhibit the manufacture of protein and nucleic acid in the cell so drastically that they are of no use for treating virus diseases.

Plants have no protective mechanism at all against virus diseases. Although it has been possible experimentally to cure some plants of such diseases, it is not an economic proposition on a wide scale.

Higher animals possess two types of defence mechanisms against virus infections. These are the normal immune response mechanism (by which specific antibody molecules are synthesized to combat any invading disease particle) and the production of a substance called *interferon*. The first mechanism is stimulated in immunization by the introduction of either dead virus particles (as in the Salk polio vaccine) or a mild strain of the virus which multiplies without causing a serious disease (as in the Sabin polio vaccine). Once the system for the synthesis of antibody molecules has been stimulated in this way, the relevant information is held in a memory store and subsequent attacks by the same virus are dealt with more quickly and much more efficiently.

Interferon is a protein which was discovered in 1957. Unlike antibody molecules, it is produced only in response to virus infections and appears to work by specifically interfering with the synthesis of viral components.

## How do viruses arise?

Ever since scientists first discovered viruses and recognized their position at the frontier of life, they have speculated on their origins. But they are really no nearer to solving this problem now than they were 50 years ago. There are three theories at present, but little positive evidence for any of them. One theory suggests that viruses have evolved from the extremely simple cells, such as those of Rickettsia, by adopting extreme parasitism. Another theory is that viruses are indeed parasites, but have really evolved only from the large molecule stage. The third theory is that they may be parts of the cell's genetic elements which have escaped.

Only the last theory has any experimental support. It comes from the fact that certain phages have a close relation with the chromosomes of their bacterial host. When the cell bursts and they are released, they often carry away with them some of the host cell's nucleic acid. If they then infect a healthy cell, the piece of nucleic acid from the first host can be incorporated into the chromosome of the second host and alter its genetic properties. This process is called *transduction* and it may be the original or a coincidental role of phage particles. But no phenomenon like it has been observed among other viruses, and so it seems unlikely that they also evolved by this mechanism.

Three men who have helped unfold the virus mystery. *Left*, Friedrich Leoffler proved some viruses were small enough to pass through a filter's sub-microscopic pores. *Centre*, Professor Beijerinck first demonstrated the existence of a virus, but was unable to contemplate it as living – 'virus' simply means poison. *Right*, Frederick Twort showed viruses occur in bacteria.

# The science behind the cure

By making basic discoveries about natural disease-combating mechanisms, biologists have provided doctors with vaccines, drugs and antibiotics which successfully attack specific diseases.

Chicken eggs provide a good medium for growing certain kinds of virus. The virus can then be used for experimental purposes or to make a vaccine against a specific disease.

DISEASE IS no respecter of persons – it can strike everyone with impartiality. For this reason progress in medicine – of all the areas of science – is perhaps the most directly important to us all.

During this century the fight against disease has been tackled more effectively than ever before and certain diseases are very much on the retreat. A great deal of this success is based upon fundamental work carried out by biologists, who have revealed many of the basic mechanisms of life and, therefore, of disease. As a result new kinds of remedy and preventive treatment have been made possible.

A first and very basic example can be seen in the work of the early organic chemists. These scientists were the first to study systematically the chemistry of living or once living (organic) matter. And their investigations are of the first importance, for here is to be found the clues to the very nature of life.

As a first step it was necessary simply to discover the exact composition of as many as possible of the organic substances (all characterized by their carbon content). One leading scientist, the German, Justus von Liebig, worked out the composition of many such substances during the nineteenth century.

His methods were notable for their elegance and simplicity; an example will suffice to demonstrate both the importance and the limitations of his work. One of the metabolites to be studied was ethyl alcohol, the alcohol present in strong drink and the product of the living process of fermentation in sugar. Liebig took the liquid and burned it, carefully trapping the gaseous products. These he weighed indirectly and so assessed the amounts of the constituent gases present in the original substance. From a knowledge of atomic weights, he was then able to calculate the numbers of each type of atom involved in the individual molecule. For ethyl alcohol, the formula $C_2H_5OH$ emerged.

But this kind of formula, called the *empirical formula,* although an important step in understanding, was of only limited use. For, as analytical methods improved and more and more organic molecules yielded up their secrets, it became obvious that two substances could have identical numbers of atoms of the same elements, yet in the end still have widely different properties.

The notion of *valency* – the number of bonds atoms make when reacting with other atoms – was used to solve this difficulty. Another German, Friedrich Kekulé von Stradonitz suggested that carbon had a valency of four – meaning that it possessed four bonds, some of which could be used to link up either with other carbon atoms or other elements present in the molecule. These bonds did not have to be only single, they could be double and even triple.

The inference of all this was clear. Two substances having the same numbers of atoms of the same element in the molecule could have different properties simply through the atoms being combined in different ways. Certain natural substances such as quinine, digitalis and willow bark were known for their curative properties whether as an anti-malarial, as a cardiac drug or as a soother of pain. The biochemists therefore set out to discover the relevant structural formulae of such substances in order to synthesize them and related compounds of these natural drugs in the laboratory. They also hoped that by modifying the structure of these natural drugs they might be able to enhance the good qualities and possibly remove some of the bad.

Cocaine, for example, is found in the leaves of the coca plant, which was originally native to South America but is now grown extensively in Java. For centuries it was used only as a pleasure-inducing drug, but near the turn of the nineteenth century an American, Carl Koller, discovered that it functioned as a pain deadener and could therefore be used in surgery and dentistry.

## Artificial drugs

There were, and are, however, real drawbacks to natural cocaine: some patients react so strongly against it that death can occur; it is addictive; the molecule is extremely fragile; a process such as heating to kill bacteria can so change cocaine's structure that its pain-killing qualities are destroyed.

Clearly, it was highly desirable to discover an artificial cocaine. The search took 20 years, during which time many substitutes turned up but none as good as novocaine, now widely used. It is stable, easy to make, and is a good anaesthetic with few side effects.

The artificial synthesis of other drugs followed similar lines, but in their voyage of discovery through the organic compounds, the biochemists made many other finds, including the composition and struc-

Louis Pasteur, who lived from 1822 to 1895, is known as the father of microbiology. He discovered that micro-organisms are responsible for fermentation and for causing certain diseases.

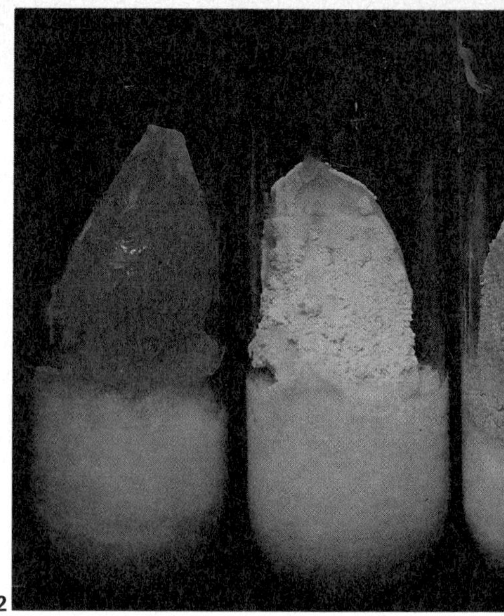

1 The discovery that penicillin – produced by a mould – stopped certain pathogenic organisms from growing led to a new era in medicine. Disease could now be controlled by antibiotics.
2 Many other micro-organisms besides that responsible for penicillin have been cultured in an attempt to find new powerful antibiotics. Sometimes this search is successful.
3 Before a new drug, food additive or antibiotic can be marketed, it must first be stringently

ture of proteins, one of the body's most important compounds. Indeed, proteins get their name from a Greek word meaning 'of key importance' and their name is well chosen. Some, called enzymes, act as catalysts in the vast number of reactions continually occuring in the body, while others are structural as, for example, the muscle protein, myosin. The body obtains its supply of proteins from foods such as meat, fish, cheese and eggs. It is now known that lack of protein in the diet can lead to all kinds of disease – at its simplest, impaired growth – both mental and physical – at its worst such terrible diseases as kwashiorkor and marasmus which take a hideous toll of life.

In 1896 the Dutchman, Christian Eijkmann, discovered that the chickens he was using as laboratory animals suddenly sickened and died – struck down by a mysterious paralytic disease. Eventually he discovered that they had been fed on rice from which the husks had been removed, and he considered that here might lie the solution to the mystery. He was right. One group of chickens fed on the husked, or unpolished rice held the disease at bay. Another batch receiving only the polished kind, soon succumbed.

Later, after dissolving this vital substance out of the husks, he found that it consisted of molecules much smaller than the proteins. He also discovered that even in doses of only a few milligrams it was extremely efficient at combating a paralytic disease in human beings known as beri beri. Later the same substance was isolated from yeast and shown to be an amine. Hence it was called *vitamine.* Subsequently, a whole host of such trace substances vitally necessary for health were discovered. These were given letters of the alphabet to differentiate them (they run from A to K), but since some were found not to be amines at all, the final *e* was dropped from the name and they became vitamins.

Having worked out the structural formulae of these important substances the biochemists were then able to synthesize them. Most of the vitamins are now synthetically made and can be taken as drops or pills, like, for example, vitamin C – the ascorbic acid of fruit.

## Regulating hormones

Along with the discoveries concerning proteins, enzymes, vitamins and mineral trace elements, biologists have also examined another group of body substances, which are quite as important in their way. These are the hormones – the regulators of metabolism. Thus the pancreas, a large digestive gland, secretes the hormone insulin which in turn controls the amount of glucose in the blood. When insufficient insulin is produced by the body, sugar accumulates in the circulatory system causing diabetes. Nowadays a doctor can treat this once killing disease simply by injecting insulin. Other hormones have similarly important functions in the body, although in some cases the exact way in which they work has still to be discovered.

All of medicine depends basically on a knowledge of the human body – the shape and interrelationships between the various organs. The father of modern anatomy, was the Belgian, Andreas Vesalius, who completed his great book, *Concerning the Structure of the Human Body,* in the sixteenth century.

His work greatly influenced the British experimental physician, William Harvey, who showed that the blood was pumped from the left side of the heart through the arteries, capillaries and veins to the right side of the heart. His description of the mechanics of blood movement was important not only to the surgeon but to medical men in general. It suggested a means by which oxygen, chemicals and some kinds of disease could be carried

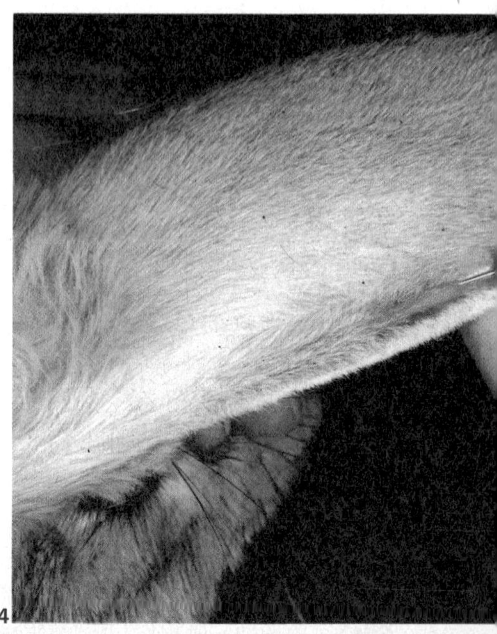

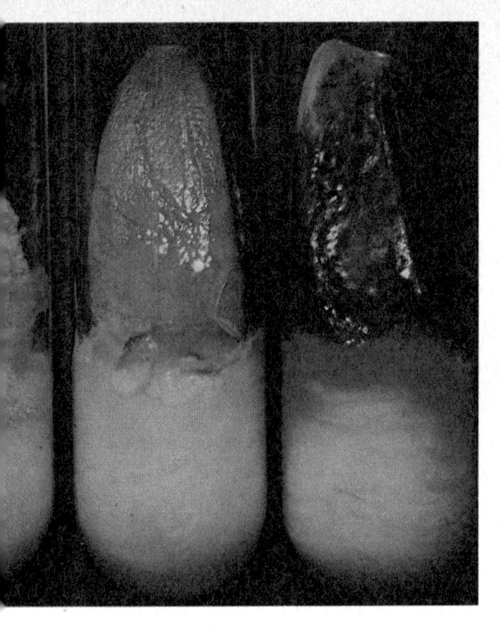

tested. Even small doses must not cause deformities to animal foeti such as these rats.
**4** By injecting a specific antigen into a rabbit the immunologist causes the animal to make counteracting antibodies. These are then isolated from the serum and used in experiments.
**5** Without anaesthesia, surgery could not have progressed, but experiments had first to be made on animals. Here Henry Hickman tests the effect of carbon dioxide on a dog.

about the body.

The confirmation of Harvey's work in part depended on the development of the microscope as a scientific tool. This revealed structural details at an even more basic level including the cell, the basic unit of all living matter.

It was Louis Pasteur, the French chemist (1822–95), who first linked the single-celled micro-organisms with the incidence of certain kinds of disease and founded the science of bacteriology or microbiology.

He and others then set about identifying the specific bacteria responsible for these diseases, and worked at methods of combating them. In 1865, the English surgeon, Joseph Lister, began to use carbolic acid, a powerful antiseptic, on surgical dress-

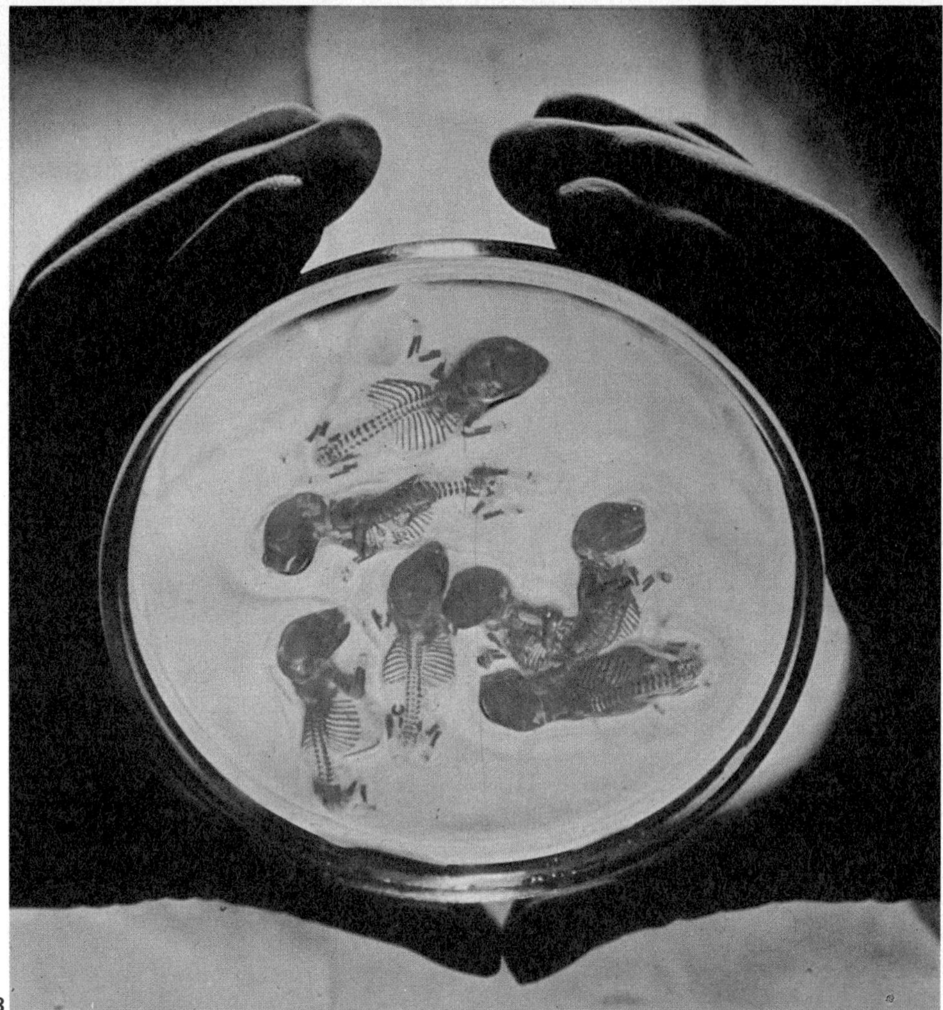

3

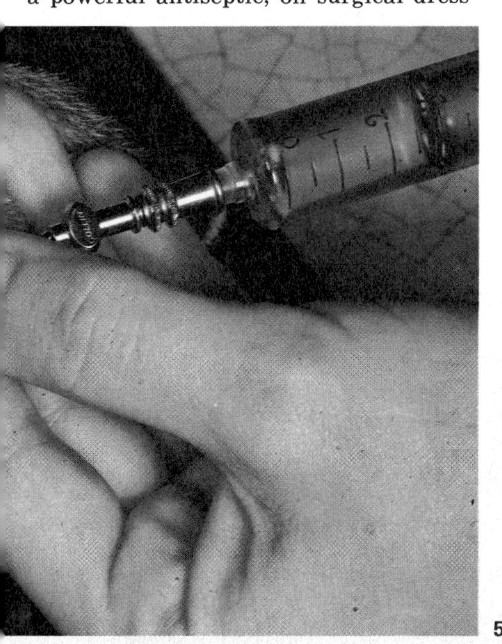

5

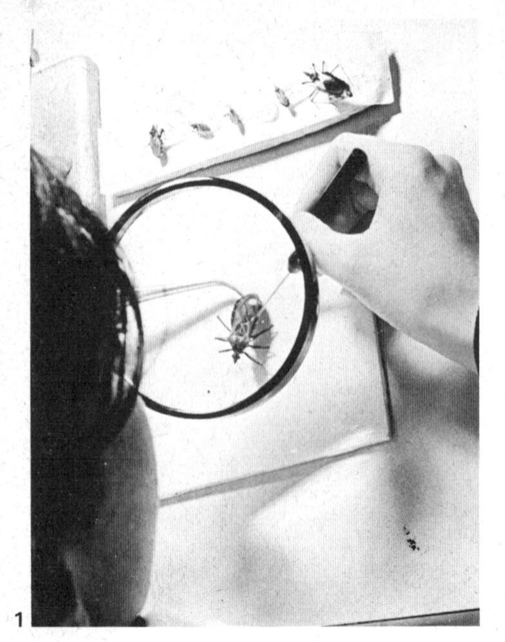

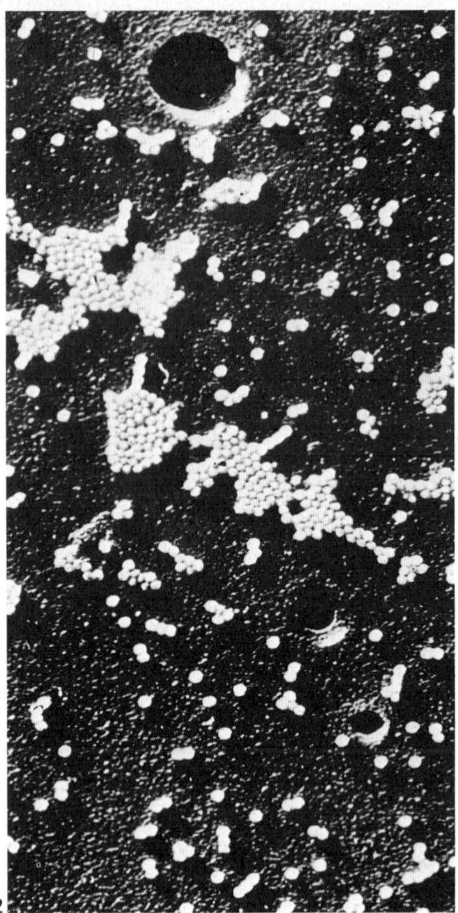

ings, and later caused it to be sprayed into the air of the operating theatre. Again, Pasteur induced surgeons to sterilize their instruments by boiling, and their dressings by steaming. Later still, antiseptics much milder in their effects than carbolic acid were found, one of which was iodine.

As year followed year, the biologists isolated the bacteria responsible for more and more diseases. And once these organisms, the cause of diseases like anthrax, tuberculosis, cholera, diphtheria and so on, were recognized, the search for chemical antidotes began.

An early and important step forward in chemotherapy came as a result of the investigation of certain dyes as possible bactericides. For example, the German Paul Ehrlich discovered one dye (Trypan red), when administered to patients suffering from sleeping sickness, would kill the trypanosomes responsible for the disease. He also synthesized many arsenical compounds to see if any of them might have therapeutic qualities. He tried out many hundreds but it was only on the six hundred and sixth attempt that he achieved what he had set out to do. In 1909 one of his students tested this arsenical compound and found that, although it was useless against sleeping sickness, it was deadly to the syphilis bacterium. They called this substance 606 'Salvarsan', or safe arsenic.

More than 20 years later, another red dye, called Prontosil, was discovered to have therapeutic qualities. The German scientist and Nobel prize winner, Gerhard Domagk, injected it into his daughter who was dying of streptococcal blood poisoning. Her life was saved. The effective fragment of the Prontosil was pinpointed as being sulfanilamide, and it became the first of the 'wonder drugs'. Subsequently a whole host of similar substances emerged, to be known collectively as the 'sulfa drugs'.

These were effective against a wide range of bacteria and were widely used, but even so their eminence was shortlived. An even more important group of drugs was waiting in the wings, the antibiotics.

For years, the biologists had wondered at the sparsity of infectious germs in

**1** Many tropical diseases, such as malaria and sleeping sickness, are spread by insects. The rhodnius bug spreads trypanosomiasis, a debilitating, often fatal, disease.

**2** Viruses are far too small to be seen with the naked eye or the light microscope. But the poliomyelitis virus – one of the smallest viruses – is seen clearly with the electron microscope.

**3** One task of the microbiologist is to select the best strain of a mould to use for antibiotic production. Here a strain of *Cephalosporin-C* – which produces the antibiotic Ceporin – is examined.

common soil – a fact that remained so although all living matter eventually decomposes and returns to the soil, taking most of its ailments with it. The biologists reasoned that the soil harboured some organisms or substances which were deadly to most germs.

In 1939 the soil organism *Bacillus brevis* was found to contain two compounds, gramocidin and tyrocidin, which would kill bacteria. These were, in fact, the first antibiotics to be produced for specifically medical purposes, but ten years before, the British bacteriologist, Alexander Fleming, had accidentally made a discovery of even wider importance. He had stumbled upon penicillin.

## Antibiotics

When purified and produced in commercial quantities during the early years of the Second World War, penicillin saved countless lives and has continued to do so ever since. Other antibiotics have followed in its wake, adding even more power to the physician's elbow. Thus streptomycin combats stomach and intestinal infections and tuberculosis; the aureo-, chloro- and terra-mycins work against ailments such as whooping cough and pneumonia.

However, bacteria are by no means the only organisms which invade the human body. Viruses are a most important group of pathogenic organisms and they are basically difficult to treat. Thus a chemical which will disrupt the working of a virus-infected cell will also upset healthy cells.

A different approach is needed, one which lies within the realm of the immunologist. Very simply, this consists of boosting the resistance of the body to infection by causing it to produce substances (antibodies) which are harmful to specific viruses. Such substances occur naturally whenever a foreign body enters the system, but illness will ensue if the antibodies are not strong enough to resist the invasion. When dead or weakened viruses are introduced into the body – a process called *vaccination* – the body reacts against these by synthesizing its own antibodies. It can now use these antibodies when challenged by the virus causing the disease against which the person has been vaccinated. Among the diseases which have proved tractable to this kind of treatment, are poliomyelitis, smallpox, measles and even influenza.

Even so, the battle against viruses in general is by no means over. Viruses change their structure, or *mutate,* with apparent ease, and the antibody which is effective against one strain may be useless against another. It is for this reason that new strains of influenza virus, for example, are able to spread with such rapidity all over the world, in spite of the efforts of the doctors who are constantly searching for new and more effective antibodies.

Finally, it is not only with virus infection that the immunologist is concerned. He is also at work on the fundamental problems of transplant surgery. Just as with viruses, the body also attempts to reject foreign organs such as heart, lungs and kidneys. Such success that has so far been achieved has resulted from the use of X-rays or drugs, like azathiprene, which suppress the immune response. However, real success still awaits the discovery of new or improved techniques by the immunologists.

# Tracing the pathways of life

Radioisotopes have become a most important tool in biology. Because of their radioactivity, they can be easily used by biologists to trace the intricate details of the metabolic pathways of life.

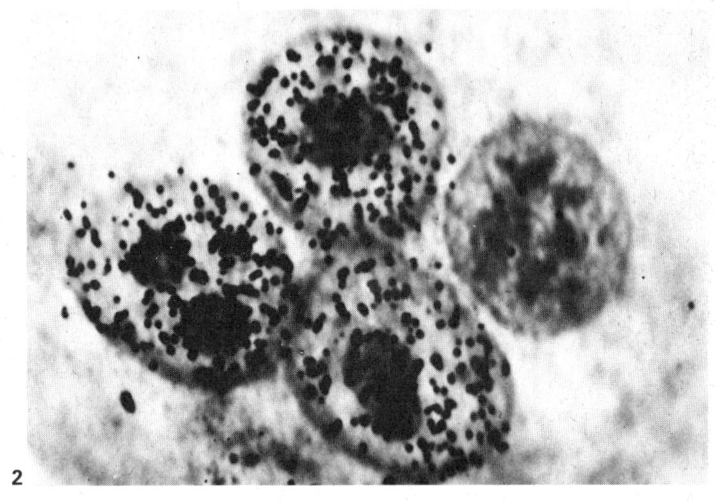

**1** Many isotopes are highly radioactive and they have to be handled with great care. By keeping them in special chambers and using gloves the technician can handle them with impunity.

**2** By labelling thymidine – one of the building blocks of DNA – with tritium, a radioactive isotope of hydrogen, biologists can follow the synthesis of DNA. The black spots indicate activity.

**3** Keeping a white rat in a special metabolic glass cage ensures that biologists are protected from radioactivity when performing experiments involving radioactive substances.

**4** The radioisotope phosphorus-32 is carried to only the living parts of the leaves of this eucalyptus seedling. The dead areas show up black and can accordingly be assessed.

SINCE 1945 biology has undergone a revolution – there is no other way of describing the progress that biologists have made in understanding the fundamental processes of living organisms. Biologists are talking about the new biology – the biology of molecules – to distinguish modern research and ideas from those of the 1940s. Ideas of biology have changed as much since the end of the Second World War as they did in the decades immediately after the theory of evolution was put forward in 1858–9. But it is not only the ideas and principles of biology that have changed, the experimental methods and the apparatus – the tools of the trade – have changed as well, keeping pace with, and generating the new ideas. Obviously it is not always helpful to think of brilliant new ideas if the tools needed to test them are not available or likely to be developed in the foreseeable future. Biology is above all an experimental science; the theory and the experiments or observations go hand in hand. The invention or the development of a technique stimulates the biologist to ask new questions which before he had to ignore because the answers seemed beyond the reach of his apparatus.

The radioactive isotope is by far one of the most powerful of all the new tools that have been developed since the 1940s. When the atom was split in the 1930s and foundations of nuclear physics laid, the way was paved not only for atomic power stations, the atom bomb and nuclear-powered engines but, what is less widely realized, they also provided biologists with an entirely new experimental approach. Radioactive isotopes have changed the whole emphasis of biological and biochemical research. A huge international industry has been developed to supply biologists with their isotopes and probably no more intensive effort has gone into any other form of instrumentation than that of detecting isotopes and radioactivity.

To understand what isotopes are, it is necessary to discuss the structure of the atom because isotopes are different atomic forms of the same chemical element. Atomic physicists now talk in a very complicated mathematical language which is meaningless to most other scientists. But there is a simple physical description of the atom, known as the *Rutherford Bohr* model, which satisfies the biologist, who is more interested in using atoms than understanding them. The Rutherford Bohr model pictures the atom as a solar system in miniature. Each atom has a central nucleus which accounts for virtually all the atom's mass and this is surrounded by clouds, or shells of orbiting electrons. By analogy with the solar system the sun would be the nucleus, the planets the electrons.

The nucleus itself is formed from two of Nature's fundamental building blocks, protons and neutrons. These two particles have the same mass but the proton carries a positive electric charge whereas the neutron, as its name suggests, has no charge and is electrically neutral. The diameter of the atomic nucleus, its cluster of protons and neutrons, is only about 1/100,000 the diameter of the orbits of the electrons, each of which has a negligible mass but carries a negative charge. The entire atom is vanishingly small, measured in ten millionths of a millimetre and, because in every atom there are always equal numbers of protons and electrons, the atom as a whole is electrically neutral.

The chemical properties of atoms depend on the numbers of charged protons and electrons that they possess but they can also exist in more than one atomic form. Each form or *isotope* has the same number of electrons and protons but a different number of neutrons. For example, hydrogen, the simplest element of all, can exist in three isotopes: normal hydrogen with one electron and one proton; deuterium with a proton and neutron and one electron; and tritium with a proton, two neutrons and an electron. All the isotopes of an element have the same chemical properties because they have the same number of protons and electrons but they have different masses and different stabilities because of the varying number of neutrons in the nucleus. Some combinations of a fixed number of protons with different numbers of neutrons, in other words, some isotopes, are inherently less stable than others. Stable isotopes, apart from those which form the bulk of the natural compounds on Earth, have their uses in biology but it is the unstable isotopes, that are radioactive, which have had the most impact in recent years on biological experimentation.

The nucleus of every isotope of every element is, to some extent, unstable, but most atoms in Nature disintegrate very slowly, otherwise the whole world would become so radioactive that all life would be killed. Each atomic isotope of every element has a characteristic probability or chance of disintegrating although it may not happen for billions of years. A convenient way to describe the rate at which disintegration occurs is in terms of the *half-life*. That is the time it takes for half a population of atoms of any isotope to disintegrate. The half-lives of isotopes can range from fractions of a second to millions of millions of years; when an atomic nucleus eventually disintegrates it emits radioactivity.

Physicists have distinguished several types of radioactive disintegration but the most important in biological research is that called *β-decay*. β-decay is the imposing name for a simple process, the emission from the atomic nucleus of either an electron or a positively charged particle, called a *positron,* which has the same minute mass as an electron but a positive instead of a negative electrical charge. This radioactivity, the β-decay, can be detected with sensitive instruments and so the radioactivity labels or traces any particular atomic isotope. This is crucially important for the biologist. It means he can feed a plant or animal with molecules, some of the atoms of which are radioactive isotopes. He can then follow the fate of

1

**1** The composition of the gases absorbed and given out by a plant can be followed using radioactive isotopes. Such experiments indicate the extent of photosynthesis and respiration.

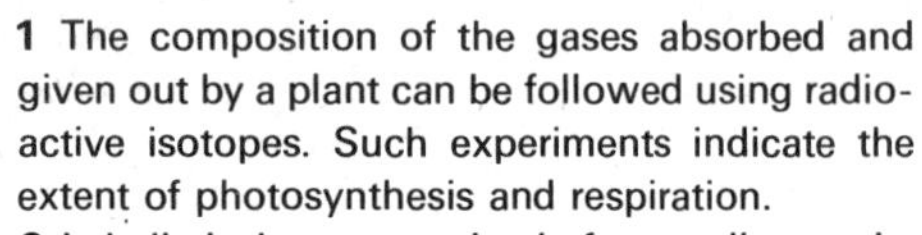

**2** Labelled glass ampoules before sealing under vacuum in the organic laboratory of a radiochemical centre in Britain where radioisotopes are produced.

**3** The United Kingdom Atomic Energy Authority manufactures a wide range of substances containing radioactive isotopes. These compounds are used by biologists throughout the world.

**4** Held in position at the end of a glass tube by suction, a single drop of radioactive insecticide solution is applied to a green fly during research into pest control.

**5** Using a Geiger-Müller counter a biologist can measure the radioactivity emitted from various parts of a plant after adding an isotopically labelled substance to the soil.

**6** By injecting a radioactive metabolite into a wild silkmoth biologists can trace what happens to the metabolite. Such research can lead to the discovery of new insecticides.

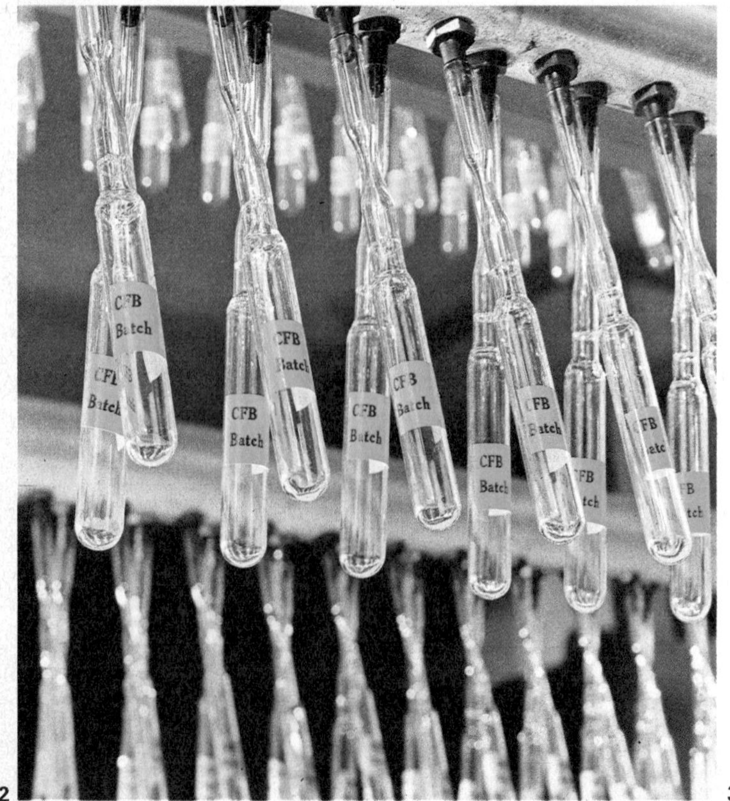


2

3

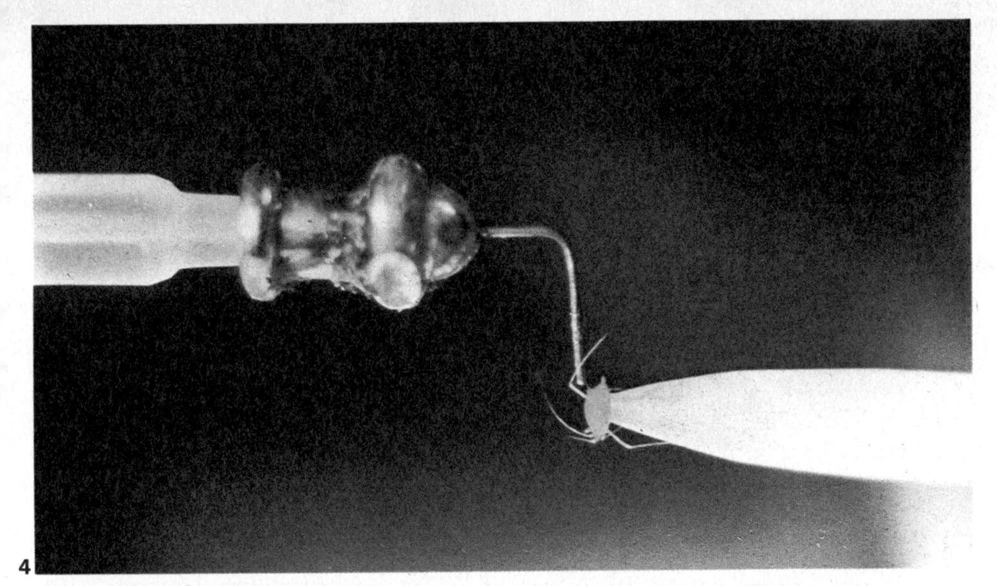

4

5

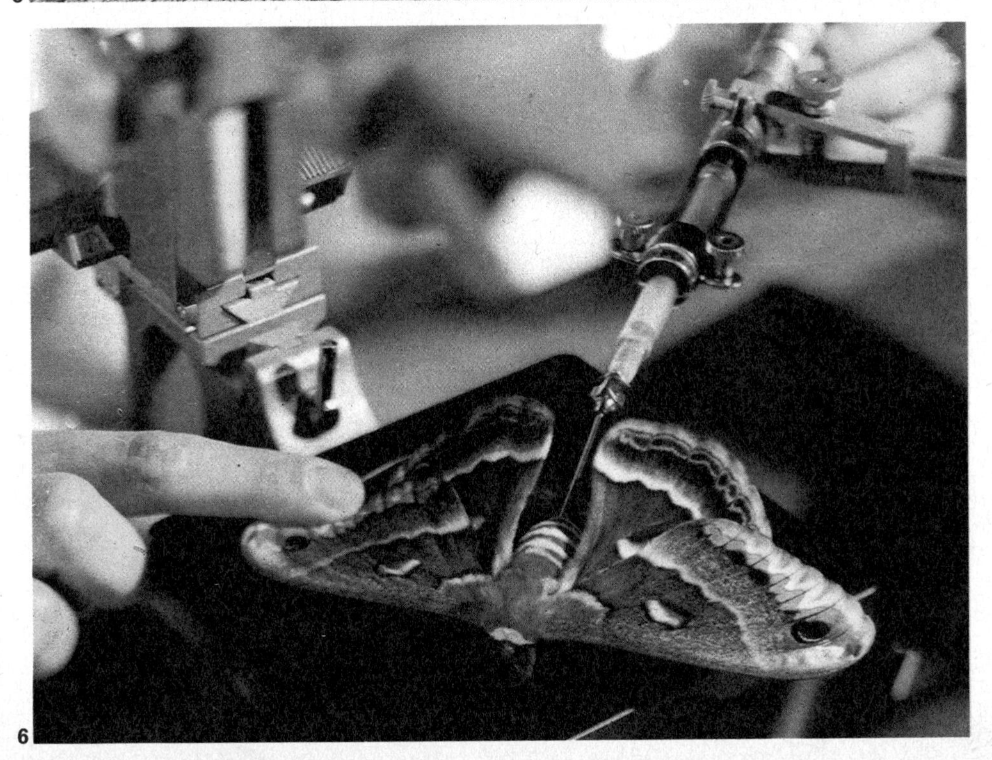

6

that molecule in the living organism – the way in which it is burned up to provide energy or incorporated into the living substance of the organism – by following the movement of radioactivity about the organism. The radioactive isotope allows the biologist to mark and follow a few molecules amongst the millions in an organism. He can study one process out of the thousands going on simultaneously; it is like being able to follow exactly the movements of one person during the rush hour of a city.

How are these marked atoms, the isotopes of the various elements, produced? Many chemical elements always occur in Nature as a mixture of isotopic forms. Usually these natural mixtures contain only traces of the less stable isotope but they can still be fractionated because the masses of isotopes differ. These mass differences in absolute terms are infinitesimally small – only the weight of one or a few neutrons – so that separation of natural mixtures is an extremely costly and very difficult business.

Natural uranium, for example, consists of about 99·3 per cent of the stable non-radioactive isotope uranium-238 and only 0·7 per cent of uranium-235, the radioactive isotope used in power stations and atom bombs. Uranium-235 can be concentrated and eventually obtained pure by gas diffusion or, now, by very high speed centrifugation because it sediments more slowly and diffuses more quickly than uranium-238. Isotopes of the lighter elements, such as hydrogen, can be separated by chemical exchange, distillation and electrolysis. But all these processes involve endless recycling and consume vast amounts of power.

## Made to order

In practice most of the radioactive isotopes used by biologists as tracers are manufactured to order in nuclear reactors. In Britain the Atomic Energy Authority has a radiochemicals division especially equipped to do nothing else. In the nuclear reactors the nuclei of stable isotopes of various elements are bombarded with beams of atomic particle 'bullets' – beams of neutrons, protons or electrons. The target nuclei capture a particle and then undergo changes which yield the required isotope.

The nuclear reactions which yield isotopes important in biology all begin with the same initial step – the capture by the target nucleus of a neutron. After this common step the reactions fall into three groups. In the simplest type of reaction a stable nucleus captures a neutron and so becomes one mass unit heavier. Spare energy is radiated away and the product is a radioactive isotope of the target element. Radioactive sodium-24, widely used in tracer studies of the blood, is made in this way by bombarding sodium-23 with neutrons.

In the second type of reaction the elements are *transmuted*. Stable atoms of one element capture a neutron in the reactor; this makes them unstable so they re-emit a proton. The exchange of a proton for a neutron in the atomic nucleus is the transmutation of one element into another because the chemical properties of the atom depend on the number of protons and electrons, the charge particles. In other words, the original atom becomes an isotope of a different element. For example, a radioactive isotope of phosphorus, phosphorus-32 which, like the radioisotopes of carbon and hydrogen, has proved to be one of the most important isotopes in biology, is made when stable atoms of sulphur-32 capture a neutron and lose a proton. The nuclei of sulphur-32 and phosphorus-32 have the same mass, the same total of protons and neutrons but a different ratio of protons to neutrons.

The third type of reaction which yields isotopes is more complex. The target nucleus captures a neutron and then undergoes a more drastic change, splitting to yield one or more isotopes of a lighter element. Radioactive iodine-131 is made in this way from the metal tellurium.

Isotopes are only useful tools for research so long as the radioactivity they emit can be measured accurately, quickly and easily. This problem of measuring radioactivity has been the subject of intensive research both in the laboratory and in industry. The stimulus for all this effort has not simply been to help biologists. Detection of radioactivity is of national and international importance in a world dominated by nuclear weapons.

Measurement of radioactivity is dominated by two processes, ionization and excitation. When an electron or positron is emitted as an isotope decays it sooner or later hits matter, some other atom, and transfers its energy to the absorbing matter. This becomes more energetic, or is excited, as a result and this forms the basis of radioactive counting. Some absorbing materials re-emit this extra energy as flashes of visible light and the number of these flashes can be detected or counted by a light-sensitive device. Radioactivity counters which work on this principle are called *scintillation counters*.

The other common type of counter is the Geiger-Müller or Geiger counter and works on a different principle. In it the charged particles, electrons or positrons, emitted when an isotope disintegrates, are accelerated to very high speeds in strong electric fields. This means that when they collide with another atom, for example an atom of a gas, they transfer so much energy to the absorbing atom that it becomes electrically charged or ionized. In the strong electric field these ions in turn accelerate and collide into other atoms. The process is repeated in a chain reaction and the net result is that an electrical current is generated which can be measured.

No counter is absolutely efficient and not all isotopes are equally 'hot'. Some emit radioactivity of high energy, others emit comparatively low-energy radioactivity which is harder to detect. For the biologist, low-energy radioactivity has the advantage that it does not kill organisms. He selects the best isotope and the most suitable counter for his experiment and armed with the appropriate isotope and counter he can now measure radioactivity as easily as he can accurately weigh a solid or measure a liquid.

## Low-energy radiation

The three most important radioactive isotopes in biology are carbon-14 which has two more neutrons than normal carbon-12, tritium or hydrogen-3 which has one proton and two neutrons instead of the single proton of normal hydrogen, and phosphorus-32 which has one more neutron than phosphorus-31. The half-lives of these three, the time it takes for half of any sample to decay, are respectively 5,000 years, 12·25 years and 15 days – all long enough to allow experiments to be made, although compounds labelled with phosphorus-32 cannot be stored for more than a few days. All three isotopes emit radioactivity with enough energy to be detected easily but, so long as the dose is regulated, not enough to kill organisms. These three isotopes are by no means the only ones used by biologists. Sulphur-35, iron-55 and 59, sodium-22 and 24 and iodine-131 are all in use.

A great many experiments involve the use of isotopes in one way or another. By labelling carbon dioxide with carbon-14 biologists have been able to follow the steps in the process by which green plants convert carbon dioxide and water into sugar using the sun's energy, and the reverse process in which sugars are burnt up as food.

The way in which proteins are assembled from their molecular building blocks is now being determined in detail in laboratories throughout the world, all using isotopes. Likewise the way in which DNA, the genetic material which determines heredity, manages to replicate itself, is being tracked down with isotopes. Indeed the whole of the new biology stems from isotope tracer work.

Even the stable non-radioactive isotopes are becoming grist to the biologists' mill. Work in the United States with a stable isotope of nitrogen, nitrogen-15, has proved the way in which new DNA molecules are divided between the two cells that result from one at cell division. With isotopes, in particular radioisotopes, biochemists have elucidated in detail the highly complicated biochemical reactions and pathways that make up the basic metabolism of living organisms. Respiration – the essential process which enables plants and animals alike to live – involves a multitude of different reactions. These reactions are all interdependent and, like all biochemical reactions in living organisms, can only take place in the presence of enzymes.

By labelling the starting chemical of respiration – in other words a sugar such as glucose – with carbon-14, the biochemist can follow through the step by step conversion of this substance to carbon dioxide and water. During the complex of reactions energy is given out in the form of special high-energy chemical bonds – the high-energy phosphate bond of ATP (adenosine triphosphate). This transfer of energy – essential to all biochemical processes in the body – has also been followed using radioisotopes such as phosphorus-32.

By elucidating the basic biochemistry of cells biochemists have made great strides in understanding what happens when the biochemical processes become deranged as during certain types of disease. This knowledge has led to the discovery of many of the drugs that are now used to combat disease as well as those which effect the complex chemical reactions controlling growth.

A single drop of radioactive insecticide is added to the leaf of a young tomato plant. Studies are in progress to see what effect the insecticide has on the plant itself.

Nucleic acids – the components of DNA – are required more and more by biologists for use in research. Here nucleic acids labelled with carbon-14 are being purified.

# Life at a simple level

Near the bottom of the scale in the animal world stand the protozoans and multicells, simple yet diverse organisms. They are the first stage in the development of true animals.

WHATEVER SIZE a living organism may be, it must carry out all those activities which enable it to continue its existence. Food must be taken in and used for energy production and building the materials of the body, while the waste must be disposed of. To do this animals move about and react to stimuli, seeking food and going from one favourable spot to another. In addition to these activities which affect the individual, the species has to be perpetuated by reproduction. With a complicated body composed of many cells, it may be comparatively simple for special parts of the body to be set aside for carrying out these functions, but what if the animal or plant consists of one cell only?

Protozoa are animals of this sort. Each one is a single cell. Within this cell must be carried out all the physiological functions which are necessary for life – and, indeed, whose presence makes us define the cell as a living thing. This complexity must be on a molecular level, not a cellular one. If we take distribution in many kinds of habitat as evidence of success, then the protozoa are a highly successful group. They are to be found in fresh water and in the sea, living on the surfaces of other animals and inside them. But like all the lower animals, they can exist only where they can be wet, for they have no defence against loss of water from the body. Once in air they face death by dehydration.

## Spots of living jelly

Probably the most famous protozoan animal is *Amoeba,* whose fame comes from the popular belief that it is a simple spot of jelly something like the first living things. But this is a misconception. Amoeba is a highly complex animal, although at first sight this is not obvious. It has a body composed of one cell with a single nucleus, just as any living cell has. The cytoplasm in which the nucleus lies is not a simple jelly, it is divided into a clear region, the *ectoplasm,* on the outside and a granular *endoplasm* within. Among the granules of many shapes and sizes are, for example, the *mitochondria,* in which energy is released from sugar in the cell.

Both feeding and movement are connected in this animal. When it moves it thrusts out a *pseudopodium* in the direction in which it will move. This is a finger-like protrusion of the body. Slowly, all the granular endoplasm flows into it, transferring the animal from one place to another. Some kinds of Amoeba seem to have a hind-end which is part of the cell specialized in some unknown way and which follows on in any movement of the whole animal.

A number of theories have been put forward to account for this amoeboid movement. What ever is going on concerns the molecules which make up the substance of the animal. Perhaps, as one theory suggests, the endoplasm contains parallel straight protein molecules. At the 'front' these become folded up, thus drawing the rest of the body forward to them as they contract in length. The completely folded molecules pass back again to the rear, as they form a tube around the folding molecules and the straight ones behind them. On reaching the 'tail', they unfold to move forward in the endoplasm once again. But the flow is not as simple as this, for it has been noticed that the pseudopodia are not in contact with the ground along their length, but are raised

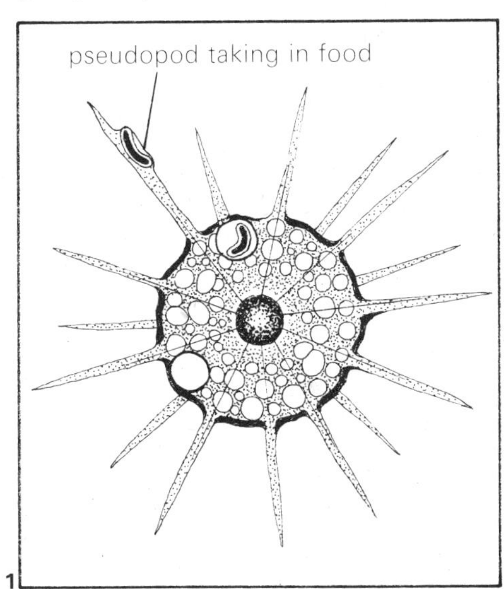


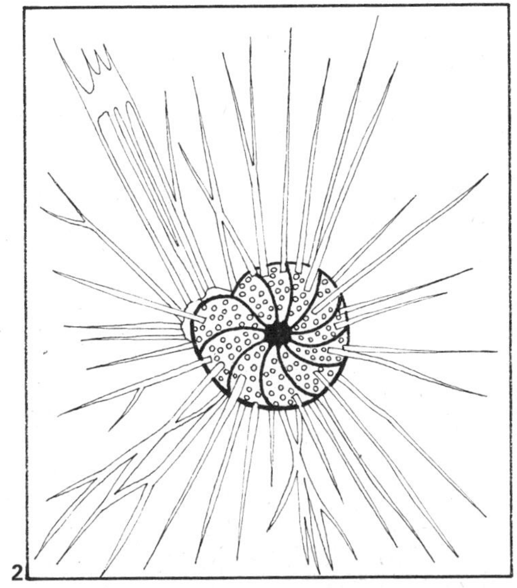

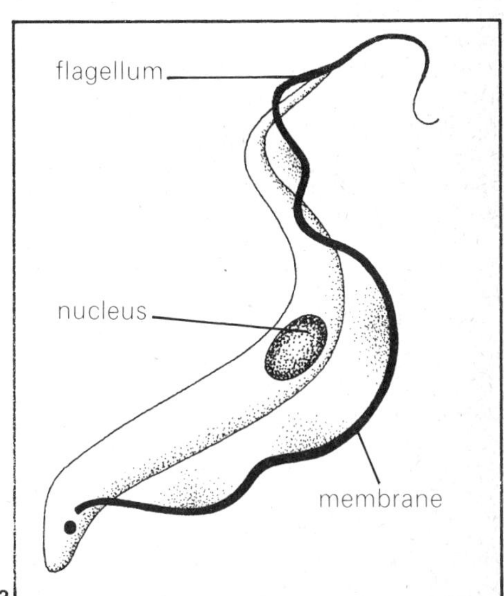


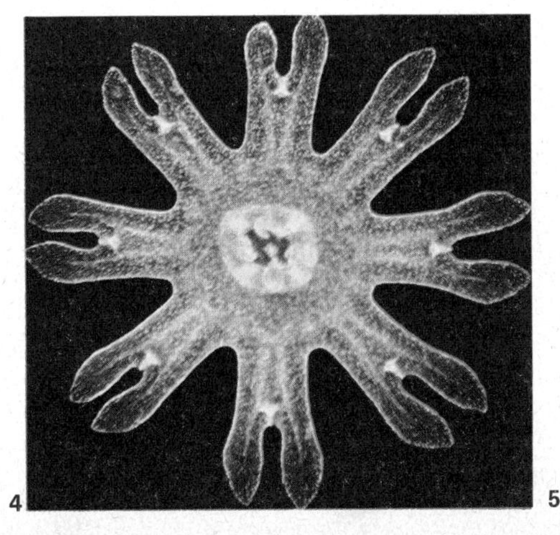

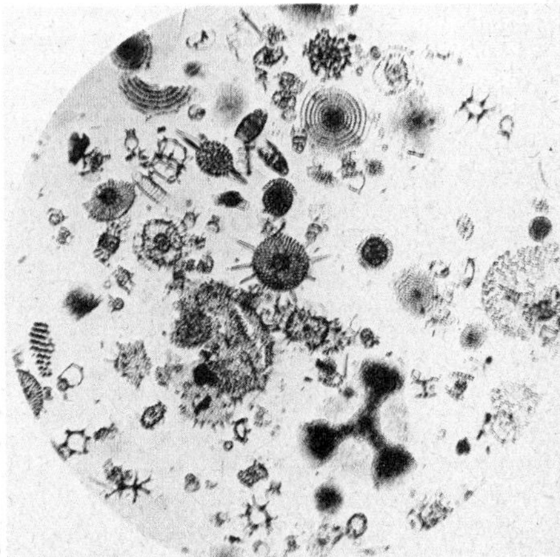

1 *Actinophrys sol* is a common Heliozoan, which is a fresh-water protozoan. The radiating pseudopods are used for taking in food, several of them working together when the object is large.

2 *Foraminifers* are common in sea water and have a chalky shell. Deposits of these protozoans have formed the chalk cliffs at Dover and the chalk beds in Mississippi and Georgia.

3 *Trypanosomes* are parasitic in both Man and animals. They are transmitted by the tsetse fly, and cause African sleeping sickness.

4 A top view of a young jellyfish shows the eight lobes containing the sense organs and the central mouth.

5 Radiolarian ooze covers vast areas on the floors of tropical seas. The individual organisms are clear when magnified.

on strut-like projections. There is still much to be learned about this apparently simple behaviour.

When it is feeding, Amoeba thrusts out its body around a diatom or some other food particle, forming a hollow like the intucked finger of a glove. This closes over, engulfing the diatom in a spherical vacuole, the food vacuole in which it is digested by enzymes poured into it by the surrounding cytoplasm.

The pseudopodia of its relatives the *Heliozoa*, found in fresh water, are long and thin. They are supported by firm rods. These animals move by rolling along on these spiky pseudopodia. When the lower ones retract they start the movement in a particular direction which is continued as, successively, neighbouring ones on the same side shorten.

## Simple yet complex

The *Radiolaria* and *Foraminifera* have skeletons, either of calcium carbonate (in Foraminifera) or silica (in Radiolaria). Outside the skeletons the cytoplasm forms a mass of finely branched pseudopodia on which food is captured. The dead skeletons rain down through the water to form radiolarian and foraminiferous oozes which are characteristic deposits on the sea bed in certain parts of the world. All these animals belong to the Sarcodina.

If Amoeba is deceptively simple in appearance, many of the ciliate protozoa look as complex as they are. Their complexity increases as we view them with the higher and higher magnifications which are possible with the electron microscope. Most of them move rapidly about by means of their *cilia* which are tiny whip-like threads. Within each is a characteristic arrangement of fibres found wherever there are cilia in the animal world. A pair of fibrils run up the centre and nine pairs are arranged around the outer part of the cilium. These must be the cause of the cilium's movement, though they are so small that there is so far little knowledge about how they produce their typical pattern of movement, but it is possible that some process not unlike that in human muscle is causing them to move.

The cilia which cover the body are grouped in pairs in some species (*Paramecium aurelia)* or singly in others *(P. bursaria)*, in small pits of a lattice-work formed in the outer layer of the cell. On the ridges of the lattice are *trichocysts*, flask-shaped objects which can discharge a fine thread which allows the animal to anchor itself as it feeds. These may also have a defensive function.

These common ciliates, the species of *Paramecium*, will be found along with many others in almost any pond. The body of the animal is slipper-shaped, with a deep trough on one side which forms a gullet. This is lined with cilia arranged rather differently from those which cover the body. The cilia in the gullet beat so that food, usually bacteria and the like, are moved down it to the small area at the end where these food particles are absorbed in the body to form food vacuoles.

The structural complexity of Paramecium, paralleled in many other ciliates, is a good example of the possibilities that are available for making a variety of structures even at a molecular level. Cilia, trichocysts, surface lattice and so forth are all contained within the bounds of a single unit; they are built up of thousands upon thousands of molecules, not hundreds of cells as the skin and muscles of a rat are.

Another large group of protozoa are those which have *flagella* rather than cilia, and which for this reason are called *Mastigophora*. Flagella are almost identical with cilia, but they are much longer. Instead of whipping to and fro, like a cilium, a flagellum moves like a snake, waves passing along it either from base to tip or vice versa. The waves press against the water and move the organism. Some of the Mastigophora are plant-like, and can produce their own food from simple substances by photosynthesis. They have one or two flagella each. But other types, generally similar to these, may be parasitic, living in the fluids somewhere in another animal's body. For Man, some of the most important of these are the *trypanosomes*. These are organisms living in the blood of human beings which cause sleeping sickness, a disease which rendered large areas of Africa uninhabitable in the past. Other close relatives cause *Kala-azar* and oriental sore, serious and common diseases in the tropics: though the use of new drugs usually means that they are no longer fatal.

The phases of the life cycle of the malaria parasite are shown in relation to the body-temperature of a malaria patient. The upper diagram shows the cycle in the mosquito.

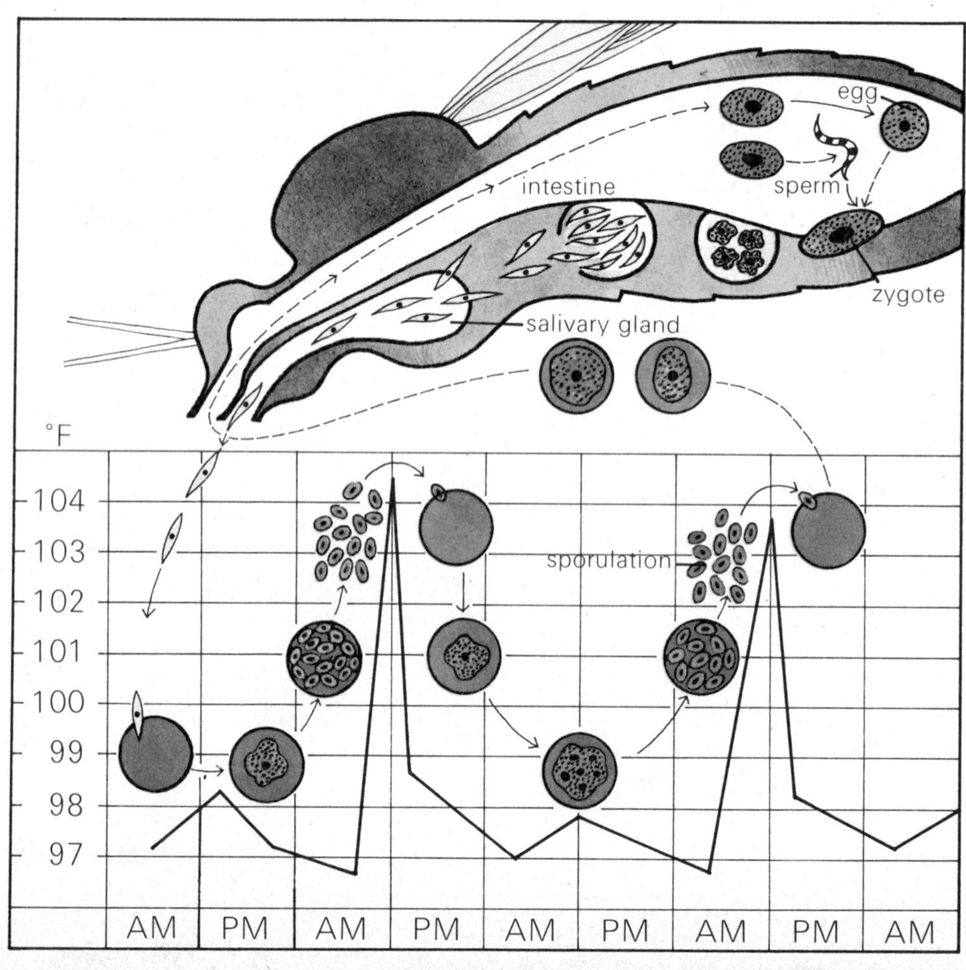


Others cause *nagana*, a wasting disease which made it impossible to keep cattle in parts of Africa. Most of these trypanosomes are carried by biting insects; the tsetse flies of Africa which carry sleeping sickness and nagana are good examples.

## Parasites

Other Mastigophora live as partners rather than parasites in the gut of some insects, such as termites. These forms have very many flagella and quite a complicated body plan, though as with ciliates, all this is in one cell. Their role is to digest pieces of cellulose – the wood on which wood-eating termites feed. Unable to digest it with their own enzymes, the termites depend on the protozoa breaking down the cellulose for them. If the protozoa are removed, the termites die.

Most groups of animals have members which are parasites, and protozoa are no exception. In addition to parasitic Sarcodina and Mastigophora, a whole subdivision of the protozoa, the Sporozoa, are parasitic. Many invertebrate animals, like insects or marine worms, have them in their gut or elsewhere in their bodies. One of these is the malarial parasite *Plasmodium* which lives in the red blood cells and in liver cells of Man. They are passed from person to person by mosquitoes which infect human beings through the wounds they make before they begin to suck blood. The parasite has a complicated life-history, reproducing in the insect as well as in men. Another parasite, *Eimeria*, lives in the gut of birds and causes a serious disease of game birds being bred for sport. Similarly, *coccidiosis* is a gut infection of domestic chickens

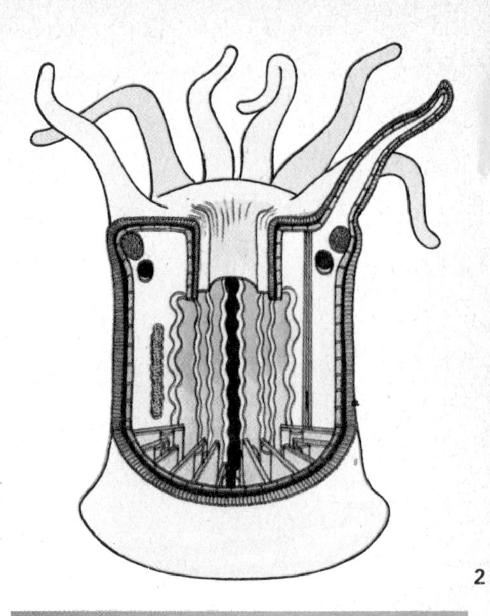

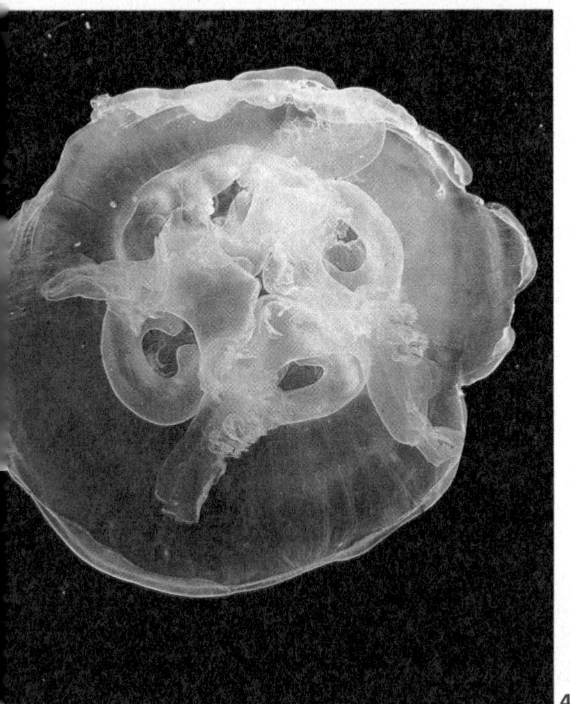

**1** Sea-anemones such as this dahlia anemone derive their name from their resemblance to land flowers. The mouth can be seen in the centre of the animal.
**2** The vertical division of the gastrovascular cavity in the anemone is revealed by a vertical section. The gullet and cavity are surrounded by a strong muscular body.
**3** Corals are the remains of *zoantharians,* and form colonies such as this brain coral in tropical seas. They form hard reefs which are capable of severely damaging the steel hull of a ship.
**4** Creatures like this moon jellyfish are often found in the pools left by the outgoing tide. The jelly within the animal consists in the main of water with amoeba cells suspended inside.
**5** *Eunicella* is a coral colony which uses the feathery tentacles to catch food which is then distributed among the members.

which can cause great damage in poultry farms.

Some of the single-celled plants form colonies with characteristic shapes, such as the round ball of *Volvox*, but this rarely happens in protozoa. Nevertheless, sponges *(Porifera)* look very much like a slightly later stage of this process of coming together to form a body.

The common bath sponge is the skeleton of a living sponge. The living tissue has been dried off in the tropical sun by the people who dived down to collect the sponges from the sea bottom. Not all sponges have skeletons which are leathery like the fibres of a bath sponge. Some have pointed spicules of silica or calcium carbonate embedded in the living material.

But whatever the skeleton may be like, the living cells are quite simple. They are of two main kinds. The outside of sponges is coated by flat covering cells through which are holes opening into the chambers within. (The numerous holes through the surface of sponges gives them their Latin name which means 'hole-bearers'.) The second type of cell lines these chambers; they are the *collar cells* used in feeding. Like a Mastigophoran, each has a single flagellum whose beat causes water to move past it. Food particles in the water get caught on the collar and carried down to the main part of the cell.

Though sponges look very highly organized, in fact each cell is to a large extent independent of the others. There are no nerve cells, for example, connecting the parts of the body of the sponge together; there is no blood system to carry food and other things about the body. Most important, the cells do not join together to form tissues.

## Specialized tissue

When cells are grouped into tissues they become specialized to carry out one main function, they can no longer do everything as a protozoan does. A group of muscle cells can contract but they cannot digest food, so they depend for their food on a supply of sugar brought to them by the blood-stream. But with this loss of some functions comes greater efficiency in doing one; the whole cell can be committed to the one activity.

The sea-anemones, corals and jellyfish are representatives of a group of animals, the *Coelenterates,* which have begun to move in this direction. Their bodies are simple, with an essential plan of an open-mouthed sack, the walls of which are formed of two layers of cells, the *ectoderm*

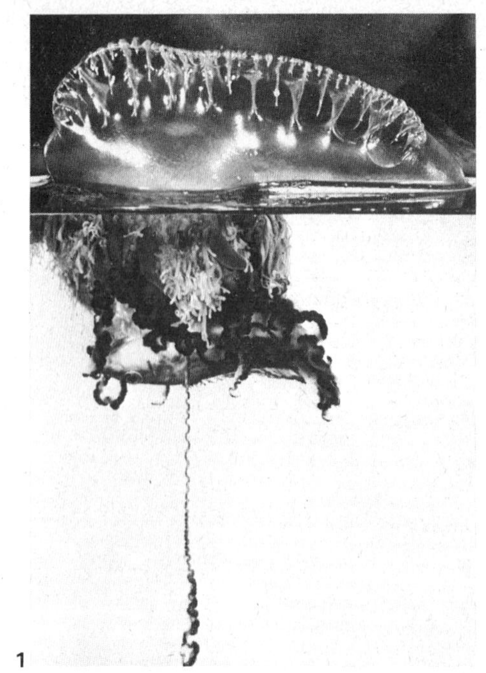

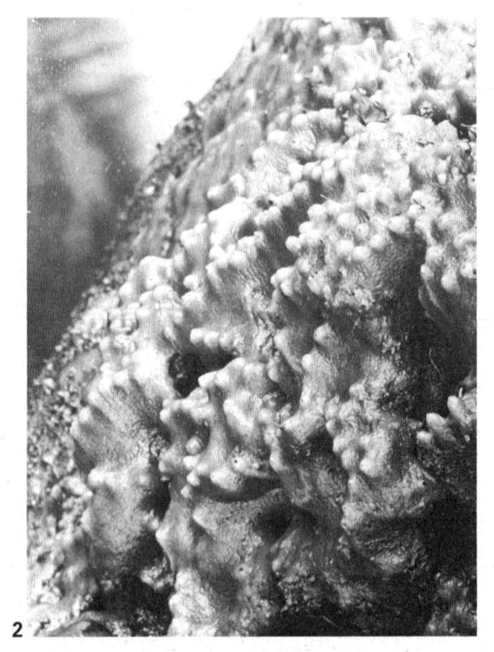

1 This Portuguese Man-of-War has just paralyzed a fish with its sting and is about to ingest it. This is one of the few types of *Physalia* whose sting can be fatal to human beings.

2 The cellular structure of sponges is essential to the taking in of food and oxygen and excretion of waste products.

3 Starting with the simple sponge, this illustration shows three types. In the centre is a more advanced type with a folded wall, while the sponge on the right has a complicated system of canals and chambers.

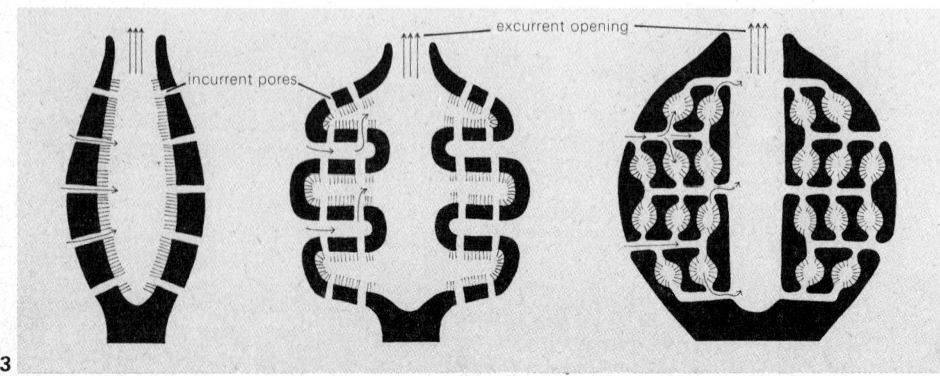


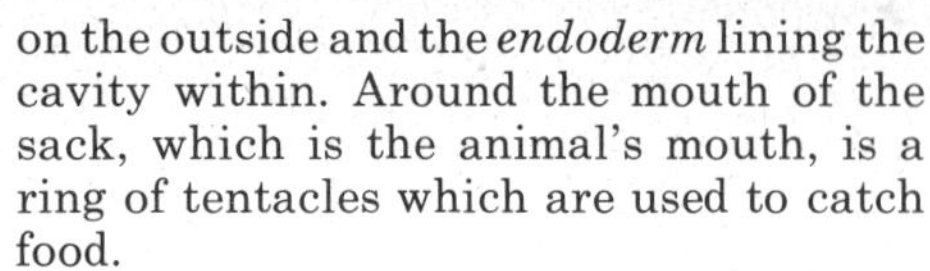

on the outside and the *endoderm* lining the cavity within. Around the mouth of the sack, which is the animal's mouth, is a ring of tentacles which are used to catch food.

Between the two layers of cells is a layer of jelly-like material, the *mesogloea.* In a sea-anemone this is relatively thin, but it is very thick in a jellyfish forming, in fact, the greater part of the bulk of the animal. The coelenterate body plan is reversed in a jellyfish, for the mouth opens downwards, often on the end of a *manubrium* hanging like a clapper in the middle of the underside of the bell.

There is much greater co-ordination in the bodies of coelenterates than there is in a sponge. Nerve cells scattered about on either side of the mesogloea are joined together to form a network on either side of the layer. There are no nerve trunks as there are in higher animals, but nervous impulses spread over the nerve net like ripples from a stone dropped into a pool. However, conduction is faster and easier in certain directions. This enables an anemone, for example, to shrink up and withdraw its tentacles into its mouth when it is touched firmly, or the tentacles to co-operate in catching food and passing it to the mouth.

Some of the cells of the ectoderm and endoderm have bases which are drawn out into *contractile strands.* These are the muscles of a simple coelenterate like the pond-dwelling *Hydra.*

## A lethal sting

Quite characteristic of coelenterates are the *nematocysts.* These are generally found on the tentacles, and each consists of a sack into which is inverted a long thread. Near the tip is a sensitive hair, the *cnidocil.* When the nematocyst discharges, the thread is thrust out turning the right way out as it goes. The threads are of various kinds; they may be long and thin to pierce the prey and inject poison, or coiled, so that they wrap round the spines or hairs of the prey and prevent it from escaping. These nematocysts will discharge when certain chemicals are in the water, or they may be primed by them so that the slightest touch on the cnidocil triggers the weapon off. They are the cause of the unpleasant 'sting' of a jellyfish. In some of the larger coelenterates like the Portuguese Man-of-War the sting may be fatal to a man.

The great coral reefs of the world, so important in warmer seas, are formed by coelenterates. For corals are living animals, often colonies of them, each individual polyp connected to the next by tubes. The stony material of the coral is sometimes laid down in the mesogloea which fill with spicules and so forth; this is the way it is formed in the soft coral *Alcyonaria* or Dead Men's Fingers. But the hard corals form their skeletons of calcium carbonate round them. As the colony grows, so more material is laid down, the living tissue always remaining on the outside. The brain corals (*Madreporine*) make thick mounds of skeleton, each polyp resting in a base whose radiating divisions reflect the arrangement of the animal's body.

# Worms - the beginnings of anatomy

**Although generally considered lowly creatures, worms display the beginnings of the development of a digestive system, a nervous system and the sense organs familiar in higher animals.**

WHEN THE AVERAGE PERSON calls an animal a 'worm', he has usually in his mind a long slimy creature without a very definite head. In all probability he will think of something which is round. But in fact this popular use of the term 'worm' throws together animals which bear only superficial resemblance to each other and which are placed by zoologists in different phyla. At the same time, it frequently ignores the many relatives which do not fit into this general description.

Probably the most familiar worm is the earthworm, a member of the phylum *Annelida*. All the worms grouped under this heading have bodies which are ringed. They represent a level of organization which is considerably greater than that of the *Coelenterates* – the sea-anemones and jellyfish. An indication of this is the relatively active searching life led by the majority of worms, but the real differences lie in the details of their bodies' make-up. Firstly, they have an extra layer of cells in the young state which gives rise to a whole new set of tissues, which no anemone has. As well as an *ectoderm* to cover the body and an *endoderm* to line the gut, they have a middle layer, the *mesoderm*. This can be thought of as taking the place of the jelly layer (*mesogloea*) of the coelenterates. New in an evolutionary sense, this layer is the one which, in every animal which possesses it, forms the muscles and blood system of the adult.

## Specialization of function

Indeed, in these worms, not only are cells grouped together for one function to form tissues, but these tissues are grouped to make organs. The gut of an earthworm has, for example, digestive and absorptive tissue lining it, with muscular tissue outside that, and a covering layer around the whole. Now that the body has increased in complexity, transport of oxygen into the body's cells from outside, of carbon dioxide outwards and of food from the gut to the cells by diffusion alone can no longer be sufficient. A transport system has to carry out all these functions. The blood system serves this purpose, passing round the body and carrying with it these materials so vital to the cells in the tissues. Many annelids have, like Man, haemoglobin in their blood.

In addition to these evolutionary innovations, annelids possess a body cavity – the *coelom*. This appears in the developing worm as a split in the mesoderm which enlarges until, in the adult, it isolates the gut from the body wall. The inner part of the mesoderm forms the muscles of the gut and the outer part forms the massive muscles of the body wall. As this cavity is filled with coelomic fluid, it permits the gut to make the movements necessary to transport food down it independently of the body wall.

These features improve the efficiency of the functioning of the body, but there is yet another factor which aids this – the body is segmented. The rings on the outside reflect divisions within the body. Each segment is to a large extent separated from the next by a muscular *septum* stretching across the coelom from gut to body wall. Within each body division is a set of certain organs which are repeated in each segment throughout the body, so that there are multiple sets of excretory organs, of muscle blocks (the longitudinal muscles stretching from one septum to the next) and of certain blood vessels. In each segment there is a collection of nerve cells (a *ganglion*), connected to those on either side, but with its own set of segmental nerves supplying the skin and organs in its own segment.

Some organs occur in relatively few segments. There are six hearts each of which lies in a segment near the head end. The various organs involved in reproduction are grouped together in another nearby part of the body and occupying six segments. In some other annelids – marine types – very many more segments contain reproductive organs.

Earthworms tend to move in one direction, so that the leading end can be called a head. In fact nerve cells there form a ring of nervous tissue around the gut. On the upper side, this is thickened, showing that there is the beginning of the trend towards forming a brain, typical of animals which have a head-end where sense organs of various sorts are grouped together. The ring of nervous tissue connects beneath the gut with the chain of ganglia which are in the other segments of the body, each joined to its neighbour by a double solid nerve cord.

The movements of an earthworm depend on nervous connections between neighbouring segments. Contraction of the longitudinal muscles of one segment is

1

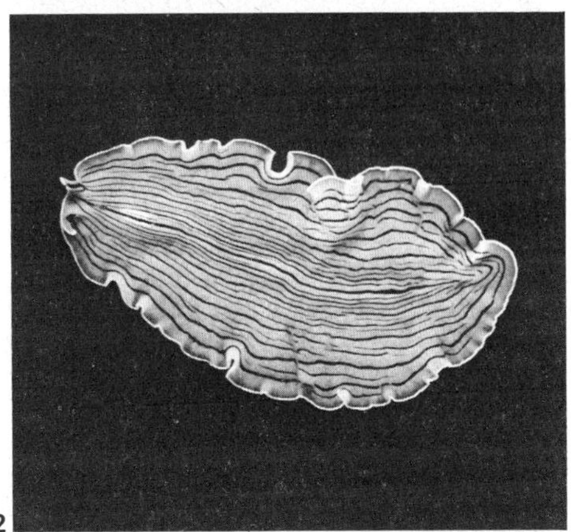
2

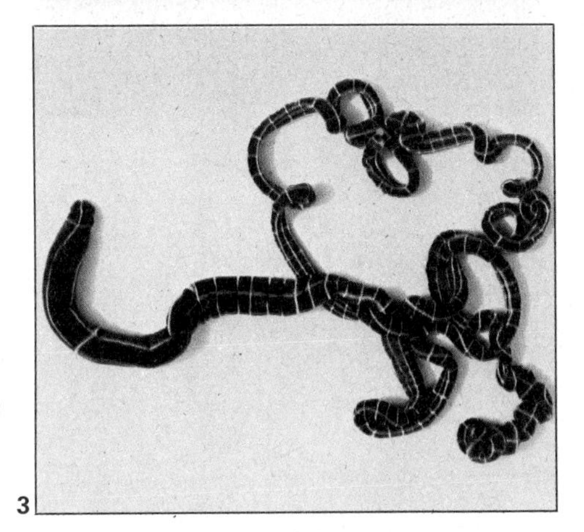
3

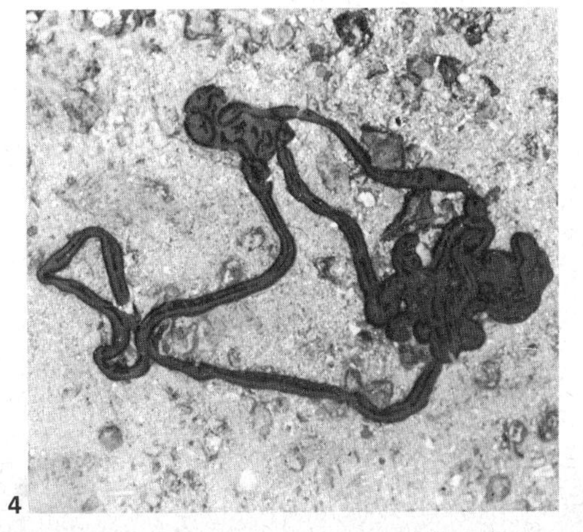
4

**1** Flatworms are found in a variety of habitats. These specimens of *Dendrocoelum lacteum* have been photographed crawling on the underside of a piece of wood.
**2** This polyclad (*Pseudoceros*), black and yellow in colour, is found on rocks or in colonies of animals (*tunicates*) which it feeds on.
**3** An efficient digestive system marks off the ribbon worm, which is a proboscis worm, and is characterized by a long muscular tube which can be projected to catch prey. It also has a fairly efficient sensory system compared with flatworms.
**4** The boot-lace worm (*Lineus longissimus*) takes its name from its shape and its ability to stretch.

followed by a similar contraction in the next segment, so that a wave of contraction passes down the animal. As the fluid in the coelom is incompressible and none can leak out, contraction of the longitudinal muscles causes the worm to fatten. Similarly, when the circular muscles contract down on the tube of fluid the worm must lengthen. Nervous connections ensure that when one kind of muscle contracts, the other relaxes.

Movement is effected by tiny spines, four pairs of which can be thrust out in each segment. These are the *chaetae,* which give their name to this class of animals. Earthworms and their relatives have few chaetae and are thus called *Oligochaetes.* Other annelid worms have many of them and are called *Polychaetes.*

Most polychaetes are marine animals, some swimming freely, others burrowing, living in a tube, or crawling on the sea bed. Like earthworms they are segmented, but each segment has a flap-like extension on either side, the *parapondium.* These are large and act as paddles in swimming worms like the rag-worm *Nereis.*

The lugworm, *Arenicola,* is a good example of a burrowing polychaete. In its habits it is like an earthworm of the shore. It burrows down into the sand, swallowing it and discharging the material in a coiled heap at the tail end of its U-shaped burrow. By moving its body it draws water through the burrow from head to tail, causing a circular depression around the head-end. The water contains oxygen which is absorbed into the worm's body through the surface of tufts of gills in segments of the front part of the body.

Many of the tube-dwelling worms have elaborate heads like those of the Peacock Worm, *Sabella.* This has radiating stiffened tentacles covered with cilia. The beating of these cilia moves food towards the mouth and also supplies the particles used for building the tube. The arrangement of the parapodia is well adapted to holding the animal within the tube. It can retreat into the tube when danger threatens.

Looking, perhaps, unlike relatives of these kinds of worms are the leeches. Despite the fact that they have no chaetae, they are part of the Annelida in a class named the *Hirudinea.* They are segmented, although there are more rings on their bodies than there are segments inside. They live in fresh water and they can be recognized by their two suckers, one around the mouth and the other at the tail.

Other worms have a less complicated body structure than the annelids. One important kind are the flatworms or *Platyhelminthes.* This phylum is unfamiliar because these worms are rarely seen. Some of them are relatively insignificant flatworms, found in ponds and streams. But many others are parasites in Man and other animals.

1

2

**1** Common lugworms (*Arenicola marina*) display their presence on the seashore by their holes and casts.

**2** Differentiation into a head and segmented body is clearly shown in this photograph of *Platynereis dumerili.*

**3** The life cycle of the liver fluke demonstrates that both hosts are essential to the worm. At one time, many sheep died because of infection by the fluke, but the disease has been almost eradicated in Europe and North America.

**4** This worm hides in rock crevices or kelp holdfasts and forages for food with long tentacles. It is brightly luminescent.

**5** The tube-dwelling feather-duster worm is sensitive to light and will withdraw into the tube when a shadow falls on it.

**6** Feathery gills extending from the tube of the peacock worm enable it to breathe, and entangle small organisms for food.

**7** Tapeworms are parasitic in fish as well as in mammals, as this picture shows. The host often wastes away as a result.

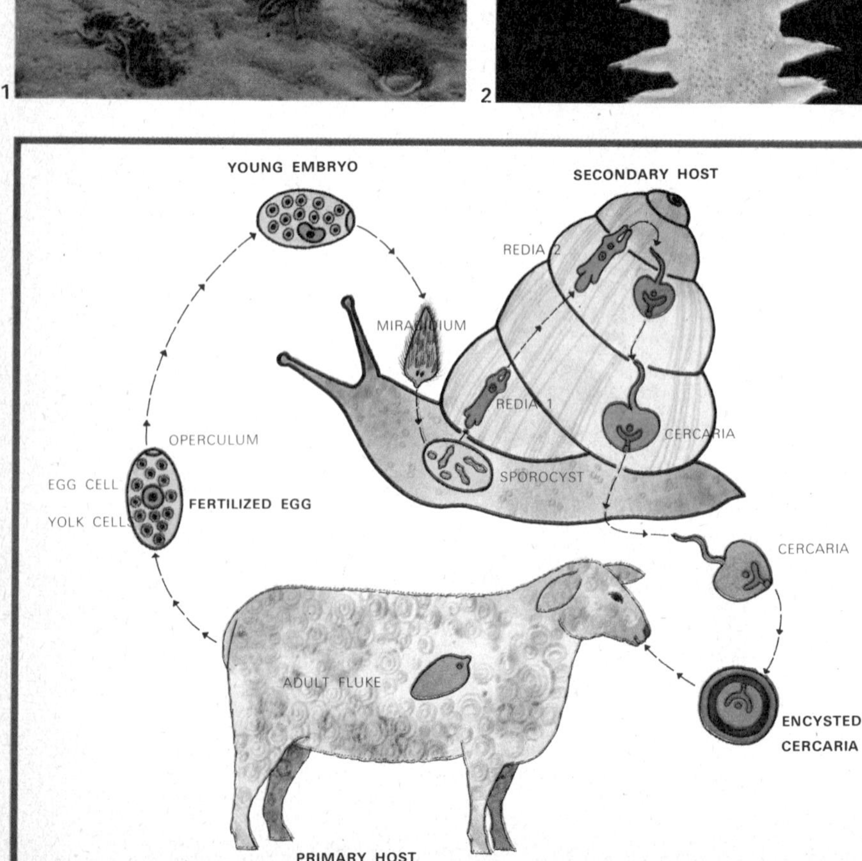


3

4

A planarian worm from a pond is not segmented; indeed this is true of all platyhelminthes. Nor do these worms have such clearly distinctive tissues as an annelid, nor have they coelomic cavities. They have heads with eyes; and although there is a certain amount of concentration of nervous tissues at the head end, the rest of the nervous system is simple. The cells which cover their bodies are ciliated and it is the beating of these which enables the worms to move steadily and apparently effortlessly along the mucus trail which each lays. Although they look like leeches, they can be quickly identified by their lack of suckers.

## Unsegmented worms

*Planaria* have guts which have three main branches, one extending forward and the other two backwards from the point mid-way down the body at which the *proboscis* arises. This proboscis is a muscular tube with the mouth at its tip. It can be moved about until it comes in contact with food, which is then passed into the gut. The animals have no blood systems and the space between the outer covering and the gut is packed with cells. The food diffuses from the branches of the gut directly to the body cells.

A few of these worms are found on land, but always in very moist places. Tropical greenhouses, for example, usually have them. Other close relatives are gutless, the space being filled with cells, and others, living in the sea, have many-branched guts. But, to Man, the most important flatworms are those which are parasitic.

The specialization of a parasite for its life within the tissues of another animal nearly always brings about changes from the body pattern of a free-living close relative. This is certainly true of the parasitic flatworms. The process of change has gone less far among the *Trematodes* (the flukes) which in many ways resemble the free-living *Turbellaria*; it is in the *Cestoda* (the tape-worms) that the greatest change has come about.

The animals in the class *Trematoda* are all flattened in shape and have a gut, although this opens through a mouth at one end of the body and is two-branched; this arrangement is never found in the free-living flatworms. However, the trematodes have suckers by which they fix themselves on to their hosts. Some of them are *ectoparasites,* attaching themselves to the gills of fish. These have elaborate arrangements of suckers which serve this purpose. Others live within their hosts, in the blood or in an organ. They too have suckers; usually one surrounds the mouth while the second is on the underside of the body, about mid-way along its length.

At one time many sheep died because of the liver fluke, a trematode worm which lives in the bile duct of a sheep. Nowadays, however, it is not so easy to find specimens, so infrequent is this worm as a cause of disease or death.

The life-history of the liver fluke illustrates very well how complex a parasite's may become. The eggs are laid by the adult worm in the liver and pass out through the rest of the gut to fall on the ground. A small ciliated *miracidium* hatches from each; this is a simple organism with light-sensitive eyes and little else apart from cells from which new generations of worm will form. If a miracidium encounters a snail as it swims through the film of water on the grass, it penetrates it and turns into a *redia* larva in the snail's body. Each of the redia larvae can bud off new individuals within itself, and each of these in its turn can continue this process, so that there is a great increase in the numbers of offspring which can arise from the original egg.

But after a time, *cercariae* appear; these

5

6

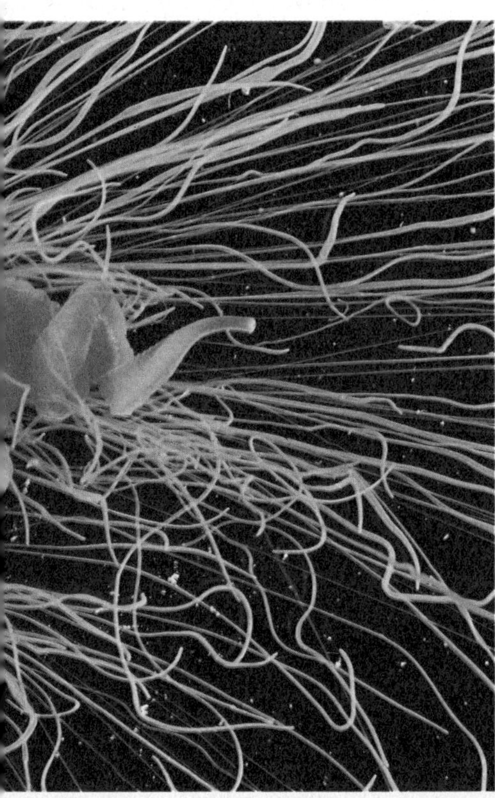
7

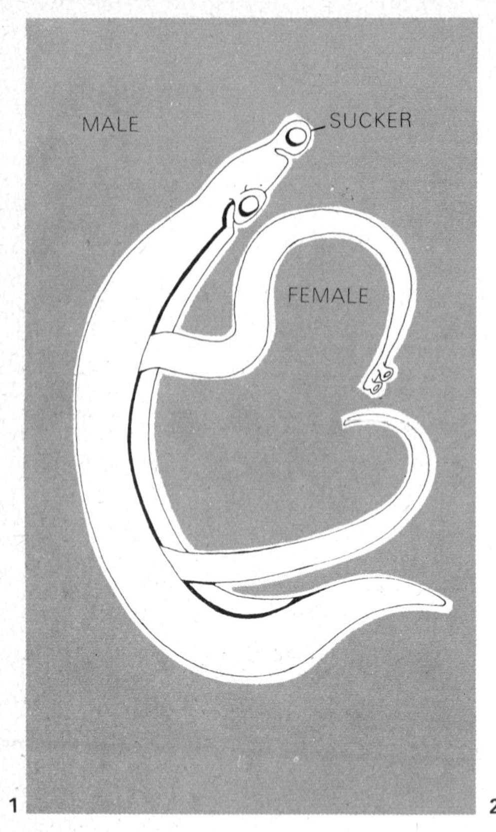


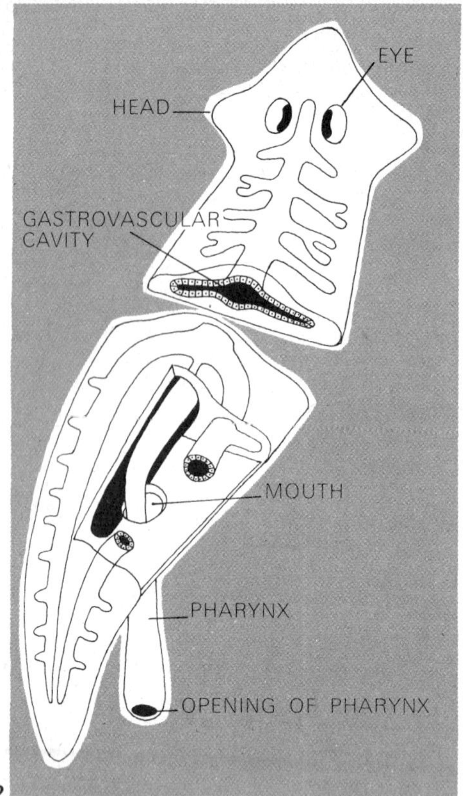


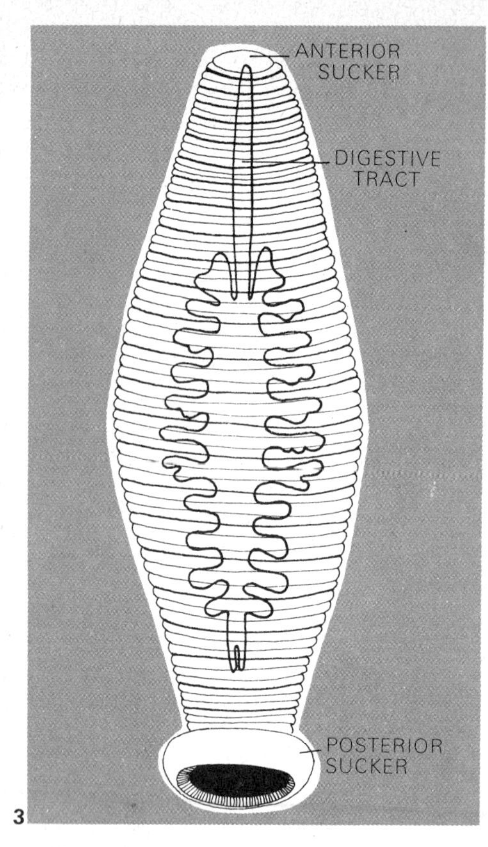


are a different type of larva, able to find their way out of the snail and swim freely using their tails. The cercariae encyst on grass blades. It only requires a sheep to eat this grass for it to become infected when the young fluke breaks out of the cyst and moves into the bile duct. This complicated life-history not only increases the number of larvae, thus increasing their chance of finding a new host, but also distributes them in places where they are likely to encounter a sheep.

## Parasites in Man

Other trematodes are the blood flukes. *Schistosoma,* which causes the disease *bilharzia,* is long and thin, well-shaped for moving about the body through the narrow blood vessels. The male worm clasps a female one in a groove along his body, so that both sexes move about together. The eggs have a sharp spike which they use to burst out of the capillaries into the bladder and are passed out with the urine. They too give rise to larvae which enter snails and multiply there. The cercariae which are finally released can penetrate the skin. For this reason, people in the tropics are advised not to wade in ponds or streams barelegged.

Tape-worms are less like turbellarians, for they have no gut and their nervous systems are very rudimentary. Often their head-ends have special attachment hooks and suckers by which they fix themselves into the wall of their host's gut. From this part of the worm, *proglottids* are budded off. These are not like the segments of an earthworm because they are not intimately connected with each other. Each is an egg-factory, and contains little more than the reproductive system. Proglottids packed with fertilized eggs drop to the ground where the eggs hatch and turn into new worms if they are swallowed by the right animal.

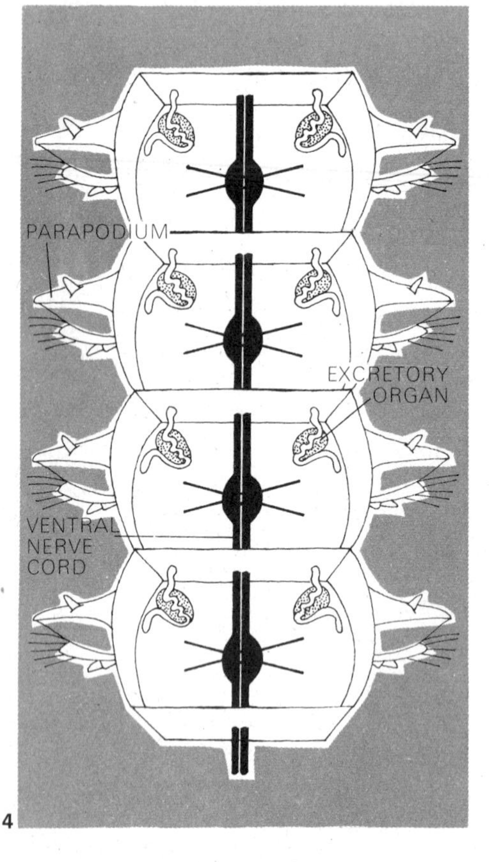


Another serious cause of disease are the roundworms or *Nematoda.* These are mainly small worms, pointed at either end and showing no sign of segmentation. Indeed, like platyhelminthes, they have no coelom. Their muscles, formed of a unique kind of contractile cell, are unlike anything found elsewhere in the animal kingdom. Their guts are simple tubes, straight from mouth to anus. Yet although their structure appears simple, they are a hugely successful group of animals which are found everywhere – even in beer mats. They may be harmless, but many are serious pests. Some, called eelworms, are parasitic on plants and cause them to die, while others live in the intestines or the tissues beneath the skin of Man. Typical of the first are the hookworms, *Ancylostoma,* which infect by penetrating the skin of the foot and moving in the blood to the intestine; and of the second, *Wuchereria* which gather in the lymphatic system, block it and cause the vast swellings typical of elephantiasis.

**1** Human blood flukes like *Schistosoma japonicum* cause a number of diseases such as anaemia and blockage of the bile duct. They are often picked up by eating inadequately cooked food.
**2** The flatworm *Planaria* has the mouth centrally placed instead of at the head. The pharynx, which is attached at only one end, is extended for feeding.
**3** Two suckers and a branched digestive tract are characteristic of the leech. The outside of the body is folded, but not all of these folds correspond with interior segments.
**4** Each segment of an *annelid* worm duplicates organs in the other parts. Only the digestive system shows much differentiation between one part and another.

There are other creatures which people would call 'worms', but they are not common and not often seen. However, sometimes beneath a stone on the shore, a boot-lace worm (*Nemertine*) may be found. These very long and thin worms have probosces which they can shoot out to catch prey. A few species are to be found on land, in moist places as are land planarians. They use their probosces for movement; having shot it out, the tip adheres and the worm pulls itself up to it.

Thus, the layman's term 'worm' covers many kinds of animal, very different in structure and habit. Some are useful, but a great many are dangerous to Man.

# Why the worm turns

**The intriguing and ingenious mechanisms which control the behaviour of primitive animals can provide a clue to the laws which govern the behaviour of higher animals and human beings.**

IN ORDER to survive the changes of any environment animals must be able to react to stimuli. The responses an animal makes are generally designed to protect it from harm, to allow it to reproduce and to maintain it in favourable conditions. The sum of these activities is called the *behaviour* of the animal.

Much of the behaviour of lower organisms like amoeba, sea-anemones and hydra consists of responses to stimuli from the environment that cause the animal to remain in an environment to which it is adapted. This class of behaviour is referred to as *orientating responses.* These responses are divided into two main classes, *kineses* and *taxes.*

Kineses are a form of locomotory behaviour in which there is no orientation of the axes of the body in relation to the source of stimulus. The stimuli eliciting such responses cannot usually guide an animal directly to their source, in the way that a beam of light can. Humidity, pressure and diffuse light are examples of such stimuli. To make responses to such stimuli the animal only requires receptor organs sensitive to variations in stimulus intensity, because it is the gradient of intensity of the stimulus, and not the source, that the animal responds to. There are two types of kineses, *ortho-kinesis* and *klino-kinesis*. In both types movement appears at first to be random, but this is not really the case.

An example of ortho-kinesis is seen in the behaviour of the common woodlouse, *Porcellio scaber*, a small creature that lives in damp areas beneath stones, boards and leaf matter. Woodlice lose water from their bodies fairly rapidly and unless they remain in a humid environment soon die due to desiccation. If woodlice are placed in a situation with a variable humidity they appear to move about in an undirected fashion, but it is found that the speed at which they move depends on the humidity. In dry air they move at a greater speed than in moist air where they may stop altogether. This variation in their speed of movement has the effect of causing the woodlice to spend a greater proportion of their time in moist areas than dry ones.

One of the effects of this behaviour is to cause woodlice to aggregate in damp areas. The way in which this comes about is similar to the way the density of motor cars on a stretch of road often depends on the speed at which the cars can travel. If the cars slow down they tend to come closer together. In the case of the woodlouse this behaviour ensures that the animal remains in the moist environment to which it is adapted. This is done without the necessity of complex sense organs; the act of walking can be thought of as a reflex action in response to dryness. The drier the air the more the animal walks.

In klino-kinesis the speed of locomotion remains constant but the rate at which the animal changes direction depends on the intensity of the stimulus to which it is responding. If a planarian worm is watched it can be seen to change direction every so often as it crawls along. If the light

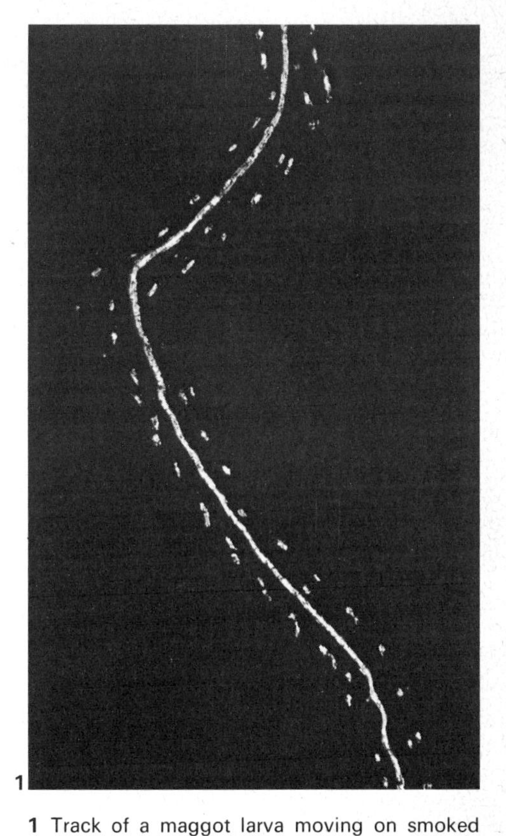

1 Track of a maggot larva moving on smoked paper away from a light source. Note the marks of the side-to-side head movements. The light position was changed during the experiment.
2 'Head' of a maggot larva showing the receptor structures. The progress and side-to-side head movements of a larva, right, in response to a change in light direction (indicated by arrows).

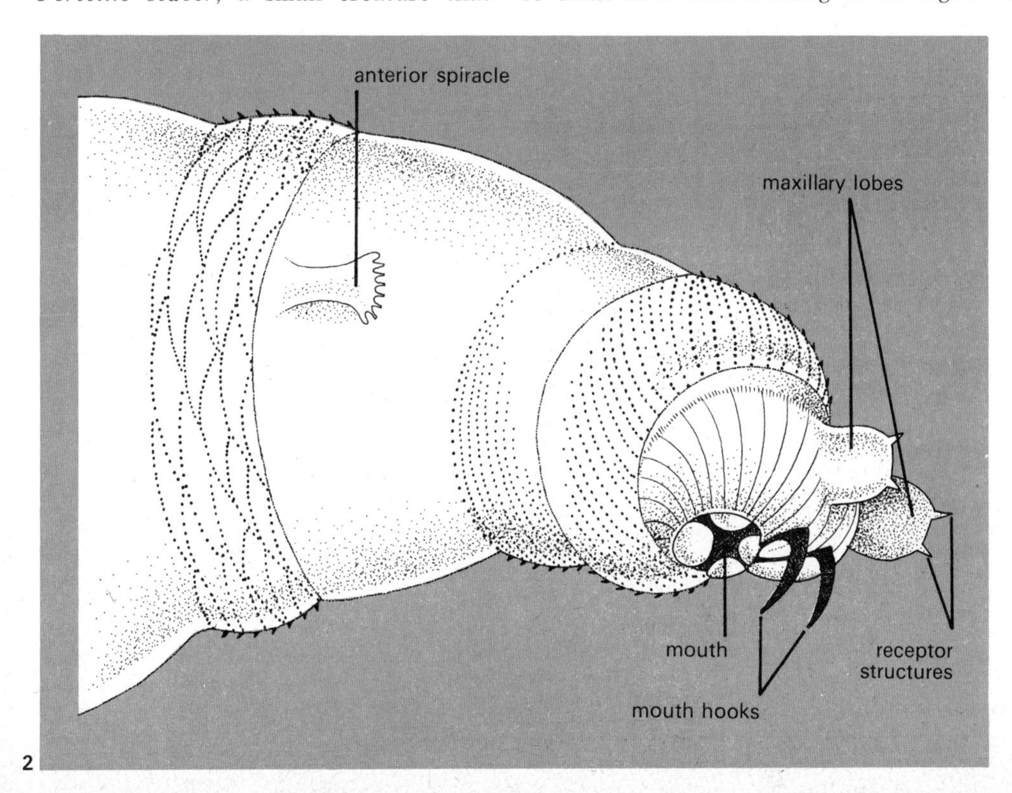


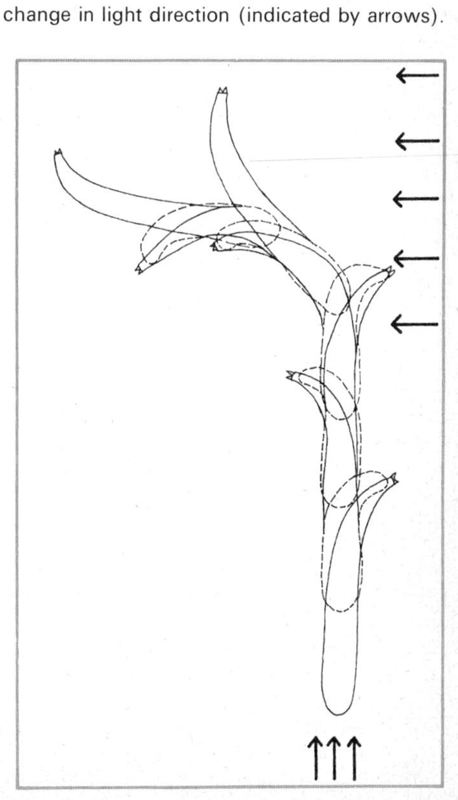

intensity above the animal is increased it changes direction more frequently but moves at the same speed. This is an example of klino-kinesis. The increase in rate of turning falls after about 30 minutes as the animal's photo-receptors become adapted to the increased light. A further increase in illumination will repeat the process. This type of behaviour – negative photo-kinesis – has the effect of causing the animal to move somewhat erratically from areas of high light intensity to areas of lower light intensity.

Kinesis is also found in the behaviour of plankton – the microscopic animals found in the sea. Some of these creatures are adapted to live near the surface, but as they are heavier than water they tend to sink when inactive. As this happens the pressure exerted on their bodies increases, and the plankton respond by increasing their activity and swimming towards the surface. This type of behaviour is called *baro-kinesis.*

Some animals, such as the cockroach, react to touch in a similar manner. If their body is in contact with something there is a decrease in activity and the animal will remain still. If there is no such contact the animal tends to move about rapidly. This is known as *thigmo-kinesis* and means that the animal spends most of its time in the crevices in which it lives.

## Inefficient behaviour patterns

Because of the undirected nature of the response, kineses tend to be an inefficient form of behaviour. Directed responses where the animal moves more or less directly towards or away from the source of the stimulus are known as taxes. A beam or steep gradient of intensity are necessary for this type of orientating response. To perform taxes an animal must have a more highly developed receptor system than needed for kineses.

In the simplest type of taxis, *klino-taxis,* the animal is able to orientate itself either towards or away from a source of stimulus although possessing only a single intensity receptor. If the maggot larva of the blowfly (the gentle used as bait by anglers) is placed on a surface illuminated by a beam of light, it will move away from the source of light in a more or less straight line. This is negative photo-taxis. During locomotion the maggot usually keeps its body straight, but every so often it will put its head down alternately to the left or right of its body.

When the light is first switched on, these lateral deviations of the head are more pronounced and occur more often. The maggot has a single light receptor at the anterior end of its body. Its primitive receptor is incapable of precise discrimination of direction; if the head is stationary it provides no clue to light direction but only to its intensity. However, by raising its head from one side to the other, the maggot can determine the intensity of the light first on one side of the body and then on the other. If the intensities are equal then the animal's body must be orientated along the beam of light. When this is the case the animal moves forward. As the anterior end of the maggot's body is smaller than the rest, the receptor will be in the shadow of the body when the animal is facing away from the light. By comparing successive light intensities the maggot is able to orientate itself so as to crawl away from a source of light, and to make periodic lateral head movements to ensure that it is still heading in the correct direction.

Maggots do not always show this photo-negative response. They perform it most readily shortly before they pupate, and the mechanism enables them to locate a dark place in which to pupate. Immediately after hatching, however, they will move towards light, a photo-positive response which has the effect of dispersing the larvae from where they hatched. This behaviour may vary according to an animal's stage of development.

Another form of taxis, *tropo-taxis,* requires a more elaborate receptor system. In this case the animal must possess paired intensity receptors such as primitive eyespots, positioned to enable the animal to make simultaneous comparisons of stimulus intensity on each side of its body. It can then orientate itself along the beam or gradient of intensity of stimulus according to the balance struck between the two receptors. Orientation is more direct than with klino-taxis. Once orientated no further deviations are required. This form of behaviour is widespread among animals with pairs of simple eyes such as woodlice, planarian worms and certain insect larvae.

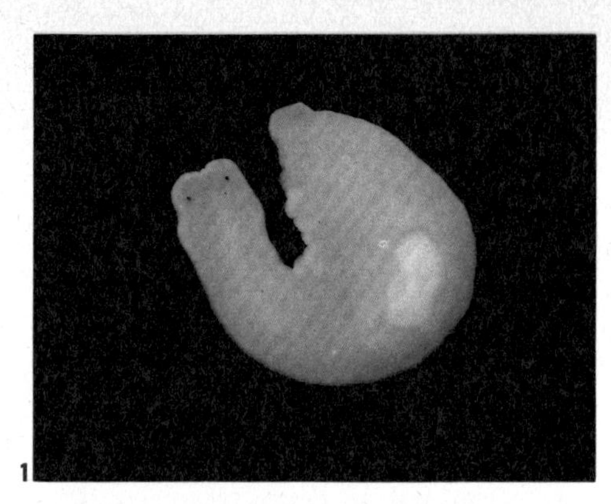

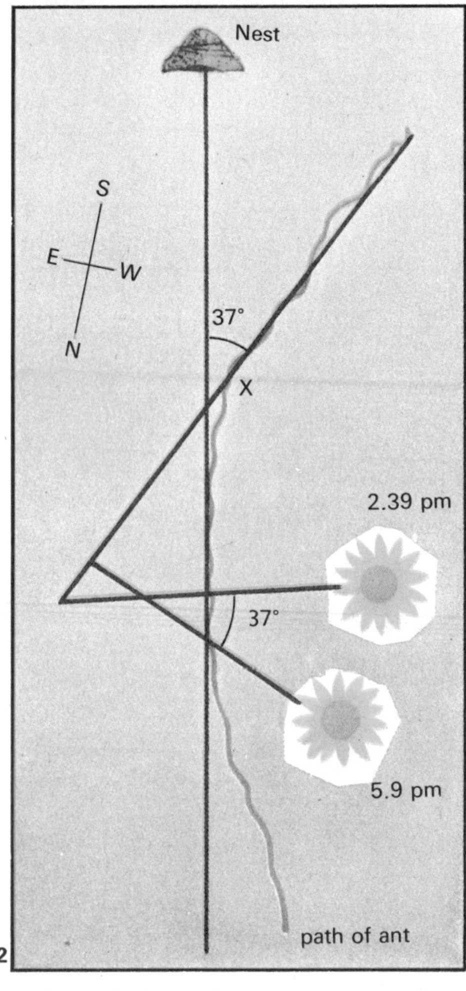


**1** The planarian worm *Dendrocoelum* periodically turns in its tracks and doubles back. When the light intensity is increased, the worm turns more frequently.

**2** Diagram of the track of an ant returning to its nest. At *X* the ant was shut in a dark box and held until the sun had changed position by 37 degrees. The ant's track changed by the same amount.

**3** Plankton respond to increased pressure by swimming towards the water surface. This response, a baro-kinesis, keeps the animals at or near the surface of the water.

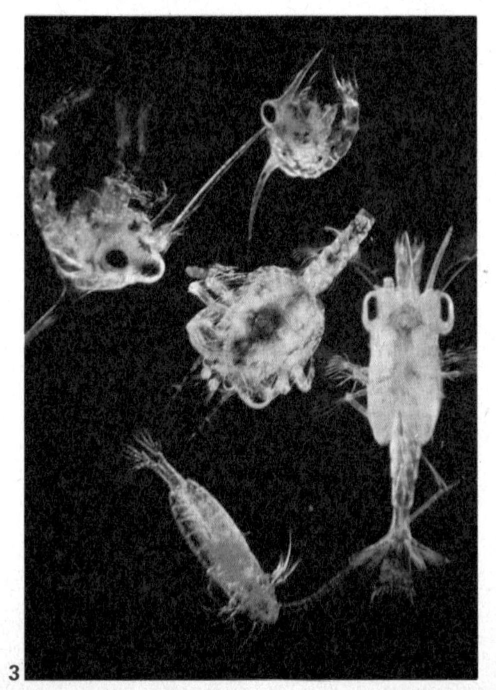

With the development of more complex eyes a third type of taxis is seen. This is *telo-taxis* and orientation to a stimulus is attained directly without any deviation. It is known only as a response to light and requires receptor organs composed of a number of receptive elements pointing in different directions, such as the compound eyes of insects. A characteristic of telo-taxis is that the animal can orientate itself as efficiently with one eye as with two. The way in which a bee released in a room flies directly for the window illustrates the speed with which this type of orientation can occur.

Kineses and taxes are orientating responses that result in the animal moving either towards or away from the stimulus sources. There are, however, two other ways in which certain invertebrates use light stimuli as a means of orientation. Dragonflies in flight and when resting orientate their bodies so that the dorsal surface is at right angles to the light

**1** A giant Madagascar cockroach. When it feels the enclosing walls of its burrow, the cockroach stays still, but moves rapidly when the stimulus of touch is removed.
**2** The fish leech orientates itself towards its host by making use of a combination of the fish's vibrations in the water and chemicals released from the fish's body.
**3** The damselfly keeps itself the right way up while in flight and resting by keeping the dorsal surface of its body at right angles to the direction of the sun's light.
**4** Snails withdraw into their shells when subjected to sudden movements. If the movements are continued, however, the snail may become habituated to them and cease to react.
**5** The fairy shrimp swims on its back by keeping its underside nearest the light. If illuminated from below, the shrimp swims with its back towards the surface.

source, usually the sun. This is known as the dorsal light response and keeps the animal the correct way up. The animal does not move towards or away from the light but at right angles to it and, for this, it requires paired intensity receptors. The water flea *Daphnia* swims with its dorsal surface nearest the surface. If illuminated from underneath the daphnia will orientate itself to the new light source and swim upside down.

## Navigating by the sun

Under natural conditions light from the sky is always present though the direction varies in a constant way. Some invertebrates can use the sun's rays as a means of navigation. This is known as the *light compass reaction*. Ants use this response to find their way back to their nests. In one experiment ants returning to their nests were retained in a light-proof box for a period of time. On being released they set off on a path different from their original one. It was found that the new path deviated from the original at an angle corresponding to the change in the angle of the sun's rays during the time the ant was in the box. The track of an ant could also be altered by using a mirror to change the direction of the sun's rays falling on the animal.

Many invertebrates respond to heat stimuli. This is of particular importance in the orientating responses of animals that are parasitic on warm-blooded animals. The warmth is only a 'token' stimulus of the host's presence as the parasite is not seeking warmth but food. Many blood-sucking ectoparasites do not remain on the host once they have sucked enough blood to satiate them. They only respond to the stimulus of the host's warmth when hungry.

The temperature range to which certain parasites respond is often quite specific. The stories of lice and fleas deserting the body of a host before it dies are an example of this. The parasites are attracted to the host by its normal body temperature, but if this temperature rises due to a fever the parasites no longer receive the stimulus to which they are adapted and leave the host.

Chemical stimuli are used by many parasites to locate their host. A fish leech senses the presence of a fish by the vibrations caused by the fish as it swims. But before the leech can attach itself to the host a secondary stimulus, a chemical secretion given off by the fish, must also be present.

The solitary wasp *Idechtha* is parasitic in its larval stage on the larva of the flour moth. The wasp lays its eggs in the eggs of the moth. A danger of parasitism is that if too many parasites are present in one host the host may die and so will the parasites. To ensure that this does not happen the female wasp will not lay in eggs that have the characteristic odour left by another wasp. If the eggs are washed free of this odour the wasp will begin to lay in the eggs but will detect the presence of the other eggs with her ovipositor and stop laying. *Idechtha* can locate a culture of the flour moth from a distance of 800 metres.

Certain moths are renowned for the ability of the male to locate a female even when released at as much as four kilometres from the female.

The responses of certain invertebrates

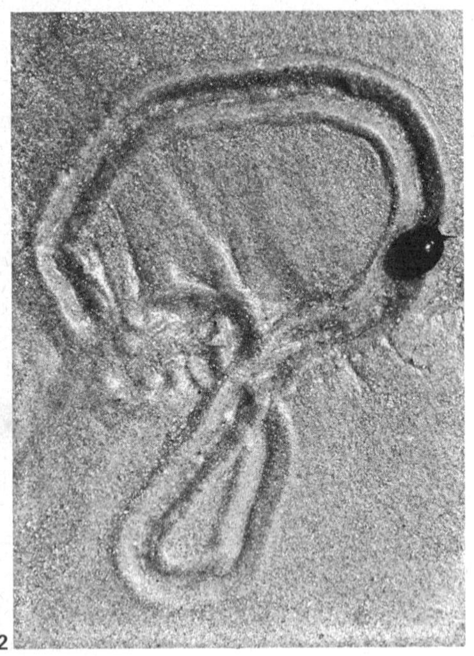

1 The woodlouse shows an ortho-kinesis. It moves more slowly in damp areas than in dry areas, thus ensuring that it spends as much time as possible in damp places.

2 The light compass reaction. The winkle maintains its position on the sand by periodically changing the direction of movement in relation to the direction of the sun's light.

3 Hydra's tentacles are very sensitive to touch. Once the sequence of cell activity that follows touching is set in motion, the hydra is unable to prevent it going to completion.

to the stimulus of food give further illustrations of simple behaviour. Amoeba feeds by moving towards its prey, wrapping itself round its prey, and slowly engulfing it completely inside its cell where ingestion occurs. This response occurs most readily to minute organisms providing a stimulus both to touch and to a weak chemical sense. A hungry amoeba will ingest a grain of sand providing the tactile stimulus only; but a well-fed amoeba will ignore such an object. This is an example of how the physiological state of an organism, in this case, can affect the behaviour of the organism.

Sea-anemones and hydra belong to a class of animals known as coelenterates. They have a tube-like body with a mouth at one end and surrounded by a circle of tentacles by means of which they catch their food. The other end of the body is used to attach them to the substratum and for locomotion. The tentacles are very sensitive to touch so that if one touches the tentacles of a sea-anemone it responds by rapidly withdrawing its tentacles. The tentacles have specialized cells called nematocysts which are thought to be able to respond to stimuli of certain chemical substances and touch without control from the animal's nervous system. These cells shoot out barbs that paralyse the prey and long threads that wrap round it. As soon as the prey touches a tentacle other tentacles move over and grasp it, and it is then moved to the mouth and swallowed. Once this pattern of responses has started, removal of the food and even a change of water will not necessarily cause the animal to stop completing the pattern. This is an example of an external stimulus 'triggering' off a pattern of responses which the animal then executes in the absence of the original stimulus. A hungry hydra will respond to a tactile stimulus only, but a satiated one requires a tactile and chemical stimulus to trigger off the response.

An animal will sometimes be seen to make an alarm reaction to a stimulus which, although not potentially harmful to it, is strange. If it persisted in making such responses to all strange stimuli whenever they were perceived the animal could not perform efficiently. In order to eliminate such useless responses some animals exhibit a type of behaviour known as habituation, by which the animal becomes adapted to a strange stimulus and no longer responds to it. If a common snail (a mollusc) is placed on a board which is frequently jerked up and down, it will at first react to the sudden movements by withdrawing into its shell. After a number of presentations of the stimulus it will no longer react in this way. It has become habituated to the stimulus which although strange did not prove to be harmful.

The various types of behaviour described can only give a brief illustration of the very varied methods by which invertebrate animals, possessing a very simple nervous system, respond to stimuli from their environment. These simple forms of behaviour play an important part in ensuring the animals' survival in an environment that is potentially and may well be actually hostile.

# Living beneath the waves

The teeming life of the oceans was for centuries known only in part, from the animals and plants which could be brought up. Underwater exploration is throwing new light on this fascinating living system.

THE AMERICAN ASTRONAUTS have shown that the predominant colour of the Earth from the vantage point of space is blue. One reason for this is that three-quarters of its surface is covered with water. In fact, there are some 330 million cubic miles of water in the world's oceans and they are truly the cradle of life. In these waters – another world with giant mountain chains and abysses so deep that Mount Everest could be sunk in them without trace – the first living creatures developed. From these waters crawled creatures which colonized and battled for domination of the dry lands.

## Living links

Many living links in this chain of evolution are still there in the oceans. Animal life has been divided in terms of form and function into 22 major groups known as *phyla* and representatives of all of these are to be found in the oceans. They range from tiny single-celled animals called *protozoa*, so small that a powerful microscope is needed to examine them properly, to the blue whales of the Antarctic, often 100 feet long and the biggest animals which have ever lived. That is not all. The oceans are rich in plant life of various kinds, life which provides the basis for a gigantic food web.

But before considering just how this enormous complex of life and habitat hangs together, we need a working knowledge of the various zones of the oceans. These divisions have been made simply for scientific convenience and are useful for visualizing the variety of fish, other animals and plants which live in the waters.

Basically, there are two main divisions. The first is the *benthic* area, which includes the whole of the seabed whatever the depth. The second is the *pelagic* area and consists of all the water overlying the bed. The benthic region is sub-divided: the area of seabed which extends from the shoreline to a depth of 200 metres is called the *littoral* system, sub-divided into *eulittoral* (high tide to 50-metre depth) and *sublittoral* (50- to 200-metre) regions. The rest of the seabed is known generally as the deep sea system, and this has two sections – *archibenthic* (200 to 1,000 metres) and *abyssal benthic* (1,000 metres onwards).

The pelagic region has been similarly divided: both vertically and horizontally. In terms of the former, the waters which overlie the littoral zone of the seabed are given the name of the *neritic* province; over the deep sea system they are called the *oceanic* province. Finally, the waters are divided horizontally into the *upper pelagic* at the top, and *abyssal pelagic* below. The line of demarcation here has been taken as 200 metres, which is the maximum depth to which daylight will penetrate.

All these areas support life but living organisms are to be found in the greatest abundance in three main areas. First there are the sun-warmed and sunlit surface waters (the top layer of the upper pelagic) which provide a home for the infinite number of tiny drifters – plants and animals – known as the *plankton*. Next there is the open sea – just beneath the surface – where the fish and other free-swimming creatures (collectively called *nekton*) hold sway. Then there is the littoral system of the benthic division, also reached by sunlight, which is notable for its many bottom-dwelling creatures – lobsters, worms, barnacles and so on.

This photograph taken at the United States Virginia Fisheries Laboratory, shows a fish being eaten by a star-fish. The fish, numbed by cold water, fell into the embrace of the star-fish.

The reason for those concentrations is very simple; they depend on food being available and, in turn, this depends ultimately on the incidence of plant life. Plants grow by employing solar energy to utilize the nutrient minerals contained in the sea water. The plants take carbon dioxide from the water and release oxygen during their growth, contributing to the aeration of the water. They not only provide food for the animals directly or indirectly, but gas for respiration as well. But where sunlight cannot penetrate, the plants will not grow, however thick the concentration of nutrients.

By far the greatest proportion of marine plant life is to be found not attached to the littoral seabed, but in the open waters. The upper 100 feet or so of the sea contains millions of tiny drifting plants; they form that section of the plankton which is known as the *phytoplankton* (the animals which make up the rest are called *zooplankton*).

Without doubt the most prominent member of the phytoplanktonic community is an alga, known collectively as *diatoms*. They hardly seem to be plants in the accepted sense at all: they are encased in

Albatrosses are among the most beautiful of the world's sea-birds. They spend days effortlessly on the wing and fish far out at sea. Here, they are shown courting on one of the Midway Islands.

transparent silica shells, and under the microscope glisten like jewels. The basic shape of the diatoms is mostly likened to that of a pill box, but in fact the silicious container (*exoskeleton*) can develop in many different ways and shapes.

Nitrogen and phosphorus are the most important of the sea-water salts for the diatoms. But nitrogen and phosphorus exist in the greatest abundance in the deep unlit waters, where without sun the diatoms cannot live. They are therefore found in the greatest quantities where upwellings of the deeper waters occur. Upwelling takes place for a number of reasons, but the most constant impetus comes from the stormy weather of winter, when the waters are most deeply stirred up. Hence, in the spring when the mineral-rich, upwelled waters are warmed and penetrated by increasing hours of sunshine, a diatomic population explosion takes place. Literally hundreds of square miles of ocean become saturated with the tiny plants, which may be so densely grouped that they tinge the water brown, yellow or green, depending on the overall effect of their individual colours. When the minerals of the upwelling have been exhausted, the diatom population dwindles to its normal level.

## Plankton

It is with the plant life of the planktonic layer that the open sea food chain really begins. This food supply serves the myriad creatures of the zooplankton, which either drift, or swim. One of the swimmers and the most numerous by far are the *copepods*, a single representative of which may devour more than 100,000 diatoms in a day. Copepod means 'oar footed', and these animals are shrimp-like in form. Their name refers to the jerky way they propel themselves after their prey with their forelegs.

The copepod is just one representative of the zooplankton. There are others in their thousands – many hard to classify clearly as either plant or animal. They are called the *flagellates*, from the whiplike tentacles which they use to swim or float, and in some cases can synthesize their food needs by use of sunlight and dissolved salts (like plants) as well as by feeding on other living organisms (like animals).

The most numerous is the *dinoflagellate*, which is itself preyed upon by the copepods. Some dinoflagellates are luminescent and flash when agitated with a brilliantly cold, blue-green light. It is the reaction of the dinoflagellates to the intrusion of an oar or fishing net which watermen sometimes see when they take a boat out on a warm night.

The copepods and other zooplankton feed upon diatoms and flagellates. They in turn provide a food source for a whole list of larger animals, which includes not only our food fishes like herring and cod but much larger creatures, like some species of the whale.

Among the plankton drift the jelly-fish and the dangerous Portuguese man-of-war. These feed on the fish which thrive on smaller fry. Both exhibit a deceptive passivity as their tentacles wave aimlessly beneath them in the water. But woe betide the fish – with one exception – which comes too near. One touch of the tentacles with their hundreds of stinging cells and the unfortunate fish is paralyzed. It can then be digested by the drifter.

The one variety of fish which exhibits immunity to the jelly-fish and men-of-war whatever their size is a small, brightly coloured creature called *Nomeus*. This lives among the dangerous tentacles and is not only immune to the poison but also makes its meal from the prey of its

**1** The tropical porcupine fish is able to frighten away its enemies by inflating its air-sac and distending its body. These two fish are from the same species, one inflated and the other not.
**2** The sea cucumber is a bottom-dweller, feeding on organic matter from the seabed. It makes its sluggish way over the slime on the bottom, scooping organic slime with finger-like tentacles.
**3** Anemones are among the most common shallow-water seabed animals. Their characteristic gaudy colours are often due to small plants living inside the cells of their bodies.

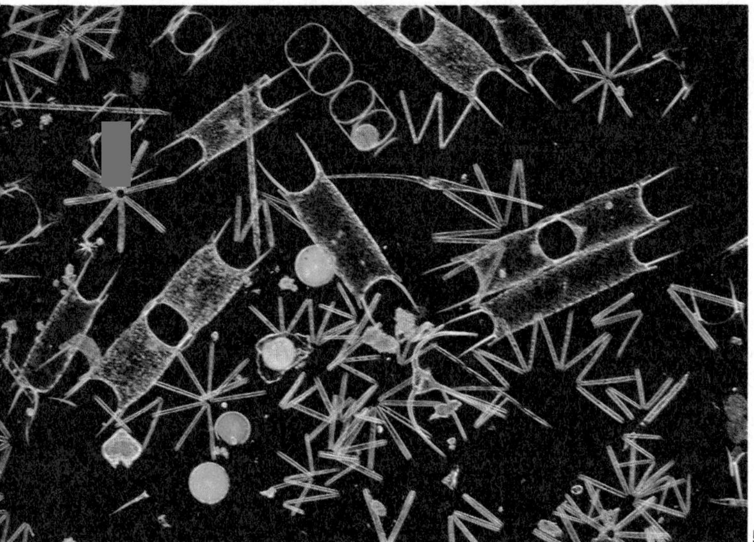

**4** Another seabed animal is the lobster. This crustacean uses its powerful claws to catch crabs, fish and shrimps on which it feeds.
**5** Many small animals and plants, some of microscopic dimensions, make up the plankton layer near the surface of the ocean. Drifting with the tides and currents they are the food for many fish.
**6** This photograph of the seabed, which shows a wrasse making its way through various types of thick vegetation, gives some idea of the appearance of the sea floor in shallow regions. The vegetation varies with the underlying 'soil type'.

host. (There is also one non-fish which seems to be able to ignore stings. It is the loggerhead turtle, and many have been seen munching contentedly through clumps of Portuguese men-of-war, apparently unconcerned by the fact that their eyes are swollen almost shut by the effect of the stings.)

Thus in the upper layers of the sea an overall pattern emerges; it rests on the admonition, 'eat and be eaten'. And it is this which brings life support to the dark waters of the abyss and the seabed below.

One of the consequences of the planktonic carpet of life at or near the surface of the oceans is that a constant rain of organic material – dead and decomposing plants and animals – falls towards the seabed and thus provides food for the deep-dwellers. These have been found in the most profound depths of the oceans, but they are significantly less numerous than those creatures in the surface waters and closer inshore. The reason is that the falling organic matter has many hungry mouths to fill. But some of it falls to the bottom and the fish it supports directly or

The bizarre shape of the sargassum fish serves it partly as a protection against predators, enabling it to blend in with the seaweed it inhabits and which forms its food.

indirectly there are sometimes odd in the extreme.

Mostly they are dull-coloured – black, dark brown or dark violet, and their bodies are often poorly developed, both in terms of bone and of muscle. Yet this is no great problem because the deep waters are calm, and call for no great physical effort to move about. Much more important is the characteristic mouth and stomach development which many of the deep-dwellers have undergone. The smaller creatures eat the organic matter direct – the larger ones eat the smaller creatures.

The angler fish, *Galatheathauma axeli*, is one of the latter category. It has an enormous mouth with rows of fierce teeth and an extensible stomach. This combination means that it can tackle meals as big as itself, and it is thought that this curious creature lies mostly on the bottom and just waits for its prey to come along. But not everything is left to chance; the fish also has a largish luminescent lure, forked in shape, which hangs suspended from the roof of its mouth. Luminescence is characteristic of many fish and has been put to good use as lures by all the angler fish. Mostly, however, the lure is not actually situated within the predator's mouth but at the end of a rod, which protrudes from the top of the head and curves over to dangle just in front of the mouth. A more typical angler than *Galatheathauma* is *Ceratias holbolli* which inhabits rather shallower waters but still lives in darkness.

This fish also demonstrates another survival problem for life in this stygian habitat: the difficulty of finding a mate. The light organs probably have some function here. But alone they would not be sufficient; the anglers lead too stationary a life. There are many more young anglers than adults, however, and

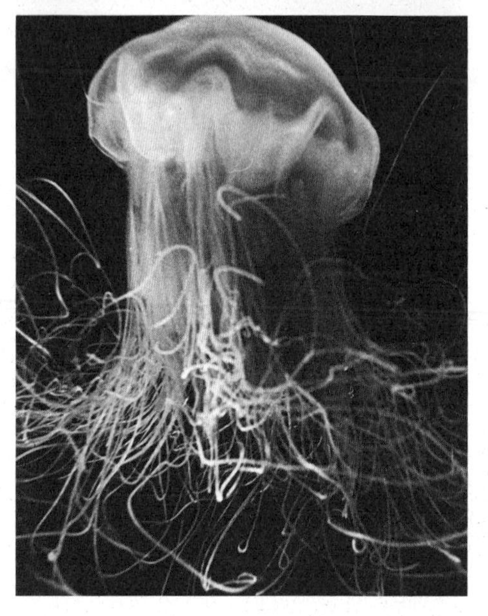

The numerous poisonous tentacles of the jelly-fish make it a very successful predator, despite its frail and boneless body. Jelly-fish float on or near the surface, trailing their tentacles.

the females are liable to come into contact with young males even before the latter are sexually mature. The outcome is a unique mating system. The immature male *Ceratias* fastens on to the much larger female with its teeth and, after a while, the two sets of body tissue fuse and the two circulatory systems become one. The puny male is then nourished by its 'wife' and eventually becomes sexually mature, when it is able to fertilize her eggs. Sometimes a single female is found to carry more than one parasite husband.

In the shallow waters and seabed along the shores it is easy to see one reason why life is so abundant; the planktonic 'soup' extends from the surface to the bottom. But the second reason is more complicated. Only in littoral waters is plant life rooted to the seabed; it is the group of plants which we know as seaweeds. They have flowers which are pollinated and they produce seeds (diatoms and others of the phytoplankton reproduce by simple cell division). They receive their nutrition, like land plants, from the soil in which they are bedded, and are able to live because sunlight penetrates to the bottom throughout the littoral system. They therefore greatly enrich the inshore food supply already provided by the phytoplankton.

But not all the plant life of the shallow waters is truly rooted, although it may be attached to the underwater surface in a rootlike way. One such plant, *Corrallinacae*, is an alga which provides a food source and is also important in maintaining the existence of coral reefs. The Corallinacae encrust the seaward faces of the reefs and bind loose coral to the whole. Consequently the wearing action of the sea is inhibited. Like most algae in the sea, the Corallinacae use rootlike tentacles to hold on, but these play no part in the feeding function. They are solely for attachment, sustenance comes from the process of synthesis.

The easy living conditions provided by plankton and non-planktonic plant life, rooted and unrooted, attract a great many varieties of fish – also a host of bizarre predators or scavengers, some mobile, some not. One mobile scavenger is the strange sea cucumber which moves slowly along the bottom, scooping up the organic slime on which it feeds, with fingerlike tentacles. Among the mobile predators are the fleet-footed crabs and lobsters which catch and tear their prey with fierce claws. Only partially mobile are the sea anemones, frequently beautifully coloured and able to move around a little from day to day. These paralyze unwary fish with their poisonous tentacles and then draw them into their tubular bodies, where the meal is digested. Sponges and oysters are unable to move and get their food by sucking in quantities of water from which they strain the organic matter.

## Sea-birds

These are some of the animals which live in the main divisions of the world oceans. There are many more, some of which live part or even most of their lives outside the water environment, such as the seals which exist largely by catching fish. And the walruses whose tastes run more to molluscs – molluscs which they bring up from the seabed and crunch up in their powerful jaws. There are also hundreds of varieties of bird. Some operate directly from the shoreline like the gannet and gull; others, like the albatross, spend most of their lives fishing far out to sea. Mostly they get their food from or just under the surface, but other birds can go much deeper. The penguin and the cormorant are able to use their wings as swim fins and so dive for their prey.

But all the creatures mentioned have one thing in common, however strangely they may contrast in outward form. They are all part of the great jigsaw of living organisms which coexist in the habitat of the oceans. The study of this vast pattern of interdependence has taught us much about the beginnings of life.

# Between the tides

In the small world between high and low tide live thriving colonies of animals and plants. How have they adapted to these odd conditions, leading a double life in water and the open air?

ONE GREAT FASCINATION of the seaside holiday is the abundance of strange life form to be found on almost any stretch of shore. The animals, like crabs, starfish and mussels, and the plants like bladderwrack and other seaweeds might almost come from another world – and indeed in a sense they do. They come from that *other* world, the oceans, and often are not found in a freshwater habitat in any form. The sea-shore stretches between the highest and lowest points reached by water during the spring tides. Many of its inhabitants are covered by water for only part of the day, or are penned into shallow pools between tides. So it is not only the curious holiday-maker who benefits; the sea-shore is also a natural laboratory for the marine zoologist and botanist where they can study marine life forms without actually entering the sea.

The periods of water cover enjoyed by the animals and plants on the shore vary according to their distance from the low-water mark. On average, the tide changes in a 12-hour cycle; an organism which lives at high-water mark may be submerged only one hour in 12. The amount of exposure decreases until, on the low-water mark, it is very short indeed.

During the time they are uncovered in warm weather, the organisms may dry up. In the winter, the threat may be frost. Whenever they are left out of water they will, in most cases, be cut off from food supplies. Shallow water will heat up or cool very quickly in accordance with the weather and again, heat may cause considerable evaporation and a consequent sharp rise in salinity. The creatures of the sea-shore must, therefore, be able to deal with and survive these conditions as they occur. Just as important are the effects of the waves. The creatures and plants of the shoreline are subjected to this immensely powerful force – it can be as great as 25 tons to the square yard – for a great deal of their lives. Were they not constructed in such a way as to withstand it, they would perish.

The features of the sea-shore are, therefore, a result of the continual battle which rages between the sea and the land. The sea always wins, but the speed of erosion varies according to the composition of rock. The sea also has powerful allies – frost and animals – which open up cracks in the cliffs. Broken rocks are pounded by the waves and reduced to pebbles, sand and even silt.

The pebbles may be drawn further out to sea. Where the waves are breaking at an angle to the shore they will be transported along the coast until the force of the wave is reduced to the point where they fall – the result, a pebble beach. Likewise the very light particles of sand and mud will be carried even further, before being deposited to form characteristic shore formations.

1 The lumpsucker grows up to two feet in length and has pelvic fins fused together to form a powerful sucker. This enables the lumpsucker to cling with great force to rocks in the tidal zone.
2 The teredo worm *(Teredo navalis)* was once a major hazard for wooden ships. Here it has burrowed into a wooden jetty pile and almost totally eroded the timber.

The process of breakdown, carriage and deposit is going on continuously, but, of course, it is happening at different rates conditional upon a number of variables such as the nature of the existing shore material, the angle of the waves to the shore and their size. Consequently the various kinds of shore may be inextricably mixed in a relatively short stretch of coastline.

The exposed faces of rock, either tumbled or sheer as in a cliff, provide probably the toughest habitat for living organisms. Here they are frequently exposed to sun, wind or frost when the tide is low, and pounded by the seas as the tide rises.

The most common animals are crustaceans and molluscs, both of which are protected from the worst rigours by strong shells.

An interesting example is the acorn barnacle, which can stand long periods of exposure to the elements, and resembles a tiny circular fort in appearance. The outer wall consists of six thickish stony plates which curl inwards near the top to surround a further four horizontal plates capping the top. The latter are hinged and can be opened by the animal when the tide is in and closed up tight when it is out.

Barnacles feed most often under the water, although some live so far up the

A flock of herring gulls in graceful flight across inshore waters. They are common on most Atlantic coasts and in the breeding season form noisy colonies along the ledges of cliff faces.

shore that they must be able to feed from splashes of water. The mollusc extends frond-like appendages through the opening to filter out the small particles of food. The tiny meal is then transferred to the inside of the shell where it is eventually digested.

The acorn barnacle does not need to move to find its food, but waits for it to come along. In fact there is no possibility of it moving, for early in life, the animal attaches the bases of the vertical plates to its rocky home by means of a natural cement. If it were not for this the barnacle would be smashed against the rocks by the sea and die.

## Conical shell

The most highly adapted mollusc is the limpet, and it differs radically from the acorn barnacle. To begin with, its shell is conical and it is not cemented to the rock – in fact, a small gap between the foot of the shell and the rock can be seen when the animal is covered with water. Instead, the limpet secures itself by means of an extremely muscular foot, in some ways similar to the undulating foot of the common snail, and this is so strong that it can resist the pull of the sea.

When submerged, the limpet is able to feed by drawing water in through the gap and filtering it in a similar way to the barnacle. But when the water recedes the foot comes into action again, clamping the edges of the shell firmly to the rock. Where the rock surface is not smooth enough for this, the limpet wriggles about until either the shell edge is worn to the shape of the rock, or it has itself worn a circular groove in the rock. In clamping down like this, the limpet also traps a certain amount of sea water and this saves it from drying up.

Periwinkles, too, have a strongly developed foot, but these creatures make no attempt to cling on when the seas get rough. They simply withdraw into their shells and close up their rounded, horny lids. Mussels attach themselves to rocks in an ingenious way – they spin fine but strong threads called *byssus*. The threads themselves are secreted as a fluid by glands in the mussel's foot and are hardened by sea water. They hold down the mussel as guy ropes hold down a tent.

Wracks are fixed to the rocks by numbers of tiny discs, which will resist a great deal of tugging. The fronds, as in the bladder-wrack, are usually dotted with swellings which contain air pockets. When the tide is in, the fronds float out of water, the wracks drape over the rock faces and provide moisture and protection for many animals. Cracks in and under the rocks themselves are just as useful for this purpose.

A more specialized means of survival is to bore into the rock. Examples of animals which are capable of this are the date mussels of the Mediterranean and another kind of bivalve, the piddock, which occurs in British waters. Both carry out their mining by completely different means.

Twisted wrack *(Fucus spiralis)* is widespread on rocky, temperate shores. This specimen shows the swollen green fronds which contain the 'seeds' of future plants.

The attack of the date mussel, which is so called simply because it resembles a date in size, shape and colour, is a form of natural chemical warfare. It burrows only into limestone, and to do so produces an acid which dissolves the rock. The piddock, on the other hand, operates mechanically. The shell carries rows of extremely sharp teeth with which to grind away almost any kind of rock. Both feed by filtering the sea water. The mussel uses the water which flows into the hole it has made, while the piddock extends a tube or siphon to the mouth of the hole, and sucks in its supply. Other animals,

The lugworm *(Arenicola marina)* is familiar to anglers who often use it for bait. The worm burrows in fine sand or mud, throwing up characteristic casts which indicate its presence.

Like many other shell-fish, the common cockle *(Cardium edule)* feeds through a fleshy outgrowth known as a syphon. Here a cockle is half buried in fine sand.

like the *teredo*, or shipworm, burrow into the woodwork of piles and boats, often with disastrous results.

It is among the rocks that the permanent pools of the shoreline are to be found. And in spite of fluctuations in temperature, salinity and other conditions, the rock pool on examination turns out to house a thriving community.

Typical plants are the pink *Lithophyllum*, the purplish coralline weed, and the dark green *Cladophora*; there are also algae and brightly coloured anemones. All are well rooted. The animal life ranges from zooplankton, through snails and crabs to quite large fish. The lumpsucker can grow up to two feet in length; its pelvic fins (separate in most fish) are fused to become a powerful sucker. Thomas Pennant, an eminent British naturalist of the eighteenth century, reported that when a newly caught specimen was tossed into a bucket holding 'some gallons' of water, it immediately attached itself to the bottom, with such force that bucket, fish and water could be lifted as one, using the creature's tail as a handle. Obviously the lumpsucker is equipped to withstand the onslaught of the tide.

After the rich profusion of a rocky shore, a sandy stretch must strike the viewer as barren. It is almost devoid of plant life, and animal life seems scarce. In fact a great deal of animal life is present at low tide, but it is mostly below the surface of the sand, for such a smooth and featureless habitat provides little shelter and no hard surface for attachment. The only way in which the animals left high and dry can survive is to burrow, and they are at home only a short distance under the surface.

Even sand appearing dry still contains a lot of water which exists as a layer around the particles, joining them together. This means that creatures trapped here do not dry up and it is also possible for them to breathe. At the same time, although contact with air may profoundly alter the temperatures of the uppermost layers, the effect penetrates no further than about ten inches.

The most common sand-dweller is the lugworm, which is responsible for the curly casts found on sandy beaches when the tide has gone out. These are formed of sand which the worm has swallowed and passed through its body after extracting particles of food.

The barnacle *(Balanus balanoides)* attaches itself to rocks, usually in the intertidal zone. Its fronds (or *cirri*) can be extended to catch food, or withdrawn at low tide when out of water.

Sand-eels lie concealed in the sand as they wait for their prey to pass. They normally live in shallow waters along the sea-shore, where food is in plentiful supply.

The most familiar sandy-shore crustacean in British waters is the shrimp. It lives in the wet sand when the tide is out and emerges to feed at night when it is covered with water. Cockles (molluscs) spend most of their time buried in the sand, even when the tide is in. They feed by pushing siphons to the sand's surface and suck in microscopic plant life with the sea water. Echinoderms are represented by the burrowing starfish, the arms of which are bounded by strong plates and spines of bony material. With all five arms working at once, it sinks into the sand. It preys on molluscs and even dying fish on the surface of the sand, and also other animals which it encounters beneath the surface.

Several kinds of fish burrow near the low-water line, which means that they are not going to be separated from their more natural medium for very long. One is the lesser weaver fish, about six inches long and grey in colour, except for a largish black fin on its back. The weaver digs in with its tail and underfins until only its eyes and black fin protrude above the surface. When the fish is aroused or startled the fin is raised to expose sharp spines along part of its edge. These carry poison, fatal to many other creatures, and extremely painful to the unwary human rambler. Other burrowing fish are sand eels and gobies.

## Shelter and protection

At some point along the shore, mud and sand are mixed in various proportions, and there may also be some largish stones as well. Here the sand-dwellers and the mud-dwellers are inclined to merge, and the stones may also provide shelter and protection for plants and animals more commonly found among the rocks.

But where mud exists by itself, living conditions become difficult for the organisms from other habitats. Mud is even more featureless than sand; it is smoother and more sticky. Nevertheless, there are some plants and animals which can survive. The former are liable to be the eel grasses which need a soft medium in which to spread their fine but extensive rooting system. The animals are mainly adapted for burrowing and include types of snail and molluscs. The common shrimp also finds an alternative home here. Conger eels, if caught by a falling tide and unable to shelter under rocks, will dig into the mud.

The pebble shore is almost barren; the pebbles roll with the movement of the water and would crush most organisms attempting to live amongst them. The water drains out of the pebble complex quickly and relatively completely, which is not the case with sand and mud. The stone is very hard and highly resistant to the attacks of the borers.

In general, however, the flora and fauna of the sea-shore are as rich as those to be found anywhere on completely dry land. Much valuable zoological information has been gathered along the shorelines of the world, and they still hold unlimited potential for the scientist and the holiday-maker alike.

1 Limpets clamp themselves so hard to rocks that they often leave a permanent mark. The upper limpet has already worn a dip in the rock, while below it is the scar left by another.

2 A whelk shuffles along the sea floor propelled by means of its giant foot. The whelk shown here is camouflaged by plants which have attached themselves to its strongly built shell.

# The highest invertebrates

Echinoderms and protochordates represent the pinnacle of specialization within the invertebrates. Their structure shows similarities with that of the higher animals, including Man himself.

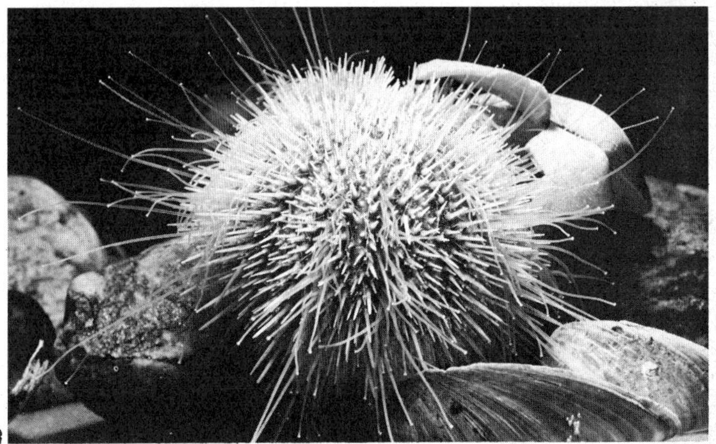

**1** An injured fish falls prey to a slow-moving starfish. Because of the speed with which fish normally move this is a rare event, but starfish often attack and eat oysters.
**2** This picture of the sea cucumber clearly shows the rows of tube feet by which the animal clings to rocks. It has five rows of feet, a common number in echinoderms.
**3** Tube feet of the sea urchin are long and slender and end in suckers. They extend beyond the spines, which are used both for locomotion and protection from marauders.

ASK ANY OYSTERMAN to name his greatest headache, and he will trot out the starfish. And anyone who has seen this brightly coloured predator glide smoothly over the sea bed and stretch its arms around an oyster, will know the reason why. Sooner or later the starfish will force the two halves of its victim's shell apart – and devour the flesh inside.

It may be hard luck on the oysterman, but the fact that the starfish is able to move at all is a matter of considerable interest to the biologist in his study of nature. One of the ways in which the animal kingdom can be divided is in terms of those creatures which can move and those which cannot. Obviously the ability to move has played a crucial part in the development of higher forms of life, and both the starfish itself and the animal group of which it is a member, the *echinoderms*, are particularly interesting from this point of view. For the echinoderms include among their number creatures which are completely stationary; those which begin life in that fashion but later become mobile; and those that are mobile throughout their lives. Since the immobile *(sessile)* types are the root stock from which all the rest spring and representatives of all types exist at the present time, it is possible for the scientist to examine quite easily both the changes which have taken place in these animals and which make locomotion possible, and to study the effects of mobility.

Echinoderm is a Greek word which means literally 'prickly skinned'. The group includes not only the starfish but such animals as the equally colourful sea urchin, the sea cucumber (which unlike its salad-bowl namesake is an animal and not a vegetable), the sea star and the sea lily.

The Greeks gave the name echinoderm to both the hedgehog and the sea urchin (the latter was studied by Aristotle and is still called 'Aristotle's Lantern'), and modern science has taken the term to denote this whole group of animals. The reason for this adoption was simply that one of the characteristics which they all have in common is that minute spicules of crystalline carbonate of lime are deposited in the deeper layers of the skin. These grow together to form plates or prickles in the skin, and resemble a layer of bony net.

The echinoderm which best represents the sessile members of this group is the sea lily (crinoid class). The sea lily consists of a globular body which is rooted to the sea bed by a stalk. The body itself is surmounted by five pairs of tentacles which are radially arranged about the mouth, itself situated on the upper surface of the body.

## Five of everything

Before considering the internal systems of the sea lily it is worth examining the tentacles in some detail, for they embody several features which are characteristic of the echinoderms as a whole.

First, there is the fact that the tentacles, or arms, are arranged in *five* pairs. The figure five is something of a magic number in the echinodermic world: most of them have five of everything, except for mouth and stomach (and by an intriguing mathematical accident, incidentally, the number of classes of echinoderms which still exist also amounts to five). In addition to this numerical similarity among echinoderms the radial arrangement of tentacles also represents a form of organization typical of the whole echinoderm family.

Next, the tentacles consist of articulated

plates of calcareous skeletal material. Finally, they incorporate both neuromuscular systems for movement and a peculiar kind of hydraulic skeleton for support.

In short, they are engineering marvels and of great importance to the echinoderm. Each tentacle carries a myriad of lateral appendages called *pinnules,* and each of these pinnules carries a groove on its upper surface. This groove runs the length of the pinnule and can be considered as a tributary in the food collecting canal of the sea lily. At the tentacle it joins a larger groove which itself runs down to reach the mouth on the top surface of the body. This complex of canals is called the *ambulacral* system, and can extend in total to a quarter of a mile.

Along each side of the pinnule groove are a set of sensitive finger-like protuberances called *podia.* When food particles come in contact with the podia, they whip down towards the pinnule groove and this, combined with the action of cilia (fine hair-like stalks) in the groove itself, drives a stream of food-laden water towards the mouth.

## Adaptation for mobility

The podia themselves are supported by the hydraulic system. More properly it is called the water-vascular system and consists of a closed water-containing canal around the oesophagus. From here, five branches lead to the paired tentacles, where they split so that a tube passes up each tentacle. Muscular movement causes the water to move through the branches and so operate the finger-like podia.

Within the globular body of the sea lily there is an oesophagus leading from mouth to stomach, which is followed by an intestine which ends in a vent near the mouth on the upper surface of the body. It is this relative intestinal complexity which separates the echinoderms from animals like sea anemones and jelly-fish, whose digestive systems are little more than internal sacs.

The sea lily, then, is an example of the non-moving type of echinoderm exhibiting the usual characteristics of skeleton, radial organization, what might be called the rule of five, and the water-vascular system. But also to be found among the crinoids is a creature which within its own lifetime demonstrates actual change from sessile to mobile. This is the feather star, one of the most beautiful denizens of tropical waters.

At the start of its life, the feather star is anchored to the sea bed, like the sea lily. But when the stem is about an inch high it breaks and the body and tentacles are free to move. The animal uses tentacles and pinnules to move about as well as to collect the water-borne food. But it also develops short attachments below the body which will allow it to anchor if required.

The fully mobile type of echinoderm is best seen in the starfish (of the group *Asteroidea*). Here, of course, the radial system can be seen more easily, while equally obviously the body and arms are fairly rigid due to the calcareous plates which are embedded in the tissues.

The starfish differs in many less obvious ways from the sea lily and the feather star. For example, there is the highly efficient manner in which it is able to move about. The chief factor here is that the starfish has ceased to use its water-vascular system as a feeding mechanism. Instead, it is employed as a means of locomotion; in effect it is a hydraulic power system.

This operation is of elegant simplicity. First, the starfish draws water through tiny pores in a sieve plate on the upper surface of its body. From there the water travels around a circular channel from which five channels radiate–one into each arm. Each of these five channels has hundreds of small branches extending to either side, into the 'tube feet' – a special development of the podia seen in the sea lily.

At the free end of each of the tube feet there is a tiny sucker; at the inboard end there is a small chamber called the *ampulla.* When the water reaches the foot, a valve closes behind it, so that it cannot return whence it came. At the same time, the ampulla contracts and the enclosed water is then forced towards the sucker end, extending the tube and pressing the sucker firmly on to the sea bed below the starfish.

By stretching out its tube feet and attaching them to the sea floor the starfish has thus taken half a step forward. The movement is completed as the ampulla relaxes and the muscles running along the foot contract and shorten the tube once again. The starfish carries thousands of such feet, and when co-ordinated they allow the animal to glide along quickly and smoothly.

Co-ordination is actually effected by a nerve system consisting of a ring around the mouth. Here again the number five reappears, in the form of five nerves radiating from the ring, one to each arm. The starfish, however, has no brain and no eyes. The tips of the arms, however, are light sensitive, and with one of these pointing the way the creature can travel in any required direction.

All of this makes it clear that the starfish does not use its adapted podia for pur-

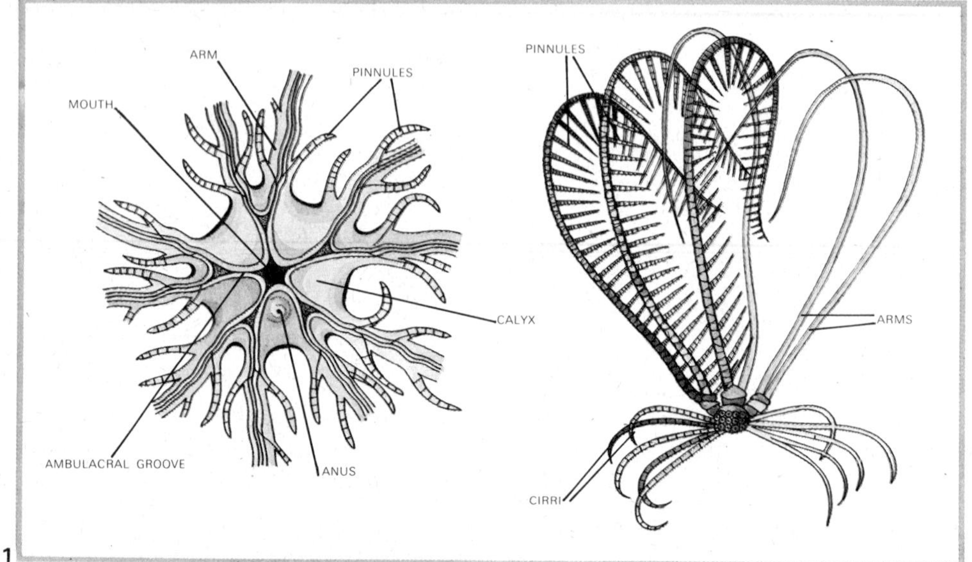

1

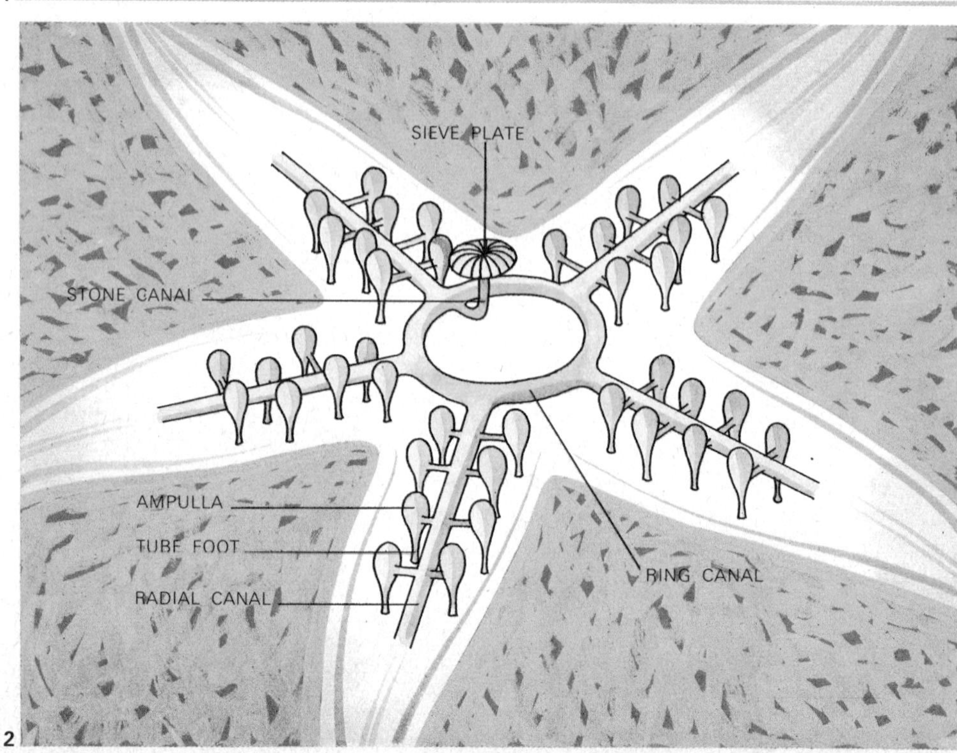

2

poses of collecting the food drifting down from above. In fact, it has completely transformed its method of feeding. Unlike the sea lily and feather star, which have the mouth and tentacles situated on the upper side of the body, the starfish has turned over so that the mouth, and obviously the feet, are on the under side.

## Muscular movement

The animal feeds then on what it can pick up from the sea bed, and its specific method of feeding is to cover its prey and eat directly with the mouth. At the same time, however, the starfish has become a carnivore, or flesh eater, hence its attacks on oysters and other animals. This particular taste often means that the food particles will be too big for entry into the starfish mouth, and so when this happens the animal neatly extrudes the lining of its stomach so that its prey can be partly digested before being taken inside.

The range of living echinoderms is completed by the sea cucumbers *(Holothuroidea)*, the brittle stars *(Ophiuroidea)* and finally, the sea urchins and relatives *(Echinoidea)*. They are all mobile and represent variations on the starfish theme although most of them look very different. The brittle stars come closest in appearance, usually having five arms, but in contrast they move by muscular action of the arms rather than by hydraulic power. They get their name, incidentally, from the fact that their arms, which are long and spiny, break easily when handled. The sea cucumbers have no radial arms as such, but these are represented instead by clusters of tentacles around the mouth.

Like the starfish, all of these are carnivores. The echinoids, on the other hand, are not. They feed on vegetation which they scrape up with their five pointed teeth. The sea urchin, the most widely known member of the Echinoidea group, also has no arms. However, its body is supported by closely fitting calcareous plates, and these are divided into five vertical sections so that the animal looks a little like a bony ball. In this case the 'seams' of the ball are really the ambulacral grooves described in the sea lily, and they run from the back of the urchin to its mouth on the underside. Particular features of the sea urchin are the long supporting spines which extend from the mass of its body like very fine stilts. The tube feet extend between these spines when the urchin is on the move.

But the echinoderms are not the only animals in the sea which exhibit within one class both sessile and mobile types. There are also the protochordates, the lower members of the great chordate group which includes Man and all other vertebrates as well. Like the echinoderms, some protochordates are able to move – others cannot.

The protochordates themselves are divided into three groups. The largest of these by far are the *urochordates,* most familiar to us as sea squirts. The squirt is the most primitive of the protochordates and is immobile, spending most of its life rooted to some object on the sea bed.

This animal depends for its livelihood on filter feeding. In other words, it draws water into its body through an incurrent siphon, and the food is digested. The water is then pushed out again through a second siphon, but on its way out it passes through the squirt's gills, where oxygen is extracted. The sea squirt's body is reasonably flexible, being covered with a layer of an interesting substance called *tunicin* which is almost pure cellulose – one of the few examples of natural manufacture of this material.

## Almost a backbone

Taken all in all, there is little here to suggest the sophisticated systems of the higher vertebrates. However, the sea squirts do produce free-swimming larvae which exhibit some of the features which are considered characteristic of the chordates. First, there is an elongated rod, or *notochord,* which stiffens the body and resembles the vertebrate spine. This is also accompanied by a dorsal nerve chord.

**1** Sea lilies or feather stars have a central mouth on the underside (*left*) surmounted by arms which bear fine pinnules as shown on the right. The tube feet are like tentacles.
**2** The water-vascular system of the starfish is based on a central ring canal with five radial canals. Water enters through the sieve plate and the rigid stone canal.
**3** This sun starfish with 13 arms is less common than the five-armed variety. But individuals with up to 25 arms are found in some waters.
**4** Sea urchins are capable of crawling. This one crawling on an aquarium wall clearly shows the mouth with teeth.
**5** Serpent stars are so called from the writhing movements which they make. They are also called brittle stars because the arms come off easily whenever they are seized by enemies. Regeneration of the broken limb is rapid, however. The tube feet are used only for respiration and feeling.

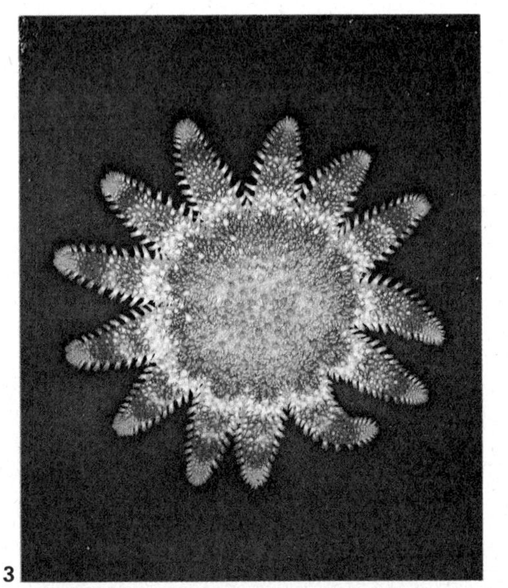

3

4

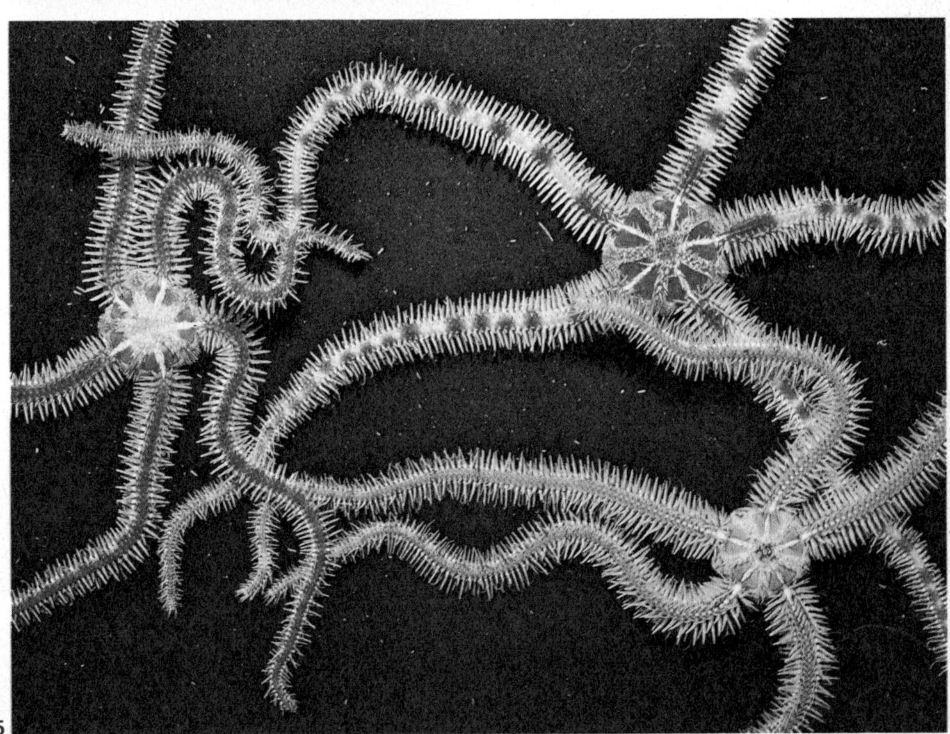

5

The other subdivisions of the protochordates are all mobile, and some of the chordate features already noted are present in these in adult life, while others are absent. The *hemichordates*, for example, include a burrowing worm which has no well-developed notochord, only a rudimentary rod in the head region. For this reason some biologists suggest that they are not true protochordates at all, but are a special case.

*Lancelets* are the best known representatives of the final protochordate division, the *Cephalochorda*. These animals – 1 to 2½ inches long – both swim freely and burrow in the sand and are truly fishlike. Not only do they have the notochord, so suggestive of a backbone, they also have a number of fins and a tail. The blood system is also fundamentally fishlike.

It is a matter of some argument in the world of biology whether or not the echinoderms and protochordates emerged from the same sessile stock. Nevertheless, together they provide a notable example of the way in which movement has been achieved and also the importance of movement in the development of higher animals. It is true that with the colourful echinoderms, progress has come to a full stop with the brainless and eyeless starfish. But on the other hand the superficially less spectacular protochordates mark the bottom rungs of a ladder which is topped by Man himself.

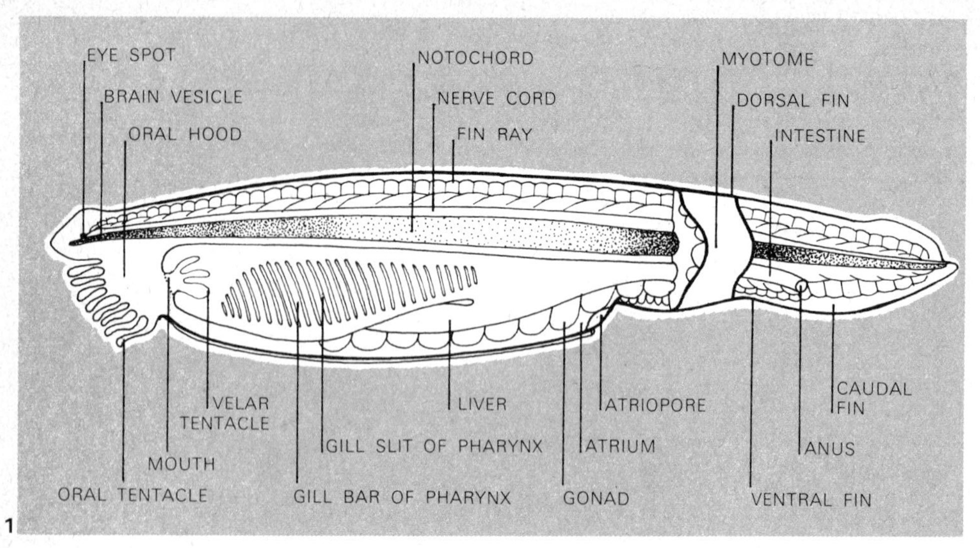


**1** *Amphioxus* (the lancelet), displays some fish-like characteristics, including the ability to swim.

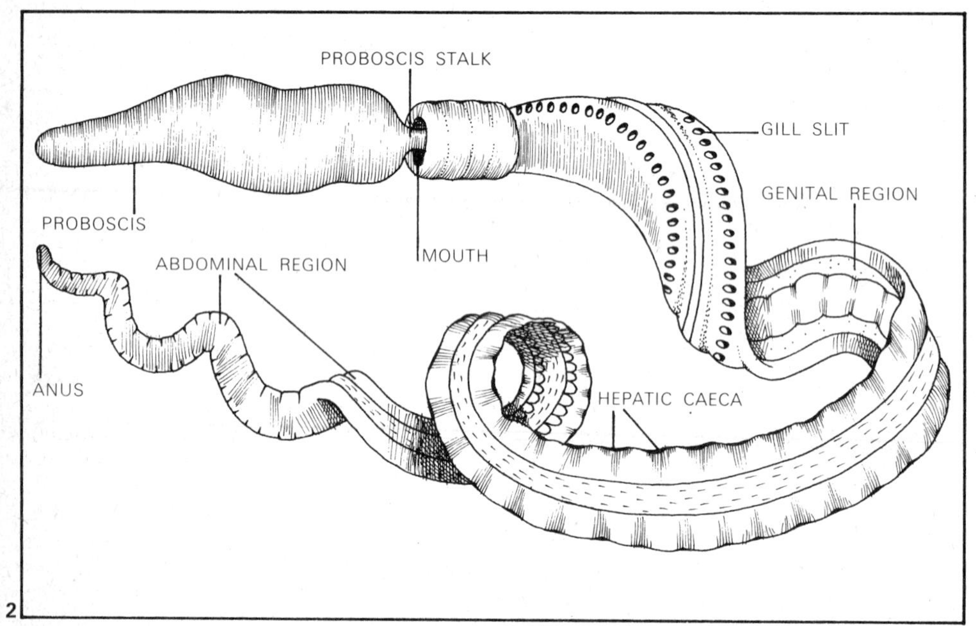


**2** Acorn worms provide a link between the chordates and echinoderms. The muscular proboscis is used to drag the animal through its sandy habitat.

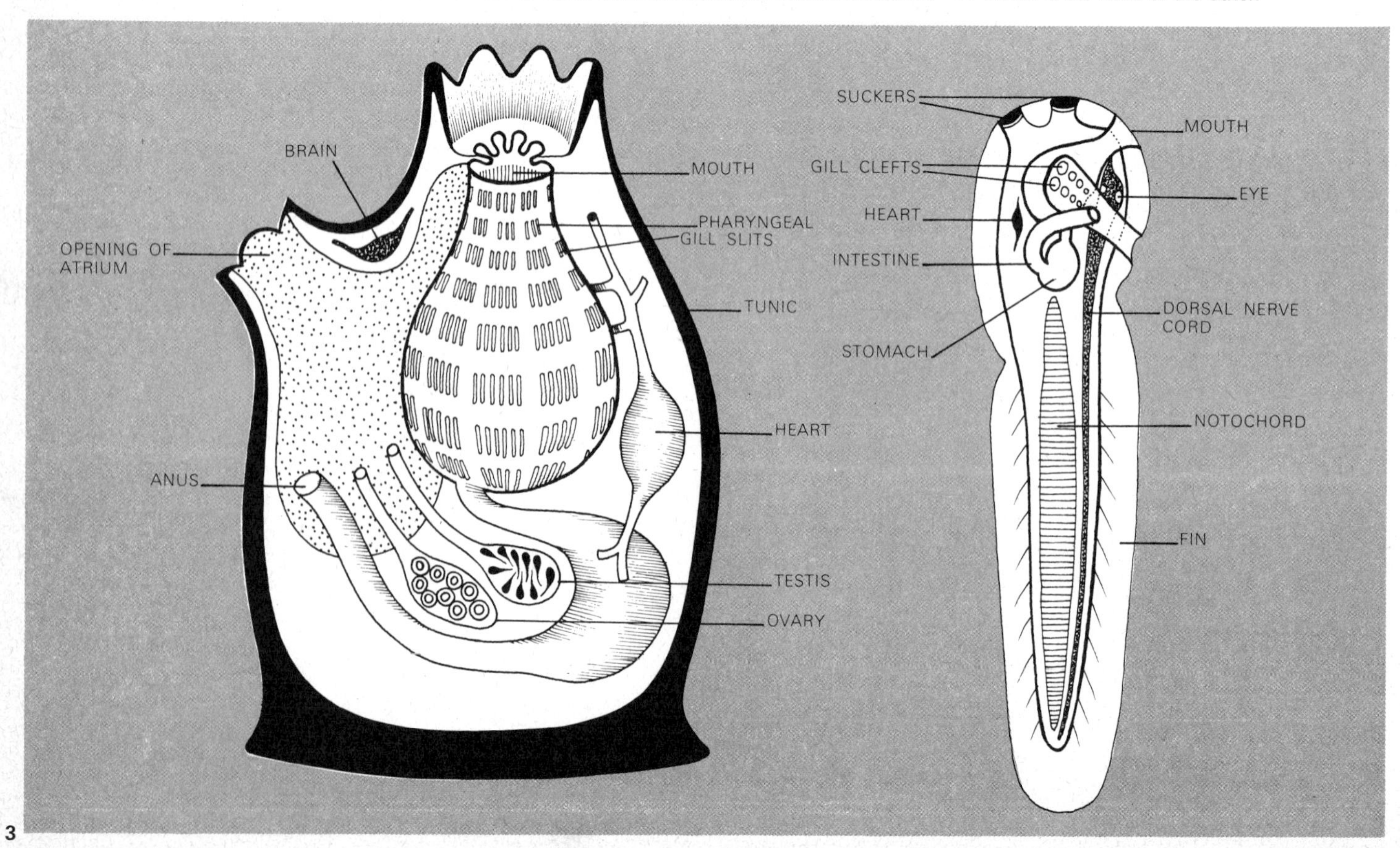


**3** Two widely different tunicate structures, one of which is the larva of the other.

# Life within a shell

Predatory squids and herbivorous snails are both members of the same diverse family – the molluscs. They represent an evolutionary milestone in the development of the senses.

EVERYBODY HAS READ TALES of giant squid locked in deadly combat with the whale. Again, few people have failed to notice the white, crystalline shells of long-dead cuttlefish lying on the beach. The pearl is highly prized throughout the world and is of course produced by oyster and mussel. These animals – like the clam, scallop and whelk – are also prized as a source of food by most of us.

Yet in spite of this background of familiarity, it still comes as a surprise to most of us that all of these animals belong to the *Mollusca,* one of the largest divisions of the animal kingdom. And that their very obvious differences in form and function all arise from the development or adaptation of a basic, primitive molluscan plan.

## Soft bodies in a shell

The major factor in the success of any group of living organisms is its ability to adapt its basic plan to meet the challenge and exploit the possibilities, in terms of food and shelter, of many different environments. In the language of the biologist this is called *adaptive radiation,* and the Mollusca provide one of the most graphic and spectacular examples of this in Nature.

The word mollusc derives from the Latin *molluscus* – which means soft – and refers to the characteristically soft body of the animal. The *chiton* is a good example. One of its two most obvious physical features is the broad, oval foot which is soft but well developed muscularly, and enables the chiton both to move and to cling with great tenacity to the undersea rocks which provide its habitat and on which it finds its food. The rest of the body is likewise soft, and also deformable.

The other very obvious physical attribute of the chiton is the hard shell. It consists of eight transverse plates and provides the animal with useful protection from marauding predators. Immediately beneath the shell is a layer of tissue called the mantle which covers the whole of the inside surface of the shell, but extends slightly beyond the shell edge to form an overhanging lip – like the eaves of a house – around the foot.

Within the space bounded by mantle and foot the vital systems are housed. These are the heart, stomach, digestive equipment, nerves and so on. Recessed under the shell at the front of the animal is the mouth.

These external and internal physical characteristics of the chiton are in most cases shared by the other molluscs, although they may have undergone great development or have been discarded altogether.

But it may be useful to examine the internal mechanics of the chiton. Thanks to its muscular foot the animal is able to move about – slowly – in search of the algae which it takes as food. The method of locomotion is by a peristaltic wave along the foot; or to put it more simply, by a rippling muscular motion rather like that seen in the ordinary caterpillar.

The mouth contains a feeding implement which is itself characteristic of the molluscs. This is the *radula,* consisting of a ribbon of tissue which carries rows of tiny teeth. The chiton employs it like a sort of zoological file. As it moves forward, the mollusc rhythmically protrudes and retracts the radula, scraping up the food as it does so. On retraction, the radula also does duty as a natural conveyor belt, the food being passed to the gut and so to the stomach.

## Breathing and feeding

Here it is sorted in terms of size by a complicated system of cilia. These are fine, hair-like appendages, some of which drive the smaller food particles to the tiny openings of the digestive gland, while others push the larger particles into the intestine for excretion. The food which actually reaches the digestive gland is absorbed by the cells which line it.

It is in the digestive system that the chiton converts its food to energy, and it is worth noting that the structure of the digestive tube (with expanded areas forming stomach and digestive gland, and coiling as it progresses towards the hind end) is also characteristic of the molluscs.

Breathing in the chiton – and for that matter most other molluscs – is accomplished by means of gills. The exceptions are certain snails which have graduated to the land, and others which, having once done just that, have later returned to the water. But in the chiton the gills consist of two lateral rows which run the length of the body. They are situated in the cavity between the overhanging lip of the mantle and the edge of the foot, and are therefore in constant contact with the water. It is in the gills that the oxygen is taken from the water and enters the blood, which is itself circulated by a heart situated in the mantle cavity at the hind end of the animal.

The nervous system of the chiton is primitive. It is no more than a nerve ring around the oesophagus (the passage from mouth to stomach) and two pairs of longer nerves. One pair serves the foot, the other takes care of the mantle, digestive system and the rest. In short, the chiton is both blind and brainless.

The *Gastropoda* – the snails and whelks – resemble the chiton in that they also

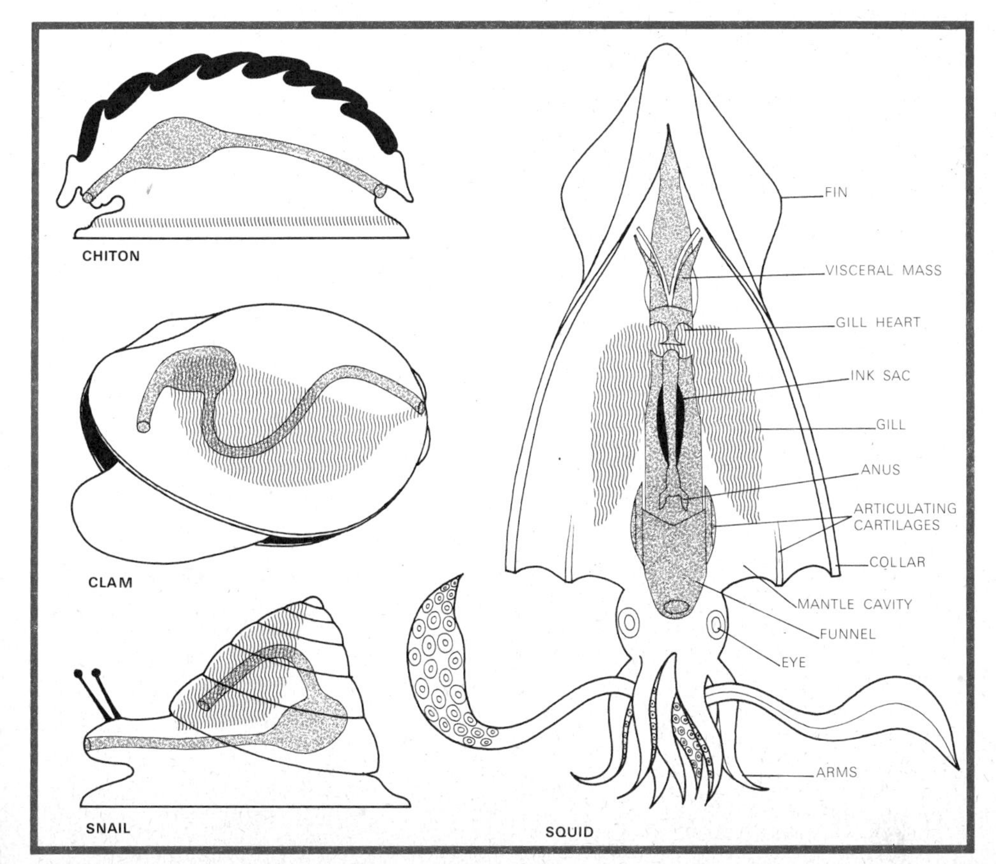


Four examples of molluscs show the development of the various systems. The chiton's digestive tract is a simple tube, while in the squid it is comparatively complex.

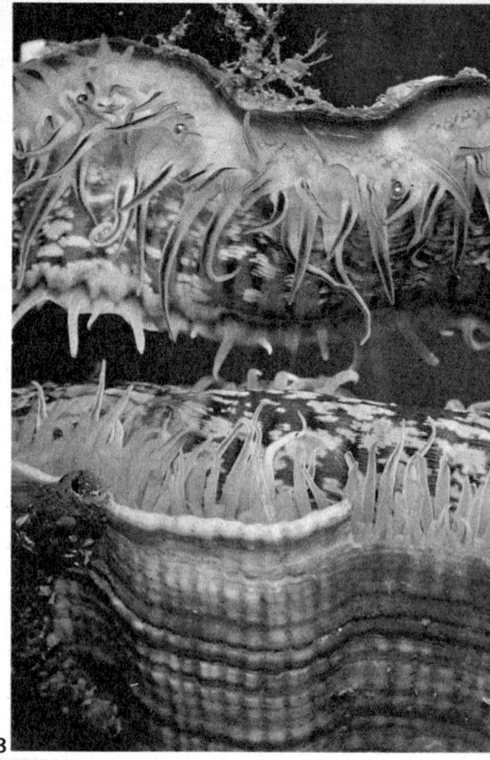

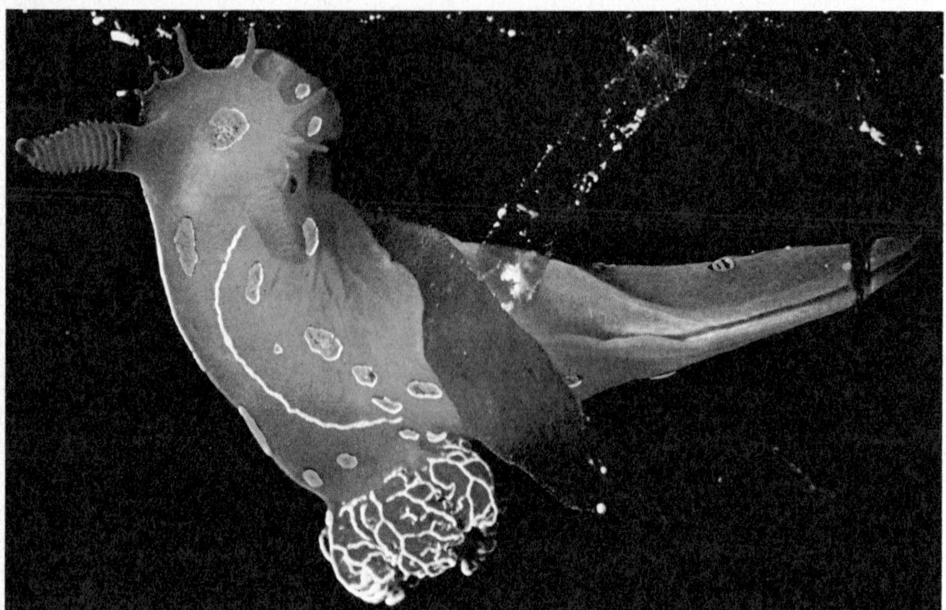

**1** Octopuses, members of the class *Cephalopoda*, are among the most highly organized of the molluscs. This class, whose name means 'head-footed', has a foot which is divided into a number of arms arranged about the head.
**2** Sea slugs are common shell-less gastropods. These strange creatures feed on sponges, hydroids and sea anemones.
**3** Bivalves include the scallop. This view of an open scallop shows eyes and marginal tentacles. The class to which it belongs, *Pelecypoda*, gets its name from the shape of the foot.

have a muscular foot, the same internal systems, and a protective shell.

But the gastropod has many differences. For example, although the gastropod foot does not differ in kind from that of the chiton, it is a much better tool for locomotion.

At the same time a head has developed – with eyes, a brain and tentacles which are located above and in front of the mouth (which incidentally also contains a radula).

## Specialization

There are, however, more specific developments which have enabled certain members of this group to exploit particular aspects of the environment. Although most of them are herbivores, some have turned to flesh for food. These use the radula to file their way into the shells of other molluscs to get at the juicy meat within, and this different food has led to changes in the digestive system. Types both on land and in the sea have discarded their shells altogether, and in consequence have become uncoiled both inside and out. Yet another particularly enterprising group within the gastropods, called the *pteropods* (wing foot), have developed the edges of the foot along the sides of the shell into flaps which they use like wings to swim through the water, thus becoming a great deal more mobile than their sea-bed cousins.

If increased mobility has been the goal of the gastropods, the bivalves (oysters, mussels, clams and so on) have developed in the opposite direction.

These animals have in the main abandoned movement. Further, they do not employ the radular feeding mechanism but depend for both food and oxygen on the manipulation of water.

Central to this process is the development of the bivalve shell. This consists of two halves, a right and a left, which extend to cover the whole of the bivalve. The two halves of the shell are joined by a ligament at the top and held tightly together by internal muscles. But within the shell, the systems of digestion and blood circulation are unchanged from the basic plan. The important differences concern the proportions of the body, in particular the mantle and the gills.

Since the bivalve depends for its existence on drawing in a constant supply of water from which it filters its food and oxygen supply, there are big changes to be seen in both gills and mantle. In most cases the latter has developed so that the edges can be brought together to seal the mantle cavity. But the seal also includes two openings, one to take in water, the other to expel it after use. In some bivalves, the area of the mantle around these gaps is also protrusible, so that in effect the simple openings become tubes of significant size, allowing the bivalve to remain buried with only these life-giving tubes extending to the surface of the sea bed.

The gills have also undergone considerable development. There are two pairs, one on either side of the foot, which as explained earlier is also modified, and the gills extend across almost the whole diameter of the mantle cavity. Gills of this size are required for the oxygen supply, but that is not their only function. The surface of each is covered once again with fine cilia which move the water through the gills but block the suspended food

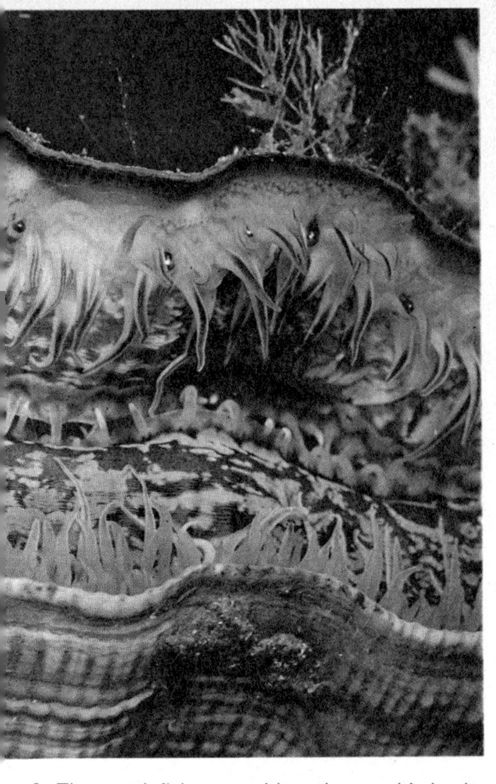

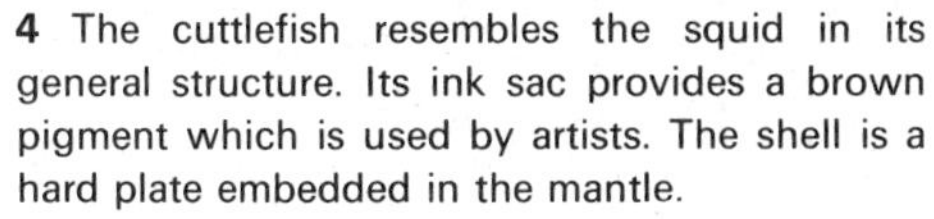

**4** The cuttlefish resembles the squid in its general structure. Its ink sac provides a brown pigment which is used by artists. The shell is a hard plate embedded in the mantle.
**5** One of the most highly developed invertebrates, the squid, shows an amazingly high degree of adaptation to its life as a predator.
**6** *Pteropods* are small molluscs of plankton size. Their discarded shells form a marine ooze in some areas of the ocean. This example is *Spiratella retroversa*.
**7** Snails are one of the few land molluscs. Part of the mantle cavity is modified for breathing. They use the toothed radula to cut off pieces from plants, and in this way they can cause extensive damage to some crops.

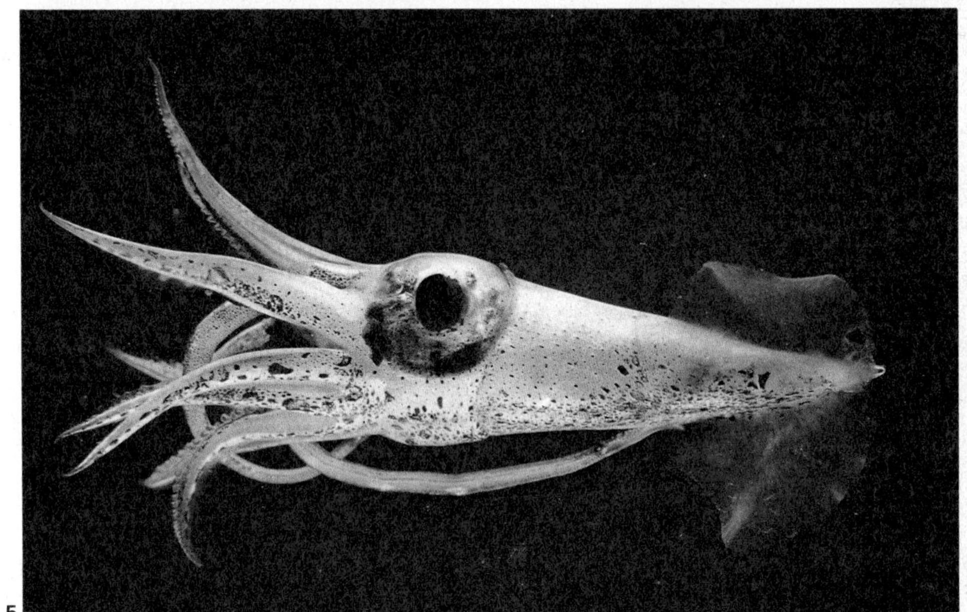

particles. Other cilia sort the food, driving the smaller particles to the mouth and the larger ones into the outflow tube of the mantle.

The bivalve foot lies most of the time within the protection of the shell, but it has been transformed from a broad base for crawling to a slender blade-like structure. The bivalve can now extend the foot between the shells for use as a digging implement or as a lever by which, from time to time, it can change its position in the mud or sand.

Some organs found in molluscs of the locomotive kind are missing in the bivalves. For example, the bivalve has no use for the radular mechanism and consequently this has disappeared. At the same time, except for the scallop, it has no eyes and no tentacles. This is an animal which has elected to stay in one place in order to live. However, they still adopt a number of habitats. Mussels attach themselves to rocks, submerged roots and wooden piles by means of a self-produced natural plastic thread (the *byssus*), and oysters achieve the same end with a naturally secreted cement. Clams and other bivalves spend most of their lives buried in the mud, feeding by means of the extendible mantle tubes. Another mollusc, the shipworm,

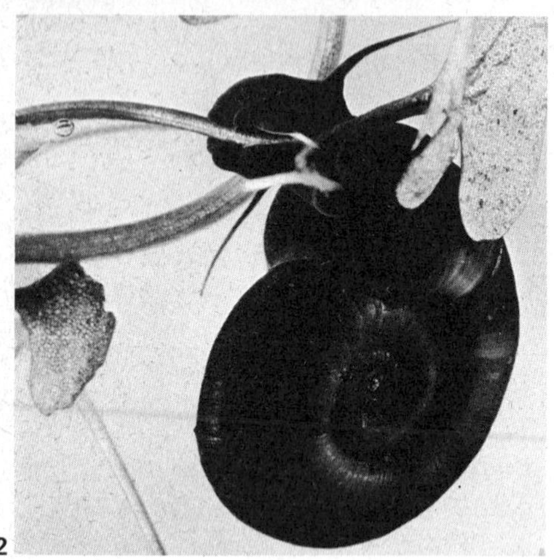

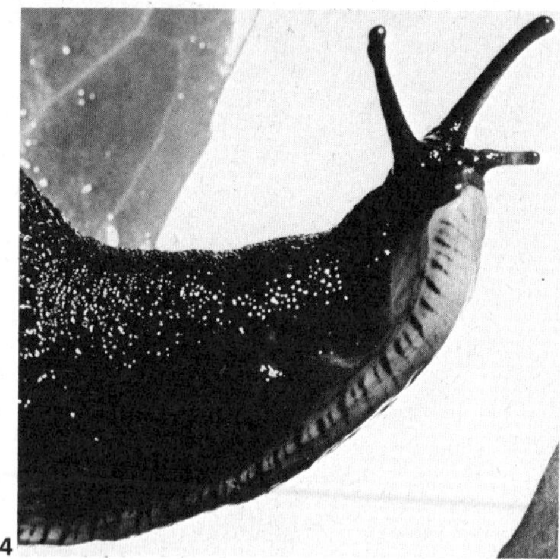

1 This razor shell *(Ensis)* is beginning to burrow into the soft sand. To the right of the picture can be seen the large muscular foot which it uses for locomotion.

2 A large ramshorn snail *(Planorbis corneus)* is seen here feeding on *frogbit,* a common weed. The radula is being used to cut pieces from the leaf.

3 Most chitons, like *Acanthochitona crinita,* are inactive during the day, moving about and feeding in darkness. They are to be found on the underside of rocks on the sea-shore.

4 *Arion ater ater* is a good example of a land slug. These are gastropods which have lost their external shell. They move along a track of slime which they lay in front of them.

uses the hinged end of its shell to bore into wooden sailing vessels and once again 'communicates' with the outside world by means of its tubular mantle. The Romans called it *'calamitas navium',* for it riddled the planking of the Roman galleys. Later on it wrought havoc on Drake's *Golden Hind,* and can still be a menace to wooden piling.

The scallop is an interesting example of special development in two directions. The mantle fringe on both shells carries around a hundred tiny green eyes, with which the animal warily surveys its surroundings for signs of predators. It can also swim by opening and closing its shell violently, an action which jerks it forwards and upwards through the water.

Without doubt the most spectacularly developed group of the molluscs is the *Cephalopoda* (squid, octopus, cuttlefish, nautilus). And among the cephalopods it is undoubtedly the squid which is king. Along with the other molluscs, it has a shell, mantle cavity containing gills, and generally the same vital systems. Unlike its lesser brethren though, it actively hunts and kills its food.

## Predatory molluscs

Some genera may have tentacles as long as 14 feet and bodies up to six feet in length. *Architeuthis,* the Giant Squid, has the distinction of being the largest living invertebrate animal, and cases have been recorded of specimens being found measuring up to 50 feet (including the outstretched tentacles). This, together with its predatory instincts, has earned the squid its formidable reputation as a sea monster.

Its first requirement is high speed and manoeuvrability, so the squid is fitted with Nature's own jet-propulsion system. The animal is able to draw in large quantities of water through one opening and expel it under pressure through another. The first opening is a slit and the second a nozzle, and both appear to be modifications of the mantle openings noted in the bivalve. The nozzle can also be turned downwards or backwards, an idea which the aeronautical engineers have only just begun to use in some vertical-take-off aircraft.

But although the squid's intake and output apparatus does provide water from which the gills can extract oxygen, the openings play no part in feeding.

The squid's body, although still soft, must necessarily move through the water at speed. It is therefore streamlined and requires stiffening. This is supplied by the shell which runs the length of the back but is situated in a pocket of the body.

It also swims backwards, and further reduces resistance to the water by trailing its ten arms straight out from its head.

The origins of the tentacles – the squid has ten, the octopus eight – are a matter of some argument. Some authorities claim that they have developed from the simpler tentacles like those found in the head of the gastropod. Others are equally adamant that these powerful tools have stemmed from the molluscan foot.

In any case, the squid uses them for feeding. Two of the tentacles, being longer than the rest, are used to capture the prey. The other eight are employed in holding the luckless captive close to the mouth cavity. A massive beak then tears the victim to pieces, from which it appears that the mouth of the cephalopod has undergone massive adaptation in the long development from the basic mollusc. Surprisingly though, it has still retained its radula, but this is very small and the use to which it is put is not known.

The brain of the squid is large – in relation to body size, the largest possessed by an invertebrate – and this backs a powerful array of sense organs. The animal depends on sight as well as speed to catch its prey and therefore possesses extremely large and efficient eyes. It also has a combined sense of taste and touch which operates mostly through the suckers on the tentacles but also extends to the whole of its body surface.

All in all, the squid is well adapted for its hunting forays through the oceans and it and the other Cephalopoda mark one extreme of molluscan adaptation. But right the way back to lowly chiton, and including the two other classes which have remained unmentioned (the *Scaphoda,* with their tubular shells, and the *Monoplacophora*), the molluscs have adapted their basic make-up in order to make the best use of varied conditions of life which Nature affords. Small wonder then that there are some 100,000 species and that their realm encompasses the world.

# A step from the sea

**Amphibians – the first animals to leave an aquatic environment, the first to colonize dry land. Today they are a very small but significant remnant of a once much larger family tree.**

ANIMALS HAVE ADAPTED in many different ways to fill the various niches in the complex which makes up the natural world. All life began in the oceans of the Earth, but later some animals moved from the waters to the land in order to exploit the way of life which was offered there. The group of animals which bridges the gap between dry land and water is of course the *Amphibia*. And though as a group they have been relatively unsuccessful – a variety of original classes having reduced to just three modern ones – they are extremely important from the point of view of their linking function.

The amphibians are placed somewhere between the fish and the reptiles in the evolutionary scheme of things, and it is necessary to go to the former for clues concerning the way the amphibians developed.

By far the largest class of fish are the *osteichthyans* or bony fish. Among these we find most of the food fish which Man exploits today, but these are only the modern descendants of much more primitive types, and it is with the primitives that we are really concerned. For the early bony fish started up the road of progress as freshwater types; they were possessed of both gills – for breathing when under water – and lungs for breathing air directly at the surface.

## Development of breathing

From this point they developed in two ways. Some gave up the use of their lungs and spread into the oceans, where incidentally they have been highly successful. Others moved in the opposite direction, eventually losing the use of their gills and taking up lung breathing completely.

This outline of the process is of course very brief and for that reason gives too great an impression of speed. The truth is that the respiratory change took a great deal of time and was also accompanied by other important changes in the physiology of the animals.

Without doubt the most important of these was the change which came about in the paired fins of these early bony fish. The significant example to take here is a

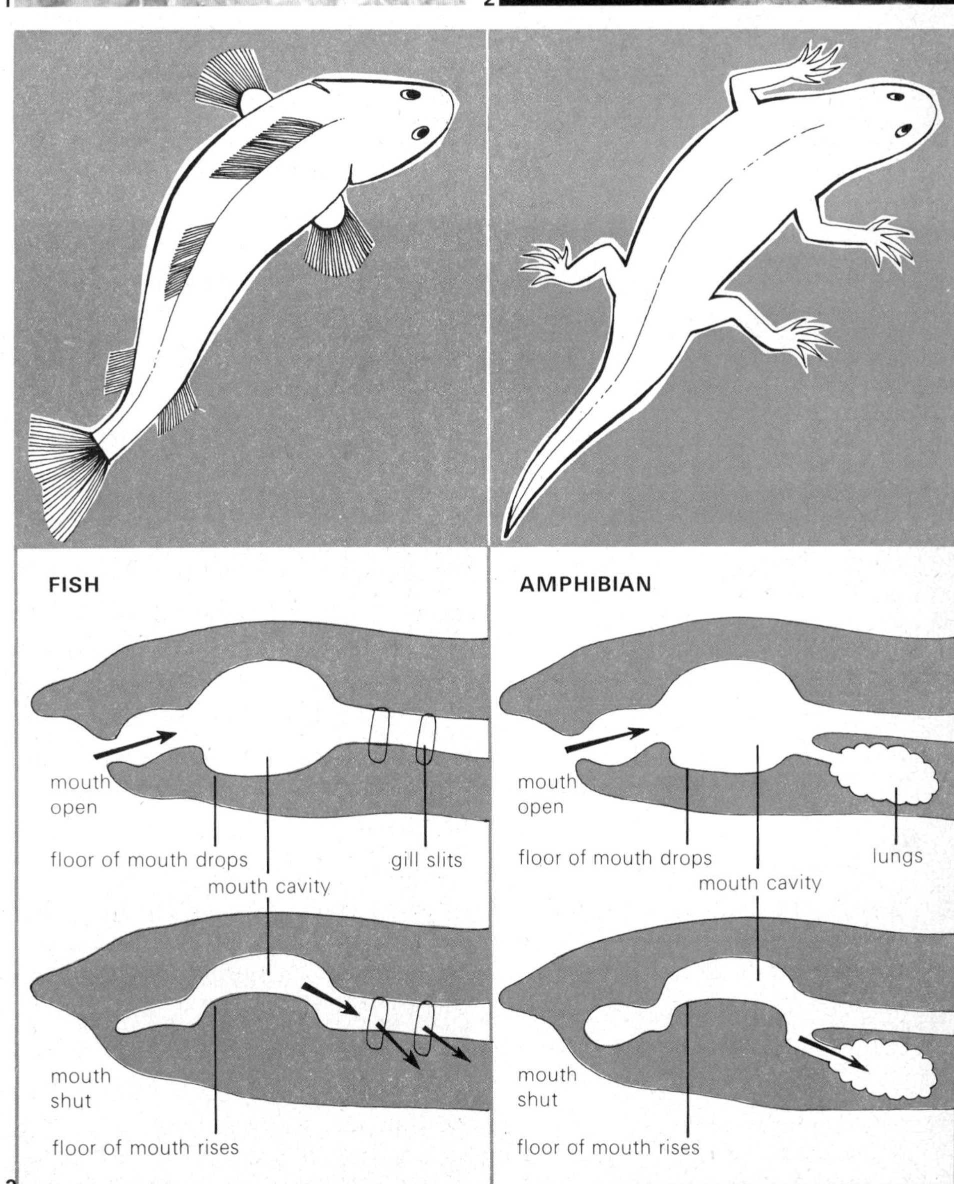


**1** The Alpine newt is a native of mountainous regions of central Europe and some southerly European countries.
**2** The Mexican *axolotl* can live in water and remain in the larval stage for years. In this neotic (non-adult) condition they are still able to lay fertile eggs. This particular variety is albino with pink gills.
**3** Fish and urodeles have similarly shaped bodies and move in basically the same manner. Breathing patterns vary only in that amphibians possess lungs for life above water.

type of fish known as the *Crossopterygii*, ('lobe fins'). These lived in large, freshwater swamps and marshes in the period of history known as the Devonian (350 million years ago) and as might be expected possessed the functional lungs mentioned above. They also had paired pectoral and pelvic fins which were fleshy in nature, and it was from these that the limbs of the amphibians are thought to have developed.

Physiological change did not stop here either. The early amphibians were fish-like in shape and were probably only capable of waddling from one water hole to the next. Other changes had to take place before they were capable of existing fully on land and these concerned the nature of the problems which land-life poses, as opposed to those met in water.

First, in water, a body is supported by its natural buoyancy, but when that precious liquid is absent an efficient system of vertebrae and limbs must be developed to support the body. Next there is the requirement of every living cell for drinking water. When any animal is continuously bathed with water then this is little or no problem, but on dry land arrangements have to be made to conserve water in the body and kidneys.

These were the changes which were necessary and which took place in the rise of the amphibians. By the end of the Devonian period some of the fish-like crossopts had developed legs and had crawled from the water. Later, in the Permo-Carboniferous period (240 million years ago) they had developed even further, although they were still ungainly sprawling brutes very different from the modern types. A typical example were *Eryops*, nearly five feet in length, with stubby legs, a tail and a big flattened and triangular head. The Eryops were also *labyrinthodonts*, a name which refers to their teeth and means literally 'labyrinth toothed'. In other words, their teeth were set in an intricate and maze-like pattern.

## Fossilized evidence

In historical terms, however, the early amphibians were not long on this world. By the Triassic (180 million years ago, and the period which saw the elevation of the continents, the origin of the dinosaur and so on) most of the early forms had disappeared. The rise of the modern forms of amphibian life are poorly documented in terms of fossils (which are in effect the only real way of discovering the form and function of departed animals) but rise they obviously did, for we still have three modern groups of amphibian.

These are the *anurans* which we know better as frogs and toads; the *urodeles* or colourful salamanders, newts and so on and finally the *caecilians*. The latter are much less well known, being worm-like burrowing animals, almost entirely blind and completely limbless. From this it can be clearly seen that the modern amphibians represent several different types of adaption from the basic plan as shown in the very early types.

Among the living types of amphibians the most successful is undoubtedly the

1

2

**1** This yellow and black European salamander is a member of the family *Salamandridae*. Like others in the group they may spend most of their lives within an area of a few square yards from where they were born – they are less visually orientated than frogs.

**2** The illustration shows a crested newt. The dorsal crest becomes prominent at the stage of the sexual cycle when the male is ready for breeding. A large tail is characteristic of the newt family.

**3** Tree frogs possess suction pads on their digits to assist gripping and are particularly good jumpers, but they still spawn in water and the eggs hatch as fish-like tadpoles. This pair are European tree frogs.

3

**1** One of the largest anurans is the giant toad (*Bufo marinus*) which lives in Central and southern America. It has the ability to create an extremely obnoxious smell.
**2** A male tree frog calling his mate. The loose skin of the vocal pouch is momentarily filled and emptied of air to produce the sound. Females do not have this vocal ability.
**3** The skin surface of the frog is either smooth or warty. It conserves water in the body. Frogs from tropical regions tend to have smooth skin, often very colourfully pigmented.
**4** This, the Common Frog, is a largely nocturnal amphibian. Although a poor jumper it can live long distances from water without fear of desiccation.

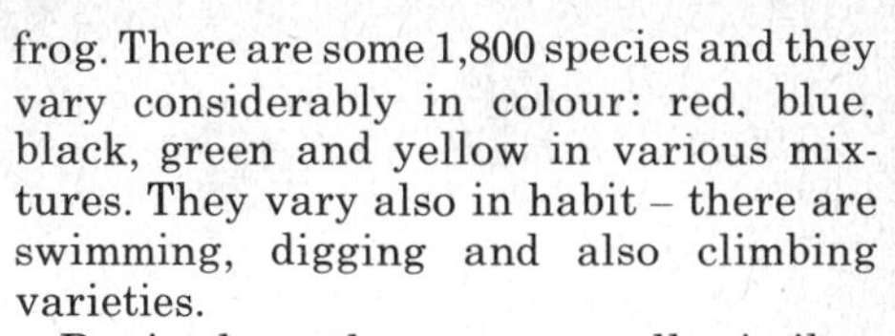

frog. There are some 1,800 species and they vary considerably in colour: red, blue, black, green and yellow in various mixtures. They vary also in habit – there are swimming, digging and also climbing varieties.

But in shape they are generally similar. They have a short squat body without a neck, and they are tail-less. Their back legs are much more powerful than the front ones, the former being used in the anuran's characteristic mode of progress, the leap. Their sense organs include those of sight and smell.

Among the amphibians, the sense of hearing is best developed in frogs, and plays a significant part in the mating ritual of the animals. During the breeding season, which usually occurs after winter hibernation, the males call the females to the breeding areas – the ponds, streams and rivers. Each species of frog has a distinctive call, of which the hoarse croakings of the bullfrog are perhaps most widely talked about, written about and indeed recorded. The females of each species are able, thanks to their hearing, to differentiate between the call of their own species and those emitted by frogs of other species.

Among the amphibians the frogs and toads also occur over the widest area of the Earth's surface. They live north of the Arctic Circle and in the southernmost tips of the continents. Of particular interest is the fact that they have been able to colonize oceanic islands, even though salt water is uncongenial to them. It is thought that they have made the journey to these distant locations on tree trunks and branches carried away during storms. It is also thought that after a particularly heavy rainfall enough fresh water overlays the saline kind to allow the creatures to survive over short distances across the seas.

## Pesticide and poison

Because they are carnivores with a voracious appetite for insects, both frogs and toads have also been introduced by Man into various areas in order to rid farming land of insect pests. An example of this is *Bufo marinus* which is something of a monster, having reached as much as nine inches in length. In fact, it is the largest of all toads and has been introduced into sugar fields in the West Indies, Australia, the Hawaii Islands, New Guinea and elsewhere. But even so, insect control is not its only use – in South America at least. Its body contains a very powerful poison which is used by the South American Indians to provide arrows with an extremely deadly payload for their victims.

It is in the larval stage of the frog and toad that its fishy origins can be glimpsed. The larvae – or tadpoles – begin as simple eggs which are laid by the adults in the water. By hatching time, they have developed the same respiratory and circulatory systems as fish; they have four pairs of gills for breathing, supported by a two-chambered heart which circulates the blood through the gills. The tadpole also swims like a fish, using its longish tail.

The change into a land-living animal is

called the *metamorphosis* and it is an extremely fascinating process. The tadpole begins as a vegetarian with horny teeth; as it grows the tail begins to be absorbed into the globular body. At the same time the gills degenerate and the vestigial lungs develop. But this is not all. In the first place back legs form and are followed by the front, the latter breaking through the body wall near the gill chamber.

The horny jaws give way to bony ones which usually carry teeth, and with this the feeding habits of the frog change radically. From herbivore it becomes a predatory flesh-eater, using a long and prehensile tongue to capture its prey.

Now the frog must literally leave the water or drown, having given up its gills for lungs. Once on land the back legs strengthen in the characteristic way, and the reason why the tail disappeared becomes obvious. If the frog retained its tail the appendage would seriously reduce its jumping powers.

One final point, the skin of the metamorphosed frog is either smooth or warty and it plays a large part in the conservation of moisture mentioned above. Again, it also provides a permeable membrane through which the frog is able to breathe as well as through its lungs.

A major difference between the anurans (frogs) and the second large class of Amphibia, the urodeles (salamanders), is that the latter retain their tails in adult life. It is also true that the metamorphosis is less spectacular than that of the frog, but just as complete.

In most cases, the salamanders produce eggs which eventually hatch into fish-like larvae, but some produce living young. In all cases the offspring have three pairs of gills, a tail for swimming and at first are limbless. Just as in the frog, the back legs develop first, followed by the front, while in most species the gills disappear as the lungs expand and grow.

## A fish on land

As noted above, the salamander retains something of its fish-like quality in adult life. Its legs are small and weak; they are not very effective in the water and are only just able to lift the body when ashore. All of this has its effect upon the way in which the salamander moves on land. When it wants to get from A to B very quickly it merely wriggles across the ground, just like a fish out of water – it does not use its limbs at all. However, when it does walk it still moves sinuously like a fish.

In short, the salamander and indeed the other urodeles like the newt and mud puppy, are much closer to fish than is the frog. This general characteristic is also to be seen in the breathing equipment of the salamander. It has already been pointed out that some salamanders do not lose their gills. But whatever the particular situation the mechanics of breathing are the same and are basically very similar to the fish.

The creature alternately lowers and raises the floor of its throat by means of muscular action. This means that it gulps in mouthfuls of either air or water and the rising of the throat floor forces whichever is concerned into gills or lungs where gas exchange takes place.

In some other respects the salamander is closer to the frog. For example, its skin is scaleless – either smooth or warty. In some species it also plays a part in respiration.

There are some 150 species of Urodela, all of which are fairly similar in structure, having typically four rather short legs all of about the same size (in contrast with the frogs and toads, where the rear pair are greatly developed for the purpose of jumping). In addition they often have a crest of skin along the upper and lower edges of the tail which are useful aids to swimming.

Newts and salamanders are found almost exclusively in the temperate regions of the Northern Hemisphere; about half of them live in North America.

The final class within the amphibian group is that of the caecilians. This contains about 70 species, all of which are roughly similar in appearance. In effect they look more like earthworms than frog or salamander and indeed were once classified among the snakes.

They spend their lives burrowing in sand and mud and for this reason have a compact head protected by a bony shield. Mostly they are to be found in Central and South America, and parts of Asia and Africa. They are elongated and cylindrical in shape and have no limbs at all. They are to all intents and purposes blind, although they do possess rudimentary eyes. Of much greater importance to them are tentacles, which most caecilians possess, which are situated on either side of the nose. These tentacles are used for both taste and smell.

These then are the Amphibia, one of the groups of animals which marks something of a dead end in one branch of evolution. Nevertheless, grotesque and exotic as they may seem, they do mark the triumphant emergence of animal life from the primeval waters. The changes which are necessary for dry-land existence can be seen in them as also can the clues to their fishy ancestry. They are also the stock from which sprang that much more efficient class of animal the reptile – and ultimately Man himself.

It is a sobering thought that we, so confident of our superiority among the animal species, have very good reason for following St Francis of Assisi in referring to that bloated croaker in the woodland pool as 'Brother Frog'.

**1** The *Eryops Permian* was an early amphibian living about 240 million years ago. A reconstruction from fossilized remains shows its numerous teeth and bulky body.

**2** Tadpoles swimming near the surface after four weeks of life. As they grow, gills disappear and are replaced by lungs. Tails are absorbed after the little frogs leave the water.

1

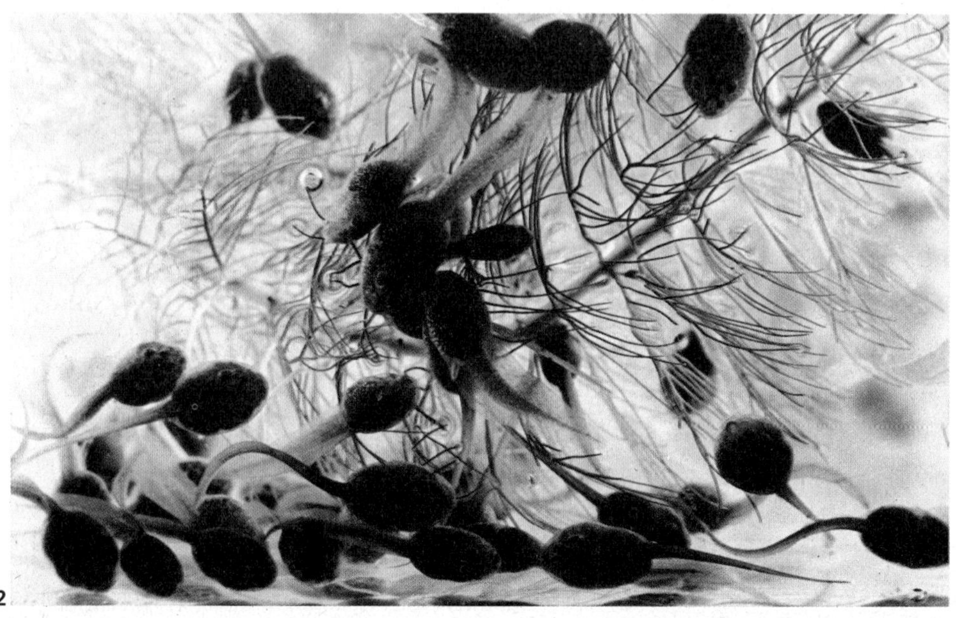

2

# Animals with external skeletons

Arthropods live in the sea, on land and in the air. They thrive in almost every conceivable environment. Their success in adapting is due in large measure to their external skeleton.

SCIENCE-FICTION WRITERS often torture their readers with the might-have-been of evolution. There are many stories about what might have happened if human beings had been beaten in the evolutionary struggle. The insects are Man's most effective rivals for control of the Earth. Together with their close allies, the marine and freshwater crustaceans, they make up more than two-thirds of the animal species on Earth. Many of these species are present on Earth in vast numbers, and in some cases there are many more representatives of a single insect species than there are human beings.

Insects and crustaceans between them have conquered every type of environment on this planet. They live on land, on the surface of lakes and the sea, underwater, between the tide-lines, in the air and underground. In fact, there is an *arthropod* to fill almost every available ecological niche. This in itself is a tribute to the tremendous adaptability of the type. Despite the tremendous variety, almost all of them can be recognized as belonging to the same general type of animal.

The name *arthropod* refers to the jointed legs characteristic of animals in this phylum. The arthropods are divided into several major groups, the most important and widespread of which is the insects. The phylum also includes the very large group of crustaceans (lobsters, crabs, shrimps, barnacles, crayfish) and the centipedes, millepedes and arachnids (a group which includes spiders, ticks, mites and scorpions).

Why are the arthropods so successful? The answer to this question is complex, but it can be summed up simply in one word: *exoskeleton*. In Man and other higher animals the muscles and other soft tissues of the body are supported by an internal core of bones which give the body its shape and make the limbs and trunk rigid. In the arthropods the tissues are supported by a rigid external covering rather like a suit of armour. The exoskeleton makes it possible to maintain a fairly constant internal environment; for example, it prevents rapid loss of water under dry conditions and prevents waterlogging when the animal is wet. It can be fashioned into all sorts of shapes so that the arthropod's shell becomes specialized for various functions suitable for its particular place in the ecological spectrum. This exoskeleton, also called the *cuticle*, is formed from a remarkable protein called *chitin*. Chitin itself is a fairly elastic substance. Where rigidity is required, it is combined with various salts to make it less liable to bend.

1 The hermit crab (*Eupagurus bernhardus*) lives inside the disused shell of other marine creatures. It has sets of legs of different lengths so that it enters the shell with a spiral motion.

In a typical arthropod the exoskeleton consists of four layers. On the outside is a thin layer of wax which makes the exoskeleton waterproof. Underneath this are two layers of chitin – a rigid layer on the outside and a flexible layer on the inside. Underneath the chitin is the first layer of the animal's cells – the *epidermis*.

## The segmented shell

The flexibility of the chitin can be varied in such a way that the arthropod has flexible joints, between which are inflexible areas, thus forming definite limbs and segments of the body. Chitin provides protection without sacrificing mobility. Contrast the hard exoskeleton of the snail, which places grave limitations on its movements.

But although the exoskeleton does much to ensure the success of arthropods, it also imposes grave limitations on them. The larger the animal, of course, the heavier and more restricting the exoskeleton becomes. For this reason, all arthropods are rather small animals, and some are minute. In fact, most of the large arthropods are found in the sea or in fresh water, where the weight of their exo-

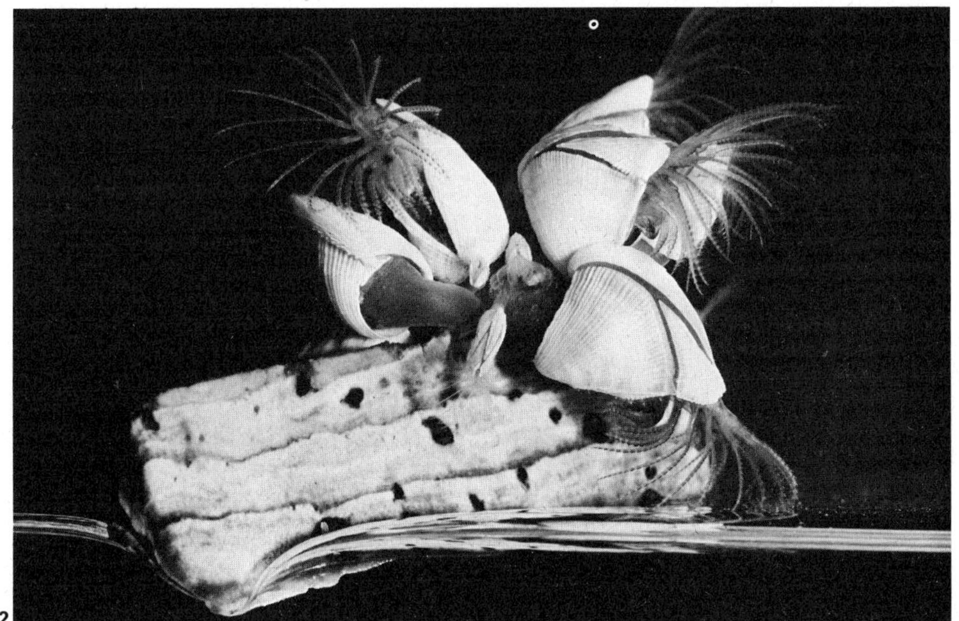

2 Barnacles were once classified as molluscs because of their shells, but the chitinous appendage which they use for gathering food identifies them as true arthropods.

skeletons is borne by the water.

The body of arthropods is divided into segments which are frequently grouped together into head, thorax and abdomen. The head of all arthropods consists of six segments, but the number of segments in the rest of the body varies from species to species. Each of the segments bears projections or appendages, but these are generally specialized to serve different functions: some may be sensitive to touch or scent, like the antennae, others may be developed to serve as wings, while still others may become legs. In some arthropods, an appendage may become so large as to be the dominant feature of the body: an example is the male fiddler crab, in which one of the claws is massively developed as a secondary sexual characteristic. The crab owes its name to the to-and-fro movements of this limb during courtship, similar to a violinist's action.

The head of the typical arthropod, as already mentioned, consists of six segments. The first segment bears no appendage, while the second and third together bear either one or two antennae. The jaws are on the fourth segment and vary considerably from species to species depending on the method of feeding. The fifth and sixth segments bear accessory jaws.

## Anatomical variation

The other main features of the head are the eyes, which can be simple, as in the spiders, or compound, as in the insects. The simple eye consists of a bundle of light-sensitive cells lying under a single lens. In the compound insect eye, however, each cell has its own individual lens, and the entire unit is separated from its neighbours by pigment cells. A compound eye produces an effect similar to a newspaper half-tone block – the image is broken up by the eye into a series of spots of differing intensities, and the eye sees a mosaic. Such a system is not quite as effective as the vertebrate eye found in human beings, although it is extremely sensitive to motion within the field of view.

The number of segments in the thorax depends on the group involved. The more primitive groups, such as the crustacea and the millepedes and centipedes, have varying numbers of segments. The insects, however, always have three thorax segments, all with a pair of legs each. The second and third thorax segments carry a pair of wings each. The wings and legs vary considerably with the species: the wings may be horny or filmy, long or short, while the legs may be adapted for a number of purposes in addition to walking. In the honey-bee, for example, the legs are modified to hold pollen.

The only appendage on the abdomen is the sexual organ. In the female this is a vagina, and there may also be an *ovipositor* for depositing eggs in the desired position. In the male, the sperm ducts open on to the surface of the body in the abdominal region.

This is only the briefest sketch of the anatomy of the arthropods. The most striking thing about these animals is the way in which this basic structure can be varied and adapted to give rise to such varied species as the ants and the crayfish, the grasshoppers and the spiders, the centipedes and the shrimps. This alone is an indication of the immense advantages of the exoskeleton and of the insect structure, making it possible for the arthropods to become dominant.

For, from a biological standpoint, the arthropods can be regarded as even more dominant than mankind. Insects and other arthropods have been able to colonize environments that would be unthinkable for Man. Indeed, in many cases insects have been effective in preventing human beings from inhabiting certain parts of the world. In many areas, until recent years, life was made intolerable by mosquito-borne malaria. In parts of Africa even today sleeping sickness (carried by the *tsetse fly*) is still an almost insuperable

1 The butterfly grows to maturity within the pupa (called a *chrysalis*) and emerges as a fully developed adult. The change from larva to adult is called *metamorphosis*.

2 Fiddler crabs scavenge on sandy beaches. They take their name from the characteristic to-and-fro movement of the male's hugely enlarged left pincer. The female has pincers of equal size.

obstacle to human habitation. Plague, carried by a flea, ravaged the population of Western Europe in historic times, and the battle with harmful insects is by no means over. Insects like the colorado beetle, the locust, the termite and the boll weevil damage and destroy many millions of pounds' worth of food and crops every year. And yet, without insects and other arthropods, large sections of the plant life on this planet would become extinct. Most of the higher plants rely to varying degrees on insects to fertilize and pollinate their seeds. This very fact indicates how ubiquitous insects are and how closely their lives are bound up with other species with which they co-exist.

Their reproductive system is another reason for the great success of arthropods. Again we can see how a relatively simple basic plan can be adapted in an almost infinite number of ways to take account of variations in environment. Arthropods lay large numbers of small eggs and the young usually hatch from the eggs in an immature condition. In order to develop further the young must be viable animals in their own right. The young animal that hatches from the egg is a *larva.* The instincts of the parent insect or crustacean have already led it to place the eggs in a favourable position for the future growth of the larvae. The parent insect may go to great lengths to ensure the right conditions for the growth of her offspring.

The most highly developed of the insects, the social bees, wasps and ants, build highly complex nests in order to care for their young, and the entire colony takes part in a complicated procedure to ensure that the young have the optimum conditions for growth. Specialized members of the colony are developed to provide for defence, construction, feeding, egg-laying and other functions.

**1** Lacewing flies live on the juices of small insects and on vegetation. They lay their eggs among colonies of aphids and the larvae feed on these while they are developing.
**2** Clusters of barnacles are to be found on rocks, flotsam, and the hulls of ships where they can cause considerable drag and loss of power.
**3** Giant millepedes (*Diplopoda*) are classed as *Antennata.* As shown, they are often host to mites, arachnids which are also found on human skin.
**4** Scorpions catch their prey with their large pincers and sting them to death with their tails. The prey, spiders and insects, are then sucked dry. The scorpion hunts at night and its sting, though painful, is seldom fatal to human beings.

1

2

3

4

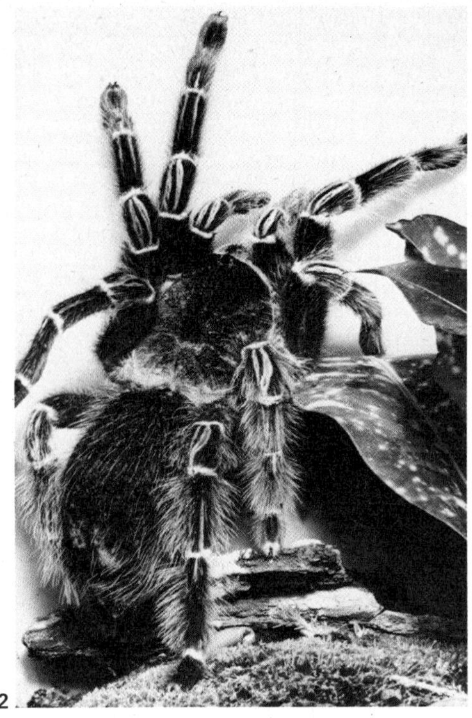

**1** There are almost 20,000 species of rhinoceros beetle, so called from the horns on the thorax. It lives on vegetation and makes its home in palm trees. Despite its heavy shell, it flies very well.
**2** South American tarantulas sometimes grow up to seven inches long, and occasionally catch small birds. Smaller tarantulas are preyed on by the *Pepsis* wasp; it lays its eggs in the body of the tarantula, which provides food for the larvae.
**3** *Lithobius forficatus*, a common variety of centipede, produces young which hatch with only seven segments, the rest being added as the animal develops.
**4** The young of *isopods* develop in a brood pouch and emerge as smaller versions of the adult crustacean.

The larvae of most insects are more specialized than the larvae of the aquatic crustaceans. The crustacean larvae are generally free-swimming forms which are rather like smaller versions of their parents. These larvae undergo a gradual change to become adults. In the insects and the higher arthropods, however, the larvae are so different from the parents that it is impossible for them to change gradually into adults. They therefore undergo a sharp change known as *metamorphosis*. Having gorged itself, the larva, which may be a caterpillar in the case of moths and butterflies, surrounds itself with a cocoon of protective material and changes into a *pupa*. The pupa appears as a quiescent stage in the life of the insect. It does not move around or eat, and it is surrounded by a protective shell. When the insect finally emerges from the cocoon, it is a fully developed adult. Metamorphosis in many insects may take a long time – in some cases many years – but the insect is heavily protected while it undergoes this change and has the best conditions for becoming an adult.

One of the characteristic features of this type of life cycle is that it allows for a division of labour during the various stages of the cycle. An animal normally has to feed, mate, and distribute the offspring. In the case of many insects these functions are carried out separately by the different stages of the insect's life. The primary function of the caterpillar in most butterflies, for example, is to feed. In some insects, like the dragonfly, the adult is not equipped at all for feeding and has only one purpose, to mate and lay the eggs. This division of labour enables some insects to exploit two totally different environments. The mosquito is an example, the larva living in fresh water and feeding on minute particles. The adult lives on land and in the air, and feeds on blood.

In the most highly developed of the arthropods, the social bees, wasps and ants, specialization has been carried a great deal further. These animals operate as a social community, in which the various members are mutually dependent, and elaborate mechanisms are developed to enable the life of the colony to proceed smoothly. In termite colonies, for example, the sterile workers build the nest, forage for food, and feed the egg-laying queen. The queen is fertilized by specialized reproductives – similar to the drones of bee colonies – whose sole function is to fertilize the queen and establish new colonies. The colony is protected from intruders by specially equipped soldiers which cannot feed themselves.

## Instinctual organization

So intricate is the organization of this type of colony that many people have been inclined to treat it as a manifestation of intelligent behaviour. But although the colony as a whole may appear to be organized along highly intelligent lines, and reacts to situations in an apparently intelligent way, the basis for this is not intelligence as known among human beings, but the operation of a complex of built-in instincts which are established even before the insects are born.

The arthropods are very well suited for life on Earth, within certain limits. Their exoskeleton protects them from variations in the environment, and is extremely adaptable for a wide range of specialized functions. Their short life-span makes it possible for their evolution to take place at a rapid rate, and they can thus adapt to gradual changes in their environment. The adaptability of the basic arthropod form makes it possible for them to specialize in thousands of different forms to suit the requirements of particular ecological niches.

The present period of time on the Earth has been called 'the age of the Insects', and we can see that there is a great deal of justification for this view. Perhaps it is as well for human beings that the anatomy and physiology of the arthropods restrict them to small size and short life-spans.

# Inside the egg

**Eggs are involved somewhere in the reproduction of all higher animals, from insects to human beings. Paradoxically, the human egg is one of the smallest eggs found in nature.**

EGGS ARE very simple yet at the same time potentially extremely complex. A hen's egg looks perfectly straightforward but it contains within its simple-looking shell all that is necessary for the growth of a bird. The case of human beings is even more striking. The 'egg' is many times smaller than the hen's, but the final product is decidedly more complicated. This paradox is one of the most interesting of all biological phenomena. The discovery of the genetic code, which shows how the cell nucleus can contain enormous amounts of information in an extremely condensed form, has gone a long way towards outlining how this age-old problem can be explained.

The egg, whether of the hen or of the human being, consists of a fusion between a cell contributed by the female and a cell contributed by the male.

The contribution of the male is the *spermatozoon,* while the female contributes the *ovum.* Some of the genetic material from each cell goes to form the genetic material of the new cell. In this way, the egg contains some of the characteristics of the male parent and some of the characteristics of the female parent.

A unique series of changes takes place in the germ cells before fusion to reduce the amount of genetic material in each germ cell. The aim of this is to make sure that the genetic make-up of the egg contains the same amount of information as is in the cells of the parent. Too much or too little genetic information would be disastrous to the developing egg – either way it would not be able to develop properly and would give rise to monstrous forms of life.

The male cells are formed in the *germinal epithelium.* In Man and other higher animals, this tissue is found in the testes, but in some of the lower animals, the tissue giving rise to the spermatozoa is less specialized. In any event, the creation of a mature sperm is a process known as *gametogenesis.*

All the cells of the germinal epithelium can potentially become spermatozoa, but only some do so. A germ cell destined to become a sperm first divides several times in the usual way giving a number of *spermatogonia,* each of which contains a full complement of genetic material. Later, the spermatogonia come to lie near the outside of the germinal tissue and then undergo a remarkable and unique type of cell division called *meiosis.* In this process, instead of giving rise to two cells each containing two of each chromosome, the cells produced have only half the number of chromosomes in the normal cell. Each of the two cells thus produced then gives rise to two other cells, also with half the usual number of chromosomes, and these cells then set about taking on the characteristic features of sperms. The exact form of the sperm depends on the species of animal involved, but all sperms have in common the ability to move rapidly and to respond to chemical stimuli which attract them towards the female germ cells. In many cases, the sperms are provided with long tails, which lash about in fluid to provide the sperm with motive power.

In the female, the process of production of the germ cell, in this case an ovum, is similar to that in the male, with the important exception that each of the primary cells produces only one and not four ova. The other three cells produced with only half the normal complement of chromosomes degenerate and form the polar bodies, which are pushed to one end of the ovum and play no further part in reproduction.

The ova vary very considerably in size from species to species but they are always larger than the sperms. The reason for this is that the ova always contain a large amount of protein and nutritive material

**1** A Rhode Island bantam hen with her chick. The chick is only a few hours old, but has many built-in reflex actions, such as pecking for food, which enable it to survive.
**2** The carpenter ant builds complex warrens inside trees and fallen wood to house its eggs. The eggs are carefully looked after by the whole community.
**3** Worker bees on a brood comb. The queen bee lays her eggs in the prepared comb, and the eggs and grubs are fed and cared for by the workers.

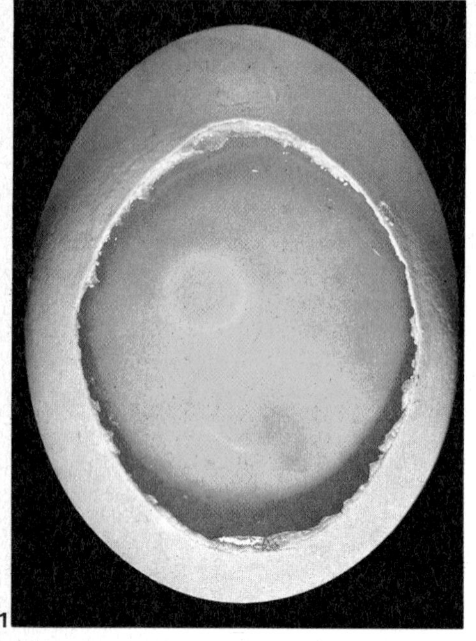

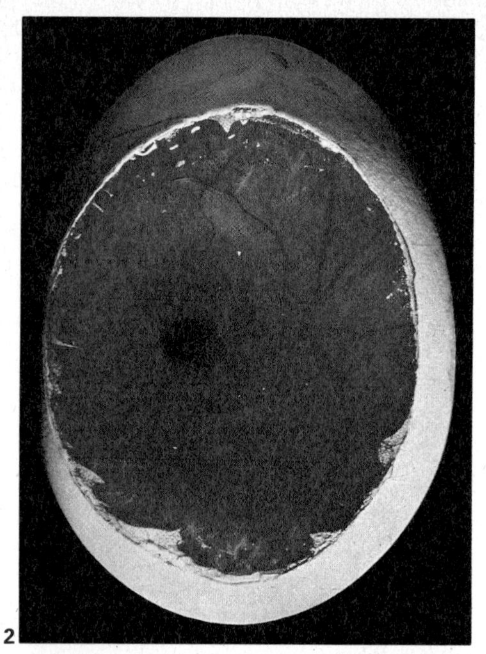

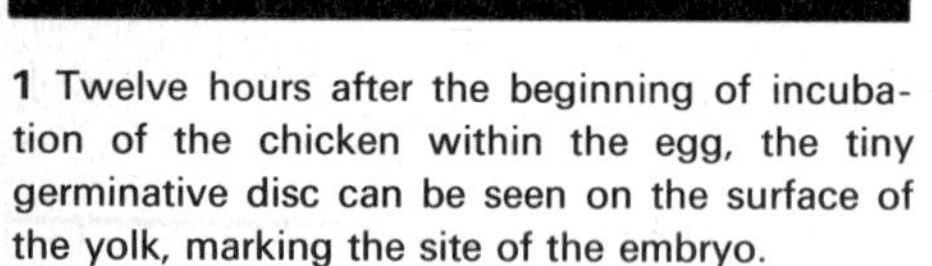

**1** Twelve hours after the beginning of incubation of the chicken within the egg, the tiny germinative disc can be seen on the surface of the yolk, marking the site of the embryo.
**2** Six days later: blood vessels now extend across the yolk, and the embryo, with its large eyes, heart and gut, is now clearly recognizable and digesting the yolk.
**3** The 13-day embryo has almost all the organs of the adult. At this stage, the muscles and cartilage are formed, and the feathers and lungs begin to develop.

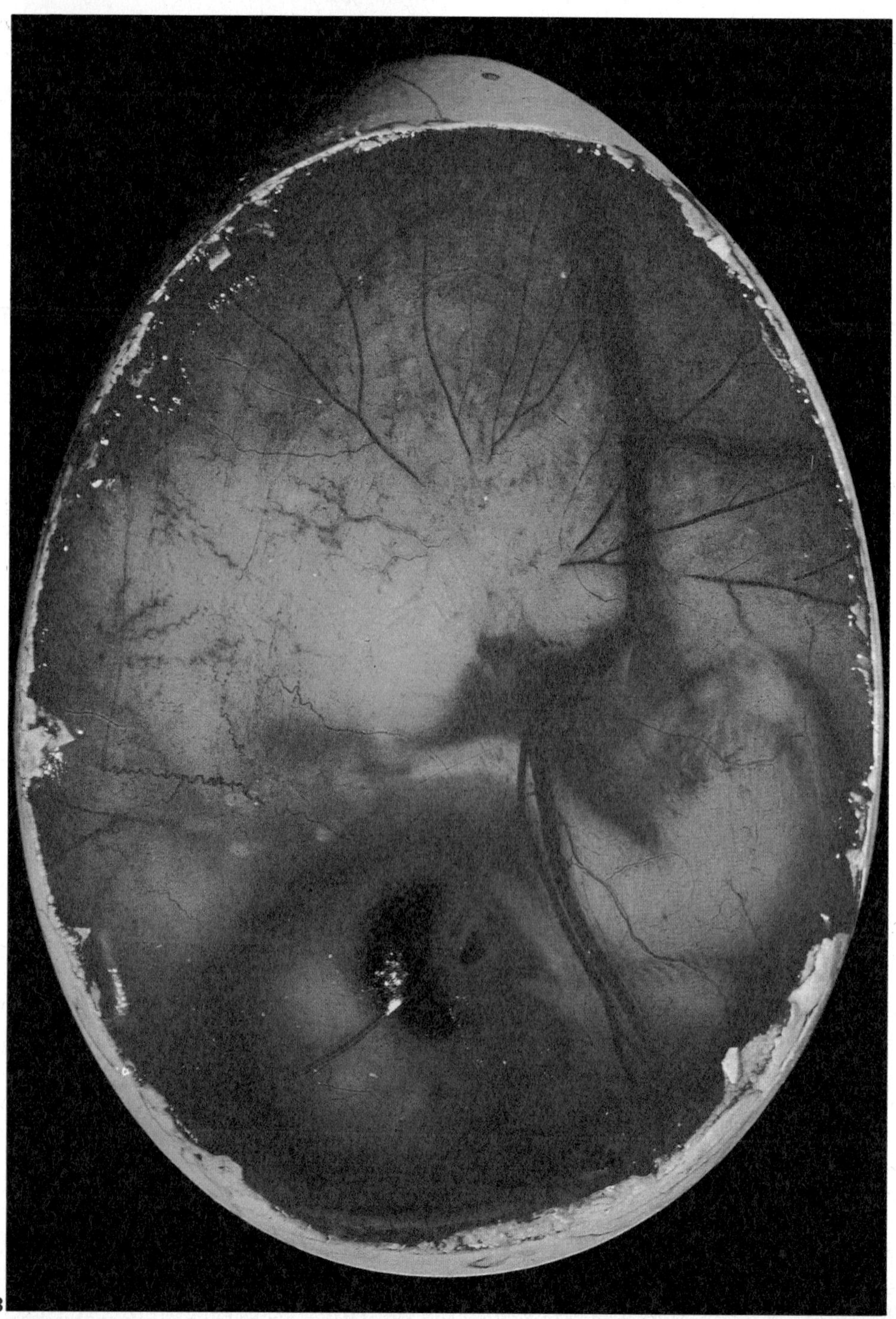

for the development of the embryo. In birds like the chicken, this provision is greatly exaggerated, and bird ova are in fact the largest animal cells known. The yolk tends to lie at one end of the cell, called the vegetative pole, while the nucleus of the egg lies at the other end of the cell, called the animal pole, in a region more or less free from yolk. In the eggs of birds, reptiles and fish the yolk present is so great that the non-yolky portion is restricted to a small cap at the animal end of the cell. The eggs of the advanced mammals are an exception to this. They do not require large amounts of yolk because the embryo is nourished mainly from the maternal blood-stream, so that a large yolk is unnecessary.

Fertilization takes place by the fusion of the sperm and the ovum to form a single cell. In this process, the sets of chromosomes provided from each partner in the union are brought together. Since each partner has provided only half the full cellular complement of chromosomes, the resulting fertilized egg cell has the same number of chromosomes after fusion as are contained in the normal cell. Once fertilization has taken place, the cells immediately begin to divide and shortly thereafter start to form the rudiments of the different tissues of the body. This process of differentiation of the cellular elements, the growth of the different tissues, and the overall development of the animal, take place in the egg according to a schedule which is similar even in such widely dissimilar species as birds and mammals. Thus, the development of a human embryo, at least in its early stages, is very like that of a chicken.

The fusion of the male and female cells depends on the species involved. In different species it is brought about in different ways. In many lower animals, such as amphibia, fertilization takes place outside the body of the female and the male frog injects his sperms over the eggs as they are produced by the female. The fertilized eggs are then left to function as independent cells and receive no protection from the adult frogs. In insects fertilization generally takes place inside the female's body, which means that the eggs are protected from the worst rigours of the external environment until they are nearer maturity. Many insects make complicated provision to ensure that their eggs are well catered for during their development. The female ichneumon fly injects her fertilized eggs into the body of a caterpillar, in such a way that the eggs are provided with the ideal conditions to

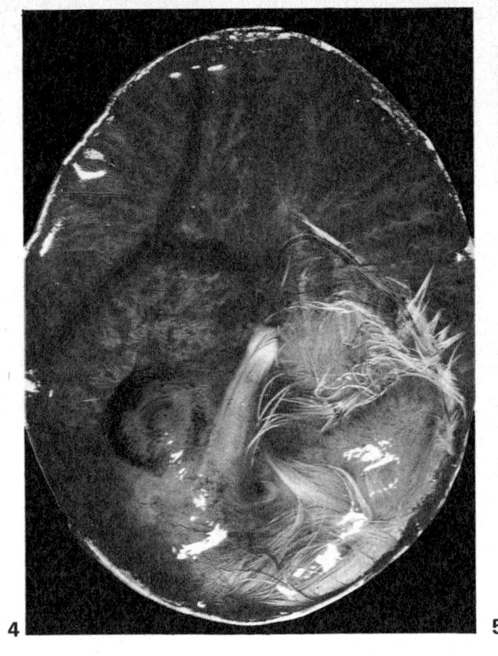

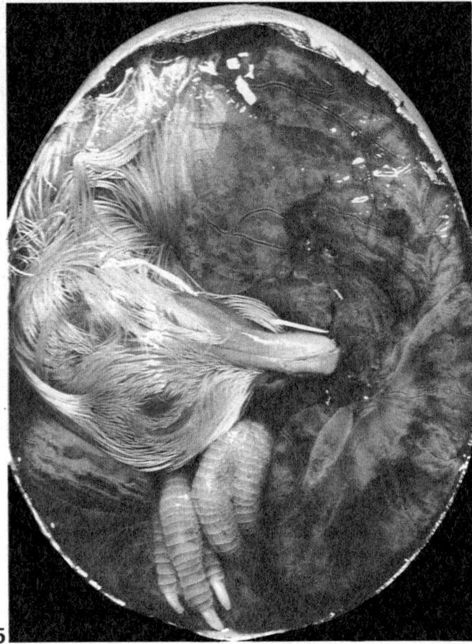

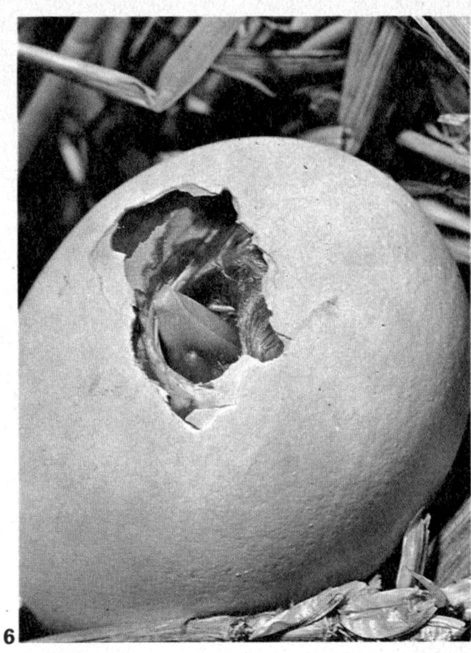

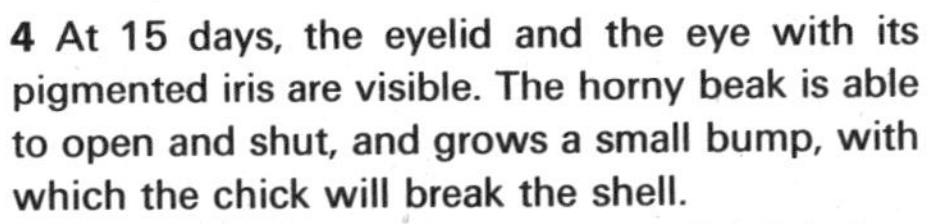

**4** At 15 days, the eyelid and the eye with its pigmented iris are visible. The horny beak is able to open and shut, and grows a small bump, with which the chick will break the shell.
**5** The 17-day-old embryo is cramped tightly into the shell. By now almost all the yolk has gone. The bird can be heard to 'cheep' at this age when it opens its beak for air.
**6** Twenty-one days old: using the bump on its beak, the chick breaks the shell and starts to peck out a circular opening to free itself. It can take between an hour and two days.
**7** The shell is cut neatly and cleanly in two and the chicken freed. Still damp from the egg, it fluffs its downy feathers and peers around at the world outside.

hatch out in a protected environment – inside the caterpillar. The larvae are able to feed on the flesh of the caterpillar during their development. Eventually, of course, the larvae eat so much of the caterpillar that it dies.

In other cases, insects go to considerable trouble to build nests for their eggs, to keep them out of the way of predators while they are developing. The logical conclusion of this process takes place among the social insects, the bees and ants, in which the whole colony centres around the nest, and eggs are provided with almost ideal conditions for their development, the right temperature being carefully maintained by the efforts of the entire hive. In these insects there is specialization of tasks so that in many cases only one member of the insect community, the 'queen', is able to produce eggs. In the flying ants, fertilization takes place only once a season, although the queen goes on producing eggs for a long period; she is able to store sperms until required to fertilize her eggs.

Most insects produce very large numbers of eggs. Instead of producing one egg which is carefully looked after, as is the case in the higher species of animals, the female produces many thousands of eggs after mating, although the rate of loss of eggs through death and predation is very high.

Many species make efforts to protect

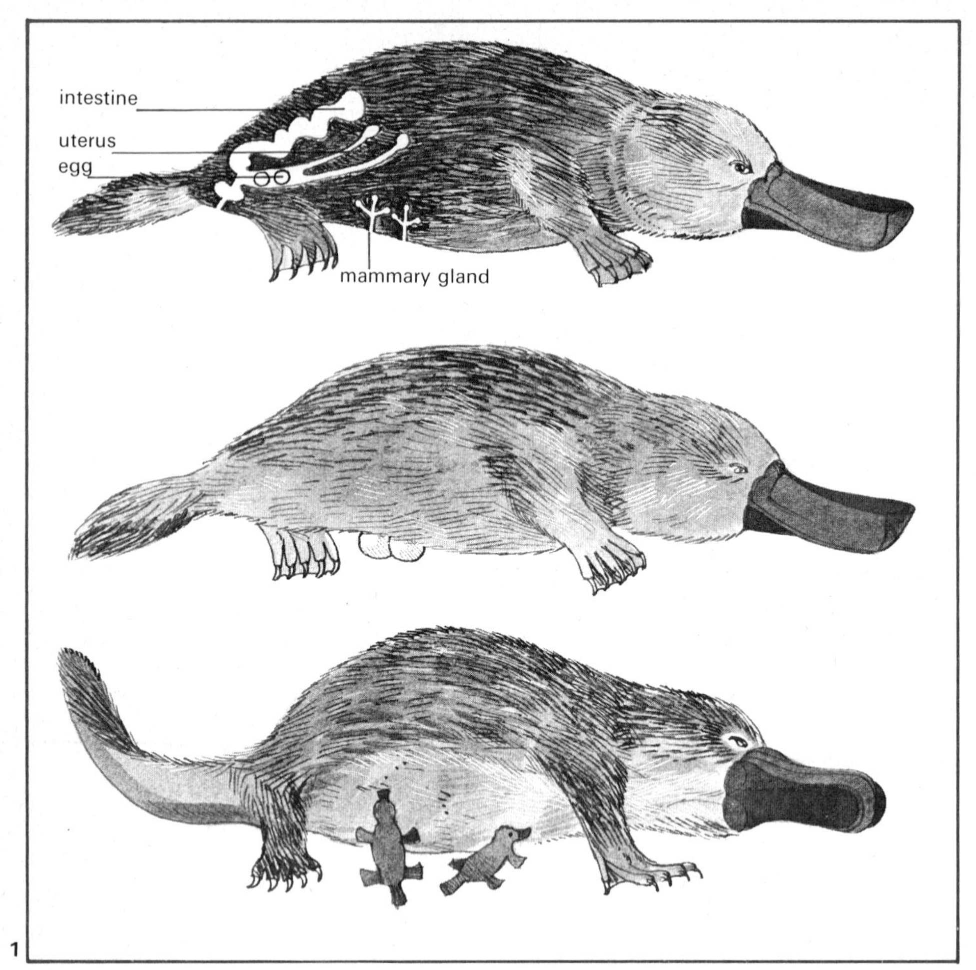


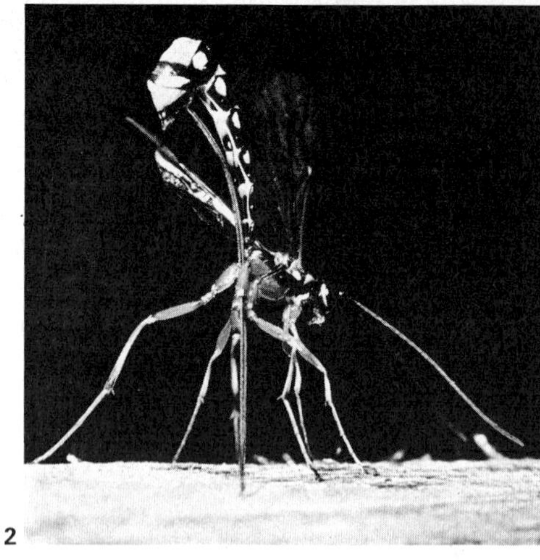

1 The Australian platypus, a primitive mammal, lays eggs and suckles its young. The fertilized eggs from the uterus are laid and hatched by maternal heat.

2 The ichneumon fly has a long ovipositor or egg-tube. It probes through tree-bark to find insect grubs and then lays its eggs inside the living grubs, which serve the larvae as food.

3 The chain king snake (*Lampropeltis*) lays its eggs in a hollow in the sand, and coils itself around them. Only some of the eggs (those in the background of this photograph) are fertile.

their eggs while they are developing. The eggs may be enclosed in some sort of protective shell as is the case with most birds, or hidden under the ground as in the turtles of the Indian Ocean. Where the egg has to develop in a warm environment, egg-laying may take place at a favourable time of the year, so that the eggs will be exposed to the sun's warmth. In the more developed species, however, particularly in the mammals and the birds, the predominant part is played by maternal care. In birds, a typical example is provided by the hen. In this bird, the egg is large and well provided with nutriments essential to the development of the chick. The embryo at the beginning is no more than a small dot at one end of the yolk. The yolk and the white (albumen) are rich in protein essential to the chick's development. In addition the egg is protected by a hard shell which keeps the chick away from harmful environmental influences.

## Hatching the eggs

Many birds camouflage their eggs to keep them from harm; they are usually laid in sheltered or protected places, and nests are built to protect the eggs and later the chicks when they hatch out. Most birds lay relatively few eggs in each clutch, but in birds maternal and paternal concern for their young is frequently highly advanced, so that the few eggs are cared for before, during and after hatching.

In order to develop, eggs must be kept at a certain minimum temperature. This temperature is relatively easy to maintain for those species that lay their eggs in water or underground. Otherwise, among birds, this is achieved by 'sitting' on the eggs from the time they are laid until the time they hatch. This job often falls to the lot of the male bird, although in many bird species the parents take it in turns. Their body heat keeps the eggs warm and provides ideal conditions for them to hatch. If the eggs are left too long without heat they will die. The instincts of the birds provide the motive for continuing this procedure, which is carried on with great dedication by many species.

Reptiles also lay eggs but they are usually left to fend for themselves once they are laid. Many reptiles go to great lengths to lay their eggs in some favoured spot. Turtles, for example, come thousands of miles to lay their eggs at traditional nesting sites in the Indian Ocean. They come out of the water and drag themselves painfully over the sand to lay the eggs at a place above the high-tide mark. In order to provide for the eggs, the female turtles dig holes in the ground, a process involving an enormous expenditure of energy, for these animals are ill equipped for digging on land, although well able to cope with conditions in the sea. Once the eggs are laid, they are covered over by sand, and the turtle leaves them to the heat of the sun. Other reptiles watch over their eggs and build nests for them. This sort of nesting behaviour is common, for example, among snakes.

The only mammals which lay eggs are the extremely primitive Australian monotremes, the duck-billed platypus and the echidna. These animals are midway between the form of reproduction found in advanced mammals and that found in reptiles. They are considered mammals because despite the fact that they lay eggs, they also suckle their young.

In the true mammals the eggs develop inside the body of the mother. They become attached to the wall of the uterus and develop in communication with the bloodstream of the mother. This form of reproduction, known as placental reproduction, carries to its logical conclusion the process of maternal care for eggs found in birds and reptiles. Instead of providing a single cell to accommodate and provide nutrition for the developing embryo, and instead of the parents having to carry out a complicated set of instinctive procedures in order to keep the embryo warm, the egg is fed directly from the mother while it is developing, and thus is given the best chance of 'a good start in life'. In mammals the development of the egg is similar to that in other forms of life, with the exception of the formation of the placenta, but mammals tend to produce only a limited number of young which are not born until after a period of development in the womb.

# Why the egg becomes a chicken

What determines the fate of the tiny egg cell? Why is it that hens' eggs always turn into chickens? Modern biology has many of the answers to this long-standing mystery.

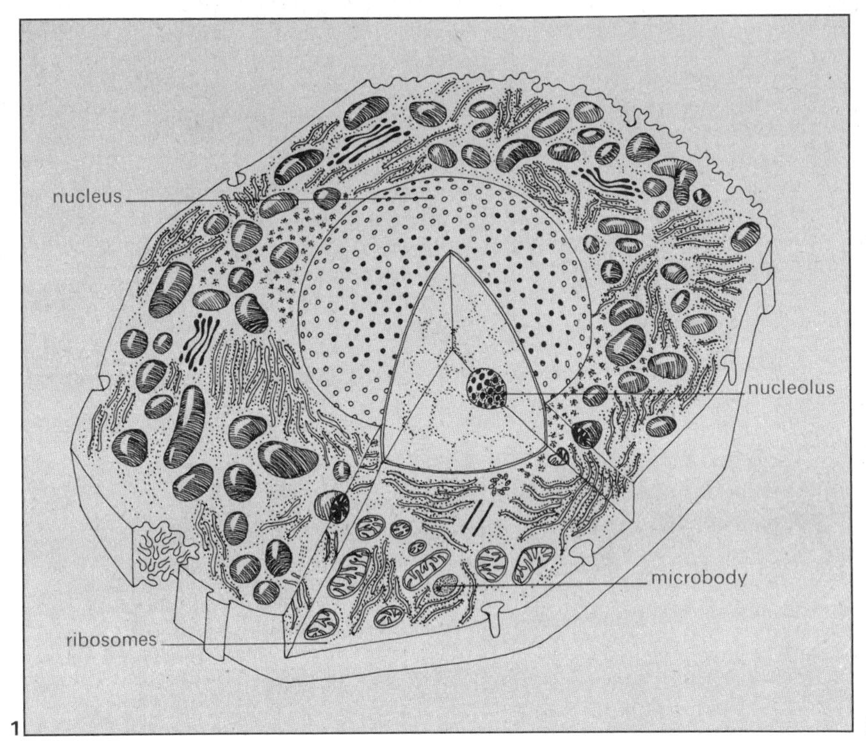


1 The structure of the typical animal cell. Outside the central nucleus is the cytoplasm, containing the ribosomes. The whole is surrounded by a cell membrane.

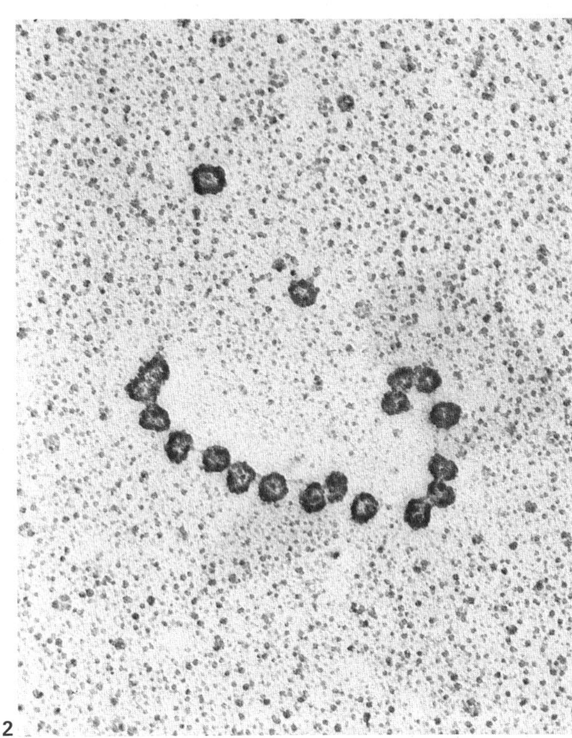

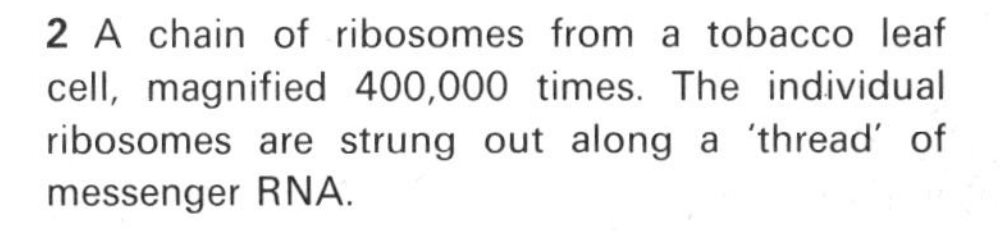
2 A chain of ribosomes from a tobacco leaf cell, magnified 400,000 times. The individual ribosomes are strung out along a 'thread' of messenger RNA.

ANIMALS AND PLANTS are made up of countless tiny units called cells. The number of cells in an organism such as Man runs into many millions, yet all these cells have come from a common ancestor. If in the life of the organism we go back far enough in time to the moment of its conception we find that all its cells have stemmed from the conjugation of just two cells – the female gamete, or *ovum,* and the male gamete, or *spermatozoon.* It is remarkable to think that all the many different kinds of cells in an animal such as Man – with his heart cells, liver cells, nerve cells, kidney cells, gland cells, gut cells, blood cells, cells for making skin, teeth and bone – should have originated from just one common predecessor; and that this single fertilized cell should therefore contain all the information necessary for bringing about the growth and maturity of a mighty oak, a myriad-legged centipede, an elephant in Africa, or Man.

What happens in the development of an organism from one single cell? The fertilized egg of the bird, for instance, is relatively enormous with its great sphere of yolk, and we find that this mass of highly nutritive food does affect what happens to the cell when it starts to develop. The fertilized egg cell, at one pole of the yolk, is minute by comparison with it. This tiny cell first divides into two identical daughter cells by a process known as *mitosis,* but it cannot divide the yolk, which remains as a single mass. The two cells thus come to lie directly on the surface of the yolk, which they begin to tap for food. Shortly, these two cells themselves divide into a total of four cells, and then these into eight cells, until in time a small mass of cells is formed – still overlying the yolk which, at that point, because it is being digested, begins to liquefy.

Now, an event occurs in the minute embryo which is the first indication that the cells, that have resulted from the con-

3 The discoverers of the genetic code. Nobel prizewinners James Watson (left) and Francis Crick. Behind them is a model of the structure of DNA, which they discovered.

tinuing division, are no longer all exactly the same. This event is the formation of a *primitive streak* by which the cells begin to separate into three layers: an outer layer, known as *epiblast*; a middle layer as *mesoderm*; and a layer closest to the yolk, known as *endoderm*. These layers are destined to become particular parts of the adult bird. The epiblast will give rise to the nervous system, to the skin, to the lining of the mouth, to certain glands and to sense organs like the ear and eye; the mesoderm to the muscles, to the bones and connective tissue, the blood and parts of the kidney; and the endoderm to the intestines, the liver, glands and other organs associated with the animal's nutrition. The primitive streak first shows as a small furrow on the surface of the epiblast, but in time it sinks deeper until, as the top layers of the epiblast close over it, it has formed a tube. This tube is the cavity of the brain and spinal cord.

At the same time the gut is forming. Where the head is developing, the endoderm cells start migrating inwards to what will become the belly of the bird. Migration is going on simultaneously, and soon, rather like squeezing off a balloon with one's finger, the endoderm has met in the belly region, and has closed off a space inside the developing embryo that is the primitive gut. A small space or opening is left in the midline which connects up with the yolk; for the embryo needs more and more nourishment. The other organs are now forming and it is very evident that each region has a particular task of development to enact and seems to know what it is doing.

## The cell's fixed fate

Birds are just one particular example of development, and every species of animal and plant has its own variation. Mammals develop in the uterus of their mothers, and nourishment is carried by the bloodstream. Part of the embryo's development is therefore to form a mass of cells, known as the *trophoblast,* which burrows into the lining wall of the uterus and develops blood vessels that make contact with the blood vessels of the mother. The blood vessels passing from the trophoblast into the young embryo are contained within the umbilical cord, which in many ways is similar to the opening through which, in the chick, yolk can pass from the yolk sac into its gut.

Whatever the animal, or plant, and its type of development, there comes a moment when the cells, which have all arisen from the one cell, begin to differ substantially from each other. Depending upon where it finds itself in the developing embryo, the cell appears to have its fate fixed and cannot normally be changed. If we take a small piece of primitive streak from a chick and graft it under the *ectoderm* – the outer skin layer – of a rabbit embryo at a similar stage of development, we see that the graft, as it would have done in the chick, develops into nervous tissue, and even affects the cells of the rabbit embryo in its close vicinity, so that they, too, form nervous tissue. This property of a cell to become fixed on a particular destiny is known as the *determination* of a cell.

But what controls this determination? Does it result from changes within the cell in question, or from outside? The answer, as is so often the case in biology, is neither one nor the other, but both. To understand what goes on inside the cell we must take a look at its basic structure and functioning. Each organism inherits certain characteristics from its parents, and the genes which determine these characteristics are carried on microscopic threads, known as the chromosomes, which are found in the nucleus of each cell. The nucleus is a membrane-bounded sac that resides more or less in the centre of the cell. After fertilization the ovum, which is about to embark on the long, tortuous course of development into the adult organism, has a double complement of chromosomes; one set coming from the mother's side, and the other from the father's. As the ovum divides by mitosis,

| DNA nucleotide | RNA translation |
|---|---|
| adenine | uracil |
| thymine | adenine |
| guanine | cytosine |
| cytosine | guanine |

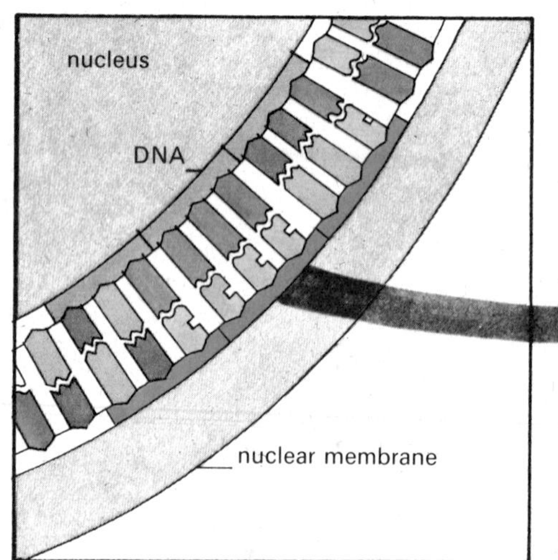


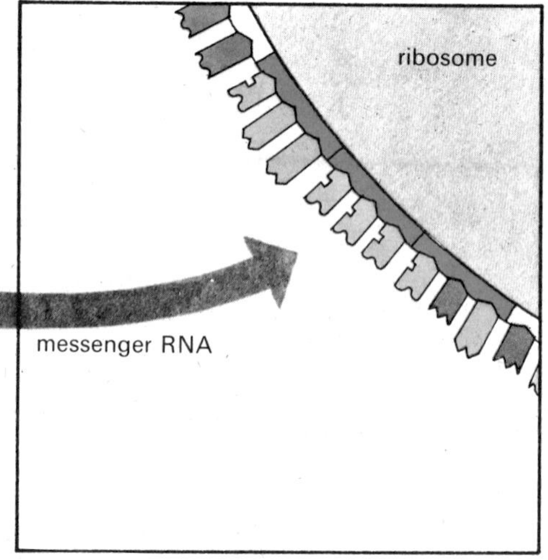


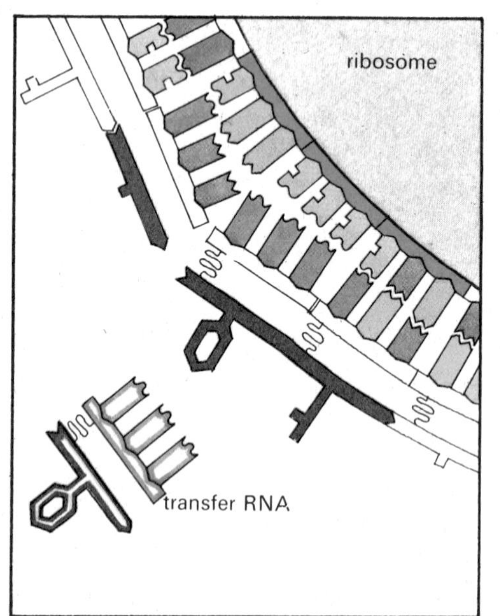


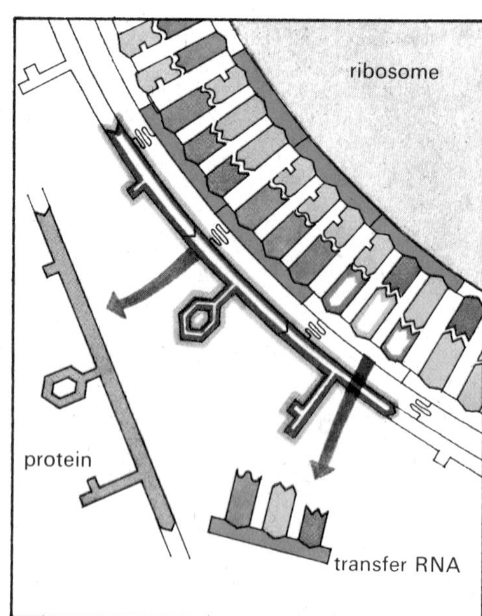


Diagrams showing the mechanism by which proteins are produced from DNA in the nucleus. A mirror image of the pattern of the DNA in the nucleus is generated on a strand of RNA. The bases on the DNA fit the RNA bases as shown. The messenger molecule then proceeds to the ribosomes, where it becomes attached. Amino acids, which form the 'building blocks' for proteins, are brought to the ribosomes by molecules of transfer RNA. The transfer RNA molecules fit along the ribosome by attaching themselves to the molecules of messenger RNA. The order in which the transfer RNA molecules fit together along the ribosome thus corresponds to the order of bases in the original molecule of DNA on the nucleus. Thus, the corresponding amino acids are brought together and linked up by enzymes (not shown) to form chains according to specifications carried permanently in the nucleus. Messenger and transfer RNA molecules move between nucleus and ribosomes, bringing together amino acids to build proteins.

the chromosomes replicate into their exact equivalents, and each daughter cell finishes up with its full complement of chromosomes. Thus, each cell, although it may be many divisions removed from the fertilized ovum, has precisely the same genetic material.

But if, as we know, it is the genetic material of the cell which determines the shape of the organism to come, and each cell has precisely the same genetic content as the ovum, why cannot each cell, independently of the others, develop into a complete organism? Given the chance and the right environment, it has sometimes been possible to make a mature cell of a fully fledged organism revert to its embryonic state and grow and develop into a new organism equivalent to the one from which the cell was first taken. In one experiment carrot cells from a mature plant were extracted and allowed to live isolated from each other in coconut milk. Coconut milk provides all the right conditions to make the carrot cell believe that it has now become an embryo, and with no cells about it to affect its own growth, it soon reverts, as we have just said, into an ovum-like cell, and is then able to develop into a mature plant. But this experiment was only successful under very special conditions. Normally, in the embryo, each cell must adapt to its situation and its neighbours. Otherwise it would be like turning up on a football pitch with a tennis racket; the place and the football players would make it impossible to play a normal game of tennis.

Thus, we have the paradox that every cell has all the genetic material necessary for bringing about complete development from scratch, yet, as the embryo develops, each cell becomes more and more specialized, or *differentiated* as it is called in embryology, so that it is incapable of turning into anything but a highly specific cell type. To understand how this differentiation can come about, we must understand what the genes do in the cell. Their function is to instruct the cell how to make proteins. These are very special proteins; they are enzymes – biological catalysts – which govern the chemistry of the cell, and therefore the cell's function. For example, every cell has to be nourished and one of the main nutrients is glucose to provide energy. But before the glucose can provide energy, it has to be broken down by a series of chemical reactions to carbon dioxide and water. In a fire, glucose would burn up in a moment and give off its energy in the form of heat. In the animal and plant this energy must be used in a controlled way, and this is done by breaking down the glucose in stages with a whole series of enzymes.

Every one of these enzymes has to be constructed on the basis of instructions received from the genes. How do these instructions get passed? The genetic material of the cell is deoxyribonucleic acid (DNA), and this DNA consists essentially of four different chemical structures, called bases, sticking out at regular intervals from a continuous backbone of a sugar (ribose)-phosphate combination. The bases are complementary to each other in that two of them, adenine and thymine, will attract each other and fit together, and the other two, guanine and cytosine, will also attract each other and fit together. Now, a single molecule, or chain as it is called, of DNA, which has a series of bases running down its length, has the particular property of being able to propagate itself (replicate) by attracting the complementary bases to it, whereupon these bases themselves get attached to a backbone of ribose sugar and phosphate. By this system of propagation parents pass on genetic material to their offspring, and each cell passes on exactly equivalent genetic material to its daughter cells at the time of division.

## The messenger molecule

DNA can also propagate a closely related species of molecule – ribonucleic acid (RNA) – which only differs from DNA by having uracil as one of its bases instead of thymine. This RNA is the messenger molecule of the cell, and it carries the instructions from the genetic DNA, and ensures that they are transcribed in the manufacture of the enzymes. The major synthesis of the enzymes takes place outside the nucleus in special particles called ribosomes, which are also composed of RNA, combined with a protein. Thus, a small portion of DNA carries the code, or blueprint, for making a particular protein – an important enzyme for example. RNA is replicated on this portion of DNA and comes off carrying the code by virtue of having a precise set, in order and in the right sequence, of complementary bases to the DNA. In the cytoplasm of the cell, outside the nucleus, this messenger molecule of RNA encounters the ribosomes, as well as special RNA called transfer RNA. This latter RNA consists of small molecules carrying the building blocks of the proteins, the amino acids.

There are some 20 amino acids in all, and a combination of three of the bases of the messenger RNA in sequence will code for one particular amino acid by attracting a particular complementary trio of bases on the transfer RNA. Thus, in all there must be as many different transfer RNA molecules as there are amino acids. The ribosomes provide the structural machinery which allows this combination of molecules to occur – the meeting of messenger and transfer RNA and the joining together in sequence of the amino acids to form a complete molecule of protein. These proteins, as enzymes, can only carry out very particular functions, and therefore, for every new process a different enzyme is needed and has to be synthesized.

The fertilized egg of the sea-urchin provides a good example of the typical stages found in the development of almost all eggs. The fertilized single cell first divides into two (**1**), and after a short period the two cells again divide along a plane at right angles to the first plane of cleavage (**2**). The cells produced in this way continue to divide and form a compact aggregation of cells. After about the sixth division, when the cluster of cells contains about 64 members (**3**), the cluster begins to form a *morula* (**4**) so-called because the structure resembles a mulberry. Soon after this stage in their development is reached, the different cells in the cluster, now properly termed an embryo, begin to carry out specialized functions.

1

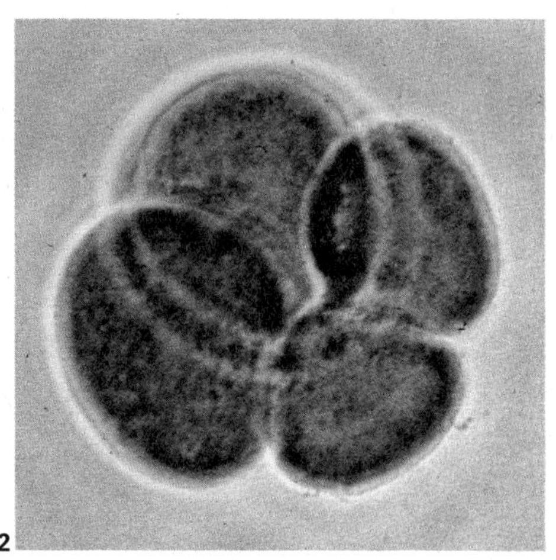

2

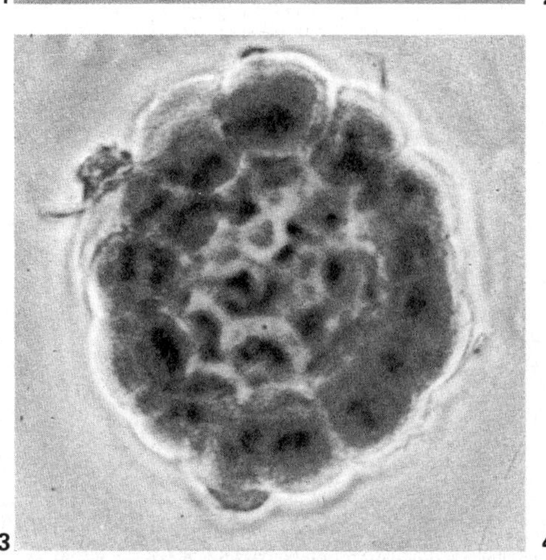

3

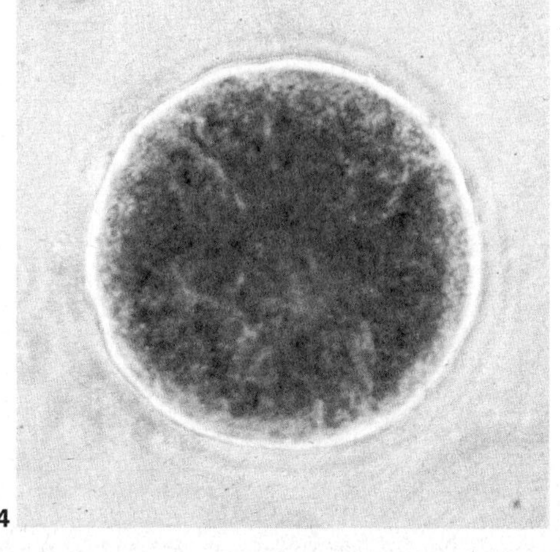

4

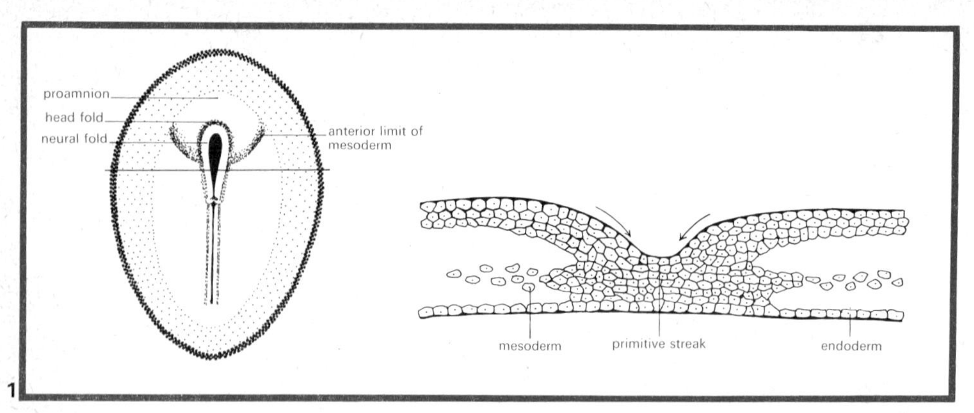

**1** The later development of the embryo showing the differentiation of the various folds and the primitive streak, and (right) the formation of mesoderm and endoderm.

**2** The long filament criss-crossing this electron microscope picture is a molecule of DNA obtained from a virus (*B. subtilis* bacteriophage). Magnification: 22,000 times.

As we have seen, only a portion of the DNA operates at any one time, and the remainder is somehow repressed. This repression of particular sequences of the DNA governs what a cell's activity is going to be and how it is going to differ from that of other cells. The DNA is not just on its own. In all many-celled organisms it is covered by a set of proteins called *histones*, and it now seems clear that when a portion of the DNA is uncovered from its coating of histones it is able to attract to it all the components for making a messenger molecule of RNA.

Bacteria are single cells, and therefore do not have to face the problems of development that confront animals and plants with many different types of cell. Nevertheless, by looking at how genes are controlled in bacteria we can get some inkling of gene control in multi-celled animals and plants. A bacterium's life is always changing; it may suddenly find itself in a situation where the type of food it was living on has run out, and instead it has to make do with another type of food. Each type of food – which in a bacterium's life is often a type of sugar – needs special enzymes to bring it inside the cell, and then to digest it, so that the energy locked up in it can be used.

But it would be a waste of the bacterium's resources if it had made all the enzymes for every type of food when only one or two types of food were available. Thus, when a particular sugar is not available a gene on the DNA chromosome produces a special repressor substance. This gene is a *regulator gene* and the repressor it makes attaches itself to another gene, the *operator gene* and prevents it from functioning. The operator gene has under its control a number of genes. These latter are the genes which carry the code of instructions for making all the many enzymes that are necessary for acting chemically on one food substance. When a particular sugar, say beta-galactoside, is not present, the genes for making enzymes to break it down are repressed and so inactivated. If now we put the bacterium in a solution containing this sugar, the sugar combines with the repressor substance and stops it from repressing the operator gene. The operator gene now activates the genes under its control, the *structural genes*, and the enzymes for breaking down the sugar can be produced. There is also a control system that works the other way round; in this the repressor substance only acts and is effective in repressing when the substrate substance (the sugar) is present.

We can imagine such systems getting very complicated if a regulator gene should control more than one operator gene, and if these in turn should regulate the activities of other operators. We therefore get a *cascade system* of gene control where by triggering off one gene we control the activities of many others. This is the kind of system we must look for in our developing animal.

## Insect metamorphoses

The insect – which can develop from an egg to a caterpillar, then after several moultings to a chrysalis, and the chrysalis (pupa) to a beautiful moth or butterfly – is a superb example of development and gene control. Insects do not have a skeleton and their shape is maintained by a hard outer skin, the cuticle. This cuticle is produced by a layer of cells – the epidermal cells – and as the cuticle gives the insect its shape as we see it, the epidermal cells essentially govern the insect. But the same cells produce all these very different forms of development – the caterpillar, chrysalis and the mature winged butterfly or moth. Therefore these epidermal cells must have a method of switching on and off genes that control at the right time the different stages. The epidermal cells are very sensitive to two hormones that are produced during the development of the insect just before it moults into the next stage. One hormone is known as the *growth and moulting hormone*, and the other as the *juvenile hormone*. The first hormone stimulates the epidermal cells to divide and get ready to moult, and the second hormone governs what form the moulting should take – whether the insect should develop into another caterpillar, or into the adult.

Hormones in animals and plants do in fact change the whole course of development of a group of cells. We know for example that hormones control our sex and our growth, including the shape of our bodies. During embryonic growth and development substances like hormones may, in fact, govern what a cell is going to become. By acting with the regulator genes of the cell a simple substance may induce or repress the activity of a group of genes, and, as in the case of the insect, change the whole course of development into an entirely new form.

# After the egg

All growth depends on simple cell division; but variations on this basic theme, from microscopic egg to mature adult, are almost endless. Some common animals never reach adulthood at all.

'MY, HOW he has grown!' This exclamation is probably heard a thousand times every day in a thousand languages all over the world, usually in response to the sight of an infant after a few days' absence. But one would hardly say the same thing about Aunt Agatha who has obviously 'put on a bit round the middle'. The reason for not saying it about Aunt Agatha is more than just good manners. To the biologist and non-biologist alike, the word 'growth' implies a *permanent* change in size and/or weight. If Aunt Agatha puts on a few pounds between visits, she 'grows' in size. But this is not true growth, because it is temporary. However, if the new baby puts on a few pounds in weight (or grows a few inches in height), this is true growth, because the change will last.

Growth results from the metabolic activities of the body. These are of two types: the building up (*anabolic*) processes, and the breaking down (*catabolic*) processes. Even when adult size has been reached, these reactions continue at a steady rate. The breakdown and renewal of tissues occurs all over the body. It affects the gut, the skin, the other organs, the blood cells and the skeletal material. In a growing young animal, the anabolic rate is greater than the catabolic rate, resulting in a general increase in size. Equilibrium is reached in an adult animal (anabolic equals catabolic), and the process is reversed during old age, resulting in very slight decrease in size.

## The 'bricks' of life

The structural and functional materials of an animal's body – apart from water and bone – consists mainly of different kinds of *proteins*. So proteins are an essential requirement for growth. Large quantities of protein are taken into the animal's body when it eats, but the proteins in the food generally are not the same kinds needed by the growing cells. So the cells remedy this defect by building their own.

Proteins are very large molecules built out of simpler units called *amino acids*. To create the proteins needed by the cells, the animal's digestive system first breaks up the proteins taken in by eating into amino acids and then the cells put them back together again in the desired arrangement, rather like building a new house from the secondhand bricks of another one. For this reason, good food plays an important part in growth. If there is insufficient food, or the food eaten is not nutritious, the animal will not grow properly.

A generalized increase in an animal's size can be achieved by cell division. The processes in which the nucleus of a cell divides, separates, and the halves draw

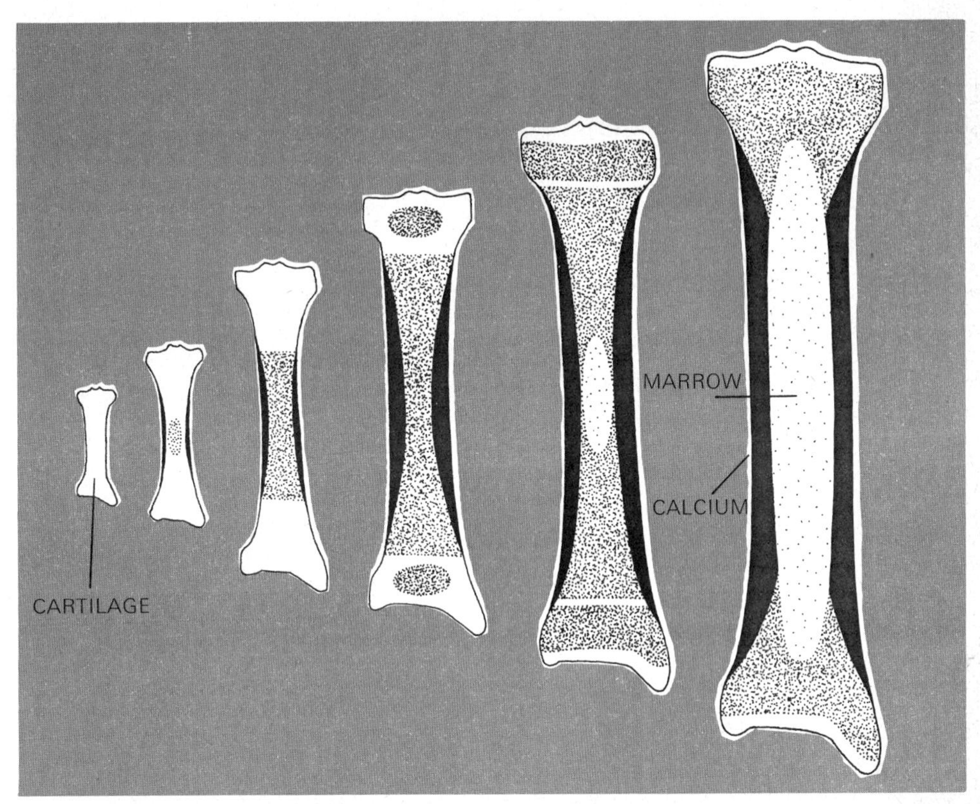


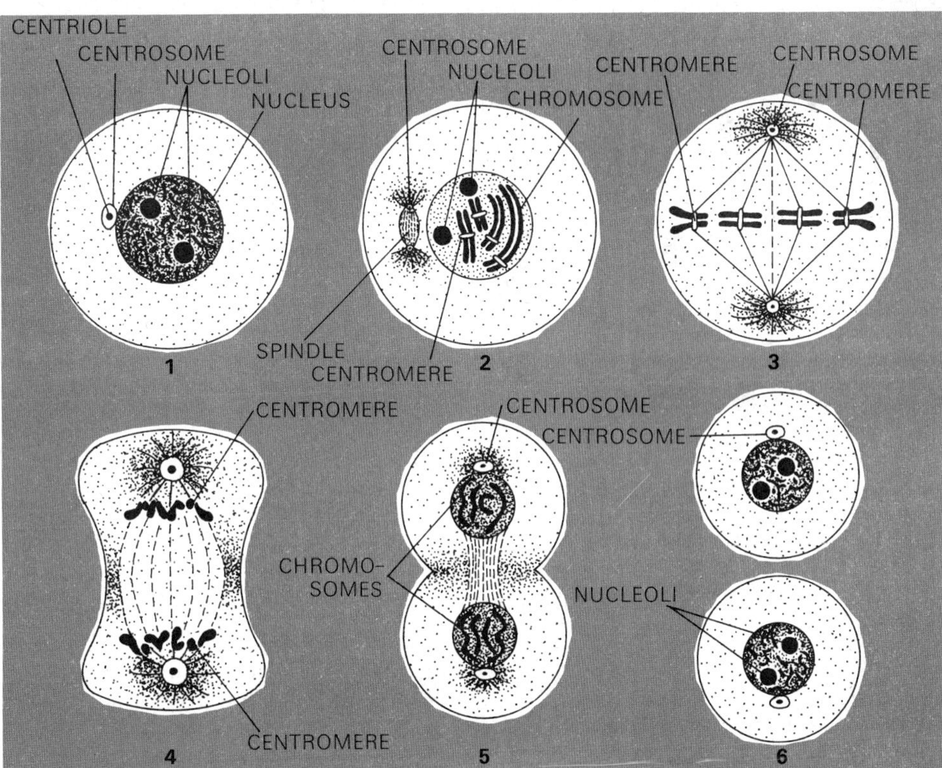


Bones develop from infancy to maturity just like any other organ of the body, starting from soft cartilage and ending with a hard calcium cover over a soft cavity of marrow, *top*. Muscles are fastened on to the lumps at the ends, allowing for movement in vertebrates. *Above*, the onset of mitosis, the splitting of one cell into two, is heralded by the centriole, **1**. Next spindles begin to grow and the chromosomes in the nucleus become visible, **2**. The chromosomes line up along the spindles and reproduce themselves in exact copies, **3**. **4** The chromosomes migrate to the ends of the cell, which then begins to divide, **5**. When the two parts have separated, **6**, the process is complete. Mitosis underlies all growth, in simple and complex animals alike.

**1** The axolotl is something of a Peter Pan of the animal kingdom, because it refuses to become an adult. **2** The salamander, a newt-like amphibian, is the fully developed adult form of the axolotl. They were not known to be larva and adult until some biologists showed that stimulation of the thyroid gland of the axolotl can cause it to mature into a salamander. Despite its juvenile form, the axolotl is sexually mature and capable of reproduction. **3** The normal process of larval development is illustrated by the tadpole. Initially aquatic, the tadpole absorbs its tail, enlarges its mouth, grows legs and becomes a frog capable of life on land.

cytoplasm with them to form two new cells is called *mitosis*. Little is known about what prompts cells to divide, although the size of the nucleus (relative to the cytoplasm) may have an effect on initiating the process. The first sign of activity comes from a cylindrical structure in the nucleus known as the *centriole*. The area of protoplasm surrounding the centriole (called the *centrosome*) is relatively liquid. The whole is enclosed by a more solid body, the *aster*.

At the beginning of cell division, the centriole divides and each half migrates to opposite poles of the nucleus. Chromosomes (threads of DNA and protein) become visible and a *spindle* connects the poles of the nucleus. The nuclear membrane then breaks down, completing the first stage, which is called the *prophase*.

During the second stage (*metaphase*), the chromosomes collect on the spindle. The third stage (*anaphase*) is characterized by the reproduction of the chromosomes and the separation of the pair, each exactly like the other, along the spindle towards the two centrioles. The final phase (*telophase*) sees the re-formation of nuclear membranes to produce two separate nuclei. Division of the cytoplasm generally occurs soon after the chromosomes have reached the poles or during formation of the new nuclei. Biologists still do not understand how all these various stages take place.

We have considered growth of protein

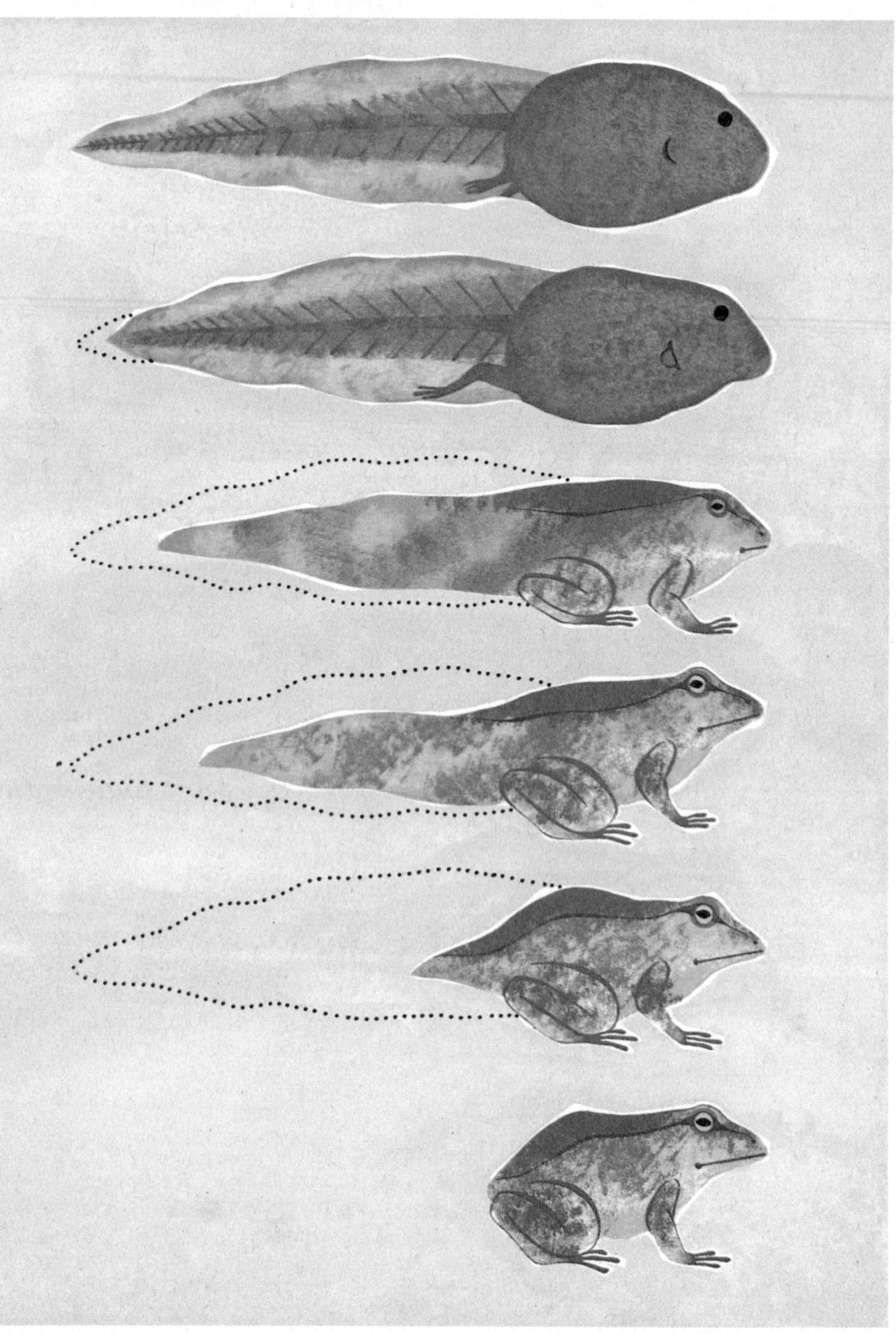

3

Some growth processes reveal themselves in seasonal changes. **4** Snakes and lizards periodically slough their skins and then grow new ones. **5–6** Other animals, such as the 'snowshoe rabbit', alter their physical appearance in order to blend with the summer and winter environments as protection against hungry predators. **7** Male deer seasonally grow antlers used in fighting for mates. At the end of the mating season, the antlers are no longer of use and drop off.

6

molecules and of cells; now let us consider how complete organs grow. If one of the two kidneys is removed from a rat, the cells of the remaining one begin to multiply rapidly, reaching a maximum rate in about 48 hours. If instead part of the liver is removed, the remainder begins to grow. These facts seem to suggest that an organ itself produces a substance that limits its further growth, otherwise it would keep on growing at maturity. If a part of the organ is removed, so are some of these inhibiting substances and it then tends to grow to make up for the part removed. For example, it is thought that some of the globulin proteins produced in the liver may also inhibit its growth.

Different organs do not necessarily grow at the same rate as each other or at the same rate as the whole body. When two parts of the body grow at different rates, growth is said to be *allometric*; when at the same rate, growth is *isometric*. For example, in the gut of most vertebrate animals growth is allometric. The walls of the gut grow faster than the whole and so they become wrinkled into folds called *caecae*. The human thymus gland shows such a marked decrease in growth rate at the end of childhood that the process can then be regarded as 'de-growth'.

Seasonal variations throughout the year markedly influence the growth of individual animals and populations of animals. These are caused by variations in climate, light intensity, and the abundance of food. We do not need to use a tape measure or a microscope to observe such changes. For example, seasonal spurts leave visible concentric 'growth rings' in the shells of molluscs and in fish scales (rather like the growth rings in the wood of a tree). These rings may be used to estimate the age of an animal, and the spacing between them may even show when the animal survived a hard winter or a winter in which food was particularly abundant.

Growth usually slows or stops during hibernation as an economy measure, to conserve the body's food reserves. The *diapause* period in insects is a time of arrested growth, geared to the season. Some reptiles, birds and mammals show seasonal cycles in their moulting and growth processes. Snakes and lizards slough their skins. Birds moult regularly or change from winter to summer plumage. Cattle thicken their coats in winter by growing special long hairs which fall out in the spring. In many arctic animals, there are two seasonal moults; the arctic hare and the ermine grow a white coat in autumn to provide camouflage among the winter snows, and replace it with a brown coat in early spring. These moults are stimulated by varying lengths of daylight, and hormones control the actual process.

## Preparing for reproduction

In a similar way, antlers of stags are grown in the spring during the spring mating season when they are used in courtship and fighting. During growth, the antlers must be provided with blood vessels and nerves and may grow as much as two inches a day. At the end of the season, the nerves and blood supply are cut off by a constriction of bone; the antlers eventually die and drop off.

In most animals, growth and development of the reproductive system coincide with warm weather so that the young are born and reared in favourable conditions. This is shown most markedly in arctic regions when spring and summer are short and relatively warm and food is abundant. For example, the insect population leaps to an extremely high level during the days of the midnight sun, and declines during autumn ready to 'overwinter' during the months of total darkness and very low temperatures.

During the spring, the *gonads* (reproductive organs) of all the animals of a given species reach maturity simultaneously so that all the animals are sexually mature and aroused at the same time. This is particularly noticeable in birds, for which the amount of daylight has a marked effect on the nervous and the hormone

The change between the summer and the winter 'coats' of some animals is sometimes so complete that it is difficult to recognize them as being the same creature. *Left,* an Alaskan rock ptarmigan takes on winter white; *right,* another ptarmigan shows off its summer plumage.

systems – mating takes place, eggs are laid, and the young are hatched at almost exactly the same times among birds of a given species. In mammals, the womb of the female becomes much smaller after the birth of the young and the mammary glands become functional to supply milk.

Most of these growth processes are controlled by hormones, chemical 'messengers' which oversee the body's functions. These substances are carried in the blood-stream to all the body tissues. Almost all hormones in vertebrate animals affect growth in some way. The glands that secrete them form the *endocrine system.* The most important hormone for growth is the *anterior pituitary growth hormone* (APGH or *somatropin*). For example, in Man a deficiency of this hormone during childhood leads to dwarfs, and an excess produces giants. An excess of APGH in adults causes the condition called *acromegaly* in which growth of bone (particularly the lower jaw) continues after maturity. It is thought that dinosaurs probably had large pituitary glands, so accounting for their vast sizes.

## Constructing the skeleton

APGH appears to promote either the growth of the cell nucleus or to increase cell division. It also appears to affect protein synthesis by increasing the uptake of amino acids by the digestive system. Its most important function is to stimulate the growth of bone.

Many people think of a mature animal's skeleton as an inert system. But it is extremely important functionally. It protects the softer organs, gives the body shape and support, and acts as a system of levers by which the contraction of muscles is transformed into body movements.

Bone formation is called *ossification.* Two types are found in young vertebrates: the formation of thin membrane or dermal bone and, more important, the formation of *endochondral* bone in which embryonic cartilage is replaced by adult bone. In this second process, the cartilage begins to degenerate within its central region. The cells of cartilage swell and become arranged in columns. Blood vessels and osteoblasts break in from the surface and bone formation takes place from the middle outwards and towards the ends. At the same time, cartilage at the ends of the 'bone' continues to grow until it, too, is caught up by the ossification process. This is timed to take place at maturity and so bone growth virtually ceases.

In higher vertebrates, *accessory* ossifications take place at the ends of bones (the *epiphyses*). These produce 'lumps' of bone for the attachment of muscles and give long bones their characteristic hourglass shape. The central filament of bone is strengthened externally by the formation of surface (*periosteal*) bone.

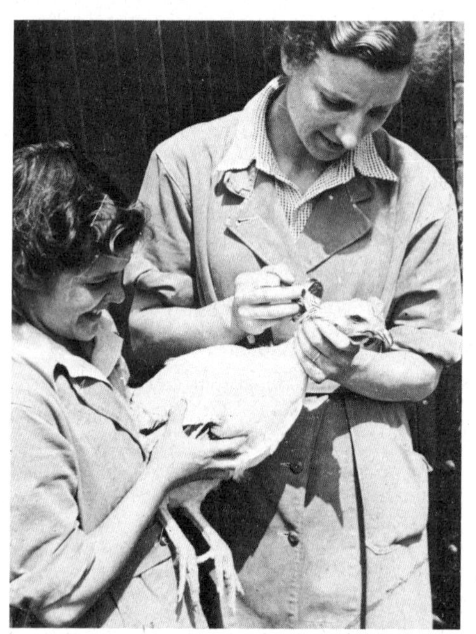

Knowledge of fundamental growth processes has important applications in the food industry. Here, a fowl is being caponized or 'de-sexed', which results in an increase of weight and size.

Another pituitary hormone, *thyrotropic hormone,* controls the growth and output of the thyroid gland. *Thyroxin,* a hormone from this gland, is important in the development of young animals. For example, many amphibians begin active life as small, aquatic larvae – such as the tadpoles of frogs. Tadpoles undergo various changes before young frogs finally leave the water for land. Over a period of about three months, these changes include the formation of external gills, their replacement by internal gills, and finally the formation of lungs. First the back and then the front legs grow, and the tail is ultimately absorbed.

## The reluctant larva

A change in diet from plant-eating to meat-eating also occurs and must be accompanied by changes in the feeding mechanism: the fish-like mouth becomes wide and gaping and the long tongue develops. The gut becomes simpler and less spiralled, since meat is easier to digest than plants.

This complete change in form is called *metamorphosis.* In amphibians, it can be greatly accelerated by giving extra thyroid hormone or by stimulating the appropriate gland by adding iodine to the diet. In some amphibians, metamorphosis may never reach completion and the juvenile form persists throughout adult life. Such an animal is the *axolotl,* which is the larval form of a newt-like amphibian called a *salamander.* For many years, people thought that axolotls and salamanders were entirely different animals. But stimulation of the thyroid gland causes the larva (axolotl) to change into the adult (salamander). If this stimulation is not provided, axolotls reach sexual maturity and can reproduce without ever changing into the adult form.

This process, by which larval forms become sexually mature, is called *neoteny* and is thought to have been an important factor in the evolution of many groups of animals. The early chordates (animals with rod-like skeletons), ancestors of vertebrates, are thought to have arisen in this way from invertebrate stock. Insects may have evolved from a millipede-like ancestor. Millipedes develop through several larval stages and are unusual in that segments are added each time the larvae moult. The primitive insect had 21 segments, and it is possible that an ancient millipede larva 'stuck' at this stage, became sexually mature (rather like the axolotl now does), and produced the insect ancestor. This method of evolutionary development is called *paedomorphosis.*

Despite the Peter Pan-like refusal of the axolotl and other neotenic animals to become adults, adulthood is generally the end result of growth. Perhaps it is not really fair to accuse the axolotl of being forever a child, for the chief biological function of adulthood is procreation. And although it may not look like its 'adult' form, the axolotl is certainly capable of reproducing itself. Otherwise, there would never have been any axolotls around for people to argue about.

# Life-histories

**Growth from egg to adult in animals is not a simple process of getting bigger. The rate of growth of different parts of the body changes to maintain function, and other complex changes occur.**

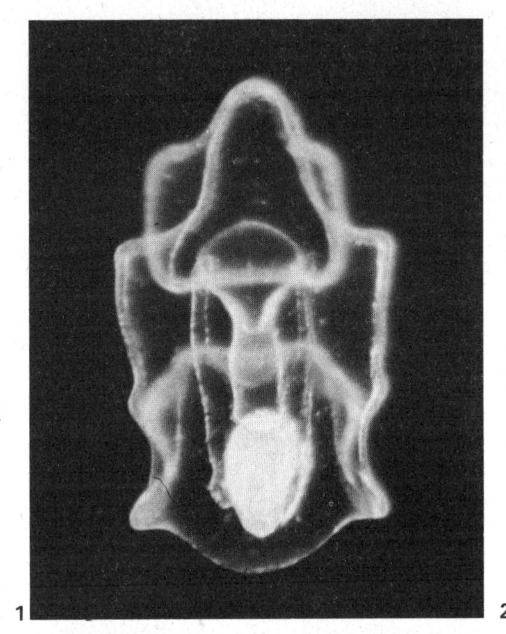

1

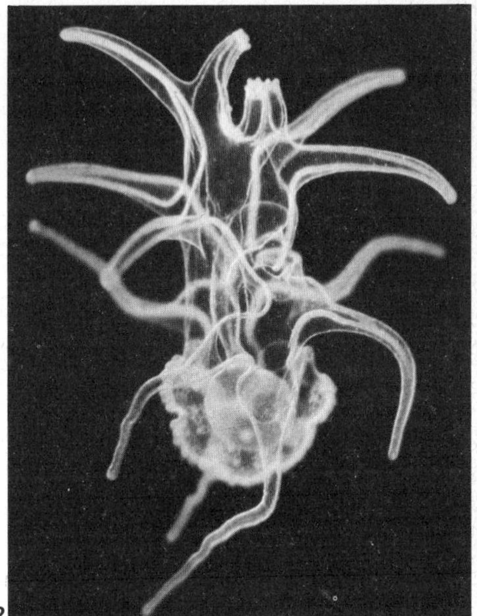

2

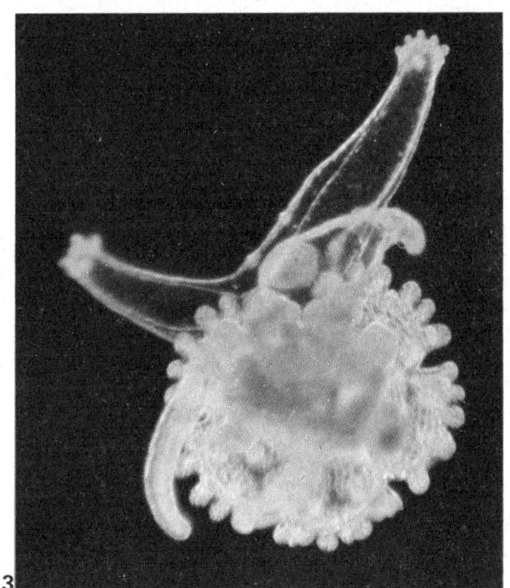

3

4

The common starfish (*Asterias rubens*) reproduces both sexually and by fission. Shown here are stages in the development of a starfish produced as a result of sexual reproduction. The egg develops into a tiny free-swimming larva or bipinnaria (**1**), which grows for about three weeks. The final stage of the larva is shown in (**2**). After three weeks or so, the larva settles down on some solid object, such as a rock, and undergoes metamorphosis (**3**). It assumes the characteristic starfish shape, and finally grows until it reaches the size of the adult (**4**).

SOME YOUNG ANIMALS are more or less miniature versions of the adult. Crocodiles are a good example. The young crocodiles have a similar environment to the adults, they have a similar way of life, and the only thing that changes throughout their lives is that at some stage they become sexually mature, and that – given the right amount of food and warmth – they get bigger.

But in most animal species the young creature is a very different animal from the adult. It is not only smaller, it is different proportionally, different physiologically, different psychologically and sometimes different anatomically. Part of the difference between young and adult results because different tissues and organs develop at different rates – but at all stages of the animal's life it must, obviously, be capable of survival. Thus a mammal's brain grows more slowly than, say, the bones or muscles of its limbs. The adult mammal generally has a proportionally smaller head than does the young mammal. Again, in the vertebrate, the bones must increase in size while at all times forming a functional, articulate skeleton. Yet it is clear that as, say, the thigh bone and shin bone increase in length and bulk the stresses and strains on the knee joint change.

## Joint development

In many vertebrates joint development tends to lag behind long-bone development, so that the young animal has weaker joints than the adult. In mammals, however, this problem is solved by the fact that joint development proceeds separately from the development of the rest of the long bone. Characteristically, in young mammals, each bone develops in three parts – the two ends, which form part of joints, are known as the *epiphyses*, and the central shaft of bone between the epiphyses is the *diaphysis*. In the young mammal the epiphyses are clearly demarcated from the diaphysis, though in the adult they are fused. The point is that the epiphyses in the young animal are proportionally larger than in the adult animal – which is why young puppies or foals appear to have such knobbly knees – and they grow, relatively, more slowly than do the diaphyses. Because the epiphyses grow more slowly the stresses and strains on the growing joint do not change so rapidly throughout life as they do, say, in the growing reptile. Hence the joints of the young mammal are always functionally very strong.

Such adaptations are imposed on the young animal because it must remain viable at all stages of its life-history, while at the same time increasing in size. The interesting point is that differences, other than differences in size, between a young and a mature animal are possible at all. Both the young animal and the adult into which it develops have derived from a single fertilized egg cell, and the genetic content of the egg cell must be exactly the same as that of the young animal, and of the adult. A single cell can give rise to many cells with an identical genetic complement to its own, though each daughter cell may be very different from the parent cell; the daughter cells might develop into liver cells, nerve cells or muscle cells, etc. This is the phenomenon of differentiation. The difference between the young and the adult animal is the same kind of phenomenon: how can two animals – the baby and adult – be so different, when each has exactly the same genetic structure?

The answer is that at any one time, in fact, an enormous proportion of the animal's total gene complement is dormant. This dormancy has been explained in two ways, and which is the right one has not yet been determined. One school says that each individual gene is naturally dormant unless aroused into activity by some 'switching-on' substance; the other school, the 'depressor' theorists, hold that genes are naturally active, unless actively

1

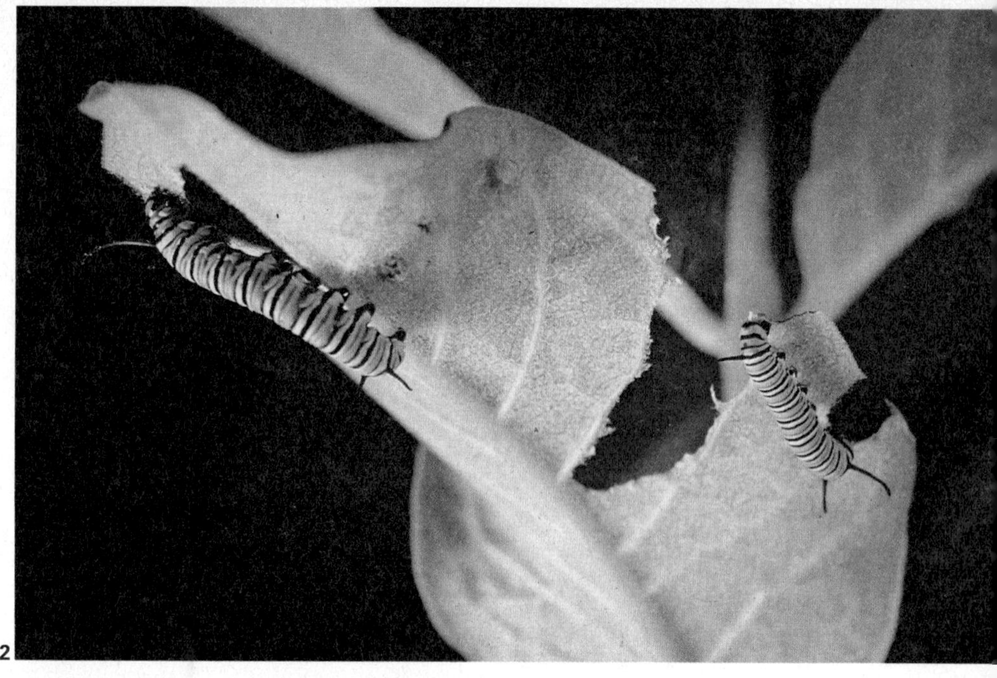

2

4

5

6

suppressed by some depressor substance. That many genes are dormant can be realized by considering the human embryo. At an early stage of its development it develops gill slits – a hangover from the days when all vertebrates lived in the sea. Later the gill slits are lost. Yet the older embryo, without gill slits, must still possess the genes necessary to produce gill slits, unless we suppose that these genes are physically lost from the baby (a very unlikely proposition). And indeed, not only the older embryo, but the baby that develops from it, and the adult that develops from the baby, must still harbour genes which, given the right conditions, could produce gill slits. In other words, every human being walking around contains within himself the potential to become something like the fish-like creature that was his ancestor.

Thus we see that the 'genetic complement' of an animal is not an economical, static quantity that can produce only one single manifestation of that animal. The development of the animal can, in fact, be thought of as a series of different genetic patterns following one after the other. Thus, in the embryo, one set of genes are operative. In the infant, some or all of these genes are suppressed, and another set takes their place. In the child, another set; in the adolescent, another set, and so on throughout life.

So far we have been talking about animals whose immature forms live much the same sort of life as the adults. But each animal could theoretically carry around with it a set of (suppressed) genes that could make up a very different sort of animal, given the right circumstances. In practice it is possible to have a young form that is *totally* different from the adult – not only physiologically and anatomically, but also in its way of life. And, in fact, more animals than not do have an 'immature' form that is very different from the adult, and the immature forms (that is, the sexually immature forms) make a very different contribution to the survival of the animal than do the adult forms.

The most familiar example of this extreme schism between immature and adult forms is seen in the insects. In the more primitive insects – cockroaches, for example – it is true that the young is more or less like the adult, the chief difference being that it cannot fly. But in more sophisticated insects – butterflies and moths, beetles, bees, wasps and ants – the young animal is totally different in form from the adult. In the bees, the totally different young form – or *larva* – contributes little to the survival of the species. The young larvae are, in fact, spivs, who are waited on hand and foot by the adult worker bees. But in the butterflies and moths, the larva – or caterpillar – is the most important feeding and growing phase. Though many adult butterflies and moths can feed through their long tubular probosci, the tissue that makes up their bodies has been accrued by the voracious caterpillars – well equipped with efficient

3

Growth and metamorphosis in the monarch butterfly. The egg (**1**), laid on a milkweed leaf, hatches out to give small, striped caterpillars (**2**). The caterpillars devour the milkweed leaves voraciously. When they have reached a certain size, and when other conditions are right, the caterpillars hang down from the underside of the leaf (**3**) and shed their skins (**4**). They then become chrysalises, apparently inert, immobile and completely different from the caterpillars (**5**). But inside the chrysalis a remarkable change is taking place. The caterpillar develops wings and becomes a butterfly. The butterfly develops inside the protective chrysalis until it is ready to emerge, a step that is largely determined by the temperature of the surrounding air. The butterfly has to fight its way out of the chrysalis head-down (**6**), and then hangs for some time from the underside of the leaf so that it can unfurl and dry its wings (**7**). Finally, the insect, its beautiful wings fully unfurled, is ready to fly away and find a mate (**8**). This type of life-cycle, characterized by sharp breaks and changes of form and function, is found in many insects. The monarch butterfly provides a beautiful example.

7

8

mandibles and an enormous gut – that they once were. The role of the adult is, in fact, only to reproduce. And many adult butterflies and moths – the clothes moth, for example – simply do not feed. They emerge from the pupa, they use their acute sense of smell to detect others of the opposite sex, they use their newly acquired wings to fly to the potential mate, then they reproduce and die. Thus in these animals, the various functions of living things that are essential to survival – feeding and reproducing – are designated to different phases of the life-cycle, and each phase is highly specialized for its particular role, and totally different from the other phases.

The totally different forms and functions that animals like insects adopt at different phases of their life-cycle is a special form of the phenomenon known as 'polymorphism'. The term 'polymorphism' – which means, literally, 'many forms' was originally used only to denote the fact that any one species of animal can appear in several different forms, each form having a different function. The most obvious example of this is the difference in form and function of male and female animals – known as 'sexual dimorphism'. A more sophisticated example is the many different forms of individual – some adapted for feeding, some for defence, some for reproduction – that go to make up the colonial jellyfish, such as *Physalia,* the Portuguese-man-o'-war. It took the genius of Cambridge entomologist V. B. Wigglesworth to see that the very different phases seen in the *single* life-cycle of an insect were, in fact, comparable with the different (though genetically similar) individuals seen in many animal populations, and to use the term 'polymorphism' to describe those different phases.

In fact, as we said, polymorphism exhibited throughout an animal's life is more common than the sort of straight-through development seen in mammals. Most animals, in fact, have a larval phase which makes a distinct and specialized contribution to the animal's life-history. This is particularly important in that enormous and highly heterogeneous mass of animals that live a sedentary life on the floor of the sea. The acorn barnacle, for example, is firmly attached by sticky glands on its head to a rock, or a shell, or a ship's bottom. It is surrounded by rigid calcareous plates that protect it from predators and from the pounding waves. It feeds by sweeping floating material out of the water by means of its brush-like legs, poking up between the plates. The distribution of acorn barnacles is world-wide, from the poles to the tropical seas. Yet the adult barnacles are quite unable to move. They can only become widely distributed because they have a larval form that floats in the plankton, where it can be carried for miles, before settling to change – *metamorphose* – into the sedentary adult form. Thus in this case the function of reproduction, which is the adult's prerogative, is separated from that of distribution – the domain of the larva.

## Parasites and polymorphism

Another group of animals to whom polymorphic changes throughout the life-cycle are a vital part of existence are the parasites. Parasites, generally speaking, have an easy time. The point is that the extremely complex biochemical reactions that characterize living things can take place only under very rigidly controlled conditions. Thus, for example, nerve cells are very susceptible to lack of oxygen, and only animals which can keep their nerves well oxygenated – that is, only animals with a good blood supply – can develop a complex nervous system. And, in fact, all animal evolution can be thought of in terms of an 'endeavour' to create a stable 'internal environment' so that more and more complex biochemistry, leading to more and more subtle behaviour, can take place. Many parasitic animals have solved the problem of finding a stable environment not by developing complex mechanisms to distribute oxygen, as all vertebrates have, or mechanisms to maintain constant temperature, as mammals and birds have, but simply by living inside animals that have already created such conditions. Thus, for example, the blood fluke, *Schistosoma,* gains all the benefits of man's marvellous blood and excretory systems and behaviour simply by living inside human veins.

But there are snags in this way of life. A horse that wants to get from one field to another can simply walk there – its feeding ground is, in fact, continuous. But an adult blood fluke cannot simply stroll from one man to another – it is not adapted to life in the outside world, through which it must pass in order to reach a new host. It solves the problem by polymorphism.

The adult worm lives generally in the veins of the bladder, and its eggs pass to the outside world in the host's urine. The eggs hatch into tiny mobile larvae clothed in cilia, which are known as *miracidia.* The miracidium does not feed, and its life is short; its sole function is to find and enter a *secondary host* – a water snail – in which to develop further, and if it doesn't find a suitable snail within a few hours, it dies. Inside the snail the miracidia change into sporocyst larvae, a strange form that, by a sort of 'budding' can give rise to many more sporocysts. This is another reproductive phase, though, unlike the adult reproductive phase, reproduction is here asexual. Eventually the daughter sporocysts, instead of giving rise to more sporocysts, give rise to yet another larval form. This form, like the miracidium, is mobile, but, unlike the miracidium, it propels itself by means of a forked tail. It is known as a *cercarium.* The sole function of the cercarium is to leave the snail and attach itself to a human being and to penetrate the human's skin. Once inside the human it is carried by the blood-stream to the veins of the liver, where it develops into the adult worm, and from thence it is carried by the blood to the veins of the bladder. Then the cycle can begin again – the cycle which was only made possible through the several distinct polymorphic larval forms, each with its highly specialized structure, physiology and 'instinct'.

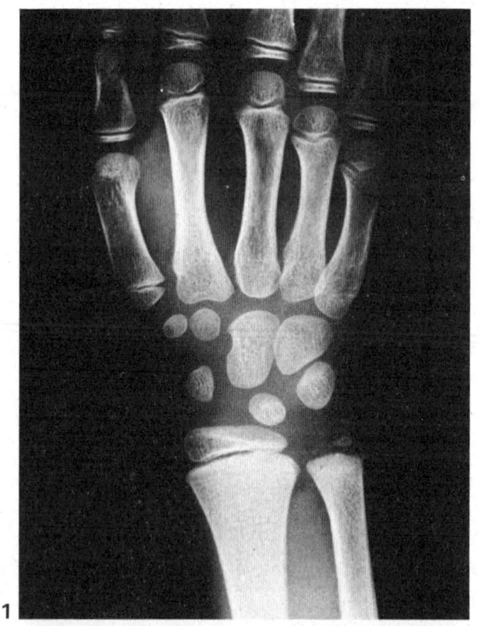
1

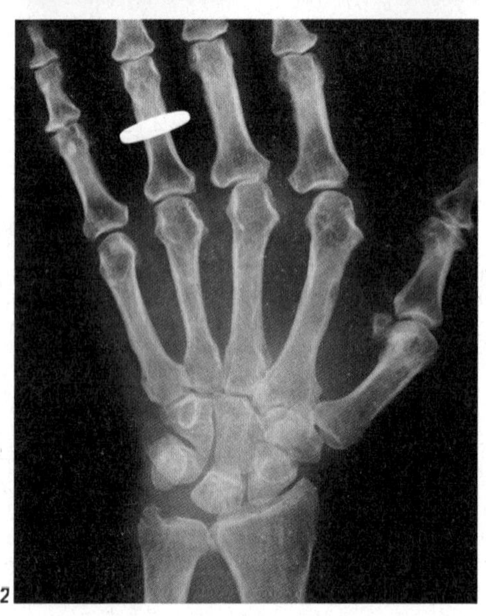
2

In an X-ray photograph, the fingers and hand of a child (**1**) appear different from those of an adult (**2**). The epiphyses at the ends of the long bones are not yet fused with the bone, thus allowing the bones to grow further without interfering with the efficiency of the joints.

The different forms through which animals pass in their life-history have provided a tremendously important source of new animal forms. Though some larvae lack the ability to feed, and many are easy prey to predators, many are complete and highly viable animals. The only thing they lack is the ability to reproduce sexually, the prerogative of the adult. If the larva can acquire the ability to reproduce sexually – if, in fact, the genes that give rise to sex organs can be caused to operate during the larval phase instead of being repressed until the adult phase – then the so-called 'adult' phase can be lost altogether, and the young need not achieve metamorphosis.

## Neoteny in Man

Perhaps the best example of this phenomenon, *neoteny,* is man himself. The young gorilla has a very man-like face – high forehead, flat face, small jaw. In adolescence it acquires the massive jutting jaw, and the skull crest that goes with it, which characterize the adult male gorilla. But what would happen if the development of the massive jaw were postponed beyond adolescence – were postponed, in fact, so long that the animal had become senile and died before it ever developed? Then the ape would stay looking man-like throughout its adult life.

We are not descended from gorillas, but we are descended from ape-like ancestors who, apparently, did have jutting ape-like jaws. It seems very likely that we have lost those jutting jaws just as our hypothetical gorilla might lose his – the genes that give rise to the big jaw have simply been postponed, that the juvenile stage of skull development lasts throughout life. We are descended not from apes, but from young apes.

Thus each animal's life-cycle, which makes it uniquely different from other animals, is the result of different permutations of its genes being switched on and switched off throughout its life.

# Animals and sexual reproduction

Highly complex reproduction processes in animals involves sexual co-operation between mating partners. This is nature's way of ensuring variations necessary to evolutionary development.

1 Mating is a hazardous business for the male praying mantis, who is often devoured by the female as her bridal dinner.

2 Eggs are laid on twigs and enclosed in a protective egg-case.

FOR ANY SPECIES of animal to persist it obviously must reproduce. Indeed, reproduction may be considered to be the ultimate biological function of an animal and the natural culmination of development to maturity. In the simple animals, *asexual* reproduction is the rule. The cells of the adult animal merely split into two, each producing two identical 'daughter' cells, which then separate to live as two new individuals.

A second type of reproduction, which predominates in higher animals, is *sexual* reproduction. This involves the fusion of two special 'half-cells' called *gametes,* one from the male (the sperm) and one from the female (the ovum, or egg), to form a new cell called a *zygote.*

A study of sexual processes throughout the animal kingdom reveals a trend of increasing complexity and efficiency. For instance, most aquatic creatures shed their gametes into the water. The male and female have to be close together; the female drops thousands of eggs and the male millions of sperm.

## Outside and inside

Fertilization is *external,* and a great number of gametes are needed to ensure that this inefficient and rather haphazard process results in a sufficient number of young – and that enough survive their early days, when they are very vulnerable to predators.

On land, however, things have to be very different. Eggs must be protected against drying up and injury, and are retained longer in the body of the female. *Internal* fertilization is necessary, after which several alternatives are possible. In birds and some reptiles, a hard protective shell develops round the egg and the female lays fertilized eggs which, if kept warm, continue to develop away from the mother. Such animals are called *oviparous.*

Another slightly more complex possibility is for the fertilized egg to be retained in the female's body, but for all development to proceed inside the egg before hatching. This is the case with many insects, snails, fish, lizards and snakes, which are said to be *ovoviviparous.* The young embryo is surrounded for most of its development by shell-like membranes (there is no need for a hard protective shell) which separate the new animal from the tissues of the mother. It may derive some nutrient from the mother, and is hatched from the egg before it is laid.

The final and most complex case is when the developing embryo spends all its time embedded in maternal tissue and is known as the *viviparous* condition. (Meaning 'born alive', the term viviparous is somewhat confusing because all fertilized eggs are biologically 'alive' on leaving the mother.) The embryo develops in the mother's uterus (womb) and gains all nutriment from it, and may make close contact separated only by a thin *placenta* with no egg membranes. Viviparity is commonest among mammals, although it does occur in other groups of animals.

One group of animals, the coelenterates, makes use of both methods of reproduction, asexual and sexual. This group includes hydra and jellyfish, which take advantage of both methods by alternating between them. During the asexual phase, hydra reproduce by growing 'buds' which develop into young animals and eventually drop off.

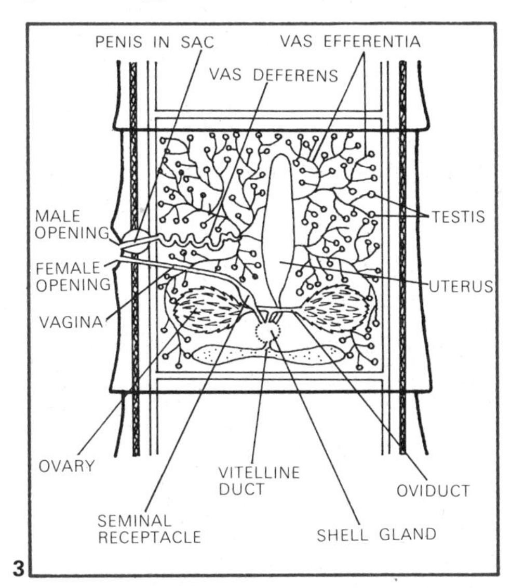


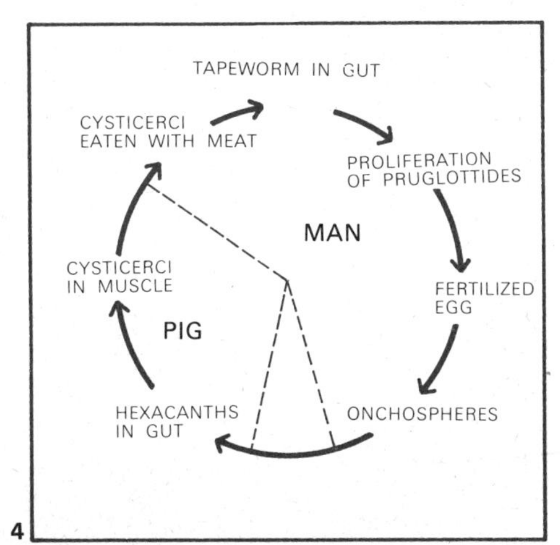


3 The cross-section of the reproductive system of the pork tapeworm reveals both female ovaries and male testis, indicating its bi-sexual nature.

4 The tapeworm is a parasite whose life cycle depends on two different hosts, one of which is Man, who carries the worm in his intestines.

## Dual sexes

During the sexual phase, ripe ova are shed into the water by the splitting of the gonads (gamete-producing organs) in the body wall. Sperm are released from the same animal in a similar way and external fertilization takes place.

Animals that have both male and female gonads are called *hermaphrodite.* Although this condition presents an opportunity for self-fertilization, this is generally prevented by the gametes of one sex (the male) maturing before those of the other (the female); biologists call this difference in the time of maturity *protandry.* Several invertebrate animals are hermaphrodite, including flatworms and some molluscs. One type of flatworm, called *dendrocoelum,*

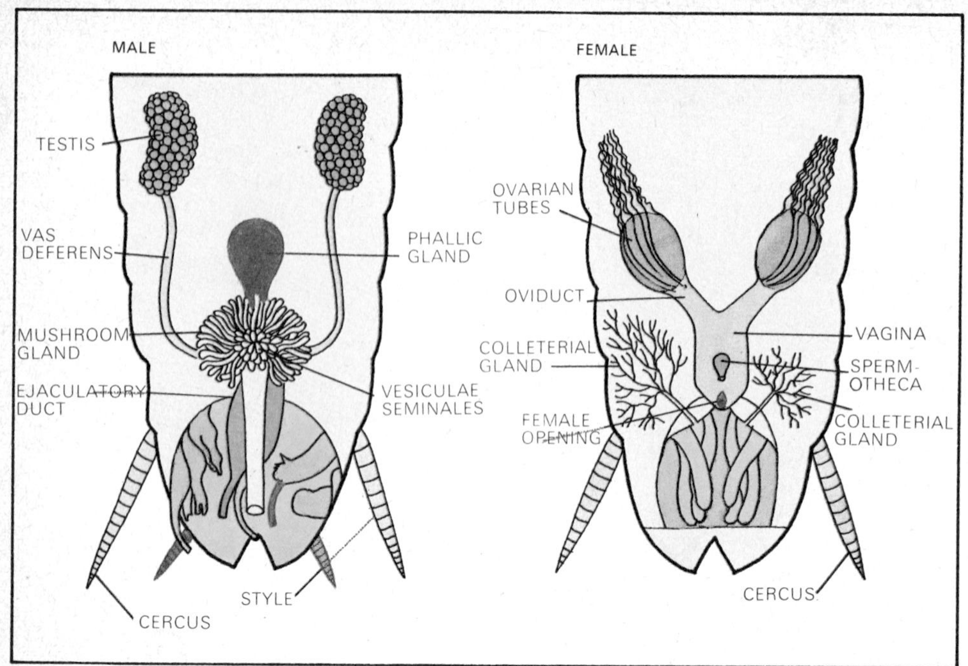


The reproductive systems in the cockroach show a definite division between the sexes. The male system produces sperms, while the female system receives them and allows for fertilization.

has both male and female genital organs located in a single opening. During copulation, sperm is exchanged by both animals. The complicated shape of the genitalia prevents self-fertilization and ensures that only cross-fertilization takes place.

The tapeworm, a parasitic flatworm, attaches itself by its head to the wall of the stomach or intestines in Man and other mammals. It consists of a series of segments which grow from the head end of the worm. Each segment bears male and female sex organs and comprises a complete reproductive unit.

## Hermaphrodites

After fertilization of the ova, the ovaries and testes disappear leaving only the uterus to house the numerous fertilized eggs. The eggs are passed out of the host animal in the faeces and remain dormant in a protective sheath. Eventually some of them are eaten by animals such as pigs and cattle. Digestive juices in the animal's stomach dissolve away the egg-cases and the young tapeworm emerges. It bores through the wall of the intestine into the blood vessels. It finally reaches the muscles where it forms a cyst. The cycle is completed when a man eats infected meat which is raw or under-cooked; the cyst breaks and an adult tapeworm emerges and attaches itself to the man's intestine wall.

The earthworm is also hermaphrodite. It has separate genital openings for its male and female reproductive systems and so self-fertilization is impossible. The sex organs are at the worm's head end. There are two pairs of testes, in segments 10 and 11. Maturing sperm pass out of the testes into a sperm sac, and when mature pass back again to the testes and along a duct to a pore on the lower surface of the fifteenth segment. There are also two sperm receptacles with openings on segments 9 and 10.

During copulation, the two earthworms lie nose to tail with their lower surfaces touching. A swollen ring called a *clittellum,* situated behind the front segments, lies opposite segments 9 and 10. Each worm sheds sperm from segment 15 which pass back along a tube of mucus to segments 9 and 10 of the partner. There they enter the sperm receptacles.

After the worms have separated, the clittellum secretes mucus and passes forward along the body. As it passes segment 14, a few ripe eggs enter it from the oviducts. When it passes segments 9 and 10, the sperm received from the other worm enter the clittellum and fertilize the eggs. The clittellum is then shed completely and forms a bag to protect the *zygotes* – the fertilized eggs.

This highly specialized reproductive system is an adaptation to life on land which provides the eggs with a very good chance of fertilization and survival. It is instructive to compare it with that in a marine annelid worm called *nereis.* Here the sex cells bud off from the lining of the body cavity in most of the segments. During the reproductive season, the females attract the males and the gametes are discharged into the sea by rupture of the body wall. The adult worms die, and the externally fertilized eggs develop into larvae.

The garden snail, like the earthworm, has a complex hermaphrodite reproductive system and cross-fertilization is again the rule. To ensure that self-fertilization cannot take place, these animals have evolved a remarkable method of copulation. Two snails approach each other and expose the male and female apertures by 'turning inside out' the chamber containing them. Each snail then uses its muscles to fire a naturally formed chalky dart at the other. (The darts travel with such force that they penetrate the body wall and may even become embedded in the internal organs.) This drastic stimulation is followed by normal copulation with a mutual exchange of sperm.

To a zoologist, a snail is a gastropod (meaning 'stomach foot', because it 'walks' on its belly). Marine gastropods, the snail's salt-water cousins, include the limpet, the periwinkle (sometimes called plain winkle) and the whelk. In these animals, the sexes are separate. The extraordinary gastropod called *crepidula* forms a colony of individual animals arranged in a column. The sexes alternate – stacked male, female, male, and so on – as each new animal is added to the column.

In nearly all insects the sexes are separate. They are primarily land animals and so fertilization is internal. A grasshopper is a typical example.

## Courtship behaviour

The male's testes discharge into a sperm duct. Glandular secretions join the sperm before it reaches the genital aperture near the tip of the abdomen. The female grasshopper has a special sac or sperm receptacle into which the male introduces his sperm. The sperm is stored in the female until egg-laying time. Eggs from the ovaries pass down twin oviducts and converge into a vagina.

The egg shell is formed round the yolk before fertilization, contrary to normal procedure. A small hole is left in the shell to permit the entry of sperm which are ejected from the sperm receptacle of the female as the eggs are laid. Strong abdominal appendages dig a hole in the soil so that the eggs are laid and fertilized virtually underground.

Mating can be a hazardous business, particularly for some male spiders and praying mantis who may find themselves finishing up as the bridal supper. A male mantis is considerably smaller than the female and he must arouse her sexual behaviour or she will eat him. Should he

Mating in insects is often preceded by the female exuding a scent to attract the male for copulation. In the case of these moths, the scent is effective at ranges of over a mile.

lose his head over her, his decapitated body can still perform its duty.

As we might expect, courtship behaviour becomes even more involved with vertebrate animals. Among the fish, the stickleback is a good example. The male is attracted to the female by the sight of her swollen abdomen which is full of ripe eggs. He begins a zigzag dance designed to show off his red colouration. The female responds and they dance together for a while, the male eventually leading her to a nest he has built among some weeds. He points at the entrance, she enters and sheds her eggs, and the male then enters and fertilizes them in the water. The female is chased from the nest and from then on the eggs are cared for by the father.

In between an aquatic and a terrestrial animal, an amphibian such as the frog is still very much dependent on water, to which it must return to breed. The croaking of the males attracts the females. The male climbs on the female's back and sheds his sperm over the eggs as the female lays them in the water.

Perhaps the most colourful courtship displays of all are those of birds. Many males have beautiful plumage which, as in the peacock and birds of paradise, they may display to attract the females. The male Australian bower bird makes up for his rather nondescript plumage by building for the female a wonderful shelter from twigs, flowers and even the bright feathers of other birds.

**1** Generally speaking, the larger and more advanced an animal, the smaller the number of young produced at a time. An elephant normally produces only one baby a season.

**2** Rodents, such as the brown rat, produce large litters. The young rats here are two days old.

**3** The blood lip snail, a native of St Vincent Island, violates the generality 'small animal, big litter' by laying only one egg at a time.

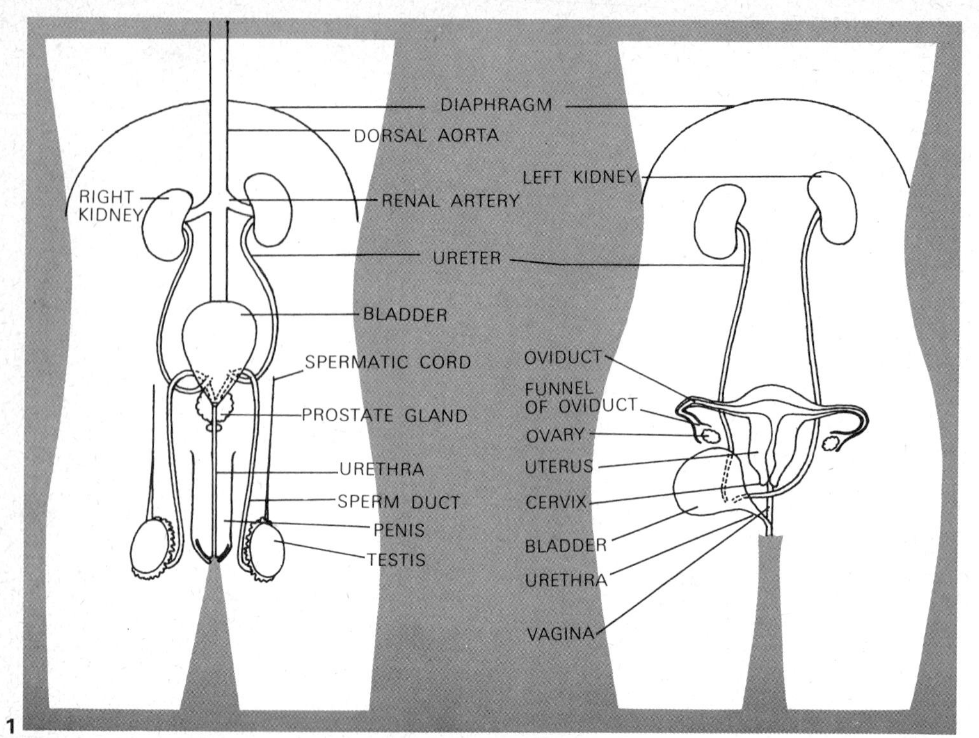


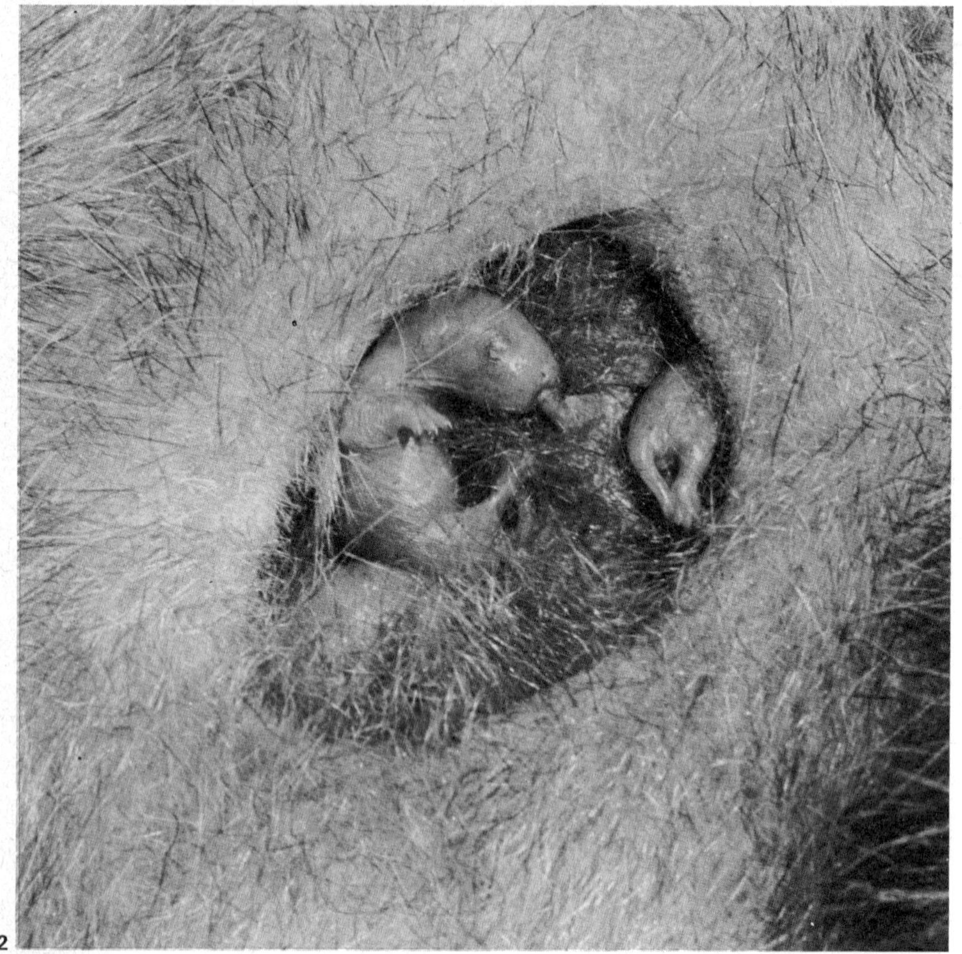


**1** The reproductive systems in Man are typical of most mammals. The male injects sperm into the female system, where the egg is fertilized and develops until it is ready for birth.

**2** After a gestation period of 12 to 17 days, the opossum gives birth to young only partially formed and about a half-inch long. They must then climb to the pouch to complete development.

Still in Australia, we find marsupial mammals such as the kangaroo and koala bear, although there are about 300 different species altogether. On the other side of the world in North America lives the opossum, which is also a marsupial. The young of these animals are very immature at birth. For instance, a new-born kangaroo is only an inch long. It is blind and naked, with only its fore limbs slightly developed. It crawls from the mother's genital opening into the pouch, the mother smoothing the way by licking the fur in its path. The baby becomes attached to its mother's nipple and continues its development in the pouch.

The time that elapses between fertilization and birth is called the *gestation period*. In marsupials, this is relatively short, about 40 days in the case of the great grey kangaroo and as short as eight days in the marsupial cat. The pregnancy period in most other mammals is much longer – and of course the young are much more fully developed when they are born. In placental mammals, a long period of development within the womb becomes possible. The gestation period in placental mammals varies from a few weeks in small rodents to nine months in a woman and 20 months in the elephant.

The number of young born at one time also varies. In large mammals it rarely exceeds one, whereas in mice it may be more than a dozen. In general, smaller litters are associated with the more highly evolved animals – quality rather than quantity. The time it takes a young mammal to develop sufficiently to be able to fend for itself also tends to be longer in advanced forms, especially in the primates. However, many herbivores (plant-eaters), such as deer, antelope and cattle, contradict this rule and give birth to young which are able within minutes to join the herd and gain protection from predators.

In most mammals, the female is receptive only during a definite season when she is said to be 'on heat' or *oestrous*. This condition may be communicated to the male by scent, as in dogs, or by colouration, as in some monkeys in which the female's buttocks become red.

## Why have sexes?

Sexual reproduction may appear to be unnecessarily complicated because it requires two separate individuals to produce a new individual. However, there are reasons for this. Since gametes contain only half the genetic material (chromosomes) found in ordinary cells in sexual reproduction, each parent contributes half the genetic material inherited by the offspring, so the offspring has characteristics of both. The recombination of genes from each parent during zygote formation leads to the possibility of variation and subtle changes in the individual. For this reason, over aeons of time, sexual reproduction allows evolution to operate through natural selection, so that only those creatures best adapted to their environment by genetic inheritance survive and perpetuate the species.

Evolution has progressed a long way from primitive almost random shedding of gametes into the sea to the long periods of gestation and post-natal parental care in higher mammals. But that is the price we must pay for our advanced development. A young stickleback, externally fertilized and deserted by its mother, can fend for itself almost the instant it is born. But a child, after nine months in his mother's womb, still has to grow for a further 12 to 15 years before he is able to survive completely on his own in his environment. But while lower animals have an initial advantage, the fact that mammals, and Man in particular, rule the land, shows that in the long run, the extra time needed for higher development pays off.

# Born alive

The most advanced animals, the mammals, and some other species, bear their young alive instead of as eggs. What are the biological advantages of this form of reproduction and how did it arise?

ANIMALS THAT PRODUCE 'live' young instead of eggs – that is animals that are viviparous – would seem to be at a great disadvantage. After all, many successful animals – like the cod, for example – are content merely to produce a whole mass of relatively tiny eggs and then 'forget' about them: reproduction seems to carry few fears or dangers for the parents. The female mammal, on the other hand, faces weeks – sometimes years – of pregnancy, and for at least part of this time is extremely vulnerable to predators or obstetric mishap. Then, during birth, the mother is a sitting target for opportunist predators (as witness the carnage among African antelope herds wrought by hyenas), while for the human female, childbirth is probably the most traumatic and dangerous event of her whole life. Yet viviparity is the hallmark of the mammals, the most influential animal group ever to walk the Earth. Why, despite the obvious drawbacks and dangers of viviparity, has evolution favoured this most complex and difficult form of reproduction?

The simplest animals – like the famous amoeba – can reproduce only by splitting in half. This is a fine method of reproducing under certain circumstances, and many animals much higher on the evolutionary scale than the one-celled protozoa may go through a frenetic phase of splitting or budding when a quick boost to the population is called for. Thus, for example, one of the larval stages of the human blood fluke *Schistosoma* lives inside water snails, and, when in the snail, it buds rapidly to produce many more larvae like itself. The point here is that after leaving the snail the larvae have only a few hours in which to find a new human host – otherwise they die. And a whole crowd of larvae has a much better chance of stumbling across a human being than a single larva has.

1 The female water bug lays her eggs in a close-packed pattern on the male's back. She then goes on her way, leaving the male to carry and defend the eggs.

2 A male marine stickleback building a nest. He has torn some finely branched seaweed from a rock and is now about to place it into the partly completed nest.

3 Sea-horses produce live young. The female deposits her eggs in a pouch under the male's tail, where they are fertilized and fed from the father's blood supply.

But animals that rely solely on asexual reproduction are doomed to evolutionary failure. Evolution implies change – change of a kind which human beings can generally interpret as improvement. Thus modern horses run faster than prehistoric horses; modern monkeys climb better than their shrew-like ancestors; and modern men think faster than ape-men did. These improvements depend on changes – refinements – in the genetic make-up of the animal. And fundamental genetic change can occur only if a gene changes its character – that is, if it mutates. So evolution depends on mutation. The trouble is that most mutations are harmful – they are, after all, random changes in a very subtle and complex coding system.

This is the paradox of evolution: an animal stock can improve only by accumulating random mutations – mutations which, *taken in isolation,* are generally harmful.

## Sexual reproduction

The answer to this paradox is sexual reproduction. For sexual reproduction means that a selection of genes form one individual. The point is that the 'classical' concept of genetics – that one gene is responsible for one characteristic – is only partly true. Genes operate in combinations – their effect can be radically modified not simply by changing individual genes, but also by re-arranging gene combinations. A mutation that is harmful in one gene combination may not be harmful – or even functional – in another combination. A mutation that is harmful – though not lethal – to a parent animal may be passed on to the offspring. But if in the offspring the mutant gene is combined in a gene combination that is different from that of the parent, the mutant gene may have no effect on the offspring. Thus animals produced by sexual reproduction can 'store' apparently harmful mutant genes that have arisen in their ancestors.

This type of reproduction means that the genetic information in all the individuals of a population can be shared. A beneficial mutation in any individual can be passed on to others, and harmful mutations can be re-arranged in different combinations in daughter animals and 'stored' without detriment to the animal. Later, these apparently harmful mutations might come in useful. (Hence the mutant black form of the pepper moth came into its own after the Industrial Revolution, when the previously lichen-covered trees of the industrial north became blackened with soot. The aberrant black moths, that had been such easy prey when resting on the greyish-white lichen-covered trees, suddenly found themselves very well camouflaged.) In fact, apparently harmful mutant genes are stored to such an extent in present-day animal populations that these populations could probably undergo enormous evolutionary change even if no more mutations occurred – simply by re-arranging and bringing to the fore latent genes that have mutated in the past. But only if all the genes in a population are 'pooled' and constantly re-arranged through the device of sexual reproduction can an animal population come to terms with the essential mutations which would otherwise destroy it. So only animals that reproduce sexually can evolve to a significant degree.

The leathery turtle, a sea reptile, comes ashore to deposit her eggs on the beach. She digs a hole laboriously with her flippers and buries the eggs under the sand.

## Dramatic events

But sexual reproduction raises enormous problems. When an amoeba splits into two, each of the daughter amoebae is a perfectly good animal – capable of feeding, reproducing and responding to its environment just as did the parent organism. But in sexual reproduction the gene complement of an animal must be split in two and then recombined with half the gene complement of another individual. Such dramatic events cannot happen on the grand scale. Special cells – the gametes – must be developed in which the parent's gene complement is split (by the process known as meiosis). The gametes from two individuals then combine to form a single cell – the fertilized egg – from which the offspring develops. But the egg, unlike the daughter amoeba, is a feeble organism. It has none of the attributes of the adult animal into which it will develop. As a single, motionless cell it is completely vulnerable to temperature and chemical changes which it can do nothing to avoid, and is a sitting target for predators. Yet, if the species is to continue, the egg must survive and develop into an organism that can forage and fend for itself.

Like most other basic animal functions, sexual reproduction evolved in the sea. There, the problems are comparatively easy. The first problem – causing gametes from two different individuals to come into contact – is solved very simply by animals as distantly related as sea-anemones, starfish, polychaete worms and barnacles by the simplest conceivable method: the animal simply releases gametes into the sea. The sea has a constant temperature, is wet, has a convivial chemical composition, and obligingly carries the gametes around until they come into contact with gametes from individuals of opposite sex. Then fusion can take place. The only difficulty is that different individuals of the same species must release their gametes at the same time. In general, each species reacts to some change in the environment that affects all members of the population simultaneously. The palolo worm, *Leodice,* for example, sheds its eggs or sperms as the day of the last quarter of the October–November moon dawns over the reefs of the Pacific.

Then, when gamete has met gamete to produce a fertilized egg, the egg may float to the surface to form part of the plankton or sink to the sea bottom. These eggs are defenceless, but because the sea provides a constant environment the eggs have only to consume the food reserves – yolk – with which they have been supplied, until they are sufficiently developed to feed. The outstanding difficulty is predators, and most eggs casually tossed into

The young of the green aphis, a common insect pest, are produced alive after gestation inside the mother's body. Here the female aphis is giving birth to a tiny young aphid.

A pipestrelle bat cleaning its young. The young bats are born alive like the young of other mammals, and are fed through the placenta while they are in the womb.

The eggs of the common toad *(Bufo bufo)* are fertilized by the male during copulation (amplexus) as they emerge in long 'ropes' from the body of the female: upper right.

the plankton are destroyed – the only limitation on destruction being that if all the eggs were eaten there would be nothing for the predators to feed on the following year. But the simple device of abandoning gametes and eggs to the tide and to chance is obviously very wasteful and it could only operate in the sea which supplies an easy environment for defenceless creatures.

Thus, though there have been a great many recidivists who have retained the profligate spawning habits of more primitive animals – cod produce 7 million eggs, turbot 10 million – the evolutionary tendency in almost all animal groups has been to make sexual reproduction less wasteful, more sure-fire. In practice, this has meant that animals have developed means firstly of protecting the gametes, and of making sure that each egg produced is fertilized; secondly of protecting the eggs, so that they stand a reasonable chance of developing into more-or-less viable organisms; and finally of protecting the young animals until they are mature enough to look after themselves.

To a very large extent the evolution of vertebrates has been a matter of developing these three stages of protection – and they have been acquired in the order outlined above. Thus, though the eggs of bony fish are generally fertilized outside the body, mechanisms have evolved to ensure that few gametes are wasted. Thus the male stickleback is attracted to the female by her swollen pregnant belly, and the female is attracted to the male by the red skin he develops in the breeding season. The female is excited by the male's movements to lay her eggs on the bottom of the pond, and the male is excited by the female's egg-laying activity into depositing his sperms on top of the eggs. This is a major advance over the method of fertilization practised by the palolo worm – female and male stickleback must respond to specific characteristics in each other, and they must co-operate. This co-operation produces much more sure-fire fertilization than would be achieved if the gametes were simply ejected when the moon was in a particular quarter.

As vertebrates left the water for the land the need to protect the gametes became not a refinement but a necessity; gametes shed into the open air would simply dry up and die. Several marine animals have independently developed means of conserving gametes by evolving means of copulation – the sperms are not shed over the already laid eggs, but are deposited inside the female's reproductive tract so that neither unfertilized egg nor sperm need ever sally into the outside world. But marine animals that copulate – notably the sharks and rays, and the squids, octopi and nautiloids – are rare. On land, copulation leading to internal fertilization is the rule.

## Internal fertilization

The beginnings of internal fertilization are seen in the vertebrates that have made the first tentative steps towards the land – the amphibia. For example, during the breeding season the male frog grasps the female around the neck – the position known as plexus – and is carried round piggy-back style for some days. In fact, in frogs, fertilization is external – the female lays her eggs in the water and the male covers them with sperm as they are released. But the action of the frogs is very nearly copulation – with very little modification the male frog could deposit his sperms inside the female reproductive tract. The most essential requirements of copulation – the extreme degree of co-operation and physical contact between animals that are not at other times sociable – are already present.

Reptiles are land breeders and fertilization is always internal. Though most

The female woodmouse builds a nest for the young and suckles the tiny mice during the first weeks of their life. Protection of the young is common among mammals.

The Mozambique mouthbrooder male protects the tiny young fish hatched from the eggs by keeping them in its mouth whenever danger threatens the brood.

The offspring of many herbivores, like this young zebra, are born with the ability to run. This calf has just been born, but it is ready to take flight if threatened.

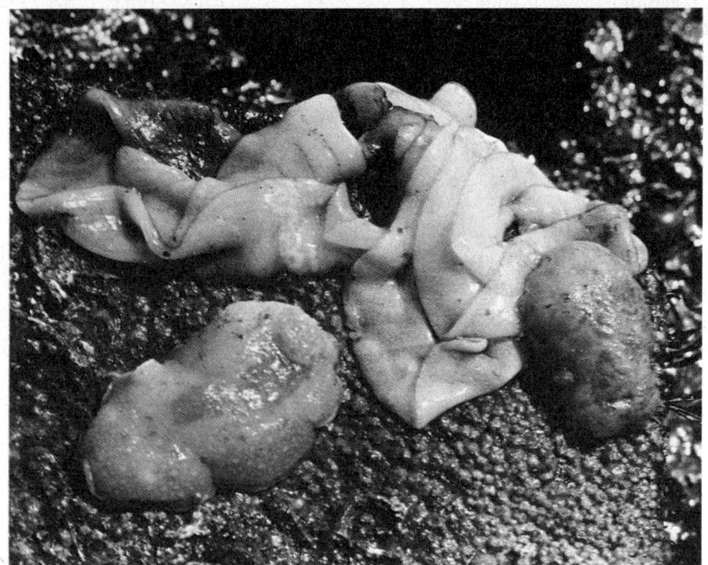

The two round jelly-like 'blobs' in the foreground of this photograph are sea slugs. Behind them is a long ribbon of spawn containing thousands of eggs.

reptiles copulate simply by placing their reproductive openings in contact (as most birds do), some – like the snakes – have developed a penis so that the sperms can be deposited deep in the female reproductive tract. Internal fertilization has one outstanding advantage over even the efficient external fertilization practised by amphibia and some fish. After the female gamete is fertilized in the reptilian reproductive tract, protective membranes and even a shell can be added to the fertile egg cell. Thus, because of internal fertilization the reptile (or bird – the same argument applies) can produce *protected* eggs that can withstand drought and can therefore be laid on land.

With most fish, amphibia and reptiles care of the young stops at the egg stage. Once the egg is laid – whether it be the protected egg of the reptile or the naked egg of the frog – it is abandoned. But a few fish, amphibia and reptiles take protection one step further. This they do in one or both of two ways – one way behavioural, the other structural 'physiological'. Thus we saw how in order to make fertilization efficient male and female animals had to evolve behaviour that made them respond to each other. Similarly in some instances one or both parents have 'learned' to respond to the eggs. While the male cod simply eats any cod eggs it finds floating in the plankton (cod are their own worst enemies), the male stickleback is so moved by the sight of its eggs that it stays near them fending off attackers, and actually fans the eggs with its tail – thus increasing their oxygen supply.

The next logical step in egg protection is not to stand guard over the eggs but to carry them around until they are developed into infants that can fend for themselves. For this, structural and physiological adaptations are needed.

The most usual place to carry around fertile eggs is in the female reproductive tract. Thus female guppies carry around the eggs until they hatch and then give birth to 'live' young. This is known as

Grass snakes copulating. The eggs are fertilized inside the female body during the spring, and laid in August, when they immediately hatch to give tiny young.

viviparity. But several amphibia and fish have developed other means of carrying around the eggs. In some catfishes the young develop within the mouths of one or other of the parents. In the seahorse and the related pipefish the male (not the female) is equipped with a kangaroo-like pouch in which he carries round the developing young. Similarly, in the so-called marsupial frog, *Gastrotheca,* the female has a large pouch on her back which opens just above the reproductive opening.

## Protection of the young

As the eggs are laid, the male – which, in true frog fashion is carried piggy-back style during mating – holds open this pouch with his hind legs, at the same time covering the eggs with sperm. The fertilized eggs pass into the pouch and are kept there until they develop into tadpoles. In such instances the structural and physiological adaptations evolved to protect eggs and very young animals are combined with behavioural adaptations.

The birds and mammals are by far the most successful land vertebrates – and indeed, the mammalian seals, sea-lions and whales dominate many marine environments. The success of birds and mammals depends very largely on protection of the young – yet this protection is produced in very different ways in the two groups. Both groups have means of protecting the gametes – fertilization is invariably internal. But whereas the bird, after supplying the fertilized egg with enormous quantities of yolk, and covering it with protective membranes, lays the egg in a nest, the mammal keeps the egg within its uterus (womb) often until it is quite well developed, and so breeds viviparously.

But viviparity in mammals is a much more refined adaptation than in lower animals. In the guppy, for example, the egg is supplied with large quantities of yolk. The egg develops in the mother more or less as it would if it were laid in the water. It gains the benefit of the very stable environment inside the mother, and it is protected from predators, but it is more or less a self-sufficient lodger.

The degree of dependence in mammals has profound implications. Firstly, the mother must develop means of retaining the young egg – after all, there is no theoretical reason why the egg, which is being propelled down the genital tract from the ovary, should not continue on its way after fertilization and be removed from the body. This is prevented through a hormone, progesterone, which acts upon the surface layers of the womb – the endometrium – and makes it capable of ensnaring the fertilized egg so that it can develop in the womb.

Thus, though some fish and reptiles are viviparous, and a few amphibia make a pass at viviparity, only the mammals have developed viviparity into a fine art. Mammalian viviparity has required enormous structural, physiological and behavioural advances – but it is largely because mammals have made those advances that they are now the most influential animal group.

# Genes - life's changing stereotypes

Children often resemble one of their two parents more strongly than the other. Nevertheless, each child born into the world is an equal mixture of both, alloyed into a unique new individual.

**1** Certain hereditary traits can remain hidden from one generation to the next, until they suddenly appear. This snowy-coated kangaroo suffers from albinism, loss of normal colour.
**2** Bengalese finches are apparently hybrids. They are found only in captivity and have no wild counterpart. They were 'created' hundreds of years ago, perhaps by a freak of nature or by Man. No one knows for certain.
**3** In some families, hereditary traits are quite obvious. Singer Judy Garland and her daughter not only look alike, they sound alike.

ON A COLD and snowy night in February, 1865, in a town called Brünn in Austria, a man got up to present a report to a group of people. The man was an Augustinian monk and his name was Gregor Johann Mendel. He was about to address a meeting of the Brünn Society for the Study of Natural History, and to tell them about some experiments he had been doing with pea plants grown in the garden of his monastery.

Gregor Mendel told his audience how he had spent the previous eight years studying problems of inheritance. He explained how he had discovered certain laws governing the inheritance of seed colour and plant height and other characteristics. His talk was received with polite but baffled silence. No one asked him any questions. After he had finished, his bewildered audience simply made their way home in the snow.

Mendel's report was published the following year in the Society's *Proceedings*. Copies were sent to many of the capitals of Europe, where they remained to gather dust on library shelves. A personal letter from Mendel to Karl von Nageli – one of the great scientists of his time – followed in 1867. Nageli replied, but was unimpressed by what Mendel had told him.

Despite these setbacks, Mendel continued his work. But upon his appointment as abbot of the monastery in 1868, demands on his time pressed more and more. He died early in 1884, aged 61, his health affected by a long, bitter fight against monastery tax laws. His work was forgotten, his genius misunderstood.

Just what did Mendel talk about on that occasion in 1865? What did he say that left his audience paralyzed with incomprehension? He told them how he grew lots of pea plants in his garden. He grew seven sets at first. Each set had two kinds of pea plants in it, and these two kinds differed in one obvious way. For example,

**1** Brown eyes dominate blue. The baby's blue eyes tells the trained geneticist that neither parent can be 'pure-bred' (homozygous) brown-eyed.
**2** The genetic make-up (genotype) of animals can be found by breeding. All-dark offspring means one genotype; mixed offspring means another.

in one set half the plants produced round seeds and the other half wrinkled seeds. In another set, half grew long stems and the other half grew short stems, and so on.

Mendel then pollinated his 'round-seed' plants with pollen from 'wrinkle-seed' flowers, and vice versa. He waited for the fertilized ovules to grow into seeds. When he opened the ripe fruits, he found that *all* the seeds were round, and *none* were wrinkled.

The following year Mendel planted his new round seeds, and let them flower and pollinate themselves. When the fruits ripened, he opened them. Round and wrinkled seeds appeared side by side in the same pods. The trait for wrinkled seeds, which had disappeared completely, had turned up again! Mendel counted the two kinds of seeds: there were three times as many round ones as wrinkled ones.

How did he set about explaining these puzzling results? To begin with, he said that the factor causing round seeds was *dominant* over the *recessive* factor for wrinkled seeds. He had to, because all the offspring produced from the cross between round and wrinkled-seeded plants were round-seeded.

## Two factor solution

For a dominant factor, Mendel proposed a capital letter; for a recessive factor, a small letter. Thus, in discussing the round seed factor, one uses R, and for the wrinkled seed factor, r.

Mendel then deduced that every plant has a *pair* of factors. Again, he had to. He had seen that plants with dominant traits could give rise directly to plants showing recessive traits. They could not do this unless they carried a recessive factor. And they certainly could not show their dominant trait without also carrying a dominant factor. So he was forced to the conclusion that a pair of factors was operating. For logical consistency, Mendel also assigned a pair of factors to those plants that were not a mixture of traits. So, for his round or wrinkled peas, the picture looked like this: round peas RR; wrinkled peas rr; hybrid from cross between round and wrinkled seed plants Rr. R is dominant over r, so all the hybrids had round seeds. When plants Rr (the hybrids) pollinated themselves, round seeds outnumbered wrinkled seeds by 3:1. Why?

The answer, Mendel saw, is easy if you assume that *pairs of factors split up into individual factors, and then recombine in pairs according to chance.* The offspring will contain the following factor combinations: RR, Rr, rR, rr. But as far as genetics is concerned, Rr and rR are the same, because the R is dominant. Thus, the result may be characterized as RR, 2Rr, rr. That is, on average, R will pair with r *twice* as often as will R with R, and r with r, so there will be twice as many hybrids as pure RR or rr strains. Since R is dominant,

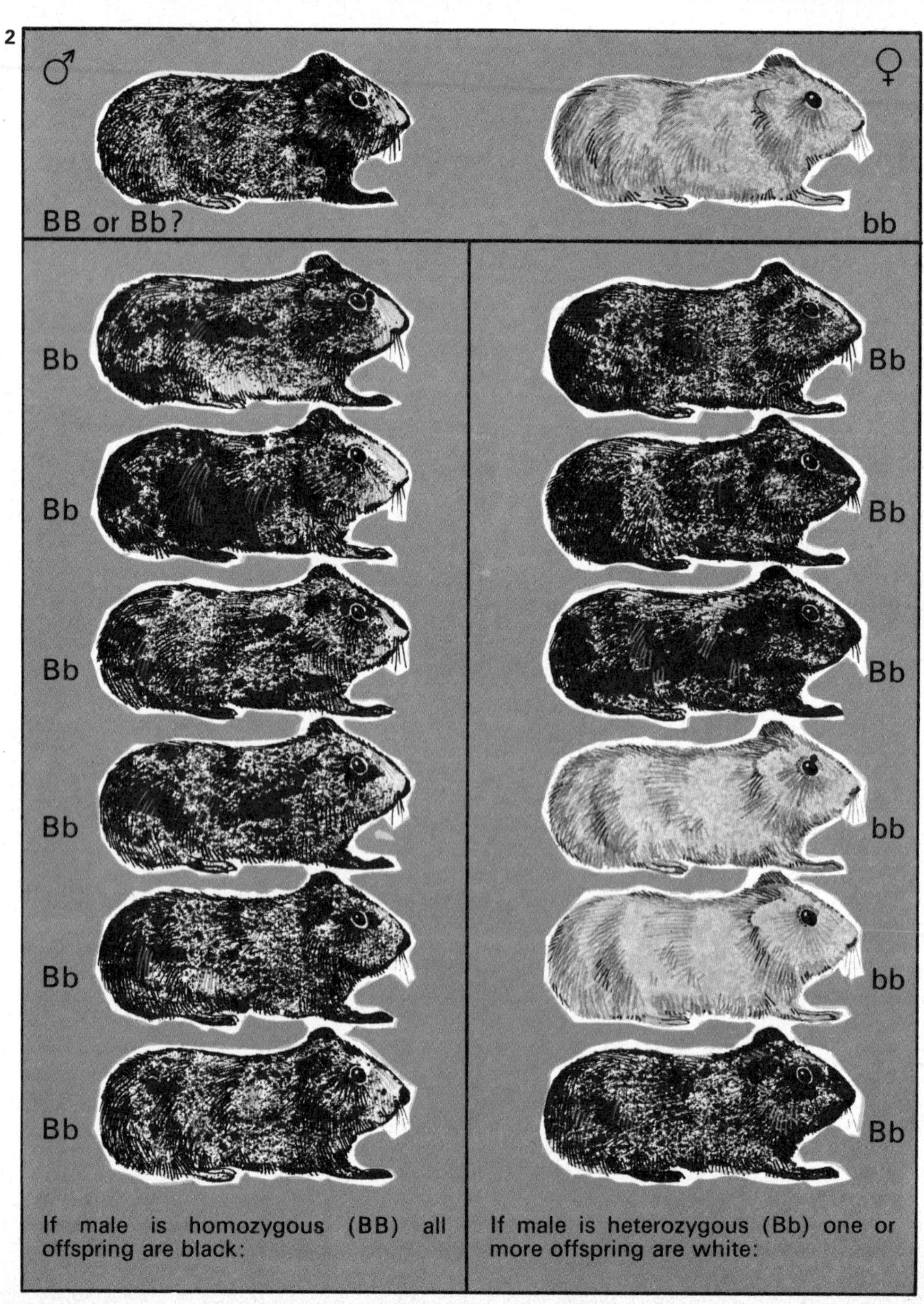

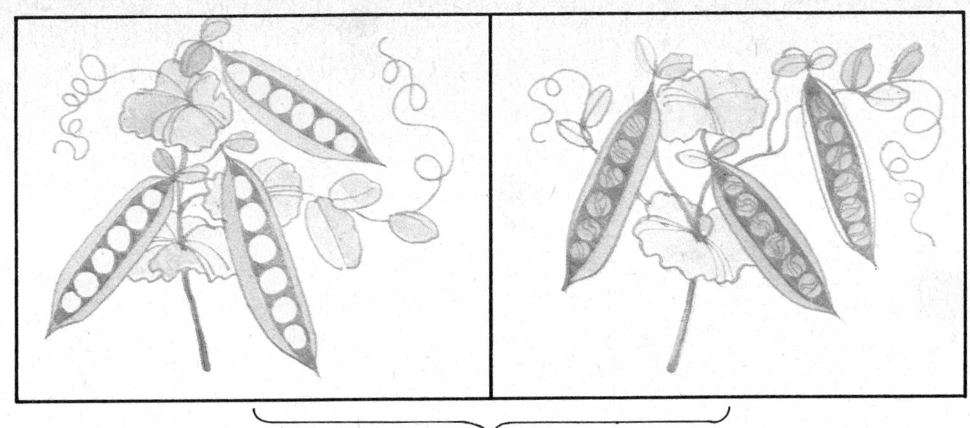

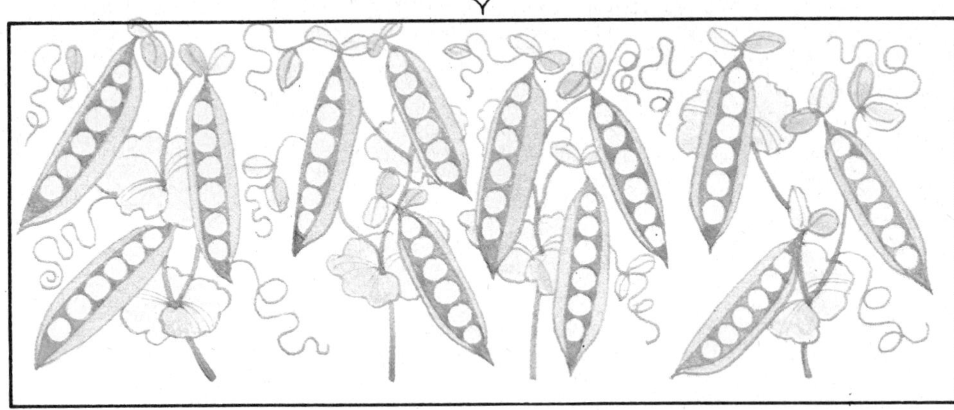

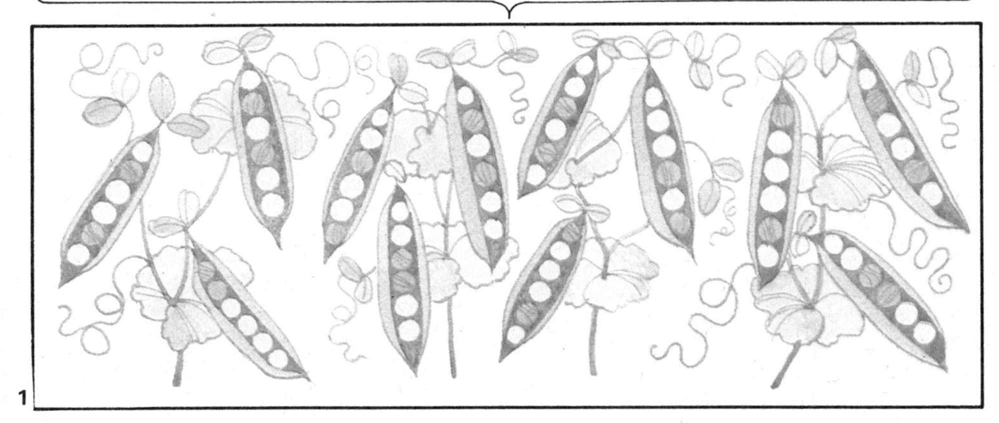

1

three out of every four of the offspring will show the dominant round-seed factor. One-fourth, with both factors recessive rr, will have wrinkled seeds.

Remember that in 1865 there was absolutely no concrete evidence of 'hereditary factors'. No one understood Mendel in 1865. In fact it was not until 1900, 16 years after his death, that three men independently discovered Mendel's paper and realized its importance. With this realization, the science of genetics began.

Today we know that every living thing consists of cells. Some organisms have just one cell. But most are made up of millions upon millions of cells. Every typical cell has a nucleus. Within this round nucleus lie a number of rod- or sausage-shaped objects called *chromosomes*.

In any single individual, the number of chromosomes in the nucleus of one body cell is the same as that in any other body cell. And the *chromosome number*, as it is called, of one individual is the same as that of any other individual of the same species. Men and women have 46 chromosomes in their cell nucleus. Maize plants have 20 chromosomes; mosquitoes have six; and cabbages have 18.

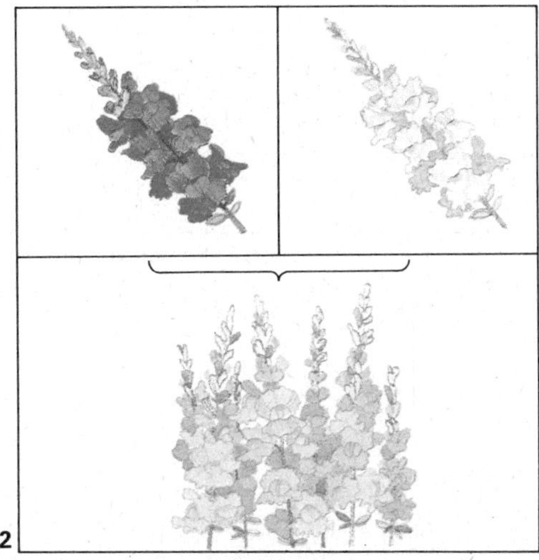

2

**1** In the middle nineteenth century, Gregor Mendel crossed 'smooth-pea' plants with 'wrinkled-pea' plants to obtain only smooth peas. But when these interbred, a mixture of smooth and wrinkled peas appeared. Mendel's interpretation of these results paved the way for modern genetics.
**2** Sometimes one genetic trait completely dominates another; at other times an amalgam results. White snapdragons crossed with red snapdragons produce pink snapdragons. The colours blend.

If you looked at a normal body cell of almost any organism under a powerful microscope you would count an *even* number of chromosomes in the nucleus (notice the numbers for man, mosquitoes and maize). One good reason for the chromosome number being even is that the chromosomes occur in pairs, as suggested by Mendel's experiments. There are, in fact, two matching sets of chromosomes in a nucleus. In animals and plants which reproduce sexually, one set has been donated by the father, and the other by the mother. Actually, the sets do not match exactly. In most animals, and in a few plants, there is a recognizable difference between the members of one particular pair of chromosomes. In a man, for example, 22 pairs of chromosomes match perfectly. But one pair demonstrably does not. In this pair, one chromosome is very much smaller than its partner. In a woman, on the other hand, all 23 pairs of chromosomes match. This difference in one of the members of one pair of chromosomes in the male accounts for the differences between men and women. Among birds and butterflies, one chromosome pair in the *female* shows a difference, while all the male chromosome pairs match perfectly.

## Divide and reduce

If every body cell contains two sets of chromosomes, equally donated by the father and the mother, it is clear that each parent provides only half the full chromosome requirement of the offspring. What this means, in real terms, is that a sperm cell and an egg cell can each contain only a *single* set of chromosomes, instead of the double set typical of all other types of cells. How do the reproductive cells manage to halve their chromosome number? They do so by means of a vitally important form of cell division called *meiosis*. During the formation of eggs and sperms, each chromosome appears to 'seek out' its partner. The matching pairs of chromosomes line up along the centre of the dividing reproductive cell, split apart, and move to opposite ends of the dividing cell. Each new cell now contains only one set of chromosomes.

The chromosomes, important though they are, are not the basic units of inheritance. Chromosomes act merely as a fleet of carriers for the fundamental hereditary particles, which are called *genes*. A chromosome carries a 'crew' of genes, which lie along the length of the chromosomes in single file – rather as though the crew were on inspection.

Each gene or group of genes carries within its chemistry the potential to recreate a trait which was present in a parent. All the genes together on all the chromosomes carry the potential to recreate an entire individual. The chemistry of the gene is the key to inheritance. A gene consists of a compound called *deoxyribonucleic acid* (DNA), which possesses the astonishing ability to copy itself. But that is not all: DNA contains a number of compounds called *bases*, arranged at regular intervals along the coiled chain-like length of its molecule. These bases determine gene action.

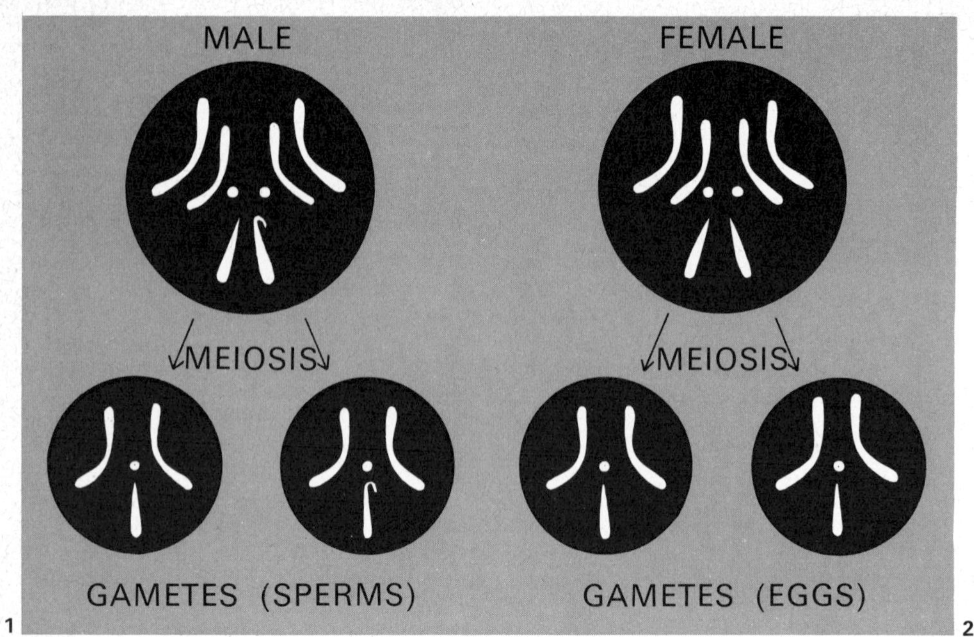

Say, for example, that a particular gene is responsible for producing a pigment in the petals of a certain species of flower. The DNA in the gene has its bases arranged in a certain way. Each group of three bases specifies a particular amino acid. As each three-base sequence is spelled out, the required amino acid is picked up in the cell and hooked on to a growing protein chain. When the base sequence is finished, the protein is complete. The protein turns out to be an *enzyme* – a catalyst whose job is to speed a particular chemical reaction in the cell.

### Beautiful brown eyes

It would be unfortunate to fall into the trap of thinking that gene action is an isolated phenomenon. Neighbouring genes undoubtedly influence each other's actions – indeed, a group of adjacent genes may be responsible for making a series of enzymes which mediate in a chain of reactions to build a complex chemical needed by the cell.

For a special case of genes affecting each other, one must go back to a point mentioned earlier. Remember that a normal body cell has two sets of chromosomes – one from either parent. The sets match – in other words the chromosomes are actually in pairs. Now this means that the genes for every single trait also exist in pairs. A pair of genes may express themselves in precisely the same way. For example, the pair of genes responsible for eye colour in human beings may both specify brown eyes. Or they may both specify blue eyes. However, it frequently comes about that one gene of the pair specifies a trait in one form, while the other gene of the pair specifies the same trait in a *different* form. For example, a child may be born with one gene for brown eyes and the other for blue eyes. The child's eyes are not blue-brown, however, they are brown. The gene for brownness completely overshadows the effect of the gene for blueness when the two are together. In other words, the gene for brown eyes is dominant over the gene for blue eyes, which is recessive in the same way

**1** In many species, including humans, male gametes (sperms) differ, female gametes (eggs) are all alike. This gives rise to the idea that the father 'determines' the child's sex.

the 'round-pea' factor was dominant over the 'wrinkled-pea' factor in Mendel's experiment. Similarly, in guinea pigs the gene for black fur dominates the genes for any other colour.

One gene in a pair is not invariably completely dominant over its partner gene. In nature, all gradations between dominance and non-dominance are known to occur. For example, crimson-flowered snapdragons, when fertilized with pollen from a white-flowered variety (and *vice versa*), give rise to seeds which grow into pink-flowered snapdragons. Here there is no dominance: the offspring's flower colour is midway between those of the parent blooms.

Chromosomes have been described as a bit like a fleet of ships, each with its own crew of genes. Like any fleet, there are big ships and little ships, and the crews vary in numbers accordingly. Whatever the size of the ship, though, it usually takes its entire crew with it, wherever it goes. In other words, the genes on one particular chromosome will usually stay together and be inherited as a unit. The genes are said to be *linked*. Notice, they 'usually stay together'. During meiosis, chromosome pairs seek each other out before they split apart to form reproductive cells. While they lie alongside one another, they contract and twist round each other. Quite frequently both chromosomes snap under the strain. It is just as likely that the broken ends then re-unite with the 'wrong' chromosome as with the 'right' one. When such a chromosome pair separates, each carries a piece belonging originally to the other. This is called *crossing over*. It is almost as though two ships have exchanged crew members in mid-ocean.

Discovery of the phenomenon of crossing over gave scientists a neat way of pin-pointing the order of genes along a chromosome. They thought rather like this: if two genes are at opposite ends of a

**2** Prominent physical traits which appear in a family generation after generation, such as the protruding 'Habsburg lip', are probably the result of a single dominant gene.

chromosome, they would get separated far more frequently by crossing over than would two genes which lie next-door to each other. In fact, the likelihood of two genes getting split up is related to the distance between them.

### Shuffling the pack

This sophisticated technique was first used to construct a map of the chromosomes of the fruit fly, and scientists were able to order and position all its known genes. Maps have also been made for many other animals, and for plants as well. Scientists are even beginning to map the chromosomes of human beings.

Crossing over means that genes get swapped about and become rearranged in various combinations. It is as though the organism 'shuffles the pack' before it deals out 'hands' of reproductive cells. Gene shuffling, particularly the dissemination of altered genes, is vital to an evolving organism. Only by turning up new combinations of hereditary factors can a species hope to keep pace with its changing environment. For survival, variety is indeed the spice of life.

It is this variety, operating in conjunction with selection and mutation, which makes possible evolutionary change, leading to new species and modifications within species. Out of Mendel's work, carried out in obscurity so many years ago, has grown the modern scientific study of the detailed mechanism of the genes and chromosomes, so that today biologists are confident that they will soon be able to tailor the characteristics of plants and animals to human needs.

For Man himself, however, the question of tampering with this mechanism is one of morals rather than science. But there seems little doubt that biologists will, one day, be able at least to remedy the disabling effects of genetic damage in human beings.

# The conforming gene

**Much animal, as well as human, behaviour is passed from parents to children through the genes. How are behaviour patterns inherited, and how are they affected by learning, trial-and-error, and reason?**

WHEN STUDYING ANIMALS, it is not so much the differences between the individual members of a particular species that are striking but the broad, general similarities. With a good eye for detail and a microscope, an expert entomologist can distinguish between most of the million and more species of insects because he knows that certain external characteristics are typical of one species only. But another way of telling species apart, however closely they are related, is to study their behaviour. Once again, within certain limits and trends, there is remarkable conformity.

Such conformity is hardly surprising. In the struggle for existence the most successful animals are those best adapted to their environment. Everything counts; their shape, their physiology and their behaviour. With time, therefore, certain elements of behaviour are discarded, while other elements, more suitable and successful, are retained. A species is the sum of its evolution; a specific solution for coping with its environment.

## Survival

Undoubtedly one single type of environment offers many different solutions, but a species cannot gamble on too many alternatives; it would soon be ousted by the other species because of its lack of specialization. An animal's behaviour must, therefore, be consistent and specialized. It must also be absolutely integrated with the animal's way of life. For example, the prehistoric reptiles discovered that by running fast on their hind legs and occasionally leaping into the air they were better able to escape their predators. By flapping their forelimbs they could go farther through the air, and the most successful were those with the broadest forelimbs. In time with this sort of behaviour, and through the agency of natural selection, the reptiles developed true wings. In birds, flying behaviour and body form have become absolutely integrated.

The inheritance of behaviour depends, like all inherited factors, on genes being transmitted from one generation to the next. While it may be comparatively easy to think of a gene controlling some specific trait, like the colour of the human eye or the number and form of the bristles on the abdomen of the fruit fly, *Drosophila*, it is almost impossible to understand how a gene, or a set of genes, can control anything as complicated as animal behaviour.

The stereotyped courtship behaviour of sticklebacks is known as a *fixed action pattern*, and it does not vary significantly from one to another. In studying the genetics of behaviour it is generally easier to look at such fixed action patterns than at other forms of behaviour, like learning, which vary from situation to situation and are dependent to a large extent on the animal's previous experience.

Although it is to the species' advantage that its fixed action patterns should all be consistent, because only then can there be true co-operation between the members of the species, particularly with regards to mating, there are variations. It is these variations which are important in evolution for they provide the basic material for natural selection. It is also these variations that give clues to the genetic control of behaviour, for they can be observed against the backcloth of the more uniform pattern of the fixed action pattern.

*Drosophila* is an extremely useful animal to study genetically because the chromosomes in its salivary glands are so enlarged that they are visible to the naked eye. Geneticists have been able to map these chromosomes by observing how certain features of the animal vary with

1 Bird-song, and particularly the mating call, is a highly specific characteristic. Stereotyped songs make it possible for birds to distinguish potential partners from non-mates.

2 The behaviour of ants has a rigid genetic basis. Every ant is born with a behaviour pattern which fits it neatly into one or other category in the ant community.

changes in the appearance of small regions of the chromosomes. They have discovered that a mutant gene, which dramatically affects some morphological or physiological character of the fruit fly, very often affects the animal's behaviour. For example the gene called *Bar* reduces the number of facets in the compound eyes, *white* reduces pigmentation in the eyes, *forked* and *hairy* affect the number and structure of the bristles, *vestigial* and *dumpy* alter the shape of the wings, while *yellow* and *black* affect the general pigmentation of the body. These mutant genes also have other effects, which may be detected if tests are carried out on the animal's metabolism, and perhaps affect its span of life. Many of these mutations even if made one at a time, have also been found to affect the fruit fly's mating behaviour, and males with such mutants are much less successful than normal males in stimulating females to mate with them.

## Difficulties in mating

There are many different ways by which mating behaviour can be interfered with. Fruit flies with the genes affecting their eyes cannot see as well as normally, and they have difficulty in finding the females to mate with in the first place. Then, having found them, they miss some essential visual stimuli generated by the females. But, as well as vision, the tactile sense is also involved during mating, and males with *forked* or *hairy* genes have bristles which are defective as tactile sense organs. Then again, as in the stickleback, a courtship sequence always precedes mating, and should it be inadequately performed the partners fail to arrive at the stage of copulating. Fruit flies with *vestigial* and *dumpy* mutant genes have grossly malformed wings which cannot be vibrated properly.

During courtship the male *Drosophila* brings one of its wings out laterally and vibrates it in the horizontal plane. This action stimulates tactile sense organs at the base of the female's antenna. A defective wing, when vibrated, fails to arouse the female sufficiently for her to copulate with the male. The reason why the mutant genes, *yellow* and *black* affect mating behaviour is less obvious. It has been suggested that perhaps the muscles operating the wings are slightly defective in some way, or the nerves to the muscles, and the wing vibration is sufficiently 'off-beat' to disturb the female.

An animal's behaviour and the genes operating it seem divorced from each other. Also, for any one behavioural

1 The greater part of its behaviour pattern is already fixed in the chromosomes of this baby American robin, though learning and reasoning play a part in its life.
2 This robin, removing a dropping from its nest, may be acting from learned considerations. But his scavenging behaviour has survival value and may be partly inherited.
3 An Australian frilled dragon lizard. Threat behaviour in lizards play an important part in enabling members of one species to distinguish their own species from similar lizards.

activity, even a fixed action pattern, a whole bank of genes is in operation. It is therefore very difficult to isolate any one gene as the operator of a particular action. Yet, a most exact piece of research has been done on honey bees by Dr W.C. Rothenbuhler. He studied the inheritance of certain characteristics which affect the bee's behaviour in cleaning out the inside of the hive.

Some strains of bee have been found to be 'unhygienic' and instead of, as is normal, cleaning out cells which contain dead larvae, they leave the cell dirty. Such behaviour has disadvantages; it can lead to disease and it prevents the queen bee from using all the available cells for laying eggs and thereby ensuring the continual emergence of worker bees. Rothenbuhler discovered that the hybrids between the unhygienic strain and a hygienic strain were all unhygienic, and therefore the abnormal gene must be dominant. He then crossed the hybrids to the recessive, hygienic strain with extraordinary results. From 29 back-cross colonies he found: nine of the colonies took off the caps of the cells, but left the corpses untouched; six did not uncap the cells, but if the caps were taken off by hand, would remove the corpses; eight colonies were completely unhygienic and would neither uncap the cells nor remove dead larvae; and six colonies were hygienic and uncapped the cells and removed the larvae.

These findings suggest there must be two main genes involved. One gene is concerned with the uncapping of cells, and the other with the removing of the dead larvae. The hybrid colony had both the dominant genes – which supplement each other in making the colony unhygienic – and their recessive alleles. When back-crossing them to the pure-strain hygienic colonies, results conformed to classical genetic theory.

It could be assumed from these results that all the genes concerned with the complicated behaviour of cleaning the cells are absent in the doubly unhygienic strains and present in the hygienic strains. But Rothenbuhler points out that even unhygienic workers perform these activities to a small extent, though quite inadequately from the colony's point of view. It is therefore much more likelv that the factor which is missing from the unhygienic workers is a gene control mechanism, which in the normal worker bee switches into action this complicated social behaviour.

In the inheritance of complicated behavioural activities like these fixed action patterns, a means can be seen whereby the total gene action becomes modified by operator genes which switch on and off certain sections. Sometimes a distinct pattern of behaviour may be incorporated into an existing fixed action pattern, and the composite action needs to be modified. This change could be effected by such switch genes.

## Gene control

It is also important for the organism that all the genes controlling a complete entity of behaviour should be as close together as possible. If not, there is every likelihood that when the chromosomes divide during reproduction the genes concerned with behaviour will become separated from each other, and the total form of the behaviour will be disrupted.

The courtship display of ducks consists of a series of patterns, most of which can be observed with slight modifications throughout the closely related family of species. The modifications spring from the operation of genes described above. Konrad Lorenz calls one such pattern the 'down-up'; in this, the drake dips his bill into the water and then suddenly raises his head and with it a plume of water. While many of their relatives possess this behaviour, both the yellow-billed teal and the pintail have lost it. When, however,

1 The ritual courtships of birds like these Indian cranes are chiefly designed to raise the sexual interest of both partners. Each stage of the routine triggers behaviour in the other.

2 Even the amorous activities of the walrus, which resemble a parody of human activity, have a large inherited component, though like most mammals, walruses have a variety of behaviour.

the two species are crossed, the hybrid is seen to have the 'down-up' pattern. The most likely explanation, says Lorenz, is that the block of genes necessary for generating this behaviour is present in both species, but cannot appear because of some inhibiting control. This control is lost in the hybrids.

Very closely related species are often widely separated from each other geographically. Although there is no contact between the species, the similarities between them may be striking. However, such species, because the natural geographical barriers between them, have broken down, may suddenly find themselves in close proximity. Because the courtship and mating behaviour are still very similar, the two species will mate as easily with each other as with their own kind. This is a danger because the hybrids are neither as viable as the distinct species nor as fertile.

Under these circumstances it is vital that the different species, through the agency of natural selection, develop modifications of their behaviour which will effectively isolate them from the other species. This happens in nature; for example, two related species of frog have a wide range in the southern United States; one tending to live more to the west and the other to the east. In the central regions the two species overlap somewhat. There the two species have developed quite distinct mating calls, which effectively keep the frogs of the two species apart. On the other hand, at the extremes of the country, where there is no overlap whatsoever, the mating calls of both species are remarkably similar.

In other species, as in the ducks with their elegant courtship display, rather than modify the details of such display, whole chunks of behaviour are blocked out, or incorporated. But there are other methods of modifying patterns of behaviour. Either the frequency with which a species can perform its display, or the emphasis placed on certain specific parts, can vary from species to species and make all the difference. Dr Aubrey Manning has selectively bred groups of the fruit fly *D. melanogaster,* to breed either faster than normal fruit flies of the same species, or much slower. Professor Niko Tinbergen has observed subtle differences in two species of gull, the common gull and herring gull, when making their 'long call'; a call equivalent to the territorial singing of passerine birds. Both birds stretch their necks forward at first, but then the herring gull jerks its head down more as the call is started.

In the next movement, when both birds throw their heads upwards, it is the common gull's turn to emphasize the movement more. The final horizontal movement is again practically the same in both birds. Another example is seen in lizards of the genus *Sceloporus* which show a curious rhythmic head-bobbing movement during courtship and also when they meet other lizards. The frequency of the bob immediately identifies the different species. Some species get three head bobs into the space of less than a second, while other species take practically three times as long and then add an extra inflection of the head. Such signals are rigidly interpreted by the species and only the right signal is recognized.

**1** Praying mantises locked in battle. Fighting behaviour can sometimes be as stylized as other aspects of behaviour, and for the same sort of reasons.

**2** Ants co-operate in carrying away a matchstick. Some ants are born with the ability to act as part of a team, while related species – the solitary ants – are not.

## Inherited behaviour

Animal behaviour is much more than a sum total of stereotyped fixed action patterns. Learning, reasoning, trial-and-error movements all play some part in an animal's behavioural repertoire. The genetics of these aspects of behaviour are less easy to determine. It has to be assumed that the intricate pattern of the nerves and their relationships with one another are somehow laid down as a result of gene control. In such cases, it is the potential to behave in a certain way that is inherited. In some animals adaptation to the environment is best achieved when most of the behaviour is stereotyped; in other animals, learning and reasoning play a much more important part. In a changing environment, patterns of behaviour must be learned.

With regard to the control of the nervous system, certain differences in behaviour definitely arise from the state, or activity, of the nervous system. Rats can be selectively bred for their emotionality. Highly emotional rats placed under the glare of a bright light in an open arena become excessively frightened and, as well as defecating and urinating, remain crouched down in one spot.

On the other hand, the brazen, non-emotional rats, under the same circumstances, continue to move around and do not defecate. This emotionality also had other consequences; the highly emotional rats were much slower in learning how to avoid an electric shock than their 'cool' counterparts. In as far as Man also shows wide variations in his emotionality, it would be interesting to assess how his different powers of reasoning or learning vary under circumstances of stress.

# Progeny without parents

**Asexual reproduction is the most primitive means of creating new life. Yet even in the modern world, this uncomplicated method of perpetuating a species still plays an important role.**

LIVING ORGANISMS are admirably suited for survival. Millions of years of tough competition in the evolutionary melting pot have ensured that the plants and animals we see about us today are well equipped to make the most of the harsh realities of their environment. The success of an individual during its lifetime is only part of the problem of survival. Survival of the species through generation after generation is vital, too, and all living organisms devote all or part of themselves to this end at some time in their lives.

Among the lowliest organisms, which carry out all living processes within a single cell, the whole body is used as a reproductive cell. But further up the evolutionary ladder, multicellular animals and plants devote a relatively small part of the body to reproduction. The remaining organs are devoted to other tasks.

But some higher species use *asexual reproduction*. As the phrase implies, this form of reproduction is achieved without the sexual paraphernalia of sperms and eggs. Asexual reproduction is the ability of an individual to produce offspring without the fusion of sperms and eggs. A potato plant is a good example.

## Life without sex

Plant a single potato tuber. Dig up the plant a few months later and there will be perhaps six new potatoes for the price of one. No hazardous fertilization is required by pollen from a nearby potato plant, and no bees or other insects need be bribed to carry the pollen to the flowers. The potato plant produces its crop on its own and could if necessary do it over and over again for countless generations. Asexual reproduction is obviously a lot simpler, less risky, and far more efficient than sexual reproduction. Why, then, do not all living organisms reproduce exclusively in this way?

The answer to this question lies with genetics. Sexual reproduction, despite its difficulties, is a means of mixing the genes and chromosomes of one individual with the genes and chromosomes of another of the same species. Genes and chromosomes occasionally change. A gene might change spontaneously, or because of exposure to X-rays, ultra-violet light, or some chemical agent. An altered gene means that the organism itself will be altered in some way, simply because the genes determine what an organism is, what it does, and what it looks like. In sexually reproducing organisms, minute alterations are swopped about from individual to individual through the generations until a 'pool' of genetic variability is created. This 'pool' is extremely important because a species can 'draw' on it to meet changes in its environment. The environment is never

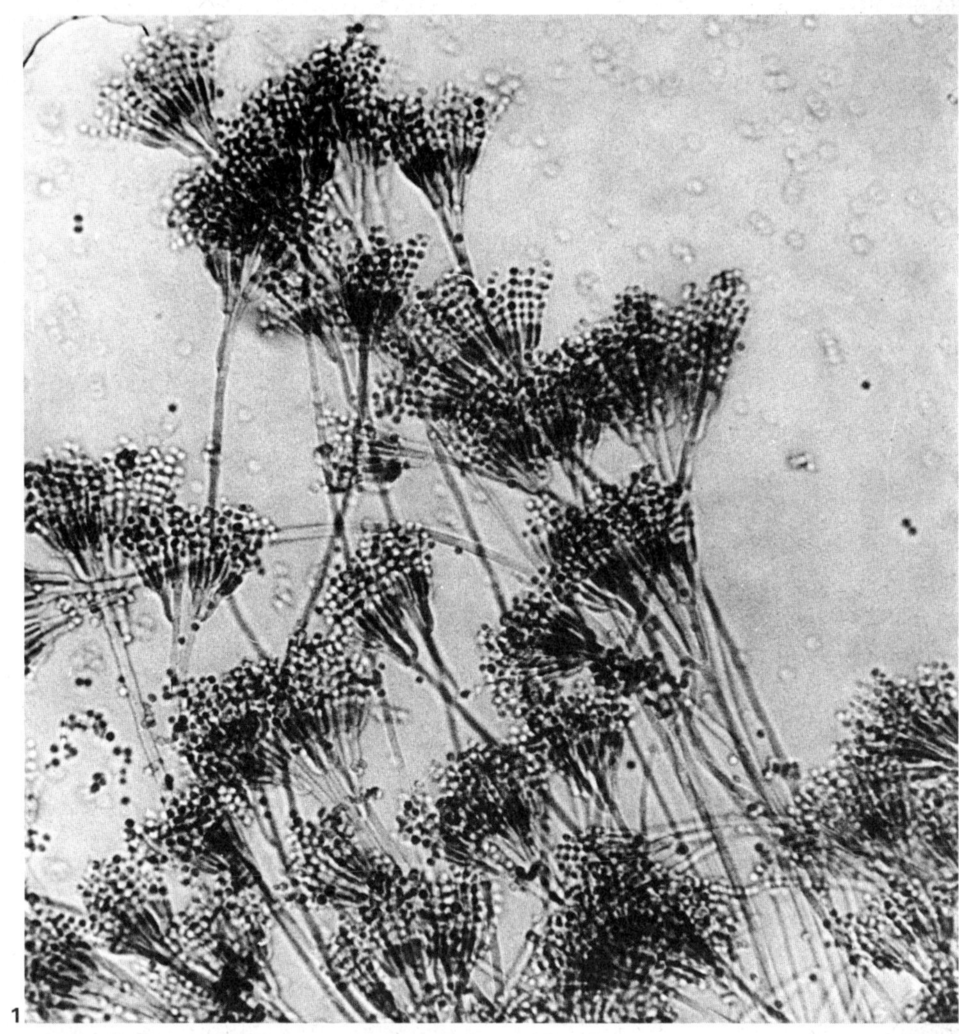

1

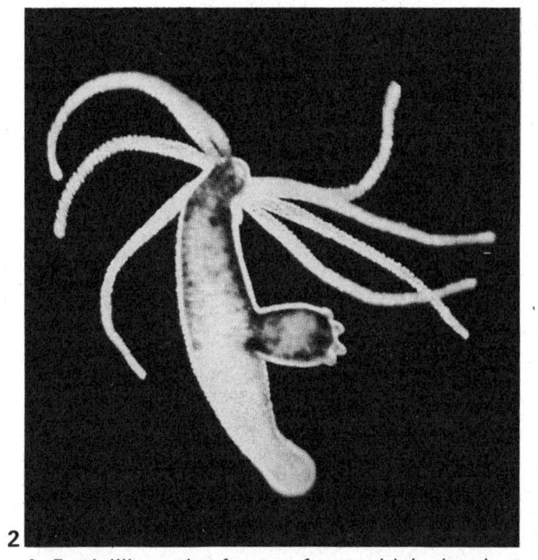

2

3

**1** *Penicillium*, the fungus from which the drug penicillin is derived, reproduces by chains of spores growing from the tip of the stalk.

**2** *Hydra* is a water-living animal which reproduces asexually by growing a bud from its side, which eventually separates from the parent.

**3** The gall fly reproduces by unfertilized eggs. The young develop protected by a huge 'gall' produced by chemicals injected into a twig.

static. The successful species is one which can adapt its form and function to suit changing conditions throughout the ages.

There is no mixing of genetic material in asexual reproduction. The new potatoes contain exact replicas of the genes and chromosomes of the old ones. This is perfectly all right as long as someone is on hand to control the potato's environment and artificially keep it static. But in a normal competitive situation, the species would be at a disadvantage in the long term, because it would not be able to adjust to changing environmental conditions. So, from the genetic viewpoint, complete reliance on asexual reproduction is a risky business. However, many animals and plants are adapted to reproduce asexually when living conditions are favourable. This fits in well with what we have just said. Conditions are favourable when an organism is perfectly adapted to them, and so reproducing more individuals equally well adapted makes biological sense. However, when conditions deteriorate, asexual reproduction usually stops and reproduction becomes solely a sexual activity.

Only a very few organisms are known which appear to reproduce *exclusively* by asexual means: a group of fungi (the *Fungi Imperfecti*), some kinds of amoebae, and a few rotifers (wheel-shaped metazoans) and insects. Even so, these organisms are grouped together here because sexual reproduction has never been observed among them. This does not mean to say that it may not occur – very, very rarely.

## Simple division

Asexual reproduction is common among bacteria and protozoans. Bacteria can take rapid advantage of food and moisture by asexual reproduction. They use the simplest method imaginable. A single cell simply divides into two. The offspring, called *daughter cells,* grow to about the size of the parent and, if conditions remain favourable, each divides again. The time between one division and the next is frequently less than half an hour. This means that in 12 hours a single bacterial parent could give birth to more than 250,000 'children'! Protozoans such as *Amoeba* and *Paramecium* also reproduce in the main by asexual means. Unlike bacteria, they possess a definite nucleus. Just before division the chromosomes duplicate themselves – form a copy – and they and the nucleus split apart. The original set of chromosomes goes one way and the copy goes the other. The cell then pinches together at the centre, cutting the organism in two.

Asexual reproduction is a common feature from the top to the bottom of the plant kingdom, although an astonishing variety of methods is used. The freshwater alga *Spirogyra* grows in streams. It looks like hanks of green thread. Each filament is a long ribbon of cells, all of which have a similar structure. These multicellular threads can separate into single cells, when they may be carried away downstream. Once they are anchored again, single cells divide over and over again to produce a new colony of threads. The seaweed *Fucus* forms masses of tangled, brown, slippery fronds on rocks by the seashore. Fragments of *Fucus,* when detached from the parent, can grow into new plants.

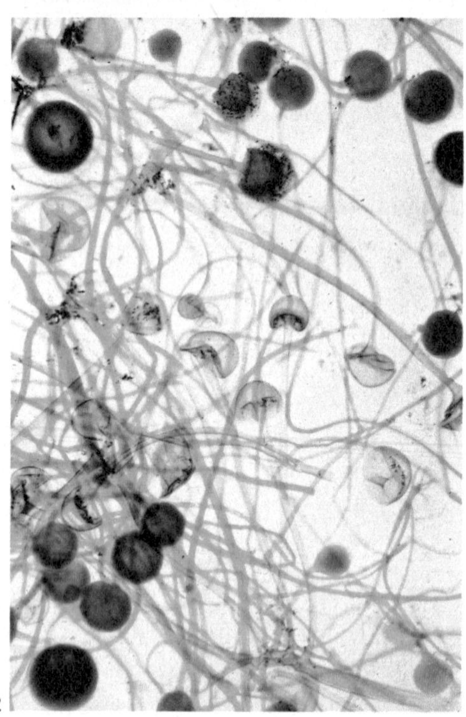

1 The liverwort *Marchantia* reproduces by gemmae stored in gemmae cups on its upper surface. The gemmae may be released to produce new plants when a raindrop 'explodes' in the cup.
2 Bread mould and many other plants store maturing spores in the capsule top of long sporangia. When the spores are ready, the capsule bursts and the spores are dispersed.

Many mosses and liverworts reproduce asexually when the older parts of their bodies die and rot away. The newer branches get separated from each other in this way and grow as individual plants. This method is used to good effect by the bog moss *Sphagnum* which grows in huge clumps on wet, acid soil. The liverwort *Riccia* grows in damp, shady places. It starts life as a little green disc with forked branches growing outwards from its centre. As it grows, the older parts at the hub of the plant die away, detaching the branches at the rim. Each detached branch becomes a new plant.

In the liverwort *Marchantia,* the upper surface of the ribbon-shaped body often bears one or two containers, called *gemmae cups,* about half an inch across. Each cup holds several tiny, flat, green discs of cells called *gemmae.* When the *gemmae* are released, as would happen if a raindrop 'exploded' into the cup, each can give rise to a new *Marchantia* plant. Among those peculiar plants devoid of chlorophyll, the fungi, the asexual spore is the characteristic method of swift reproduction. The asexual spore of a fungus is a blob of protoplasm containing one to many nuclei, surrounded by a wall. In fungi which live in water, the wall is thin and the spore has one or two whip-like hairs jutting from the protoplasm. They use these hairs to swim away from the parent to a new location.

Fungi which live on land produce asexual spores with thick walls which prevent the protoplasm drying out. They have no hairs, cannot move on their own, and are simply blown away by air currents. In common pin-moulds which grow on bread, asexual spores are born in thick-walled spore-cases. The spore-case is carried aloft on a long, thin stalk. When the spores ripen, the wall of the spore-case splits, peels open and the spores are blown away. Bear in mind that each spore-case contains hundreds of spores. This gives some idea of the colossal potential of this form of reproduction.

## Fungi and yeast

In many kinds of fungi, asexual spores are born not internally in spore-cases, but externally on single or branched stalks sticking up from the fungus body. Chains of spores, looking like tiny strings of poppet beads, stick out from the tips of spore stalks in all directions. The spores are produced in vast numbers and are so light that they are whisked away by the gentlest breath of air. Under the microscope, these spores are easy to see on fungi such as *Aspergillus* or *Penicillium,* which grow as blue or green patches on food left around in the open for a few days.

Before leaving the fungi, mention of one form of asexual reproduction employed by yeasts is in order. Yeasts are one-celled organisms. Yet if some yeast cells are viewed under a powerful microscope, the cells are often found linked together in

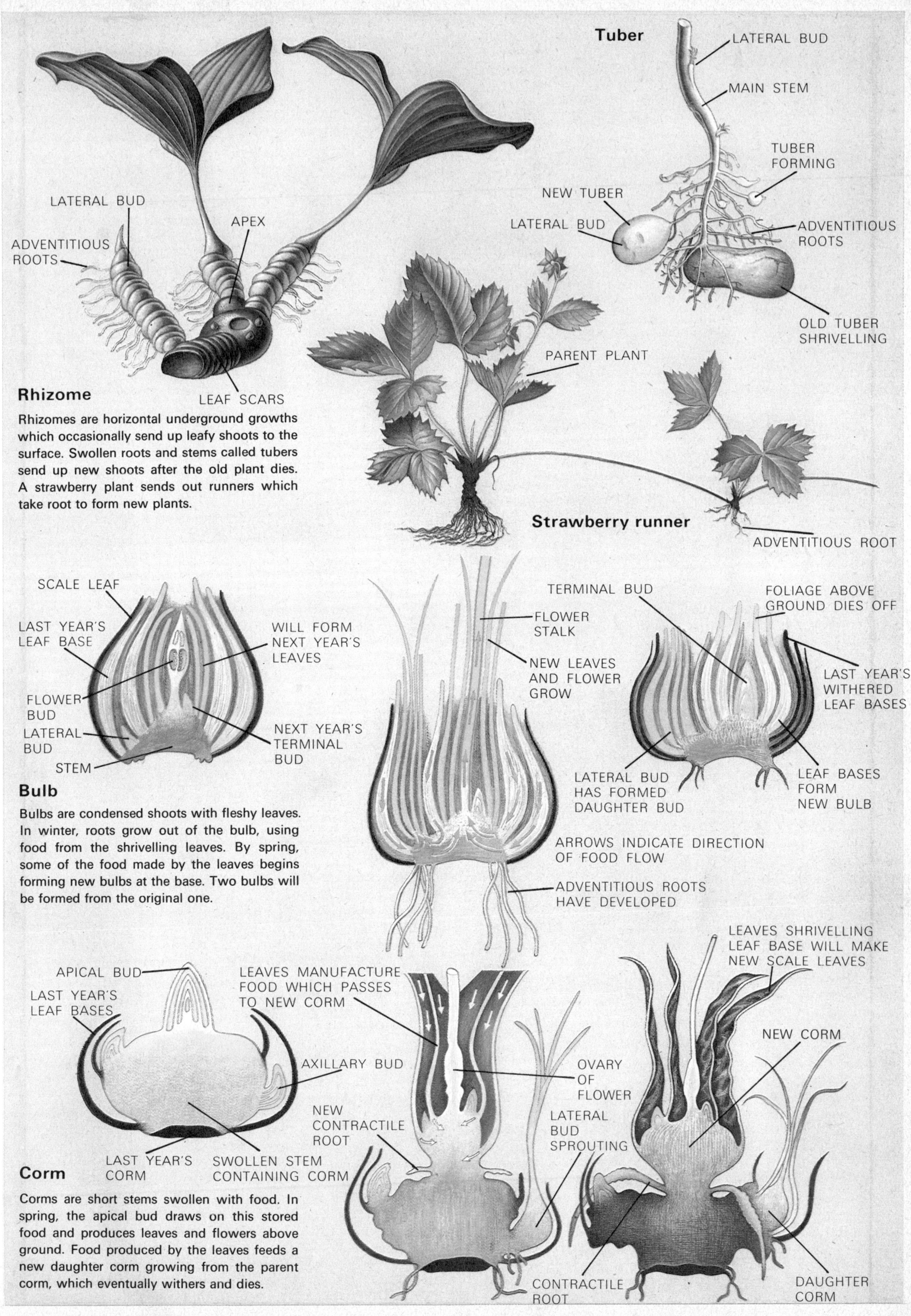


**Rhizome**

Rhizomes are horizontal underground growths which occasionally send up leafy shoots to the surface. Swollen roots and stems called tubers send up new shoots after the old plant dies. A strawberry plant sends out runners which take root to form new plants.

**Bulb**

Bulbs are condensed shoots with fleshy leaves. In winter, roots grow out of the bulb, using food from the shrivelling leaves. By spring, some of the food made by the leaves begins forming new bulbs at the base. Two bulbs will be formed from the original one.

**Corm**

Corms are short stems swollen with food. In spring, the apical bud draws on this stored food and produces leaves and flowers above ground. Food produced by the leaves feeds a new daughter corm growing from the parent corm, which eventually withers and dies.

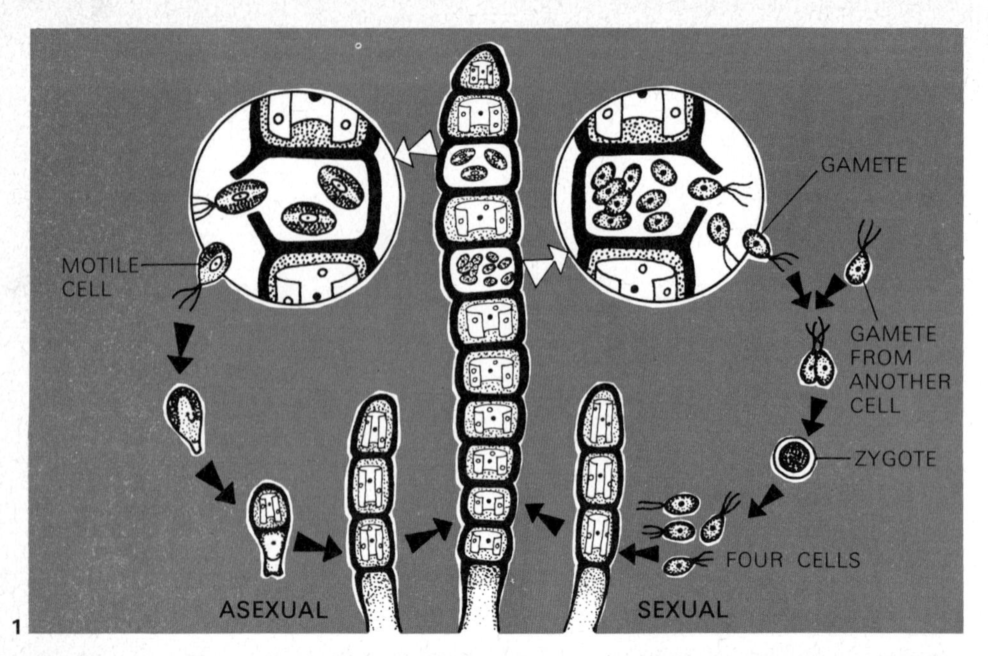


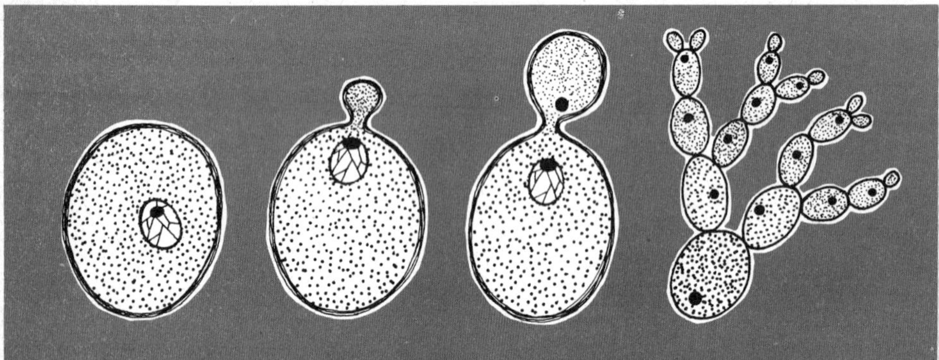


**1** The green alga *Ulothrix* reproduces asexually from cells which rupture the plant wall and sink to the stream floor. Sexual reproduction requires union with another *Ulothrix* cell. The resulting zygote then divides into four daughter cells.

**2** In yeast, a constriction forms in the parent cell, a nucleus moves into the bud and the constriction closes. The buds often do not separate from the parent cell, so large branching colonies of yeast plants may develop.

small colonies. The explanation is that a yeast cell commonly reproduces by little outgrowths called *buds*. A bud starts as a swelling at the side of a cell. As it grows bigger, it receives a nucleus and cytoplasm from the parent cell, and is then cut off from it by a wall. The new cell may itself bud before it separates from its parent, and in this way quite large colonies may build up.

Flowering plants, apart from having a highly evolved system of sexual reproduction with flowers, seeds and fruits, also use numerous methods to reproduce asexually. Various plants employ such organs as runners, suckers, rhizomes, tubers, corms and bulbs.

Strawberry plants produce slender branches called *runners* which grow rapidly along the ground away from the parent plant. Every so often they set down roots and form a new strawberry plant. The connecting branch then rots away and the young plant becomes independent.

## Asexual animals

Apple trees and poplar trees commonly grow *suckers*. These are underground shoots which grow up above the soil surface to produce new plants. A great many flowering plants reproduce asexually from *rhizomes*. Rhizomes grow horizontally beneath the soil, but at intervals they develop leafy shoots which grow up above the soil surface. Irises, lilies of the valley, and many grasses reproduce in this way.

*Tubers* are underground portions of stems or roots which swell with stored food and remain in the ground after the parent plant has died. They begin to grow from buds on their surface in the following year. Potato tubers are swollen stems, and dahlia tubers are swollen roots. Crocuses reproduce asexually from *corms*. A corm develops from the base of the plant's flowering stem. It is a roundish mass of hard tissue densely packed with food. Bulbs are formed from the lower parts of leaves which have become packed full of food. The leaves surround one or more buds which will grow into new plants the following year. Leaves and buds arise from a stem, which is reduced to a flat disc at the bottom of the bulb. Tulips, daffodils and onions all grow from bulbs.

Asexual reproduction is a good deal less common among members of the animal kingdom than it is among plants. Planarian worms (flatworms) and some freshwater annelid worms regularly reproduce by dividing their bodies into two pieces. Coelenterates such as *Hydra* and *Obelia* produce new offspring by a process called budding – the same name given to asexual reproduction in yeasts. *Hydra* is a green pond animal that grows up to half an inch long. It has a thin, cylindrical body with a tuft of tentacles at one end. From time to time a hydra grows a bud from the side of its body. The bud enlarges, grows its own set of tentacles at the free end, and then breaks away from the parent to live on its own. *Obelia*, a common inhabitant of rock-pools, also grows buds, but these frequently remain attached to the parent so that colonies of animals are formed.

A curious form of asexual reproduction, called *parthenogenesis*, occurs in several animal species. Parthenogenesis is the ability of an egg cell to produce offspring whether fertilized or not. Among ants, bees and wasps, for example, eggs which are fertilized develop into female offspring. But the unfertilized eggs do not perish: they grow into males. Some gall flies and a few kinds of microscopic freshwater animals called rotifers appear to reproduce exclusively by parthenogenesis and to have dispensed with males altogether! There is some evidence to suggest that parthenogenesis very occasionally occurs in higher animals. It certainly can be induced artificially in animals such as rabbits.

## Artificial asexuality

Among plants, dandelions are quite capable of producing seeds without fertilization of the egg cell. And the seeds of citrus fruits often contain a number of embryos, all but one of which have developed from cells other than the fertilized egg cell. Parthenogenesis in plants is called *apomixis*.

Asexual reproduction in the animal kingdom becomes less and less common as one ascends the evolutionary scale, so it may be a surprise to learn that human beings, in a manner of speaking, sometimes reproduce in this way. When a fertilized egg undergoes its first division to form a multicellular embryo, the first two cells formed may very occasionally separate. When this happens, both separated cells continue to divide and develop quite independently and two identical embryos are formed – identical twins in fact.

Of course, the production of human twins by the chance splitting and independent development of a fertilized egg is not asexual in the common sense of the word. To begin with, the egg must first be fertilized by union with a male sperm, which is definitely a sexual process. But the production of human twins may be considered asexual from an entirely different and more convincing point of view.

It is possible, even today, to think of culturing a fertilized egg in an artificial medium and splitting the daughter cells formed after the first few divisions. By implanting these separated cells into the wombs of foster-mothers, a biologist may be able to create 2, 4, 8, 16, 32 or even more identical children. Such things have already been done in lower animals. For human beings, the achievement is still far off, but it is something to think about. The fact that it can be done does not mean that it should be done. This decision must rest with the voters and the leaders they elect.

# Network of the nerves

**Most animals are made up of millions upon millions of different cells, all of which must work together to maintain life. The nervous system co-ordinates and controls this vital activity.**

WHEN WE sit on a pin, our reaction is immediate – we leap up. We do not consciously think: 'I have a pain; I must have sat on something; I must get up.' The reaction is completely automatic.

Such automatic responses are common to all animals, from the highest to the lowest. If a simple amoeba is pricked, it automatically shies away; if a torch is shone on an earthworm at night, it automatically dives back into its hole. What sets Man and other higher animals apart from amoeba and worm is the complex bodily organization required to control their responses. This complex organization is known as the nervous system, and its primary function is communication – receiving messages from one part of the body and sending messages to another part.

Like all vertebrates, Man has a tube of nervous tissue running the length of his body. This tube, called the spinal cord, is responsible for the co-ordination of nerve actions. The brain has evolved from the specialized front end of the spinal cord and constitutes a central control system. But such a system exists in relatively few animals.

## Bypassing the brain

The spinal cord and the brain together make up the central nervous system (CNS, for short). All sensory nerve fibres (which detect stimuli) run *to* the CNS, whereas all effector nerve fibres (which cause muscular actions) run *from* it. In most animals, the links between the sensory nerve fibres and the effector (motor) fibres occur inside the CNS, either in the brain or in the spinal cord.

A *reflex* is a nervous response that does not require a brain, or bypasses the brain. A familiar reflex reaction is used by doctors to test the functioning of part of the nervous system in humans. This is the knee-jerk reflex in which the lower leg jumps forward and the leg straightens in response to a blow just below the knee-cap. There is a straightforward communication link between the stretch receptors in the ligament below the knee-cap and the muscle above the knee-cap which pulls on this ligament.

How does this reflex work? In the very short space of time between the tap and the jerk, a 'message' in the form of an electrical impulse passes up a nerve from the knee to the base of the spine and back down again – a distance of about three feet – causing the knee to jerk.

Such a simple type of reflex is called a *spinal reflex*. It involves at least three nerve fibres: one *to* the CNS, one *from* the CNS, and one connecting these two *within* the CNS. It is the range and complexity of the connections between the incoming and outgoing signals which determines the number of responses possible for a given stimulation – the bigger the telephone exchange the greater the number of calls it can handle.

In lower animals with a simple nervous system, it is possible to understand much of behaviour in terms of nervous connections. For example, sea-anemones are simple animals which have no central nervous system. Instead they have nerve cells which connect with one another to form a simple intermeshing *nerve-net*. These cells conduct in all directions, so that stimulation of the animal's body in any one place causes muscular contractions to spread outwards in a circle from the point of stimulation, rather like the way ripples spread out from a stone dropped into a pool. With no central system, these animals have an extremely simple direct form of behaviour, and different parts of their bodies can react to different stimuli at the same time. Even so, conduction along the nerve-net is faster in some directions than in others.

Slightly more complex animals, such as the annelid worms, have longitudinal nervous systems. As a result, the nerves from the various segments are co-ordinated to a certain extent but the 'brain' is poorly developed, with little overall control.

In higher animals, the nervous system has evolved into something more than merely simple point-to-point communication links. It has become a network complete with complex exchanges and switchboards capable of controlling their own operation. In Man, where the whole of the part of the brain called the cerebral cortex may be involved, the connecting pathways between incoming and outgoing systems become incredibly complex. We experience the millions of correlation processes as memory and insight.

A nerve consists of a bundle of fibres. The fibres are made up of nerve cells or *neurones*. Long thin branches called *processes* radiate from the main cell body. A neurone can therefore be thought of as a special type of cell which in some way can conduct a 'message' from one side to the other.

The 'message' actually takes the form of an electric current. The conduction of a

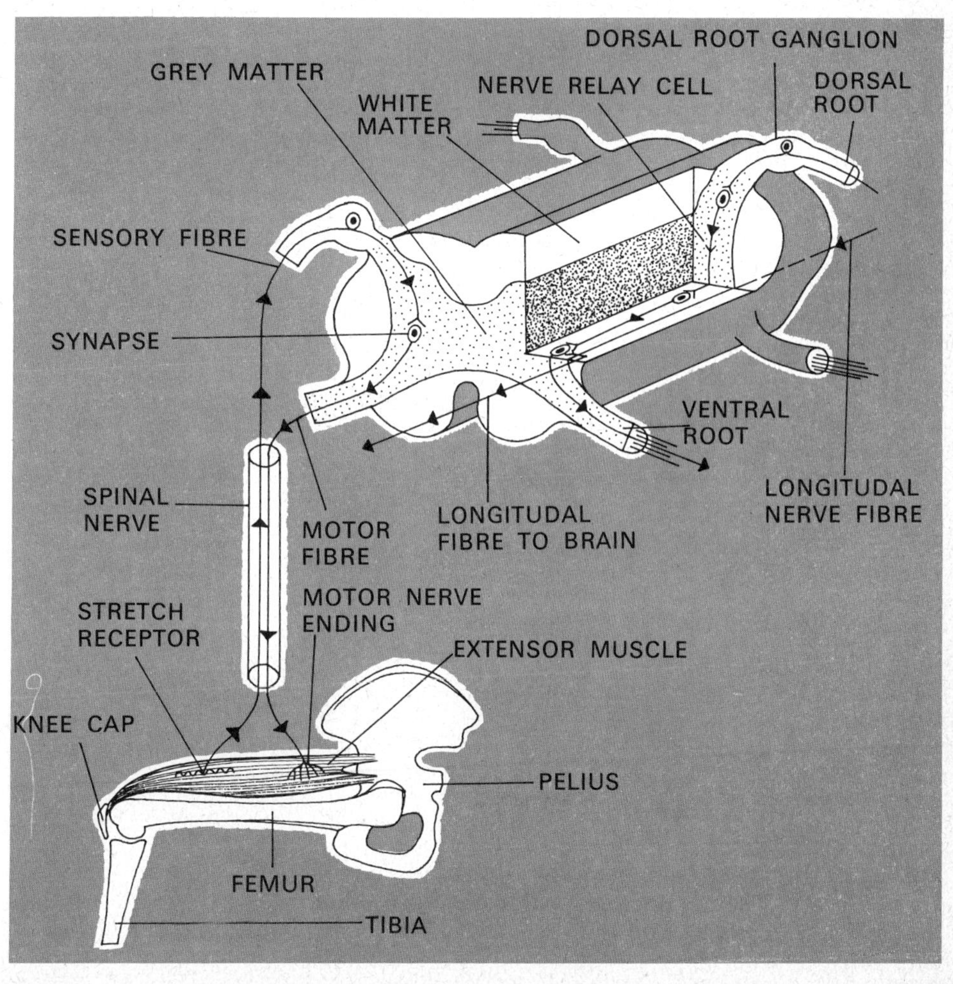


Even in higher animals, many body actions are not controlled by conscious thought. In a reflex arc, a message is sent through a sensory neuron to the spinal cord and out to a muscle through a motor neuron, bypassing the brain.

'message' is brought about by a brief change in the electric potential of the neurone, when a positively charged electric pulse passes along it. The change in potential is caused by a brief influx of positive sodium ions ($Na^+$), which are normally kept out of the cell by the continuous osmotic activity of the cytoplasmic 'pump'. The stimulation of the neurone causes its membrane to become permeable to sodium ions, the electric potential changes, and the next neurone along the fibre is stimulated. The actual value of electric potential involved is about 100 thousandths of a volt (written as +100 millivolts).

Because the energy used to transmit the electric pulse is contained within the relaxed nerve, it is called the *resting potential*. An impulse travels from one side of a neurone to the other without losing any of its strength. The nerve can transmit only one sort of information – a brief pulse of positive charge. There can be no variation or gradation in the size of the charge or in the duration of the pulse, although of course a rapid or a slow series of pulses may be transmitted (up to 500 impulses a second are possible). In other words, all nervous impulses are of exactly the same type whether they originate from the eye, the ear, or the skin where we sit on a pin.

Most nerves conduct in only one direction, although some can conduct both ways. When an impulse reaches the end of a neurone, the 'message' is passed across a space to the receptive end of the next neurone. This space is known as a *synaptic space* and the junction between neurones is a *synapse*.

Transmission of the message across a synapse is thought to be a chemical and not an electrical phenomenon. The arrival of a nerve impulse causes the ends of the nerve fibre to produce a chemical called acetyl-choline. This substance diffuses across the synaptic spaces and either excites or inhibits the receptive ends of adjacent neurones. Many nerve cells have thousands of synapses reaching them and branching out from them. Since thousands of such cells may be interconnected, giving millions of possible pathways, the complexity becomes very great. And by varying the proportion of stimulating and

*Below,* owls fly and hunt at night, so they have a keenly developed sense of sight. In general, the higher an animal on the evolutionary scale, the more specialized are its nervous responses.

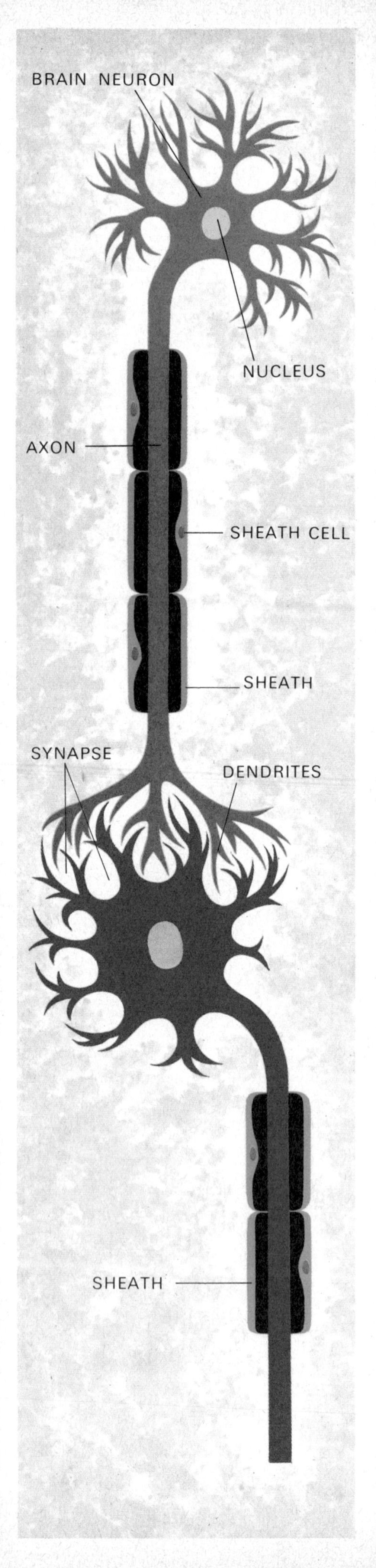

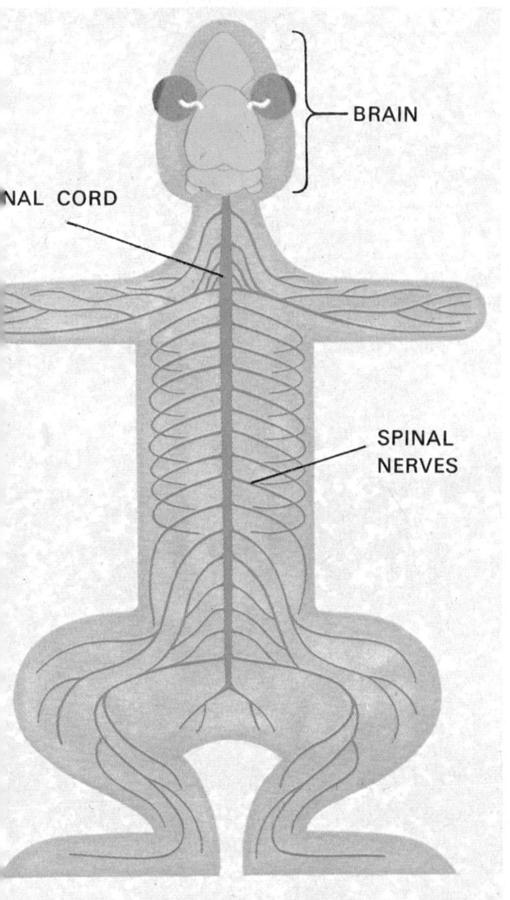


*Left,* nervous impulses are transmitted from the axon of one neuron to the dendrites of a second neuron across an open synapse. The two neurons do not actually touch one another, but relay the message by producing chemicals which flow across the synaptic gap. *Top left,* some animals are almost completely helpless at birth and must have time until their nervous system and other organs reach maturity. *Top right,* for other animals, it is imperative that they be ready to defend themselves almost at once. A foal can stand and run almost immediately after birth. *Above,* a diagram of the central nervous system of a rabbit is typical of most higher animals. The brain acts as a complex communications exchange, receiving messages from – and routing messages to – nerve endings throughout the body.

inhibiting impulses, a very fine balance can be achieved.

The single unalterable electric pulses passing along nerves are very similar to the 'language' used by a computer. In both cases, an 'all or none' binary system is at work and information is passed as a series of either 'on' or 'off' pulses. And in both cases the components making up the system are comparatively simple; the complexity and flexibility come from the ways in which the simple components are assembled to form the various interconnections inside the system.

We saw earlier how a spinal reflex arc can cause a stimulus to give rise to the same response every time. We can now understand how more complicated responses are possible. Imagine that most of the impulses passing to the spinal cord of a man can travel along branch connections to the brain. Then at any one time, the number of nervous impulses passing round the co-ordinating centres in the brain will be enormous. The pattern of these impulses will give a sort of 'picture' of the condition of the man at a given instant. But the situation will be continually changing as environmental changes alter the pattern of the incoming signals.

Sensory inputs will also influence what messages are sent out to activate the various muscles. It is the overall complexity which makes the study of animal behaviour so difficult, and in higher animals there is often no obvious or direct relationship between stimulus and response. The same stimulus may evoke quite opposite responses under different conditions.

Even in a thinking animal such as Man there is still a great deal of co-ordination and 'decision making' which completely bypasses the conscious parts of the brain. Instead they depend on the way in which the nervous system is built. For example, control of breathing rate, heart rate, movement of food along the gut, and so on, all take place without any conscious effort. Indeed, most of them are *beyond* the control of the conscious mind – we cannot alter our heart rate merely by thinking about it.

The special part of the nervous system which deals with these 'automatic' activities is called the *autonomic* nervous system. It has its own co-ordination centres in the brain and its own network of nervous fibres which largely lie outside the central nervous system. The autonomic nervous system acts as a very complex series of reflex actions and keeps the machinery of the body running without involving any conscious thought. Imagine the nuisance of having to remember to breathe every few seconds. This leads us to realize that these automatic actions are the fundamental ones, and conscious thought is a much later development of the nervous system.

## Life without thought

Nerves that carry messages to activate muscles under the control of the conscious mind form the *voluntary* nervous system. The nerves of the voluntary and autonomic systems are made up and 'work' in much the same way. Most of our daily activities are of the voluntary type. Whether we are brushing our teeth, running for a bus, or doing our daily work, most of our actions are controlled, not reflex or instinctive. In terms of stamina, strength, or agility, Man is not an extraordinary nor a particularly outstanding animal. Where he does score is in his ability to think and translate his thoughts into conscious actions.

If we can imagine life without any conscious awareness of anything at all, then we are probably close to the state which exists in simple animals. Our own sophisticated nervous system, awareness of ourselves and things around us can easily trap us into the error of anthropomorphism – that is, assigning to all animals attributes and emotions requiring conscious thought.

Discussing the ability of animals to think can lead to profound philosophical arguments; but it is necessary to try to envisage life without 'thought' in order to be able to assess the advantages which conscious thought gives to an animal. Conscious thought allows an animal to translate information about its real

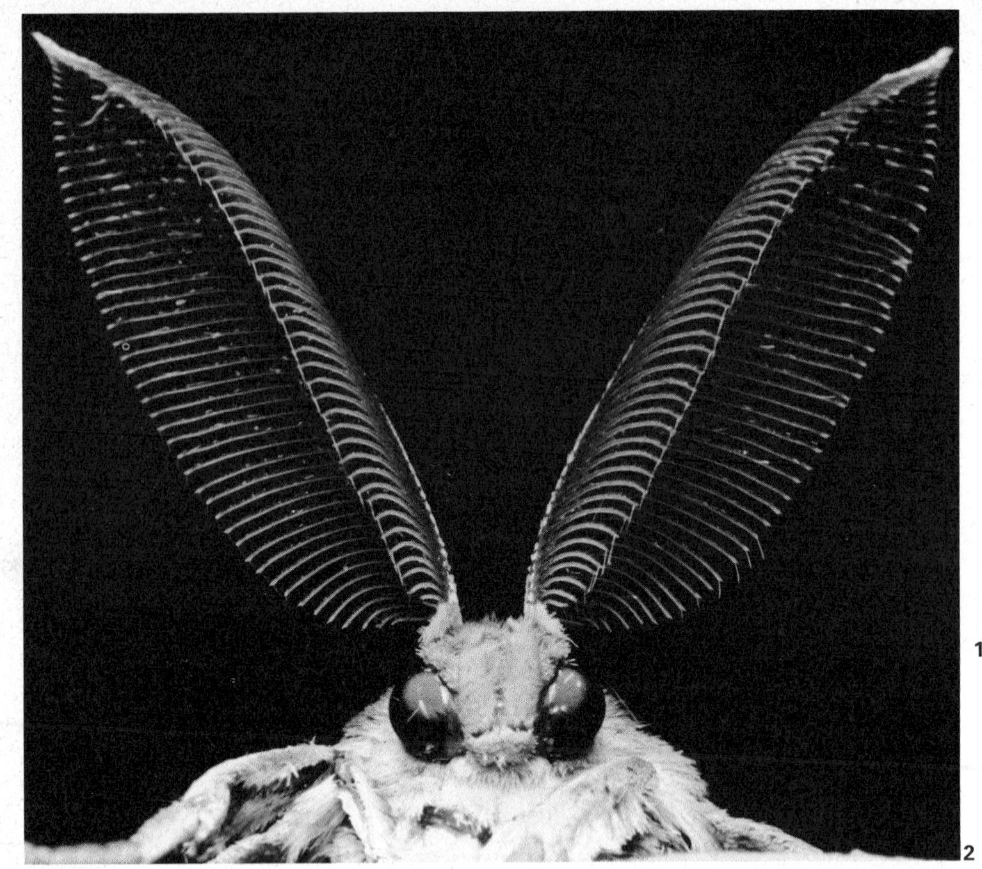

1 The whiskers of a cat are sensitive to touch, but felines also rely on night eyesight and mental agility to make their way in the world. 2 Sensory acuity in moths has reached a very high stage of development. These leaf structure antennae are the principal receptors. 3 The dog's acute sense of smell is well known, and is put to good use in hunting, as the criminal whose scent this police dog is following well understands. 4 Many activities of birds appear to result from conscious thought, but are really reflexes or 'species memory'. This mother bird reacts to anything with a gaping mouth, be it her own young or, in this case, hungry fish.

environment, given by its sensory organs, into a language of nervous impulses. By this simplification it is possible to record events in the memory and to call on these – that is, to use experience – in making new decisions.

The further ability of being able to pass on experience from animal to animal seems to have developed in only a few instances. It reaches its peak in Man where the 'language' of the nervous system is further simplified to the languages which we speak and write.

Perhaps the best contrast with the condition reached in Man is provided by the complex behaviour of many birds. Whereas Man and some mammals have developed the powers of thought and individual memory, birds have tended to develop a set of 'species memories'. Many of the complex activities of birds are completely instinctive and are fixed at birth as surely as are factors such as the colour of their feathers or the sizes of the beaks.

This is not to say that birds are incapable of learning, but most of their essential behaviour is controlled by instinct. This is the fundamental difference between the bird type of behaviour and the type found in higher mammals. Perhaps the greatest consequence of conscious memory in mammals is that mammals are capable of behaviour modifications from generation to generation, whereas birds can change only by evolution over many hundreds of generations.

# 'Kill and be eaten'

Living things reveal their interdependence in the ways in which they gain and expend energy. The cycles of carbon and nitrogen and the pattern of life in a pond are taken as examples.

THROUGHOUT THE WORLD matter is constantly on the move. Much of this movement is caused by man-made machines and the weather, but much is also due to the activities of living things. For example, a green blade of grass takes in carbon dioxide from the air. A rabbit appears and eats the grass, and an eagle may seize and eat the rabbit. When the eagle dies, its body decays and passes into the soil, where bacteria break it down into gases such as nitrogen and carbon dioxide, which once again pass back into the air.

Consider the movement of a single carbon atom in this process. It starts as part of a molecule of carbon dioxide. The grass incorporates it in hydrocarbons, such as starch. The rabbit, eating the grass, may convert the starch into glucose. The eagle eats the glucose and may store it as glycogen. Bacteria decompose the glycogen from the dead eagle and re-form carbon dioxide. The cycle is completed. The same carbon atom may undergo the whole process again many times.

All the chemical compounds in the world exist in one of two states: in living things, which make up the *biosphere,* or in non-living things, which make up the *geosphere*. The chemical compounds move in cycles between the biosphere and geosphere, and within each of these spheres. Two cycles of matter are of great importance in biology, the carbon cycle and the nitrogen cycle.

Carbon exists in the biosphere as carbon dioxide, carbonates, and complex compounds such as proteins, carbohydrates and fats. The carbon of the geosphere is combined as carbon dioxide, calcium carbonate, and complex carbon compounds such as coal and petroleum. The carbon dioxide of the atmosphere is *fixed* (incorporated into other compounds) by the action of green plants.

This process yields molecules which can be made into complex compounds. The green plants are eaten by animals, which digest and oxidize many of the compounds, producing some carbon dioxide. Green plants and animals die and are caused to decay by non-green plants such as fungi and by bacteria, in this way releasing more carbon dioxide.

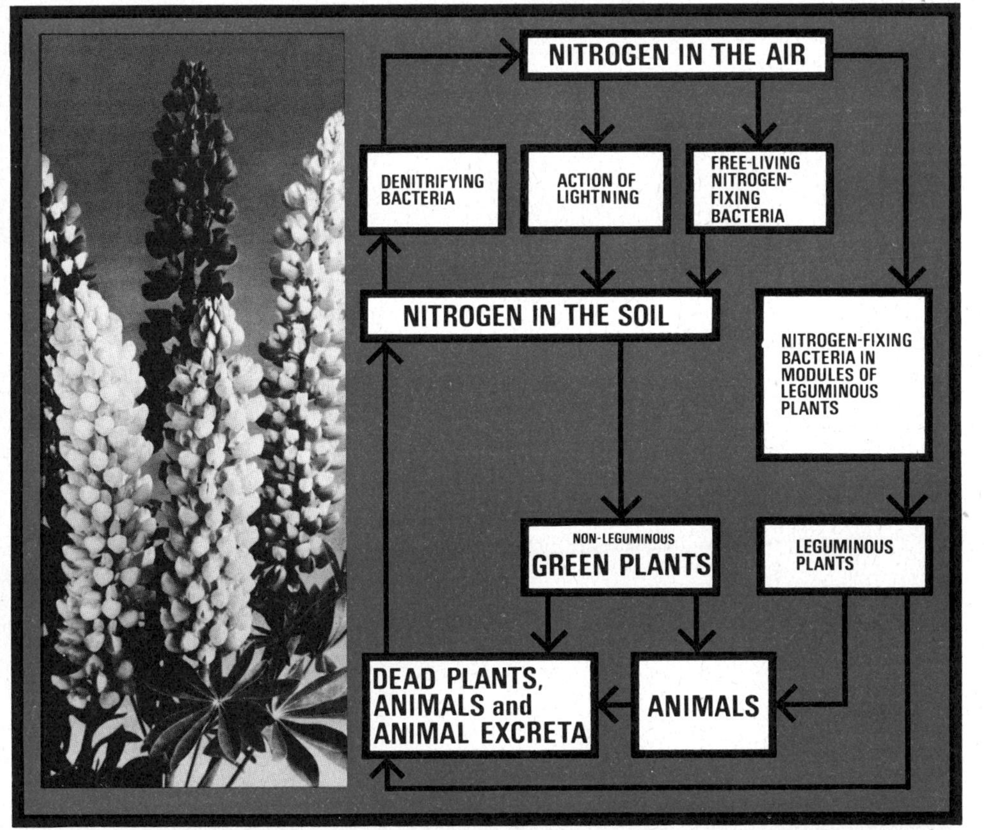


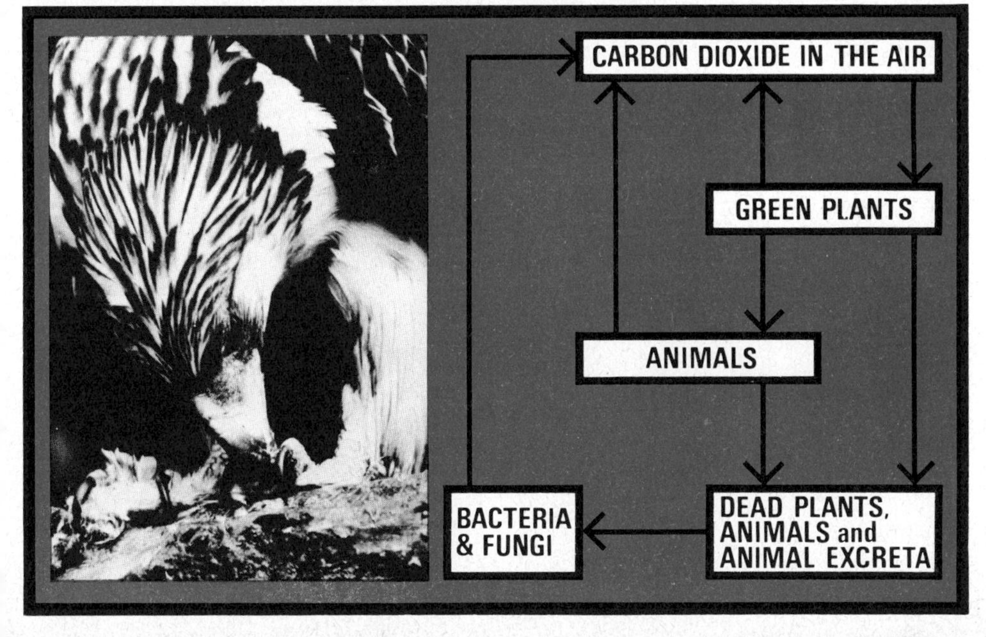


## Lightning and legumes

All the carbon dioxide released in these processes can be re-used by green plants. Some carbon compounds produced by living things are not so readily made available again. For example, many living things deposit carbonates (usually as calcium carbonate) in their skeletons and shells. Calcium carbonate is not readily usable by living things and so it tends to accumulate as limestone or chalk. The 'white cliffs' of Dover, those famous landmarks, are the remains of the skeletons of countless millions of small marine animals called *Foraminifera*.

Nitrogen is an important constituent of such compounds as proteins and nucleic acids, which are found almost exclusively in the biosphere. The nitrogen of the geosphere is made available to living things in several ways.

Nitrogen gas makes up about four-fifths of the Earth's atmosphere. A little of it may be converted into nitrogen oxides by lightning, and the oxides are then carried into the soil by rain. Certain kinds of

*Top left,* the lupin plant is specially adapted to its role in the nitrogen cycle, for attached to its roots are nodules which contain nitrogen-fixing bacteria. These bacteria may also live free in the soil, and convert nitrogen into nitrates.

When it dies, the body of the golden eagle, *left,* will be invaded by millions of decomposing bacteria. Once these have converted the glycogen stored in its body back into the original carbon dioxide another carbon cycle will be complete.

Within the pond ecosystem, there are untold numbers of living things existing together in a close-knit, interrelated community. When studying energy changes in nature, biologists first determine the distribution of living things within the ecosystem, and then classify them according to their different trophic (feeding) levels, numbering four in all. *Top left,* fish, if carnivorous, are classified as secondary consumers (level three), and feed off primary consumers such as the waterstrider, *top right* (level two). *Above left,* this frog could have suffered the same fate as the tadpole, *centre,* being attacked by the larva of the great diving beetle. *Right,* another temporary pond dweller is the dragonfly nymph.

bacteria and algae are able to fix nitrogen directly and convert it to nitrates. These nitrogen-fixing bacteria may live free in the soil or in *nodules* on the roots of leguminous plants such as clover and lucerne. The nitrogen oxides formed by lightning, as well as the nitrates formed by bacteria and algae, are made available to other plants. The plants then convert them to nitrogen-containing compounds of the biosphere.

Nitrogen is made available to most kinds of animals only in the form of complex compounds. The animals then digest and oxidize these compounds. Some of the products are used to form new nitrogen-containing compounds; others are excreted in the form of ammonia, urea, uric acid, and so on. Excreted compounds are used by bacteria and plants to form other complex nitrogen compounds. Some of the nitrogen from the excretory products of animals and from decaying plants and animals is returned to the atmosphere. This is accomplished by denitrifying bacteria, which can remove the nitrogen from ammonia, nitrates and other compounds, and release it as a gas.

## Energy and pond life

These cycles of matter demonstrate the interdependence of all living things. They also appear to demonstrate that 'nothing is wasted'. This is an illusion, however, as becomes clear when we analyse the energy changes which accompany the matter cycles. The cycles of matter are vast generalizations which may cover the whole of the biosphere. But when we come to study energy changes, we can no longer make such broad generalizations. We must confine our study to closely interrelated groupings of living things. A specific grouping, which can be studied closely, is called an *ecosystem*. We may illustrate such a study by considering an ecosystem that consists of a small pond.

What do we want to know about the pond ecosystem? We want to know how much energy is put in, how much energy leaves, and how much energy stays in the pond. In order to know how much energy stays, we must first know how much energy there is to begin with. And although the overall energy content may change little, the distribution of the energy may change significantly.

The first step is to take samples from the pond and discover what kinds of living things there are and their numbers (generally expressed as a density such as numbers per square metre). Then all the living things are classified in terms of their method of nutrition or *trophic* (feeding) level. There may be plants growing in the bottom of the pond and microscopic algae

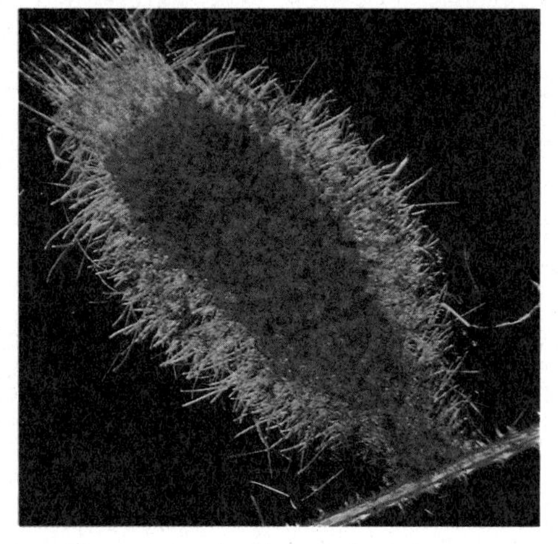

*Top,* shimmering strands of algae obtain their brilliant green colouring from their chlorophyll content. All pond plants can be classified as primary producers (trophic level one). The fourth trophic level is made up of decomposers such as bacteria and fungi. *Above left,* a great water beetle, his back legs specially equipped for swimming, nibbles a plant shoot. *Above right,* although it has the appearance of a plant, the freshwater sponge is actually animal in nature.

floating in the water. Since these are all green and can photosynthesize, they are called *primary producers* (trophic level one). Living among the algae may be microscopic animals such as water fleas and other kinds of tiny animals. There may also be snails, plant-eating fish, and some kinds of aquatic insects living among the rooted plants. These herbivores (plant-eaters) are called *primary consumers* (trophic level two).

Preying on the herbivores may be carnivores (meat-eaters), such as insect larvae, crayfish, fishes, and so on. These are called *secondary consumers* (level three). Finally, there will be bacteria and fungi present which are *decomposers* (level four). They bring about the decay of different organisms from all the other trophic levels. They release some nutrients into the environment for use by the producers, and absorb others for their own nutritional purposes.

Even in an area as restricted as a pond, it would be almost impossible to count all the living things. Representative samples are therefore taken from all the different areas in the pond where things live. The living things are then counted and weighed, and estimates made of the total numbers in the pond.

The relative abundance of organisms in the various trophic levels can be expressed by making what is called a pyramid of numbers. This shows the pattern of distribution, and generally indicates that the primary producers are largest in number and the secondary consumers least, giving in effect a pyramid.

A much more meaningful measurement, in terms of the use of energy, is that of weight or *biomass*, since the mere counting of numbers may distort the picture. For example, a square metre of a pond may contain one fish weighing, say, 15 grammes. It may also contain several million algae whose total weight may not exceed a few grammes. Since the use of energy is related to weight, it is likely that the single fish needs more energy than do the several million algae.

In studying the energy of trophic levels in ecosystems, biologists make an assessment of the weight of all trophic levels. They measure the surface area of the water and take samples of the various areas where organisms are found. Fish and larger aquatic organisms may be netted, dried and weighed. Small organisms, such as algae, bacteria and protozoa, are captured on filters, which are dried and then weighed. The biomass is usually expressed as dry weight.

In estimates of energy flow through an ecosystem, biomass must be related to energy. This may be done in a number of ways, such as by burning a given weight of biomass and measuring the amount of heat (in calories) released. This experiment gives a factor which can be used to convert any other biomass to energy. The information it gives is not very precise, but even approximate values may be both useful and informative. The amount of energy put into the ecosystem can be calculated by measuring the sunlight falling on a square metre of the water surface. This energy can also be expressed in calories.

## The availability of food

When a biologist has made all his measurements, he can draw an energy-flow diagram. This diagram shows the energy changes which occur for each square metre of pond surface during a year. The energy is expressed in kilocalories (units of a thousand calories, or Calories with a capital C) to avoid having to use very large numbers. A kilocalorie is the amount of heat energy necessary to raise the temperature of a kilogram of water through one degree centigrade. It takes about 90 kilocalories (or 90 Calories) to boil a quart of water.

The usable energy falling on a square metre of the pond is about 400,000 Calories a year. Of this amount, the primary producers fix 24,000 Calories, or about 6 per cent. This energy is fixed in the form of plant biomass. Respiration (tissue oxidation) in the plants accounts for 14,000 Calories a year, and the balance is available for the next trophic levels. Decomposers use up about 6,000 Calories, leaving only 4,000 Calories (16·7 per cent of the original) available for the primary consumers. Of this amount, 2,400 Calories are lost as respiration heat, and 1,200 Calories are lost by decomposition and exportation. (*Exportation* is the loss to the ecosystem of animals which leave it, such as insects like the dragonfly emerging from its mature nymph, tadpoles that develop into frogs, and so on.) As a result, only 400 Calories are fixed as biomass in the secondary consumer level, representing only ten per cent of the biomass of the primary consumer level. Of this amount, 300 Calories would be lost in respiration. So we see that a predator, such as Man,

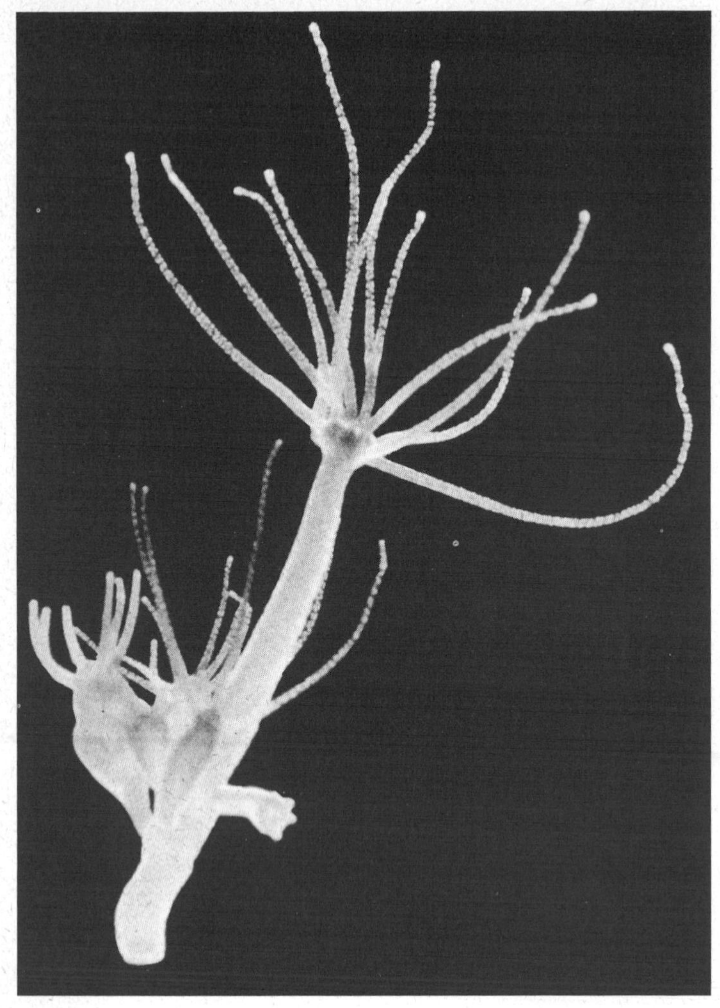

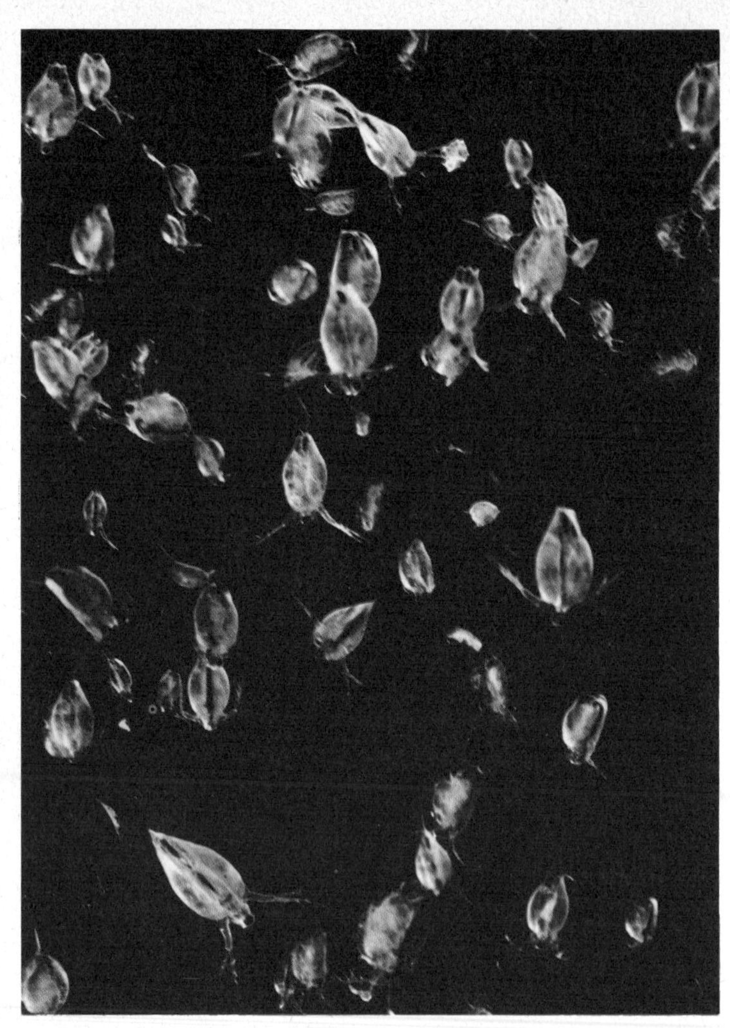

*Left,* the common hydra is one of the very few coelenterates (such as sea-anemones), which lives in fresh water, not salt, and is usually found on the leaves of water plants. Here a species is shown firmly anchored to the glass of an aquarium as it lies in wait, with tentacles extended, for likely prey to pass by. A large part of its diet is made up of the tiny, crustacean, freshwater 'water-fleas' or *Daphnia,* seen *right.* These beautiful, translucent creatures feed on minute plants, and are able to swim in water by means of their delicate branched antennae.

feeding on secondary consumers (for example by fishing), would have only 100 Calories available from the original 24,000 Calories. Since a man needs an average daily food intake equivalent to 3,000 Calories, one might say that he should go and fish in a bigger pond!

Energy-flow diagrams, however, do have a serious implication for the future of Man's food supplies. It is obvious that the higher the trophic level at which Man finds his food, the less food will be available in proportion to the amount of energy put in. Primary producers represent about 6 per cent of the usable energy input and primary consumers represent 1 per cent. The secondary consumers represent only 0·1 per cent. Since the amount of usable energy put in cannot be increased, the way in which the energy is used must be improved. The shorter the food chain, the greater is the amount of food available. If Man could adapt himself to a diet consisting exclusively of plants, he would automatically increase his food supply many times.

Of course, there are a number of factors other than theoretical biology which determine the suitability of food, not least of which is palatability. But the solution to the shortage of food threatening mankind probably lies in making better use of the food supplies we already have. Studies of energy-flow in food-producing ecosystems are one way of showing how this can be done if the theory is understood.

The rate at which primary producers fix energy in the form of biomass is called *gross primary productivity*. It is usually stated in terms of weight per area per day or year. We can roughly convert the energy value of primary productivity in our pond example by taking a quarter of the number of Calories. Thus 24,000 Calories is equivalent to about 6,000 grammes per square metre per year, which is roughly 24 tons per acre per year, a high rate of gross productivity.

The term 'energy cycle' is, in fact, not completely accurate. Matter may cycle, but energy does not. To see why this is so, we must briefly consider the laws of thermodynamics.

## The sustaining sun

The first Law of Thermodynamics states that the total amount of energy in an isolated system does not change. As far as we know, the Universe is an isolated system. But the Earth certainly is not. Energy is transferred from one part of the Universe to another as light energy and other forms of radiation, but the total amount does not change. The Earth is being continuously bombarded by energy, coming mainly from our own private star, the sun. On the Earth, the total amount of energy *does* change. It increases, due to the living things, the biomass. Living things convert the energy of sunlight into usable energy in the form of more biomass.

The conversion of energy from one form to another is described by the second Law of Thermodynamics. This law states that in the conversion from one form of energy to another, energy is degraded – that is, the capacity to do work decreases.

Discussion of the thermodynamic laws in relation to energy may seem rather academic and remote. But this is not so. The implications of these laws are fundamental to the very existence of life of Earth. Energy is continually being put into the biomass of the Earth as sunlight. The Earth's biomass then converts part of this energy to forms of energy which are less and less usable. As we saw in our discussions of trophic levels in a pond ecosystem, much of the energy fixed at any trophic level is lost as heat. Thus energy is degraded, and the second Law of Thermodynamics obeyed.

By their activities, living things convert some of the sun's energy into forms which they are able to use, carbon dioxide and oxidizable complex carbon compounds. Non-usable forms of energy, such as heat and non-oxidizable complex carbon compounds, are also produced. It is therefore fortunate that the Earth is not an isolated system. The continuing input of energy from the sun makes up the deficit between total energy and usable energy. If this were not so, life on Earth would eventually extinguish itself.

# Fresh-water life

Varied and complex forms of life have adapted to the special conditions required to survive in fresh-water rivers and lakes. Both plants and animals are found in abundance under the right conditions.

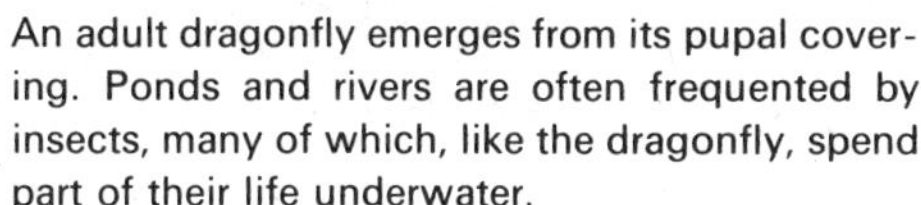

An adult dragonfly emerges from its pupal covering. Ponds and rivers are often frequented by insects, many of which, like the dragonfly, spend part of their life underwater.

Common toads mating. The female ejects a long 'rope' of mucus-covered eggs which festoon underwater vegetation and provide food for a number of underwater species.

GREAT AMOUNTS of water fall on dry land as rain. Some is absorbed; some is evaporated by the heat of the sun. But for the rest there are only two courses open. According to the land on which it falls, the water will either run down slopes, gullies, rivulets and so on until it collects as a lake in some low-lying and enclosed area; or it will progress along similar roads to a river and make its way eventually to the sea.

Such collections of water, be they lakes or rivers, are very important. They provide fresh water which can be used for drinking, watering livestock, and in agricultural irrigation. And in varying concentrations, they harbour another important food source, fish. Rivers are also useful as a means of transportation. And finally, but not least, many inland waters have a natural beauty.

In the more static lake, although water will run in constantly from the surrounding land, and while some is removed by evaporation and seepage, the water itself is not flowing. Why, then, does it not become stagnant and foul and life disappear?

Part of the answer lies in the gas exchange which takes place between the surface of the water and the air. Living organisms requires oxygen and/or carbon dioxide to survive. But although these gases *are* taken from the air above the water, they can enter only the top layers in any great quantity when the water is still. Natural mechanisms are necessary to distribute the oxygenated water to other levels. In part the job is done by the heat of the sun which at certain times of the year, sets up convection currents in the water. More important are winds which cause the lake water to drift from side to side; some of it returns to lower levels of the lake allowing oxygen-reduced water to the surface for recharging.

Another major necessity for life is heat. The heat of the sun can only be absorbed by the top layers of the water – it can penetrate no further. This layer is called the *epilimnion* and it mixes slightly with the water below it to form another less warm layer called the *thermocline*. But below this, the area called the *hypolimnion*, the water is cold.

Green plants need a wide range of mineral nutrients – calcium, iron, potassium, sodium and so on – to grow, as do animals. In the main these minerals find their way into fresh water from the surrounding soil when they are washed loose by rain.

Finally light is extremely important to any living community. Without it, plants cannot grow, and it is the plants which give the dissolved nutrients to the animals in a form (organic material) which the latter can eat.

Light also can only penetrate to relatively shallow depths even in crystal-clear water. If the liquid contains suspended material, then penetration is proportionally reduced.

These are the basic necessities for life in the lake: certain gases, a range of mineral nutrients, heat and light. What kinds of plant and animal do they support?

The 'average' lake divides itself into three general regions. First, there is the area of bed which stretches out from the shore to the greatest depth which daylight can penetrate: this is the *littoral zone* and surrounds the area of bottom which is without light, the *profundal zone*. The water which covers the whole is known as the *limnetic region*.

The shoreward rim of the littoral region differs in appearance. Some of it will be masked by clumps of emergent vegetation (rooted underwater, but with the tops standing clear of the surface) like bulrushes. Elsewhere it may be smooth sand, or a carpet of pebbles and rocks.

Further out, where it is too deep for emergent plants to keep their heads above water, there is another type of vegetation of which water lilies are a common example. These are rooted plants, the leaves and flowers of which float on the surface, and this is called the *zone of floating leafed plants*. Still deeper, where even the larger plants cannot make the surface, plant life is still likely to be dense, but here it is wholly submerged (*zone of submerged vegetation*), and contains waterweed, shining pondweed and the like. These plant zones may not always be sharply defined, but may be intermixed according to the formation of the lake bed. Likewise, algae are liable to occur elsewhere on rocky beds in the littoral zone.

In the profundal area of the lake, no plants grow on the bottom at all because there is no light. But there is plant life on the surface and this can be divided into two kinds. First there is the plant section of the plankton, called *phytoplankton,* which includes the algae called *diatoms*: they are enclosed in a glassy case, often beautifully sculpted. Then there are the surface-dwelling weeds, which are not rooted but float. They include the flowering frogbit and chickweed.

The animal life of the lake can also be divided according to environment. First there are the *surface dwellers,* among which the most obvious are the whirligig beetles, so called because they whirl rapidly about the surface of the water using their short flattened legs as paddles.

## Floaters and swimmers

Next come the *floating forms* – the zooplankton section of the planktonic mix – which include only one insect, the so-called 'phantom larva'. The larger animals are crustaceans: the water fleas named for their jerky motion and the copepods which have no shells and are pear-shaped. Also there are the *rotifers* with their small crown of *cilia* (hair-like appendages) which beat incessantly.

The *swimmers* – the next group to be considered – include, of course, the fish. Various species thrive in various parts of the world; in Britain the common types are trout, pike, char, perch and minnows. But there are 45 British species in all. It should not be forgotten also that a number of the higher animals – amphibians like frogs and toads, mammals like otters and water rats, birds like the spectacular kingfisher – make some or all of their living from the water.

Fourthly, there are the stone and weed dwellers. They include a whole host of insects, some of which like the dragonfly nymph can extract oxygen from the water, while others, like water beetles, have to make trips to the surface in order to catch their breath.

All fresh-water snails are numbered among the stone and weed dwellers, as also is the fresh-water shrimp. This animal can swim well but spends most of its time rooting about among the weeds and stones at the bottom. It resembles its marine cousin reasonably closely but, of course, is much smaller. The male fresh-water shrimp carries the female around with it nearly all the time.

Finally, there are the animals known as *burrowers,* a name which speaks for itself. Important among them are the Annelid worms which wriggle through the mud of the bottom, straining from the slime the organic matter they need to live. There are also the fresh-water mussels, which are more or less stationary and vary in size from more than six inches to less than a quarter-inch long.

The food chain begins with the plants of various kinds which utilize the energy of the sun to build proteins. In the open water it is algae – diatoms and others – which do the job, and these in turn are eaten by the planktonic crustacea – although some of these crustaceans are carnivorous and may eat their own kind.

Some of the carnivorous fish, like char, eat zooplankton. Perch do the same but only up to a certain point in their growth. Others like trout feed on zooplankton some of the time and in other periods snap up the tiny creatures which fall into the water. The surface dwellers themselves live almost entirely on this source of food, while they themselves are preyed upon but little.

The creatures like molluscs and worms of the profundal zone where no plants grow depend largely on the manna which drifts down from above, dead plankton and the larger animals. A few bottom dwellers are carnivorous, and some fish – like perch – prey happily on profundal creatures.

In the littoral region, plankton also operates as a primary producer, but of course it is joined in this by the rooted plants and the attached algae. Most of the herbivorous creatures in this area seem to live on the algae, but some insects and snails eat the higher plants. Most of the insects are carnivorous.

1

2

Fresh-water shrimps are scavengers – they live on the leftovers of other creatures or the remains of dead ones, and where this detritus is divided finely enough, it also gives sustenance to the sponges and so on.

## Predatory fish

In the littoral waters, the fish prey on all the animal organisms during some part of their lives. Later on they prey on smaller fish. This is true even of the fierce and predatory pike, but only when very young. It may be prepared to accept a diet of large insects during this time, but later on it takes to an exclusively fish diet.

It has been necessary to dwell on life and its interrelationships in the lake at such length, not only to give as clear as possible a picture of a complicated system, but also because many of the factors involved also play an important part in river habitats.

Oxygen and carbon dioxide, nutrients,

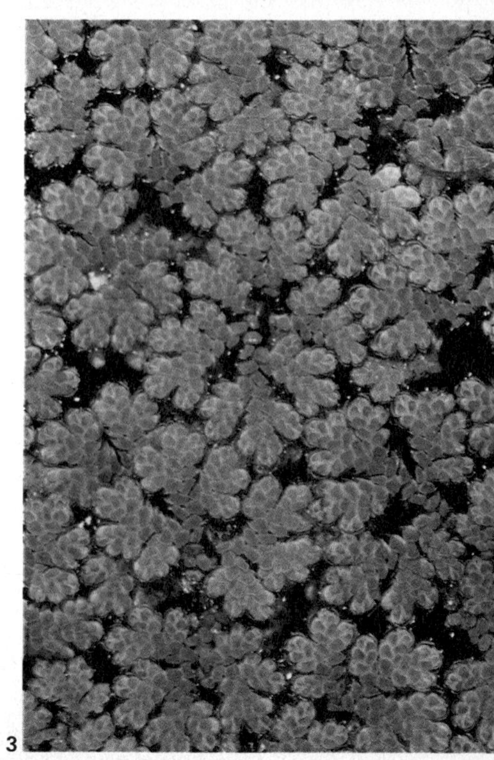

3

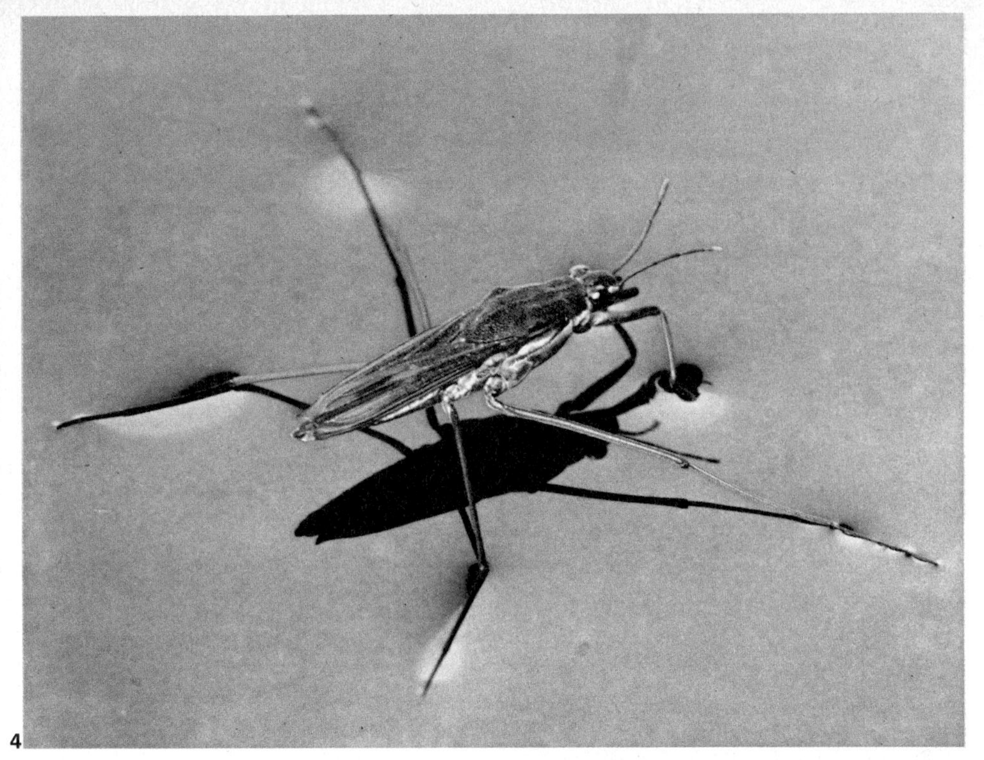

and animals themselves? Clearly the mixing action of turbulence means there are few difficulties about the capture and distribution of oxygen and carbon dioxide. Similarly the valuable minerals, washed in from the soil, and to some extent the sun's heat are well distributed – except in the very deep portions of sluggishly moving rivers. However, heat (and light) may be kept from the surface of the water by high banks and overhanging vegetation. In general, the basic life necessities are there in the river for animals and plants to co-exist as they do in the lake.

The living organisms of a river are divided into three groups: the sedentary; the drifting; and the swimmers. The representatives of each which are found in any particular section depend on the combination of those general characteristics. In the plunging waters of a head-stream, the higher rooted plants have a difficult time surviving – their foliage presents great resistance to the water and they are likely to be swept away. In their place there are generally algae of different kinds, even the diatoms so important in the economy of the lake. But they are likely to

**1** The giant water-lilies on this African river give the illusion that this handsome jacana bird is walking on the water.
**2** Like a tiny version of the familiar water-rat, the water shrew dives for its food, which consists of insects and small river animals taken from the river bottom.
**3** The water fern is Britain's only true aquatic fern. Instead of being rooted in the mud, *Azolla* floats on the surface of the water, drawing its mineral intake from dissolved salts.
**4** The water strider literally does walk on the water, in fact it spends most of its life on the surface of quiet ponds and backwaters, supported by the surface tension of the water.
**5** This lush-looking field is in fact an African river infested with 'Congo cabbage'. A herd of hippopotamus is half-submerged in the greenery, while egrets wait to catch passing fish.

heat and light are required by river plants and animals as well as by those in lakes. The food chains are very similar and many of the living organisms are common.

Where differences occur, they do so because river water is constantly in motion, though the direction is not uniform along the length of the waterway; there are a number of factors which can cause reverse currents or eddies. Neither is the velocity of the flowing water uniform. It changes from point to point with changes in the gradient, changes in the cross-section formed by bank and bottom, and variations in the amount of matter suspended in it. Again, river water is turbulent water – to a greater or lesser extent according to the formation of the river. At various times it may encounter slopes, from gentle inclines to spectacular rapids.

The flow of the river also affects the clearness of its water. It can wash organic and inorganic materials from the bed or banks and if they are gathered in sufficient quantities the water becomes cloudy (turbid) and light penetration is affected.

What effect does this complicated set of variables have on the fresh-water plants

The coypu, a large aquatic rodent, is a native of South America. Accidentally introduced into Britain, it has flourished on the Norfolk Broads, where it is now hunted as a pest.

be specially adapted for life in a swift current, and may have stalks with which to cling to the rocks.

Rooted plants are better able to exist further downstream, where the water flow is less fierce, or where some peculiarity of the bank makes for still water, and emergent plants like bulrushes may be found. But the majority of the higher plants stick to the slowly meandering reaches.

As might be expected the range of sedentary animals, like plants, broadens significantly where the flow is slower. There are many more insects and the bottom houses burrowers, such as mussels and dragonfly larva. Some burrowing mayfly larva are able to survive in fast and slow waters. They are an important link in the food chain, for they are voracious herbivores and at the same time provide a choice diet for many fish.

## Turbulence

Rivers are not ideal habitats for drifting life. The velocity and turbulence can damage the organisms by dashing them against rocks and logs and the drifting organism may be carried from one type of habitat to another, where often the conditions for life are not suitable for it.

Plankton is therefore largely absent from fast-flowing water, although there may be some in transit. Lower down it is able to reproduce in the backwaters and still sections of the river and includes some bacteria, various algae and diatoms. These are joined by rotifers and other larger plankton and some organisms which the water has torn from their hold on the sides or bottom.

Swimming life includes frogs, toads, snakes and otters, but perhaps the most important denizens are the fish. In the upper waters these are likely to be relatively few, being limited to strong swimming types, such as salmon and trout. In the lower and slower reaches the variety of fish life is much wider.

In the River Tees in Britain, for example, only trout and minnow are found in the upper reaches, but lower down they are joined by such fish as grayling, dace, chub, and occasionally pike or perch.

The threat of pollution is an increasing danger for life in rivers and lakes. Pollution comes from a variety of sources: run-off of agricultural chemicals; industrial waste and domestic sewage; overheating due to power stations. The need for constant vigilance over waterways was vividly illustrated early in 1969 when the discharge of a small amount of organic poison into the Rhine in Germany killed millions of fish. Similar incidents have occurred in a number of other countries. Clearly there is much that can be destroyed in the way of living matter and its various habitats. If the destruction is allowed to continue, then equally clearly the fresh waters of the Earth will largely cease to give us significant benefit or pleasure.

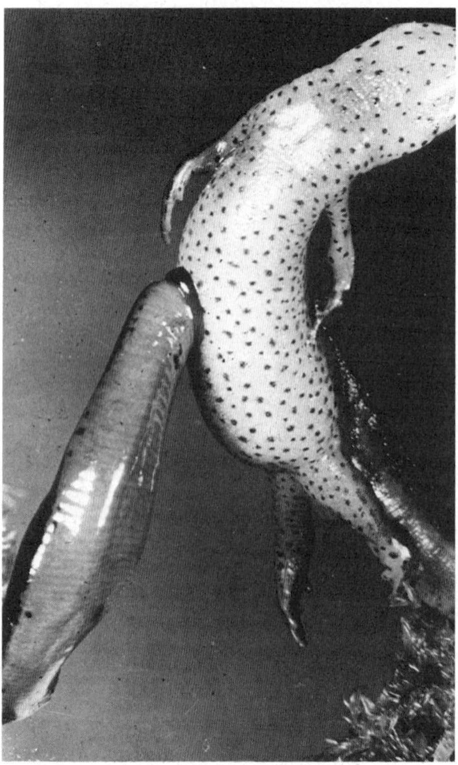

A fish leech attaches itself to the belly of a newt. Leeches abound in rivers and waterways, particularly in the Tropics, wherever there is sufficient water to keep them from dehydration.

An eel comes close to the river bank on its journey to the spawning grounds to breed. Like salmon, some eels divide their time between rivers and the sea, breeding in the Atlantic.

# Pond pygmies and sea giants

Giant masses of floating seaweed can be a hazard in the shipping lanes of the world. Surprisingly, the scum which forms in ponds and water tanks is a member of the same family, the ubiquitous algae.

IT HAS BEEN ESTIMATED that there are over a thousand million tons of usable seaweed easily available throughout the world. This alga, which contains many chemicals essential to modern industry, represents a virtually untapped and inexhaustible source of raw materials. Modern technology has now developed to the stage when this vast storehouse of algae can be tapped for the benefit of the human race.

Algae, which range from single cells to enormous colonies containing many thousands of cells, are a primitive form of plant life which has sidestepped the process of evolution, and are probably the ancestors from which other forms of plant life developed.

There are some 30,000 different species of algae ranging in size from microscopic plants 1/25,000th of an inch in diameter to trailing seaweeds hundreds of feet long. All algae are simple structures without roots, stems or leaves. They thrive on damp rocks, walls, treetrunks and palings; in caves, crevices and along seashores; in lakes, rivers, ponds and puddles and even in the depths of the ocean. Indeed, they are found in any damp environment. The smallest are the single-celled *motile* or moving algae, and the biggest are the giant kelps of the Pacific Ocean, which have been known to exceed 400 feet in length. In general, the smaller algae are found in fresh water or terrestrial habitats, while the bigger are marine.

Biologists have arranged algae into a complex system of groups, sub-groups and classes. Algae constitute a major group of the plant kingdom and were at one time included with bacteria, fungi, mosses and ferns in a division called *Cryptogamia.* Subsequently, the algae and fungi were grouped in a separate division called *Thallophyta*.

Algae are now recognized as forming a separate division, but this can be simplified into five major groups based on pigmentation: Green Algae; Blue-green Algae; Yellow-green Algae; Brown Algae; and Red Algae.

Algae range in size from single-celled plants to seaweeds, such as this giant kelp, which grow to lengths of up to 400 feet. These kelps cling to rocks on the sea bed.

## Uses of Alginates

| | |
|---|---|
| **Thickening (viscosity)** | |
| Food and bakery | Filling creams |
| | Lemon curd, soups |
| Pharmaceutical and cosmetic | Toothpaste |
| | Hand creams |
| | Shampoos, lotions |
| | Liquid detergents |
| Textile | Printing pastes |
| Rubber | Latex |
| **Emulsifying, stabilizing and deflocculating** | |
| Food and bakery | Ice cream |
| | Soft drinks |
| | Baker's emulsions |
| Pharmaceutical | Emulsions |
| General | Polishes |
| | Emulsion paints |
| | Welding electrodes |
| | Insecticides |
| **Gelling and binding** | |
| Food and bakery | Confectionery jellies |
| | Packing jellies |
| | Milk jellies and puddings |
| Pharmaceutical and cosmetic | Tablets, hand and anti-burn jellies |
| Dental | Dental impression powder |
| Medical | Haemostatics |
| Ceramics | Glazes and engobes |
| General | Sintered products |
| **Film and filament forming** | |
| Food | Sausage casings |
| Pharmaceutical | Barrier creams |
| Medical | Absorbable dressings |
| Textile | Soluble yarn |
| | Warp sizes |
| Paper | Transparent paper |
| | Coated papers |
| | Washable wallpapers |
| General | Anti-stick and mould release agents |
| | Leather |

A typical green alga common in ponds and puddles is *Chlamydomonas.* It collects in such quantities that it imparts a bright green colour to the water, although each individual cell is invisible to the naked eye. Its shape is usually oval and somewhat pointed at one end, where there are two whip-like threads of protoplasm, called flagella, by means of which the alga 'swims' about. Most of the cell is occupied by the *chloroplast,* a cup-shaped granule containing chlorophyll, within which is embedded a protein mass called the *pyrenoid.*

The exact function of this has not been established, but around it starch is deposited as it is formed by the chloroplast. Near the pointed end of the cell is the nucleus and two *vacuoles:* these latter are spaces in the protoplasm containing air or partially digested nutrients. Immediately within the pointed end of the cell is a mark called the red spot, thought to be light-sensitive, which induces the plant to swim towards light to aid photosynthesis.

Biologists have difficulty in drawing a dividing line between certain motile (moving) algae, such as *Chlamydomonas*, and a somewhat similar group of protozoa which also move by flagella. Some protozoa, although unicellular, exhibit animal qualities such as lack of chlorophyll and their ingestion of solid food. On the other hand there are protozoa that combine animal characteristics with the plant characteristics of motile algae. These protozoa give support to the theory that plants and animals had a common origin in the very remote past, and that their ancestors were similar to the unicellular and flagellate plant and animal life existing in water today.

## Teeming pond life

One of the most interesting of the floating green algae is *Spirogyra*. It consists of a row or string of cylindrical cells, each bounded by a cell wall, and grows in masses at or near the surface of freshwater ponds, lakes or slow-moving streams, or clings to submerged rocks and tree roots. The whole string or filament of cells is enclosed in a sheath of mucilage which makes it feel slimy to the touch. When a mass of the filament is lifted from the water, the individual strings cling together, due to their sticky, jelly-like covering.

Each filament is made up of cylindrical cells joined end to end and one cell wide, without branching. Just inside the thin, transparent cell wall is the chloroplast, which is shaped like a flat spiral spring and gives the alga its name. Spaced along the chloroplast are pits or protein bodies, the pyrenoids, where starch collects from photosynthesis. The nucleus is near the centre of the cell.

During spring and summer, *Spirogyra* filaments steadily increase in length by growth or by division of individual cells, until a swirl of water or the movement of stones or fish breaks them. The broken strings then form new and distinct filaments. With the approach of autumn, filament growth stops and many filaments die. The survivors then go through the sexual spore-formation process called conjugation, by which two filaments exchange nuclear material.

## A world of constant movement

A more simple species of alga is *pleurococcus viridis*. Looking like a smear of green paint, it is often seen on the trunks of trees, where it is particularly conspicuous in damp, winter weather. Examined under the microscope the smear is seen to be a mass of tiny, ball-shaped cells in clusters of fours and eights. The alga reproduces by simple division of the original cell into two cells which cling together for a time, their sides flattened where they press against each other.

One of the most curious algae colonies is formed by *Volvox*, common to freshwater ponds. Thousands of individual cells arrange themselves side by side in a hollow sphere.

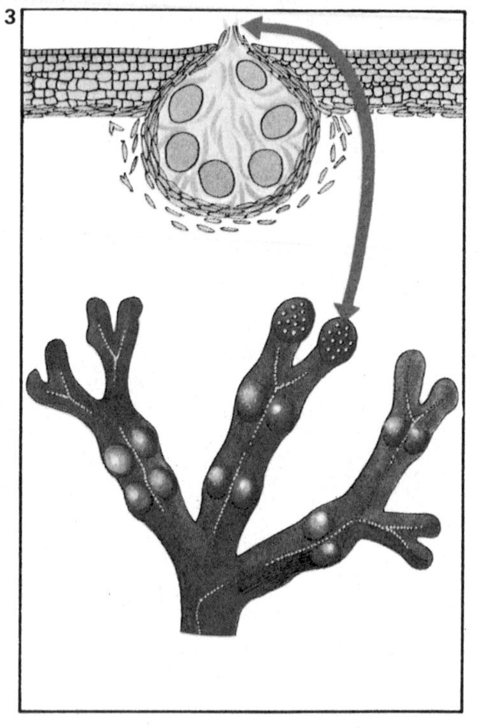

1 Green algae like this seaweed (*Codium tomentosum*) derive their colour from chlorophyll, which they use to make food.

2 Seaweeds exhibit many different forms and colours. Colour variations are caused by masking of the chlorophyll by other chemicals.

3 Reproduction in *Fucus vesiculosus* is by sex organs which develop inside conceptacles growing at the tips of the branches.

Each cell has flagella and these project beyond the sphere like the nap on velvet. As the thousands of flagella whip about in the water, they impart to the sphere a slight rotating motion. Within a main sphere there are often smaller sphere-colonies which remain enclosed inside until the outer sphere is ruptured.

*Cyanophyceae* is the collective name for those species of algae commonly called blue-green. In addition to chlorophyll, they contain a blue pigment called *phycocyanin*, as well as other pigments. Blue, the dominant colour, is dissolved in the protoplasm and masks out the other hues, so that most species are a dark blue, though sometimes varying to blue-green. Other species range from orange to black.

Some *Cyanophyceae* exist as individuals and others form filament, ball, and sheet colonies. Colonies are in general held together by a protective film of jelly secreted by the individual cells in the colony. Species of the algae are found in most parts of the world where there is sufficient moisture to sustain them. Reproduction of all species is asexual.

One of the most interesting of the motile blue-green algae is *Oscillatoria*. It has neither flagella nor cilia, but moves about by a wave-like oscillating movement, hence its name. Oscillatoria exist in filament colonies made up of rectangular cells arranged side by side. The filament increases in length through cell division at either end. Gelatinous partitions form at intervals along the filament, which eventually breaks up at these junctions. The short filaments thus formed then produce new cells at the ends, in the same

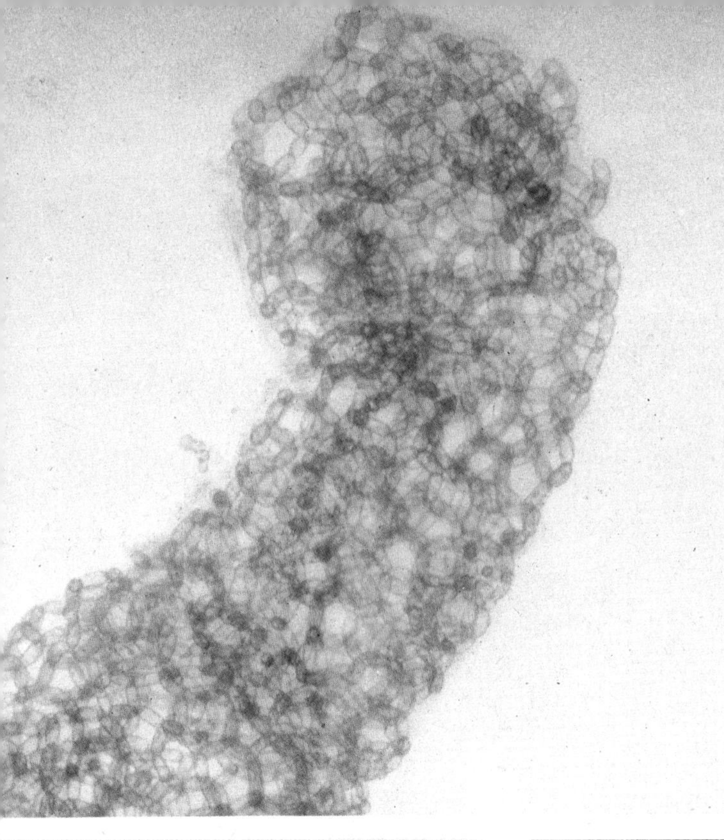

**1** Colonies are common among algae such as *hydrodictyon*. They almost always contain a fixed number of member cells.
**2** In outward appearance many algae, especially seaweeds, resemble higher differentiated forms of plant life. Now, they are being processed to provide food and raw materials for Man.

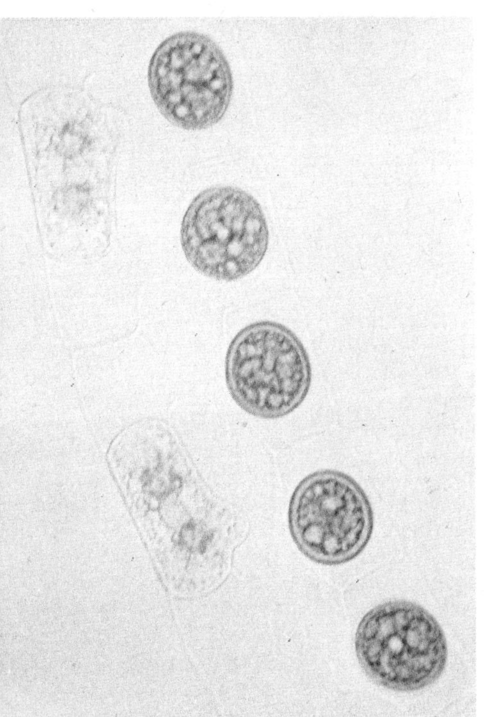

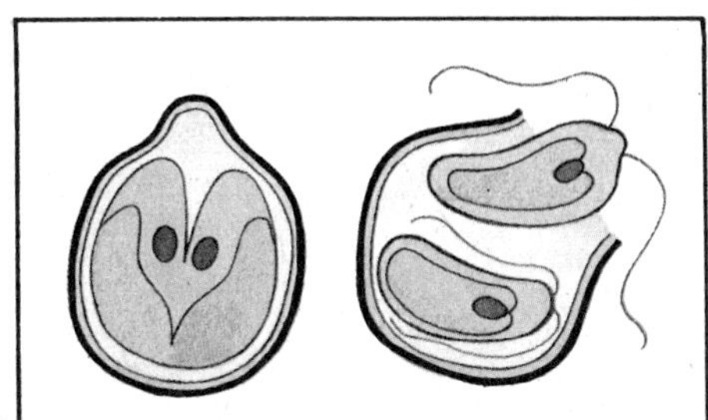

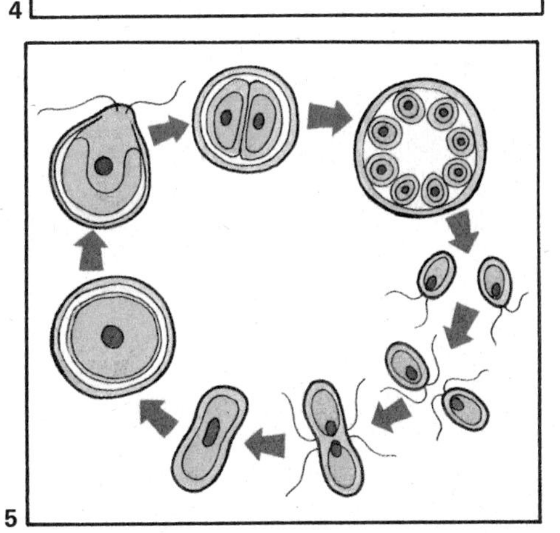

**3** Reproduction in *Zygnema* is by the formation of zygospores within the cell walls.
**4** *Chlamydomanas* reproduces asexually by longitudinal division of the cell to form two daughter cells.
**5** It also reproduces sexually. Gametes form within the parent cell and each unites with one from another plant to form a zygospore, which develops into a new adult plant.
**6** *Volvox* colonies, usually of 16 cells, are enclosed in an envelope of mucilage. Movement is by the whip-like flagella.

way as the parent, until another long filament forms.

There are approximately 1,500 species of Oscillatoria, and they have an extraordinary variety of habitat. Some flourish in Arctic snow and others are equally at home in hot springs.

Usually occurring as a slimy coating in caves and on damp rocks and walls, the blue-green algae called *Gloeocapsa* normally exist as individuals, though they are occasionally found in colonies of three or four enclosed in a film of jelly. *Anaboena* is another of the blue-green algae that exist in filament colonies. The cells are roundish oval so that the filament looks like a string of microscopic green pearls.

*Phaeophyta* are nearly all marine algae, and show considerable variety of structure. This is particularly true of those popularly classed as seaweeds. Though some of the latter have structures resembling the leaves and stems of higher plants, they exist and derive their nutriment in exactly the same way as do the most microscopic of algae.

Seaweeds occur as filaments; many branched; in flat sheets; and as long, thin ribbons. In many species there is *alternation of generations*. Parts of the plant develop organs called *sporangia*, which produce asexual spores. These spores give rise to new plants that produce sex cells, which unite to form new plants which in turn reproduce by spores.

Seaweed algae are generally attached to rocks or other underwater objects by sucker-like discs called holdfasts, and they are buoyed in the water by bladders. Many seaweeds grow in the shallow water of areas covered by tides, where they perform a vital function in preserving marine life. Not only do seaweeds such as bladderwrack form a cushion to protect rocks from the force of tides and waves, but they provide many marine creatures with shelter and moisture when the tide goes out.

Other species of seaweed grow clinging to rocks at depths far beyond the tide line. The giant kelp, for example, thrives at depths of over 50 feet. It is probably the longest plant in the world, and specimens have been reported 400 feet long. Large masses of seaweed drift about in the ocean. One such species is *Sargassum,* which has leaf-like structures set in a stem and pear-shaped floats for buoyancy. Vast quantities of *Sargassum* are carried by ocean currents to collect in floating mats. An example is the so-called Sargasso Sea.

## Giant plants from the sea

Red algae are similar to the brown algae seaweeds, but derive their colour from a pigment called *phycoerythrin.* Most species are found in ocean waters, but a few are fresh-water, particularly in cold, fast-flowing streams. Both ocean and fresh-water species are between one and two inches long and appear as filaments, ribbons or fern-like growths. Most species show alternation of generations. Neither the spores nor the male cells are motile. The male sex-cells simply drift about until they come into contact with an egg cell and fertilize it.

*Diatoms* are found in the sea, in lakes and ponds, in rivers and streams, on moist rock and even in cultivated soil, in fact anywhere with enough light and moisture. The surface area of the sea is inhabited by countless millions of diatoms, which make up the bulk of *plankton,* the mixture of animal and plant life forming the marine pasture on which whales and other sea animals feed.

When diatoms die, their skeletons fall to the bottom of the sea or lake in which the algae lived. This happens to vast numbers of them every minute of the day. The ceaseless rain of diatom skeletons to the ocean floor over millions of years has resulted in extensive areas, especially in Antarctic regions, becoming covered with a fine ooze, chiefly of diatom remains. The deposits of the diatomaceous earth are in some places hundreds of feet thick.

Dredged up, cleaned and refined, diatomaceous earth has a host of industrial applications. It provides a first-class insulating material for refrigerators and boilers, and when finely powdered acts as a mild but valuable abrasive in metal polishes, cleaning powders and toothpastes. It is also used as a filter for clarifying liquids.

For many years seaweeds have been a human food in the form of laver and Irish Moss, though on a relatively limited scale. Of recent years, however, there has been considerable scientific study of the nutritive value of algae in general, and many dieticians see in these plants a valuable food source if they can be cheaply and efficiently processed and made palatable.

If that can be done, a major breakthrough will have been achieved in solving the problem of feeding the underdeveloped countries. Already advanced experiments show promising results in the cultivation of algae in spaceships, as a food reserve for astronauts undertaking prolonged missions.

Diatoms, taking many different forms, occur wherever there are damp conditions. They form the main constituent of plankton.

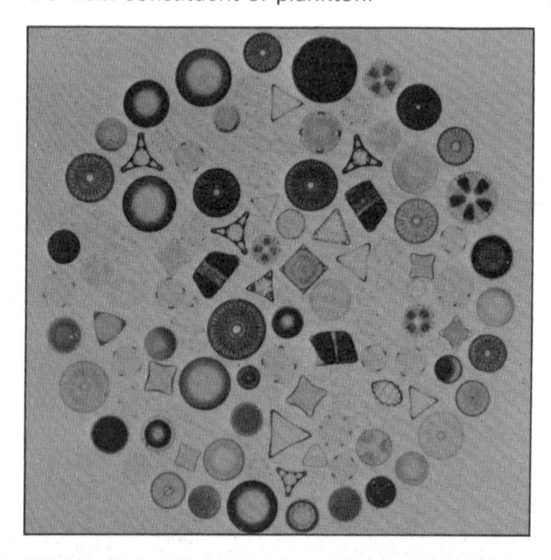

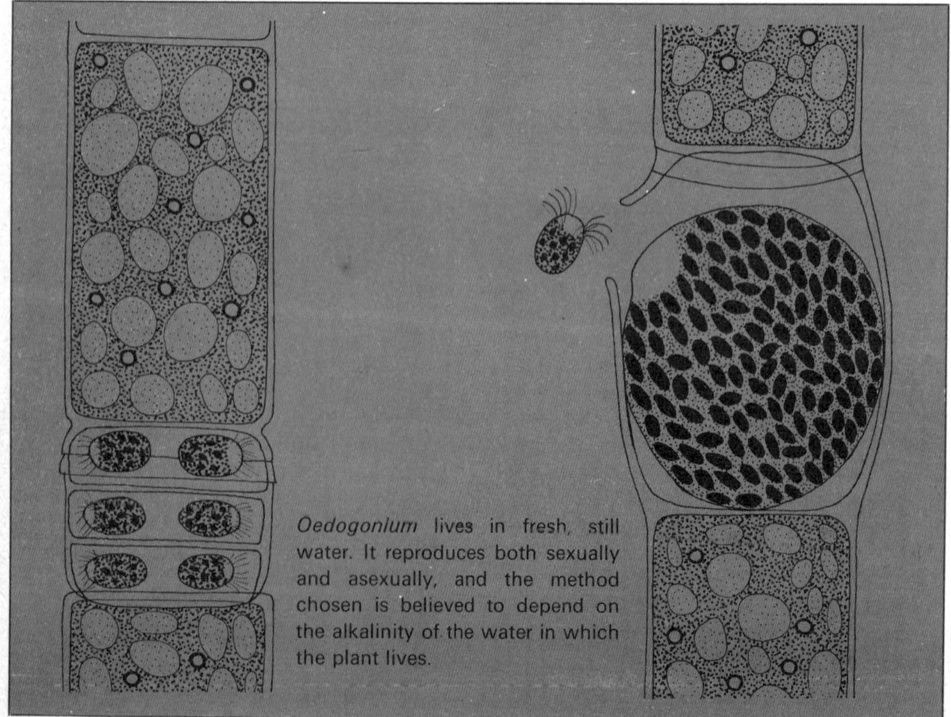

*Oedogonium* lives in fresh, still water. It reproduces both sexually and asexually, and the method chosen is believed to depend on the alkalinity of the water in which the plant lives.

Apart from its limited use as a food for human consumption, seaweed has numerous industrial applications. Its value as a fertilizer has been known for centuries, but it is expensive to transport and until the middle of the nineteenth century it was an important source of potash and iodine. Recently the chemistry of seaweed has become better known, and it is now recognized as a valuable source of industrial raw material.

## Algae's new-found riches

*Colloids* are now commonly extracted from seaweeds; from certain brown seaweeds come the alginates and from red seaweeds come agar-agar and carragheen. These colloids act as a structural filler in the same way as concrete does in buildings with a steel frame. In seaweed, as in trees, the steel frame is cellulose.

From alginic acid, which is chemically extracted from seaweed, various salts can be made, but sodium alginate has the widest range of industrial uses. This is a pale yellow powder which can easily be made up into a colourless, odourless and tasteless but highly viscous solution. Sodium alginate is widely used for its thickening, gelling and film-forming properties. It is used in the food industry as a stabilizer, most commonly in ice cream, but as food processing becomes more widespread the need for colloids will grow too and sodium alginate is well established in this field. Toothpaste and dental impression powders are the most important of a host of pharmaceutical outlets.

Sodium alginate can be spun into a synthetic fibre which is soluble. This is used in sock manufacture so that socks can be knitted continuously, and separate when they are washed. This yarn makes a fluffy lightweight synthetic wool which is used for reducing bleeding in surgical operations and for making gauzes and sutures that can be left inside the patient, to be dissolved in the body after they have done their work.

Agar-agar makes a first-class culture medium for growing bacteria. Carragheen is a food stabilizer with slightly different stabilizing and gelling properties from alginates. These find their main application in canned pet food and chocolate milk stabilizers.

Until very recently, algae have been virtually ignored by all but biologists. The discovery of their vast potential as sources of food and raw materials has now put them at the front of scientific research and industrial exploitation.

In a century when the world is faced with shortages of both food and essential chemical raw materials, all the sources in the plant and animal kingdom must be exploited. Fortunately, much of this storehouse, like the algae, is readily available, and its uses are already well known to chemists and industrialists.

At present, industry relies very largely on naturally-occurring algae growths, except in cases where specific types are grown for food. It is not beyond the range of science that algae farms, producing chemicals should be flourishing before the end of the twentieth century.

# Bryophytes live on land - breed by water

Why is water vital to mosses and liverworts, when they seem able to live happily in dry locations? Their curious reproductive system provides the answer to this apparent contradiction.

1 *Polytrichum commune* is a species of moss which is common on damp moorland, where it forms a dense, bright-green carpet. It is shown here slightly smaller than life size.

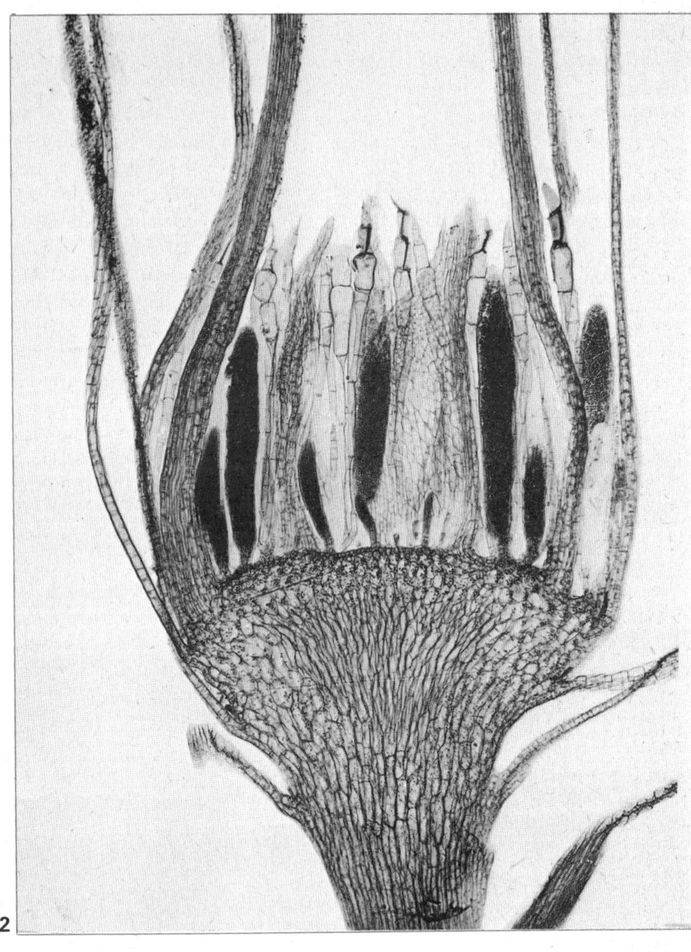

2 This section through the tip of the male shoot of a moss shows the antheridia (male reproductive organs) and the hairs (paraphyses) which separate them.

FEW PLANTS can live under conditions of more extreme dryness than some mosses. They grow on tree trunks, in cracks in old walls, between paving stones, and in other places where, for most of the time, they hardly ever see a drop of water. Yet, curiously, the mosses and their relatives the liverworts, which together make up a class of plants called the *bryophytes,* are utterly dependent on water for the continuation of their species. The reason for this paradox is that when they reproduce the sperms produced by the male organs must swim to the female organs with their egg cells. Unless the surface of the plant is covered by a film of water at this time, fertilization cannot take place and the reproductive efforts of the plant have been wasted.

Not all mosses, of course, live in dry places. Most mosses, and nearly all liverworts, prefer damp, shady situations, where the danger of drying up is not so great. Should a moss happen to become completely desiccated, however, it does not necessarily spell disaster. Most mosses have a remarkable power of reviving from a dried-up condition when they are given water, provided that the drying-up has not gone on too long.

Everyone knows what a moss looks like, but the liverworts may not be so familiar. Liverworts are not conspicuous; normally they are only noticed by people who are looking for them, common though they are.

There are two kinds of liverworts. The *thallose* liverworts are usually found beside streams, in culverts, and in other damp places. Unlike mosses, they are not divided into stem and leaf: they consist of branched, green ribbons, called *thalli*. In contrast to them, the leafy liverworts have tiny stems that bear leaves and are, at first glance, not unlike mosses.

## A typical moss

It is easy to distinguish between a moss and a leafy liverwort by examining the arrangement of the leaves. In a moss, the leaves are usually arranged in a spiral round the stem, while in a leafy liverwort they are in two rows, one on each side of the stem, with a third row of smaller leaves on the underside of the stem, which tends to lie along the ground.

*Funaria hygrometrica* is a typical example of a moss. It is very common, especially on the ground after a heath fire, where it forms dense, bright green tufts. The tiny plants are not much more than half an inch high, the branched stems bearing small, spirally arranged leaves. Near the base of the plant are a number of hair-like rhizoids that serve to attach it to the ground; as in all mosses and liverworts, there are no true roots.

If a section of the stem of *Funaria* is cut and examined under a microscope, three layers of cells can be distinguished. On the outside is the epidermis, which forms an outer skin covering the plant. Inside this is the cortex, consisting of a mass of small cells, and, in the centre of the stem, we have a core of cells, with thin walls, that are greatly elongated. This central core of cells is thought to have the function of conducting water up the stem, but this is not certain. Another possibility is that it may conduct sugar, manufactured in the leaves, to other parts of the plant. It may even do both.

The leaves of *Funaria* are triangular, and attached to the stem by their broad bases. They are extremely delicate and, except for a central 'nerve' or midrib, they are only one cell thick. The cells of the leaf contain chloroplasts – minute, lens-shaped bodies containing the green chlorophyll that enables the plant, with the aid of sunlight, to manufacture its own food from carbon dioxide in the air, by the process called photosynthesis.

The presence of a thickened midrib running down the centre of the leaf gives another way of distinguishing a moss from a leafy liverwort. Most (though by no means all) mosses have leaves with a central midrib, but the leaves of leafy liverworts never have one.

It is in their reproduction that the mosses show the remarkable way that Nature has adapted them to their particular mode of life. A moss has two forms of reproduction: a sexual one, followed, later on, by one in which sex plays no part.

## Two stages of reproduction

In *Funaria*, the male sex organs arise at the tip of the main shoot, where there is a conspicuous rosette of leaves, coloured reddish in the middle. These are easier to see in the hair moss *(Polytrichum)*, a large moss that is common on acid soils. To see the actual sex organs, a microscope is needed. They consist of ovoid structures called *antheridia*. Within the antheridia are formed the male sex cells, or sperms.

The female sex organs of *Funaria* are called *archegonia*, and they are borne at the tip of a side branch from the main stem; in the course of growth, however, the male branch is pushed to one side, so that the female branch may appear to be the main one. The archegonia, as seen under the microscope, are long and thin, with a swelling near the base where the female reproductive cell, or egg cell, is housed. This swollen portion of the archegonium is called the venter, while the long, thin portion above it is called the neck. The neck contains a row of neck canal cells, which, when the archegonium becomes ripe, disorganize, leaving the neck of the archegonium open.

The ripe archegonia of *Funaria* produce a certain amount of cane sugar, which attracts the wandering sperms. For their journey from the male to the female branch they must have water in which to swim; that is why mosses – and liverworts, too – are absolutely dependent on water for their reproduction. In a small moss such as *Funaria*, where the male and female branches are on the same plant, the voyage is not too difficult, even allowing for the very small size of the sperms, but in mosses where the male and female branches are carried by different plants, as they are, for instance, in the hair moss, the sperms may need a little assistance. This they may get from insects, which transport the sperms on their legs, or they may be splashed by raindrops from male to female plants. In the hair moss the rosette that contains the antheridia forms a 'splash cup'. During rain, it gets filled with water; a further direct hit by a raindrop sets up a violent wave movement in the water filling the cup, with the result that some water, containing sperms, is flung out, often to a distance of a foot or more.

When a sperm reaches a ripe archegonium, it enters the neck, passing down until it reaches the egg cell, with which it unites. This is the act of fertilization.

The plant that grows from the egg of a moss is a very simple one. It consists of an egg-shaped capsule, which is attached to the old moss plant by a stalk called the *seta*; the bottom end of the seta, or foot, is anchored firmly in the tissues of the mother plant, and remains so throughout the life of the capsule.

When the capsule matures, the seta elongates greatly, carrying the capsule up aloft to the dizzy height of an inch or more, where it nods hither and thither in the breeze. Within the capsule are formed the spores of the moss – the asexual bodies which form its second means of reproduction. These are extremely minute bodies which, if they fall in a suitable spot, can germinate to produce a new plant.

## The need for dry weather

They are formed in a spore cavity in the upper part of the capsule, and are released by the falling off of a lid, or *operculum*, at the tip of the capsule. When the operculum falls off, however, the spores are not immediately released, for they are kept in the capsule by a double row of teeth – the *peristome teeth*. In dry weather, the peristome teeth move apart, releasing some of the spores, while if it is wet, the peristome teeth close together again, retaining the spores in the capsule. This arrangement ensures that the spores shall be liberated in dry weather, when they will have a better chance of dispersal.

When the spore of a moss germinates, it does not give rise directly to a moss plant, but forms a green filament called a *protonema*. Buds form on the protonema, each bud growing into a new moss plant.

There are thus two distinct generations in the life history of a moss. The moss plant is one, and, since it bears the sex cells, or *gametes*, it is called the *gametophyte generation*. The other generation is the capsule, and, since it produces the spores, it is called the *sporophyte generation*. The gametophyte and sporophyte generations alternate regularly with one another, the gametophyte always giving rise to the sporophyte, and the sporophyte, in turn, producing the gametophyte.

One important thing should be noticed about this alternation of generations. The gametophyte needs moist conditions,

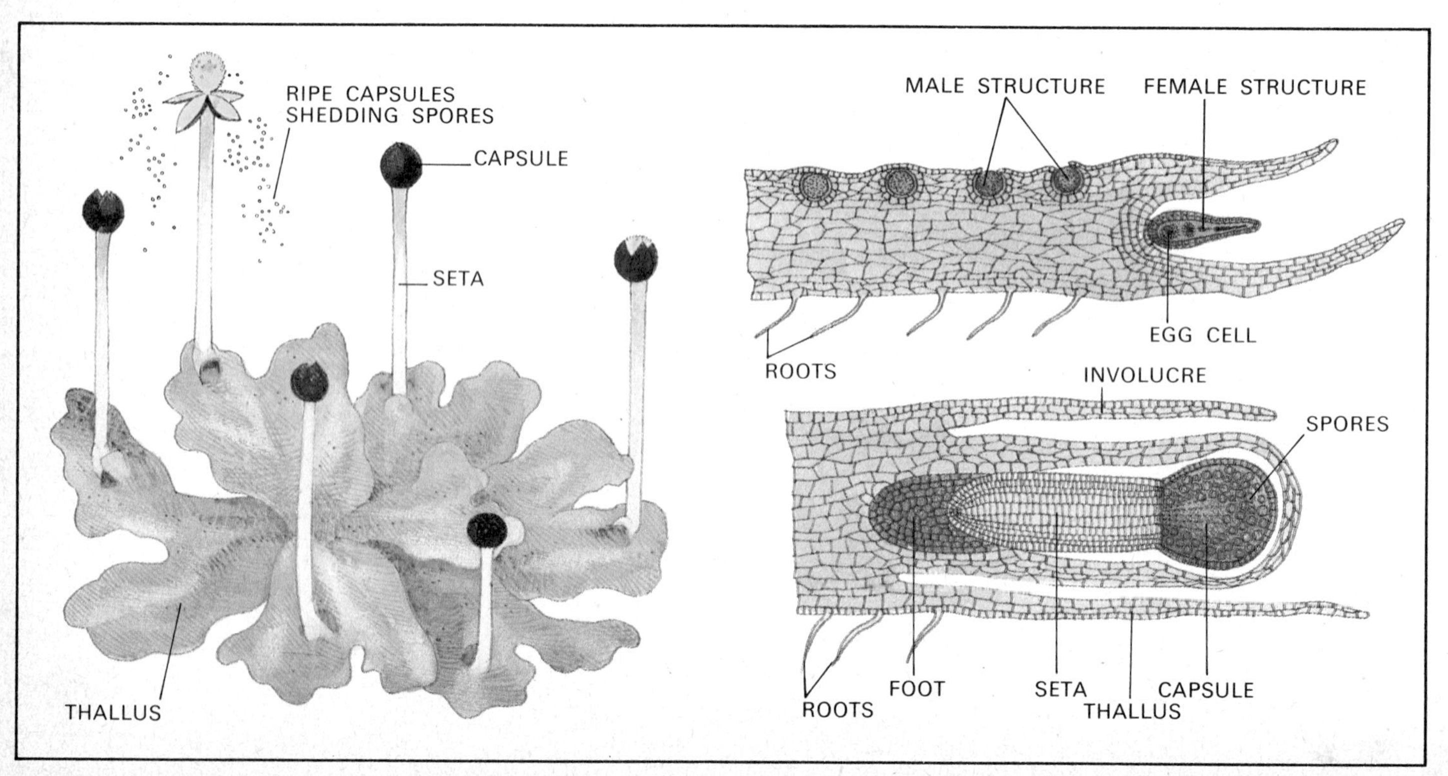


The spore capsules of bryophytes often grow on stalks from the thallus, and shed the spores when ripe. On the right are the male and female reproductive structures, showing how they are embedded in the protective tissue of the thallus and the involucre.

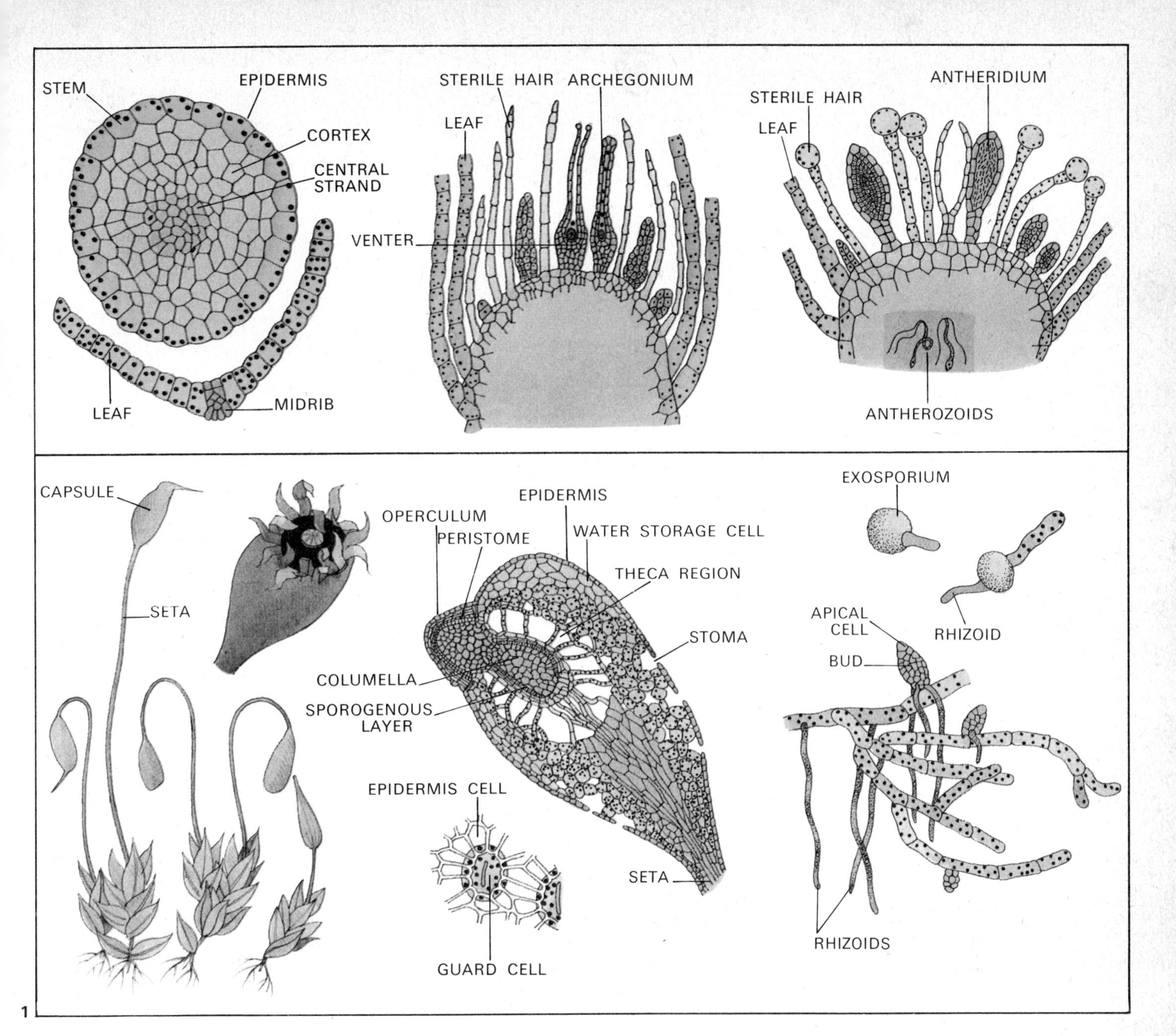


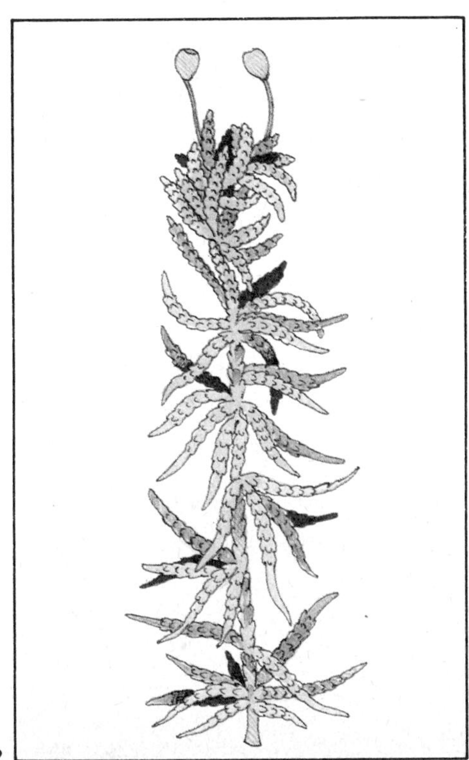


**1** A transverse section of the stem and leaf of *Funaria* shows the differentiation between the thick-walled epidermal layer and the cortical tissue. Male and female sex organs are carried on the apices of the main axis or its branches. *Below:* The ripe capsule ruptures and releases spores which germinate into a branched structure known as the primary protonema.

**2** *Sphagnum palustre,* one of the bog mosses, has complex branch leaves mainly composed of hollow cells, and possessing a small hole through which water can be absorbed.

because of the swimming sperm. The spores, on the other hand, function best if conditions are dry. Notice how, in a moss, the gametophyte is a small plant, hugging the ground, where there is more moisture. The capsule, on the other hand, is carried bodily aloft, where air currents can blow the spores away. The same thing is true of the liverworts.

In the ferns, and their allies such as the club mosses and horsetails, the main plant is the sporophyte. The gametophyte is a tiny plant, often less than a centimetre in diameter, which hugs the soil. The ferns are more completely adapted to land life than the bryophytes. In the seed plants – conifers and flowering plants – terrestrial adaptation is carried even further, for the gametophyte generation is entirely hidden inside the pollen grain and the ovule, or immature seed. They have evolved to a point where they no longer need water for sexual reproduction, for they have got rid of the swimming sperm.

The bog moss *(Sphagnum)* is of great importance in the formation of peat. There are many species of Sphagnum, and all grow under acid conditions, and particularly in bogs, where they may completely dominate all other vegetation. Sphagnum is a comparatively large moss, and has most peculiar leaves, built up of a network of long, narrow cells, with large, empty cells separating them. The presence of these empty cells gives the leaves of Sphagnum an amazing power of absorbing water – like blotting paper, only more so. For this reason, it is used in surgery as a dressing for wounds; its power of absorbing blood or pus is extraordinary.

Peat is formed largely of the remains of Sphagnum plants which have died and undergone a slow incomplete decomposition. The acid conditions in a Sphagnum bog severely limit the action of bacteria responsible for decomposition, with the result that the decaying vegetation retains much of its structure indefinitely. Thus peat is formed. In an old bog, the deposit of peat may be many feet thick, and represent the accumulation of plant remains over thousands of years. In some parts of the world peat is an important fuel, both in the home and in industry.

A thallose liverwort has quite a different structure from a moss. There is no division into stem and leaf, the plant body consisting of a branched, green ribbon. Such a structure is called a *thallus*. In some of the liverworts the thallus may be extremely complex. In *Marchantia*, a common genus, the surface of the thallus is marked out into minute, diamond-shaped areas.

## Mechanism of food production

If a section of the thallus is examined under a microscope, each of these areas can be seen to mark the boundary of a chamber inside the thallus, filled with slender filaments of cells, rising from the floor of the chamber and containing many chloroplasts. It is these filaments that carry out most of the work of photosynthesis, manufacturing food for the thallus. Air can enter the chamber by a small pore in the roof, which is just visible to the naked eye.

Not all liverworts show this extreme complication of the thallus. In *Pellia*, another common liverwort, the thallus consists of a solid mass of cells, without internal differentiation.

Some liverwort thalli are provided with means for vegetative reproduction. *Marchantia* has small, cup-like organs called *gemma cups* on the surface of its thallus. The cups contain minute bodies called *gemmae* which, when they become detached from the cup, can grow into new thalli. In *Lunularia*, a relative of *Marchantia* that is common in greenhouses, the gemma cups are shaped like half-moons – hence its name.

1 The liverwort *Marchantia polymorpha* often occurs as a weed in greenhouses. It is easily identified by the prominent round gemma cups occurring on the branched thallus.

2 The female receptacles of *Marchantia* have nine rays, each of which contains spores and elaters. They are easily distinguished from the disc-shaped male receptacles.

The life history of a thallose liverwort follows closely that of a moss. The sex organs (antheridia and archegonia) are usually formed on the surface of the thallus, but in *Marchantia* and a few other genera they are formed on antheridiophores and archegoniophores that rise up on stalks above the general level of the thallus.

Fertilization of the egg cell is followed by the formation of a capsule, as in mosses. The capsule of a liverwort, however, is simpler in structure than that of a moss. It contains no chlorophyll, so that it is completely parasitic on the parent thallus. The capsule, in liverworts, opens by means of four longitudinal slits; there is no peristome apparatus to limit the dissemination of the spores. Liverworts do, however, often have curious empty cells, called *elaters*, mixed with their spores. The elaters have spiral bands of thickening material on their walls, and, as they dry up, they perform twisting movements which help to free the spores from the remains of the capsule.

The leafy liverworts superficially resemble mosses, but they can be distinguished from them on careful examination, though, in a few cases, a microscope may be needed. In liverworts the leaves are arranged in two rows down the sides of the stem, with a third row of smaller leaves on the lower side of the stem. Mosses nearly always have their leaves spirally arranged, and the few species that have two rows of leaves may be distinguished by the presence of the thickened nerve or midrib running down the centre of the leaf.

The bright orange or red flower-like male 'inflorescence' is a conspicuous feature of *Polytrichum juniperium*, a moss which thrives on fairly dry heaths.

## Spotting the difference

The leaves of leafy liverworts are often lobed or segmented, but those of mosses never are. The leafy liverworts are usually – but not always – smaller plants than mosses.

Bryophytes are indeed plants dependent on water, even if some of them can grow in dry situations. They have the marked alternation of generations that is characteristic of nearly all plants, but they are peculiar in that the spore-bearing generation, or sporophyte, is partially (in mosses) or completely (in liverworts) parasitic on the parent gametophyte. The bryophytes form a distinct group of the plant kingdom, easily distinguished from all others. Unfortunately, fossil bryophytes are almost completely lacking. We cannot tell whence they came, or what their relationship is with other plants.

# The evolution story 1

**Did all living organisms develop from common ancestors? The case is still not proved, but Darwin showed how they could have done, and presented a mass of evidence in support of the theory.**

FOR HUNDREDS OF YEARS thinking men have been asking the question, 'How did life as we see it today, in all its diversity and complexity, come to be present on Earth?' There have been many attempts to answer this question, perhaps the earliest being the Theory of Special Creation.

The Theory of Special Creation is fundamental to many religions because it says that at some time in the past some 'outside force' (God) created all forms of life, and since the 'time of creation', there have been no changes in the species.

Another theory, that of Spontaneous Generation, suggests that some forms of life suddenly appeared from non-living things, and are still doing so now. This theory was proposed to account for various observations, such as the appearance of maggots in cooked meat left on a plate, or even mice in a closed barn. The work of Louis Pasteur (1822–95) with micro-organisms led many men to believe that organisms do not arise except as offspring of pre-existing organisms. Maggots were found to be the offspring of flies. Mice and other rodents, of course, have a host of ways to appear where they are not wanted.

## The Theory of Evolution

As a result, the theory of Spontaneous Generation was largely abandoned, but not completely. It survives, greatly modified, in the widely held Theory of Evolution, which states that non-living things (chemical compounds) gave rise to living things (simple one-celled organisms). However, the theory further suggests that spontaneous generation occurred only once. Then these single-celled organisms gave rise to the many-celled organisms up to and including Man.

Evolutionary views had in fact been held by a number of people long before that time, even before rival theories were discredited, but they did not gain general acceptance because there was no satisfactory explanation of how the changes necessary to create one species from another could have occurred. This lack was filled by the British naturalist Charles Darwin (1809–82) when he put forward his views, together with those of another great nineteenth-century naturalist Alfred Russell Wallace (1823–1913), in the book *Origin of Species*. This book contained Darwin's *Theory of Natural Selection*. Darwin became greatly interested in Nature while a student at Cambridge University, and so when H.M.S. *Beagle* left Devonport in December 1831, the young unpaid naturalist was aboard. During his voyage on the *Beagle* between 1831 and 1836, he had noticed how the geographical distribution and variation of species could be explained by assuming that related species have evolved from a common stock. In 1854, he wrote of the finches on the Galapagos Islands (in the Pacific), 'seeing this gradation and diversity of structure in one small, intimately related group of birds, one might really fancy that . . . one species had been taken and modified for different ends'.

Darwin was also greatly influenced by the social and economic conditions of his times, and by the writing of Malthus, who in 1802 wrote an *Essay on Population*. Referring to human populations, Malthus stated that the population is capable of increasing indefinitely in geometric progression, and must therefore be held stable by limiting the amounts of food available. For this last part, that food supply could limit the population, there is no proof, and herein lies one of the greatest problems confronting the human race – how to provide enough food for an exploding population.

Darwin also noticed that many animals and plants produced more offspring than ever survived, and that there must be some factor, such as shortage of food, which kept the populations at a stable level. There was, therefore, a 'struggle

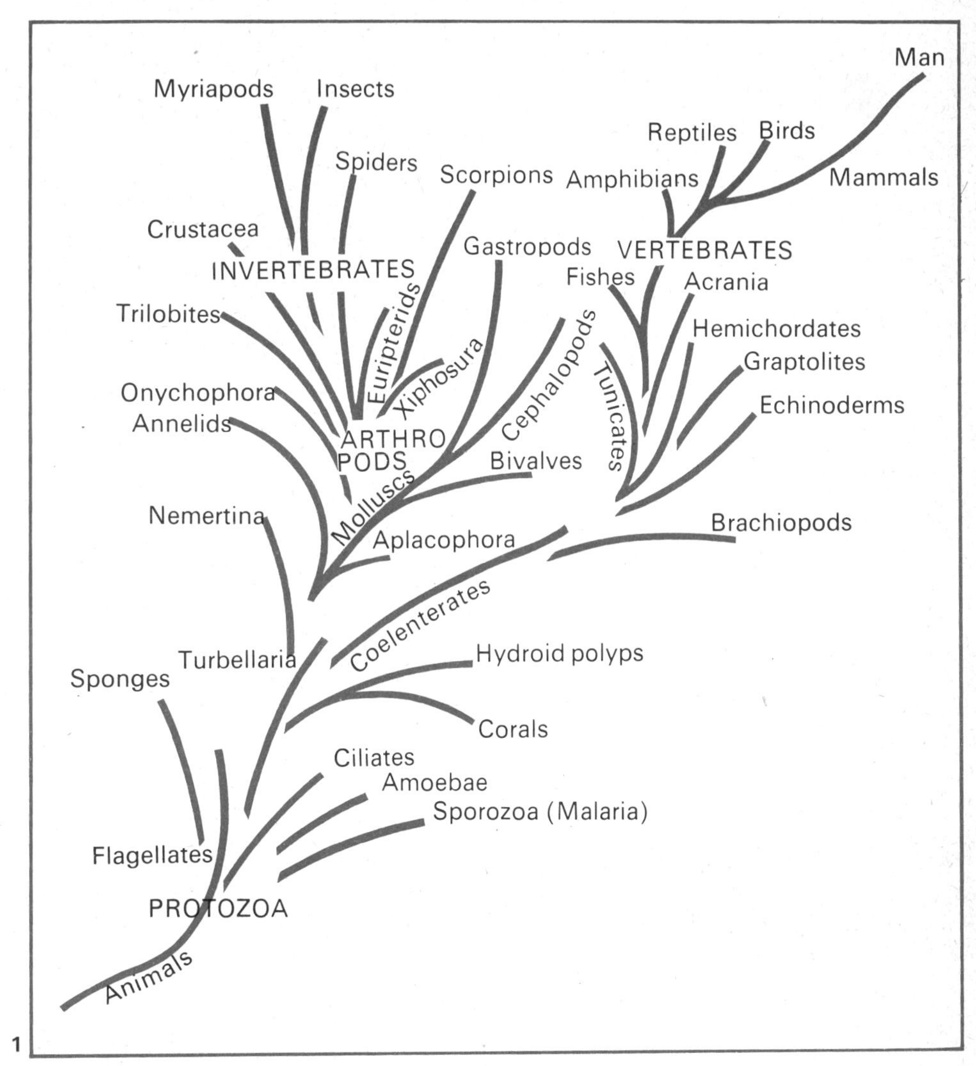

1 Relationships between the organisms occurring in the animal kingdom are clearly shown in this diagram. The development of any species can be traced back through its intermediate stages.
2 Much of the evidence for evolution comes from fossil remains. In the case of soft-bodied animals or plants such as this fern, the organism rots away leaving behind an imprint in the rock.

for existence' in the natural environment. He also observed that any variation which better suited the individual to its particular habitat would have two effects: to give the individual a better chance of survival, and, if offspring could inherit this characteristic, they, too, would have a better chance of survival.

In 1859, Darwin's *Origin of Species* was published, which provided a coherent theory for the evolution of life. It included three major points. Firstly, there exists in Nature a struggle for existence, such that not all the progeny of a species will survive. Secondly, the individuals within a population differ from each other in small details (the concept of continuous variation) so that those animals and plants best adapted to survive have an advantage. This corresponds to 'the survival of the fittest'. Finally, an individual which has the advantageous characteristics is more able to live and reproduce, and so the characteristics will be passed on to the offspring by the phenomenon of heredity.

There were a number of weaknesses in Darwin's theory, due mainly to the ignorance during his times of the concepts of mutation and genetic (sex cell) inheritance. The theory lacked a convincing account of the origins of variations and inheritance. In fact, Darwin accepted two ideas that today are not acceptable, that inheritance took place via the blood (and so characters were a kind of alloy of all previous ancestry), and that the variations induced in an organism by the environment could be passed on to the next generation. This latter idea was due to the French naturalist Jean-Baptiste Lamarck (1744–1829) who tried to suggest a way in which an animal can change according to its needs (the Law of Use and Disuse and the Transmission of Acquired Character). This idea can best be explained by the well-known example of the giraffe. Lamarck believed that because the animal was constantly stretching its neck to reach food high in the trees, its neck had become increased in length, and the increase could be passed on to the next generation. In the same way, the fact that some birds found it unnecessary to use their wings led by the Law of Disuse to the evolution of the 'flightless birds' (ostriches, emus, rheas, and so on). However, although later work on genetics showed that such characters could not be produced in this way, Lamarck had grasped the importance of the environment in producing changes, which was so strongly stressed by Darwin.

The Dutch biologist Hugo de Vries

1

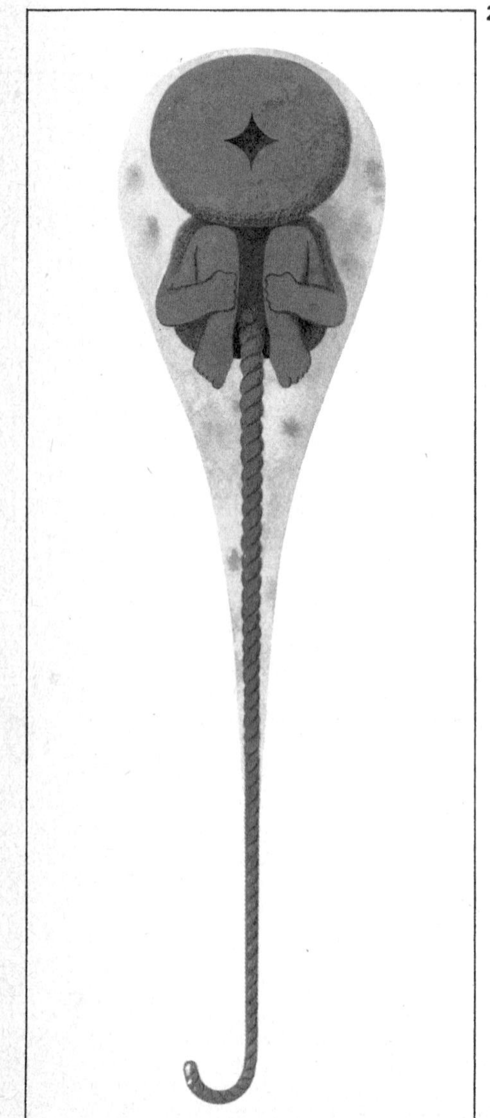

2

3

4

**1** Michelangelo's painting shows the Biblical version of the creation of Man.
**2** Early drawings showed 'little men' in human sperm cells, an idea in flat contradiction to evolutionary theories.
**3** Even after the publication of Darwin's work, many people still preferred the traditional view, as shown by this *Punch* cartoon of 1882.
**4** Fossils such as this ammonite shell provided evidence of links in the evolutionary chain.

Certhidea olivacea
ALBEMARLE ISLAND

Geospiza fuliginosa
BARRINGTON ISLAND

Catamblyrhynchus diadema
EAST ECUADOR (Mainland)

Geospiza magnirostris
CHATHAM ISLAND

Geospiza fortis
INDEFATIGABLE ISLAND

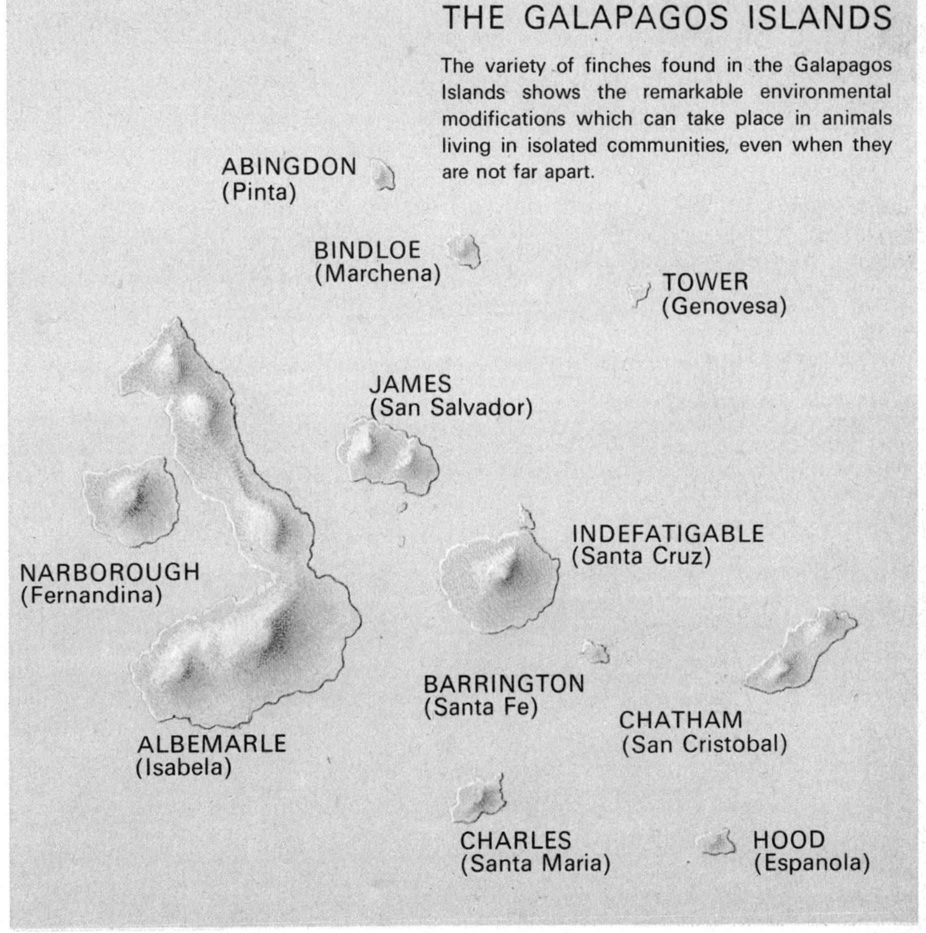


## THE GALAPAGOS ISLANDS

The variety of finches found in the Galapagos Islands shows the remarkable environmental modifications which can take place in animals living in isolated communities, even when they are not far apart.

(1848–1935) showed that chance occurrences (induced by radiation or other means) can produce marked changes in the genetic make-up of an individual, and that these changes are inheritable. So if an individual is born with exceptionally good eyesight because of a genetic mutation, his children will probably have exceptionally good eyesight, because this characteristic is carried by the sex cells from one generation to the next. (Genes are chemical units strung together on chromosomes, which determine the characteristics of an individual when born.)

Darwin's theory of natural selection (survival of the fittest) could account for small changes within a species, but mutations were needed to explain how the large changes leading to the establishment of new groups of animals could occur. So in the 1930s, the modern theory of evolution (often called the Synthetic Theory) was proposed. This theory is based upon the theory of natural selection, but includes the concepts of mutation and genetic inheritance.

Fundamentally, this theory suggests that when a spontaneous gene mutation is such that it provides the offspring of the animal with a characteristic favourable for survival, i.e. makes them better equipped to compete for the available food or to withstand the stresses of a changing climate, the animals carrying this gene will become more and more numerous. Thus, the new gene will become 'established' and the species will acquire a new characteristic.

Having considered the theory of evolution, we must now deal in more detail with how new species are created. Although Darwin did not believe in the existence of the species as a separate entity (in his own words, 'I look at the term *species* as one arbitrarily given for the sake of convenience to a set of individuals closely resembling each other'), it is generally accepted today that a species is in fact a unit. Ignoring one or two exceptions, we may say that a species is considered as a group of individuals which are able to breed amongst themselves, but not with individuals of another group (for example, a bear does not mate with a monkey). Therefore, a species forms a reproductively isolated group.

Over very long periods of time, species can begin to change into new forms when two or more groups of one species are separated in such a way that they are unable to interbreed. This allows them to change (i.e. to evolve) in isolation from each other until a stage is reached where they cannot, even if they are brought together, mate and produce viable

1 Comparison of this Galapagos turtle with other members of the species on other islands led Darwin to conclude that geographical location could produce adaptive changes in organisms.

2 H.M.S. *Beagle* was the ship in which Darwin sailed round the world. Data collected on this trip provided evidence for the theories of evolutionary development and adaptive changes in organisms.

offspring (hybrids capable of living and reproducing). By this time, the differences may be obvious, for example as they now are between a lion (*Felis leo*) and a tiger (*Felis tigris*), but this is not always the case. The differences between the various species of the fruit fly (*Drosophila*), for instance, are often so minute that they are virtually indistinguishable except to an expert.

The most important way in which populations may become isolated is by being separated by geographical features, such as an expanse of ocean, a large river, or a mountain range. A classical example of the effects of geographical isolation is to be seen on the Galapagos Islands, where each island tends to have its own particular species of giant tortoise. These species have resulted from the tortoises being unable to cross the stretches of sea between the individual islands.

Once isolated, two such populations will be acted upon in a number of ways which will result in their having different genetic make-ups (*genotypes*), such as natural selection and gene mutation. When the genotype of local populations are such that they cannot interbreed with those of other local populations, they are then usually considered as separate species.

## Preserved in rock

The evidence that such changes are occurring or have occurred in the past comes from a number of sources, including classification, effects of physical influences, the natural appearance of new species and races, comparative morphology and anatomy, embryology, geographical distribution, comparative physiology, genetics and palaeontology. Man-made variations through artificial selection (animal and plant breeding) show that these changes can be made to occur, but do not necessarily prove that such changes have occurred in nature.

Even the study of fossils (*palaeontology*) does not prove evolution, but it certainly provides strong evidence that evolution has occurred in the past, and enables scientists to build up a picture of the past history of animal and plant groups. A fossil is the remains of an organism, or direct evidence of its previous existence, preserved within rocks. There are three main types of fossils. There are the *trace fossils,* for example worm-holes or footprints, which obviously do not involve the death of the organism. Then there are the two types of *body fossils*: one which is a whole organism or part of it (such as the skeletal remains of an extinct dinosaur); the other, which like trace fossils does not involve the death of the organism, occurs when for instance an insect moults and leaves its cast skin for preservation.

Fossils are produced only when remains are situated in such a position that they quickly become covered with sediment. This can occur when an animal or plant drops into a peat bog and quickly sinks down beneath the surface, or when a landslip, or volcanic ash and lava cover it up. However, such instances are comparatively rare, and by far the most common place for fossils to be formed is in the sea or in large lakes where sediment is constantly being deposited at the bottom. Apart from being quickly covered, in the case of body fossils, there must also be present some hard skeletal parts (such as bones or shells) as the soft parts soon decay and are lost. For this reason, 'soft' organisms such as jelly-fish are seldom found as fossils.

Once the remains have been covered by sediments, they are acted upon in a number of ways before we come to dig them out of the rocks. Only rarely is an organism found unaltered, as for example in the rare finds of whole mammoths, extinct relatives of elephants, preserved intact in frozen mud and ice in Siberia (their meat was still edible), or insects encased in fossilized resin (called amber) found on the shores of the Baltic Sea. Usually the remains are altered, the hard parts being converted to rock such as calcite or silica, or they may be leached (dissolved) away, leaving a space which is filled with minerals resulting in the formation of an internal mould or replica.

## The fossil record

Although there are gaps in the fossil record enough fossils exist to suggest strongly that most groups of animals and plants have undergone a gradual series of modifications from prehistoric times to the present. For example, by examining the fossil ancestors of the horse, a number of trends can be identified, culminating in the modern horse (*Equus*). Modern horses are considerably larger than their Eocene ancestor, *Hyracotherium,* and their legs are longer and thinner with reduced skeletal elements (early horses having feet somewhat similar to those of a dog).

Evolution is not complete; it continues at the present time. If climatic conditions on the Earth undergo dramatic changes during the next million years (as they have in the previous million years), then new species will evolve from those existing today. Man may still be master of all he surveys, but he will be a creature very different from the one which bears that name today.

3 Charles Darwin (1809–82), the British naturalist, whose Theory of Natural Selection suggested how changes could have taken place in an organism to give entirely new species.

4 Jean-Baptiste Lamarck (1744–1829) was the first biologist to grasp the importance of environment in producing adaptations, a point which was strongly emphasized by Darwin.

# The evolution story 2

**Darwin expounded the what and why of evolution. Modern biological research goes a long way towards explaining the how – the mechanism of evolutionary change which may lead to new species.**

EVOLUTION IS such an extremely slow process that it is almost impossible to observe significant changes in the structure of a creature over a short period of time. For this reason many people find evolution is a rather difficult idea to understand. When zoologists first began to study the great variety of animal life on Earth, they began noticing marked similarities among various species. For instance, the group of animals called the *Amphibians* – comprising frogs, toads, newts, and the like – all have moist skins for 'breathing', all have rudimentary lungs, all have similar skull structures, and so on.

Classifying the animals by their physical characteristics gives support to the theory of evolution, because there seems to be a logical progression of structures from simple to more complex. It is by examining the physical structure of an animal that its place on the evolutionary ladder may be found.

It is possible to study the physical features of extinct species, which may have vanished from the Earth millions of years ago, by their fossil remains. The vertebrates (animals with backbones) are easier to study than invertebrates (animals without backbones) because the vertebrates' bony structures have provided a good collection of fossils, whereas the invertebrates' soft structures are nearly always lost without a trace in fossilization.

## Fish out of water

Fossil remains show that *Crossopterygian* fishes, believed to be the evolutionary ancestors of modern amphibians, had what are called lobed fins. Part of the body extended into the fin, giving it extra support. The fleshy lobe was supported by bony structures. Similar bones are also present in the limbs of amphibians, although they may be enlarged and differ a little in shape. It is therefore reasonable to assume that when these fish were stranded by drought on the beds of the lakes and streams in which they used to live, they used their fins to move from one pool to another. Thousands of years later, perhaps owing to climatic change or a mutation enabling a few individuals to possess better developed 'limbs', the fish evolved into walking amphibians able to lead both an aquatic and a terrestrial life.

Throughout the vertebrates, it can be seen that many of the bone formations are similar. It is easy to find bones present in an amphibian's fore-limb also present in, say, a reptile's or a mammal's. The difference may be only in size, or the structure may be slightly modified to fit the new function. The best example of this can be seen in the pelvic girdle

1

2

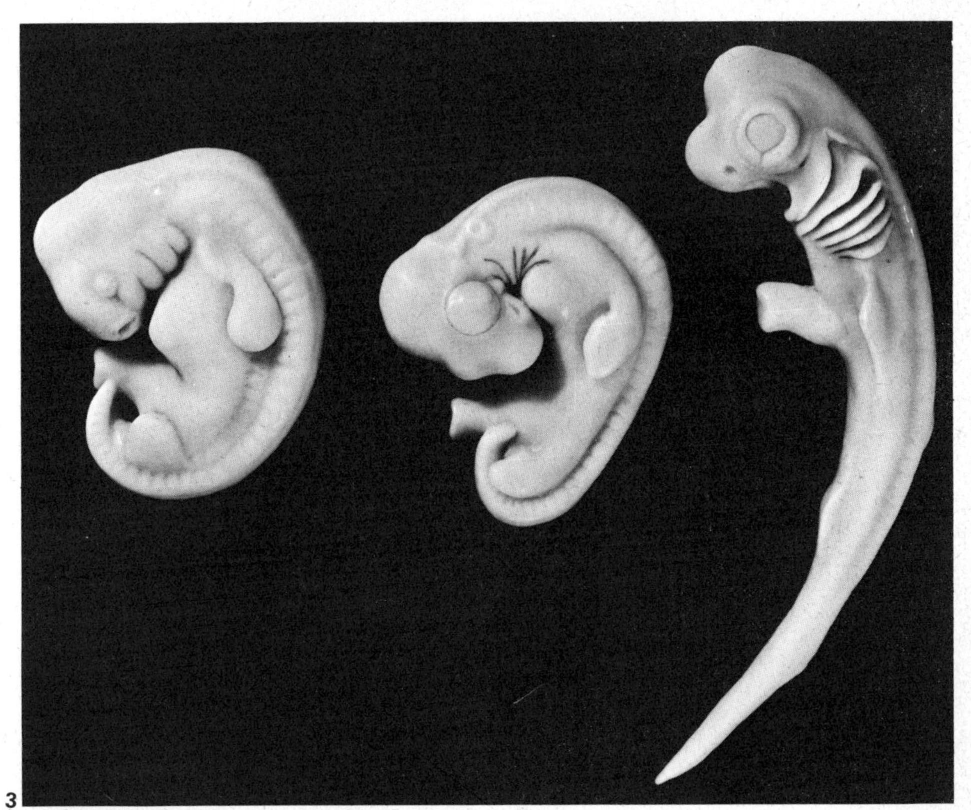

3

**1** Fossil remains of a coelacanth. Until about 20 years ago, this unusual fish was thought to be extinct.
**2** Discovery of this modern coelacanth enabled biologists to establish that it has not changed from its fossilized predecessor.
**3** Embryos of a man, a chicken and a dogfish, showing the remarkable similarity between them. The gills of the dogfish and its elongated tail distinguish it as a marine creature.

**1** Drawing of Rhodesian Man (*Homo rhodesiensis*) showing the probable appearance of this early cave-dweller.
**2** Cranial remains on which drawing of Rhodesian Man was based. Note the low receding forehead.
**3** Skull of *Zinjanthropus biosei,* with reconstructed jaw. The ridge of bone on the crown of the head provided additional area for the *temporalis* muscle.
**4** Resemblances between anthropoid apes and Man lend credence to the evolutionists' arguments.
**5** Woodpeckers have adapted to their environment in a number of ways. Their beaks are hard and bony, a rigid tail gives support, and grubs are taken from the tree by the long tongue.

bone (corresponding to the hip bones in Man) during the change from the aquatic life of fish to that of land amphibians – and sometimes back to the watery life again.

A fish has a very small and rudimentary pelvic girdle which is not attached to the vertebral column. Locomotion is achieved using muscles running along the trunk and tail. The pelvic (hind) and pectoral (fore) fins are not used for locomotion at all but for maintaining or altering the fish's position in the water. However, when fish had moved on to land, locomotion by means of the tail was exceedingly clumsy and energy consuming, requiring extra food. As a result, the fins became enlarged into limbs to 'lift' the body from the ground. Simultaneously the limb girdles grew in order to support the extra weight and fused to the backbone to distribute it throughout the body. (In the water, the fish did not have to worry about this problem because most of their weight was carried by the surrounding water.) Of course, all these evolutionary changes required thousands of years to take place.

Reptiles evolved from amphibians and eventually superseded them as the 'ruling' animals. Some remained on the land and evolved more powerful limbs. With the reptiles also came the first two-legged creatures, so that the pelvic girdle had accordingly to be further modified. Some reptiles returned to the water and as a result underwent a reduction of their supporting skeleton. The girdles slowly dwindled to rudiments and dissociated themselves once more from the vertebral column.

The extinct *Plesiosaurs* were such reptiles which returned to the water. The neck was elongated and the limbs became flippers for paddling. The girdles were still attached to the vertebral column. The *Ichthyosaurs* were also secondary aquatic forms. They became streamlined and fish-like, even reverting to the old method of locomotion, that is by using the entire posterior trunk region as a paddle.

## All shapes of limbs

Other members of the reptiles took to the air – a feat demanding different modifications altogether. In this case the backbone was made rigid by fusion of the vertebrae, and the pelvic girdle was enlarged so that it could support the animal in the standing position. The girdle was fused to the backbone as in the terrestrial forms. These flying reptiles were called *pterodactyls*.

Among the modern mammals as a group there are also good examples of *homologous* organs, which are basically the same organ but have been modified during evolution in different ways to suit their different functions. One of the most noticeable examples, perhaps, is the difference between a man's arm, a bat's wing and a whale's flipper. A man's forearm is adapted for doing a variety of jobs. The upper arm consists of one bone, the *humerus*. The lower arm has two, the *radius* and *ulna*. The wrist is made up of nine *carpals* and the hand of three *metacarpals,* the digits being made up of 14 *phalanges*. This arrangement is modified in the bat where the radius and ulna are partly fused to increase the strength (although decreasing adaptability). The wrist bones are reduced and the metacarpals and phalanges are elongated to support the wing-tip surface.

The whale, also a mammal, has become adapted for life in the ocean once more. The fore-limbs are now modified as rudders for 'steering' the animal. The power for movement comes from the trunk on which a large tail-fin has developed. This beats up and down, propelling the animal forward. The fore-limb is much reduced in the region nearest to the body. The humerus, radius and ulna are short, the carpals are small and insignificant and embedded in cartilage. It is only digits two and three which are elongated, with an increased number of phalanges.

The whale also shows how, as a result of evolution, some organs can become *vestigial* (no longer have a useful task to perform, and so become reduced in size and efficiency). It is believed that the whale evolved from a creature which was once terrestrial and had two pairs of limbs. Since it has returned to the sea and swims instead of walking, the hind limbs have become very reduced and are not visible from the outside. In fact, all that remains are the vestiges of the pelvic girdle, femur and tibia – not attached to the backbone but 'floating' inside the body wall.

It is believed that flightless birds, such as the kiwi, emu, rhea and ostrich once possessed the power of flight. They are descended from other birds, but since they lived originally in parts of the world where it was not necessary to escape from predators, the wings slowly degenerated over hundreds of generations into small vestigial stubs not capable of flight. Instead, the hind limbs have become enlarged and strengthened to support their large body weights. These birds are also specially adapted in several ways to compensate for their inability to fly. Thus, for example, they are all very swift runners, enabling them to travel almost as quickly as birds equipped to fly.

Man also has vestigial organs. The muscles of the ear are a good example. Whereas dogs, cats and most other mammals can turn their external ears towards the source of sound, most humans cannot, probably because Man is two-legged and walks upright. This fact enables him to move only his head to face towards a sound, instead of his whole body as he would have to do if he walked on all fours.

## Convergent evolutions

In the early days of zoology, it was sometimes wrongly supposed that two animals were somewhat related because they lived in the same habitat or looked very similar. For example, in the sea, all the vertebrates are equipped with a similar method of locomotion. They all have a powerful tail for propulsion and have fins or flippers. The body shape is streamlined so that it passes through the water easily. It might be tempting to say that if two animals possess all these characteristics, they have evolved along the same path and are consequently closely related to each other. It is here that anatomical examination of the organisms is necessary to determine whether or not the two types with common features are closely related.

For instance, the porpoise and the shark are both marine, streamlined and eat fish; perhaps they are related? Closer examination shows that they are not, for several reasons, the most important being that the shark is covered in scales whereas the porpoise is not; and the shark breathes by means of gills whereas the porpoise must surface to use its lungs. The two animals have in fact undergone *convergent evolutions* (evolved side by side, influenced by the same environmental factors). In other words, both animals have evolved a basically similar design to cope with similar environments. At the same time, one remains a mammal and the other a fish.

Towards the end of the nineteenth century, scientists began to study the development of animals from the egg. This new science, called *embryology,* contributed to our knowledge of evolution. The problem at this time was to find out how the many-celled (*metazoan*) animals have evolved from the primitive one-celled (*protozoan*) animals. This investigation of the developing embryos has yielded many clues to the way in which organisms evolve.

From a study of the larval forms of invertebrate animals, it was revealed that many are alike in many ways. This could be due either to convergent evolution or to a common origin (that is, the groups concerned may have evolved from a common ancestor). In 1870, the German biologist Ernst Haeckel (1834–1919) established his *Law of Recapitulation,* based on the evolution of the metazoans but applicable to all other groups.

Haeckel thought that the original 'stem' metazoan was a *Blastaea,* a hollow ball of flagellated cells (cells with hair-like tails) which could easily have been formed from protozoans aggregating and forming a colony. He suggested that it moved through the water in one direction, and so caused a vortex at the back where food particles would collect. As a result, the colony got food more easily than could an individual. He said that the cells in the rear region would become adapted to absorb these food particles and would eventually

Darwin's experience in the breeding of domestic pigeons led him to the conclusion that there is much more variation in domesticated plants or animals than there is with organisms in the wild state. He found that he could breed desirable characteristics into his birds by careful selection. The varieties of pigeon in the illustration show how different in appearance these birds can be. However, there is still a basic similarity, showing their common ancestry.

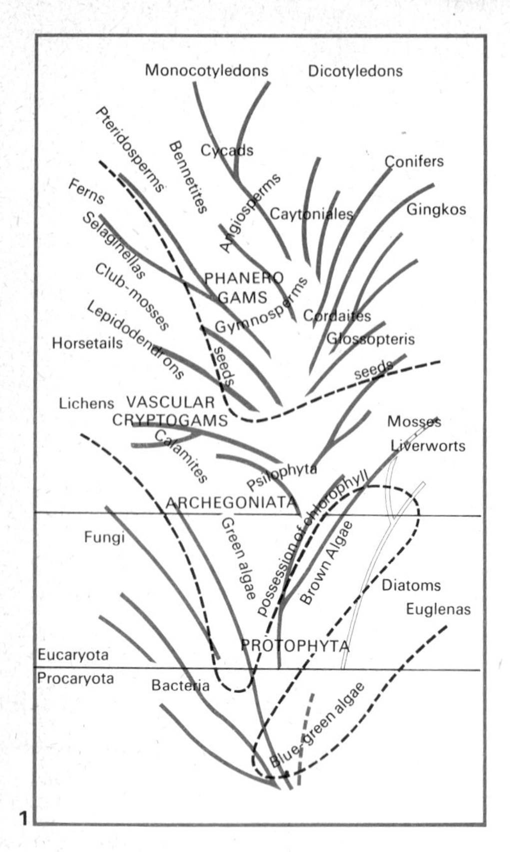


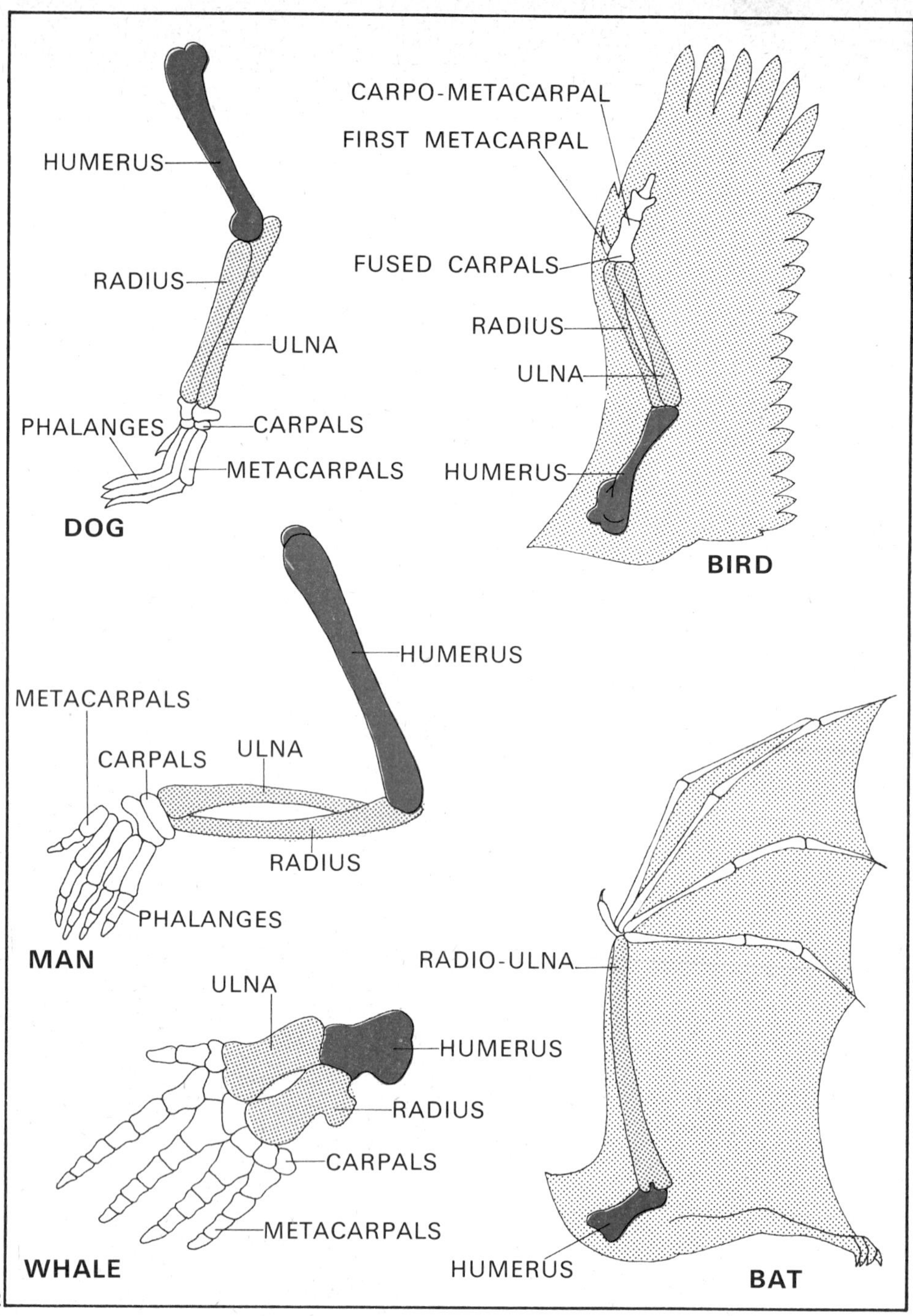


**1** An attempt to show the main lines of evolution. The original organisms gave rise to bacteria, blue-green algae and plants. Further development eventually gave rise to seed-plants. As indicated in the diagram, the origin of fungi is obscure. **2** Modifications of the skeletal structure of the limb are clearly demonstrated in this picture. Structures are modified to suit the needs of the animals' environments, although the individual bones retain some common characteristics.

form an inward-facing cavity with a primitive mouth and gut. This stage was called a *Gastrea*.

## Evolution in miniature

Haeckel's hypothesis was largely accepted. His Law of Recapitulation stated in effect that the stages in the development of an individual (called *ontogeny*) are a short recapitulation or summary of the stages in the history of the development of the whole group of animals to which it belonged (called *phylogeny*). This hypothesis means that some stage in the development of an advanced animal would closely resemble a more primitive animal, and that phylogeny is the cause of ontogeny. For instance, supporters of the theory would see a close resemblance between the early foetal stages of a human baby and the adult forms of some amphibians.

Then in 1922, the modern theory of evolution was put forward. Haeckel's original law was re-stated and it is now thought that the evolutionary history (phylogeny) of adults is the product of a succession of complete developments (ontogenies) – ontogeny does not recapitulate phylogeny but *causes* it. In other words, each life history of an individual producing offspring will slowly change the structure of the animal, so causing evolution.

For a long time after the theory of evolution was first formulated, there remained the grave problem of explaining how variations occur in the first place. Darwin proposed his theory of natural selection without any knowledge of genes, genetic mutation and heredity. The laws of heredity had, in fact, been worked out by an Austrian monk, Gregor Johann Mendel (1822–84), whose work went unrecognized until long after his death. Then, in 1900, Hugo de Vries and two other scientists unearthed Mendel's original papers.

But de Vries made one big mistake when he formulated the laws of heredity. He stated that mutation (a change in a gene, the fundamental unit of heredity) was the main cause of evolution. In fact natural selection – the moulding of an animal by its environment – is the *force* for change, and mutation provides the *opportunity*. Mutation and natural selection work in conjunction. Mutant genes create the possibility of a new species arising; natural selection can make this possibility a reality.

As its name suggests, natural selection takes place without any interference from an outside agency, such as Man. But good confirmatory evidence for the correctness of the theory of evolution comes from *artificial selection*. For instance, numerous varieties of pigeons have been created by controlled breeding. 'Man-made evolution' has also given rise to 110 separate recognized breeds of dogs (all belonging to the same species), as well as dozens of breeds of cats, cattle, horses, sheep and chickens. The fact that Man has caused evolution does not *prove* the theory of evolution. But until evidence to the contrary turns up, most scientists will continue to accept that over millions of years, what Man has done by intent, Nature has done by natural selection to give rise to the thousands upon thousands of life forms existing in the world today. Future forms of life in the ages to come will inevitably be moulded by these same forces.

# Forming the new generations

**The ultimate goal of living things is to produce more living things in their own image, but evolution demands continual variations. The processes of reproduction accommodate both needs.**

ONE OF THE CHARACTERISTICS of living things separating them from non-living things is that they reproduce themselves. The legacy of the old to the new is the genetic information or 'blueprint' which will enable the new organisms to develop and function in much the same way as the organism which gave rise to them. Since this 'blueprint' is contained in the genes inside a cell's nucleus, most of the essential mechanisms of reproduction are concerned with securing the passage of this information from the parent to the progeny.

The simplest way of reproducing is to split in two by a process called *replication*, producing an exact copy of the parents. As this involves duplicating everything so that one of everything passes to the new individual, it includes the formation of a duplicate set of genetic information. Bacteria can divide once every 30 or so minutes; as replication continues at this rate, the population arising from one bacterium may reach many millions in a day. Amoeba, too, is an organism which reproduces by splitting.

## Pairing for procreation

The nucleus divides first by *mitosis*, the process by which the *chromosomes* (strings of genes) are replicated so that the second nucleus contains exactly the same number. Each new chromosome under normal conditions, is an exact replica of the original. When a cell in an animal or plant's body divides to form new tissues – when a wound is being healed, for example – they divide in this way.

The single-cell individual can reproduce in this way without the need of a second member of its species. In much the same way, spores of fungi or ferns can grow into a new individual without further change. So the process of budding off a new individual, whether it is from some part of a plant or from the base of a sea-anemone, is similar in nature. No other plant or anemone is necessary. Reproduction of this sort is called *asexual* because only one organism is involved.

Reproduction in most plants and animals, however, involves two individuals each contributing a set of chromosomes to the offspring. The ciliate protozoan, *Paramecium*, for example, undergoes exchange of genetic material. These ciliates each have two nuclei, a macronucleus (controlling the feeding activities and so forth) and a micronucleus (smaller and concerned with reproduction). Two individuals swim alongside each other to come to lie with the sides on which their mouths are together. The macronuclei in both disintegrate; the micronuclei divide (mitotically) until there are four of them, three of which also disintegrate. The remaining one then divides to form two; one nucleus of each pair passes over into the body of

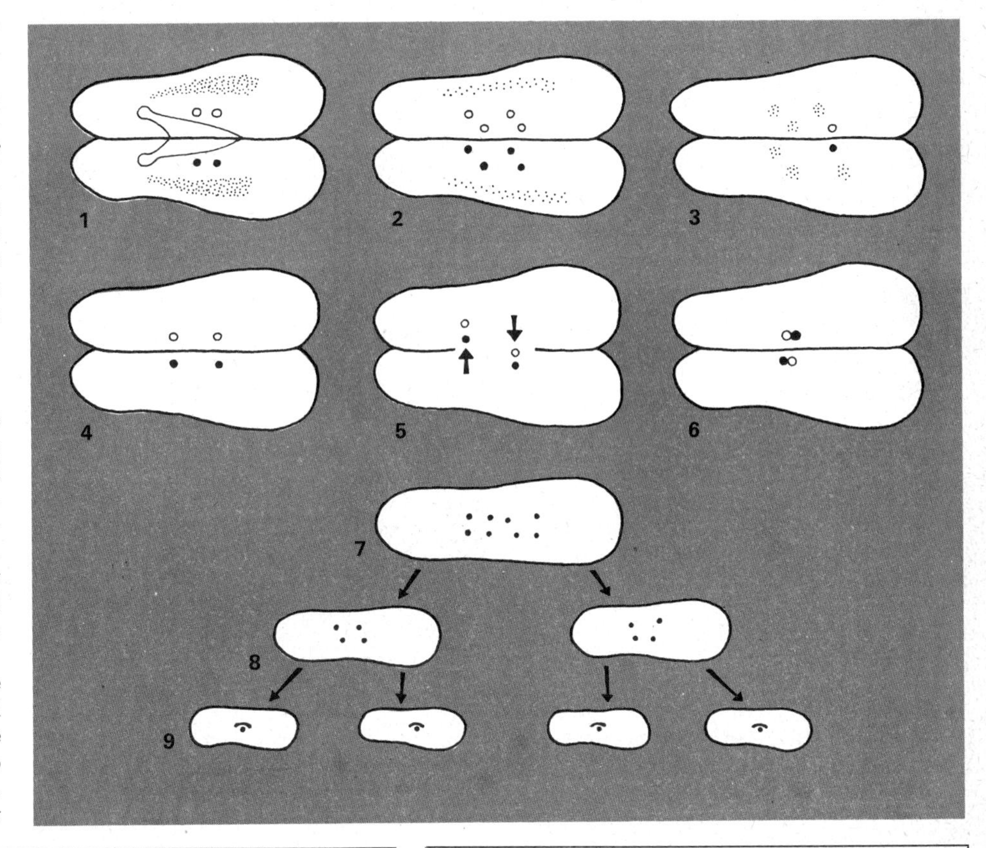


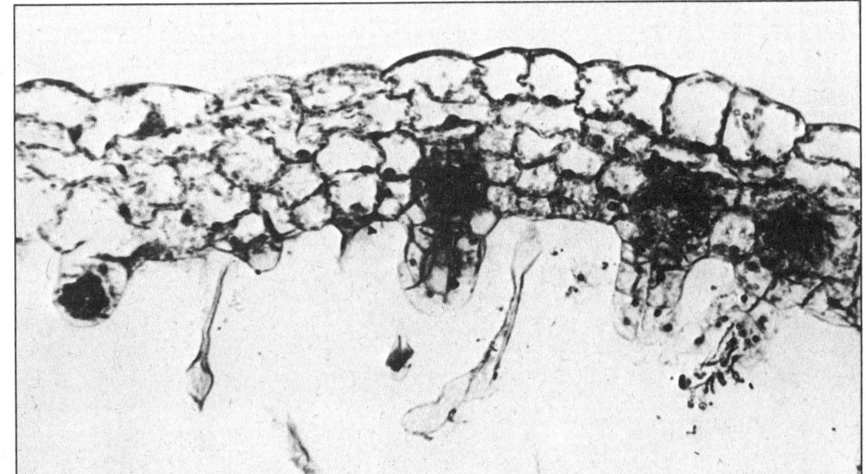

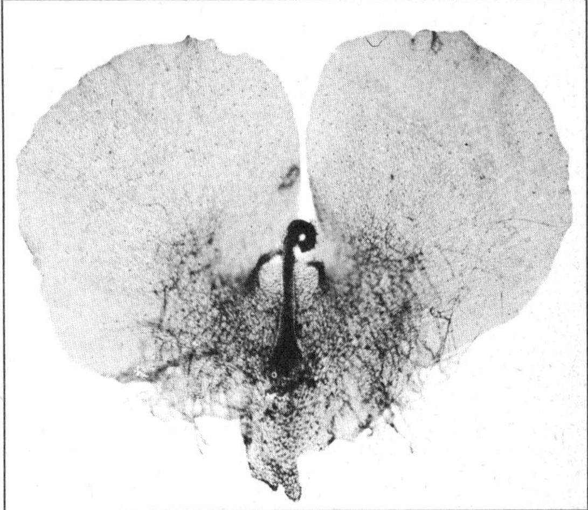

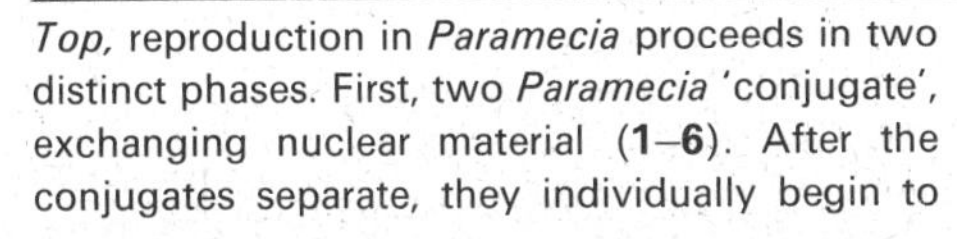
*Top,* reproduction in *Paramecia* proceeds in two distinct phases. First, two *Paramecia* 'conjugate', exchanging nuclear material (**1–6**). After the conjugates separate, they individually begin to divide. In this way, each conjugate is capable of producing four daughter cells which swim away as new individuals. *Above left,* a section through a fern prothallus shows a (male) antheridium and three (female) archegonia. In reproduction, sperms swim through a water film on the prothallus to reach an archegonia. *Above right,* a complete fern prothallus with embryo.

the other partner, and fuses with the nucleus which has been formed in it in the same way.

The conjugants then part and swim off. Thus there has been an exchange in nuclear material but no actual reproduction, for no new individuals have been formed. This comes later when each conjugant divides to form four new protozoa in each of which a macronucleus is reformed to give the normal complement of nuclei. This example underlines the fact that the exchange of nuclear material is not all there is to reproduction, for new individuals must also be produced.

There are no obvious differences between the two partners in *Paramecium*; each one receives the same from the other. Yet there must be some difference between the partners, probably ones of a biochemical nature, for a *Paramecium* will not mate with just any other *Paramecium*, its partner must be of a different 'mating type'. *Paramecium aurelia*, for example, has at least 16 varieties, each with two mating types. Effectively this means that the *Paramecium aurelia* has 32 different sexes'.

## Settling for two sexes

'Sexual' differences are also found in *Spirogyra*. Strains of this green filamentous alga are simply labelled + and −. Only if a + strain filament comes close to a − strain filament will the gamete formed in the cell of one filament emerge along a conjugation tube to fuse with a gamete from a cell in the other. The result is a hard-covered zygote from which a new filament will grow.

The more familiar gametes, such as those in Man, are unequal in size and plainly different. Often the male sperm can propel itself by a long whiplike tail. The head of the sperm contains little else than the nucleus. But the female egg is a larger cell, with its cytoplasm packed with reserve food. It usually moves very little, and has to be located by the active sperm for fertilization to take place. It seems as if early in evolution all manner of different combinations of 'sexes' were tried, but finally this arrangement of having only two sexes, male and female, proved the best, and so is the rule in higher species.

Among some invertebrates which live in the sea, it is common for both eggs and sperms to be set free into the water. In the clouds of gametes liberated by numbers of sea urchins, for example, fertilization of the eggs will take place by sperms from another individual. Although chemical signals ensure that numbers of the urchins release their gametes together, many gametes are wasted. In other organisms some of this wastage is reduced, because eggs are retained on their parent. Then the sperms must be able to locate the egg and this they usually do by chemical cues.

One of the disadvantages of the fertilization process is that it has to take place in a fluid to allow for the sperms to swim to the egg. Additionally both are unprotected and therefore could dry out were they not in fluid. The egg, at least, can be protected to a large extent if it is retained in the parent organism. But whereas a male frog can fertilize a female's eggs merely by spraying them with sperms as they leave her body, an organism which lives entirely on land cannot simply release the sperms in this way, for the sperms need fluid in which to swim and they would dry up in the air. Therefore many means of transferring sperms to the female have appeared in evolution.

The pollen grain of a flower is one method. The courtship behaviour of a mammal is another. By this procedure, physical mating becomes possible and the male can introduce his sperms into the female's body. Some animals, the scorpion is one of them, deposit their sperms in a small mucus packet, the spermatophore,

*Top,* the *Pellia* is a very common liverwort which grows on damp soil in wooded areas and other shady spots. *Above,* sporangia grow like stalks from the *Pellia*. The capsule at the top contains spores which will be released when the capsule bursts. *Right,* the capsule has burst, releasing spores. Reproduction by spores is inefficient. Thousands of spores are released, but only a handful ever grow to adult plants.

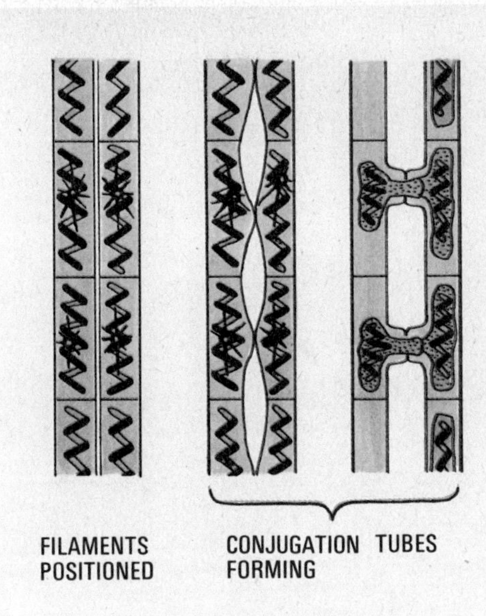


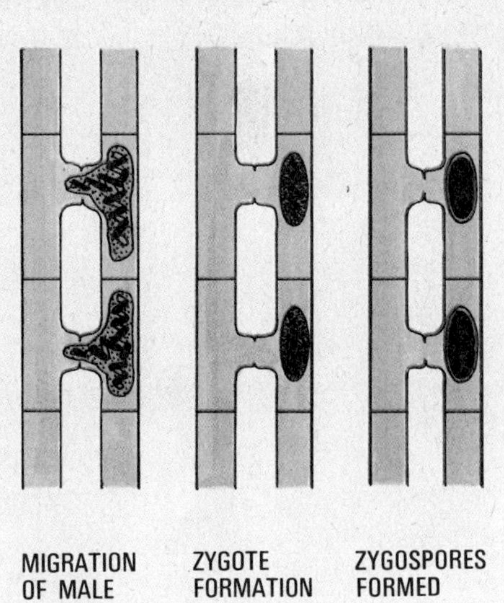


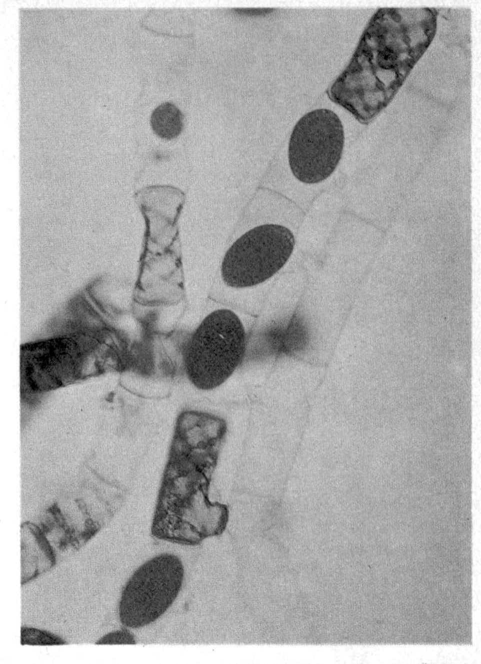

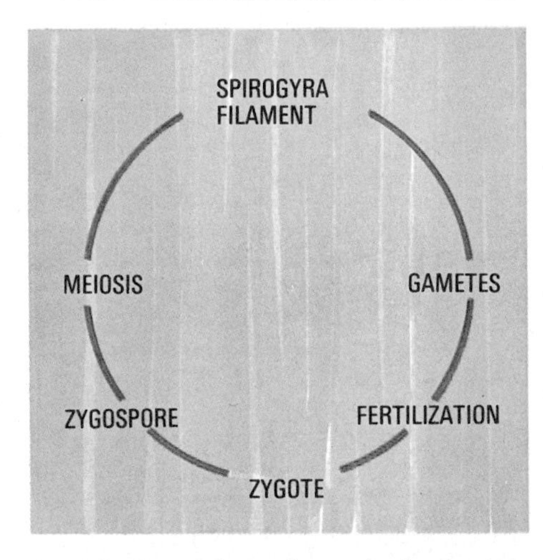

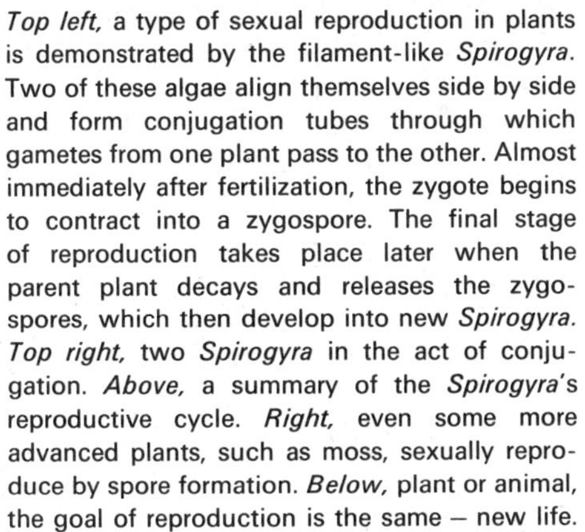

*Top left,* a type of sexual reproduction in plants is demonstrated by the filament-like *Spirogyra*. Two of these algae align themselves side by side and form conjugation tubes through which gametes from one plant pass to the other. Almost immediately after fertilization, the zygote begins to contract into a zygospore. The final stage of reproduction takes place later when the parent plant decays and releases the zygospores, which then develop into new *Spirogyra*. *Top right,* two *Spirogyra* in the act of conjugation. *Above,* a summary of the *Spirogyra*'s reproductive cycle. *Right,* even some more advanced plants, such as moss, sexually reproduce by spore formation. *Below,* plant or animal, the goal of reproduction is the same – new life.

leaving it on the ground for the female to pick up. The next stage in evolution is for the male to put the spermatophore directly on to the genital appendages of the female – this is what a male grasshopper does. Then, finally, the spermatophore is abandoned altogether and the male uses some copulatory appendage (penis) to convey the sperms directly on to the genital system of the female where the egg is protected by the mother's body.

All these methods reduce the wastage of sperms and help to ensure that the eggs are fertilized. In addition, the fact that the eggs themselves are kept in the body of a female means that they can be particularly well supplied with food reserves such as

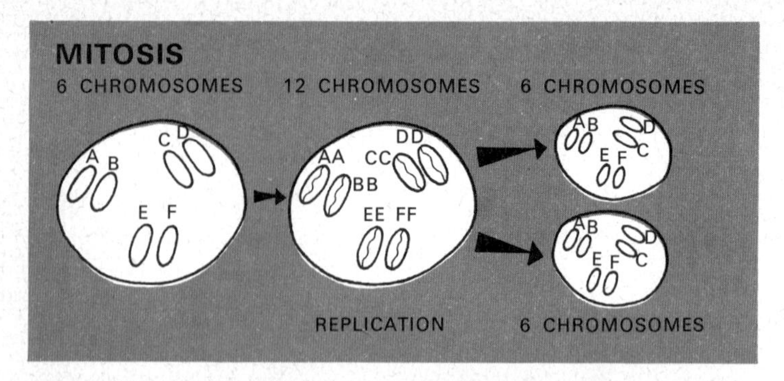


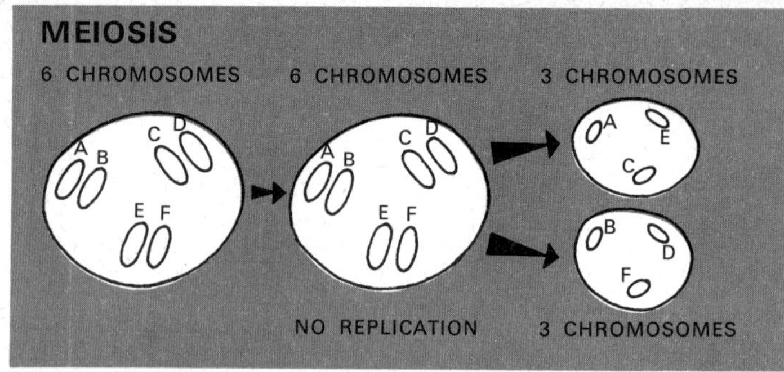


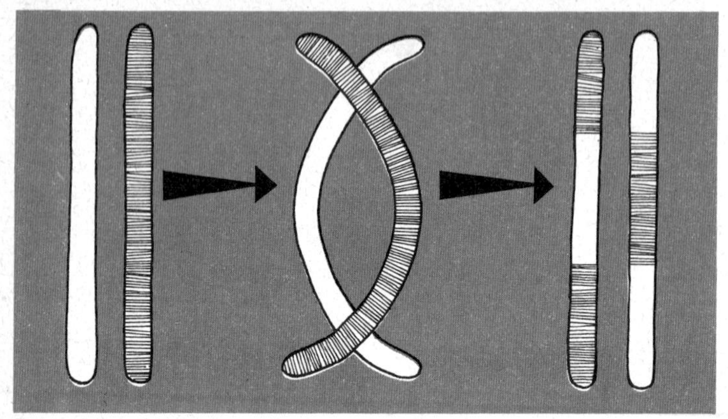

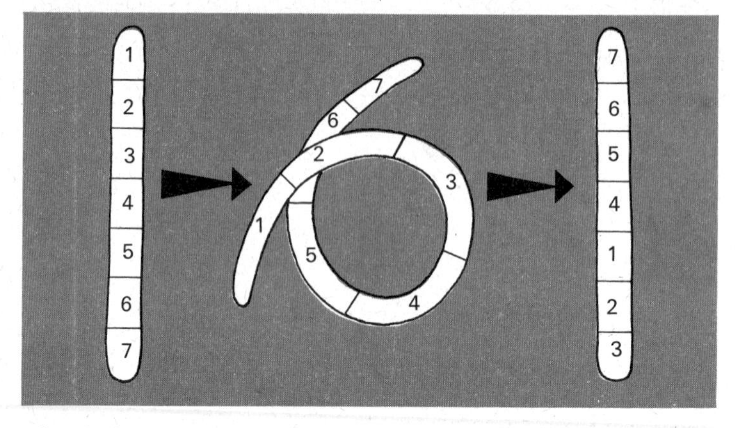

*Top,* it is convenient to think of meiosis as mitosis with a step missing. In mitosis, each chromosome replicates (creates a duplicate of itself) before the cell divides, so each new cell has exactly the same content as the parent cell. In the final phase of meiosis, no replication takes place. Thus, each of the two new cells has only half the number of chromosomes of the parent cell. Mitosis is ordinary cell division, meiosis produces gametes for sexual reproduction. *Above left,* chromosomes sometimes 'cross-over' one another, interchanging parts. *Above right,* it is also possible for a chromosome to interchange parts with itself. Such mutations help explain the process of evolution.

the *yolk* in animals and *endosperm* in flowering plants.

Also special protective layers can be put round the fertilized egg. The egg membranes, the albuminous 'white' of the egg and, around everything, the shell, are added to a bird's egg by the various parts of the oviduct of the female bird. The fertilized egg cell is the whole of the yolk – one very large cell swollen with the yolky reserve food.

Occasionally an egg will develop without being fertilized. A frog's egg will commence the cell divisions which herald the beginning of development after being pricked with a needle. The mechanical stimulus replaces the natural one of the penetration of the egg by the sperm. Development without fertilization is *parthenogenesis* and happens to the eggs of a number of invertebrate animals. The unfertilized eggs of a honeybee queen develop into males, (drones) while fertilized eggs give rise to females, workers and queens. There is no evidence for parthenogenesis among higher animals such as mammals.

## Variety and consistency

But, nevertheless, there is more to fertilization than a mere mechanical stimulus, for in this way genetic information is brought from two sources – the two parents. In this way greater variation can result. However, if we examine the way in which the mature egg and sperm are produced we shall see that they themselves contain the possibility, almost the certainty, of a further increase in variation.

Unlike ordinary cells, which divide so that each new cell has the same number of chromosomes as the original, gametes (sperms and eggs) are formed after a cell division in which the number of chromosomes is reduced to one-half. This type of reduction division is termed *meiosis.* So if a normal cell has 32 chromosomes (in 16 pairs), the gametes will have only 16 chromosomes.

In the meiotic cell division, chromosomes pair off, so that in Man, for instance, 23 pairs of chromosomes are formed. But before meiotic division is complete, the two partners of each pair become intertwined round each other, and frequently sections are exchanged in this *crossing-over.* On the whole, one of each pair comes from the set of chromosomes derived from the mother and the other from the father of that particular organism. So the exchanges are taking place between chromosomes which are slightly unlike.

The material which passes from one chromosome to the other will contain genes, and therefore the changes will bring about a re-sorting of the genes on those chromosomes. Later in the division, one of the two changed chromosomes goes into each new sex cell. As a result the gametes are themselves different from each other. It is a matter of chance which a sperm happens to fertilize or if either is fertilized at all. Thus, the distribution of the chromosomes is quite random.

One important result of the altering of pieces of chromosomes is that the genes on parts of the chromosomes will now have different ones on either side of them, in other words, their genic background will be changed. This often alters the way in which the genes express themselves in the organism's make-up when it is born. Again, this produces more possibilities of variation from individual to individual.

By doing this they form new organisms which may be like the original ones or may differ from the old in various degrees. These variations are the essential material from which the evolution of new forms can proceed. If everything were an exact replica of what had gone before, there could never have been the evolution of the huge variety of living organisms which exist in the world today, or in the ages long past. The introduction of variation is one of the main, if not the main, advantages of sexual reproduction involving two partners.

## A kind of immortality

In a number of organisms, a cell which will give rise later to the sex cells is set aside very early in development. The remainder of the body of the organism which acts as a carrier and a nurse for the reproductive cells is called the *soma.* The somatic part is mortal, for it dies while the sex cells pass on to the next generation. An amoeba which divides its whole body is potentially immortal, for two new individuals are made and nothing is left behind. Who is to say which is the parent cell? It has been distributed between the two new cells.

But the somatic part of an organism protects the sex cells against the direct influence of the environment. This may be of major importance in preserving the integrity of the genetic information needed for determining the next generation. To a very large extent they are also isolated from the influence of the remainder of the organism's body. Thus, changes which the organism acquires do not change the genetic information which is being preserved for posterity. For fertilization is only the beginning; development of new individuals must follow, if reproduction is really to be attained.

# The continuing struggle

The concept of natural selection is basic to modern biology. It explains how different species of animals and plants developed and how it is that living organisms 'fit into' their surroundings.

1 The ancestor of the modern domestic pig, the wild boar. This ferocious forest animal is still found in some parts of Europe.

2 The boar's domesticated descendants would not last long in the wild. Selected by breeders for their meat yield, pigs are sluggish animals.

THE WHOLE EDIFICE of modern biology rests on the discoveries of the great biologists of the nineteenth century. The greatest of these discoveries, and the one which opened up the whole subject of biological evolution to scientific investigation, was the theory of natural selection put forward by Charles Darwin in 1859. His book, the *Origin of Species,* is probably the most important single biological work ever published: it revealed clearly for the first time that the development of animals and plants could be explained not on mystical or biblical grounds but on the basis of a continuous struggle between the make-up of organisms and their environment.

The discoveries of scientific geology made at the beginning of the nineteenth century showed that many of the forms of life in past ages were related to present-day animals. How could this be explained? Darwin's great achievement was to provide an over-all theory which has stood the test of time.

## Darwin's finches

As a young man, Darwin spent some years voyaging round the world on H.M.S. *Beagle.* During the voyage he landed at the Galapagos Islands and there he noticed that some of the animals on the islands had diversified into a remarkable variety of related, but different, forms. Thus, birds of the finch family on the islands had become specialized to live in every type of habitat and eat every type of food: some to live on seeds, others on insects or berries. He surmised that all these different varieties had sprung from a single form which probably came to the islands from South America in an earlier period.

How could this variety of forms have come about? Darwin's analysis of this problem led him to formulate his theory of natural selection.

Reproduction is one of the fundamental characteristics of living matter. The offspring have most of the characteristics of the parents. But at the same time they are subtly different. Animals and plants produce far more offspring than will survive to propagate the species; for example, fish like the stickleback lay thousands of eggs though only a small proportion of these eggs ever become adult. This profligacy on the part of Nature seems merely a waste but in fact it has an important purpose. Although each offspring is very similar to the parents, each differs from the parents in various ways. For one thing, no offspring inherits the exact genetic make-up of its parents. Secondly, the genes that are handed down from generation to generation in this way are subject to slow but continuous change. This change, which biologists call mutation, is horrifically demonstrated by the effects of radiation on animal and plant life after the explosion of atomic weapons. But mutation is in fact going on constantly in nature. Most of these mutations are harmful. They are random changes in the chromosomes which are handed down from parent to offspring and determine in detail the characteristics of the organism.

Although the vast majority of mutations are harmful, a few are actively advantageous to the animal or plant and enable it to do things that its parents were not capable of. Animals that inherit these favourable mutations have an advantage over others competing for food or for living space. Unfavourable mutations tend to be rapidly eliminated.

Of course, some mutations are favourable in one place and unfavourable in another. One mutant of the tobacco plant, for example, was found to be unsuitable for life in its native Virginia, but was more suited than the parent strain for life in more southerly regions. In the absence of conditions which would destroy potentially harmful mutations, of course, they survive.

3 During the breeding season, red deer stags fight over the does. Only the fittest and strongest of the herd mate with the females.

This has happened to many species of cave fish. These animals live the whole of their lives in darkness and there is thus no advantage in efficient vision. In most of these fish, the eyes have totally degenerated, and in some they have disappeared.

By constant small changes in the genetic material combined with a struggle for survival in which no more than a small proportion of offspring can survive, Nature has provided a very delicate mechanism for 'fitting' species to their environment. It is this process that Darwin dubbed the 'survival of the fittest'. He wrote in the *Origin of Species* that 'the ultimate result of natural selection is that each creature tends to become more and more improved in relation to its conditions. This improvement inevitably leads to the gradual advancement of the organization of the greater number of living beings.'

## Order out of chaos

The efficiency of this natural process led many biologists before Darwin to postulate the existence of a creator, others attributed biological development to the workings of 'life force' or to some similar mystical conception. It was Darwin who saw that random processes *do* produce order. Not only does natural selection provide a unifying concept for the evolution that has taken place in the past, but it can be observed in operation at the present day, a startling example being industrial melanism.

Natural selection can also be observed to operate among bacteria. The bacterium *Escherichia coli*, for example, is normally killed by the drug *streptomycin*. But when the bacterium is grown in a medium containing streptomycin it is found that the few survivors rapidly become resistant to the action of the drug. Studies of this process have shown that this is not

1 Practically blind, and with its forelimbs adapted for digging, the mole has been refined by selection for its life underground.

2 A crab spider waits to catch flies inside the flower of an arum lily. This seemingly 'intelligent' behaviour is a product of selection.

3 These Characins, found in underground pools, are blind. Their eyes have degenerated because vision confers no advantage in the dark.

4 The red underwing moth has camouflaged forewings. A second line of defence is the threatening colour of its hindwings.

due to all the individuals in the bacterial colony becoming more resistant to the drug but to the fact that in every colony there are always a few individuals which have, quite accidentally, mutated so that they are resistant to streptomycin. The drug weeded out all those individuals not resistant to it, and left only those that could withstand its action.

This is the explanation for the finding of 'hospital strains' of common bacteria: these strains are frequently exposed to the action of bactericidal drugs and there is thus a strong selection pressure favouring the resistant mutants. These come to make up the majority of the population. Similar changes have been found in insect populations exposed to the action of insecticides. The selection of resistant strains of malarial mosquitoes has created difficulties for malaria control programmes in many parts of the world. The first effect of the insecticide is to kill most of the insects, so that the problem appears to have been beaten. But later, the mutant survivors of the insecticide multiply and give rise to a more intractable problem.

Another example of selection in action is the way in which mutant strains of insects are selected back towards normality. This phenomenon was first found in the fruit fly *Drosophila melanogaster*. This insect has been much used to study mutation, as it reproduces very rapidly and the geneticist can follow developments through many generations. One of the mutants found in the fruit fly is the so-called 'eye-less' strain. This mutant is rare in the wild because the effects of the mutation are harmful. It can, however, be bred as a pure strain in the laboratory, where the fly can be cushioned against the harmful effects of mutation. Such a strain has been bred. But it was found that when the 'eye-less' strain was bred for a number of generations the characteristics of the population became more and more like those of normal flies. In fact, what was happening was that the odd normal mutants occurring in the population were at an advantage compared with the rest

1 The wasp beetle protects itself from predators by 'mimicking' the coloration of a wasp. Mimicry of this type is common among insects.

2 The pine hawk moth, by contrast, conceals itself against the bark of the pine tree by blending into its surroundings.

3 Most of this brood of ring-neck pheasants will die young. The survivors will be those best able to cope with their environment.

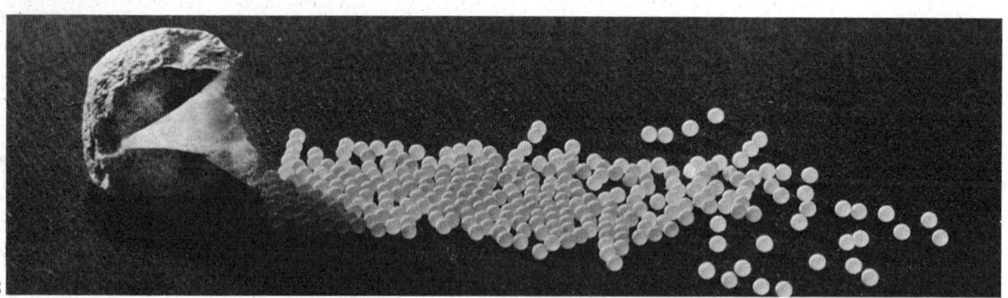

**1** The large family of this black bullhead (a form of catfish) are a guarantee against the wiping out of the species by predators.
**2** Palaeontologists are able to reconstruct ancient life forms from their fossil remains. The animals shown in the diagram lived 600 million years ago.
**3** Eggs of the black widow spider. Like many other animals, the spider produces many eggs but only a few of them reach maturity.

of the flies. Natural selection comes into operation to produce a more and more normal population. In fact, after about ten generations, the 'eye-less' strain was very little different from normal populations of fruit flies.

But how can the development of diverse animals and plants, the rise and fall of species and the development of entirely new types of animals with very widely differing modes of life, be explained on the basis of random mutation picked out by the struggle for survival? Many people confronted with the evidence for natural selection or with the concept of evolution find it hard to believe. It seems to violate some deeply held preconceptions. There is no doubt, however, that this theory provides the only rational explanation for the development of life. The all-important element that many people forget is time.

## High degree of improbability

Natural selection has been described as 'a mechanism for generating a very high degree of improbability'. What this means is that if the changes in living matter had been left entirely to chance, without the intervention of any form of selection, that is, if living matter had developed so to speak in a vacuum, it would be very unlikely to look as it does today. It has been estimated that the probability of producing a racehorse in this way is something like ten to the power of 1,000,000,000!

The fundamental weakness in earlier theories of the development of life was that they considered living matter to be fixed and unchanging, whereas in fact it is capable of being moulded into very different shapes and types. Mutation is, of course, in one sense a rare and abnormal event. Perhaps only one in 1,000 mutations is favourable, while most of the remainder will be unfavourable. Again, the frequency of mutation itself is low. For some genes it may rise to as much as one in 50,000 but the average frequency is more likely to be of the order of one in 100,000. Once a favourable mutation has emerged, it may take anything up to 50 or more generations to become widespread in the population. But in the time-scale of evolution, 50 generations is not very long.

Evolution has been studied in action through careful examination of fossil remains. These provide a means of comparing the theory with reality. The work of examining fossils in this light is highly skilled and requires a detailed knowledge of the changes not only in the fossils but in the environment. The classic work in this sphere was carried out on fossils of horses. These are relatively numerous, and it has been possible to build up a fairly complete model of the evolution of the horse. These studies exploded a number of old myths. The most notable exploded myth was that evolution has proceeded in a straight line. The studies showed that this was seriously in error. Dr G.G. Simpson points out in his book *Horses* that there is not one line of evolution of horses, but a whole number of lines, branches and splits, most of which can be correlated with changes in the horses' environment. Many of the lines of evolution reached dead ends and died out after longer or shorter periods. The most marked split is between two types of horse, one group of which became specialized for grazing on grass and the other which became adapted for eating the soft foliage of trees and shrubs.

The early horses were relatively unspecialized, smaller than the present-day examples of the species. Their brains were less developed than those of present-day horses. Interestingly, the development of the horse brain appears to be tied to the developments in the way of life of the horse: the parts of the brain that became developed were those concerned with speed and the detection of predators. Once these aspects of brain function had become fairly fully developed, the rate of brain evolution, as shown by the size of the brain-cavity in the skulls of fossils, slowed down markedly.

## Climatic changes

Again, the sharp changes in the course of horse evolution can be shown to correlate with changes in the environment. For example, during the Miocene period (25–12 million years ago) the climate became drier and led to the formation of savanna-type country where previously there had been large forests. This development favoured the grazing type of horse. The sharp change in the climate is mirrored in a marked stepping up of the rate of evolution. This has been studied particularly in relation to the teeth. These became progressively more specialized to take account of the grinding processes needed to digest foliage and particularly grass. During the sharp environmental changes of the Miocene period, the teeth became relatively rapidly higher and flatter, and then later the rate of evolution slowed down as the teeth became more perfectly suited to the horses' way of eating.

The basic mechanism of selection seems to underlie the whole development of life on Earth and provides a means by which the blind chance of mutation can be harnessed to the struggle of living matter to survive.

# Mammals 1 - The lower orders

From duck-billed platypus to Man, the variety in size and structure of the mammals is astounding. Even the egg-laying monotremes and pouched marsupials have the ability to suckle their young.

HUMAN BEINGS, together with most of their domestic animals, belong to the class of animals known as *Mammalia,* or mammals. Members of the group range in size from the gigantic blue whale, the largest animal ever known on Earth, weighing up to 120 tons, to the tiny tree shrews, not much more than an inch long and weighing about three grams. Mammals are found all over the world – polar bears and arctic foxes have been found close to the North Pole, while whales, seals and dolphins are adapted to life in the cold oceans. Generally regarded as the most advanced animals, mammals are *craniates;* that is, they have skulls and backbones, but differ from the amphibians, reptiles and birds, by possessing a larger brain, hairy skin and an ability to suckle their young. It is this last ability that gives the mammals their name (Latin, *mamma,* breast). Like the birds, mammals have a four-chambered heart – venous blood flows into the right side of the heart through the right atrium and ventricle and to the lungs. The blood then returns from the lungs bearing oxygen and is pumped to the tissues by the left ventricle. Apart from three species (the platypus and two ant-eaters) the mammals produce their young alive. All are warm-blooded, like the birds but unlike the reptiles, and have elaborate internal mechanisms for maintaining body temperature within a very narrow range.

## Learning how to live

A large brain means that a much greater proportion of behaviour is learned than is the case with other animal types. In birds, for example, the brain is smaller and less developed than the typical mammalian brain. This restricts the bird very largely to instinctive behaviour. The young mammal requires a considerable period of protected life while its parents and other members of the species teach it to cope with enemies, to find food, to seek a mate. The role of instinct decreases in the higher mammals, playing a relatively minor part in Man.

Control of body temperature means that the body processes take place in a constant environment. The kidneys and lungs ensure that the acidity of the tissues is maintained within a narrow range; the kidneys are also responsible for conserving the salt content of the body. This temperature stability makes it possible for mammals to develop a more sophisticated biochemistry than is possible for lower animals.

As soon as they are born, the young are fed with milk manufactured inside the mother's body. This makes them to a large extent independent of the availability of food in the environment and they can rely on the mother to provide the essentials of life until they are able to feed themselves. This period of dependence is essential for animals that must be trained by their parents.

The four-chambered heart is an extremely efficient way of ensuring that the blood is washed completely free of carbon dioxide in the lungs, and that all the oxygen accumulated by the blood in passing through the lungs is made available in the tissues throughout the body.

**1** Domestic cats have litters of five or six kittens. They are fed from eight abdominal teats and at birth are blind and completely dependent on their mother for food and protection.

**2** The common opossum is the United States' only marsupial. It has two litters of nine each year; the young stay in the pouch for three months, then travel on their mother's back.

More than 8,500 species of mammals are at present alive on the Earth. The history of mammals is unclear, but it is certain that they are descended from reptiles. One group of reptiles, the *Synapsida,* appeared on the Earth about 60 million years ago. They were heavy animals, some reaching the size of large dogs. These animals were abundant in the Permian period, about 30–40 million years ago. The bone structure of fossilized specimens shows that they were extremely similar to primitive mammals. It is difficult to be certain about the ancestry of the mammals because the only evidence of the early reptiles is in fossils. There is no way of knowing whether these animals suckled their young, had four-chambered hearts, were hairy or warm-blooded. However, the weight of evidence suggests that mammalian origins were among the Synapsida.

The difficulty of determining the early history of the mammals makes it difficult to classify modern mammals according to their evolutionary history, but zoologists are now generally agreed on the basic classification of the mammals. The living mammals can be divided into three sub-classes.

The sub-class *Prototheria,* which is now largely extinct, has three surviving species. All three are *monotremes,* and are extremely primitive. All are confined to Australia and New Guinea and are very different from the rest of the mammals. Although they have milk-glands, hair and a relatively large brain, they lay eggs. The platypus, commonly but inaccurately referred to as 'duck-billed', is the best known representative of this sub-class. It is confined to Australia, and lives in pools and streams. Although the platypus has some ability to control its body temperature, this ability is not well developed; its temperature often falls by as much as 15 °C. Its close relatives, the spiny anteaters or echidnas, are found in New Guinea and Australia. They live on ants, lay eggs like the platypus, and have no teeth; the upper part of the body is covered with stiff spines, and the skeleton, like that of the platypus, is very different from other living mammals. All three monotremes have probably been able to survive because they have few natural predators and are highly specialized for their particular habitats. The platypus was at one time hunted almost to extinction because of its fine fur, but it is now rigidly protected by the Australian government.

The sub-class *Allotheria* is now entirely extinct, but it is thought that this group of mammals evolved independently of the modern mammals. They existed for almost 70 million years, and fossil evidence shows that they were quite successful. Their ecological position may have been similar to modern rabbits.

## Competition for space

The sub-class *Theria* contains three groups, one of which is totally extinct. The other two groups are the *marsupials* and the *placental* mammals. The latter contain the vast majority of mammalian species and are the most highly developed.

The marsupials are now confined largely to Australia and South America. They are basically similar to the placental mammals, but their young are born in a less developed condition and usually finish their development inside the mother's pouch. Some marsupials, however, do not possess a pouch; in others the development of the young before birth is very similar to reproduction in placental mammals.

The oldest fossil remains of marsupials have been found in Canada, but the animals were fairly common all over the world until about 15 million years ago. In the Old World they have been eliminated by competition with the more highly developed placental mammals; in Australia, however, marsupials had few competitors until the arrival of Europeans and they have developed a considerable variety of species. Although they have evolved separately from the mammals of Europe, Africa and Asia, the marsupials of Australia and New Guinea have in many cases developed species which have close counterparts in the Old World. This phenomenon, known as *convergence,* is a striking illustration of natural selection. Some marsupials came to fill the equivalent position of mice, cats and moles, and many remarkable resemblances between these animals and their marsupial counterparts can be found.

Even in Australia, isolated by the sea

**1** The duck-billed platypus is an egg-laying mammal. It is about 20 inches long with webbed feet for swimming, a beak for grubbing for food but no pouch. The young are taken into a fold in the mother's skin where milk is discharged.
**2** A New Forest pony suckles her young foal. The composition of milk varies from mammal to mammal – cow's milk is the most balanced.

1 The dark-grey fur seals are protected from the cold by a thick layer of fat. These aquatic mammals look after their young for four months – but many do not survive their first year.

2 On the alert for danger – a lioness and her cubs. Two or three cubs are born at a time and are weaned at six months. After five months they accompany the male on his hunting trips.

3 The dingoes are believed to be the descendants of domestic dogs brought to Australia in prehistoric times. Today they prey on sheep and in this case a not-so-agile wallaby.

4 The offspring of an opossum still in the pouch. They crawl there a short time after conception when only half an inch long and feed from internal nipples.

5 Like the platypus, the echidna or spiny anteater is an egg-laying monotreme. It has strong claws and a sensitive snout to search out termites and ants. When alarmed it can roll into a prickly ball or burrow into the ground. It lives in rocky areas of Australia and New Guinea.

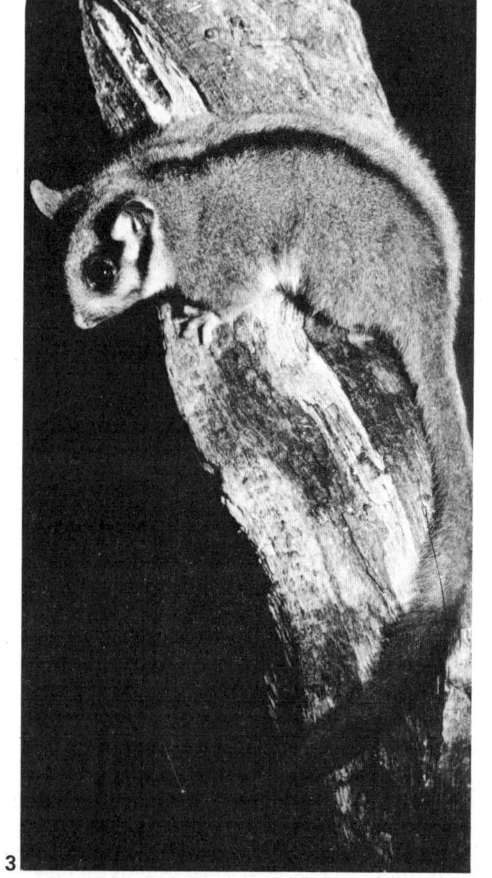

1 The 'badger' of Australia is the common wombat. It is a nocturnal, herbivorous animal which digs burrows up to 100 feet long. The female raises one baby at a time.
2 The kangaroo licks her fur to aid the migration of her newly born young to the pouch. After two months it can leave the pouch to find food but returns at all other times for a period of up to a year. Only one offspring is born each year.
3 The Australian possums resemble dormice or squirrels and their habitat is the trees. This is the long-tailed Leadbeater possum.

from the rest of the world, the marsupials were not entirely left to themselves. Bats flew into the area, while rats and other rodents arrived, perhaps on pieces of drift-wood. These rats flourished and gave rise to a large number of native species. They probably eliminated some of the smaller marsupials by competing with them for food and living-space. Originally, there was a marsupial species similar to the wolf, but by the time Europeans arrived on the Australian mainland, the marsupial wolf was extinct, having been ousted entirely by the dog or dingo. In Tasmania, however, there were no dogs, and here the marsupial wolf still flourished at the time of the European colonization. The Tasmanian aboriginals themselves are now extinct, but a few of the marsupial wolves have survived.

## Agile kangaroos

The best known of the marsupials are the Australian kangaroos and wallabies. These animals are adapted for swift travel over land. They are vegetarians, equipped with powerful hind legs with which they move in a series of long jumps. Most have large pouches, or marsupiums, in which the females carry their young after they are born. At birth the baby kangaroos are extremely small, in some cases not much bigger than a man's thumb-nail, and are almost incapable of any independent activity. The kangaroo assists them into the pouch by licking her fur in a broad band from her vagina to the pouch. The tiny babies then 'swim' up the bank of wet fur. They remain in the pouch for as much as a year feeding on milk from nipples inside the pouch. Once the tiny foetuses become attached to the nipples they swell, thus ensuring that the offspring do not become accidentally displaced from the pouch.

The largest of the kangaroos is the great grey kangaroo which reaches a height of six feet; the smallest is the rat-kangaroo, about the size of a hare.

In the same general zoological grouping as the kangaroos are the Australian possums, the flying phalangers, the wombats and the koala bear. The large family of possums includes a number of tree-dwelling species. Some, such as the sugar glider, have long feathery tails and webs linking their front and hind limbs. They are able to glide from tree to tree. The possums were once extensively hunted for their beautiful fur, but are now protected and have become much more common.

The wombats, heavy and rather sluggish vegetarians, live in underground burrows and emerge at night to feed.

The koala bear, the original 'teddy bear', is a sluggish tree-living animal, and not a true bear at all. It will only eat the leaves of a few species of eucalyptus tree. It never drinks, but absorbs sufficient water from the leaves on which it feeds. It does, however, eat earth, presumably in order to obtain essential minerals. The pouch of the female koala is downward facing and the young are born only 34 days after conception. They have to make their way without assistance to the pouch; after eight months the baby emerges as an eight-inch youngster. For some time afterwards, the baby koala is carried around by the mother, on her back or in her arms.

## 'Playing possum'

The Tasmanian wolf is representative of a large group of flesh-eating marsupials found in Australia. Some of these are similar to the cat family, and include the so-called tiger-cat. These animals are easily able to hold their own against 'imported' cats and dogs, but are hunted down where possible because of their ferocious raids on poultry farms.

The South American marsupials are somewhat removed from the Australian species although both groups probably arise from a common stock. The American species have undergone a process of selection in competition with placental mammals. At one time there were marsupial 'bears', carnivores rather like the modern grizzly bear, but these were ousted by similar placental species. There are also fossil remains of a marsupial superficially similar to the sabre-toothed tiger.

The best known of the American marsupials are the opossums. They occur all over the American continent, live in trees and feed on insects. Some of the species of opossums in America have the remarkable habit, not shared with their Australian counterparts, of shamming dead when threatened. This is the origin of the expression 'playing possum'.

The survival of these animals that have not achieved the level of development of the true mammals is certainly due to geographical isolation in the case of Australia and New Guinea. In all probability South American varieties have not been extinguished because of the late arrival of true mammals to the continent.

# Mammals 2 - Man's closest relatives

At the summit of the animal kingdom are the true mammals. Their young are born in a more advanced condition than any other group – a common feature which classifies a wide variety of creatures.

1 Barely two inches long, the harvest mouse is an agile little mammal which uses its prehensile tail to perform fantastic balancing feats.

2 Deer have less developed hooves than other ruminants and are still four-toed. This red deer stag is 'in velvet' – growing new antlers.

THE PLACENTAL or true mammals form the largest and best developed group of Mammalia. They are generally regarded as the highest point of the evolutionary tree. Man is a placental mammal, as are the great apes, the whales, all the mammals of the Old World and most of the mammals found in the Americas.

This group of animals are called 'placental' because their young are carried in the mother's womb and born alive, the blood circulation of the unborn young being linked with the blood-stream of the mother by a complex of membranes. These membranes, bathed on one side by the mother's blood and on the other by the blood of the offspring, transmit substances required for the growth of the offspring, and carry away its waste products. This system of membranes is called a *placenta*.

## Ancestors of the mammal

The early placental mammals appear from fossils to have been rather similar in appearance to today's shrews. Zoologists believe that these early mammals lived in trees, as indeed some of the shrews do today. For reasons that are not fully understood, the dinosaurs and large reptiles disappeared rather rapidly from the Earth, while at the same time there was a rapid development of the mammals. They spread quickly across the surface of the Earth and diversified into a large number of species and types.

The early mammals probably lived largely on insects, as moles and ant-eaters do today. Modern mammals feed on an astonishing variety of foods: *carnivores* like dogs and cats eat the flesh of other animals; *herbivores* like cows and elephants eat grass, tree leaves, and other vegetable matter; *rodents* – rats, mice, squirrels – also live mainly on vegetable matter but obtain their food by gnawing rather than by chewing; *omnivores* such as Man will eat almost any food available. Of the aquatic mammals, seals eat fish, sea cows eat only sea plants, others like the whalebone whales, live on plankton.

Adapting to their needs carnivores have become well equipped for catching their prey with sharp claws, strong teeth for tearing flesh, and an ability to run faster than their prey. Most have developed good eyesight or sense of smell for tracking down the animals they wish to eat. Herbivores, on the other hand, often require special internal adaptations in order to digest their food. The four stomachs of the cow, for example, make it possible for it to digest cellulose, the main constituent of grass. Cellulose is normally indigestible for carnivores because they lack the necessary enzymes to break down this substance in their stomachs.

## Escaping the killer

Other vegetarian animals are well adapted for flight from their predators. The gazelle, which is preyed upon by the lion and hyena, has long legs and quick reflexes to enable it to escape. Other herbivores, like the elephant and the hippopotamus, are large and powerful enough to deter any meat-eater.

The carnivores alive today are generally separated by zoologists into two main groups. One group contains cats and similar animals; the other, dogs, bears, weasels, and animals like them. The cats are extremely pure examples of carnivores; their teeth are adapted solely for tearing flesh and they have no equipment for chewing their food. This restricts them entirely to flesh, because flesh can be swallowed whole and digested, whereas vegetable matter cannot. Cats tend to be individualists, unlike dogs, and do not hunt in packs. They cannot run for long distances and catch their prey by stalking and springing on them. Lions and tigers are the best known big cats. Lions and tigers have been successfully interbred, notably at the Paris Zoo, producing 'tigons' with some characteristics of both. These artificial hybrids are, however, sterile. A mammal closely related to the cat is the hyena. This animal was once thought to be a scavenging species; but detailed studies of hyenas in African national parks have shown that these animals do not generally scavenge. They catch living prey, such as antelopes, by hunting them down.

Unlike the cats, the dogs, foxes and wolves have retained some chewing ability and have some molar teeth. They tend to hunt in packs and can run for long distances. Some of the wild forms found today, such as the Australian dingo, are probably descended from domesticated dogs that have reverted to the wild state. The bears are closely related to the dogs and are also capable of eating a mixed diet. The only purely carnivorous bear is the polar bear, which has little choice in an area where fish is the the only available food.

The marine carnivores are probably descended from land carnivores of the dog type. They include the seals, which live almost exclusively on fish, and the walrus, which uses its huge canine teeth or tusks to open the shellfish on which it feeds. In these animals, the legs have become adapted for swimming.

The most adaptable and successful of all mammals are not the carnivores, but the rodents, the gnawing mammals. Best known are the rats and mice, but the family also includes squirrels, porcupines, rabbits, chipmunks and guinea pigs.

1 Lemurs, or 'half-apes', are the most primitive primates. The ring-tailed lemur of Madagascar prefers thinly wooded country to thick forest.
2 The 'tiger' of South and Central America, the jaguar, hides during the day and hunts at night. This ferocious big cat can be a man-eater.

1

3

2

3 The 'white' rhinoceros is, in fact, a muddy grey in colour. Despite its four tons weight and menacing horns it is quite placid unless provoked.
4 The American black bear is a quiet animal, a good climber and is partial to fish. Protected in national parks, it is elsewhere hunted as a pest.

Rodents are found in every part of the world, and some live in close connection with Man. The rodents are almost entirely vegetarian. Characteristic of the group are prominent incisors or front teeth which grow at a rapid rate. If the animal for some reason ceases to gnaw for a period, the growth of the incisors tends to force the jaws apart and the animal may die.

Many rodents dig burrows in the ground; some, such as beavers and musk-rats, are partially water-dwelling. Others live in the trees, and while there are no flying rodents, some of the squirrels can glide long distances using webs of skin between their limbs and trunks. The extraordinary ability of rodents to adapt is shown by the rats. These animals were the only placental mammals to enter Australia unaided by Man, and have developed a number of forms well suited to their new environment.

The guinea pig and the porcupine are representatives of a group of rodents which penetrated into South America

when North America was a separate land mass. They include the largest living rodent, the capybara, or water-pig, which grows as large as a domestic pig. Hares and rabbits although successful are unlike the other rodents because they have four upper incisor teeth.

The *ungulates* contain the mammals which are most useful to Man. This is a large and diverse group of animals developed from different evolutionary lines. Almost all the large herbivorous mammals are ungulates: cows, horses, sheep, elephants, camels and other animals domesticated by human beings. The ungulates are not a single group and are classified together more for reasons of convenience than because all the animals are closely related. All, however, have certain similarities, which are chiefly related to their method of feeding.

**5** Shrews are very small insectivores and have a three-hour cycle of sleeping and feeding. The common shrew, like other species, lives alone.
**6** Common red foxes generally live in burrows, or earths. During daylight they lie low and at night hunt birds, rabbits, mice and moles.

5

4

6

The obvious similarities are in the teeth of the ungulates. Their food is generally grass or vegetable matter which must be thoroughly chewed before it enters the animal's stomach. This has given rise to molar (grinding) teeth of large size and surface area.

## Swift-toed horse

The ungulates are usually highly mobile, either to escape from carnivores, or because they must traverse a wide area to find food. Many African species, the antelopes for example, may travel thousands of miles in the course of the year and migrate from winter feeding grounds to summer pastures. The horse is a typical example of an ungulate well adapted for rapid motion, but a fallen horse finds it difficult to rise. The horse's legs are typical of many fast-running ungulates; the first part of the limb is relatively short making it possible for the second, longer segment of the limb to move rapidly, giving a powerful muscular thrust to the drive of the leg. The third section of the horse's leg corresponds with the hand or foot in Man. In animals like the horse, the bones of the foot are lengthened and the animal really runs on its toes. The horny hooves are adaptations of the claws found in the early primitive mammals. Claws, where they do persist among the ungulates, are generally blunted and have the function of protecting the feet.

The horn is typical of the defence mechanisms developed by the ungulates against hostile predators. Another defence, developed, for example, in the pig family and by the elephants, is the elongated tusk. In reality this is a canine tooth, valuable as a weapon of defence or attack.

The ungulates are divided into odd-toed and even-toed; typical of the former is the horse. It runs on the middle toe, the other toes being reduced in size and no longer used in running. Three-toed horses are found in fossil remains, but today this type of foot is found only in the rhinoceros. The only truly wild horse now living is the rare Prezwalsky horse of the Mongolian steppes, although there are other species, like the native ponies of the British Isles, which have reverted to a semi-wild existence. The other major representative of the odd-toed ungulates is the tapir of Malaya. This animal retains a very primitive foot formation; four toes on the front feet and three on the hind feet.

The even-toed ungulates are represented by a much wider variety of living species than their odd-toed relatives. They include the diverse cattle family, with such wild species as the buffalo of North America. To these are related the deer and camel families and the giraffes. They form a large group of *ruminants,* pure vegetarians with a complex arrangement of stomachs for digesting grass and leaves. After being taken into the mouth, the food travels into one of the stomachs where it it is partly digested and then regurgitated to the mouth to be chewed over again. The camels and their relatives the llamas are descended from North American species and there were native camels in the United States until quite recent times. The giraffe is another ruminant; the formation of its long neck does not involve the addition of any bones to the animal's skeleton. Almost all mammals have seven neck bones; the giraffe is no exception, its bones are just extremely long.

The elephants belong to another group of ungulates, or more properly subungulates. Their group, the proboscidians, was originally widespread in the Northern hemisphere where mammoths were once common animals. Well-preserved mammoths are found regularly in the frozen bogs of Siberia; it has been reported that the flesh is often still edible. The proboscidians also include another bizarre species of mammal – the dugong or seacow. These belong to the *sirenians,* so-called because the appearance of these vegetarian beasts off tropical coasts probably gave rise to legends about mermaids. Despite their specialized habits, the seacows are closely related to the elephants.

Whales are the largest group of aquatic mammals and the best adapted to life in water. They are able to withstand the major pressure changes involved in deep diving and are insulated against cold by a thick layer of fatty blubber. They are also streamlined for fast and efficient movement. Some of the whales appear to have a very high degree of intelligence, and species like the dolphin are friendly towards human beings, easily learn complicated 'tricks', and appear to have a well-developed method of communication.

## Primates – born in the trees

The most intelligent of the land mammals are the primates, the group to which Man himself belongs. The lemurs, monkeys and apes are derived from tropical tree-living forms, and indeed most of the present-day primates still live in trees. They are omnivorous, eating both flesh and vegetation, although many species rely more or less exclusively on vegetable food. Their mode of life in the trees has given rise to a well-developed sense of sight, and the necessity for quick reactions and muscular co-ordination in order to swing around the forest has given rise to a highly developed brain. The lemurs are generally considered to be the most primitive of the primates. The monkeys are divided into Old and New World types. The New World monkeys are less advanced from an evolutionary point of view than the Old World monkeys and are chiefly distinguished from them by their flattened snouts. The Old World monkeys include the great apes and Man. The most developed of these are the gibbon, orang-utans, chimpanzees and gorillas. Of these, the last two have relatively large brains and a fair degree of intelligence. Both are large animals, and both have begun to move out of the trees and on to the ground.

But the highest form of primate, *Homo sapiens,* is another story altogether. . . .

1

2

3

**1** The incisors of a beaver are used for gnawing; flaps of skin prevent wood chips from entering the mouth. Teeth grow quickly to compensate for wear.

**2** At night, the Brazilian tapir feeds on leaves and fruit with the aid of its prehensile muzzle. It is an odd-toed ungulate having four toes on each front foot and three on the back.

**3** Wild rabbits are smaller than hares; they live in large groups in complex warrens.

# Fish 1 – Evolution and development

Were fish the ancestors of land animals? The evolutionary evidence and study of the existing 20,000 species of fish indicates this. They are the first stage in the development of a skeleton.

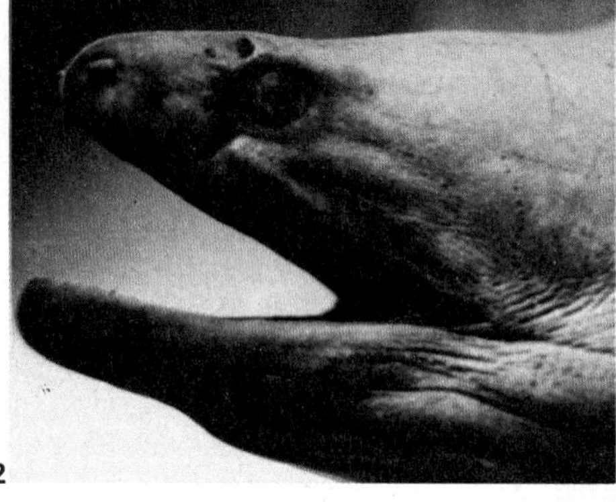

FROM THE VERY EARLIEST TIMES the fish has figured largely in the folklore of Man. And the reason is easy to see. Fish exist everywhere in the waters of the world – fresh and salt – in great numbers. This makes them relatively easy to harvest, and once ashore, they provide not only high-quality food, but are also a source of other valuable materials. They supply products like oils, for example, and also fertilizer, meal, glue and fine leather. Again, in some societies their teeth and bones are prized as ornaments, used as money, or employed in the making of spears, arrows and harpoons.

Paradoxically, their very great value and ubiquity may sometimes have led Man to turn his back on the idea of exploiting them. For they have been considered sacred in some parts of the Middle East and Africa, and therefore were hardly exploited at all. Even so, in most areas of the world such restraints have not and do not operate and the fish is of the very greatest importance to the majority of the human race.

At the same time, it is equally important to the balance of nature within the oceans, the rivers and ponds themselves. Fish serve as consumers of small organisms which they convert into food for larger organisms, thus supporting their own food chain as well as contributing to ours.

**1** The sting ray *(Dasyatidae)* has well-developed pectoral fins and a sting which is positioned above the tail.
**2** Vicious, sharp-toothed moray eels inhabit coral reefs and are a danger to swimmers. Their gills are reduced to no more than pores.

And if all this were not enough in itself to make fish worthy of close study, there is also the fact that they are vertebrates, a class which also includes Man, so their study can add important detail to our knowledge concerning the rise of the 'lord of Creation'.

## What is a fish?

In the world at the present time there are more species of fish than any other vertebrate, but in spite of this and their undoubted importance to Man, there is still some confusion concerning what is a fish and what is not. Commonly the name is given to any aquatic creature which employs gills to breathe, moves through the water by means of fins, and possesses scales. But this simple definition will not do. Some fish are finless, some breathe with lungs, some are able to leave the water altogether for a time, and some do not have scales.

Sharks are predatory and live in almost all waters. They produce broods of as many as 30 living offspring at one time.

To define the fish more accurately and usefully it is necessary to be more technical. To begin with there is the characteristic common to all fish which has already been mentioned: the spine. No other ocean animal has a true backbone. It is made up of separate pieces – the *vertebrae* – which fit together to form a structure which, while it is rigid enough to support the body, also allows a great deal of flexibility. The fish typically has lidless eyes. It has a skin containing mucous glands, and a heart consisting of a single folded tube with several chambers.

These then are subdivided, however, into five classes which it is proper to examine and compare since they outline the evolutionary progress of these animals. The fish originally evolved, it is thought, from a type similar to the *Amphioxus* (lancelet) which possesses physiological equipment which seems to foreshadow the backbone and other facilities later found in fish.

The most ancient class of true fish which we know of are the *agnaths*. Their name means 'jawless' which describes their major peculiarity, for indeed that was their condition. The agnaths dominated the fish world for some tens of millions of years before subsiding and finally disappearing as more efficient animals evolved.

One direction in which this develop-

As the chart on pages 194 and 195 shows, there are five basic classes, and the chain of evolution leading to present-day fishes has been established from the fossil record. However, there are still many gaps in the chain.

The fish shown as present-day types are merely representative examples of the various classes. It can be seen that the spiny fish are the most numerous.

Fish are the first vertebrates in the evolutionary scale. The chart shows how the various present-day types have developed from their remote ancestors. The different forms of fish illustrate the changes which have taken place to adapt them to various environments.

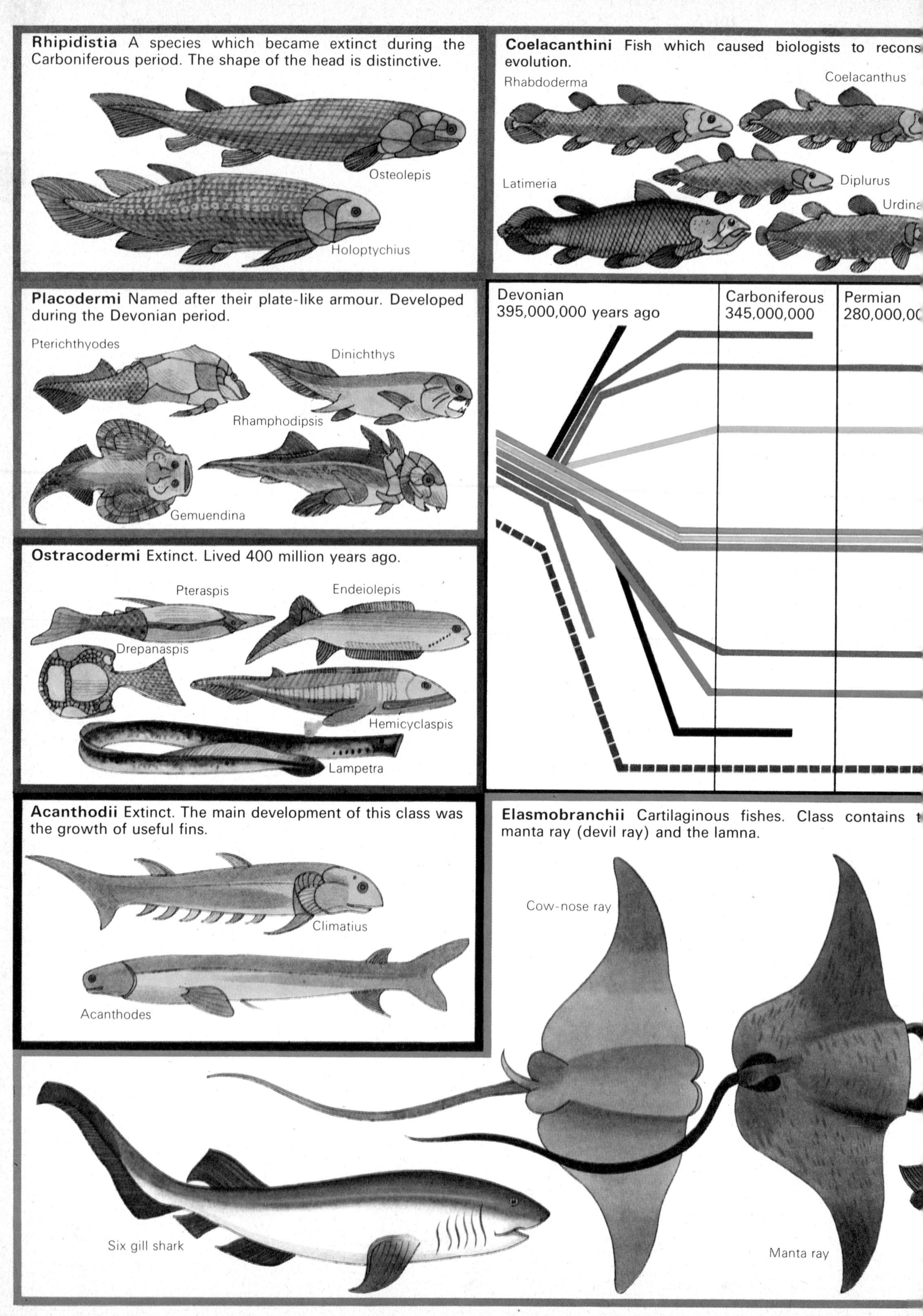
Rhipidistia A species which became extinct during the Carboniferous period. The shape of the head is distinctive.
Osteolepis
Holoptychius
Coelacanthini Fish which caused biologists to recons
evolution.
Rhabdoderma
Coelacanthus
Latimeria
Diplurus
Placodermi Named after their plate-like armour. Developed during the Devonian period.
Pterichthyodes
Dinichthys
Rhamphodipsis
Gemuendina
Devonian
395,000,000 years ago
Carboniferous
345,000,000
Permian
Ostracodermi Extinct. Lived 400 million years ago.
Pteraspis
Endeiolepis
Drepanaspis
Hemicyclaspis
Lampetra
Acanthodii Extinct. The main development of this class was the growth of useful fins.
Climatius
Acanthodes
Elasmobranchii Cartilaginous fishes. Class contains
manta ray (devil ray) and the lamna.
Cow-nose ray
Six gill shark
Manta ray

**pnoi** A term reserved for lungfishes and fossil forms by some logists, although others include coelacanths in this class.

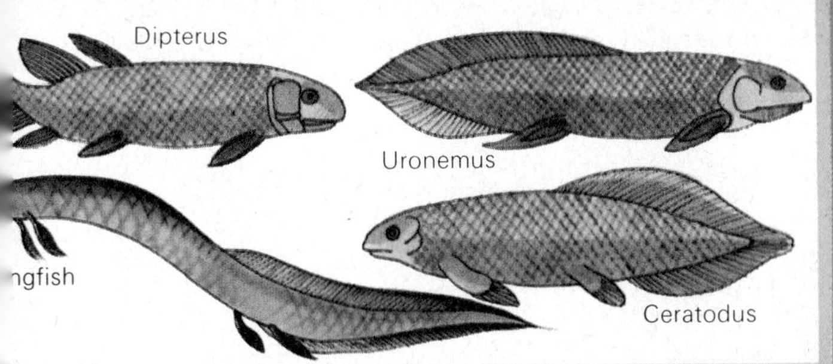


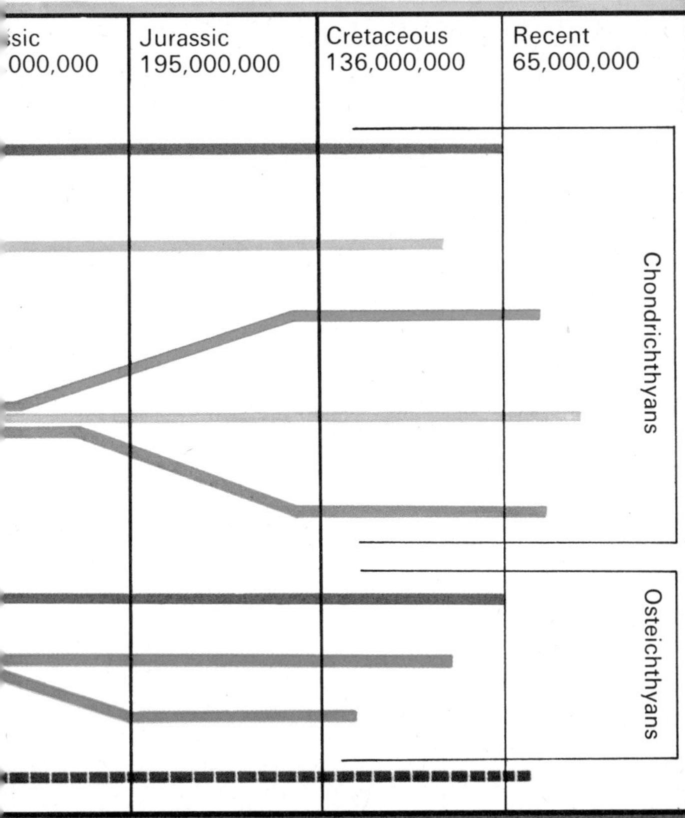


**Teleostei** A class which includes many of the customary food fishes like herring and salmon.

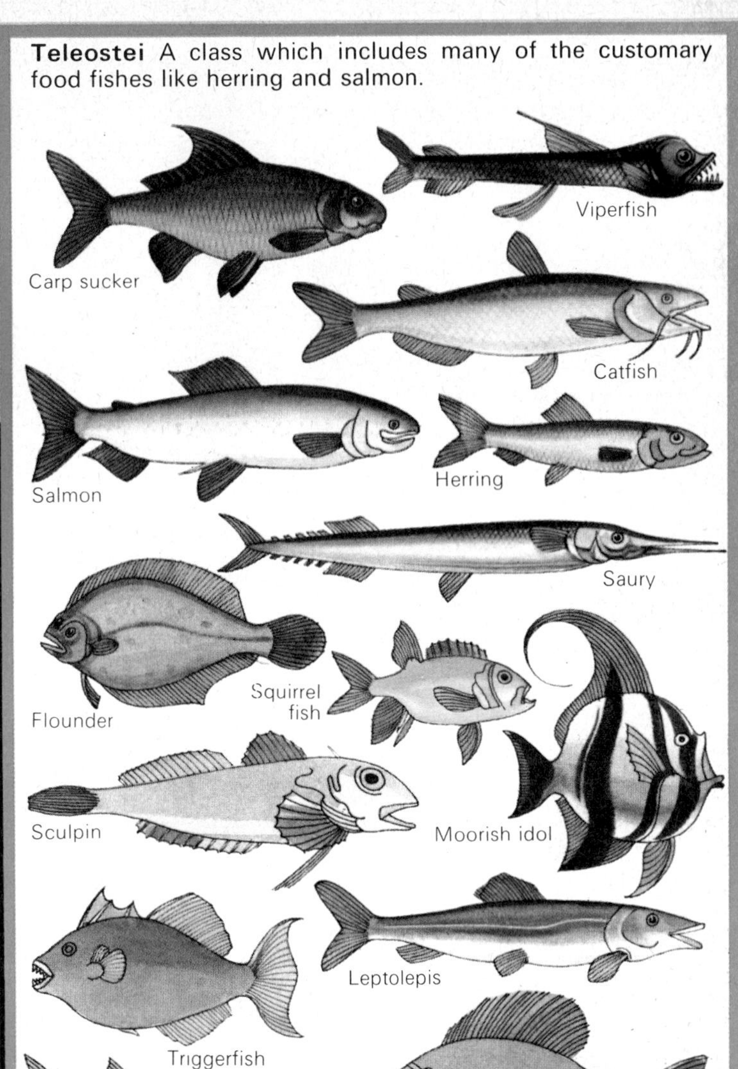


**himaerae** Also called rat-fishes. A member of the class olocephali, which includes Helodus.

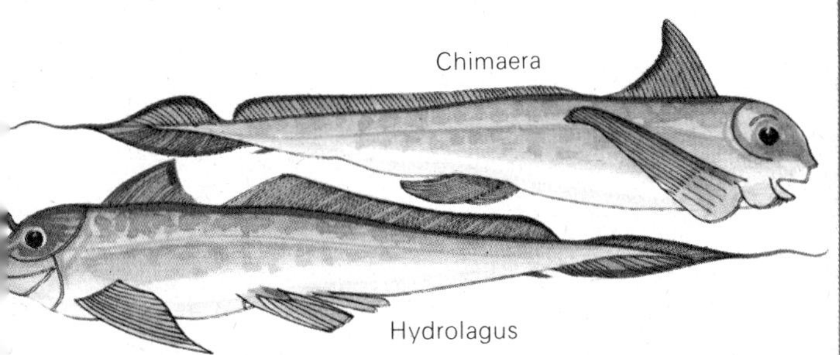


**Holostei** Includes the well-known gar and bowfin fish.

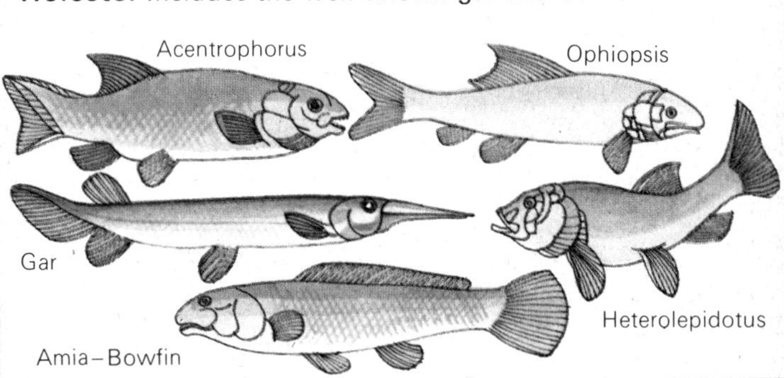

**Chondrostei** Replaced by more advanced forms of marine life during the Jurassic period. A few survived to the Cretaceous.

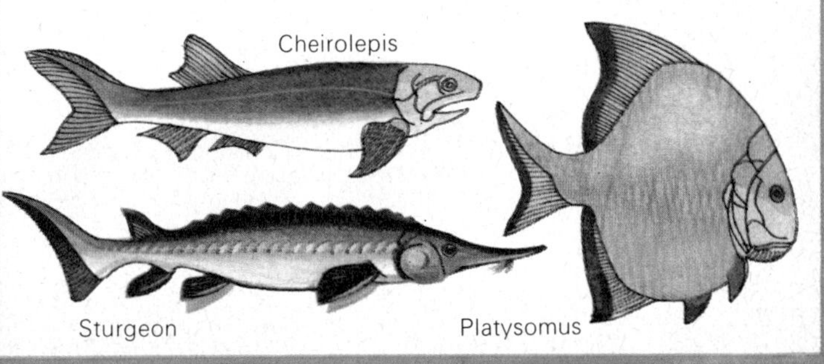

ment took place can be seen in a second class called the *Cyclostomata* which are still much in evidence today in the shape of lampreys and hagfish. Both of these are jawless in the accepted sense and in shape are long and eel-like. For feeding they possess a round sucking funnel lined with teeth, and the technique of both is to attach themselves by means of the sucker to their prey. In the case of the lamprey, the teeth are then used to rasp a way through the skin so that it can suck the blood; and indeed it is no uncommon thing to find other fish which carry the scars of one or more visits from a lamprey. Even more destructive, though, is the unpleasantly named hagfish. Once these have become attached, they eat their way right into and through their prey.

## Predators and prey

Another line of development from the agnaths encompassed a truly remarkable evolutionary change – the development of a jaw. Most of the early agnaths probably lived by sucking up the bottom mud and extracting their living from the organic matter which the mud contained. Clearly jaws allow the fish to take a wider variety of foods, and in the third class of fish, the *placoderms* ('plate skin' because many had bony armour plates), hinged gill supports.

The placoderms, however, did not last for long, being replaced by the two remaining classes of fish. These are *chondrichthyans,* which in the shark and ray contain two of the most dangerous animals in the sea, and the *ostychtheians* or bony fish, which include not only most of the world's food fishes, but also some pretty dangerous customers as well – the notorious barracuda, for example, and the aggressive moray eel.

But the two classes also benefit from another interesting comparison. The shark and its relatives were originally developed in order to live in and exploit the salt waters of the Earth, and subsequently only very few have moved into fresh-water habitats. The bony fish, on the other hand, were specialized for life in fresh water. Here they have continued to dominate but have also spread into the seas.

But even though the chondrichthyans have to compete with some 30,000 species of bony fish, they have held their own and have not been wiped out. One reason for this might be their fearsome defensive and offensive equipment as seen in the sharks. But they are also designed in one respect in a much more efficient manner than the ubiquitous bony fish.

This is the mechanism by which their cells are kept supplied with water. This is all a matter of the osmotic pressure of the body fluids within the fish. If this pressure is lower than that of the surrounding water – as it is in the bony fish – then they tend to lose their body water continuously through the gill membranes. So in order, literally, to prevent their cells from dying of thirst, the bony fish must use comparatively large amounts of energy to gulp water continually, thus making good the loss, and then excrete the dissolved salts.

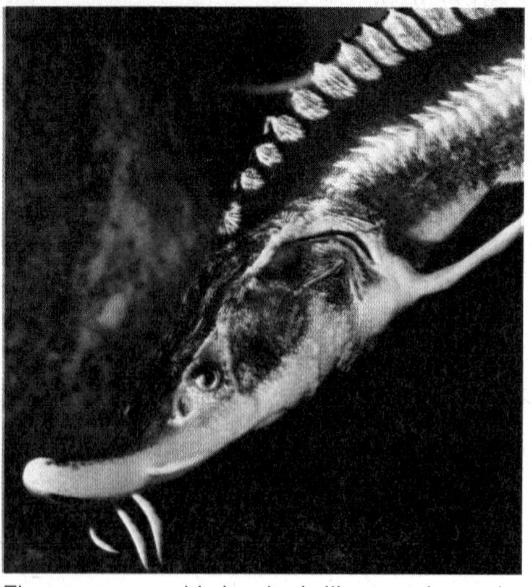

The sturgeon, with its shark-like mouth on the underside of its body, feeds on small marine creatures. Its eggs (caviar) are a delicacy.

In the shark and its relatives, the whole business is carried out in a much simpler manner. In short, the chondrichthyans retain large amounts of urea in their body fluids. In most other animals such a concentration would be fatal but here, together with other salts, it maintains the internal fluids at the same osmotic pressure as the water outside, so the shark, or other chondrichthyan need do much less work in supplying its cells with water.

The other factors which characterize the chondrichthyan include of course its cartilaginous skeleton (indeed the name means 'cartilage fish'); its absence of a swim bladder; and the fact that none of them have lungs.

The bony fish get their name from the fact that most have well-developed bony skeletons. (As mentioned above, the skeleton of the shark is composed of cartilage, the tough gristly material which in bone skeletons is reserved for connective tissue at the joints.) In a few species though, like the sturgeon, the bone has retrogressed and the skeleton consists largely of cartilage.

The most primitive bony fish were equipped with lungs as well as gills for purposes of breathing. This probably stems from the fact that during their fresh-water beginnings they found themselves in semi-stagnant surroundings in which the oxygen content was very low and gills were therefore ineffective. With subsidiary lungs they would have been able to rise to the surface and breathe air directly.

In most cases the lung has now fallen into disuse in the context of breathing and has become the subject of a particularly interesting adaptation. It has developed into a very important part of the bony fish's equipment: the swim bladder. In most such fish this is a simple gas-filled sac which reduces the animal's specific gravity, and like a pair of internal water wings maintains it at a depth suitable to its mode of life. That, however, is not the swim bladder's only function.

In some fish it operates as a large ear. Sound waves reaching the creature pass through its outer tissues and strike the taut membrane of the sac: from there they are transmitted mechanically to the brain through the small bones of the vertebrae.

But as ever in nature, here there are exceptions to prove the rule. Some bony fish *have* retained lungs, and these not very surprisingly are called lungfish. They are to be found in rivers in Australia and Africa where the water is too foul to support fish having only the more usual gills.

## Mammalian forebears

So in all of this we can see the interrelationships of the five classes of fish, but a truer and perhaps more spectacular picture of their range and diversity and the wonderful mechanisms they embody requires more detailed study.

The diversity of forms which the fish adopt provide a number of valuable clues to the ways in which land animals have developed from their aquatic forebears. This is particularly the case in relation to the amphibians and reptiles, whose origins and vestigial fish characteristics are apparent even to the casual observer.

In recent biological research into evolutionary process, the coelacanth has provided a valuable link in the evolutionary chain. But there are many other types of fish which retain their anatomical and physiological forms intact, untouched by the processes of evolution. In many ways, they can be considered as living relics of an age of animals which has long since passed. Their study is a vital part in the completion of the history of the animal kingdom and in the origins of the higher animals, including even Man himself.

The carp, a native of North American and European waters, has an unusual scale formation. It is preyed on by the pike.

# Fish 2 – In the waters of the Earth

Bony, jawless, herbivorous, carnivorous – the variety of fish swarming in the rivers, lakes and seas of the world is seemingly endless. How do they relate to each other?

THE NUMBER of species of fish, approximately 20,000, pales into insignificance when compared with the vast number of insect species. And yet, in their diversity of form, habitats, breeding methods and adaptation, the fish surpass the insects. They range in size from tiny animals to the sharks and rays.

And although they are the Earth's oldest vertebrates, living in their strange environment for many ages before the first of them ventured on dry land to give rise eventually to the mammals, very little has been known about them until comparatively recently. The water which nurtures them and has shaped their physiology and life-cycle has also acted as a considerable barrier between them and investigating scientists.

Despite the diversity of form, all fish are in the end conditioned by their environment. Their watery existence has determined their shape, their means of locomotion, their feeding and breeding habits, and their means of respiration. Furthermore, as many fish live in conditions which make the senses as we know them virtually useless, some of them have developed a sixth sense which has no counterpart among other classes of animal. This alone is enough to make the fish unique among the animal kingdom.

## Anatomical development

In most cases fish have moved a long way from the elongated spindly shapes of the first vertebrates. While this may not be so obvious in the cyclostomes (lampreys, etc.), which have become long and snakelike, the cartilaginous fish like the shark have become streamlined for speed, with fins so fleshy that the Chinese are able to make soup from them. Their cousins, the rays, have become flattened and their ventral fins have become extended and winglike. The bony fishes show perhaps the greatest variation in shape of all. They range through almost all shapes – from the long and snakelike moray eel, through the shortened and side-to-side flattened butterfly fish, to the streamlined herring and barracuda.

To return to skeletal matters briefly, it is interesting to note that the fins have a variety of uses apart from propulsion. In some cases they are paired and it is thought that these paired fins in the higher vertebrates have become limbs.

**1** The cod family (*Gadidae*) includes a number of food fishes, most of them common in the Northern Hemisphere. Characteristically, they live in shoals.

**2** Coral fish have a delicate sense of touch which enables them to dart between rocks which they cannot possibly see. They are also able to change colour very rapidly.

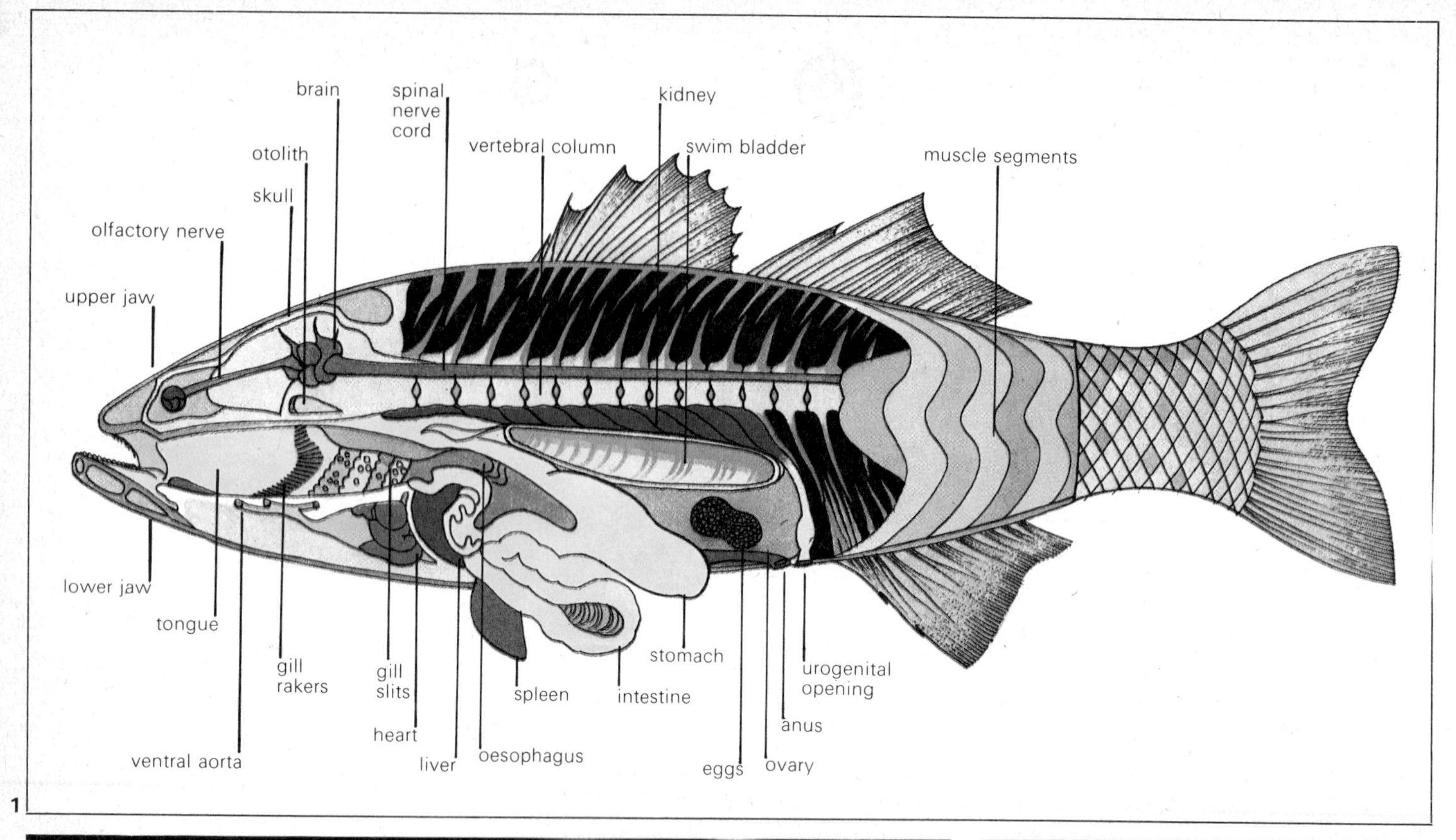


1

2

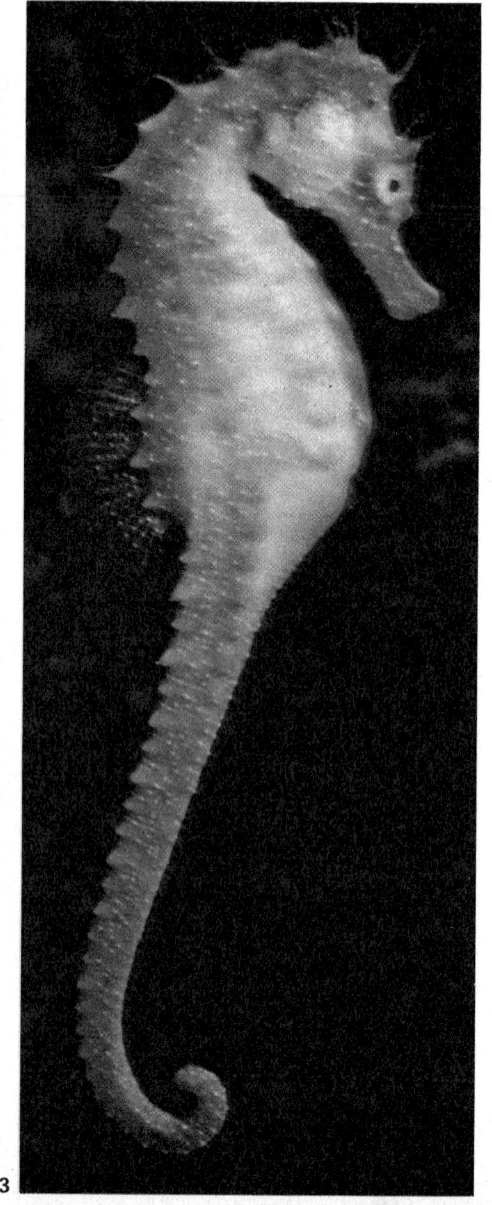

3

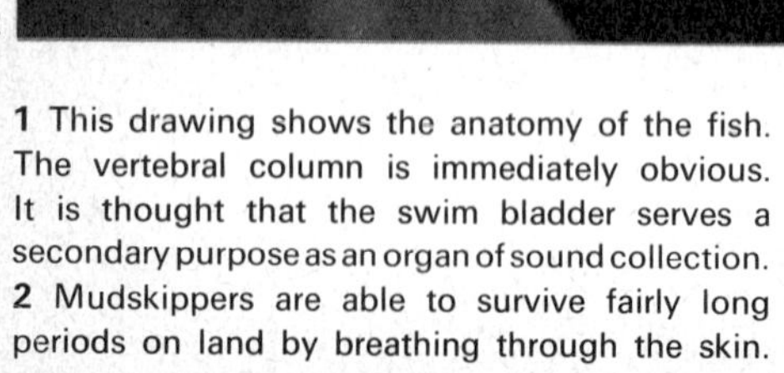

**1** This drawing shows the anatomy of the fish. The vertebral column is immediately obvious. It is thought that the swim bladder serves a secondary purpose as an organ of sound collection.
**2** Mudskippers are able to survive fairly long periods on land by breathing through the skin.

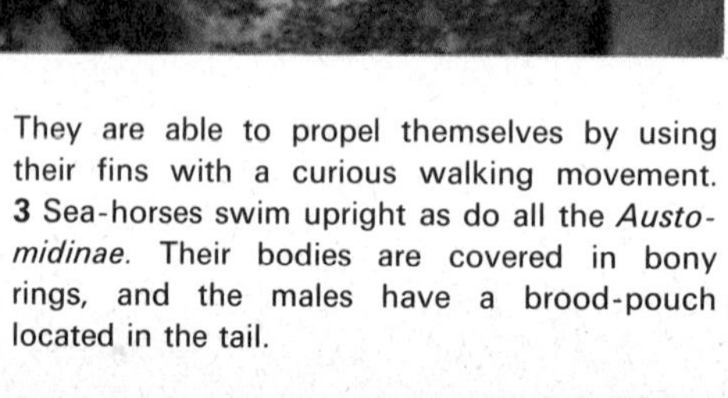

They are able to propel themselves by using their fins with a curious walking movement.
**3** Sea-horses swim upright as do all the *Austomidinae.* Their bodies are covered in bony rings, and the males have a brood-pouch located in the tail.

**1** The smooth trunk fish has an outer covering made of scales which have fused together. It is a poor swimmer and relies on its armour for protection against predators.
**2** Porcupine fish, as shown here, are able to dilate their bodies and erect their spines as a protective device. The spines are not poisonous.
**3** Catfishes are mainly found in fresh-water habitats in South America, Asia and Africa. They often build nests for the protection of their young, and sometimes the eggs are carried in the mouth of the male.
**4** Butterfly fish, found in tropical waters, have thin fins covered with scales and brush-like teeth.
**5** The lamprey is one of the jawless fishes. It seizes its prey with a powerful sucker in the centre of which is the mouth and teeth. Lampreys cause extensive damage to fisheries.

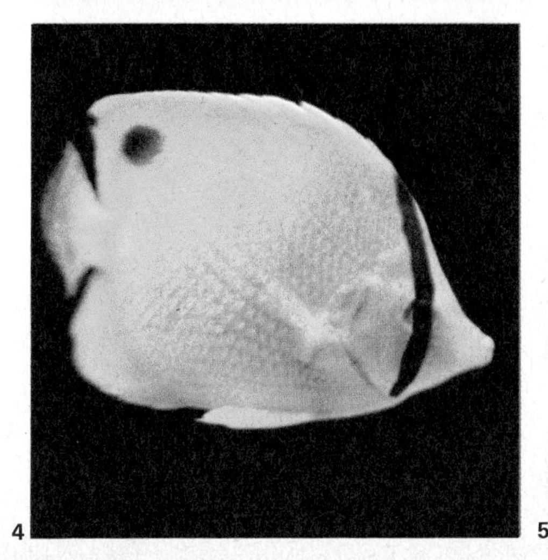

Some fish, like mudskippers, in fact do use pairs of specially developed fins to 'walk' across the sea bed.

The skin of the fish is a highly complex thing. Mostly it is smooth and flexible and dotted with various glands designed to do various jobs. For example, poison glands occur in the skins of many cartilaginous fish and, needless to say, they are extremely useful as a means of protection, often backing up to sharp spines. In very deep sea forms, there are often *photophores,* or luminous organs, embedded in the skin, and these operate as lures. The other small fry are attracted by the bright glow given out by their bigger brother and usually end up providing a meal for him.

## Gills and scales

Then there are the scales. These are divided into five categories, one of which is not found in any living animal and need not concern us here. The others include, first, the *placoids,* which are found in the skins of cartilaginous fish and are spiny and tooth-like – human skin which has been rasped by the pelt of a shark looks much as though it has been treated with coarse-grade sandpaper. Primitive bony fish sometimes carry a second class, *ganoid* scales, which are inclined to be thick and usefully protective. *Cycloid* scales are found on carp and similar fish and are what we usually mean when we talk of scales in everyday life. They are thin, relatively large, and round or oval in shape. They overlap on the skin. Finally, there are the *ctenoid* scales, which occur in the more developed of the bony fish and carry spines or teeth on their free edge.

Even so, some fish are entirely without this kind of protective armour, including the lampreys, and some bony fish, like the eel.

As already noted, most fish have gills and these are extremely important to them, for it is with this equipment that they are able to get the oxygen necessary to life. Gill openings vary in the different groups but inside they are in principle entirely similar. The gills contain finely divided blood vessels which to look at resemble a broad and dense red fringe. Water is continually taken in by the fish through the gill openings and inside comes into contact with the fringes. The fine membranes which house the blood vessels allow oxygen to pass into the blood-stream where it is distributed to various parts of the body by the pumping action of the heart.

The fish heart is placed behind and below the gills and consists of a folded tube with three or four enlargements. Contractions of the heart drive the blood to a bulb at the base of a main artery, through which it travels to the gills. After the oxygen has been picked up, the blood progresses via capillaries into another main artery – running the length of the fish beneath the backbone – from whence it is delivered to most parts of the body. While giving up its load of oxygen, the blood removes waste products and returns to the heart for recycling.

Colour plays an important part in the life of the fish. They are as colourful at times as the resplendent birds and butterflies of the tropical jungles. A beautiful if tiny example which is known to every home-aquarium owner is the vivid neon fish.

Some fish can also change the intensity of their colouring. Simply, the mechanism is as follows: the pigment cells in the skin of the fish are comparatively large and when it is necessary for the particular colour to be intensified the pigment floods through the whole of the cell. A lightening of the shade is accomplished when the pigment is concentrated into a tiny dot at the centre of the cell.

## Hiding and feeding

Since the fish can also change their colour they are adept at camouflage. This colour-change ability rests upon the fact that the colours of the fish skin are made up by relatively simple mixtures of one-colour cells. By suppressing certain of these cells the animal is able to change its overall colour. Thus a fish, which might normally be seen as green by virtue of sporting a mixture of blue and yellow cells, can become either of these colours by suppressing the other.

Vision is extemely important to many fish and it has been established that most of them are capable of distinguishing between certain colours. There is some physiological evidence to suggest that fish are near-sighted, but some at least are certainly not. The ease with which certain of them distinguish between flies is proof of this, as is the skill of the dolphin which is capable of following the track of a flying-fish when it leaves the water in order to snaffle it when it plops back to the surface. Again, there is the archer-fish which squirts a jet of water at its prey – insects and the like – so knocking them off overhanging branches and into the water where the archer-fish can deal with his meal at leisure.

The hearing mechanism employing the swim bladder has already been covered, but there is another sense-organ system unique to the breed. This is called the lateral-line sensory system. It is thought to be concerned with the apprehension of changes in pressure and is a system of pit organs, or pressure-sensitive cells, usually arranged laterally along canals situated on the animal's head and body.

1 Parrot-fishes are unusual in that they are herbivorous, and they also chew their food. They are equipped with a proper beak to snip off plants.

2 Sterlets are one of the smaller species of sturgeon, most of which periodically ascend rivers to deposit their spawn. They spend the rest of the time in the oceans.

It is possible that the system works as follows. The fish when moving through the water sets up a pressure wave ahead of it. Any solid object in front of the creature would cause this wave to bounce back, and it is thought that the lateral-line system allows the fish to tune into this invisible signal. Now, many fish are capable of emitting sounds at will – as Cousteau, the famous French underwater explorer, has pointed out, the 'silent deep' is anything but silent. In this case it is also suggested that the fish amplify the naturally-occurring pressure waves with sound waves, and thus have an effective echo-location system similar to that used by Man in underwater warfare and exploration. This faculty is often regarded as the fish's sixth sense.

The sense of smell is well developed in fish, particularly those with poor sight. For years men have marvelled at the way in which salmon and other types are able to return to the stream of their birth in order to breed. Now it is thought that they are able to distinguish the specific water course by its smell. Other species, like the shark, apparently locate their prey by the smell which it gives out, and it is also a fact that an injured or distressed fish emits a particular odour which warns its fellows of danger and causes them to disperse or swim about agitatedly.

In size, fish range from the tiny – half an inch long or so – to what is probably the largest of all fish, the whale shark. This can measure up to 70 ft. The largest sunfish and sturgeon may exceed 2,000 lb.

In terms of habitat, there is scarcely any permanent stretch of water which does not carry its quota of fish – from the oceans to the tiniest stream, and again they can exist at great depths and in extremely shallow waters. Finally, there are so many of them that their true numbers can never be known: a graphic example is that it is reckoned the Atlantic Ocean holds some trillion (million million million) of herring.

It is no surprise then that the fish bulks so large in the mind and welfare of mankind, and lucky for the scientist that this important branch on our evolutionary tree is everywhere so abundantly available for study.

# Birds 1 - Feathers and flight

The combination of wings, beaks and feathers sets the birds apart from other animal classes. From reptilian beginnings each has adapted to its own environment – even reverting to flightlessness.

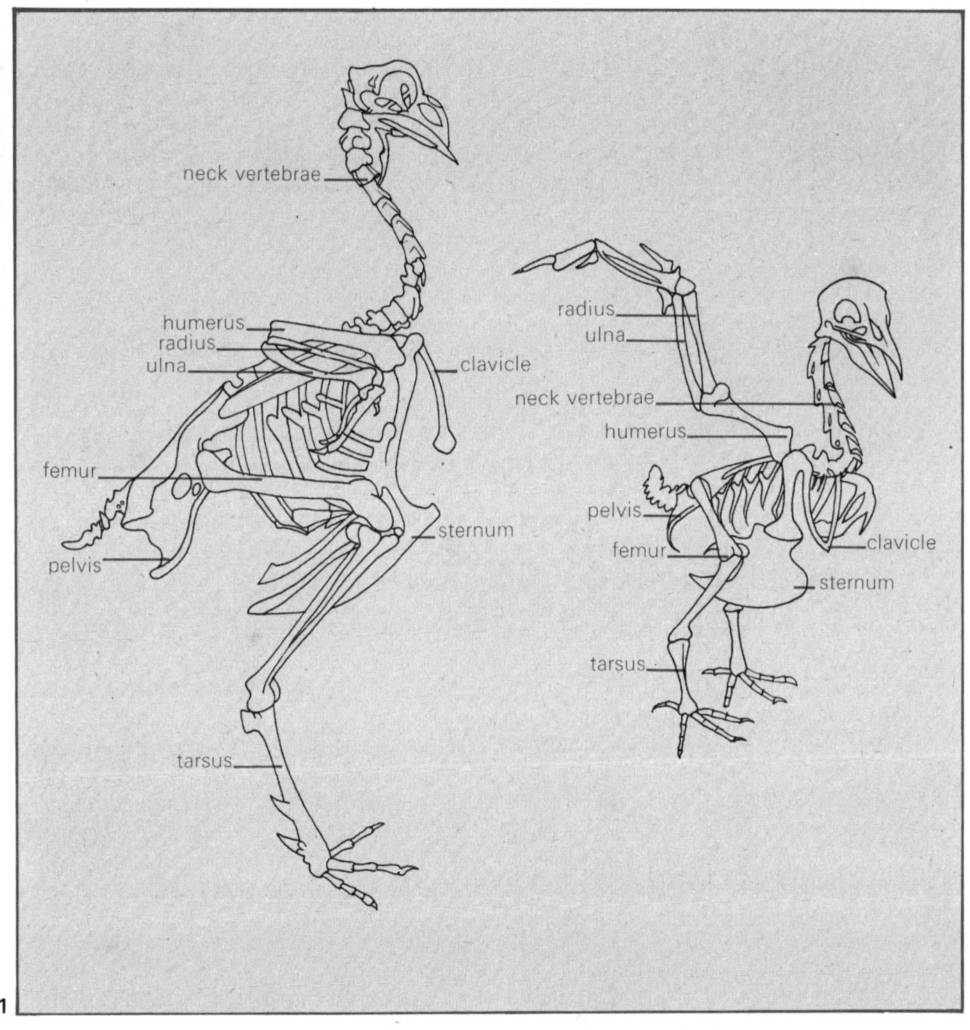

**1** Flying birds have a relatively light skeletal frame with strong and well-developed wings (right). The hen (left) is an almost flightless bird with small wings and a bulky body.
**2** White storks, once paired, remain together for life; they build their nests, frequently in exposed places, and return to them each year, gradually adding more and more material.

LIFE BEGAN in the oceans; after millions of years of development it progressed to the land and diversified slowly. At this point there only remained one area suitable for the support of animal life, the atmosphere. But progress from Nature's drawing-board to a living flying machine was slower and more complex than any process imaginable in terms of aeronautical engineering.

The birds, a branch of the vertebrates, have their origins among a group of reptiles called the *thecodonts* which were able to run about on their back limbs; the front limbs of one group of animals developed into wings.

## Learning to fly

First to appear were the *pterosaurs* which were truly winged reptiles. Their wings were not as sound in aerodynamic terms as those of the true birds and were much more easily broken.

The structure of their legs from fossil evidence seems to suggest that they had difficulty in taking off from flat surfaces, and would in any circumstances have been ungainly on the ground. Though the largest animals ever to fly must be counted among the pterosaurs, they represented something of a blind alley in the progress towards unhindered flight, and died out with most of the other reptiles at the end of the Mesozoic era.

Perhaps the most important acquisition of the animals comprising the second line of development was the feather. It is widely accepted that feathers themselves evolved from reptilian scales, but the change could hardly have been more drastic. The only similarities are that they, like the reptilian scales, are made of *keratin* (a substance produced by the skin, also responsible for hair and horn), and that they both occur in a regularized pattern over the bird's body and wings. The modern bird, incidentally, has retained scales on its legs.

Unlike scales, feathers are enormously intricate in construction and it is worth looking at them in some detail. Each feather has a quill or main shaft from which extend some 600 hair-like barbs on either side. But the resemblance to hair is extremely superficial, for each of the 1,200 offshoots carries about 800 smaller ones, and each of these smaller offshoots carries as many as three dozen tiny hooks. The whole of this complex is locked together by means of these hooks, and the marvellous interweave which results is so finely meshed that air can only just pass through. If you pick a feather from the ground and handle it roughly all the smoothing in the world will not return it to its original shape. To fit all those tiny hooks accurately together again is just not possible.

Of course in normal life the feathers of the bird do become spoiled. But they, in some unknown way, are able to re-engage the hooks by rubbing the feathers with their beaks. Eventually the feathers become irreparable and drop out during a period which occurs once or twice a year in most birds and is called the *moult*. Since the feather is so important to flight, birds tend to become less active during the moult, which lasts until the lost feathers are replaced by new ones.

Associated with the feathers are muscles which enable the bird to raise and lower them. They are, therefore, important for flight, but more relevantly at this point they also play a vital role in regulation of the bird's body heat.

Living cells are extremely vulnerable to damage by fluctuations in external temperature, so the body temperature must be kept fairly even. In the reptiles, including the extinct pterosaurs, the mechanism of heat control is not very effective; they rely on moving into shade when it is hot and the open when it is cool. Obviously then, outside factors can wreak havoc upon a reptile population; drought can wipe out suitable shade with the sudden destruction of vegetation.

By means of its feathers the bird is able to overcome this heat control problem. The feathers trap air beneath them and, as with the large-mesh string vests used by Arctic explorers, this layer of air becomes heated and proves an effective method of insulation from the cold.

But even so the usefulness of the feathers does not end here. They are vital to successful flight since the way they are distributed over the body and wings produces effective streamlining. The main supporting surfaces of the wings are comprised of long flight feathers. Banks and turns impossible for an aeroplane are open to the bird through movements of particular sections of the wing feathers.

## Wind and weather proof

Feather colouring is important both for purposes of camouflage and mating. Feathers are also associated with both waterproofing and the sense of touch. Most birds have two oil-producing glands situated near the tail; the bird when preening presses its beak against the glands, whereby it receives a coating of oil which it then transfers to the feathers, so enhancing their ability to repel water. What is not clear is how other species – some parrots, for example – manage without oil glands at all. As to touch, nerve fibres around the base of each feather provide birds with extensive sensitive areas.

Even though the feathers are crucial to both flight and temperature control, they would have been of little use in the development of the modern bird without other extensive physiological changes from the reptilian pattern.

The wings, as in the pterosaurs, depend upon the adaptation of the bone structure of the reptilian forelimbs. The wing is supported first by the upper arm (the humerus), then by the forearm (the ulna). The 'wrists' are relatively simple and the skeletal system terminates in a much extended second finger. The supporting bones are hollow and reduced to a minimum while still retaining sufficient rigidity for action; lightness is absolutely vital. An indication of the kind of weight saving which is achieved is that the frigate or man o'war bird, although having a wingspan of more than seven feet, has a skeleton which weighs a mere four ounces.

1

2

3

Apart from the wings, the rest of the skeleton consists of light, hollow bones and is suitably adapted to the bird's natural element. The breastbone, or *sternum*, extends along the bottom of the animal's body – from the base of the neck to the tail – like a thick knife-blade. Strengthened also by ribs and backbone, it forms a massive and rigid anchor for the muscle system of the wings.

When not in the air, the bird is able to walk or hop about the ground. It can do so because of the formation and positioning of its leg bones. The legs are toward the front of the body which means the bird's

**1** The most common owl in Britain, the tawny owl, has plumage consisting of fine feathers of varying colours which confuse its enemies.
**2** In America the swallow is known as the barn swallow because of the bird's close association with Man and his environment. It often builds its nest in man-made nooks and crannies.
**3** The strong, sharply curved beak of the peregrine falcon is well suited to the job of killing and dismembering its prey.
**4** A coot's nest is built among the reeds, often floating on water. The six to nine eggs are brooded by each of the parents in turn.
**5** The family *Paridae*, of which the long-tailed tit is a member, build intricate spherical nests of

moss and lichen. Through the round entrance a female feeds her young.

6 Puffins, once on the verge of extinction in Britain, are now protected birds. They are equally at home on land or in water, but are particularly good at swimming and diving for food.

7 Long, pendulous nests hanging in groups from a tree belong to weaver-birds. On closer inspection the intricately woven patterns become more apparent.

8 Oyster-catchers in profusion. Their long red bills are well designed for opening mussels, limpets and, occasionally, oysters. The female lays eggs in the smallest of hollows.

centre of gravity is situated over them; the thigh bones slant forwards and, in conjunction with the muscles of the legs, also help balancing. Thus a bird such as the flamingo is capable of standing easily on one leg, and even of going to sleep in that state.

Feet consist in most cases of four toes, three pointing forward and one back. This configuration makes it easier to move fast on foot and explains the advantage which the modern bird has over the extinct flying reptiles on the ground.

Apart from containing a relatively large brain, the bird's head is dominated by the beak, or bill, which is essentially a tool for seizing and handling food. The neck normally carries many more vertebrae than are found in mammals, and consequently has considerable mobility. In fact, such power of movement is essential in conjunction with the bill for the gathering of food.

The bird's muscular system needs to be supported by an equally powerful and efficient system of circulation and respiration. The heart is divided into left and right sections, and relatively speaking is much larger than the heart of the mammals.

## Blood, breathing and brain power

The right section pumps blood to the lungs where it takes up oxygen; the left side pumps the oxygenated blood at high pressure to the muscles of the body. The red blood cells – those which actually carry the oxygen – are capable of transporting large quantities of the gas which they are able to give up very quickly, thus keeping high the oxygen level of the tissues.

The lungs of the bird are relatively small, but that does not mean to say they are not highly efficient. The reason is that they are supported by thin-walled air sacs which help once again to lighten the body and even extend into the actual bones of the animal.

The intake of air is greatly increased in this way beyond the capability of the lungs themselves. On breathing out – expiration – it is thought that the air in the sacs passes through the lungs again where further gas exchange takes place within the circulatory system. It also makes sure that stale air is cleared fully from the lungs themselves.

The brain of the bird is well developed; it has very effective senses of hearing and eyesight. Birds react to other bird calls over fairly large distances. Likewise the excellent eyesight of this class of animals can be gauged from the way in which they are able to spot airborne predators, hawks and buzzards, when they are flying very high or a long way off.

On the other hand the sense of smell in birds is not so good. The sense of taste is good in some varieties; most will reject strongly salted food.

A bird's song is one of the greatest pleasures which animal life can give us. The voice-box of the bird is a complicated system of membranes and cartilaginous rings, and these are activated by the column of air drawn down the windpipe.

The sounds which a bird is able to emit are of the utmost importance to it. They enable the adult animals to warn of approaching enemies, to attract mates, and to let intruders know that they are entering a particular bird's territory; the young can keep in touch with their parents and show when they are hungry. The birds have inherited from their reptilian ancestors the kind of egg necessary for successful reproduction on dry land. First and foremost among the requirements is that such an egg should have a hard shell which is capable of holding the contents together. A natural consequence

1 The microscope reveals that a feather is not merely a shaft with barbs extending from it. Filaments with minute hooks lock together to form an almost airtight mesh.

2 An outsized baby for this unfortunate hedge-sparrow. The cuckoo lays eggs in the nests of other birds; when the young bird is hatched it pushes out the rightful occupants and continues to be fed even when it grows larger than its 'foster-parents'.

3 Green woodpeckers cling to the tree with their claws and inspect the bark for insects with their long beak and tongue. Nests are built in a hollow tree-trunk.

4 A brooding red-legged partridge is disturbed in the long grass. These birds lay 10 to 16 eggs in a depression in the ground.

5 Found near lakes, the black and white Australian mudlark constructs its nest with mud reinforced with hair, feathers and grass.

is that the egg must be fertilized by the male before it leaves the body of the female, and in some cases the male bird possesses a penis although more usually the sperm is transferred by external bodily contact. Hatching is sometimes aided by the parents sitting on the eggs; sometimes, as in the case of the cuckoo, by other parents. In warm climates, however, the mother may simply leave her eggs behind and allow the sun and the warm earth to do the job.

Periods of incubation vary enormously. In some smaller birds it can be less than a fortnight; in the larger ones such as eagles and albatrosses it can range from two to three months. The variety of nests built for the eggs is enormous. Some merely use the ground, others build the classic cup shape of mud and interwoven grasses, and yet others rest their brood on nothing more substantial than a pile of twigs.

Clearly the animal which can fly has a number of advantages over his land- or water-locked compatriot. When danger threatens on the ground it can move at high speed to safety. If the right kind of food or vegetation is destroyed in an area, the bird can take to the wing and look for new pastures.

It is, therefore, something of a surprise that some species of bird are flightless, while retaining all or most of the other characteristics of the breed. It might be thought that these were types which had not progressed so far along the evolutionary road, but this is not so. In fact, they have degenerated from types which *could* fly but have since lost the ability.

Why this should have happened is not known for sure, it is only possible to guess. For one thing it has been found that many flightless birds occur or have occurred on islands, and the likelihood is that they were not bothered by mammal predators. In New Zealand, where there are no native animals of this type, not only the kiwi but also the duck, owl and penguin are flightless.

## Flightless and flying high

For the ostrich, a native of Africa, this theory does not hold true because the continent has perhaps more than its share of predatory mammals. In this case it has been suggested that the large size of the birds, and perhaps their fleetness of foot, has allowed them to live on without the ability to fly.

Whatever the reason for the flightlessness of these animals, they are mavericks or degenerates from the normal. Birds have achieved their extraordinarily wide distribution in the world because they are able to fly. They have conquered the skies in a way that Man, even in a modern aeroplane, can never hope to emulate.

# Birds 2 - Soaring far and wide

Almost 9,000 species of bird live in the world today. Through their ability to fly, birds have inhabited almost every corner of the world – even to the edges of the great polar icecaps.

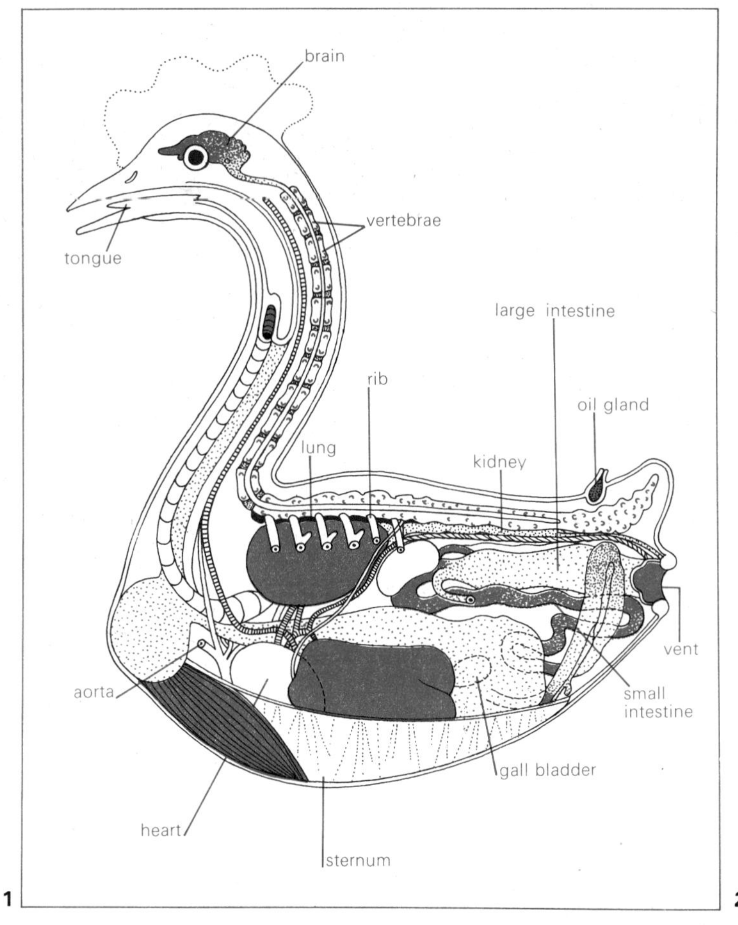

1 The internal structure of a male domestic fowl. Red jungle fowl from Asia were first domesticated about 5,000 years ago. Members of descendant species now outnumber the human race.
2 Dull brown in colour, the emu is the second largest living bird – but it cannot fly. It inhabits the Australian deserts. The male builds the nest, incubates and broods the chicks.

'FREE AS A BIRD.' How many times must these words have been used to describe a blithe and carefree state, shorn of all depressing restrictions? In one sense, the expression represents our wistful yearning to be able to get away from it all with as little trouble as these flying vertebrates apparently experience. It also reflects, by implication, the admiration which Man has felt from time unremembered, for the grace and efficiency with which the birds exploit the skies.

Nobody can forget the majesty and power in the wingbeat of a circling Golden eagle or a transitory swan. Smaller birds – in particular the tiny, colourful hummingbird – possess a manoeuvrability which is breathtaking.

The internal structure of the bird is designed for lightness. It has slender and hollow bones, and its lungs are supplemented by air sacs. Similarly its feathers, while important for maintaining body heat, are also light and effectively streamline the bird's body. But it is the wings which really do the job of raising the bird into the air and maintaining it there. They provide lift and propulsion unlike the wings of the aeroplane which provide only lift.

The important wing movement to gain altitude is the downstroke, for it is during this movement that the under surface of the wing presses down upon the air beneath it. Naturally the air offers resistance to the wide-spread wing, and this levers the bird upwards in much the same way that oars propel a rowing boat.

The most important part of the wing in this context is the tip. Its vertical arc is greater than that of the rest of the wing and, like the blade of the oar, it produces the greatest amount of leverage.

It is important for propulsion. For forward flight, the leading edge of the wingtip is held slightly lower than the trailing one, which means that the tips not only press downwards against the resistance of the air, but backwards as well. The analogy with oars is even more fitting in this case.

When it comes to the upstroke of the wingbeat cycle, the front edge of the wing is raised relative to the trailing edge. As the bird is still moving forward by the force of the previous downstroke, the air through which it is passing builds up against the underside of the wing. At the same time the wing assumes a delicate curve so that the flow of air across it is smooth and as little speed as possible is lost. This situation cannot last long. In most conditions the bird will be gradually descending and will continue to do so, unless it begins the wingbeat cycle again, with another downstroke. What is called level flight, is nothing of the sort when it comes to bird movement. In fact, the creatures progress in a series of arcs, though these may be so short that the flight path may appear level.

## Soaring and gliding

There are important areas of flying which do not depend upon the flapping of the wings, but on spread enabling birds to soar and glide. When gliding the wing is held in the same configuration – that is, with the leading edge held higher than the trailing one – as in the upstroke of level flight mentioned above. But, since in this case there are no downstrokes to maintain height for the bird, it must sink, however gradually, even though it moves forward.

Soaring involves the use of the wings solely as sails. They perform a relatively passive role and are used merelv to collect the pressure of air currents which are moving upwards from the surface of the Earth. The upcurrents consist, in one form, of air which is heated at ground level by various means – a town, for example, emits a good deal of heat – and consequently rises. These are called *thermals*. Upwelling occurs when a surface breeze rushing across the ground is deflected upwards by meeting a cliff or other obstruction. Either way, the birds are capable of employing these columns of air to carry them to great heights.

The formation of the wings of a bird clearly reflect the type of flying it does. Creatures like the buzzard and frigate-bird have long and broad wings because they spend a great deal of time gliding or soaring. A long wing cannot be moved through its arc as quickly as a short wing with the same expenditure of power, so birds which depend for a living on very quick and agile movement – the sparrow hawk, for example – have wings which are short and broad. Because air will not flow smoothly over a very broad wing at speed, the fast flying birds tend to have narrow swept-back wings.

The highest flyers seem to be found in the region of the Himalayas; the alpine chough, a rather dull-looking black bird, has risen as high as Everest – about 29,000 feet. Other champions from the same area are the lammergeier, which has reached 25,000 feet, and the red billed chough and wall creeper which have attained 21,000 feet.

Fantastic claims have been made for the speeds which birds have achieved in the air. As much as 200 mph has been attributed to the brown-throated spine-tailed swift of Asia, but the observer was not equipped with reliable timing apparatus. In all such cases the claims emerging must be treated with caution. However, it has been proved conclusively that peregrine falcons have achieved as much as 180 mph when swooping on their prey, but here it might be said that they are falling rather than actually flying.

## Humming-bird 'helicopter'

In level flight the racing-pigeon has reached a creditable speed of 94 mph. Other speedy birds are the loon (90 mph) and once again the high flying lammergeier (79·5 mph). Most birds, of course, never exceed 40 mph, but an interesting exception is the ruby-throated humming-bird, which can hover like a helicopter – maintaining its position with 55 wingbeats a second – and fly at 60 mph.

Some birds habitually cover enormous distances on their migratory flights, the journeys which are, it is thought, prompted by changing climatic conditions. 'One swallow does not make a summer', but when there are plenty of them around it usually means that the British summer is well under way. Few people realize, however, that these relatively tiny birds have flown all the way from Africa. The Manx shearwater has been known to travel 3,000 miles and the white-fronted goose commutes from Greenland to Ireland, a distance of some 2,000 miles across the choppy featureless surface of the Atlantic.

There is some evidence to suggest that birds navigate by the sun during the day and the stars at night, but exactly how the brain uses this positional information as a basis for action is not at all clear. At other times it is known that the creatures do depend upon visual clues from the ground below. They have been seen following the indentations and outcroppings of shore lines. No doubt they also find the meanderings of rivers valuable from a navigational point of view since these make strong visual patterns against the green, brown or other colour of the land.

There are about 8,600 living species of bird and there is no area of the world which does not support some avian life. Some areas, however, are more abundantly populated than others. The North Pole

**1** To discover migration routes and other bird movements, ornithologists ring the legs of selected specimens – in this case it is the common black-backed gull.
**2** The male whinchat calls for a mate after returning to England from winter migration. A female that likes the bush the male has chosen will nest with him beneath it.
**3** Flamingoes in Europe and Africa live in large flocks in shallow water. They possess a beak for filtering food from the water and can stand for a long time on one leg.
**4** The great crested grebe flies poorly and is unhappy on land. If the female is disturbed on her nest she covers her eggs and then dives into the water.

3

1

4

2

**5** The delicate wings and fantail of the Chinese bluepie are beautifully depicted in *Birds of Asia* by the famous British ornithologist, John Gould.
**6** Long-tailed macaws from Central and South America, the largest and most colourful parrots, are good 'speakers'. Note the nut-cracking beaks.
**7** A circling vulture is the sign of impending doom. The king vulture from southern America is a scavenger feeding on carrion. Its wing-span can reach over six feet.

has been visited by at least four species of bird, but only skuas visit the South Pole. The Antarctic continent supports 16 species of bird, mostly along its shores and on its islands but also many miles inland.

Other poorly endowed areas are oceans, deserts, or systems of islands (archipelagos). Few birds inhabit islands because remoteness has made them difficult for the birds to reach from the larger land masses, and thus colonization has been restricted.

The number of species increases considerably in the temperate areas of the world – Great Britain and Ireland, for example, have about 450, Japan has 425. But the really big counts are reserved for the densely forested areas of the world like the Congo and the Amazon belt of South America. The country with the largest share of the world's bird life is Columbia, where a total of 1,700 bird species have been noted. In their splendid and comprehensive guide to ornithology, *The World of Birds,* James Fisher and Roger Tory Peterson call Columbia 'the heartland of ornithological variety on our planet'.

This distribution pattern has naturally required considerable special adaptations in the animals; it is instructive to look briefly at the subdivisions of the class from this point of view.

Some 600 living species are adapted for life on or in water. They include the beautiful and stately flamingoes. These birds stalk through the shallows of the warm African lakes repeatedly dipping their strongly curved bills into the water to feed. They suck the liquid into their beaks in a steady stream and eject it from the corners of their mouths. On its way it passes through a filter system which collects the food content. Similarly, the heron moves about in the shallows on its stilt-like legs, but is able to spear luckless fish and other small animals with rapier-like thrusts of its sharp beak. Webbed feet are another modification for life in water – to be seen commonly in the swans, geese and ducks.

## Life without land

Most of the water birds of this type feed by poking their heads beneath the surface of the water; others bob right under or use their webbed feet for swimming beneath the surface. They may be carnivores or vegetarians; an interesting example of the former, and one which is specially adapted, is the oyster-catcher. Its bill is so constructed that it can be used like a powerful chisel to knock limpets and molluscs from the rocks.

Most of these birds confine themselves to fresh water but there are about 260 further species which have taken to life at sea. In some instances adaptation has gone so far that they drink only sea water and spend many years without touching down on dry land at all. An example of this is the albatross, but the majority, such as puffins and gulls, live at least part of their lives ashore. The cormorant is one of these but this bird has taken to the water with such relish that is uses its wings like giant fins to swim about beneath the surface in search of food. In the East, incidentally, these birds are used to catch fish for fishermen. The bird is attached to a thin line so that it can be recovered once it has dived; and it is prevented from eating its catch by a ring placed around its neck which stops it swallowing.

The birds of prey are divided into two groups: the day hunting types, or *Falconiformes;* and those that operate at night, the *Owls.* These predators generally have very powerful talons, with which to grab their prey, and sharply hooked beaks with which to tear it up if it cannot be eaten whole.

The daylight hunters are broad winged and soar to great heights, dropping like stones to take their victim on the ground, or in some cases, if it is a smaller bird, while still in flight. The daylight group includes eagles, ospreys and falcons, but there are others less well endowed with talons – vultures, buzzards and the like – which feed on dead meat, carrion. The group varies greatly in the size of individual species. Apart from the large ones already mentioned it also includes the tiny falconet, which employs all the fierce skills of its bigger cousins to seize and kill insects.

The owls dispose of their victims in the same way as the daytime predators, that is with beak and claw. But obviously they have eyesight which is adapted to seeing in the dark and their hearing is extremely acute, allowing them to assess the range and direction of sounds.

The most brightly coloured of all the birds are to be found in the equatorial forests, and a great many of these belong to the fruit and seed eating group. They exist in great numbers because the forests provide a never-ending supply of their dietary requirements. Seeds and nuts often have hard shells so the nut-cracking species, which include some parrots, have a strong beak with sharp edges to do the job. Much more remarkable are the birds which live, at least in part, on honey. Among these are the humming-birds, which carry out their feeding while still in flight; they push their beaks into the flower as they hover above it and suck out the honey. The sword-billed hummer is found in the Andes and has a five-inch bill which is longer than the rest of its body.

A further division in the family of birds is provided by the *omnivores* – those that will eat vegetable matter, insects and even small mammals. In Britain, for example, the skylark eats both insects and the seeds of weeds, a relatively sedate diet; but the scarlet-rumped tanager from Central America is much more adventurous. Its intake ranges from bananas, through spiders, to mice and eggs.

Birds which feed on insects also occur in great numbers. Many of them hunt on the wing and are capable of great speed and manoeuvrability. Among these are the swifts and swallows, both of which fly enormous distances back and forth over the same area during a day's feeding. Most birds give the wasp a wide berth when it comes to eating, but not so the shrike, which has learnt how to pluck the sting out of the insect before it is eaten. This is, of course, a behavioural adaptation rather than a physical one. Also of interest here, are those birds like the South American ant pipit and tanager, which follow the ant armies and feed on both the ants themselves and the other insects which the marching column disturbs.

Next, there are the *ratites,* or flightless birds, of which there are 46 living species. The ostrich, emu and kiwi are included in this group.

## Birds for food

The game birds are much hunted by Man as a source of meat. They include the pheasant, partridge, grouse and quail, and the turkey. Some of these are able to fly efficiently but others are less well equipped for aerial manoeuvring. Most of them are very quick on their feet and often use this method combined with short flights to evade danger.

Other birds used for food were long ago domesticated by Man. Most of these have been bred specifically to provide meat and are ill-adapted for life in the wild.

The ability to fly has enabled birds to conquer both land and ocean throughout the world. They have adapted in many different ways to meet the challenges of colonization, but there are many qualities which even now we do not understand.

**1** The northern gannet lives around the northern shores of the Atlantic. It hunts fish and is an excellent diver and flyer. Although nesting in colonies each pair has only one egg.

**2** Reminiscent of a sentry dressed in the traditional uniform of some exotic state, the Californian tufted quail also keeps watch for enemies, its plume erect on the crown of its head.

# Reptiles 1 - Life on land

**How they breathe and reproduce, their skin texture and limb development are features which mark the reptiles as one of the most critical stages in the evolution of the higher vertebrates.**

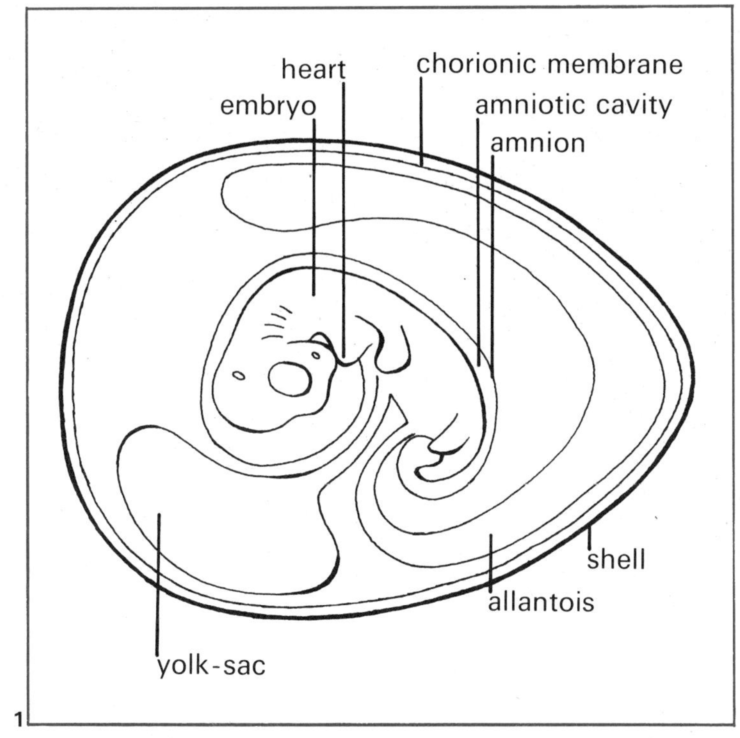


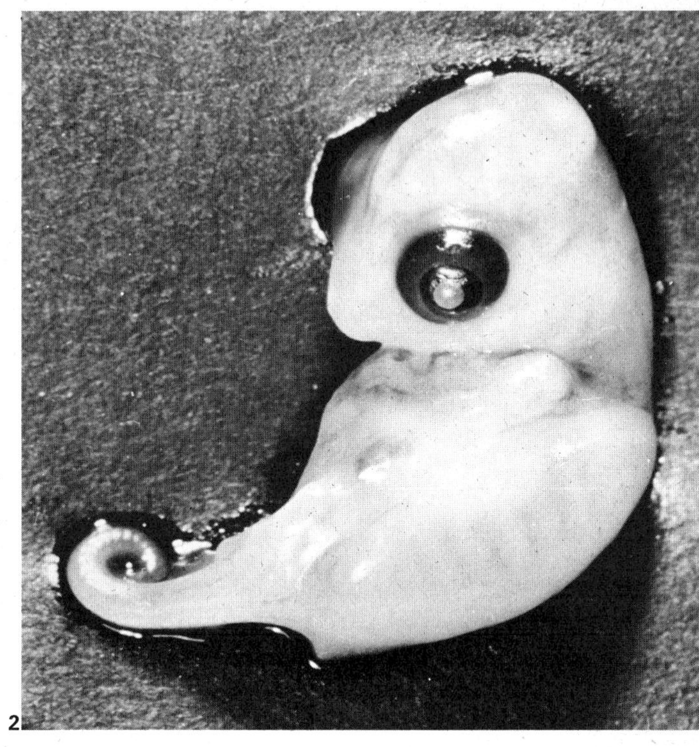

1 Diagrammatic representation of a reptilian egg shows the four sacs or membranes, the *chorion, amnion, yolk-sac* and *allantois,* which are essential for the growth of the embryo.

2 The two-month-old embryo of a snapping turtle is exposed by removing part of its shell. In later life this variety spends most of its time in water and can be very aggressive.

LIFE WOULD HAVE no chance of reaching the level which we see around us in the higher vertebrates if it had not adapted in ways to make it possible to leave the water for dry land. The change was not easy, and Nature had two attempts at the job, both involving members of the animal group, the vertebrates.

From the first partially successful attempt, the amphibians, there stemmed the class of animals called *reptiles*. These have become fully adapted for life on dry land, although some still spend a great deal of time in the water. A hundred million years ago this class of animals was dominant, but outside pressures eventually brought the Age of Reptiles to an end. Now their numbers are reduced to a mere handful of types: the crocodiles, turtles and tortoises, snakes and lizards.

But before looking at the extinct or even the living species of reptile in any detail, we should first examine the general physical characteristics which have allowed reptiles their independence of water as a habitat.

From their amphibian forebears, the reptiles inherited lungs. These vary in sophistication, but in general they are superior to the lungs possessed by amphibians. In the case of the latter, the lungs are not efficient enough to supply the animal with all the oxygen it needs for life. Intake has to be supplemented by breathing through the skin. The reptile lung on the other hand has no such limitations.

Again, the reptilian system by which air is actually taken into the body is more advanced. The frog (amphibian), for example, gulps in air by expanding the muscles of its throat. These are then contracted and the air is pushed into the lung, the same air being used again and again until the oxygen content is exhausted.

The reptile, on the other hand, possesses a system of muscles which enables it to expand and contract its rib cage. This causes the lungs to work like a pair of bellows and breathing takes place in a more steady and controlled fashion.

This improved breathing apparatus has freed the reptilian skin from its breathing function and allows it to be used for another purpose, water conservation. Since the skin of the amphibian is permeable to air, it also tends to be permeable to water and one reason why frogs and toads are clammy to touch is that they are permanently undergoing a process of evaporation of body liquids through the skin. Constant replenishment of this supply of water in the body is yet another reason why amphibians customarily live close to water. The reptile has overcome this problem by retaining a physiological attribute of a more distant ancestor, the fish. These are scales.

Reptilian scales are overlapping and

3 Crocodilians lay clutches of about 30 eggs. At the end of its snout the emerging crocodile has an *'egg-tooth'* for breaking out of its hard, waterproof shell.

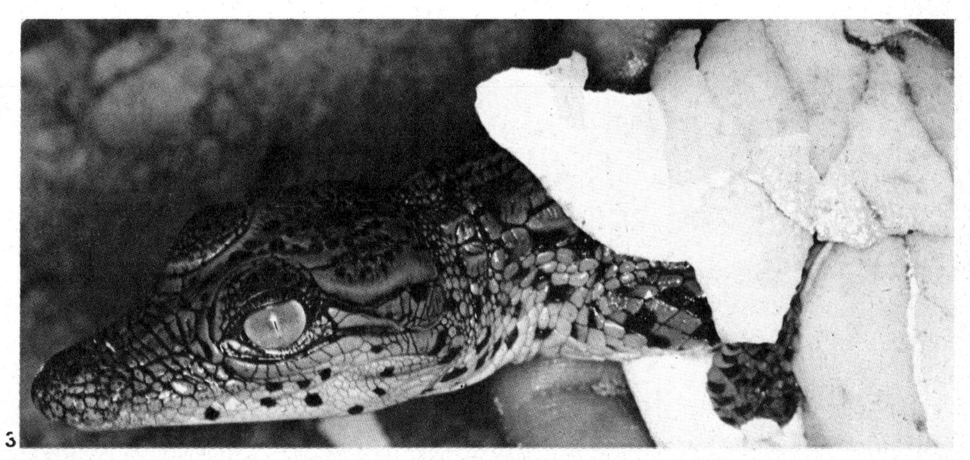

**1** Confronted with an adversary, the harmless grass snake puffs itself up menacingly; if this fails, it acts as though dead.

**2** Slender European whip snakes are extremely well camouflaged to live in the trees, their natural habitat.

**3** The slow-worm, despite its snake-like appearance is a harmless, legless lizard. Here a female is surrounded by her young.

consist of a hard, dry substance called *keratin*, which is virtually impermeable to water. It is therefore both a form of lightweight but effective protection to the body and also precludes loss of body fluids by evaporation. The crocodile or snake, if provided with sufficient drinking water, is unlikely to suffer the fate of desiccation which so often befalls the frog and toad.

However in one other aspect reptiles are not well equipped – dealing with violent changes in temperature. It is obvious that beneath the surface of the water such fluctuations are much smaller than they are on dry land. This is concerned on the one hand with the physical nature of water and its potential for storing and losing heat, and on the other with changing seasons experienced on land where warm day inevitably gives way to relatively cold night.

Reptiles, like fish and amphibians, are what is generally termed 'cold blooded'. This is a splendidly inaccurate but widely employed term for what in science is called *poikilothermy*. What is really meant is that the blood heat of these animals tends to move up or down until it coincides with the temperature of their environment.

A very wide range of temperature would, however, cause irreparable harm to the delicate mechanism of the animal cells. To combat this possibility the reptile has been forced to develop ways of maintaining a fairly constant body heat.

In this the class has been only partially successful. Some lizards possess a reasonably elegant system by which they are able to change the intensity of their colouring in response to temperature change. They do so by contracting or enlarging the pigment contained in the cells in their skin. Thus they will become darker – with enlarged pigmentation – on cold days so that their skin absorbs as much of the available heat as possible, while on hot days the pigmentation is contracted and consequently the skin becomes lighter. The effect of this is to reflect the heat in much the same way as the white headcloth of an Arab.

This is only partially effective and most reptiles tend to hide from the sun when it is very hot and even burrow in the ground. In short they are better able to deal with cold than with excess heat, although they do need the average temperature of their surroundings to be fairly high in order to flourish.

Yet another important consequence for animal life of the change from a watery habitat to existence on land is that the body no longer has the support afforded by its buoyancy in water. For the animal to get about it needs limbs strong enough to support and move it.

Most reptiles, therefore, have four relatively powerful legs. (In the turtle these have become adapted for such purposes as swimming; in the snake, the legs have disappeared completely.) These limbs are paired, the forward set being connected to the bones of the pectoral girdle, the rear set to the pelvic girdle.

The legs are thought to be a development of the paired fins found in fish, and in bone structure they resemble the skeletal organization of the fins occurring in some extinct and some modern fish. In both, the fin or limb stems from one basal length of bone; there are two bones in the 'forearm', several smaller bones in the 'wrist', and the system ends with a fan of five articulated bones.

But perhaps the greatest factor in the freeing of reptiles, and thus all the higher vertebrates, from dependence on water as a habitat is to be found in birth and reproduction.

As we saw, the amphibian is forced to return to the water in order to produce its young. This is first and foremost because the infant needs water to support its life processes in both the egg and larval stages. Amphibian larvae are essentially fishlike; the tadpole, for example, has both fins for swimming and gills during its life up to the *metamorphosis* when it changes into the adult form.

On the other hand, reptiles have evolved an egg which can be laid and hatched out on land. There is no fishlike larval stage; the young emerge from the egg as small replicas of their parents. In some cases the egg is held inside the mother until it hatches, and the young therefore come into the world live.

The importance of the development of the land-adapted egg is to make it even more unnecessary for reptiles to live where there are large stretches of water, and it is no surprise that they have been able to colonize, at one time or another, most of the land surface of the Earth.

1 The Indian python is also to be found in the Malay Peninsula. The female coils around her eggs and acts as an incubator.

2 Hermann's tortoise is found almost exclusively on the northern coasts of the Mediterranean even though it is a land animal.

3 The common iguana is a vegetarian and lives in South America. The throat sac, or *dewlap,* distends when the animal is excited.

But what are the requirements for an egg which will be successful on dry land? The first quality needed is without doubt a shell, which at one and the same time must prevent desiccation and also hold the contents together. The egg must contain sufficient food and water for the embryo to go through all its stages of development right up to adult shape before leaving the shell. Finally, it must have some means of storing or disposing of the waste products of the developmental process in such a way as to protect the embryo from poisoning.

All of these requirements are met in the reptile egg, one of the most elegant examples of natural design, a design which the reptiles have passed on to some mammals and birds.

It works like this. The egg is provided with a hard shell – unlike that of the fish and amphibia – and it is made of rigid calcareous material which at one and the same time is rigid enough to support the contents and is also impermeable to water. It is not, however, impermeable to gases.

Within the shell the infant is usually cushioned by a layer of *albumen*, of which almost 90 per cent is water. Next comes the embryo itself with its attached sacs, each of which has an important duty to perform. The *yolk-sac* provides the developing reptile's food; the *amnion* sac contains the embryo's supply of water in which it is constantly bathed. It is from this sac that this kind of egg gets its name. – the *amniotic* egg.

## Caring for the embryo

The *allantoic* sac deals with all the waste products of the embryo. First, it holds liquid waste in its interior, and secondly, since it is connected to the circulatory system of the embryo, it is able to carry the gaseous waste to the inner surface of the shell through which it passes to the outside world. By the same means the sac collects in its blood system the oxygen coming in through the shell and passes it back to the embryo. In this sense it is both a respiratory organ and a waste-disposal unit.

Finally, the *chorion* is the sac which surrounds both the *amnion* and the *allantois*. It assists the former in the job of providing the aquatic medium which is so necessary to the development of the embryonic reptile. Further, though the allantois and shell are separated by it, the chorion still allows the gaseous exchange to take place.

The amniotic egg is a complicated arrangement, but although it frees the reptile from the need to breed in water, it has required one other adaptive change in these animals. The hard shell of the eggs makes it necessary for them to be fertilized before that shell is formed – while the egg is still within the mother. Most male reptiles, therefore, possess some type of intromittent organ, or penis, for the injection of the sperm.

1 Lizards are preyed on by snakes, weasels – and human beings. If part of the tail is lost, it will grow again, but with uneven scales different from those of the original tail.

2 Tortoises lay their eggs in the ground. A 'nest' is excavated and the eggs placed in it. The mother then leaves the job of incubation to the warmth of the earth.

The modifications so far discussed are backed by changes in the nervous and sensory systems. Such changes are necessary for the simple reason that without them the reptiles would be unable to make full use of the other faculties which make fully terrestrial life a possibility.

Crucial among these developments is the sense of hearing. In simple terms the reptilian ear, like that of other land vertebrates is made up of two parts: the sense organ itself and the means of transmission of the sound waves.

The device for performing the latter function is called the *tympanic membrane*, or *eardrum*. In many reptiles this membrane is visible on the side of the head. In others it lies protected in a pit.

What happens is this; the airborne sound waves beat upon the taut tympanum and are then transmitted across a cavity called the *middle ear* by a slender bone, the *ossicle*. Travelling along this the signals finally reach the second part of the hearing mechanism, called the inner ear. This is where the actual hearing is done in the sense that the sound waves are turned into signals which impart information to the brain.

Again, the eye of the reptile is adapted to do the job of seeing out of water where the refractive index is different and for that reason exhibits significant differences from the eye of the fish. For example, the *cornea* in the fish eye is nothing more than a transparent window. It has no function in focusing the image on the retina. In the reptile the cornea has become curved and plays a considerable part in image formation.

As the reptile eye is now out of water for a good deal of the time its surface must be kept clean by some mechanism in the animal itself. The reptilian eye has therefore developed eyelids – usually three in all. The first two are an upper and a lower lid to each eye, of which the lower is the larger and more mobile. However, it is the third lid which is thought to do the cleaning. This is almost transparent and sweeps backwards from the inner corner of the eye across the surface of the cornea. In mammals this third eyelid has degenerated and exists only vestigially in the inner corner of each eye.

As a footnote, the colour of the reptilian eye is often bright red or yellow, and it has been shown that many of them have the ability to distinguish between colours, although, for some reason, this is thought not to apply to the crocodile.

## One per cent brain

The move from water has also brought about the disappearance of the nervous systems associated with gill breathing and also that peculiar organ found in fish called the *lateral line system*. This is generally accepted to be a means by which fish receive information about changes of pressure in the water around them, and by which they may even locate objects in their path and maintain formation with other fish in their particular school. Clearly the terrestrial reptile has no further use for such mechanisms and consequently they have disappeared.

Although the brain shows some development in terms of size from that of amphibia and fish, it remains relatively small in comparison to that of mammals and in comparison to the reptile's own size. It is unlikely to amount to more than one per cent of the animal's body weight. Even in the mighty dinosaurs, some of which weighed as much as 20 tons, it is unlikely that the brain accounted for more than a few ounces and was probably only a few inches long.

All these adaptations have enabled the reptile to survive without dependence on an aquatic environment. Without ignoring the variations and peculiarities which characterize individual types within the reptile family, the physical attributes of this class of animals sets them apart from their antecedents to form perhaps the most important link in the evolutionary chain which has led to the higher vertebrate life on Earth today.

# Reptiles 2 - The defeated conquerors

The kings of the Earth, the mighty dinosaurs, have long since faded into extinction. Only four of the original 16 orders have survived, but reptiles still inhabit most corners of the world.

A resting place for a large number of 'grinning' American alligators. The short, broad head distinguishes the family *Alligatoridae* from the slimmer and longer-headed crocodiles.

SAY 'PREHISTORIC ANIMALS' to the average person and they immediately think of the dinosaurs. Yet even then they are not usually thinking of dinosaurs in general but of the giant *Brontosaurus,* merely one of the group. There is little notion of the range and diversity of the reptiles which existed, or that the way the number of species have dwindled is one of the most dramatic happenings in natural history.

The Age of Reptiles – that is the period during which they dominated the land areas of the Earth – was in fact the whole of the Mesozoic era, which began about 205 million years ago, although reptiles did exist in some numbers before that. In fact, they began their climb from origins among the *labyrinthodont amphibians* much earlier in the Paleozoic era.

The dinosaurs were without doubt the most impressive of the reptiles in the Mesozoic era, but they were not only large like the brontosaurus.

The savage *Tyrannosaurus,* about 50 feet long, walked on its hind legs and was a meat eater. Its enormous and powerful head was equipped with sharp sabre-like teeth, but its tiny front legs were rather feeble in marked contrast to the rear ones. The *Stegosaurus* (the name refers to the armour plates which ran down its back and suggest roofing tiles) had only weak teeth and jaws and is considered therefore to have been a vegetarian. Also in contrast to the tyrannosaurus it walked on all fours. Some reptiles moved towards exploiting the air; these were the *Pterosaurs* or winged reptiles, which though they did not lead directly to birds as we know them, were certainly successful for a time.

That the pterosaurs could fly was due to the extraordinary development of their forelimbs. In the pterosaur the fourth finger of the forelimb became enormously extended, the fifth finger disappeared and an area of skin stretched from this extension to the sides of the body to form the wing. Some were no bigger than modern bats, although others boasted wing spans of up to 29 feet and were the biggest animals ever to fly.

Birds as we know them also emerged from a reptilian root, the *thecodonts,* which also produced the dinosaurs. In its early life this line progressed less quickly than that which produced the pterosaurs but ultimately it emerged superior.

But what brought about the end of the Age of Reptiles? Why were the number of reptilian species so reduced at the end of the Mesozoic era? At this distance of time it is of course extremely difficult to answer these questions, and many of the reasons given can be dismissed as fanciful. There was probably more than one causal factor.

First, it may be that the temperature of the Earth rose towards the close of the era and all reptiles found difficulty in dealing with increases in temperature. There is fossil evidence that plant life took on a sudden spurt in the later Mesozoic and this

Crocodiles lie submerged with only their eyes above the surface. They can eat in this position – folds of skin inside the mouth prevent them from gulping large quantities of water.

The Egyptian cobra, although smaller and less dangerous than his Indian brothers, is still a man-killer. These snakes kill by ejecting venom into their wounded prey.

1 Almost a 'living fossil', the Tuatara is the only survivor of a group of reptiles common during the Mesozoic era. Today it lives on a few islands near New Zealand and is protected.
2 Tiny hooks on the undersides of the gecko's toes enable the animal to run very fast and cling to almost any surface. The name is derived from the repetitive 'geck-o' call of some species.
3 The Gila Monster is one of only two known poisonous lizards. It lives on small birds, eggs and young mammals, but can fast for long periods after storing food in its tail.

could be accounted for in climatic terms (which would support the temperature-increase theory), but it might also be due to geological changes.

However, if the climate did fluctuate in this way, it may be that the reptiles perished simply because things got too hot for them. With the evaporation of the lakes the animals would be without facilities for hiding from the sun.

## The problem of heat

It is likely that the larger reptiles disappeared leaving the relatively smaller forms of life, because the greater the surface area which the animal presents to the sun, the bigger are its problems in terms of resisting overheating. Many could not overcome this inability to deal effectively with temperature fluctuations outside the water.

Modern *Reptilia* are represented by four different orders. The three most common are the *Squamata* (lizards and snakes); the *Crocodilia* (crocodiles, caimans and alligators); the *Chelonia* (turtles and tortoises). The fourth order is the *Rhynchocephalia* and this has only one surviving species, the Tuatara which is found only on small islands of the North Island of New Zealand. Of the four orders, the Squamata is by far the largest. There are over 2,000 species of lizard and about 2,400 species of snake.

The typical lizard has an elongated body with two pairs of limbs terminating in five-toed feet. Some less typical kinds, however, resemble snakes more closely in that they have no limbs at all, or at best merely rudimentary ones.

The difference between lizards and snakes lies firstly in the distribution of scales. The snake has transverse scales across its belly, while in the case of the lizard that area is covered like the rest of the body in small horny scales. Secondly there is the formation of the jaw. A snake is able to swallow meals much bigger in diameter than itself. This is because the jaws are cunningly articulated, the lower one being split into halves connected by rubbery tissue. The lizard has no such ability.

In one way, however, all lizards are snake-like. This lies in the way their bodies curve as they move across the ground, and is a function of the way the legs are constructed. Where legs do not exist, the lizard gets about in even more of a snake-like style.

Most of the sub-order live by hunting and are flesh eaters. Those that do eat vegetable matter are not strictly vegetarian.

The lizards have an interesting trick or two up their sleeves when it comes to survival. Some can go without water for extremely long periods, slaking their thirst by sucking the dew from stones. Some varieties are able to lose their tail when seized by another animal leaving the lizard to scamper off to safety, apparently unharmed. The reason for this is that such animals have a disc of gristle inserted into the middle of their tails, between two of the vertebrae. The muscles and veins in each part are so designed that they will easily break apart at this point and the damage is minimal. Later a new tail will grow, but it is unusual for it to reach the length of the original. Because of their survival equipment, lizards are to be found all over the world, except in polar regions. However, they flourish most happily along the equator and decrease in numbers progressively towards north or south.

The sub-order of lizard is itself divided into several families, and of these the *monitors* contain the largest types. The

A blue-throated tree agama. The *agamids,* similar to the iguanas, comprise 200 species of lizard found in warm parts of Asia, Africa, Australia and southern Europe.

*Chamaeleo bitaeniatus* inhabits the mountains of eastern Africa. Chameleons possess a prehensile tail for climbing, a prehensile tongue for catching insects, and all-round vision.

greatest of all is the Komodo Dragon which can weigh up to 290 pounds and can be over ten feet in length. It was first discovered in 1910, and lives on Komodo Island, which is east of Java and a mere 18 miles long by 12 wide, and a few smaller islands nearby. In spite of their large size, they are capable of a good turn of speed. Usually they remain on land, but can swim, and they burrow a hole in the ground in which to rest at night.

The *Helodermatidae,* another family of lizards, boasts some formidable specimens of its own. These include the only two existing species of poisonous lizard. One at least, the Gila Monster, has a bite which can be fatal to Man and very soon dispatches small mammals. It is a sluggish animal which moves mostly by night, and grows to nearly two feet in length. When disturbed it hisses loudly and froths at the mouth.

Chameleons and geckoes make a pleasant change from the rather unattractive monsters already mentioned. In the former the body carries a sharp ridge down the back and is best known for its ability to change colour to harmonize with its surroundings. In a rage it turns deadly white. The gecko is very common around the Mediterranean and is most notable for its ability to run across the ceiling of a house with its 'hook-pad' feet.

The snake, the second sub-order of Squamata, is a beast for which Man seems to feel an innate repulsion, but only about 250 species out of a total of some 2,400 are in fact poisonous to Man. All snakes have the jaw mechanism already mentioned which allows them to take in large quantities of food at one time. This in turn means that they eat at fairly widely spaced intervals.

The teeth of the snake are thin, pointed and tip backwards towards the throat. In the poisonous varieties the venom sac is situated in the upper jaw, and the associated teeth have either grooves running down the outside or a canal running

Although they have the longest snout of all crocodilians and grow up to 20 feet long, gharials are not dangerous to Man. They keep almost exclusively to their diet of fish.

The leathery turtle is the largest marine turtle. A fully grown adult may be six feet long and weigh up to 1,000 pounds. A female returns to the water after laying her eggs.

A mouse is swallowed whole by a boa. The flexible articulation of the jaws enables the snake to engorge prey of much greater diameter than itself.

through them to carry the poison to the bitten victim.

These creatures, of course, have no legs; however, they do have a great many ribs – commonly a pair to each of as many of 200 vertebrae. They use the tips of these ribs to get them about much as a millipede uses its vast number of limbs. Snakes slough (discard) their skins at regular intervals throughout their lives.

The boas and the pythons are non-poisonous snakes but are well known for the manner in which they kill their prey. Both grow to a considerable length and attack by striking at the victim with their jaws and then squeeze the life out of it. The largest boas are probably the South American anacondas, which have been recorded as growing to as much as 37 feet in length.

The major difference between the boas and pythons is that the former bears its young alive, while nearly all the latter lay eggs, The python, however, provides perhaps the most spectacular example of the snake's ability to eat animals much bigger than itself in girth. One nine-foot Reticulate Python (from South East Asia) was observed to swallow a monitor five feet long; another dealt with a deer weighing 123 pounds.

The crocodilians (crocodiles, alligators, caimans and gharials) are examples of reptiles which live most of their lives in water. However, they are fully equipped to move about on the land and commonly do so to find new stretches of water and to lay their eggs.

All species closely resemble one another. They have long heads with powerful jaws and tails for swimming. Their legs carry five toes on the front pair and four on the back and the toes are usually webbed.

## Eating under water

The crocodilians are able to lie submerged and yet open their mouths to take in their prey. This is due to a physiological mechanism consisting of a fold in the tongue and a flap hanging from the roof of the mouth. When these are brought together they prevent the lungs and bodies from flooding even though the mouth is open. The largest of the group are probably the gharials (or gavials) of which there is only one species, found in the Ganges. It is characterized by a very long and slender nose which contains teeth finer than those of other crocodilians. Gharials have been known to grow to 21 feet but they do not attack Man.

The true crocodile has a shorter snout than the gharial and exists in most continents other than Europe. It is prepared to attack Man and even larger animals, should they venture too close.

The alligators and caimans comprise a family of seven species of which all but one live in America. The odd one out is found in the lower reaches of the Yangtse-Kiang River, China, and has been studied relatively little. One peculiarity is that its toes on the forelimbs are not webbed. This may be due to the fact that it spends the winter in a hole which it digs in the mud – presumably any webbing on its front feet would become torn in that process.

The black caiman which is abundant along the Amazon departs from the usual method by which crocodilians get their meals. Instead of seizing the victim in its jaws and dragging it to the bottom, the black caiman stuns the fish or other animal with a swipe of its powerful tail. They have been known to leave the water during the night for hunting trips, killing sheep and small animals.

The Chelonia (tortoises and turtles) are particularly easy to distinguish from other forms of reptiles since they carry a *carapace* or shell which is usually hard but not necessarily so.

They all possess four limbs and breathe in the characteristic reptilian manner through systems of muscles forcing their lungs to contract. The aquatic turtles can take oxygen from the water and emit carbon dioxide through the skin.

Chelonians can live to 100 years old. They live in the tropics, although a few are found in temperate regions. They usually spend the winter in hibernation.

Finally, the Tuatara, which resemble lizards to the casual observer, exhibit internally a number of features which show them to be related to more extinct forms. It is mainly nocturnal in habit and moves about slowly feeding on worms, insects and frogs.

In all of this we can see the decline of a once dominant class of animals and some of the reasons for its decline. However, the modern forms which remain are well adapted to the lives which they lead, and it is likely that without some disastrous intervention by Man they will survive for millions of years to come.

The European pond tortoise is a strict carnivore feeding on fish, frogs and insects. In autumn it hibernates by burrowing into the mud and remains there until the spring.

Largest of the monitors is the Komodo Dragon, which can reach ten feet in length. It has an enormous appetite and eats small deer, wild pigs, carrion – and is also cannibalistic.

# Inside the breath of life

A fish gulps air at the pond surface. Man's breath on a frosty morning steams from moisture in the lungs. The dividing line between air and water dwellers is less sharp than it looks.

IN WINTER, worms are commonly seen on lawns and in gardens. But where do they go in summer? After a spell of hot, dry weather, they are extremely difficult to find because they are deep down in the soil where there is still plenty of water. Worms have to live in the damp because they breathe through their skin. Oxygen dissolves in the slimy moisture on the skin surface and diffuses into the worm's body. In this way, the worm uses its skin as a *respiratory membrane.*

A large land animal, however, could not possibly breathe through its skin. Its surface area is nowhere near large enough to absorb the amount of oxygen its body requires. Its skin would also need to be thin – and therefore practically defenceless – and it would have to stay moist the whole time.

Evolution has solved the problem for large land animals: they have their breathing apparatus tucked away inside their bodies in the form of lungs. The skin is then free to play its protective role and it can stay dry. The development of an internal

Drawing in a deep breath, the goldfish pumps oxygen-rich water over its gills, *above.* The gills, which are basically not very different from lungs, contain a thin skin surface which is folded into filaments to save space in the animal's body. Blood, running close to the surface, picks up oxygen from the water, *right. Top.* The structure of the bronchial arches, which lie between the gill slits and which do the job of absorbing oxygen, is in the diagram, *bottom right.*

respiratory membrane is an evolutionary triumph. The only connection to the outside is through the windpipe, nose and mouth. This means that the wet lung surface can be made large enough to absorb sufficient oxygen for the animal's needs, without losing too much precious water vapour to the atmosphere.

Thin and delicate lung tissue forms countless folds and pockets which enormously increase its surface area. The tissue in a man's lungs, if spread out flat, would cover about a thousand square feet of area. Any land animal with an outer skin of that area would be at the mercy of

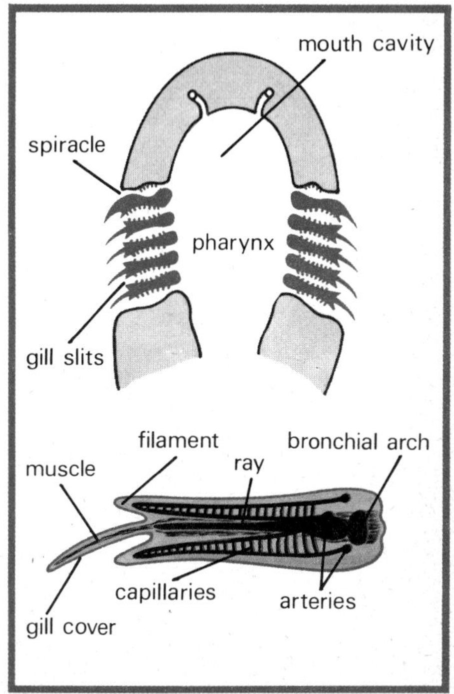

the environment. It would lose water at an alarming rate and soon be as dry as a crisp. So we can see that, for large land animals, an internal respiratory membrane is essential.

Apart from an efficient oxygen absorption mechanism, animals require other systems. The gills of a fish and the lungs of an animal occupy only a part of the body. There must also be a means of transporting oxygen from the gills and lungs to every other part of the body. Blood is the transport medium which does this. The blood circulates round a system of blood vessels (or blood spaces in molluscs and arthropods) under the pumping action of the heart.

Blood which arrives at a respiratory surface is poor in oxygen: it has recently returned from body cells which have taken up most of its supply. But the water on the outer surface of a lung or gill is rich in oxygen. If we plot a graph of the amounts of oxygen in the various cells, from those of the blood to those of the respiratory membrane, we get a sloped line which runs down from the higher 'gill' or 'lung end' towards the lower 'blood end' of the graph. We say, therefore, that there is a *gradient* of oxygen concentration. Oxygen diffuses from the oxygen-rich gill or lung through the thin membrane to the oxygen-poor blood, along the oxygen gradient.

## Steepening the gradient

A respiratory surface becomes more and more efficient as the diffusion gradient across it becomes steeper. That is, the greater the difference in concentration of oxygen on one side of the membrane in comparison with the concentration of oxygen on the other side of the membrane, the more quickly and easily it can be made to flow to where it is needed. This, then, is another way of overcoming the problem of large size. First, an animal can evolve in such a way as to increase the area of a particular part of its body and make a respiratory surface of it. Second, it can evolve in such a way as to maintain a steep diffusion gradient across this surface. As we shall see, there are several ways of doing this.

In an animal, the blood is continuously moving past the respiratory surface. In other words, as the blood picks up oxygen, it moves away and makes room for blood poorer in oxygen. In just the same way, air or water moves continuously over the other side of the respiratory surface so that the steepest possible diffusion gradient is maintained across it. Blood is moved along by the action of the heart. Water or air is drawn over a membrane, usually by muscular actions known as respiratory movements.

In primitive molluscs, which use gills, the respiratory movement of water is maintained by the action of thousands of hair-like cilia. But more highly evolved molluscs, such as squids and octopuses, drive water over their gills by muscular respiratory movements.

Crustaceans such as crabs and lobsters use their legs to create water currents over their gills. Fishes use the muscles of their mouth and throat to pump water

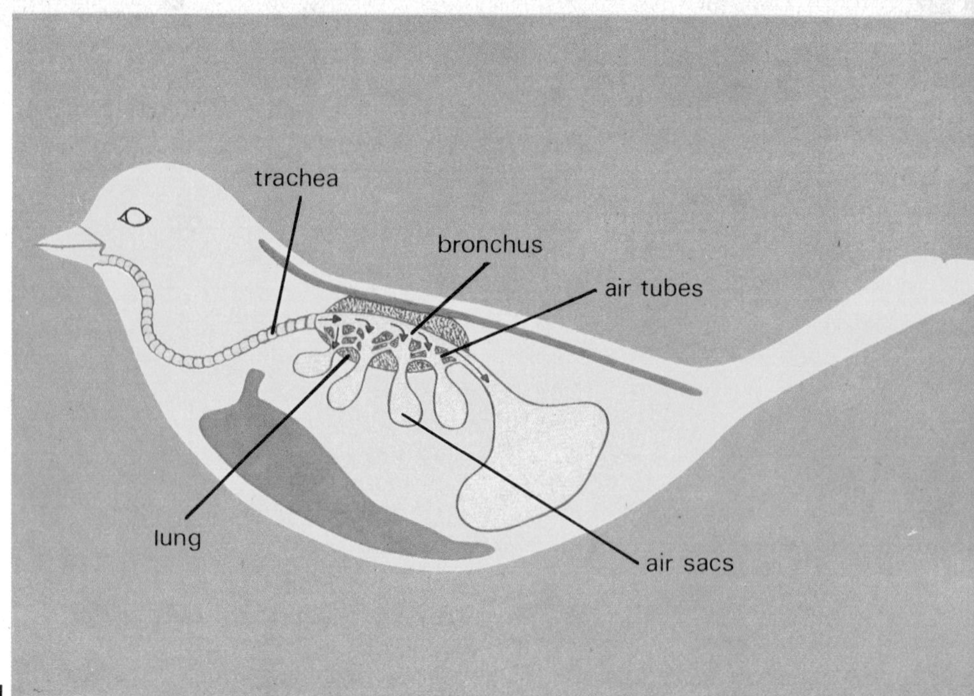


1

4

Birds, **1**, use energy at a faster rate than mammals, so their respiratory system gives their lungs two chances to take oxygen from the same air. As the bird breathes in, air passes over the lungs into air sacs. As it breathes out, the air sacs deflate, passing air over the lungs a second time. Man's inability to breathe water hampers his exploration of a major part of the Earth's surface, **2**. But the barrier between air- and water-breathing creatures is not so great as it might appear – even in air-breathing animals, oxygen dissolves in the water which forms the moisture of the lungs. In the human lung, **3**, muscular action pumps air in, while the heart pumps blood past the respiratory surface to collect the oxygen. Though aquatic animals, the playful dolphins, **4**, are mammals and must surface periodically to replenish their lungs with air, but the shark, **5**, is a fish and must pass large quantities of water over its gills to extract oxygen. The frog is equipped with lungs, but can breathe through its skin as well. A closed network of blood vessels just below the surface of the skin, **6**, gathers in the oxygen for transportation to other parts of the body.

over their gills and out through their gill slits. In bony fishes, the mouth pumps water into the gills, and the *operculum* (gill flap) sucks it out. Sharks and rays do not have the 'suction pump' part of this system, and some sharks have to swim all the time to pass enough water over their gills. If they stop swimming, they quickly suffocate.

Gills are generally on the outside of an animal's body, although they may be covered for protection. As a result, water is able to pass over them and between the many gill filaments. Lungs, on the other hand, are bags inside the body; to renew the air in them, they must be continually emptied and refilled. For instance, frogs and toads gulp down air and blow up their lungs like balloons.

Other backboned animals with lungs use a different system. By moving their ribs, they cause the space around the lungs to get larger and air is sucked in. More precisely, they lower the pressure around the lungs by increasing the volume of the rib-cage, and the air pressure forces air down into the lungs through the windpipe.

Reptiles rely on movements of the ribs alone, but mammals have a *diaphragm* which converts the rib-cage into a closed chamber. Birds have a slightly different system. They have extra air sacs connected to the lungs. When a bird breathes in, air passes over the lungs and into the air sacs. When the bird breathes out, the same air is passed over the lungs a second time, giving two chances for the lungs to pick up oxygen. This system is more efficient than that of mammals, and means that birds can use energy at a faster rate than their earth-bound brethren. Indeed, if it were not for the extraordinarily efficient respiratory system, birds would be unable to muster enough energy to get off the ground.

If we compare this mechanism with that of the air-breathing spiders and land snails, we see that snails empty and refill their lungs just as higher animals do. But spiders do not. The oxygen merely dif-

2

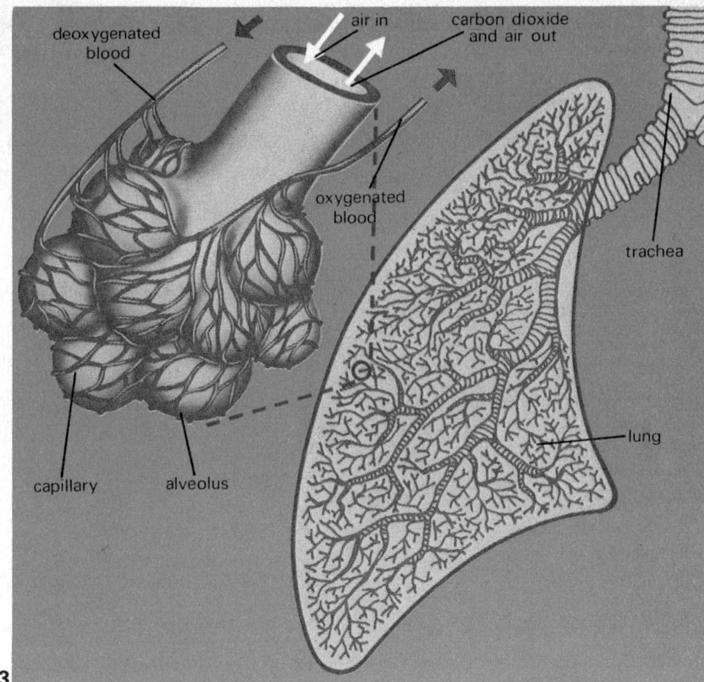


3

5

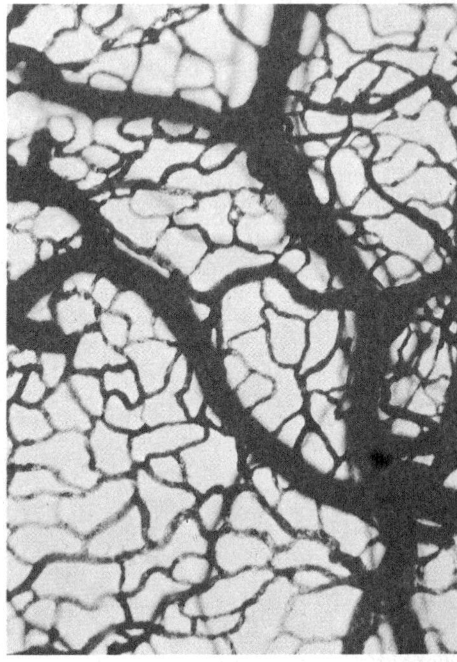

6

fuses through the book-lung. Fresh air enters as the air in the lung becomes depleted with oxygen.

We have seen how, in higher animals, an increased surface area is formed and a steep diffusion gradient is maintained across it. An efficient blood system is also developed, and blood has special properties which make it a very efficient carrier of oxygen.

The blood of most animals is coloured. This colour is due to a material in the blood which is used to carry oxygen. It is called a *respiratory pigment*. Actually, the colour is not important – it is just one of the properties of the compound concerned. Backboned animals, and some insects, have red blood with haemoglobin as the respiratory pigment. The blood of crustaceans and molluscs has a different pigment called haemocyanin, which is blue. Some worms have green blood pigment called chlorocruorin.

Although they have different colours and chemical structures, these respiratory pigments all serve the purpose of carrying oxygen. They combine chemically with any oxygen present near them at a high concentration, and the compound formed releases oxygen when its surroundings are low in oxygen. In practice, this means that oxygen is picked up in the lungs or gills, which are surrounded by a relatively high concentration of oxygen, and released in the tissues, which are poor in oxygen. The presence of a respiratory pigment means that blood carries much more oxygen than it could if the gas were merely dissolved in solution.

Oxygen is only one of the gases in air or water. Others include nitrogen, carbon dioxide and rare gases. Each gas exerts a pressure. The contribution to the total pressure made by each gas is known as its *partial pressure*, and the sum of the partial pressures of all the gases equals the total pressure of the air – the atmospheric pressure. The gas with the highest partial pressure is the one which is most abundant in the air.

Respiratory pigments pick up oxygen when the partial pressure of oxygen is high, and release it when the oxygen partial pressure is low. Each respiratory pigment works within its own particular range of oxygen partial pressures. These vary with the ways of life of the animals concerned and the different amounts of oxygen available in their environments.

## Exertion requires oxygen

Respiration must be able to keep pace with the muscular exertions of an animal. The harder a muscle is working, the more energy it is using, and so the faster will its food be broken down by tissue respiration to release energy.

Tissue respiration needs a supply of oxygen and involves the production of carbon dioxide. As the oxygen content of the tissue is used up, more oxygen leaves the blood, and more must therefore be supplied by the respiratory surface.

There are many ways in which the need for this increased supply is met by the

When the bat, *left,* hibernates, his breathing and temperature drop to a minimum. The bird, *above,* has a different kind of problem. Feathers, unlike bat skin, retain heat. To prevent overheating, cooling air is diverted to spaces within the bones as the bird breathes.

body. The carbon dioxide produced by tissue respiration is carried in the blood, and certain areas of the blood vessels are sensitive to the amount of carbon dioxide in it. These areas 'inform' the brain of the concentration of carbon dioxide in the blood. As the concentration increases, the brain acts to boost the rate at which oxygen is made available in the tissues. For example, the rate of lung ventilation or the rate of flow of water over the gills can be increased to make more oxygen available at the respiratory surface. At the same time, the rate of the heart beat can be increased, and oxygen is moved more quickly around the body by the circulatory system. Also, the blood supply to areas of the body not actually being used can be reduced, making more of the oxygen-carrying mechanism available to the muscles and the brain.

The energy needed to make muscles contract comes from the breakdown of ATP to ADP. ATP is a high-energy compound important in all kinds of cell reactions which need a shot of energy to make them 'go'. But ATP is not the only energy-rich compound in muscles. Another one, called *creatine phosphate,* is present in much greater amounts. It is the muscle's store of energy. When muscles contract, they use up ATP. The ADP formed is quickly recharged to form ATP by transferring high-energy phosphate radicals from creatine phosphate (which ends up as creatine). As soon as the muscles relax, the creatine phosphate store is built up again from fresh ATP made by glycolysis and the Krebs cycle.

Anyone who has ever run long and hard knows the agony of muscle fatigue. As a person starts to run, the ATP in his muscles breaks down, and the muscles contract. The ADP is recharged to ATP from the reserves of creatine phosphate, and his muscles keep going. Eventually, however, the creatine phosphate runs out. The muscles must now draw their supply of ATP directly from tissue respiration. Most of this ATP comes from the Krebs cycle, and the Krebs cycle runs on oxygen. But the blood cannot supply oxygen fast enough to a muscle that is working at maximum capacity, and so the system begins to seize up.

Fortunately, the first part of tissue respiration – the conversion of glucose to pyruvic acid – can work without oxygen and, although not much ATP is made during these reactions, the muscles will continue to work. But the pyruvic acid is not allowed to accumulate; it is converted by muscle cells into lactic acid. If a person is courageous or desperate enough to keep running flat out, the lactic acid in his muscles piles up, the agony starts, and he stops!

## Paying the 'oxygen debt'

The accumulated lactic acid must now be removed. Part of it is re-converted to pyruvic acid, which is shunted round the Krebs cycle to make ATP. This ATP is used to push the remainder of the lactic acid along the glycolysis pathway to glucose. ATP is also needed to recharge the creatine phosphate store. Manufacture of these large amounts of ATP requires oxygen, since it is made by means of the Krebs cycle. That is the reason why the person goes on panting for air a long time after he has staggered to a stop. He is repaying his 'oxygen debt'.

Although higher animals have developed very complicated methods of obtaining oxygen from their environment, their cells and tissues still respire in much the same way as does the most primitive protozoan. Although respiratory mechanisms may differ markedly from one organism to another, the basic need for oxygen has remained the same throughout the plant and animal kingdoms.

# How nature draws breath

What practical reason prevents a beetle from growing as big as an elephant? To find the answer, look more closely at the many ways by which living things go about the vital business of breathing.

MANY MOUNTAIN CLIMBERS and athletes find difficulty in taking part in violent physical exercises at high altitudes. For instance, some people were worried about the possible effects of holding the 1968 Olympic Games in Mexico City, which is situated at about 7,000 feet above sea level. At high altitudes the air is thin and oxygen is scarce. Some people feared that under these conditions an athlete's body might become so short of oxygen during moments of great physical exertion that the strain would kill him.

What makes oxygen so important? Why is this gas indispensable to life? The short answer is because oxygen has a remarkable partiality for electrons and can be readily reduced to water by biological systems. To understand the meaning of this answer, we must know something about how living organisms get energy from food.

Most people know that glucose gives them energy. The energy in a glucose molecule is locked up in the chemical bonds which hold the molecule together. If we set fire to some glucose in plenty of air, it burns away completely to carbon dioxide and water. It also gives out a lot of heat energy as its bonds are torn apart. Oxygen must be present for glucose to burn away completely and give out all its energy.

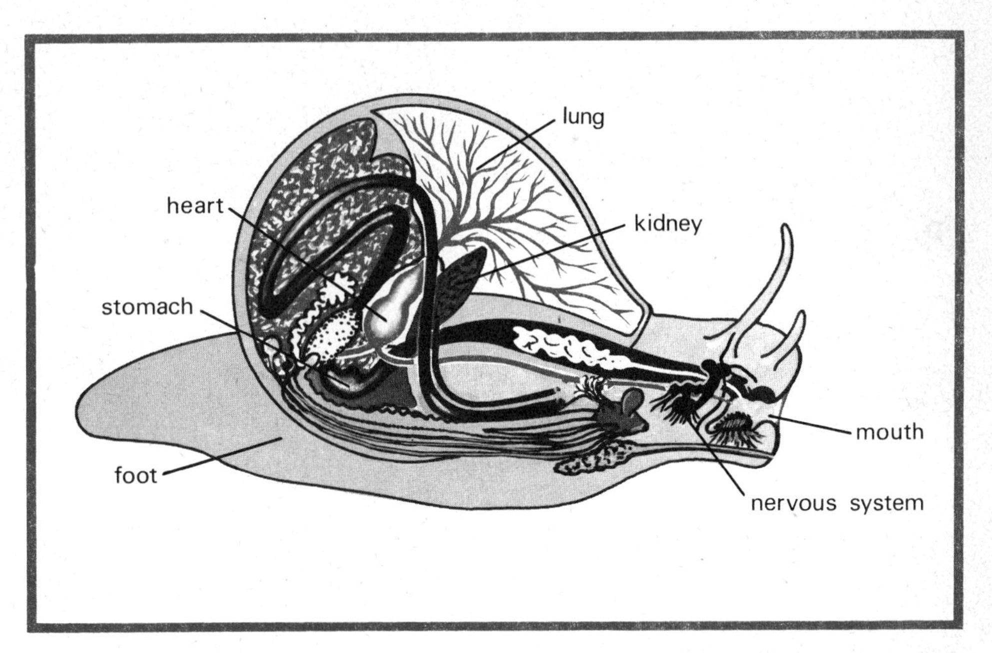


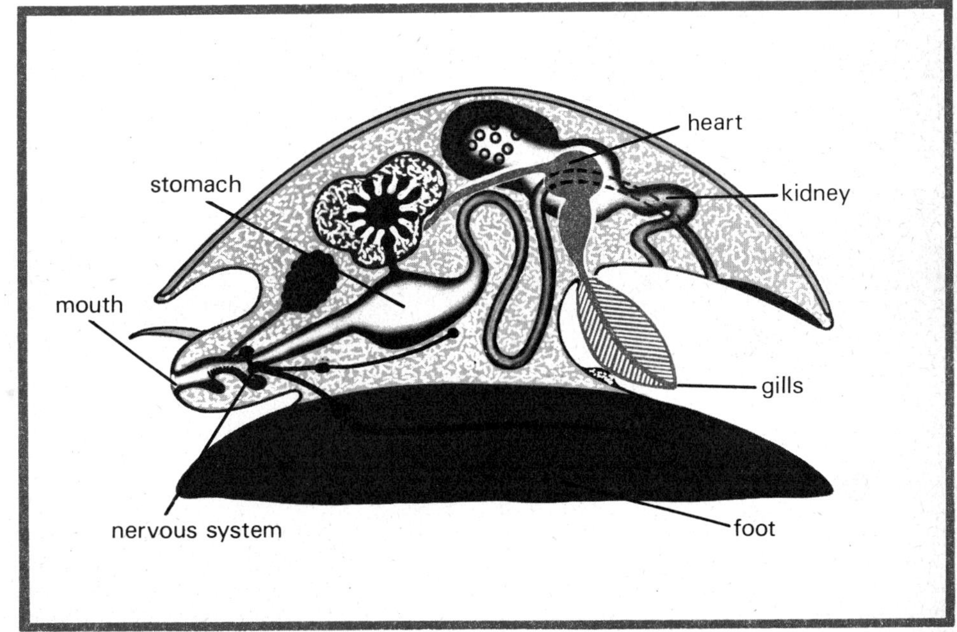


Which way to breathe? Winkle, *above,* and garden snail, *top,* demonstrate nature's two main ways for creatures to catch oxygen. For the water-dwelling winkle, fronded gills serve well. But out in the open air, they would collapse – just like a bunch of seaweed wrested from its bed. In the snail, as in men, the respiratory surface is inside the animal: it breathes through lungs.

## Subtle use of sugar

Heating a substance is a good way of activating it and getting it to react chemically. But living things obviously cannot set fire to glucose in their cells. They activate glucose molecules in a more subtle way by grafting phosphate radicles on to them. The phosphorylated glucose is then ready to start giving up its energy. Of course, glucose molecules cannot be allowed to give up all their energy at once within a cell. If they did, the heat output would kill it. Here again the cell has a subtle mechanism of its own. It possesses biochemical machinery in the form of enzymes which *degrade* the molecule a small step at a time. The energy released during each step is not great, and is stored away as ATP (adenosine triphosphate).

Various enzymes chip away at the glucose molecules, changing them into smaller and smaller molecules containing less and less free energy. During the final stages of this process carbon dioxide is removed by means of *decarboxylase* enzymes, and hydrogen ions and electrons are drawn off with the help of enzymes called *dehydrogenases*.

In living organisms, electrons and hydrogen ions are shuttled along a chain of acceptor molecules, each succeeding member of the chain having a greater affinity for electrons than its neighbour. They are ultimately delivered to a group of enzymes called *oxidases,* the most important and widespread of which is *cytochrome oxidase.* This biological game of 'pass the electron' stops at cytochrome oxidase, which hands on electrons directly to oxygen atoms. The oxygen ions so formed combine with hydrogen ions (derived from glucose breakdown) to form water.

These processes go on entirely inside the cells of tissues and, for this reason, constitute *internal respiration.* This is to distinguish it from *external* respiration, which is any process for getting oxygen from the environment and into the cells where it is needed. The reactions which comprise internal respiration fall into two stages. The first stage starts with glucose and ends with pyruvic acid; this stage is called *glycolysis.* The second stage starts with pyruvic acid and ends with carbon dioxide and water; this stage is called the citric acid cycle or the Krebs cycle, after the man who deserves most of the credit for working out its details. Glycolysis can proceed without oxygen, but the Krebs cycle cannot.

Having stressed the importance of

oxygen, we are bound to say that some organisms can get along quite well without it. Yeasts and bacteria, for example, get their energy from glucose by breaking it down by *fermentation*. Fermentation follows the same pathway as glycolysis to produce pyruvic acid. The pyruvic acid is then reduced to ethyl alcohol by yeasts, or to lactic acid by some kinds of bacteria. In neither case is oxygen necessary. But the amount of energy recovered from glucose by converting it to alcohol or lactic acid is trifling compared with that gained from the complete breakdown to carbon dioxide and water. A cell can make about ten times as much ATP from the Krebs cycle as it can from glycolysis. So we see that oxygen is essential to practically all forms of life. We will now consider the various ways in which living things get the oxygen they need from their environment.

Plants live on land or in water. Aquatic plants acquire oxygen (which is dissolved in the water all around them) by diffusion. Diffusion is a slow business, however, and puts a limit on size. Since oxygen diffuses in through the outer surface of an organism's body, the bigger its surface compared with its volume, the more efficiently will oxygen enter. The trouble is that any increase in size increases volume much faster than it increases surface area. For example, oxygen would diffuse into a one-celled alga of thickness one-tenth of a millimetre in a few seconds. But if the alga were 1 millimetre thick, oxygen would take several hours to diffuse right into the cell. Nevertheless, some seaweeds (which are kinds of algae) are among the largest plants known. They have solved the area problem very well by having thin flat blades which expose a huge surface to sea-water.

## Underwater air storage

Large, freshwater plants solve their oxygen problem in another way. Apart from having finely divided leaves which give a large surface area, their leaves and stems contain air space. Oxygen given off during photosynthesis is not released into the water, but collects in the air spaces and is used later for respiration. Luckily, not all plants do this or animals, which depend on oxygen from plants, would soon die.

Land plants have to conserve water or they would quickly wither and die. Their leaves and stems have a *cuticle* which is impervious to water. But at the same time the cuticle is an effective barrier against diffusing oxygen. Plant leaves are also dotted with pores called stomata, through which carbon dioxide and oxygen can diffuse freely. Although stomata normally close at night, oxygen from photosynthesis and from the atmosphere is abundant in the leaf intercellular spaces, and is quite adequate for the plant's respiratory needs during the hours of darkness.

Animals, too, have a size problem. Single-celled protozoans such as *Amoeba* and *Paramecium* get their oxygen from water by diffusion. Even some simple multicellular animals such as *Hydra* and *Planaria* use the same method. But beyond a certain size an animal has to develop a

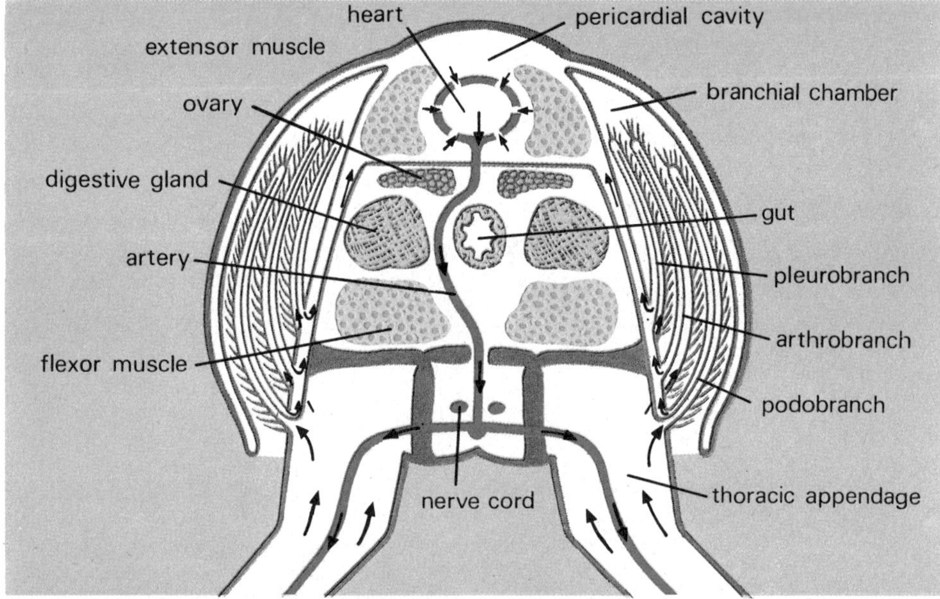

Gills feather the shrimp's legs, *top far left*. Better protected, gills of the crayfish, *far left*, and crab, *left*, are cased within jointed armour. Diagram, *above*, shows the crayfish gill system in a cross-section across the thorax. All told, the crayfish has 18 gills, arranged in three series – the podobranchs, arthrobranchs and pleurobranchs – named after the site of their growth. Once every second, an organ that serves as a bailer drives water sucked in between the bases of the legs over the gills – reversing direction occasionally to clear them of debris. Arrows show the path of the crayfish's thin but blue blood about its body. *Top*, in a crowded rock-pool scene, white and yellow shelled dog whelks, gills tucked away under their shells, are feeding on edible mussels, with the company of acorn barnacles, limpets and beadlet anemones.

special 'respiratory surface' where the efficiency of obtaining oxygen from the environment (water or air) is greatly increased.

In water, the respiratory surface takes the form of feathery structures called gills. But in land animals, the air does not provide enough support for delicate gills and so the respiratory surface is generally inside the animal – as lungs. Making one area of the body into a special respiratory surface has the added advantage that it allows the rest of the body surface to be developed as a protective covering. If the whole body surface is used for breathing (as it is in earthworms), there can be no hard scales or thick skin on the body to interfere with the flow of gases in and out.

Jointed-legged arthropods and soft-bodied, shelled molluscs have some members which live in water and some which live on land. Of course, an aquatic animal can be an air-breather if it rises to the surface for oxygen (as do dolphins and whales).

The earliest snail-like animals lived in the sea, and most molluscs are still marine creatures. Animals such as whelks and winkles have gills which are tucked away in cavities under their shells. This is how all the ancestors of the molluscs breathed, using gills just as fish do. Molluscs that now live on land lost their gills, and the cavity that used to hold them is developed to work as a lung. For example, the garden snail lost its gills as it came to live on land and developed a lung-like respiratory surface (as did frogs and other backboned land animals). We can even find the counterparts of the whales and dolphins among the molluscs – some land snails that have returned to the water still breathe air by means of a lung. Like whales, these freshwater snails must rise to the surface to breathe air.

## Gills and book lungs

If we consider the jointed-legged arthropods, we find that all those which live in the sea, and many which live in fresh water, use gills for breathing. The arthropods of the sea (crustaceans such as crabs and lobsters) have feathery gills which are attached to the tops of their legs. They are usually covered by protective shields, as they are in fishes.

Spiders, and their relatives the scorpions, live on land and breathe air. They have developed a peculiar respiratory system and have in their bodies pouches which hold many sheets of soft, hanging respiratory tissue. Under the microscope, these sheets look like the pages of a book, and for this reason these air-breathing organs are called *book lungs*.

Insects, which are the chief arthropods of the land, have developed their own system of breathing. All through an insect's body runs a network of tubes which carry air from the surface of the body to the tissues. Some insects live in fresh water, and once again, like snails and whales, they must rise to the surface to breathe air. The respiratory system of insects carries air right into the tissues, and there the process of respiration takes place,

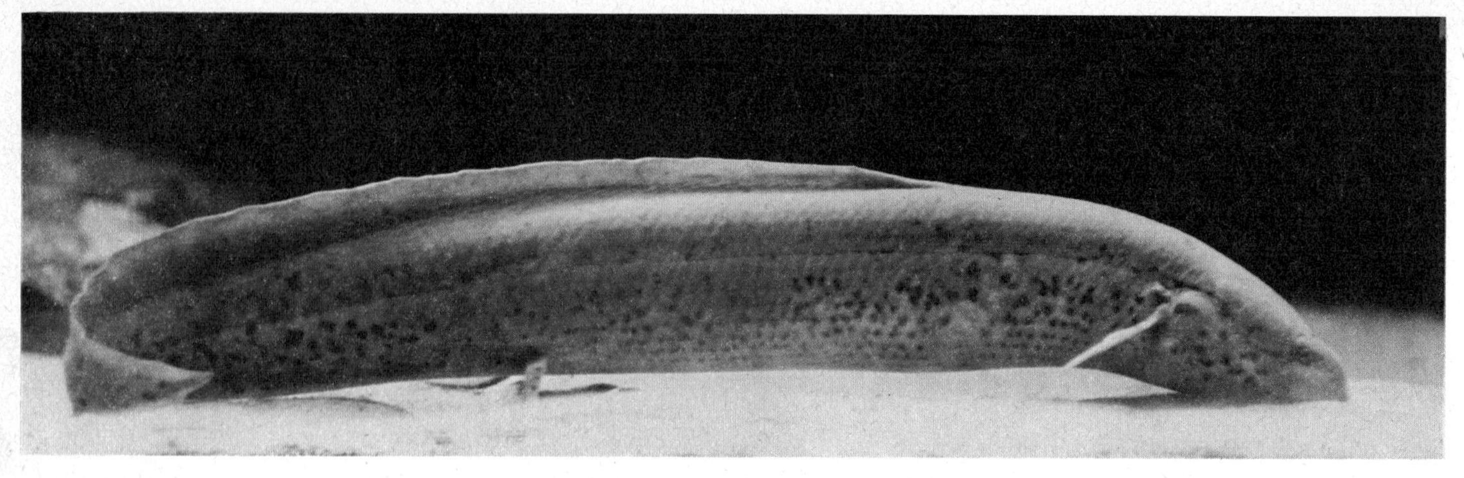

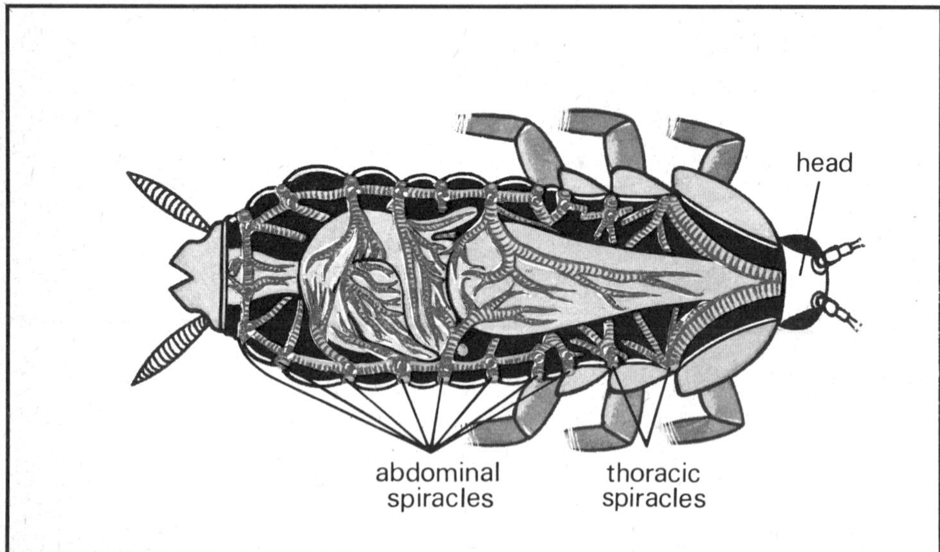


breathing tube
gills
trachea
food channel
thorax
eye
feeding brush

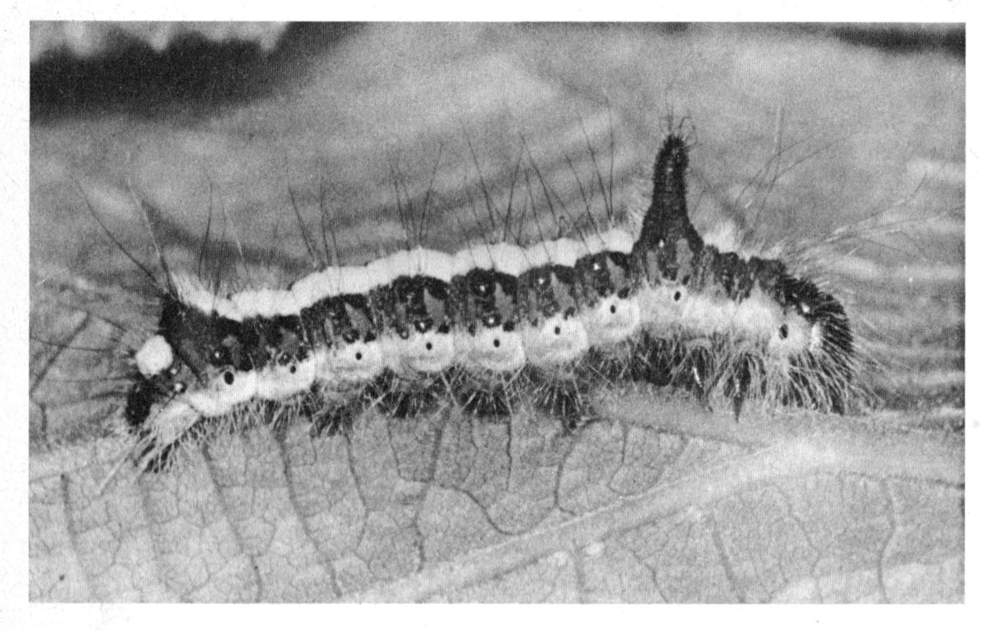

Like the man who wears braces and a belt, the lung fish, *top,* switches from gills to lung breathing when its favourite muddy pool dries up. *Centre left,* no lungs, no gills for the beetle: in insects, a direct tube service transports air to diffuse oxygen among the tissues. The system would not work in a large body. That is why insects are small. *Above right,* aquatic insects, such as the mosquito larva, boost the tracheal tubes of their air-intake system by gills. *Left,* the inlets to the insect's air tube system are called spiracles. Like black port holes, they line the caterpillar's flank.

just as in protozoans, by simple diffusion through the cells.

Pairs of openings called *spiracles,* generally one pair to each segment, line the outer skin of an insect's body. These spiracles lead into many branching tubes, called *tracheal tubes,* which terminate beside the cells of the body tissues.

At their thickest parts, tracheal tubes are stiffened by a spiral of thicker tissue round their walls. By the time they have narrowed to a twenty-thousandth of an inch in diameter or less, they are called *tracheoles,* and their walls no longer need stiffening. Diffusion carries the oxygen down the tracheal tubes and along the tracheoles right into the cells. In times of great activity, some insects can supplement the diffused oxygen supply by 'pumping' more oxygen to these cells by muscular action along the tubes.

Diffusion is a slow process and there is a limit to the depth of tissue that can be penetrated by tracheoles and adequately supplied with oxygen at a sufficient rate. This depth is about half an inch, which, in turn, imposes a limit on the size to which an insect – able to use only this form of respiration – can grow. As a result, there is no insect with a body much more than one inch thick.

Highly evolved vertebrate animals have solved the problems of increased size and activity by a different method of respiration. They have developed special large respiratory surfaces in special organs inside their bodies. But they must have a mechanism for getting the oxygen from this surface to the tissues where it is needed. Once it gets there, as with all living things, the processes of tissue respiration are exactly the same.

# The beat of the blood

Animals emerged from the prehistoric oceans to conquer the land millions of years ago, but they never lost their need of a liquid environment. So they learned to carry it with them – as blood.

PLANTS AND ANIMALS need energy to maintain their life and growth. The chemical reactions involved in supplying this energy generally take place in solution, so that living cells which are not in direct contact with fluids, especially water, must be supplied by some mechanism of the body. In higher animals, particularly those which are not aquatic, this 'distribution system' can become quite complex, but the function is always the same, to supply the living cell with vitally needed materials to carry on life processes.

The simplest system is found in the single-celled protozoans. Their minute size gives them a very high surface area in proportion to their volume, which enables them to absorb oxygen from their watery surroundings by passive diffusion. Similarly, food and excretory products in solution can diffuse in and around the whole animal. It has been estimated that an animal of up to 1 millimetre in diameter can maintain a high metabolic rate by this method.

## Blood carries fluid

But in larger animals, the ratio of surface area to volume is inadequate for passive diffusion, so they must either reduce their oxygen and food demands and become less active, as do sponges, or they must develop an efficient internal transport system. In more highly evolved animals, diffusion is replaced by convection and by a circulatory system. A *blood system* is developed, which aids the continuous and fairly rapid movement of fluids to all parts of the body.

The first rudiments of a circulatory system is found in a group of worms called the *nemertines*. Each of these worms has two vessels running along its length, with cross-connections joining the ends of the vessels. The main vessels have in their walls circular muscle fibres that can contract and expand and 'pump' fluids along the vessels. In nemertines, the system is probably used only for the transport of metabolic, cell-building substances, because it is located too deeply to be used for respiratory purposes.

The group *Annelida,* which includes the earthworm, the marine ragworm and many other related forms, shows several advances over the nemertines. They have a well-developed body cavity (*coelom*) and gut-like tissues (*mesoderm*). The circulatory or vascular system is derived from mesodermal tissue, and it is not surprising to find a circulatory system which has become associated with the uptake and transport of oxygen and carbon dioxide. In the earthworm, for instance, blood vessels lie just beneath the thin moist *epidermis* (outer skin), enabling gases to diffuse freely between the blood system and the body surface.

Blood not only transports nourishment and waste products to and from body cells. In the case of the dragonfly, *top,* pressure created by blood is essential in freeing a new adult from its pupal shroud. Pressure then aids the insect to unfold its moist wings, *above,* for drying in the sun.

The circulatory system of the earthworm consists basically of a contractile vessel running dorsally (along the length of the animal's back) and acting as the main collecting vessel. In it the blood flows forwards, propelled by rhythmic *peristaltic* waves of muscle contractions. Blood is distributed via a non-contractile ventral vein in which the blood flows backwards. The anelid body is made up of a series of segments, in which blood flows from the ventral (lower) to the dorsal (upper) vessels through capillaries in the body wall.

Near the front end of the gut, dorsal and ventral vessels are directly connected by five pairs of muscular transverse vessels. Those act as hearts, pumping blood through the ventral vessel. Blood is prevented from flowing the wrong way by valves in the hearts and in the dorsal vessel. Transverse segmental vessels supply the segmentally arranged kidneys and the musculature of the body-wall with blood which is then returned to the dorsal vessel. This flow is reversed in segments 7 to 11, where blood flows down from the dorsal to the ventral vessel through the hearts. Blood supplies the head region and also flows back from the hearts to supply the transverse vessels. The gut is supplied by branches from the ventral vessel. In this way, absorbed food material is transported up to the dorsal vessel and then around the body.

The annelid circulatory system is known as a *closed blood system,* because the blood is always enclosed within definite walled vessels such as arteries, veins and the capillaries which join them. The blood flow in the invertebrates is generally forwards in the dorsal vessels and backwards in the ventral vessels; but in the vertebrates it is reversed, being forwards in the ventral vessels and backwards in the dorsal vessel.

## Insects have hearts

A second type of circulation, found in many invertebrates, is called an *open blood system.* Here, the blood is pumped forwards in the dorsal vessel, which has a series of contractile hearts incorporated into it, and out into body cavities where it bathes the organs of the body. Blood returns to a large cavity (*sinus*) surrounding the dorsal vessel and is drawn into the hearts through paired lateral apertures called *ostia.* The open blood system is characteristic of arthropods, such as insects, spiders and crustaceans, and of molluscs, such as garden snails and marine shell-fish.

Insects are unusual in that their respiratory demands are met by a system of tubes which are ingrowths of the hard exoskeleton. These tubes carry oxygen directly into the tissues. As a result, the blood system plays little or no part in the transport of oxygen and carbon dioxide (except in a few aquatic forms). Insect blood is called *haemolymph* and is made up essentially of plasma and *haemocytes,* which are cells capable of *phagocytosis* (the ingesting of tissues and micro-organisms) and stabilizing the effect of chemical metabolites in the blood.

Insects also have accessory circulatory organs which meet special demands. For instance, organs which pulsate rhythmically are found at the bases of the antennae of certain butterflies and cockroaches. The 'heart' is composed of from one to 13 serially repeated chambers in the dorsal vessel.

Other important functions of the blood of insects include transporting hormones (the chemical regulators of the body functions), maintaining the body fluids at a constant concentration, and assisting in egg laying and moulting. In the case of the last two, blood is used to create a pressure and is particularly important in enabling the insect to break out of its old cuticle at moulting and in expanding the wings after pupation. The blood also acts as a water storer.

Blood is essentially a suspension of cells in a liquid tissue called *plasma.* The plasma is predominantly water containing proteins, inorganic salts (mainly sodium chloride and sodium bicarbonate) and substances being transported from one part of the body to another. The proteins include albumen, globulin, prothrombin and fibrinogen. Each has a high molecular weight, and in mammalian blood in solution they exert a high osmotic pressure. The proteins provide an emergency supply of food, and help to give the blood its viscosity and facilitate blood clotting (particularly prothrombin and fibrinogen). They also prevent major changes in the level of acidity of the blood.

Glucose, some fats and amino acids are also carried in the blood. But unlike plasma proteins, they have relatively small molecular weights and can pass directly into the tissues and cells where they are used to provide energy and form structural proteins.

Waste products are found in the plasma during their passage from the cells to the excretory sites. Carbon dioxide is usually carried combined as sodium bicarbonate, nitrogenous wastes are found as either uric acid or urea, and some lactic acid may also be present. In addition to these substances, various amounts of hormones and enzymes are found in the plasma.

An important function of the blood is to transport oxygen to the tissues; but plasma can absorb only very small amounts of the gas. More oxygen can be carried when it is chemically combined with a *respiratory pigment.* Such pigments are found in most animals, and may be present in the blood plasma (as in many invertebrates), or in the red blood corpuscles (as in vertebrates). A respiratory pigment consists of a metallic ion (iron or copper), a porphyrin group (haem) and a protein group (globin). The best-known pigment is *haemoglobin,* which is found in the blood of vertebrates and some invertebrates. Other pigments found among the invertebrates include *haemocyanin, hae-*

The lowly earthworm **(1)**, a member of the Annelida group, contains within it a circulatory system exhibiting most of the fundamental parts of more advanced designs. The cutaway diagram **(2)** reveals the dorsal and the ventral vessels, plus the five transverse blood-pumping vessels, or 'hearts'. Very much further along the scale of complexity and efficiency is the heart of a sheep **(3)**, the four-chambered mammalian design. The two upper chambers, or auricles, receive the blood; while the two lower chambers, or ventricles, pump it throughout the body **(4)**, carrying food and oxygen to the billions of living cells. The actual work is carried out in the countless networks of microscopic capillaries **(5)**, sometimes so small that the blood cells have to queue up in order to reach their destination. **1**

**2**

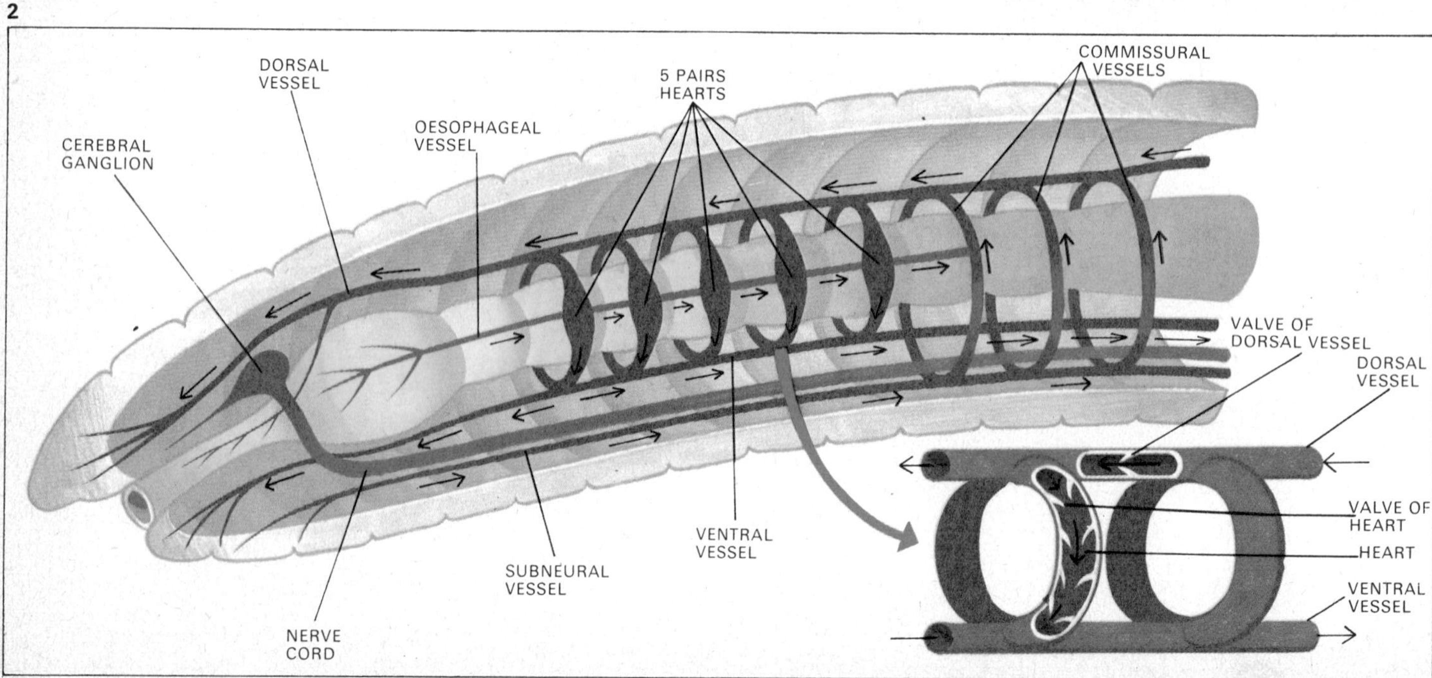

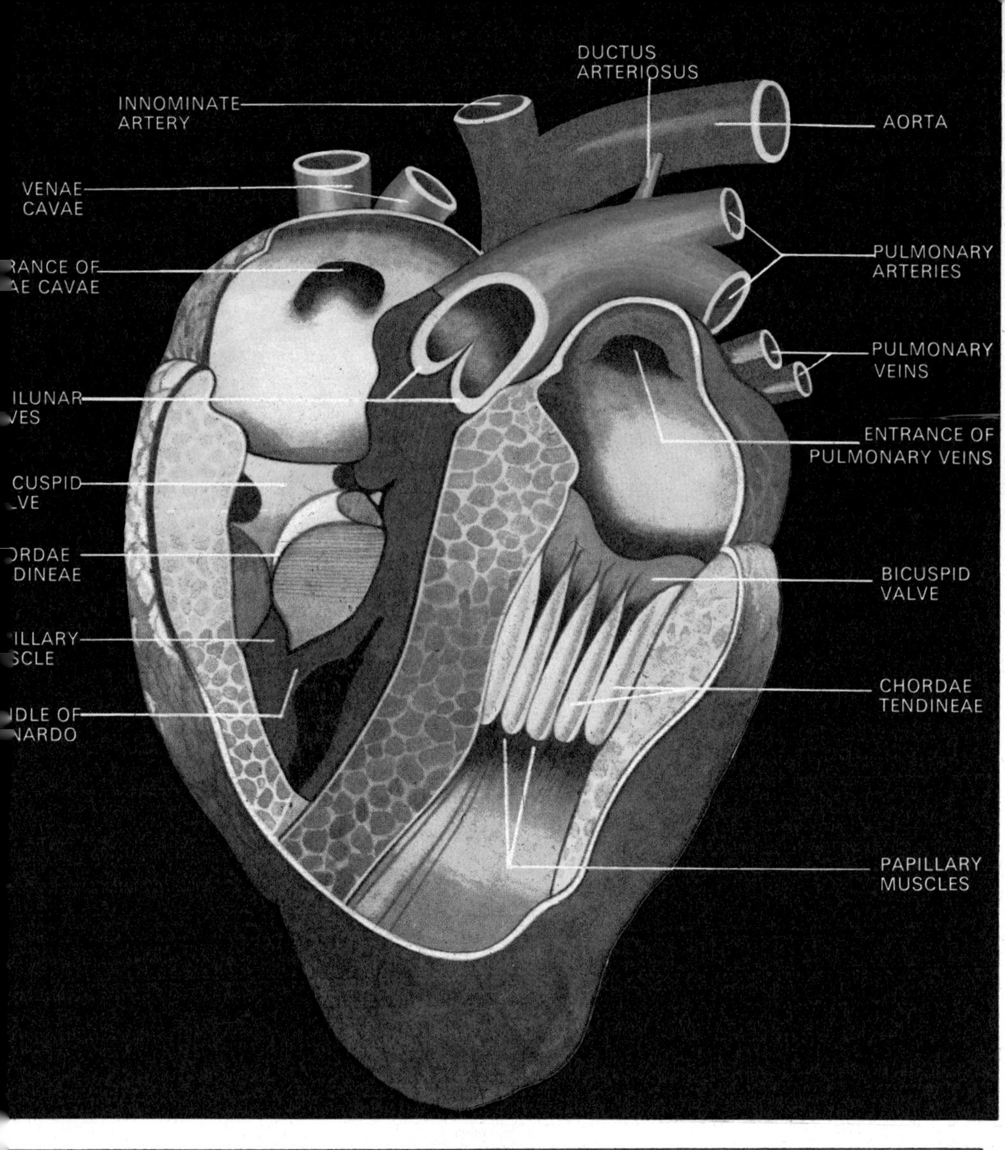


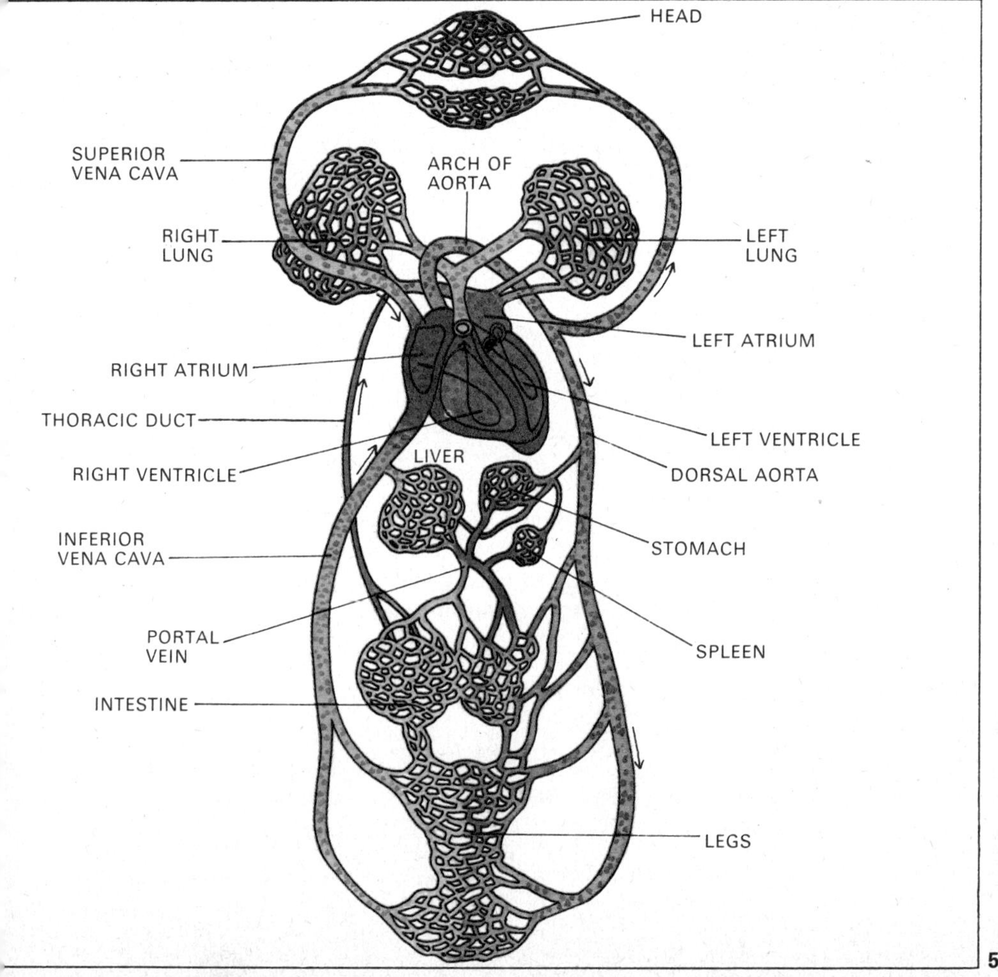


5

*merythrin* and the green *chlorocruorin*.

An important advance shown in vertebrate circulatory systems is the development of a chambered heart. In its most primitive form, it consists of four successive chambers. Starting from the back, these are called *sinus venosus, atrium, ventricle* and *conus arteriosus*. Contraction of the primitive heart begins in the sinus venosus and spreads forward towards the conus arteriosus. The musculature of the sinus acts as a 'pacemaker' for the rest of the heart. The arrangement becomes slightly more sophisticated in higher vertebrates but the basic pattern remains the same. In advanced vertebrates, only the atrium and ventricle retain their identity and these are subdivided to give the four-chambered heart. The heart lies ventral to the gut and remains 'free' in the body cavity, attached only at the points where blood vessels enter or leave it. This enables it to constrict and relax – that is to beat – without hindrance.

## The heart's own blood supply

In all higher animals, the heart is surrounded by a *pericardial membrane*. The heart 'wall' has three layers; the predominant one consists of connective tissue and muscle and is called the *myocardium*. A series of powerful valves prevent backflow, and in advanced vertebrates these may be furnished with tendons and muscles. The heart receives its own blood supply from the coronary artery. Fibres of the autonomic nervous system modify the heart rate, but heart muscle is able to beat without stimulation for a considerable time even after removal from the body.

In the embryonic development of lower vertebrates, the heart curls to form a compact S-shaped structure. Blood enters and leaves the ventricle on the dorsal plane, enabling it freely to perform vigorous contractions. In the primitive gill-breathing vertebrates, all blood leaving the heart flows forwards in the ventral vessel or *ventral aorta*. This vessel has paired branches which arch upwards towards the gill-slits where they break

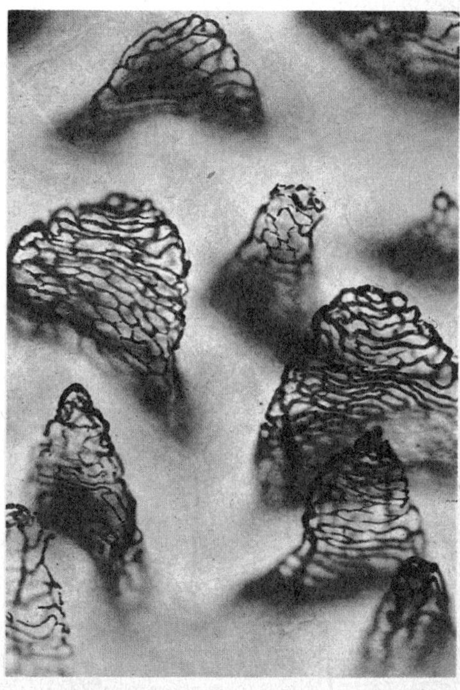

into capillaries at the sites of oxygen uptake. The capillaries then come together to form arteries near the animal's back, which run into the *dorsal aorta* and from there to the various tissues of the body. The paired vessels which supply and drain the gills are called aortic arches. There are generally five gill-slits and a spiracle, giving a total of six pairs of aortic arches.

The arterial arches of all other vertebrates are based on this six-fold pattern, although the development of lungs causes fusion, loss and specialization of the vessels, and the basic arrangement becomes heavily disguised. For instance, in adult mammals only three pairs of arches are found, one of them forming the pulmonary supply to the lungs.

Let us consider now the changes in the vertebrate circulatory system which enabled this group of animals successfully to conquer the land.

In fish, the heart is essentially a muscular tube pumping blood forwards, into the aortic arches, through the gill capillaries, and round the body. This process involves the blood passing through at least two sets of capillaries before returning to the heart, and requires a considerable pressure.

## Circulatory systems

To add to the problem, nearly all fishes have portal blood systems (a portal vessel is one which has capillary systems at both ends). The *hepatic portal* vessel carries blood directly from the gut to the liver, and the *renal portal* vessel runs from the tail and hind limbs to the kidney. These systems put an even greater demand on the blood pressure. In fish, blood passes through the heart only once during one circulation around the body; this condition is known as a *single circulatory system*.

With the evolution of lungs in the amphibians and the loss of paired gill-slits, a more efficient circulatory system developed. The lungs are provided with a separate circulatory route, so that after the blood has been oxygenated in the lung capillaries it is returned to the heart before being pumped round the remaining tissues. This reduces the number of capillaries through which the blood must flow. The renal portal system is retained, and the ventricle remains undivided so that oxygenated and deoxygenated blood is mixed. In reptiles, the renal portal system is reduced and the ventricle becomes at least partially divided.

Birds require a very quick and efficient method of oxygen transport to meet the high demand of their very active flight mechanisms. To fulfil this need, the heart is relatively large and beats considerably faster than that of most mammals. The blood contains an increased number of red blood corpuscles to enable more oxygen to be absorbed, and the arteries supplying the flight muscles are greatly enlarged.

But the highest circulatory efficiency is found in mammals. The mammalian circulation has no renal portal system and the ventricle becomes completely divided into two. This results in the typical four-chambered heart with which we are familiar, composed of left atrium, right atrium, left ventricle, and right ventricle.

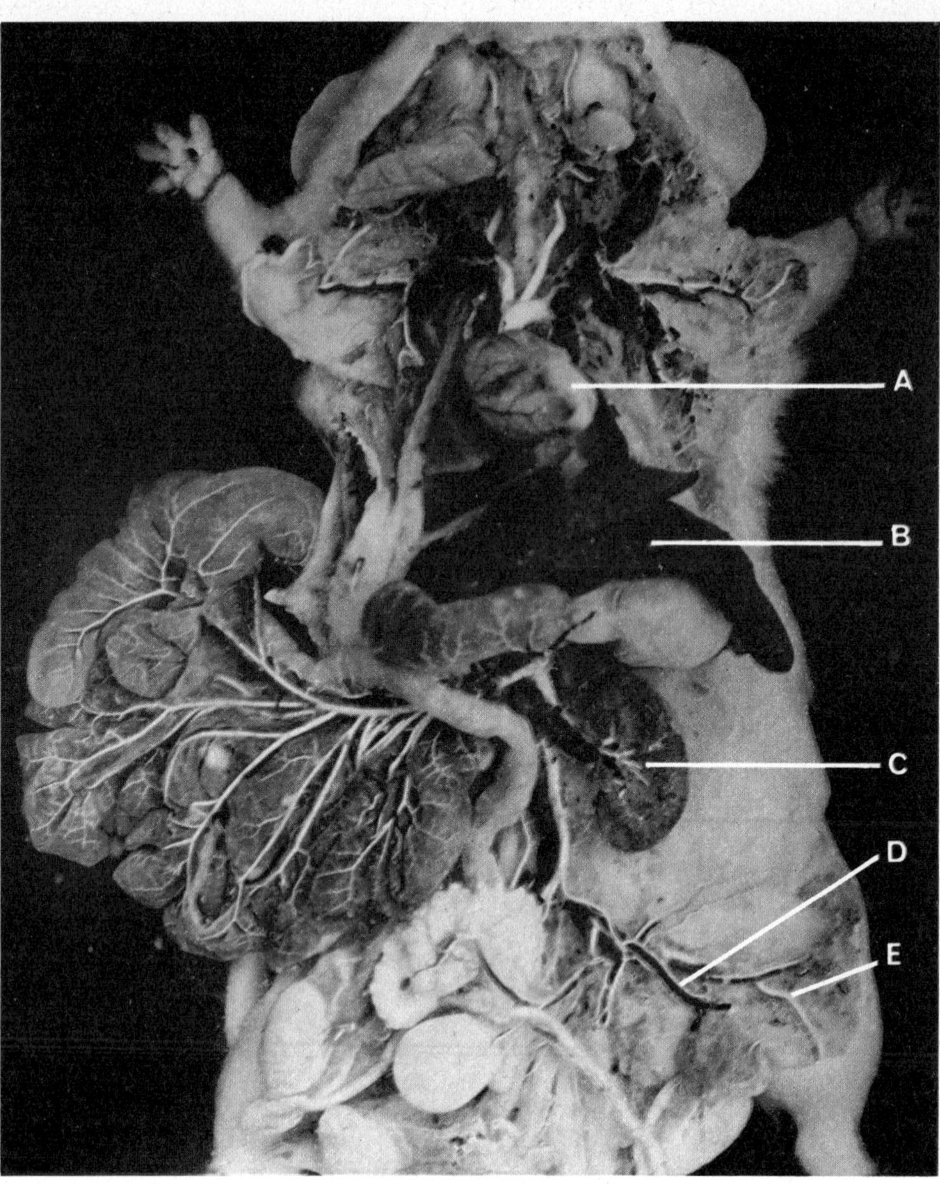

In mammals, such as this mouse, the circulatory system is differentiated into several distinct organs. The heart **(A)** is of course the pump, the veins **(D)** and arteries **(E)** are the transport tubes. The liver **(B)** and kidneys **(C)** act to filter waste products carried in the blood.

The mammalian circulation, of course, shows slight variations to meet the needs of animals as varied as mice, bats, horses, whales, monkeys and men. But the fundamental arrangement remains the same. Basically there are two pumps at work (the right-hand side of the heart and the left-hand side) and two sets of vessels in series (the systemic and pulmonary circulations). The systemic circulation supplies the body muscles and organs, and the pulmonary supplies the lungs.

Blood enters the right atrium in two large collecting veins, the *superior vena cava* from the head and neck region and the *inferior vena cava* from the trunk and limbs. The auricle contracts and blood is forced through into the right ventricle (back-flow is prevented by valves and the closing of the openings of the collecting vessels). The blood is then pumped by the right ventricle into the pulmonary artery to the lungs, where it is oxygenated and then returned to the left auricle via the pulmonary veins. From the left auricle blood is pumped into the left ventricle, which is more muscular than any of the other chambers. From there it is pumped out into the aorta. The aorta divides, carrying blood forwards in the carotid artery to supply the head and neck region and backwards in the dorsal aorta to the remainder of the body. The arteries of the systemic system therefore supply the head, trunk, limbs and main organs (except lungs). The pulmonary artery contains deoxygenated blood, and the pulmonary vein contains oxygenated blood. This is the opposite of the condition of blood circulating in the systemic vessels.

The connection between an artery and a vein is a system of capillaries. These carry gases, food materials and wastes between the blood and tissues. A vessel which has a system of capillaries at both ends is called a portal vein, for example the vein that carries blood rich in absorbed food materials from the intestine to the liver is called the hepatic portal vein.

The evolution of an efficient and well-developed vascular system has enabled animals to reach considerable sizes and to maintain a high rate of activity. It has overcome many of the limitations imposed on animals that rely on diffusion or on only a poorly developed transport system.

# Windows on the world

An astonishing diversity of eyes is found in nature, from the primitive eyespot to the insects' compound eyes. How do they work, what can they see, and how are they suited to their owner's way of life?

THE VERTEBRATE EYE is like a camera. Light enters it through a transparent 'window' at the front, known as the cornea. It is focused by a lens (which in the case of Man is flexible, and in the case of fishes is not) on to a layer of light-sensitive cells, which collectively form the retina. The amount of light passing through the lens to the retina is controlled, as in the camera, by the iris – a muscular ring overlaid with light-absorbing pigment which closes when the light is bright and opens when it is dim. The eye's shape is maintained in the same way as a football's: fluid inside the eye, at carefully regulated pressure, pushes against the tough fibrous 'husk' of the eye, known as the sclera.

## The 'simple' eye

This extremely complex camera-like organ is known, seemingly ironically, as a 'simple' eye to distinguish it from the compound eye of insects. That the vertebrate eye is, in fact, complex, is not in itself surprising – most things in nature are complex if you look at them closely enough. The puzzling thing is how such an eye developed. For the various parts of the eye are not related structurally or embryologically to each other; the retina develops as an outcrop of the embryonic brain; the cornea develops from transparent ectoderm at the surface of the embryo; the sclera is mesodermal. Yet each part of the eye is – apparently – useless without the other parts. How could a sophisticated, flexible lens evolve, unless the animal already possessed a retina capable of picking up and interpreting the image

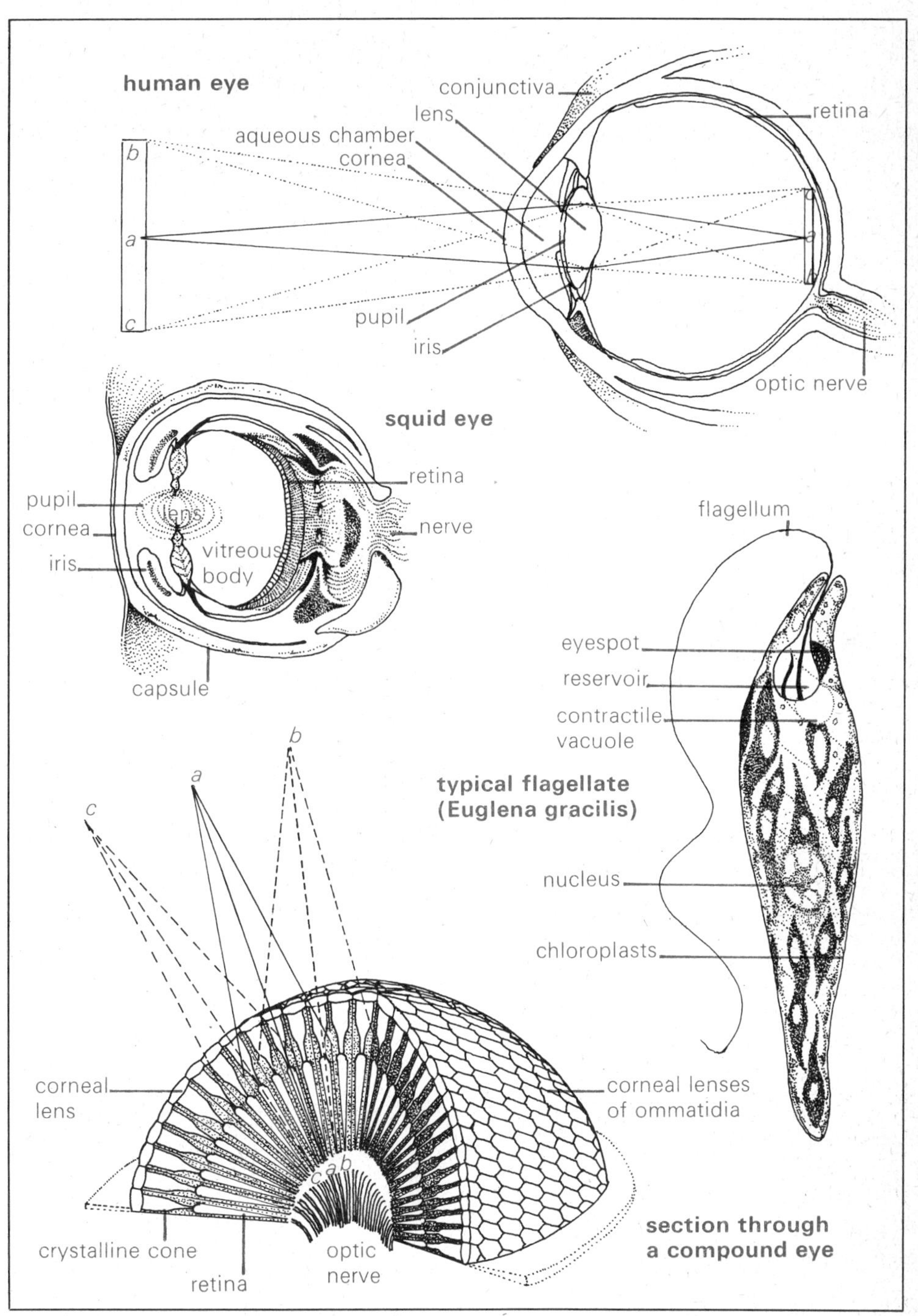


Four different types of eye. The most primitive, in *Euglena,* is a simple light-sensitive spot, while the compound eye is highly complex. Squid and human eyes look similar but develop differently.

Built for night vision, this owl's eyes reflect an image of the photographer. The large pupils catch as much as possible of the incident light so that the owl can hunt in darkness.

projected on to it? And, conversely, how could such a retina develop unless the animal stock already possessed reasonable lenses capable of focusing light? It is the chicken and egg problem all over again. Nor is this the whole problem. We can see that the vertebrate lens is very useful. But what use would a lens be that was only half evolved? What were primitive lenses like before they were sophisticated enough to focus light properly – what function did they serve the primitive animals that possessed them?

Before we seek to answer these questions, let us make the problem still more complex. The things that we 'see' around us – solid objects, each with a definite form, each standing separately from all the other objects – bear very little obvious relation to the 'image' that is focused on our retinas. For this image – a mere patch of light – is distorted (since the retina is a curved surface); it is granular (since the retina is composed of separate cells, not all of which are functional at any one time); and it is two-dimensional. And this image, in turn apparently bears very little relation to the flurry of electrical impulses that travel from the retina down the optic nerve, to the visual cortex of our brains.

For these impulses do not travel down the nerve like electrodes rushing down a cathode-ray tube in a television, to re-create the retinal image on our brain as if it were a television screen. And even if a retinal-type image were re-created inside our brains, this would not explain vision; for we would still need some means of interpreting the image projected on our brain; we would need a second eye in the brain to see that image. In fact, of course, both the retinal image and the nerve impulses that arise from it are part of a rarefied and stylized visual code, just as the printed words on this page are a stylized code of the thoughts they are intended to convey.

## Half-way eyes

Thus even when we have explained how all the various components of our eye might have come into being (which is the theme of this article) we have told only half the story. To glean meaningful information about the outside world through the medium of light energy, it is not enough simply to have good eyes. Graft a man's eye into an earthworm (if such a thing were possible) and it would 'see' no better than it does now, for it lacks the nervous equipment needed to make sense of the esoteric and very individual code of nervous impulses that would come from the eye. Eyes and brains have evolved in concert, just as have the various components of the eyes of higher animals.

If an animal is to respond to light it must 'know' that the light is there. The first requirement, then, is that light should produce some chemical change in the animal. The simplest animals – like amoebae – can respond to bright light (generally by shunning it) simply because the large amount of light energy hitting the animal produces somewhat generalized chemical changes in much the same way as heat or sound energy would.

The next stage in perception is for the animal to possess special chemicals that respond to light much less intense than that needed to produce generalized chemical changes – and furthermore, that are reversibly alterable, so that having once been changed by the light they can then be restored in their original form, and thus become capable of responding to the light a second time. Several such chemicals exist in nature. Of necessity, they absorb light. They therefore appear coloured and are known as pigments.

Even very simple animals possess blobs

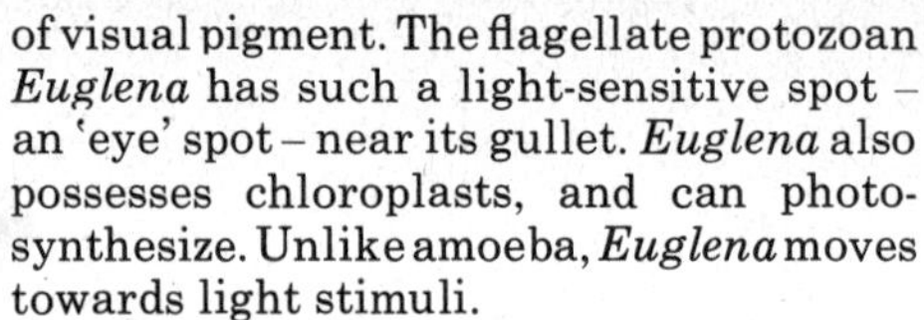

of visual pigment. The flagellate protozoan *Euglena* has such a light-sensitive spot – an 'eye' spot – near its gullet. *Euglena* also possesses chloroplasts, and can photosynthesize. Unlike amoeba, *Euglena* moves towards light stimuli.

*Euglena* with its single eyespot, can learn very little about its environment beyond the fact that the prevailing light intensity suddenly decreased – as when a shadow fell over the animal; or that it pulsed a signal only when the light suddenly increased, signifying that the shadow had passed. Already we would have

**1** The almost human eye of the conch peers out from under the animal's shell. This type of eye is probably capable of forming a reasonable image of undersea objects.

**2** The hawkmoth caterpillar keeps its predators at bay by simulating an 'eye' on its trunk. The 'eye' is simply a form of camouflage.

**3** The squid, a very advanced mollusc, has a number of eyes which appear superficially very similar to those of vertebrates. In fact, the squid has well-developed vision.

**4** The loris, a nocturnal primate distantly related to Man, has large round eyes which take up a considerable portion of its face. They help it see in the dark.

**5** In the snail, a primitive mollusc, the eyes are projected on the ends of the animal's antennae. A pit of light-sensitive cells is sunk into the tip beneath a layer of transparent cells.

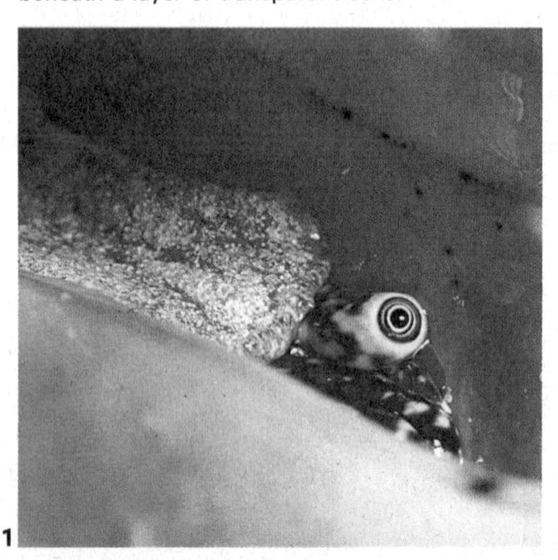

1

2

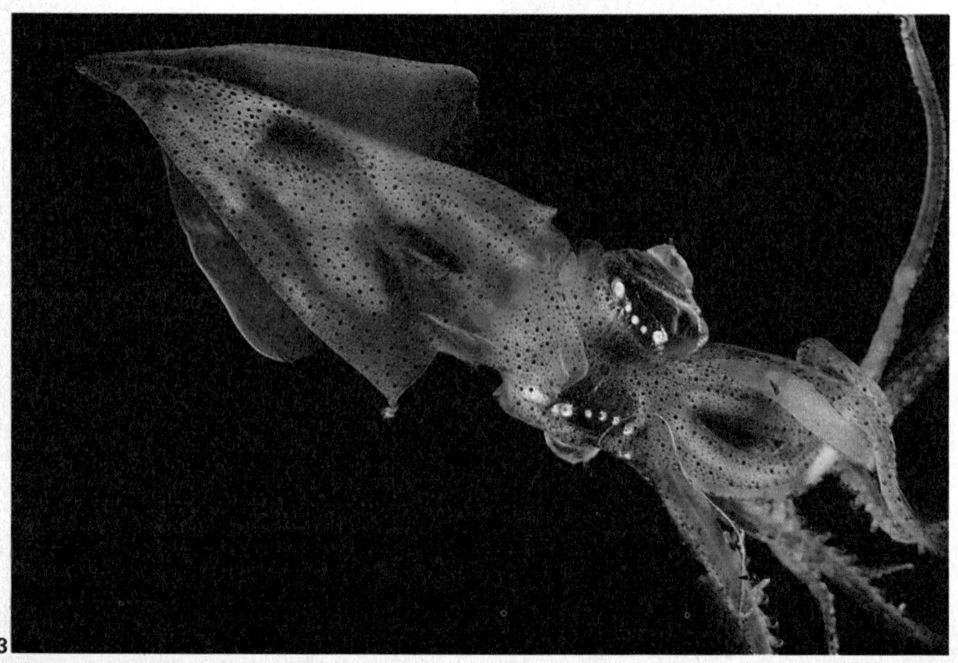

3

4

5

a coding system that could tell an animal with a suitable nervous system that something in the environment is moving.

Animals whose bodies are made up of many cells – the *Metazoa* – generally have specialized light-sensitive cells. In the simplest conceivable situation, these cells are scattered over the body surface. Thus the flat-worm *Planaria* – besides having recognizable eyes at its front end – also has light-sensitive cells scattered over its body surface. The earthworm's light-sensitive cells are similarly scattered, but it is doubtful whether this should be regarded merely as a 'primitive' feature. The earthworm is a burrower, and it generally surfaces only at night. It needs to know only if it is dark or not. Animals more primitive than the earthworm – like *Planaria,* and like *Nereis,* a marine segmented worm that hunts its food – have perfectly good eyes.

The cat is another vertebrate with good eyesight, to suit its nocturnal habits. The pupil in this case is slit, and can be widened to accommodate more light when it is dark.

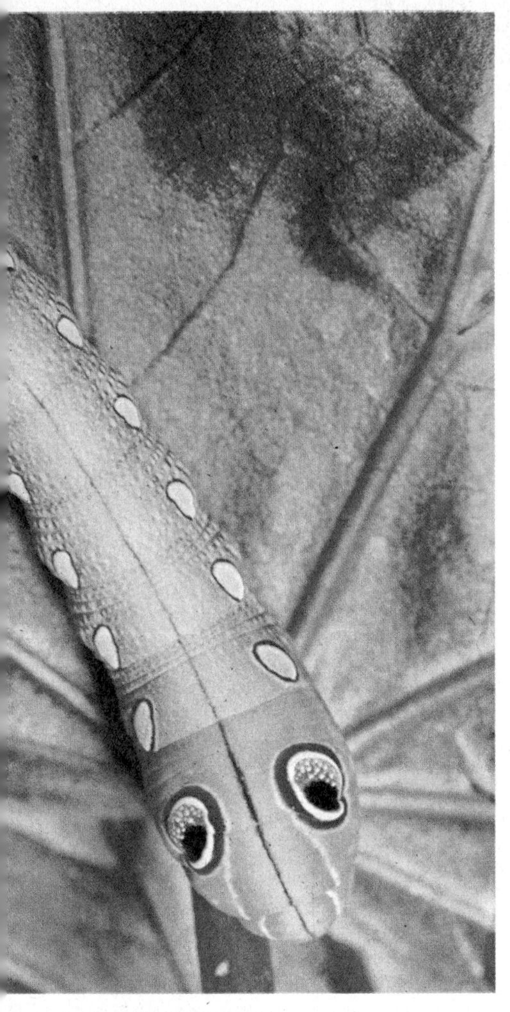

But in most animals, even in primitive things like *Planaria,* the light-sensitive cells are mostly grouped together into recognizable eyes. This is no accident; most mobile animals move in one direction only, and there is obvious selective advantage in having light-sensitive cells at the front: it is better to have information about where you are going than where you have been.

## Eyes front

That light cells became grouped at the front of the animal might seem obvious and of no great significance. But the point is that *unless* light-sensitive cells had become grouped together then they could never have been used co-operatively in the way that is necessary to form images. Yet they originally became grouped together long before any animal had a brain big enough to cope with images, and long before animals even had means of focusing light on to the cells to make image formation possible. A very primitive retina – which at its simplest is no more than a patch of light-sensitive cells – might have evolved simply because animals tend to move in one direction only and it is best to have the receptors at the front.

In fact, even lowly *Planaria* uses its very elementary group of light-sensitive cells to tell it from which direction the light is coming. The whole eye lies beneath a patch of specially transparent surface ectoderm. Each group of light-sensitive cells whose ends project directly into the 'brain' is surrounded by a bowl of black pigment cells, which shade the receptor cells from light coming from all directions but one.

Usually, however, the light-sensitive cells in lowly animals are not buried beneath epidermis; they generally are at the surface. A common arrangement is seen in the limpet, where the light-sensitive cells line a shallow pit on the body surface. Possibly light-sensitive regions became pit-shaped so as to protect the light-sensitive cells from mechanical damage. But having cells in pits also has a visual advantage. The ancient Greeks found that they could look at the stars in the daytime by looking straight upwards from the bottom of deep pits, because that way the view of the stars was not obliterated by the glare of the sun. Similarly, light-sensitive cells sunk in pits are shielded from glare, and so the possibility of image formation is enhanced. Again, limpets probably cannot form images; but if their eyes were wired to a better nervous system, possibly they might perceive some sort of image.

And indeed, very similar eyes in the

The eight eyes of a spider. Not every animal has only two eyes – many insects have numerous light-sensitive organs. In this case, the eyes give the spider an all-round view.

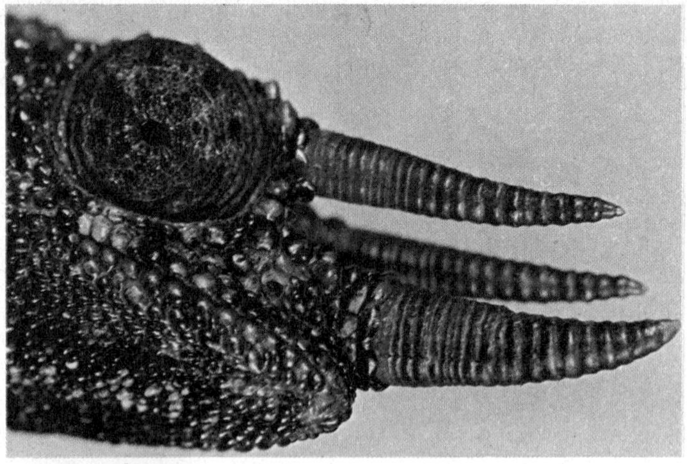

The horned chameleon has a turret for its eye – rather like the turret of a tank. By swivelling the turret round, the chameleon can look round without turning its head.

head of the cephalopod *Nautilus* (primitive relative of the squids and octopuses) undoubtedly serve to form respectable images. The eye-pit has deepened in *Nautilus,* and the edges of the pit have closed over, leaving only a small hole. In fact *Nautilus*'s eye is exactly like a pin-hole camera, which though primitive can produce images which are extremely sharp – though not very bright.

You have only to combine the very primitive features of limpet and *Nautilus* eyes – the deep cell-lined pit of one and the protective and refractive transparent covering of the other – to produce eyes like those of spiders or scorpions – predatory animals that use their eyes in hunting. In these animals, the thickened secretion that has come to serve as a lens is on the surface. In the predatory marine worm *Nereis* development has gone one step further; the cup of light-sensitive cells, with the lens secreted over them, has sunk beneath a transparent cuticle. In the snail there is a similar arrangement, except that the external transparent cuticle is replaced by an external cell layer.

## Snail eyes

Snails are in many ways primitive molluscs: squids and octopuses (which, like *Nautilus,* are cephalopods) are very advanced molluscs. No one is saying that squids evolved from snails; but they do belong to the same phylum, and it is easy to see how a snail-like eye could be modified into a squid-like eye. And the squid's eye, though in detail very different from the vertebrate eye, bears a strong superficial resemblance to it; it is of comparable efficiency, and, like the vertebrate eye, it works on the camera principle.

The vertebrate eye, though it has all the components of a squid's eye, is in detail totally different. And, of course, vertebrates are totally unrelated to squids – their evolutionary lines diverged when the Earth was still young. The most striking difference between vertebrate and squid eye is that the vertebrate retina, compared to that of the squid, is inside out. The nerves running from the squid's retinal cells run directly from the back of the retina. The nerves from the vertebrate's

The head of the dragonfly is dominated by an enormous pair of compound eyes, bulging out to give almost all-round vision. This type of eye is very sensitive to tiny movements in the field of view.

retinal cells actually run forward, so that the nerve fibres lie inside the retinal cells, between them and the light.

Thus we see how the complex and closely interrelated components of the camera-like eyes of squids and vertebrates are reflected in more primitive creatures. But there has been one important evolutionary diversion that has produced eyes that work totally differently. This diversion led to the compound eyes of the primitive trilobites and the modern insects. We can see how camera-like eyes may have evolved by looking at simplified versions of them in simple animals, but the compound eye apparently appeared complete in the trilobites which lived more than 500 million years ago. There are no fossils older than these trilobites, so the origin of compound eyes is uncertain.

The compound eye has a great many – sometimes hundreds – of separate vase-shaped components known as *ommatidia.* Each ommatidium consists of a cluster – usually seven – of light-sensitive cells, surrounded by a hexagonal pattern of six pigment cells. At the outside of each ommatidium is a thickened piece of cuticle that serves both as protector and lens, and is called therefore a 'corneal lens', or a lens facet. Behind this corneal lens lies a second lens, the so-called lens cylinder. Now, the vertebrate lens – like those of pretty well all other animals – works as a lens by virtue of its shape. Not so the lens cylinder. The refractive index of the centre of the lens cylinder is greater than at its edge; thus light is funnelled down the cylinder, in a way that is unique.

One of the silliest misconceptions about insect eyes is that each ommatidium forms a separate image; according to this idea the fly sees a thousand views at once, as if it were looking through the dimpled glass that is used for bathroom windows. This is impossible on anatomical grounds; for each group of light-sensitive cells in each ommatidium is served by a single nerve fibre, and single nerve fibres, though more versatile than one might think, cannot form images. In fact each ommatidium works on an on/off basis – the ommatidium probably signals only when there is a sudden change in the intensity of light hitting it. In fact, the insect eye is primarily adapted to detect movement – and very efficient it is too, to judge from the speed of a fly's reaction to the swatter.

## Evolution of vision

Thus animals glean information from light stimuli in a remarkable variety of ways, and the information they glean differs markedly in quality. At the most primitive level, only the presence or absence of light can be detected. More advanced animals can detect light's direction; then movement was detectable; then eyes and brains combined to form images; and finally, of course, animals became able to detect the subtlest differences in the quality of light in the images they formed: they developed colour vision. We cannot know how the vertebrate eye developed – the most primitive vertebrates have quite good eyes and the fossil relics of the pre-vertebrate line are virtually non-existent – but we can infer how the functionally similar eyes of squids, for example, might have been built up from simple components, and presumably vertebrates' ancestors showed a similar step-wise progression. But the early development of compound eyes, the hallmark of insects, remains something of a mystery.

# The deceptive eye

The all-seeing eye is a myth. In all animals, vision is tailored to the animal's way of life. Many species see the world very differently from humans as their eyes are designed for other purposes.

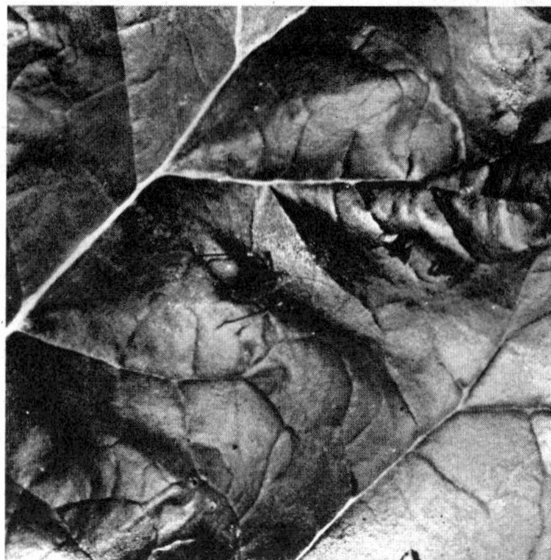

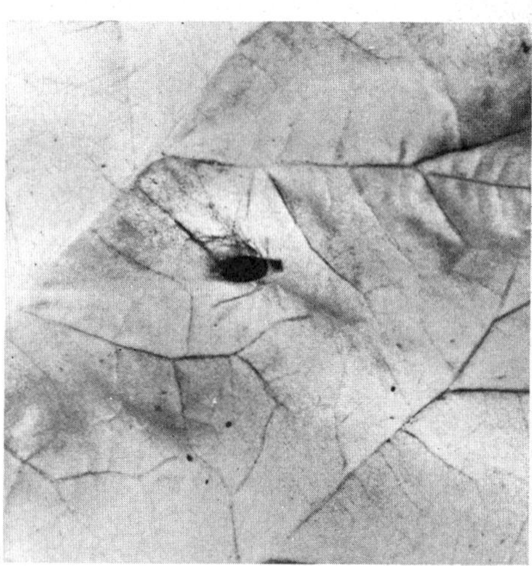

1 An all-round view of London's Trafalgar Square. Many animals, frogs for example, have a far wider angle of view than human beings, and their eyes are often placed to look fore and aft.

2 On a visible-light photograph, this grasshopper looks 'camouflaged'. 3 Photographed on infra-red film, however, it stands out. Not all animals see the grasshopper's camouflage.

HUMAN EYES are not the best – birds, for example, can see better – but they are reasonably good. We can see the electromagnetic spectrum at wavelengths between about 4,000 and 7,000 angstroms – and we can distinguish between light of different wavelengths, which is to say we can see colour. We have a good idea of shape – we can distinguish immediately between, say, a square and a circle, and even between a circle and a polygon. And we see things in depth – we have a good idea of perspective.

We tend to forget that other animals have very different visual equipment from ours, and that their view of the world is therefore very different from our own. For example, it is extremely unlikely that the compound eyes of insects – though they are in some ways very good – can form images. For each individual facet of the compound eye – each *ommatidium* – cannot possibly form an image, because it is served only by a single nerve fibre. Neither, by the same token, can each ommatidium form part of an image, like a piece of jigsaw. All the ommatidia can do is to tell the insect whether or not the intensity of light is changing; and, in some instances, the colour of that light. Thus the insect eye is primarily adapted to detect movement, for which it is obviously very efficient, as anyone who has watched a dragonfly hunting on the wing will testify. And the speed at which the insect eye can register movement is phenomenal – for example, if a fly went to the cinema it would not see the continuous movement on the screen that we see: it would see each frame separately, as a series of 'stills'.

Difficulties arise for insects that need to distinguish between static objects in order to live: the bee needs to distinguish between the shapes of different flowers, and indeed does so with remarkable accuracy, even though its eyes are poorly adapted to do so. In fact, bees cannot distinguish circles from squares, or squares from polygons. But they can distinguish objects with irregular edges – like daisies – from objects with smooth edges – like buttercups. We can assume that the irregular edge creates an impression of flicker in the bee's eye as the bee moves its head, whereas the smooth-edged objects set up no such impression. Thus the bee uses an eye which is designed to detect movement to distinguish shapes – crudely, perhaps, but well enough to enable bees to live successfully.

The colour-vision that we take for granted is foreign to most animals. The distribution of colour-vision in the animal kingdom seems a bit haphazard. It seems that among the mammals, only the primates – men, apes and monkeys – can distinguish colour. Yet birds see colour perfectly well. Among the reptiles, the turtles and lizards can appreciate colour – if we are to believe the evidence of the few behavioural experiments that have been done; whereas it is doubtful whether crocodiles and snakes can. (This distribution is very odd, as snakes and lizards are very closely related.) Insects, crustacea, the bony fishes and a few lowly invertebrates can appreciate differences in hue; many lower fishes, most amphibians and most invertebrates cannot.

Colour tends to play a big part in the lives of animals that have developed colour-vision. Birds, insects and fish are the most highly coloured of all animals, and they often use their bright colours to communicate with each other – either in mating, or, in the case of birds, sometimes to warn others of the same species of impending danger. Many animals that do not themselves see colour have developed bright colours in order to communicate with other species that can: a lot of poisonous frogs and toads have very bright colours – which they themselves cannot appreciate, but which are intended to warn birds that they are not good to eat.

The observation that all colours – even white – can be made by mixing together various combinations of three coloured lights – blue, red and green – has led to the so-called 'trichromatic' theory of colour, first put forward in 1801 by Thomas Young. Young's idea was that the eye contains three kinds of light-receptive 'elements', each responsive to only one of the primary colours, and that when various combinations of these three elements are stimulated, we distinguish colours other than the primary hues. The primary colours stated here are different from the primary colours of the paint-box. This is because coloured light is fundamentally different from pigment. When burning sodium gives out yellow light it does just that – rays of wavelength around 6,000 Å exude from it. A yellow pigment, on the other hand, *absorbs* all light hitting it except that with a wavelength of 6,000 Å. The effect of mixing different light *absorbers* is different from that of mixing different light *sources*.

1 A normal human retina seen through an ophthalmoscope. The blood-vessels radiate from the 'blind spot' near the centre of the field of vision, where the optic nerve leaves the eye.
2 The bright red coloration of this tropical frog warns its predators that it has an unpleasant taste.

Colour plays an important part in protecting animals and in communication.
3 Bees see a different portion of the spectrum from human beings. While they can perceive ultra-violet, they cannot see red. Flower colours undoubtedly appear quite differently to them.

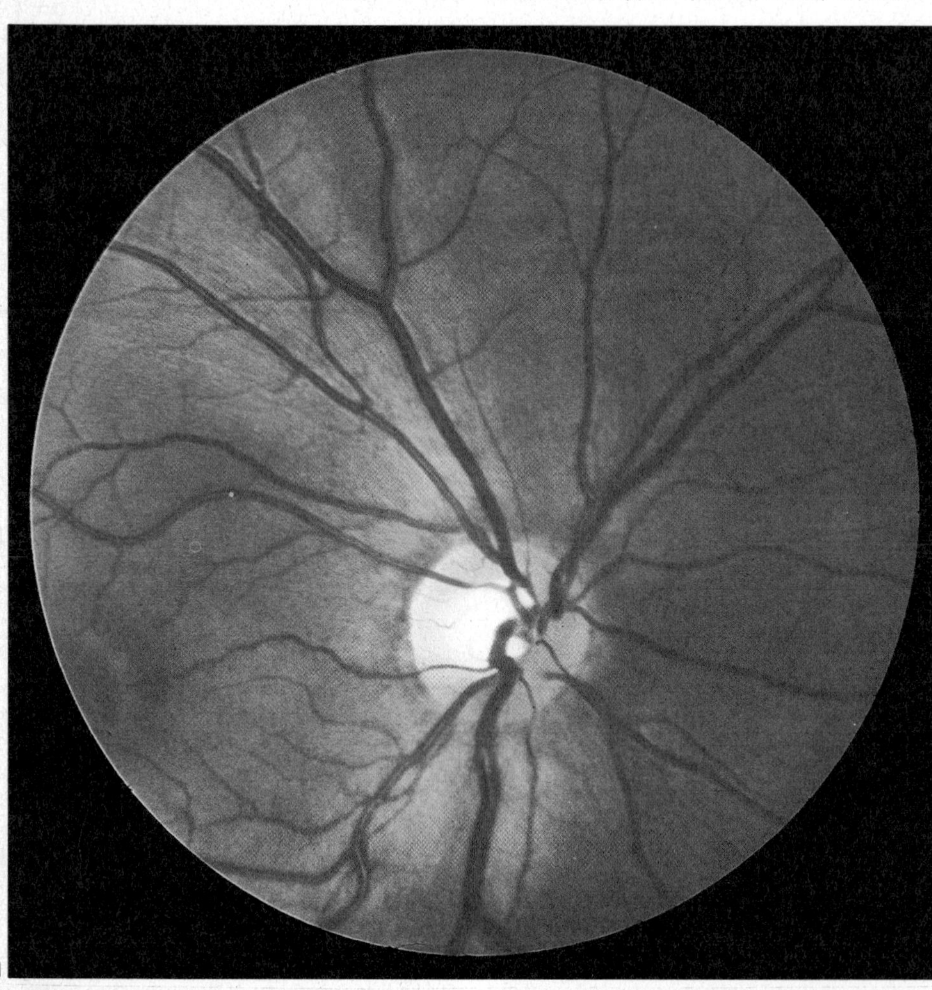

1

2

3

Young's hypothesis has a number of weaknesses: for one thing, the eye does not contain three different kinds of light-sensitive cell, and for another, though several visual pigments have been identified, we have not yet found three that correspond to the three 'elements' that Young's hypothesis demands. It is not quite true to say that you can form *all* colours by mixing the three primaries: you can't form brown, for example, or ginger. The young American genius Edwin Land (inventor of the Land polaroid camera) showed that under certain special circumstances an eye can 'see' a whole range of colours even when only one colour – in Land's experiment, red – is shone into it.

Despite these drawbacks, we know that Thomas Young must have hit on something, and his ideas still form the basis of modern experiments on colour-vision.

## Bee vision

Not all animals with colour-vision 'see' the same colours as we do. The bee cannot see so far into the red end of the spectrum as we can, but it can see what we call 'ultra-violet'. If we apply the Thomas Young trichromatic theory to bees we could say that the bee's primary colours are ultra-violet (equivalent to our blue), yellow (equivalent to our red) and blue (equivalent to our green). Because bees see ultra-violet and not red, wild flowers must look very different to bees than they do to us; and since wild flowers evolved to attract bees, and not to attract human beings, you could say that our impression of wild flowers is not what nature intended. Thus red flowers presumably appear to the bee to be ultra-violet since they reflect both ultra-violet and red, and we know bees cannot see red. And we cannot be certain that two flowers that appear to us to be the same colour appear that way to the bee. Bees can be taught to distinguish between two identical looking shades of white flower, presumably because one reflects ultra-violet and the other doesn't. Similarly, two flowers that appear to us to be different colours may well appear to the bee to be the same colour.

Before we judge the 'significance' of a particular colour in nature we must first find out what impression that colour is likely to have on the animal it is intended to impress. A parallel example is seen in

This picture, of a stickleback swimming past the open jaws of a wrasse with a starfish in the background, was taken through the lens of a cod's eye. This is how fish see their world.

certain animals which apparently disguise themselves by merging themselves with the background. If you photograph a grasshopper sitting on a leaf it appears very well camouflaged – both leaf and grasshopper are green. But if you photograph the same grasshopper with an infra-red camera the grasshopper stands out very clearly – because it reflects infra-red light and the leaf doesn't. Before we decide that the grasshopper's colour is intended as camouflage we must decide whether or not its possible predators can appreciate infra-red. If they can, then the green pigment would be not camouflage, but – if anything – warning coloration.

Another thing that bees can do which we cannot is to appreciate the direction in which light is travelling; even when the sun is hidden, they can infer its position. This ability to appreciate polarity is essential to the bee's communal way of life. Bees may travel miles to find food, and when they do so they return to the hive, and, by means of the famous symbolic 'dance' described by von Frisch, they tell the other bees where that food source was, in relation to the sun's position. This system can only work if the bee has a highly developed sense of geometry and if it is capable of using the polarity of sunlight as a grid to direct its movements.

Animals with eyes much more like ours than bees' have very different visual capabilities from our own. One of the most striking points of difference is in acuity – the ability to distinguish detail.

Visual acuity depends on a lot of things. It depends first on how much light gets into the eye: too much, and there is 'glare'; too little, and much of the visual scene disappears simply because no light is being reflected from it. Acuity also depends on how well the light is focused on to the retina, which contains the light-sensitive cells. Finally, it depends on the light-sensitive cells themselves – how close they are together, and how they are connected to the nervous system.

The visual acuity of vertebrates does not depend simply on how 'advanced' the animal is; we cannot assume that mammals see better than fish simply because they took longer to evolve. Indeed, as we saw earlier, fish have the advantage over most mammals in at least one respect – they can see colour. In general, the acuity of the eye – as of a microscope or a camera

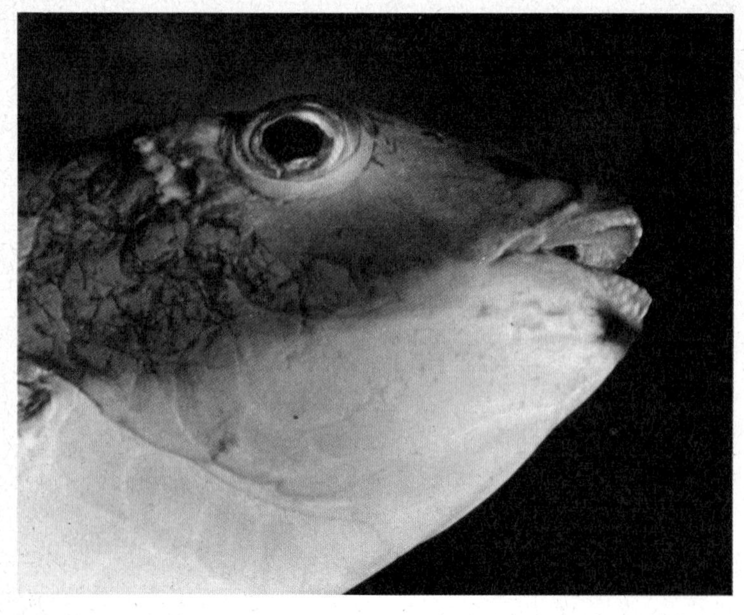

The eye of a parrotfish. Because the cornea can take little part in focusing, many fish are able to move their lenses forward or backwards in a similar way to a bellows camera.

The bulging eye of an octopus. Though it seems improbable, the octopus eye rivals vertebrate eyes in its efficiency and is extremely well adapted for underwater vision.

– must be a compromise between different requirements. An eye that is adapted to take in as much light as possible, for use in near-darkness, will not see the detail that our eyes can (and still less than some birds' eyes can) but it will be useful for a nocturnal animal.

## The focusing mechanism

Consider first the easiest part of visual acuity – the focusing mechanism. The vertebrate eye is roughly like a camera in this respect. Light enters through the transparent cornea at the front, passes through the lens, and is focused on to the light-sensitive retina. But there the parallel with the camera ends. For one thing, most people assume that the cornea is simply a 'window' – a transparent front to the eye. In practice, in land vertebrates the cornea does most of the focusing – the lens serves merely for fine adjustment. Though the lens is extremely useful, people who have had their eye lenses removed because of cataract (opacity of the lens) can still see perfectly well provided they wear reasonably thick glasses. (In fact they can possibly see better than many normal old people, whose lenses have started to become opaque and have become too stiff to focus properly.)

The importance of the cornea in focusing is obvious if you apply physical principles to the eye. For focusing depends on light being bent, or *refracted,* as it passes from a medium of one optical density into a medium of greater optical density. The optical density of the cornea is much higher than that of the air, and so, in a land animal, light entering the eye is refracted very significantly as it crosses the air/cornea interface. After passing through the cornea the light travels through the *aqueous humour,* a watery fluid that separates cornea and lens, and then it passes into the lens. But the lens, which is made of *cytoplasm,* is itself almost 100 per cent water, and so its optical density is very little different from that of the aqueous humour. So comparatively little refraction occurs at the aqueous humour/lens interface.

In practice, then, the lens serves for fine adjustment. Light coming from distant points is parallel when it enters the eye. Parallel light needs very little refraction to make it converge on the retina. For distant focus, then, the lens is almost flat – flat lenses are less convergent than spherical ones. But light coming from near points is diverging as it hits the eye – it needs to be refracted more strongly to make it converge on to the retina. So for near focusing the lens assumes a more spherical shape.

Mammal eyes focus by changing the lens shape – and not, as does the camera, by moving the lens nearer or further from the place of focus. But fish find vision more of a problem than land animals for their eyes are surrounded by water, and the optical density of that water is very like that of the cornea of their eyes. Very little focusing can be done by the fish cornea – it must all be done by the lens. Most fish have given up the attempt to focus with the cornea – their corneas are flat (hence the expression 'cod-eyed'). The lens, left with all the focusing to do, tends to be almost spherical. And focusing is achieved not by changing its shape but, as in the camera, by moving the lens nearer or further from the retina. Some fish can also focus by changing the shape of the eyeball, thus altering the distance between lens and retina – a technique which parallels that of the bellows camera.

Lenses that are almost spherical pick up more light than flattened lenses, but, though their refracting power is greater, they focus less accurately than flat lenses. Daytime animals, like Man, which can afford to 'waste' light but which need to see detail, tend to have flat lenses with a long focal length, positioned a long way from the retina. The mouse, a nocturnal animal, needs to pick up all the light it can get, because there is not much around at night. And it needs to see vague outlines, but not detail: it might help a mouse to see the shadow of the owl overhead, but it would not help it to know whether it was a barn owl or a tawny owl because they are equally fearsome predators.

So the mouse's lens is nearly spherical – to pick up all possible light – and it occupies most of the mouse's eye, so the distance between the mouse's lens and retina is very small. On optical grounds we can be pretty certain that the mouse sees little detail. (Owls, which need to see detail at night, have beautifully designed lenses shaped like microscope lenses – cut away at the edges, where focusing is least efficient.) Fish, as we have seen, have spherical lenses for other reasons; but deep-sea fish also need to pick up all the light they can, and besides being spherical, their lenses are enormous. This is why deep-sea fish have telescopic eyes – their heads are too small to contain the vast eyeballs.

## Compromise solutions

Similar compromises between, say, the need for acuity and the need to see in near-dark, are reflected in all the components of vertebrate eyes – in the shape and *modus operandi* of the iris; in the retina; in the presence or absence of 'damping' devices in the eye to prevent glare. Man has a damping device in the form of a layer of pigment cells behind the retina which 'soaks up' surplus light just as the damping mechanism in a modern concert hall soaks up echoes. Cats on the other hand, which contrive to see in the dark, have reflectors in their eyes – which actually increase glare and reduce acuity, but ensure that no light is wasted.

In this respect, the eyes are like almost every other body organ. What they are able to do depends on the requirements imposed by the animal's way of life. Eyes cannot do everything at once.

So, although eyes must have certain features in common – they are all devices for converting light energy into electrical impulses – they are extremely varied in their applications. They have as many different uses as limbs or teeth or pelts.

# Making sense of sounds

**Most animals respond in some way to sound. In higher animals, special sense organs – ears – concentrate and sort out the various sounds around the animal. Many species rely heavily on their ears.**

ALMOST EVERY MOVEMENT that takes place on Earth leads to some kind of noise. The ability to detect sounds and react correctly to the disturbances they produce is thus an asset of considerable value to living beings.

Response to the vibrations of sounds is found even in very primitive forms of life. Earthworms retreat into their holes when they feel the vibrations of footsteps through the earth. They are able to respond even though they have no 'ears' as such.

In the same way, an amoeba would not be regarded as 'seeing' light, although it will move away from bright light. But hearing is generally associated with special sense organs which have developed the ability to respond to vibration to a higher degree than the rest of the body's tissues.

The basic plan of all sense organs is sufficiently similar to show a common origin. Each consists of a *receptor cell* or cells specially modified to receive a stimulus. These initiate an impulse through nerves to the brain or spinal cord where the impulses are 'interpreted' and acted upon.

This basic model of receptor, nerve and brain is found not only in the eyes, the ears, and the organs of taste and smell, but also in the cells in the skin dealing with touch and pressure senses, and in the muscles. The ear is designed to convert the energy of sound, that is, the energy of the movement of air or water molecules, into electrical energy that can then be detected by the brain.

The human ear, a fairly typical example of the type of organ required to detect sounds, acts not only as a *transducer* – turning sound energy into electrical energy – but is also able to amplify the energy received.

The external appearance of the ear is of a flap, the *pinna,* which is designed to concentrate sound into the cavity, the *meatus.* In Man the pinna is rudimentary compared with that found in animals like the horse or the rabbit, which rely far more on their sense of hearing than do human beings. But the pinnae do serve a useful purpose in so far as they tend to cut out sound coming from behind the head and help locate the source of a sound more accurately.

The meatus of the ear is really a tube in the bone leading to a stretched membrane, the *ear-drum.* Behind the ear-drum is a cavity, the *middle ear,* which is normally closed, except during swallowing. The cavity acts as a resonant chamber to increase the efficiency of the ear-drum. The outer and middle ears are solely concerned with the transmission of vibrations, and act merely to pick up sounds and pass them on their way to the inner ear. For this purpose, the ear-drum is connected to the inner ear by a train of small bones, the *ossicles* (*malleus, incus* and *stapes*), which are so arranged that they give added leverage to the small membrane which covers the entrance to the inner ear. The inner ear itself is safely concealed

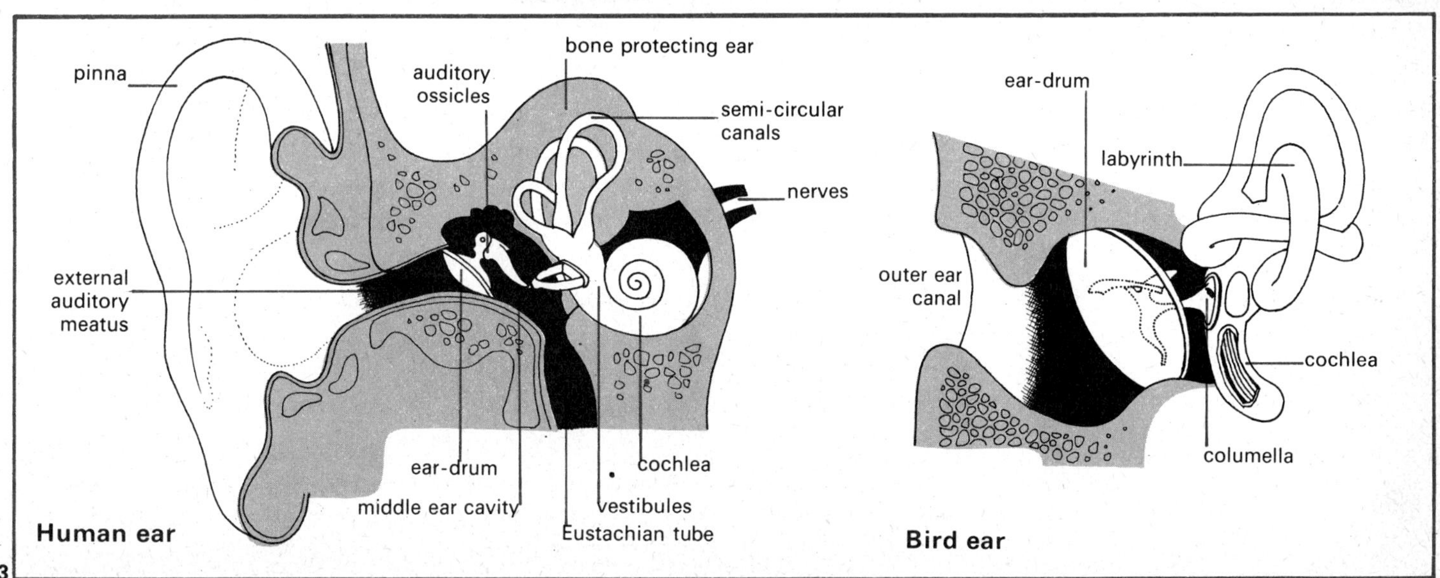


**1** Hares – like this East African species – live close to the ground and require acute hearing. Ear pinnae are well developed and can be swung round to catch sounds from all directions.
**2** The hippopotamus has small ears but like the eyes they are set close to the top of the head so that the animal can listen to its surroundings without raising its body from the water.
**3** Diagram contrasting the human ear with the ear of a bird. The bird has no pinna and its outer ear canal is broader than Man's. The ear-drum is relatively larger and the middle ear shorter.

1 In the green crested lizard (*Calotes cristatellus*) the membrane covering the ear-cavity shows up on the side of the head as an oval brown spot with a central depression.
2 Wild dogs in Murchison Falls Park, Uganda, show the well-developed external ears of hunters. Their acute hearing enables them to detect their prey at considerable distances.
3 The large membranous ears of the African elephant are chiefly concerned with temperature regulation. Blood flowing through the pinnae is cooled by the air.
4 The ear of this occipital vulture can be clearly seen behind the eye. The form of the ear in birds betrays their reptile ancestry, although in birds the ear-drum has sunk below the surface.

1

2

inside the bones of the skull so that it is unlikely to be damaged except by a major catastrophe.

The vibrations which reach the membrane of the inner ear are transmitted to a fluid which fills the cavity of the inner ear. This fluid communicates with a spiral cavity, the *cochlea,* where the real work of the ear is carried out.

The *cochlea* is lined with nerve cells which have hair-like projections. As the vibrations in the fluid set these 'hairs' in motion, they cause the nerve cells to set up impulses which are transmitted through the auditory nerve to the brain.

The shape of the cochlea is such that sounds of different frequency set up vibrations in different parts of the cochlea. This is the basis of our ability to distinguish notes and to hear the pitch of sounds falling on the ear.

The human ear is not equally sensitive to vibrations of all intensities. In fact, we hear only in a comparatively narrow band of frequencies spanning about ten octaves from 20 to 20,000 cycles per second. Below this level, if the vibration is strong enough, it is detected by feel, whereas above 20,000 cycles the sounds are outside our senses altogether.

In fact, human beings have only a moderately developed sense of hearing compared with many other animals. We rely far more on our eyes than on other sense organs. No doubt this is related to the mode of life of the ancestors of human beings who were probably tree dwellers. Good vision was obviously more important than well-developed hearing under these

3

circumstances.

Every dog-owner will have noticed his pet pricking up its ears even when human beings in the vicinity have noticed nothing. This is because dogs have a larger range of hearing than Man. This property is exploited in the so-called 'ultra-sonic' whistles, which emit notes too high for the human ear to detect, but which are readily audible to dogs. The same ability to hear sounds outside the human range is found in many insects. One American research team set out to study the sounds made by crickets. They took tape-recorded imitations of the crickets' chirps, but even when they played these in an area full of crickets, they were apparently unable to get any of the crickets to reply. The reason for this is that the crickets communicate with sounds that are far higher than the human ear can detect: the sound made by the crickets in scraping their wings is entirely incidental to the real communication.

The human ear becomes less sensitive to high notes with increasing age. The ear-drum gradually grows thicker and the tiny bones which link it to the inner ear become less flexible and tend to fuse together. The loss of sensitivity can be charted, and it has been found that in middle-aged men, the loss runs at a rate of about 160 cycles per second lost every year.

The human ear is most sensitive to sound in the range of about 3,000 cycles per second, about four octaves above middle C. This sound is about the same pitch as a woman's scream.

The fact that the ear is relatively insensitive to very low-frequency vibrations is important in preventing hearing being swamped by the sounds of ordinary bodily activity. Some of the problems this might pose can be found by stopping up both ears with the fingers. The low humming sound one can then hear is caused by the continual tiny contractions of muscle cells in the arms.

## Hearing aids

Stopping the ears, and thus shutting out the airborne vibrations shows that the air is not the only medium that transmits sound to the inner ear. With our ears stopped, we can still quite clearly hear ourselves humming. In this case, the energy of the sound is transmitted through the bones of the head. Because the inner ear is surrounded by bone, it is able to detect easily vibrations passing through the bone. This principle is exploited in the treatment of some types of deafness, particularly those due to damaged ossicles (middle-ear deafness). Hearing aids for these types of deafness amplify the sound and apply the vibrations to the bone just behind the ear, thereby by-passing the middle ear.

The ability to hear is the basis of language and this form of communication is widespread throughout the animal kingdom. Many bird songs and animal cries are familiar sounds but until recently the sounds made by fish and sea creatures were almost unknown. In fact, water is a better medium than air for carrying sound. One startling demonstration of this fact was the picking up by a microphone off the American coast of the sound of the explosion of four pounds of TNT off the coast of South Africa.

The sound-transmitting properties of water are used to the full by fish and other marine and freshwater animals. If a microphone is lowered into an aquarium, the fish are found to be making a cacophony of sounds. Some species of fish have specially developed muscles surrounding their swim-bladders which cause the taut surface of the sac to vibrate like a drum. Others rub their gill arches together to make sounds which are meaningful to others of the same species. Fishermen trying to sleep in their thin wooden ships off the coast of China have long found that the noise from certain types of croaking fish keeps them awake at night. The same noises disrupted American anti-submarine defences during the Second World War. These defences made use of microphones under the water connected with loudspeakers above ground. The sound made by large shoals of croakers was almost deafening, and the apparatus had to be redesigned,

Fish are not the only marine animals with the ability to communicate with one another by sound. Dolphins, the intelligent friendly marine mammals which follow ships and can be trained to perform tricks,

4

**1** The ear of the bullfrog (*Rana catesbeiana*) is covered by a stretched membrane continuous with the skin of the head. The bullfrog ear is particularly sensitive to low notes.
**2** The fennec is the smallest known fox, being only 16 inches long. Its striking external ears reach a length of four inches and serve mainly to regulate temperature in its desert habitat.
**3** Bats have extremely sensitive hearing, particularly for high notes, and navigate in the dark by emitting squeaks and picking up the echoes with their large external ears.

are now known to have a well-developed language and seem to be able to express a wide range of feelings. Dolphins are also accomplished mimics; captured species can imitate the human voice.

One question which puzzles many people about hearing is why it should be necessary to have two ears. The reason for this can be more readily appreciated by considering the ears not only as sound-receiving devices but also as direction-finders. When a sound is heard, the head turns slightly to find out where the sound is coming from. But even if the head were fixed in one position, it would still be possible to detect where the sound is. With only one ear functioning, however, and in the absence of other clues, it is hard to tell where a sound is coming from.

The brain can detect very small differences in the time of arrival of a sound at each ear. Differences of as little as 1/10000 of a second can be easily detected, an ability which enables Man to place the source of the sound. The illusion of stereophonic noise can be simulated by a device which delivers sound to one ear and then to the other after an almost imperceptible delay. By varying the delay, the sound can be made to appear to come from various points around the listener.

Blind people are forced to develop the ability to respond to sound to a very high degree. Many of them claim to be able to 'feel' objects through the pores of their skin. In fact, however, they make great use of the direction-finding ability of the ears, and are extremely sensitive to echoes which most people do not notice.

The echoes produced from objects along the side of the road during the course of a car journey are probably familiar to most people. The sound is a regular hiss normally, but passing a car or a pedestrian produces a more pronounced note for a split-second. Much of the time, our ears ignore the echoes produced when we make noises. For example, if you shout in a forest, the echoes are scarcely noticed, if at all. On the other hand, if the sound is recorded and then played backwards it becomes clear that there is really quite a loud echo, and one which is somewhat higher in pitch than the original sound. It is the presence of these echoes that enables blind people to locate objects and to avoid obstacles in their path.

This ability to navigate by ear is found in certain bats. These animals have small mouths which produce a note far outside the human range of hearing, with frequencies up to 130,000 cycles per second. Almost all the smaller bats can use this very high-frequency note as a form of 'radar' to detect obstacles in their path. Their ears detect the reflections from even quite small objects, and they are able to take avoiding action. This ability depends on being able to emit a note at very high frequency: only at this sort of frequency are the echoes from small objects really detectable. Lower notes, with longer wavelengths, need larger surfaces for adequate reflection. To give an efficient echo, the object acting as a reflector needs to be about three times as wide as the wavelength of the sound being reflected. In the case of a note like middle C, for example, the wavelength is just over four feet, so only an object larger than 12 feet by 12 feet has a reasonable chance of producing a good echo. This explains why the spectacular echoes are generally found either in large buildings with big reflecting areas or in mountain districts, where walls of rock act as natural reflectors.

Not many animals can hear as well as the bat but there are few animals that are totally deaf, and no fish has yet been found which lacks completely the ability to hear. Hearing, in fact, is probably the basic sense for communication between members of the same species.

# The feel of things

**The sense of touch, widespread throughout the animal kingdom, plays a predominant part in many animals' lives. In human beings, its potential for communication is only now being explored fully.**

THE ABILITY of animals to detect and react to objects with which they come into physical contact is so widespread that it may almost be classed as a fundamental property of living matter. Every animal shows this property in some way, even the simple one-celled amoeba; while among plants it is also found in many species.

The living cell consists of a complex chemical structure which is constantly undergoing change. Objects in contact with the cell will clearly affect the way in which chemical change proceeds in the cell.

In most lower forms of life response does not rise above the level of a simple reaction. A typical example is the one-celled animal *Paramecium*, a tiny organism found in ponds. The paramecium swims by means of a cilia or tail which it moves convulsively to force its way through the water. When it encounters an obstacle to its progress, the animal 'back-tracks' and approaches again from a slightly different angle. The organism can clearly notice in some way that its path is blocked and take some form of avoiding action.

Sea-anemones not only pull in their tentacles when they protrude above the level of the tide – a necessary reaction if they are to avoid becoming dehydrated by

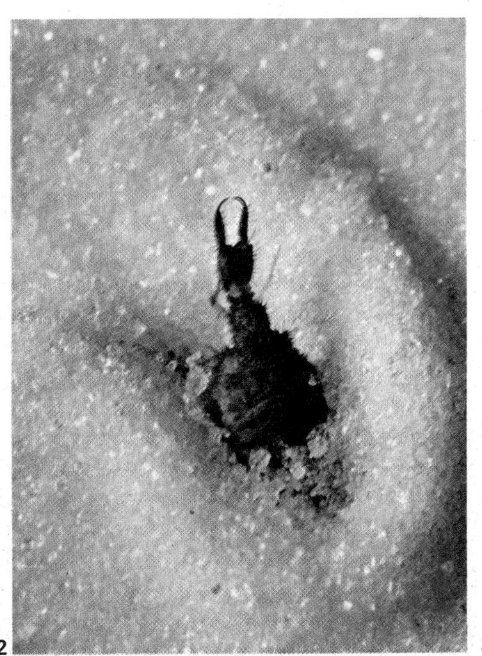

**1** Spiders rely heavily on their sense of touch to tell them when insects land on their webs. The spider's reaction varies according to the magnitude of the vibrations of the web.
**2** Ant-lions lie in wait for their prey at the bottom of shallow pits in sand. When an ant (**3**) blunders over the edge of the pit, the ant-lion throws sand over it and drags it down.

being left high and dry – but they also seem to be able to distinguish food from other underwater objects. The anemones which 'ride' on the back of hermit crabs are frequently bumped against rocks by the movement of their 'chargers', but in these cases they scarcely bother to contract. They pull in their tentacles actively only when they feel the motion of a small fish or shrimp that brushes against their fronds. Thus they can tell 'touching' from 'being touched'.

## Privileged fish

This distinguishing ability is even better developed in one particular anemone. *Actinia quadricolor*, a Red Sea species, works in close conjunction with the common small fish *Amphiprion bicinctus*. The fish drive away the anemones' enemies, while the anemones will not open out if they do not feel the frequent touches of the fishes passing and repassing over them. In normal circumstances the anemones make no attempt to sting the fish, which pass through the fronds unharmed. However, if the fish is passively pushed on to the anemone's tentacles, the anemone can no longer tell it from food and will sting and eat it if it is small enough.

The catfish of the Mississippi, like the cat itself, relies heavily for information on the whiskers fringing its mouth. In the case of the catfish, the whiskers droop on to the bed of the muddy river, trailing over it and warning the catfish when they come into contact with anything unusual. Unlike those of the cat, however, the catfish 'whiskers' are not hairs. Instead they are fleshy outgrowths of the face, but they serve the same function.

Shrimps, too, make use of their antennae as probes. The tropical barbershop shrimp keeps its extensions in constant motion, probing the surrounding water with them. Each of its antennae is two or three times its own length, and they clearly provide it with a great deal of information.

Touch is particularly developed where the senses of sight and sound are unable to operate effectively. In the cat, a nocturnal hunter, the face is fringed with sensitive whiskers which provide instant information about the whereabouts of small prey that may have been tracked down into a dark corner. If a mouse touches its whiskers, a cat will react with hair-trigger speed, and is instantly aware of the mouse's position.

## Feeling ability

The sense of touch is capable of giving accurate information, particularly of a comparative kind. In human beings, for example, it is sufficiently well developed to make it easy to tell a smooth pane of glass from one that is etched to a depth of only 1/2500 inch. This ability has been put to professional use by 'cloth-feelers' whose job it is to feel cloth to tell its quality and type. Many of these men can tell the exact type of a cloth merely by rubbing it with a stick. Others can distinguish a particular type of cloth even if the only contact they have with it is a momentary tap with a fingernail.

Unlike that of the primitive paramecium, but like that of most higher animals, Man's sense of touch is linked with and mediated by a complex nervous system. Cells within the skin are capable of reacting to touch, pain and pressure. These are linked with fine nerve-endings which transmit messages back to the brain. The activity of the brain itself influences what is felt. We have all seen the person, who, absorbed in some task, suddenly starts looking for his spectacles, which are all the while on his nose. This situation is in fact evidence that our nervous systems profoundly influence what we can feel. The central nervous system, after a while suppresses our consciousness of objects which we are constantly touching. Thus we do not, after a short while, feel our clothes on our bodies unless they get in our way. The brain stops 'telling' us that we are wearing them. At the same time, however, the touch cells in the skin are still sending out their messages whenever our clothes rub against them.

For human beings, of course, touch is not the most important sense. It plays a large part in the minutiae of our lives, but has relatively little survival value.

One stage of life in which touch plays a predominant part, however, is in the very young child. A baby gets most of his information about his restricted world from the things he touches. His contact with his mother is even more important. Unless he is nursed and fondled during these early months and years, his development will be impaired. During his childhood, he will feel a need to take part in rough play with other children, involving considerable amounts of touching and contact.

Experiments with animals have shed light on this problem. A third of the rats in one experiment were left in their cages without being handled at all. Two other groups were placed by hand at intervals into special boxes, where one group was given mildly painful electric shocks regu-

**1** The baby macaque monkey in this experiment faces a choice between two 'mothers' – one cloth-covered, one made of chicken-wire. Though feeding from the wire doll, he prefers the cloth one, and runs to 'her' when in danger.
**2** These armoured catfish find their food in murky water by trailing their fleshy barbels along the river floor. The barbels are outgrowths from the face, but they serve the same purpose as whiskers.
**3** Books written in Braille, a code of raised dots, can be read quickly after practice by blind people. Many blind people acquire a remarkably acute sense of touch.
**4** The queen bee, top, determines what sort of egg to lay in a particular honeycomb cell by feeling the cell's dimensions with her antennae. In large cells, she lays unfertilized eggs that later become drones.
**5** These fish swim unconcernedly around the fronds of an anemone. The anemone ignores them so long as they are not pushed passively against it. If they are it stings and kills them.

2

larly while the others were merely left alone once inside. The interesting result was that the two groups of rats that had been handled, both those that had been shocked and those that had not, were friendly and 'tame' when they grew older. It was the third group, the unhandled, unstimulated rats, that showed a difference. As they grew up, these cowered timidly in the corners of their cages, showing all the signs of fear and anxiety. When they grew older, they underwent brain surgery which turned them into

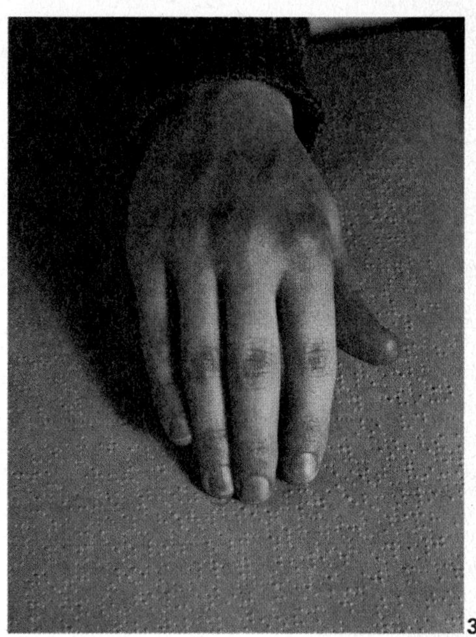
3

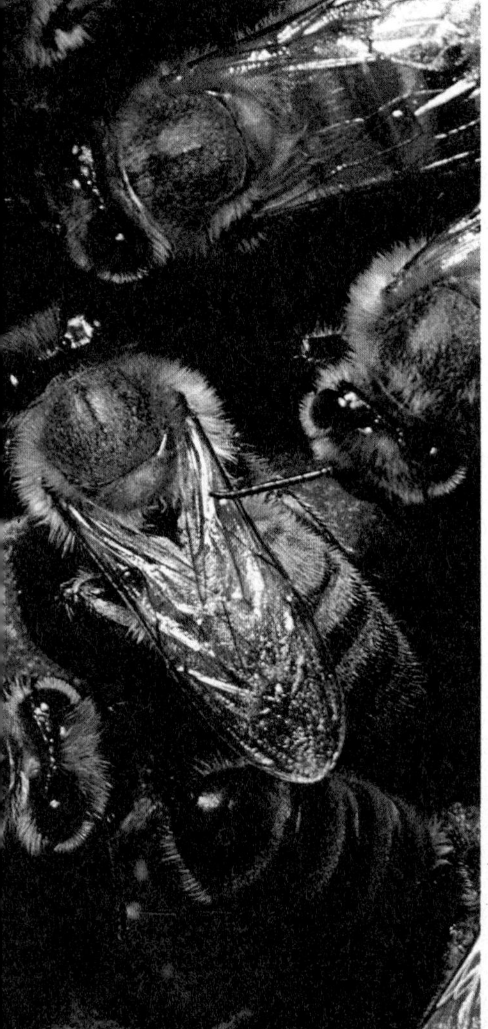
5

Play, involving touch and mock fighting as well as affectionate gestures, is essential to the full development of the young animal. Here a kitten and a Shetland sheepdog pup play together.

When the tide goes out, the shore-line animals like these anemones, feel the lack of water and draw in their tentacles to prevent loss of body water from the action of wind and sun.

extremely vicious rats. The other rats after similar surgery remained comparatively tame. It appeared that the presence of stimulation rather than its quality was the vital factor.

This experiment, with emphasis on the role of the sense of touch in the development of sociability, leads on to consideration of the role of the mother in raising normal children. Here again animal experiments throw some light on the intricacies of this problem. A group of scientists at the University of Wisconsin under the leadership of Dr Harry Harlow took new-born macaque monkeys from their mothers and put them into cages at the age of two days with a dummy mother, a life-size doll fitted with a teat delivering milk. One type of doll was made of chicken wire, while the other was covered in soft cloth.

## Gained confidence

The baby macaques fed from the nipples of either type of parent, but only the cloth-covered doll gave rise to any affectionate feelings. The chicken-wire mother was treated solely as a source of food, while the babies placed in cages with cloth-covered mothers also came to regard them as a source of protection and would run to them if threatened. The reactions of the two groups of monkeys to unfamiliar objects thrust into their cages was also different: The 'chicken wire' babies, frightened of anything new, cowered in the corners of their cages for long periods without venturing to examine the objects, while the 'cloth' babies ran first to their 'mothers' and seemed then to gain sufficient confidence fairly rapidly to venture out and examine the objects.

This illustrates the powerful part that touch plays in the development of maternal love and in the normal development of the infant

All parts of the body surface are not equally sensitive to touch. The palms of the hands, which we use constantly in touching, are among the most sensitive parts. Under the skin of the palms is a maze of nerve-endings. This heavy *innervation* is reflected in the cortex of the brain, where the nerves eventually terminate. The part of the cortex which deals with conscious touch sensations can be represented as a distorted image of the body, in which the parts are not life-size, but are scaled according to their innervation. The fingertips and the lips are among the most sensitive areas of the body. These are the parts of the body with which babies constantly explore the world around them.

A remarkable example of touch in insects is the ant-lion, an insect common in the southern deserts of the United States. The ant-lion lies at the bottom of a pit of sand and waits for ants to land on the edge of the pit. A few grains of sand falling on the ant-lion triggers off its sensitive nervous system, and the insect begins to shower the ant with grains of sand. In its state of confusion it becomes easy prey for the ant-lion.

The activity of the queen bee is also triggered by touch. She wanders over the face of the honeycomb, weighed down by her enormous egg-filled abdomen, feeling the cells of the honeycomb to decide what type of egg to lay in each. If the cell is small, a reflex of her nervous system releases a valve inside her reproductive organs and allows a few sperms to pass through to fertilize the next egg. Shortly afterwards, she deposits the egg in the small cell, where it will eventually become a worker bee. If the cell is large the reflex does not operate and an unfertilized egg is deposited which can develop only into a drone.

Many species of spider extend their sense of touch by building webs so that they can detect instantly any insect which lands on the web. In the spider, the sense of touch is especially well served by sense organs on her legs, and she is able to sit at the edge of the web and sense what is happening over a wide area.

The female spiders which build webs are sensitive to the size of the movement of the web. If the vibration is too small, the spider will not respond. On the other hand, if a large insect, a beetle for example, becomes caught in the web, the spider will cower in a corner of the web while a considerable part of it is destroyed by the beetle's struggles.

## Braille

Touch thus plays a predominant part in the lives of many insects, enabling them to find food and guiding them in many other activities. In human beings, while touch is important, and vital in early life, it is not as powerful a sense as sight. But for specialized purposes it can be immensely useful. In blind people, for instance, training and experience combine to develop enormously the sense of touch, and the language of Braille gives a clear example of the way in which touch can be used for communicating abstract information.

Scientists are now studying new ways of communicating by the use of touch. One such device makes use of a vibrator attached to the chest, which sends out a form of Morse code. The recipient can distinguish different vibrations and can use the results to form a mental image of what is being 'said'. Such a device would be extremely useful for people to communicate rapidly in situations where the noise level is too high for hearing. Airline pilots are now testing such devices.

With the increasing noise involved in many occupations, and even in everyday living, such devices utilizing touch sensations may become even more common.

It has also been suggested that similar devices might be of considerable value for spacemen, who need to be able to take in large amounts of complex information very rapidly and whose sensory channels might otherwise be overworked.

# Taste and smell

Taste and smell are less important for human beings than sight and hearing. Many animals, however, use chemical senses to seek their mates, find their food and keep out of the way of dangerous predators.

SMELL AND TASTE are very much bound up with each other, and when we talk of 'tasting' a substance particularly something with a lot of flavour, we very often mean that we are 'smelling' it. We have only to have a heavy cold, or to hold our noses while eating to find our food with little taste. The reason is simple; the tongue can only distinguish between four main classes of flavour – sweet, sour, bitter and salt – the other flavours that we taste are in fact selected by our noses.

Although most of us can tell between good and bad smells, a sense of smell is not as important for Man as sight or hearing. The aroma of good cooking or a subtle perfume will certainly arouse us, but we will not, like the dog, be able to track down our food simply by sniffing the ground or air. In fact Man, together with the apes and most marine mammals, is somewhat exceptional among the higher animals in having a relatively poor sense of smell.

## Powers of smell

Animals with poor or non-existent vision rely heavily on their senses of smell and taste. Using their olfactory powers (*olfaction* is the sense of smell), they learn to recognize their territories, can track their food, and avoid predators. Sometimes, too, mating is contingent on the male being able to smell when the female is ready and receptive for him; the cat on heat, for example, releases a strong sex attractant. Some animals have extraordinary powers of smell. The salmon can find its way back across miles of ocean to the freshwater river where it was reared. It is believed that once back at the mouth of the river the salmon finds its way back to the spawning ground by remembering the smells of various parts of its outward journey.

Even the lowest forms of animal – the single-celled protozoans – can react to changes in their environment, and they will either be attracted towards a pleasant stimulus like food, or try to escape a noxious one. Thus, squirting a drop of dilute acid near to the protozoan *Paramecium* makes it swim furiously away. Every substance is basically chemical and therefore capable of reacting with other chemical compounds. The ability to detect such a change in the environment depends on a process called *chemoreception*: the most elaborate forms of chemoreception are the sensory cells of taste and smell.

The simplest animals to have these sensory cells are the coelenterates – the sea-anemones, the jelly-fish and hydra. Their chemoreceptors are modified nerve cells, and their structure is very similar to the receptor cells of mammals.

Insects have probably developed the most sophisticated ability to smell and taste. Very often communication between one insect and another is effected by means of substances that are liberated by one insect and picked up by another. Thus bees and ants depend on smell and taste to recognize members of the hive or nest, and any intruder is promptly dealt with. The sense of taste is very often on the tip of the proboscis; the housefly is able to sense the presence of sugars or salt through special receptors on its feet. Sometimes the antennae are used for taste, as in the wasp; more often, they are used to distinguish smells. A cockroach can therefore smell its food with its long, pointed antennae and will follow the trail to a piece of cheese. A few insects, like the cabbage white butterfly, smell with their *palps*, which are small projections on their mouths. Whether they are for taste or smell the sense organs have very similar structures and they are, in fact, derived from the same cells, the *ectodermal* cells. As in the coelenterates the receptor cells are connected to nerve fibres which run to the insect's brain, and the insect's behaviour can be completely governed by what it smells. For example, the male silkmoth is endowed with large feathery antennae, and these are so sensitive that they can pick up the scent of a female silkmoth that may be several miles away.

## Phenomenal ability

It has been calculated that only a few molecules of the scent need strike the antennae for them to be stimulated. This phenomenal ability to smell the female is one way in which reproduction is ensured. The adult silkmoth does not feed and at most only lives for about nine days after emerging from the cocoon. In that short span of time the silkmoth must mate and lay its eggs. To attract the male, the female thus secretes a volatile substance into the air from special glands on her abdomen. This substance – called a *pheromone* because it is a secretion of one animal that can change the behaviour of another animal – is the substance the males are so sensitive to, and once they have picked up the scent their sole object in life is to find

Snakes and lizards use their tongues to touch and sense the surroundings. The tongue is flicked back into the mouth and inserted into a sensory pit behind the upper lip.

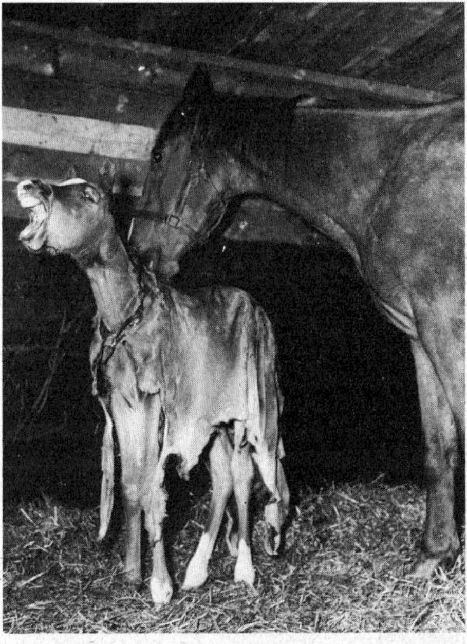

This colt's foster-mother accepted and nursed him after he was encased in the skin of her own dead colt. Smell clearly plays the predominant part in the mare's recognition of her offspring.

the source and mate with the female.

Cockroaches live for much longer than the adult silkmoth and they go through several reproductive cycles. The female only mates at certain times when she releases a pheromone and only then is she attractive to the male. If a filter paper touched by a receptive female is put into a cage containing male cockroaches, they immediately go beserk and clamber over each other to get to the source of the pheromone. The secretion of the pheromone is under the control of hormones and these hormones are released from glands associated with the brain of the insect. There is thus a tie-up between the season, the year, the animal's reproductive state, and the animal's behaviour – and as we have seen smell plays an important part. The gypsy moth produces a pheromone known as gypsol and this has now been synthesized by chemists. In the United States plagues of gypsy moths are controlled by putting out containers of synthetic gypsol. The male moths are attracted to the containers, where they are trapped and can be destroyed.

Female mammals on heat, also produce substances to attract the males. It is believed that women release a special substance when they are at the most fertile periods of the menstrual cycle. If they do, it is unlikely that men have sufficiently good noses to know.

## Olfactory lobes

We think of the nose primarily as an organ through which we breathe, but the origin of the nose and nostrils was undoubtedly for smell. If we look at fishes, particularly the sharks which have a very good sense of smell, we see that the nostrils lead into a small blind-end chamber – all the breathing in fishes is done through the mouth and the gill slits. Inside the chamber the *surface epithelium,* which is the skin layer that has the olfactory cells, may be in a series of folds. By this means the number

1

2

3

**1** Salmon leaping a waterfall on their way to spawn. Smell may play a considerable part in guiding these fish in their long and perilous journey to the spawning grounds.
**2** The feathery antennae of the male silkmoth are sensitive to minute concentrations of the female sex attractant. Only a few molecules of this volatile scent alert the male to the female.
**3** The housefly tastes with the tip of its proboscis, the trunk-like organ it uses for feeding. By brushing objects with its proboscis it can taste whether they are sweet or salty.
**4** Taste and smell in human beings. Food on the tongue can be smelt by the olfactory organ at the top of the nose as well as being tasted by the taste buds on the tongue.
**5** Plagues of gypsy moths in the United States are controlled by 'fooling' the male moths with a synthetic female attractant, gypsol. The pheromone draws the males into traps.
**6** Otter hunting is almost entirely based on the hounds' well-developed sense of smell. Here, the otter has tried to throw the hounds off the scent by swimming a river.
**7** Giraffes licking salt from the edges of a dried water hole. Many animals when short of salt exhibit a craving for salty-tasting foods and will go to considerable lengths to satisfy their needs.

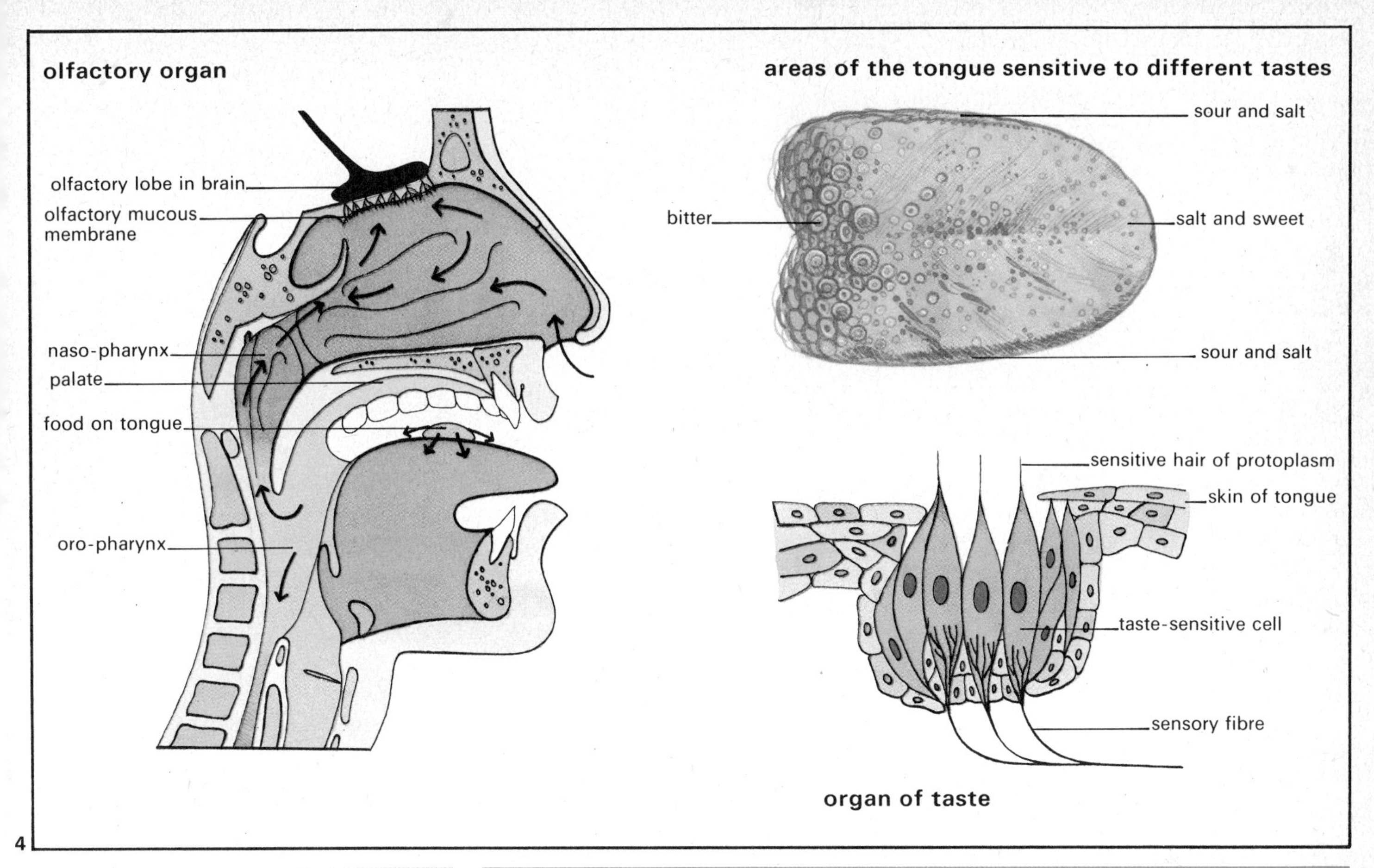

4

5

6

7

of sensory cells that can be contained is increased enormously. The cells are also very well supplied with nerves from the olfactory lobes in the brain. These lobes lie at the front of the brain and they are relatively large in animals with a good sense of smell, like the man-eating shark, the blacktip, where they are clearly the largest portion of the brain.

In the amphibians the nostrils connect with the roof of the mouth. As the animal breathes it is taking in at the same time a sample of air to be tested for any interesting smells. Frogs, and most reptiles, are, however, lacking a 'true palate' and the air and food intermingle in the mouth. The true palate, where the air is almost entirely shut off from the mouth and filters through a network of fine porous bones, is only found in the mammals. However, amphibians and many reptiles have developed a small pouch called *Jacobson's*

The erect siphon of the common whelk draws a current of water over the animal's organ of smell. In this way, the whelk can smell out its prey and proceed to catch it.

A skilled wine-taster also makes considerable use of his sense of smell. 'Nosing' is the technical term for the preliminary examination of a wine's bouquet.

*organ* leading off from the main respiratory passages. This small organ contains many olfactory cells. The tongues of some snakes lie on pads in the mouth. When testing their environment these snakes flick their tongues out of their mouths and pick up traces of scent. When they retract their tongues the scent is brushed off on to the pads, from where it passes into Jacobson's organ.

The sensation of taste in many vertebrates can be confused with that of olfaction. The catfish has a number of antennae-like barbels projecting in all directions from its head. These barbels contain assemblages of taste and touch sensors, and using them the catfish can follow a food source upstream. However, in most vertebrates the sense of taste is confined to areas within the mouth.

## How man tastes

In contrast to catfish, adult Man has 100,000 taste buds, some 9,000 taste receptors, placed mainly on the peripheral parts of the top of the tongue. In children the taste buds may be much more numerous and distributed widely over the tongue and even on the cheeks. The taste bud is an oval structure consisting of a thin receptor cell surrounded by supporting cells like the staves of a barrel. Each taste cell ends in a hair process which projects upward through a small pore on to the surface of the tongue. The four main flavours of taste are distinguished for the most part in different areas of the tongue. Thus sweet tastes are most easily perceived at the tip of the tongue, bitter at the back, sour at the edge and salt both on the tip and the edge.

How we taste is not really known, although it has been suggested that a substance which has a characteristic taste somehow depresses or excites the activities of enzymes – biological catalysts – which are known to be secreted by the cells surrounding the taste buds.

There has been some attempt to discover if a sensation of taste can be tied in any way to appetite. The association is certainly tenuous, and one of the main factors in feeling satiated is undoubtedly when the stomach is full. Nevertheless, if animals are deprived of certain basic substances like salt they will in preference choose to drink water that has a high salt content; it is well known that miners and other hard-working labourers who sweat a great deal like to drink salty water to replace the loss of salt. There are some strange anomalies with taste. Although all normal people can taste the four basic flavours, some people are unable to taste substances which to others have a distinct flavour; this is governed by inherited characteristics. Substances like saccharin, which we think of as sweet, are very bitter to the cat, which cannot taste sweet substances. Animals are often sensitive to the smells of their own species; the dog, like the tom cat that goes round its neighbourhood spraying musk, leaves its 'visiting card' to warn other dogs in the area of its presence. In one sense the dog is staking out his territory. Many animals use musks or scents to indicate their presence.

Scent is also very important to colonies of animals. We have already mentioned the insects. Rats, too, live in colonies, and each member of the colony has a distinct smell of the colony by which he is recognized by his fellow rats. Should he be an intruder or have his scent masked in some way, he is likely to be driven away or even killed.

Some social insects, like the ants, when they have found a food source, leave a pheromone trail as their abdomen brushes the ground on the return journey to the nest. This trail attracts other ants of the nest to the food source; they themselves leave trails, and by this method maximum ant-power can be brought to play in the search for food. Bees also taste the food brought back by foraging bees, and this stimulates them to join in an all-out effort to bring back food for the hive from the source. Bee communities depend on substances being passed all the time between one bee and another. The smell and taste of these substances determine the social behaviour of the hive. Indeed, the queen bee retains her status by secreting a special substance which is tasted by all the bees of the hive.

## The sense of flavour

The close relationship between smell and taste means that it is often more accurate to speak of a single 'sense of flavour'. Certainly, people who lack a sense of smell (anosmics) seem to have a different sense of taste from other people.

In recent years, there have been considerable advances in research into the mechanism of smell. One of the centres of this research is the University of British Columbia, where Dr James Wright has recently put forward a theory of smell based on the observation that there are seven 'primary' scents. Receptors in the nose are shaped to receive molecules of these primary scents, and the extent to which a particular molecule fits a receptor determines how much of that smell we detect in it. Dr Wright's theory explains a number of hitherto puzzling facts about smell, though it may not be the whole story.

Smell and taste are part of the same phenomenon, and Man depends very much on both operating at the same time for the sense of flavour. A sprinkling of salt on our food often makes it taste better, although much of what we are tasting is perceived in the nose. Throughout the animal kingdom taste and smell have a certain universality – the bee seems to be able to recognize the same perfumed scents, such as tincture of orange, as Man, but there is a difference – the bee can smell it a thousand times better.

# Processing the information

Scientists are beginning to grapple with the extraordinarily complex processes which make up the activity of the brain and central nervous system and determine most of our activities.

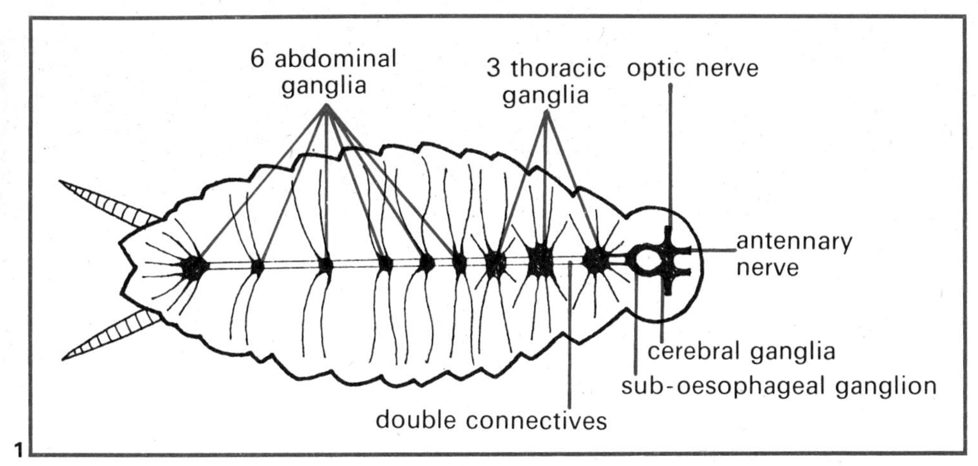

IT SEEMS DIFFICULT to us to visualize the functions of the brain without speaking in the language of computers. The comparison between the brain and a computer has become a *cliché,* even though sometimes a powerful and appropriate one. At the same time, this train of thought has proved valuable to scientists studying the brain, particularly in providing them with a powerful mathematical armoury for looking at the processes taking place among the millions of nerve cells that make up the nervous system in human beings and in the higher animals.

But although brains and computers both handle information this is really where the strict analogy between the brain and a computer ends. The methods of the brain in handling information are not the same as those of the computer. Unlike that of the computer, the basic unit of the nervous system in higher animals is the neuron. The neuron is a very highly specialized cell, built to handle very weak electrical impulses. There are many different types of neuron, but perhaps the most typical representative of this type of cell has a body from which a large number of processes protrude. The body itself contains the nucleus and the cell organelles that are normally present in every animal cell. The processes, some short, at least one often of great length, terminate in a nerve ending, where they contact another process from another neuron. The processes from the two neurons almost but not quite touch – the slight gap between them is essential to the transmission of the nerve impulses they are built to carry. The interconnections of these processes from the different nerve cells form a huge network, the complex connections of which play an essential part in setting up circuits for transmitting and processing information.

The second component of the nervous

**1** The nervous system of a cockroach consists of a number of ganglia connected by nerves. There is no central 'brain' in insects.
**2** Four electrodes contact the exposed brain of this anaesthetized cat. One is used for stimulation and the other three record the resultant changes in the electrical activity of brain areas.
**3** The brains of fish, reptiles and mammals compared. The cerebral hemispheres become more developed in the higher animals.

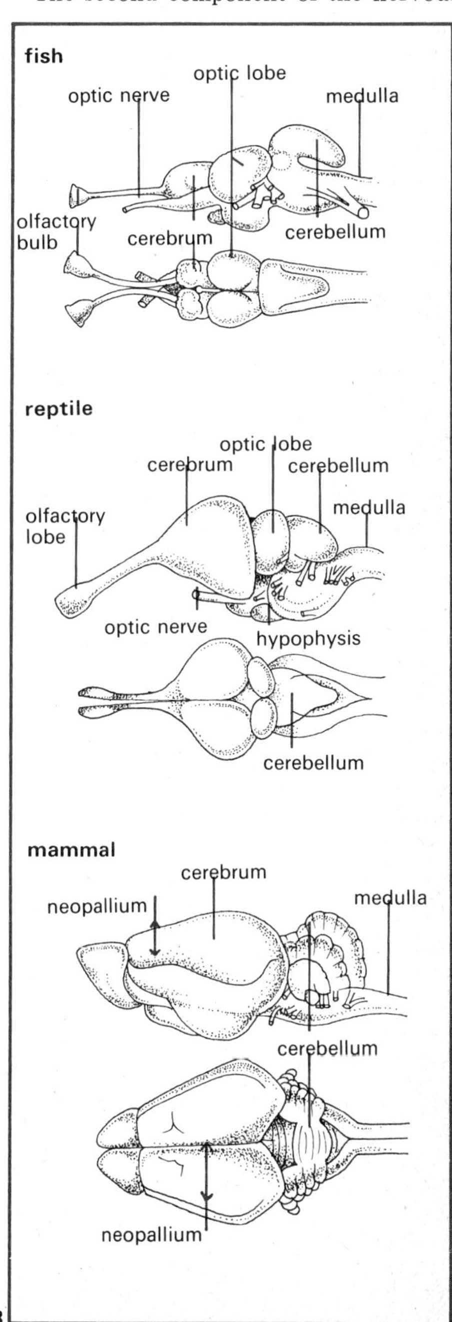

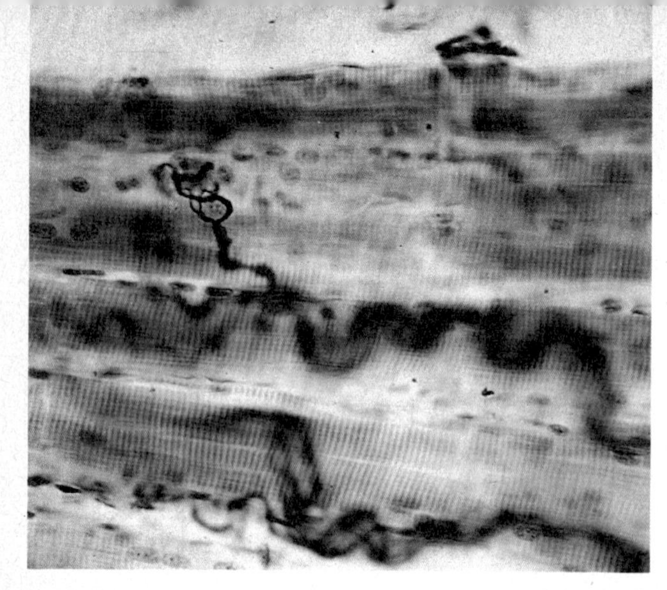

Peripheral nerve endings in voluntary muscle fibres. Note how the nerves, which cause the muscles to contract, terminate in close proximity to the muscle fibres.

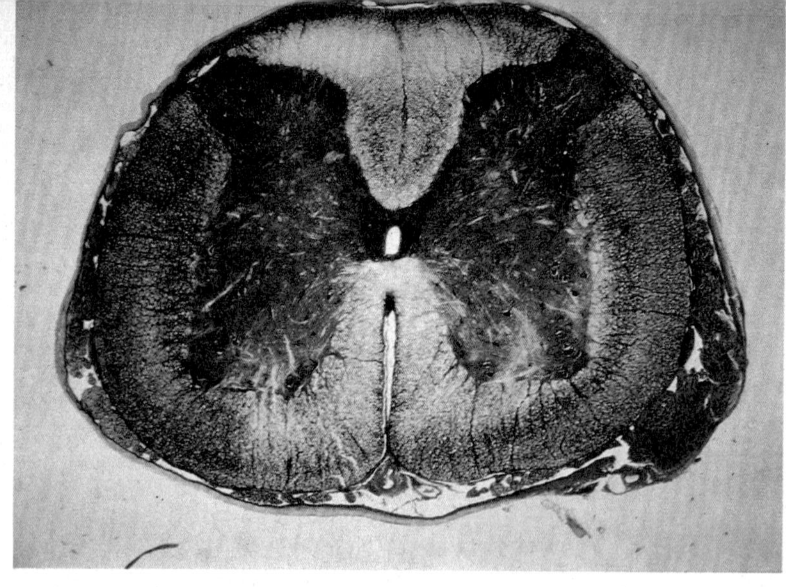

Cross-section of the spinal cord of a cat. The brown butterfly-shaped area in the centre of the cord contains the bodies of neurons, the outer white area consists of nerve fibres.

system is a complex arrangement of cells which support and supply nourishment to the nerve cells. This second function is particularly important when one considers that the processes of some neurons may be more than a metre in length, and the areas at the tip of the process would have a thin time if they had to be supplied with nourishment from the body of the neuron. Each nerve cell outside the spinal cord is thus surrounded by Schwann cells which nourish and maintain the vitality of the nerve process. Without their Schwann cells, the nerves would die quite rapidly of starvation. In the brain and spinal cord, too, there are cells with similar functions.

Through the millions of nerve endings in the skin, in muscle, in the blood vessels and in all the organs of the body, the brain is kept in constant touch with all the activities of the body. But here we come to a difficulty. We all know that we cannot consciously feel much of our body activity, particularly when we are asleep or when we are concentrating on some other problem. If we are asleep in an awkward position, for example, we can lose all feeling in a leg, say, without being in the least conscious of a loss, until we wake and find we have 'pins and needles'. Again, a whole range of everyday body activities, the workings of the liver and kidneys, digestion, heart-beat, even breathing, go on entirely without our noticing consciously.

In many animals, too, the entire activity of the body can be said to take place without any consciousness.

The reason for this situation is that by no means all the brain is concerned with conscious experience. Indeed, only the highest level of the brain, the cerebral cortex, is directly concerned with conscious thought and feeling. Below this area, which is well developed in Man and the higher animals, are other regions concerned with the more or less automatic functions of the body, with co-ordination, respiration, heartbeat, posture, visceral activity, and so on. The nervous system is thus required to select which parts of the brain require to have the incoming information, and this is done by ensuring that the tracts of nervous tissue which carry impulses from the peripheral nerves to the brain and spinal cord terminate at various levels. The second and more important way in which this is done is an arrangement by which nerve impulses can not only be advanced up the spinal cord to higher levels of the brain, but suppressed at various levels and allowed to proceed no further. The great advantage of this system is its extreme flexibility. The brain is not a static system for codifying incoming information, but is rather a highly dynamic apparatus for sifting and sorting information.

The central nervous system is generally divided by anatomists into brain and spinal cord. This division applies, of course, only to the higher animals. In lower animals, like insects and earthworms, and, of course, in one-celled and primitive multi-celled animals, the nervous system is very much less well developed. In many such animals the nervous system consists of a series of

The muscular grace of an accomplished ballet dancer owes a great deal to carefully trained reflexes. Skills like dancing involve both cerebrum and cerebellum.

The brain is able to select essential information reaching it from sense organs. These polar bears sleep undisturbed by trivial noises but wake immediately danger threatens.

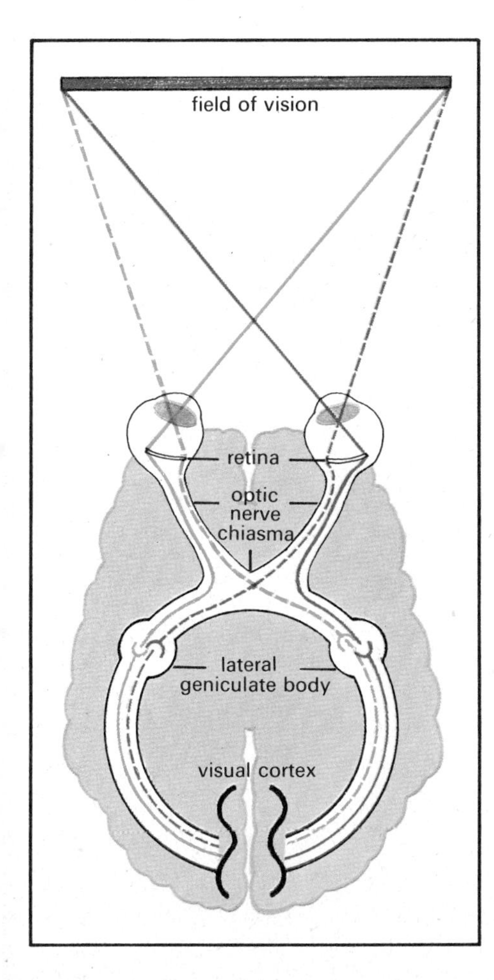


Diagram of the nerve tracts which deal with vision in Man. From the retina impulses travel through the optic chiasma (crossover), relay in the geniculate body and terminate in the cortex.

ganglia, connected by nerve tracts running between them. This is the system in the earthworm and in animals like the cockroach. But in the higher animals, the spinal cord, derived from embryonic tissue called the neural tube, is developed at the head and into a more elaborate and specialized organ – the brain. The brain itself can be further subdivided. The part immediately above the spinal cord appears little different from it, but contains a number of important centres concerned with the control of respiration, maintenance of temperature and similar activities which never or rarely become conscious but are extremely vital to life. From the hind brain also arises the cerebellum, a part of the brain concerned mainly with the control of muscle tensions and the maintenance of posture. The mid-brain consists of the optic lobes, through which the fibres from the optic nerves run on their way to the cerebral cortex, and the hypothalamus which is closely connected with the system of hormonal control in the body.

## The seat of consciousness

The forebrain, from an evolutionary point of view the last part of the brain to develop, is dominated by the cerebral cortex, concerned with consciousness, an area of the brain that is highly developed in Man, less highly developed in lower animals. In the cortex are areas devoted to sensation from all parts of the body and to such functions as hearing, speech and association. The part of the cortex behind the forehead in human beings is concerned with higher mental activities, such as moral judgement. The part of the cortex in front of the back of the skull is concerned with vision.

The brains of different animals, of course, vary this basic pattern according to their mode of life and their position on the evolutionary scale. In animals like the dogfish, for instance, in which the main special sense is that of 'smell', the part of the brain devoted to smell, the olfactory lobes, is highly developed, while the part devoted to vision and hearing is relatively small. In human beings, of course, the optic cortex is more heavily developed than any other part serving the special senses, because vision plays such an important part in the lives of human beings.

A characteristic of all mammals, compared with other animals, such as reptiles or even birds, is the high degree of development of the cerebral cortex. This part of the brain is much more important as a co-ordinating centre in the higher animals, and its loss is correspondingly more serious. A frog with the cerebral cortex removed continues to behave in a similar way to before, and most of its activities are not very seriously affected. In higher mammals, and particularly in human beings, loss of the higher centres of the brain is a crushing blow. It removes all possibility of initiative from the subject and turns the animal into a virtual vegetable.

The detailed activity of the nervous system is perhaps best explained by considering the simplest kind of complete nervous transaction, the spinal reflex arc. The reflex arc is a miniature and simple version of much of the activity of the nervous system, although the higher centres of the brain involve much more complex interactions than the simple reflex, interactions that may involve hundreds of separate nerve cells, and conscious decisions which are only remotely connected with reflexes, although they may have similar physiological bases.

When one places a finger on a hotplate,

it is withdrawn before one feels the pain, and the arm jerks upward apparently automatically. Behind this is a rapid passage of impulses to and from the spinal cord in the following way: the heat from the hotplate causes pain fibres and other nerve endings in the finger to set up impulses in the nerves running back to the spinal cord from them. These nerves synapse (connect) in the spinal cord with other fibres running to the muscles of the arm. The impulses pass directly from one fibre to another, or via intermediate fibres in the cord, thus arousing the muscles and contracting them before awareness of the burn reaches the higher brain centres. The spinal reflex arc demonstrates in a simplified form the basic mechanism of the nervous system which controls inputs in such a way as to control the output and the ultimate action taken on the basis of the information received.

**1** Alcoholism causes rapid deterioration of the sensitive nerve cells in the brain. Once these cells have been poisoned by alcohol, they are not reproduced and are lost for good.
**2** Spastics suffer from brain damage, sometimes contracted at birth. The brain loses some of its ability to control muscular movements and has to be retrained patiently to do so.

The other main process in the nervous system is inhibition. In the case of the burn reflex the impulse from the pain receptors in the hand passed to the spinal cord and set up an impulse in the outgoing nerve. In other cases, the impulses activate repressor fibres running to the nerve cells serving the outgoing nerves. This may also occur during the passage of the nerve impulse up the spinal cord to the higher centres. One purpose of this mechanism is to prevent the brain being overloaded with trivial information. An example of the way this operates in practice is the proverbial tale of the absent-minded professor who pushes his spectacles on to his forehead and 'forgets' they are there, later spending hours looking for them. Here, the touch sensations coming from the nerve endings on the forehead have been suppressed because they have become part of the 'background' noise in the nervous system. The brain does not want to be overwhelmed every minute with the information that the glasses are still in place. The nervous system is far more sensitive to unusual or sudden changes in the information coming into it than to information that everything is still the same. This latter type of information can be handled at levels well below the conscious level.

## Sifting vital from trivial

At the same time, the brain has to be extremely selective in what it suppresses. This by no means depends solely on the volume of information received – the volume of sound, say, reaching the ear. A good example is found with elephants, which sleep lying one against the other, moving their vast bodies against each other without disturbing sleep. But the whole herd will wake immediately a human being in the vicinity takes the slightest step. Again, a mother may sleep soundly in a house overlooking a main road, with all the noise of traffic and gear-changing, and yet wake immediately her baby begins to cry. This ability to select from a mass of sensations the vital information which must be acted on and to reject the background information which is less directly of value, is a remarkable one, when one considers the difficulty of designing a computer to distinguish a baby's cry from traffic noise, or pick up a human footstep amid the noise of sleeping elephants.

Of course, these two mechanisms do not exhaust the activity of the brain, but they do provide a basis for the complex operations of the central nervous system. In human beings the activity of the brain is far more complex than this simplified picture might suggest.

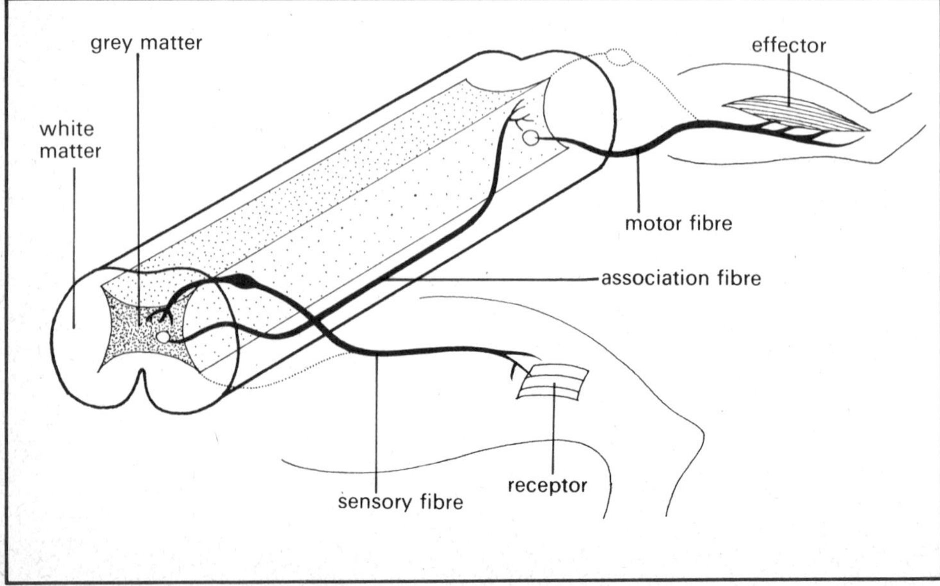


Diagram of a spinal reflex arc. The sensory fibre from the skin receptor synapses in the cord with a second fibre which in turn passes the impulse to the motor nerve.

# The sense of self

Traditional physiology recognized only five senses – touch, smell, taste, sight and hearing. But a sixth sense – proprioception – is just as essential as the other five, though it is much less obvious.

IF A CLOCKWORK MANIKIN, which can shuffle its legs to and fro to simulate walking, is set to struggle up a small incline, it will probably get only so far and then, hopelessly, fall over backwards. It has nothing in its simple mechanism to control its posture, nor the tension in its rigid, unjointed legs, so as to bring its centre of gravity further forward over the incline. Of course, we don't suffer the same fate when we try to walk up a hill or climb stairs, and although we may be quite unconscious of it, we have a built-in mechanism to ensure that, come what may, our bodies can be co-ordinated to do what we want with them.

Indeed, throughout our bodies – in the skin, in the connective tissue, in the muscles and joints – are special sense organs, which assess information about tensions, pressures and positions of every conceivable part of the body. This information is relayed to the central nervous system, where it is sorted and from which messages are transmitted via the nerves to the muscles to increase their tone or relax depending on the need at that particular moment. The constant, ceaseless activity of these special sense receptors is known as *proprioception* – a word coined to suggest a 'sense of self'.

Much of this sense of self is unconscious and we are not really aware of any particular muscle contraction or relaxation, but there is a conscious side to proprioception, too, and we can become all too sensitive to a burning pressure on our feet when we have had to stand too long, or to a crick in our necks and backs after sitting uncomfortably as during a long bus journey.

The sense receptors in the skin are for the most part little more than naked nerve endings. Different ones respond to different types of sensation, such as touch, pressure, pain and temperature. All these sensations can be felt consciously. There is also a more complex sort of receptor which responds to a sudden mechanical stimulus. This receptor is known as a *Pacinian corpuscle,* and it is found in the skin and deeper inside the body. The corpuscle consists of a naked nerve ending surrounded by a series of skin layers, rather like a miniature onion. Between the skin layers is liquid, and as soon as the corpuscle is pressed the liquid transmits a pressure wave through the skin to the naked nerve endings. This is a rapidly adapting nerve and becomes relatively inactive after a short burst of impulses, in spite of the pressure still being applied. Then when the pressure is taken off, the nerve fires briefly again. The Pacinian corpuscle, therefore, transmits information about a sudden change in pressure, but does not record the continuing presence of the mechanical stimulus.

Proprioception, concerned with maintaining balance and muscle control, plays a vital part in the complex routine of these circus artistes.

The most important proprioceptors, however, are in the muscles and joints. The *Golgi tendon organs* are found close to the junction between muscle and tendon, and they consist of a number of tendon fibres enclosed in a fibrous capsule penetrated by one or two nerve fibres which divide up and branch in all directions. Tension on the tendon distorts the endings of these nerves and fires them. Recordings made from the nerves using electrophysiological apparatus show that they respond to tensions only above a certain value, thought to be in the region of 200 grams or half a pound. The precise function of these receptors is not known, but it has been suggested they are a type of safety device to prevent the joint or muscle being overburdened. Thus, when they do fire, the tension being in excess of 200 grams, they cause the muscle attached to that joint to relax completely.

## Muscle spindles

The Golgi tendon organ is in series with the muscle and joint and gives a precise measure of tensions because all strains have to pass through it. The *muscle spindles* – the receptors in the muscles – are in parallel with the muscle, and they do not measure precise tensions; indeed it is possible for them to be under no strain at all although the muscle itself may be fully contracted. The role of the muscle spindles is more to maintain tone in a muscle, whether it is bearing a load or not. They are the main receptors of the complex servo-mechanism of proprioception. Muscle spindles are found in the body of the muscle. Each spindle consists of thin muscle fibres enclosed within a capsule of connective tissue in the central region. These are known as *intrafusal* muscle fibres and their ends are connected to the tissue surrounding the main *(extrafusal)*

**1** The lateral-line system of this tench can be clearly seen running the length of its body. Proprioception probably evolved from such systems.
**2** How the lateral-line system works. The sensory nerves terminate in special pressure-sensitive organs in the wall of the lateral-line canal.

1

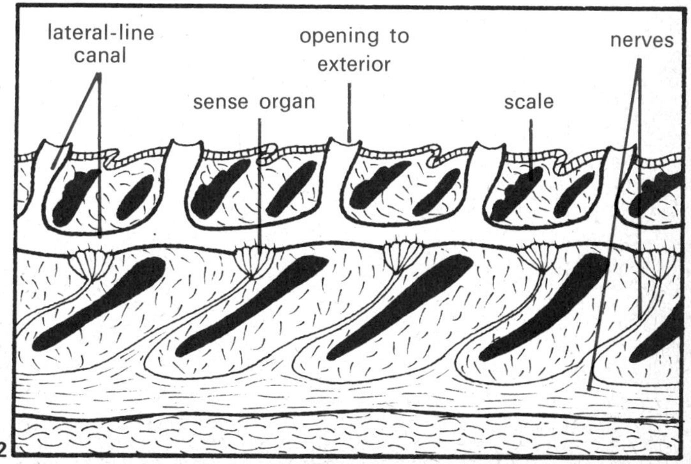

2

fibres of the muscle. These intrafusal fibres are of two types, *nuclear bag* and *nuclear chain*, the former having a central bag of nuclei and the latter a chain of nuclei in the middle region. The sensory nerves, which take information back from the spindle to the spinal cord and central nervous system, enter the capsule, and, as in the Pacinian corpuscle, lose their protective myelin sheath.

Recordings have been made from these nerves and it has been shown that a change of tension in the muscle of as little as 1 gram is sufficient to fire the primary nerve endings; a strikingly different picture from the Golgi tendon organ. If the muscle is stretched and the stretch is maintained we can see two types of nerve response. The primary nerves give an initial sharp peak when the tension first comes on, and then the rate of firing falls to a lower level, until as the tension is taken off completely, the rate of firing falls momentarily to below the resting level (the level at which the nerve was firing before any tension was put on the muscle). The response from the secondary nerve endings is very different. They show no peak of discharge during the stretching of the muscle, but their firing frequency does rise to a plateau which is proportional to the amount of stretch. The different structures of the nuclear bag and nuclear chain fibres account for the difference in behaviour of the nerves. Nuclear chain fibres contain contractile fibres throughout, and we would expect them to resist a stretch evenly. Nuclear bag fibres consist instead of contractile fibres at each end separated by a watery bag of nuclei. Stretching of this structure is all taken up by the central region, and the nerve response is likely to be initially high. As the stretch is maintained the tension on the watery region falls off and instead gets taken up by the contractile ends; the rate of discharge therefore falls.

## How muscle spindles work

As we can see, a muscle spindle can become almost switched off when the muscle surrounding it contracts, for the tension is taken right off it. Nonetheless the intrafusal fibres are under motor nerve control and, like the muscle fibres on all sides of them, can be made to contract. This contraction has the immediate effect of increasing tension within the spindle, and its sensory nerves are stimulated to fire. The extrafusal muscles, which actually move joints, are under the control of large motoneurons, the alpha-motoneurons; instead the intrafusal fibres of the muscle spindles are under the control of small motoneurons known as gamma-motoneurons.

The muscle spindles are not therefore simple indicators of muscle length or of muscular contraction; rather they behave as though their function were to detect differences in the state of contraction of the intrafusal and extrafusal fibres. When the extrafusal fibres alone are contracted the sensory discharge from the intrafusal fibres decreases, but when intrafusal fibres alone are contracted the reverse situation applies and the discharge from the nerves goes up. During the normal working of the body neither the extrafusal fibres nor the intrafusal fibres are ever completely relaxed and there is constant interplay between them. We can see what happens when we look at a simple stretch reflex like the knee tendon jerk. The knee is stretched fairly tightly over the other leg, then a tap on the tendon between the knee cap and the tibia causes the quadriceps muscle to stretch slightly, and a moment later the leg kicks forward because of the contraction of that same muscle. Any muscle can be made to respond in this way. The muscle spindle is responsible for this type of reflex. As the quadriceps muscle is stretched it pulls on the muscle spindles and these immediately discharge. The discharge is taken by the sensory nerves into the spinal cord, where it makes contact with motoneurons supplying the quadriceps muscle. This type of response of a muscle is known as a *simple reflex arc*.

The knee jerk may seem to have little relevance in our lives, other than being something we go through to please the doctor. Yet, imagine what happens when you are standing upright – the muscles on both sides of your leg are relatively tense so as to make a kind of column to support the body. But when you sway forwards slightly you are immediately off balance. The muscle that has been stretched now stimulates its own increased contraction via the sensory discharge from the spindle fibres, and brings the leg back into line.

There is obviously more to movement than a series of simple reflex arcs which take place only at one level in the spinal cord. The brain plays an enormous part in

1

2

3

**1** Surfing is a skill which requires a high degree of balance and muscular co-ordination. The surfer must learn to 'feel' the motion of the board and react without thinking.
**2** In many animals, such as this harvest mouse, the tail plays a large part in maintaining the animal's equilibrium. The tail muscles come under close cerebellar control.
**3** The limbo dancers on the island of Grenada, must have very fine control of their balance. Once learned, the skills required become 'second nature' as the cerebellum takes control.
**4** The leopard, like other cats, owes much of its lithe grace and its climbing ability to its well-developed proprioceptive system. This takes the clumsiness out of its movements.
**5** Proprioception accounts for our ability to control our muscular activities. Without it, our movements would be clumsy, and an active life would be impossible.

4

5

the control of movement. Conscious thought probably originates only in the cortex of the brain; and it is in this region that voluntary movements come into being. However, without another part of the brain to control these movements and bring about finesse we should be very clumsy creatures indeed. This part of the brain is known as the cerebellum, and it is constantly receiving information about the tensions in the joints and the relative contractions of the extrafusal and intrafusal muscles throughout the entire body. Although we can survive without the cerebellum – and there are unfortunate people who have lost this part of the brain through a war injury or motor accident – without it movements become extremely gross and if such patients try to touch their noses with their hand they are likely to strike themselves in the face as this hand overshoots the mark. Indeed any control of movement in people without a cerebellum is only possible if they can see what they are doing.

As well as receiving information from all the muscles and joints, and from the cortex which gives the orders as to what activity must be carried out next, the cerebellum is linked up via nerves with a part of the ear known as the labyrinth. The labyrinth is concerned with measuring the position of the body in relation to gravity and any accelerations that the body is being subjected to. Although the labyrinth has nothing to do with hearing, its organs are very closely connected to the hearing apparatus in the inner ear. The labyrinth consists of two chambers, the utricle and saccule, and three semicircular canals. The utricle and saccule both contain a ridge of cells topped by hairs embedded in a gelatinous material. There are many chalky particles, called otoliths, embedded in these hairs, and as the body tilts from side to side the hairs are pulled in the corresponding direction. These organs are therefore assumed to assess the plane of the body with regard to gravity. The three semicircular canals are at right angles to one another. At its origin each canal has a dilatation, the ampulla, into which projects, rather like a swing door, a barrier called the crista. This is also a ridge of tissue surmounted by a column of matted hairs, the cupola. Each canal contains fluid and on rotating the head the fluid swirls in the canals at a slower rate than the movement, rather like tea in a cup which we are turning in our hands. The crista is therefore deflected in a direction opposite to the movement.

## Gravity and acceleration

All these organs, the utricle, saccule and semicircular canals, are extremely well supplied with nerves that terminate in the cells of the cristae. These nerves fire all the time in what is known as a resting discharge. If the cells they supply should be pulled in one particular direction the nerves fire more, if, on the other hand the cells should be pulled in the opposite direction, the nerves fire at a slower rate than the resting discharge. This information indicates to the brain exactly what is happening to the body in terms of gravity and acceleration. Of course, if you should spin on your tracks and then stop suddenly, the liquid in the canals will continue to spin, but this time the spin will be in a different direction to the walls of the canal which before were moving faster than the liquid. Your eyes will tell you you have stopped moving, but your ears will tell you you are moving in the opposite direction. This conflicting information makes you feel giddy. Now we can begin to understand what is involved in the control of movement and muscles in the body. The cerebellum receives its 'marching orders' from the higher centres of the brain; at the

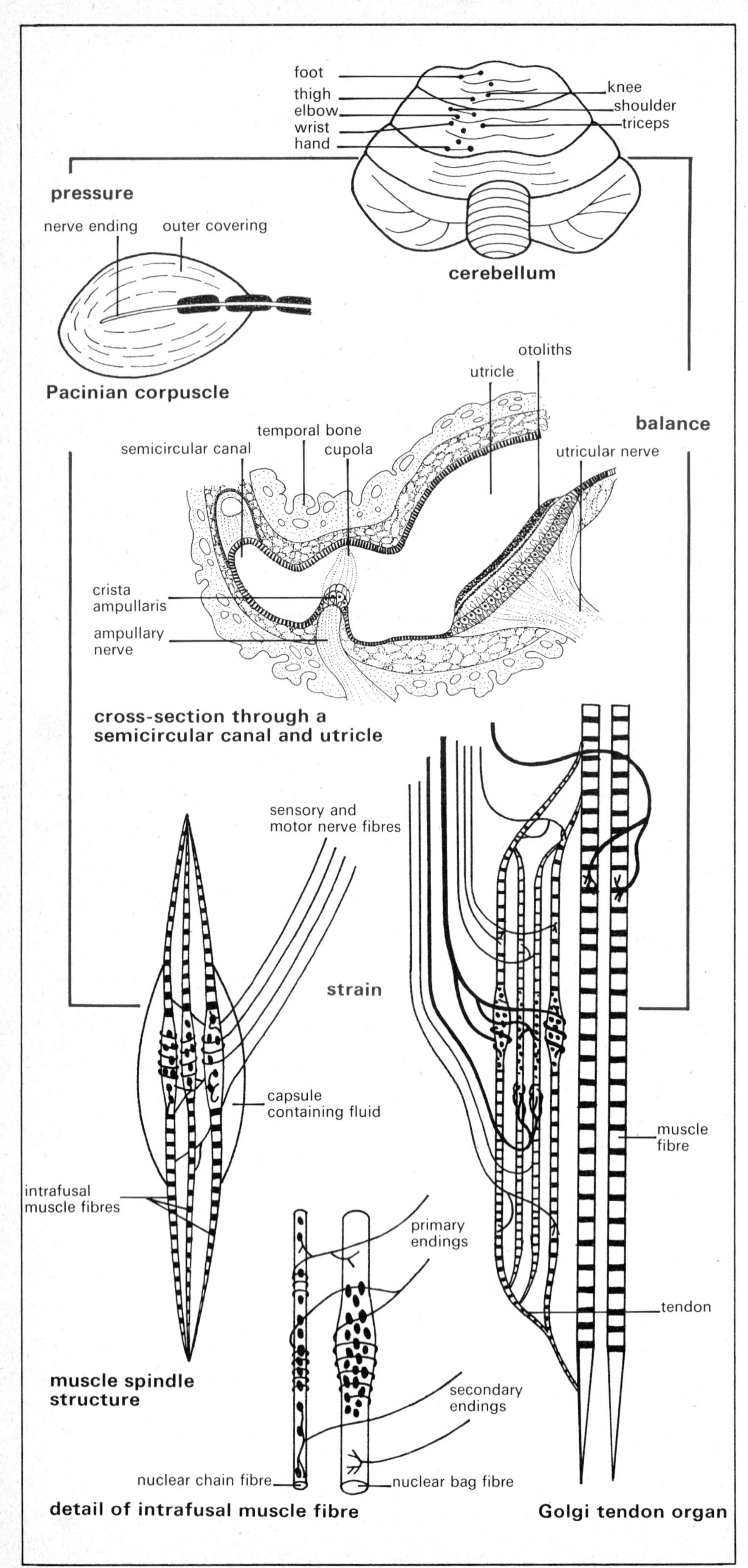


Diagram of some of the organs concerned with proprioception. The various peripheral receptors supply information on posture which is co-ordinated by the cerebellum.

same time it is assessing the position of the body in relation to the space around it and the state of the joints and muscles. The cerebellum has nerves linking it with the main motoneurons going to the muscles of the body and also linking it with the gamma-motoneurons going to the muscle spindles. When the cerebellum receives information that a particular muscle is getting too lax it can stimulate it to contract via the alpha-motoneurons, or by means of the gamma-motoneuron pathway which has the effect of increasing the sensory discharge from the muscle spindles.

The situation is further complicated by what is known as inhibition of one muscle as another one contracts. This inhibition takes place between what are known as antagonistic muscles. We can imagine it would be hopeless to try and contract the biceps muscle to pick up an object if the opposing triceps muscle was contracting hard at the same time. So, when one muscle is stimulated to contract, it somehow inhibits the activity of the opposing muscle.

## Controlled movements

A controlled movement, like walking, does not consist of complete inhibition of one set of nerves or complete excitation of another; otherwise we should be thrown by our muscles forwards and backwards like a badly managed puppet. Instead, all movements consist of a careful interplay between the two sets of muscles, the synergists – or those that work in one direction – and the antagonists.

When you first learn a complicated movement like cycling, or playing an instrument like a cello, you have to think hard and consciously about every individual movement, and you seem to be very clumsy. As time passes, the movements, however complex, appear to become easier and less thought-out, until all of a sudden you are no more aware of doing them and they are part and parcel of your subconscious. This change from conscious to unconscious control occurs when the cerebellum has taken over completely from the cortex. All the cortex now has to do is to dictate that the particular movement be done and without any more concern as to how it is going to be done the movement is perfectly carried out. This is the moment when playing an instrument that you can begin to put expression into the music and feel what you are doing, or, if you are rowing in a race, can put the pressure on, to drive on to win.

Proprioception governs all our movements and activities however simple and slight; even when sleeping, control is being exerted and muscles never completely lose their tone. The basis of proprioception is a feed-back of information to the control centres which then respond accordingly. Without this vital mechanism, our movements would be extremely limited and very clumsy.

# Sense and sensibility

The outside world is not identical with what we perceive of it, and the study of illusions generated by the conflict between perception and reality gives an insight into the brain's workings.

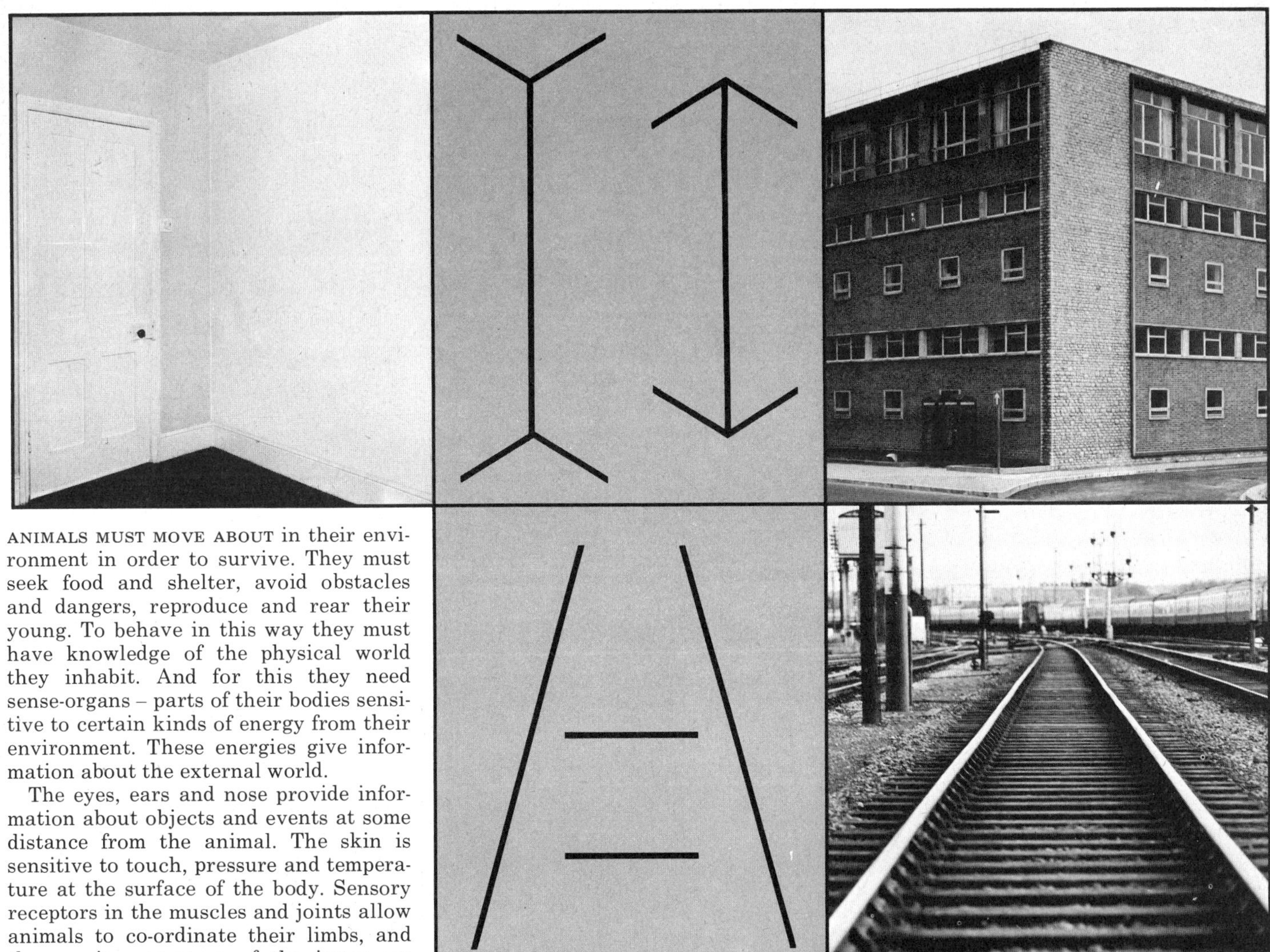

ANIMALS MUST MOVE ABOUT in their environment in order to survive. They must seek food and shelter, avoid obstacles and dangers, reproduce and rear their young. To behave in this way they must have knowledge of the physical world they inhabit. And for this they need sense-organs – parts of their bodies sensitive to certain kinds of energy from their environment. These energies give information about the external world.

The eyes, ears and nose provide information about objects and events at some distance from the animal. The skin is sensitive to touch, pressure and temperature at the surface of the body. Sensory receptors in the muscles and joints allow animals to co-ordinate their limbs, and the gravity receptors of the inner ear enable them to maintain a constant position with respect to the ground.

## How do we perceive?

Traditionally, a perception was thought to be a combination of sensations received by the sense organs, in the same way as the substances of the Earth are combinations of the 100 or so basic elements. Sensations were colours, touches, sounds and smells which were not things in themselves. On this view the physical world, as well as imagination and thought, was constructed from sensation by the mind. How these sensations were combined into perceptions was not clear, and although we do sense colours and touches in everyday life, objects and events seem to be just as immediate.

This theory also raised a number of problems for which there seemed to be no answers. If the eyes only sensed colours this would not permit us to see objects as separate from their backgrounds, nor could it help us to see the world in depth. Light entering the eye falls on a two-dimensional surface – the retina. If the sensations of colour were the only information present in the light, how could a perception of the third dimension be possible? One could argue that space or depth was a sensation, but this would just be an evasion. Although the term 'sensation' is used when referring to apparently simple impressions, and 'perception' for more complex events, there is no justification for this dichotomy.

The Muller-Lyer or arrow illusion can be simulated by the inside corner and the outside corner of a building. The lines in the illusion are the same length. The Ponzo (railway lines) illusion causes the upper of the two lines to appear longer than the lower, though both are equal.

The problem of how we perceive the real three-dimensional world with a two-dimensional eye did seem to be real. In fact, it is no more of a problem than is the relationship of a written word to the sounds of the word when it is spoken. The written and the spoken word correspond to one another because there is a lawful transformation between them which we have to learn. If there is a lawful relationship between the real world and the patterns of stimulation on the retina, then they, too, can be said to correspond. Since the optical system of the eye is subject to the laws of physics, a particular view of the real world will always produce the same pattern of stimulation on the retina. When we see in depth it is because this information is present in the pattern of light entering the eyes.

A similar problem is that the lens system of the eye inverts the real world to form an upside-down image on the retina. Philosophers wondered how we were able to see the world the correct way up. Again, there is no problem since 'up' in the real world always corresponds to 'down' on the retina. 'Up' and 'down' are directions relative to an organism which is subject to the law of gravity and

not to the orientation of the retinal image.

If an animal moves across our lines of sight its image on the retina changes position. If we move our eyes the image of the world on our retina also changes, but in the latter case we do not say the world has moved. Since in both instances the position of the image on the retina has changed, this is puzzling. The answer seems to be that when we move our eyes the brain takes this into account and cancels the movement of the world. In the case of a movement external to ourselves, no eye movements occur and the external movement is not cancelled. If you press firmly on the side of one of your eyeballs – cover the other eye with your hand – you will see the world jump each time you push. It must be that the signal to the eye to move is also the signal to cancel the external movement, which will result from the eye movement, since passively moving the eye does not cancel the external movement.

Movement is a relative displacement of objects or surfaces. How do we decide which object or surface is actually moving? This is not a ridiculous question. If, whilst travelling in a train, you are overtaken by another train you perceive that both trains are moving in the same direction, but also that the other train is moving faster. Occasionally, if the overtaking train obliterates your view of the scene, you may imagine you are standing still or even travelling backwards. At the same time you may be aware that it is an illusion because the rocking of your train indicates that you are moving.

All perception entails a decision between two or more possibilities. If in a darkened room you view the illuminated outline of a large frame and a spot of light within it, and the frame but not the spot is moved, you will see the spot of light, not the frame, move. In situations like this, which do not allow certainty, one makes the most likely choice, and since large objects are more likely to be stable than small ones, you perceive the spot to move.

The impression we have of the world stretching into the distance is very strong; it is virtually impossible to see the world as if in two dimensions. If you close one eye and concentrate you may eventually get some conception of the importance of two eyes for seeing depth. Objects seen with one eye do appear to be less solid and even flat. Our two eyes, which are about two and half inches apart, are an aid to depth vision because each eye has a slightly different view of the world. If you fixate the wall opposite you and place a finger a few inches in front of your nose you will see two fingers. Closing each eye alternately will demonstrate that each eye sees a different view. These two slightly different images in some way indicate depth. The stereoscope, which presents each eye with a slightly different view for the same scene, gives a vivid impression of depth, but each picture is relatively flat when viewed singly. If you doubt the usefulness of two eyes for depth try to thread a needle with one eye closed, making sure that your hands do not touch one another. This binocular vision is, however, only effective up to about 20 feet, and beyond this point we are essentially one-eyed.

We have already noted a number of signs which indicate depth and distance. These are called monocular cues because they do not depend upon the use of two eyes. One is *size perspective*, or the decrease in the size of things with increasing distance. This size, at the retina, of an object at six feet is twice that of the same object at 12 feet. *Linear perspective* refers to the size/distance relationship of rectilinear contours. The sides of a road or the lines of a railway track appear to converge as they run away from us. The *texture or*

**1** The texture of the cobblestones on this street at Clovelly, North Devon, provides the eye with an important clue to distance, as the street appears smoother further away.

**2** The position of the sun or moon in the sky determines how large it appears to us. At its zenith it appears considerably smaller than it does on the horizon.

**3** Experimental studies show that people brought up in a 'rounded' environment, like these Zulu,

*grain* of surfaces, such as a cobbled road or the waves of the sea, appears finer and more densely packed with increasing distance. *Motion parallax* is the effect whereby if you move your head, near objects appear to move a greater distance than further ones. This can clearly be seen from the window of a moving train. If you observe the middle distance, objects nearer move more rapidly, in the opposite direction to yourself, than do objects at the level of your gaze. Even more striking is the apparent slow movement of further objects in the *same* direction

These signs or cues are usually considered as indicative of distance, and so they are. However, it is possible that they are the results of our sophistication and experience of paintings and geometry. The real world is not composed of lines and angles, but shades of colour, brightness and texture, so that we cannot be certain that these are the cues we use in everyday life.

Although an object at a distance gives a smaller image to the eye than the same object seen close to, we do not usually see the distant one as smaller. A 6-inch square is seen as approximately the same size over a considerable distance. It is because we perceive the square at a certain distance from us that we see the size as the same. If these cues to distance are eliminated, as is done in the laboratory by viewing the stimulus through a reduction tube, so that we can see only the object, then we judge the distant object according to its retinal size; it appears to be smaller.

In the real world objects differ in many ways, size being only one aspect. We usually see familiar objects as constant and do not compare their size, shape or colour. A circular dinner plate lying on the table is elliptical in shape at the eye, yet we do not observe an elliptical dinner plate.

The size of an object can only be meaningful with respect to other objects. The moon is an example of an object with no other object near enough for comparison. This makes it difficult to see the moon as constant. At the horizon it appears to be about one and a half times as large as it is when high in the sky. This is true whether it is viewed over buildings, fields, desert or water. If, however, the terrain is masked, the horizon moon is reduced to the size of the zenith moon. The cues to distance present in the

4

are less sensitive to line illusions than are people living in more 'rectangular' environments.

**4** A form of brain damage makes it hard for this girl to see shapes as a whole. Here she is being trained to 'build' a face to help her overcome her handicap.

**5** Seen from a speeding train, the foreground of this landscape appears blurred, although the background is clearly in focus. The eye fixates on the apparently slower-moving background.

as yourself. Because we view the ground at an angle, distant objects are seen to be 'above' nearer objects, that is if you imagine the visual scene without the third dimension. With *aerial perspective* distant objects are less sharp and colours are less bright.

Objects at a greater distance than 20 feet still appear as solid and three-dimensional and monocular cues are possibly operating to give us this solidity. A very important cue is provided by shadowing, which enhances edges, curves and textures of objects.

5

terrain in conjunction with the lack of change in the size of the retinal image produce the apparent increase in size. Remember, if two objects form the same size retinal image, then the further one must actually be the larger. The importance of the terrain in producing this illusion can be judged if you view the horizon moon through your legs, when it will be reduced to approximately the same size as the zenith moon. The cues to distance given by the terrain are not as effective from this position; they normally lie at our feet, not above our head.

## Conflicting information

Errors of perception, such as the moon illusion, are not common. They usually occur when there is lack of information or when conflicting information is present. A simple experiment, using temperature sense, demonstrates this. Fill three bowls with water – one hot, one iced and one at room temperature. Place one hand in the hot and one in the iced water and keep them there for about three minutes. Then place both hands in the water at room temperature. The peculiar impression which results is due to the expectation that the water in a single bowl cannot seem hot and cold at the same time.

Geometrical illusions are a special case of conflicting information. Two common ones are illustrated. In the *Muller-Lyer* illusion the identical vertical lines appear to be of different lengths. In the *Ponzo* illusion the upper horizontal line appears to be longer than the lower one. There have been many attempts to explain satisfactorily this type of illusion, but the most reasonable one supposes that they represent perspective outlines. One of the figures of the *Muller-Lyer* illusion can be seen as representing the corner of a room or a roof viewed from below. The other figure can be imagined as the edge of a building or a roof viewed from above. If these figures are seen as transparencies in the dark they appear in depth. This situation eliminates the conflicting information provided by the paper on which the figures are drawn. The paper indicates both vertical lines are at the same distance but the perspective shape implies distance. The vertical line of the figure in which the two short lines would, with perspective, be nearer is therefore seen as longer. Of equal-sized objects at the retina, the apparently more distant one must be larger. This is probably the correct interpretation for many of the geometrical illusions.

It has been suggested that these geometrical illusions are enhanced because of our man-made environment, in which rectilinear forms are very common. It has been found that African tribesmen who live in round huts with no rectangular windows, no straight roads and few corners and edges, are less susceptible to these illusions.

This idea has been tested experimentally and found to be true: Americans and Europeans see a greater difference between the vertical lines of the Muller-Lyer figures than do many African peoples. Indeed, social factors, particularly the early training of the child, probably play a larger part in perception than is generally realized: we see the world as we are taught to see it.

## Painting and perception

This explanation of geometric illusions suggests that our perception of space and distance dominate our approach to painting. This is not true of all cultures, some of which do not attempt to convey space in their art. Western children's paintings are similar. Six-year-olds, if asked to draw trees on an outlined mountain slope, place them perpendicular to the slope instead of vertical to the ground. If the same children are allowed to plant model trees on the slope of a mountain of sand they do so correctly – vertical to the ground. It is not that children do not perceive space correctly but that they are not capable of representing it correctly according to convention. The vertical direction is given in the real world by information from the gravity receptors and it is usually at a right angle to the Earth. The child confuses the line representing the slope of the mountain with the flat ground from which the mountain rises. To draw the world according to our conventions it is necessary for 'up', 'down' and 'side' to be referred to the edge of the paper and distance is created by means of perspective drawing. Representational art is an illusion of the real world created by the artist.

Perception involves other senses apart from sight. A musician playing the organ, for example, has to co-ordinate the sounds he hears with the sensations in his fingers and his feet.

When the eye is held still, the image of a moving object runs over the retina, but if the eye follows the movement, the image remains on the same point. The two systems can disagree.

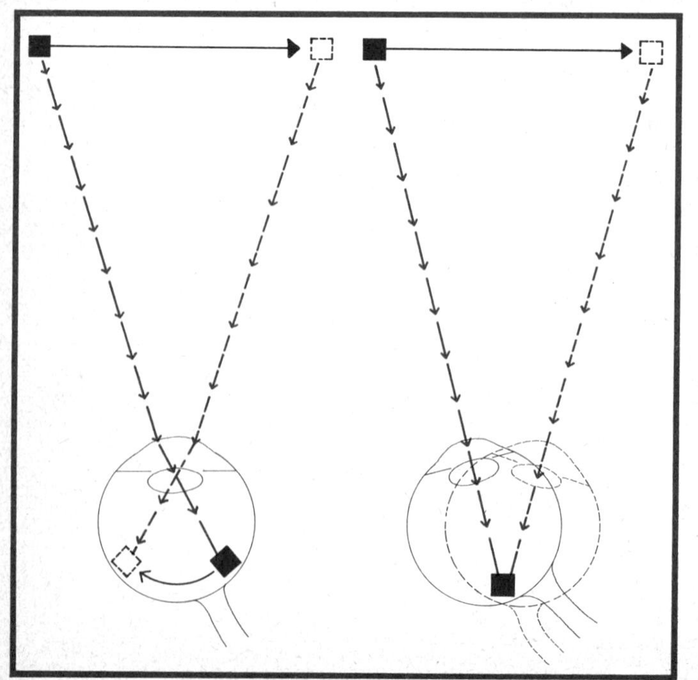

The visual cliff leads to conflict in the baby's mind. Although the glass is there, he refuses to crawl out over the drop because he can see the 'cliff' and the danger.

# The fuel of life

All life on Earth depends on the sun's energy. Plants can use this directly, but animals cannot. Complex 'food-webs' of prey and predator among animals have developed to overcome this.

1 A privet moth caterpillar feeding on privet leaves. Caterpillars are voracious eaters – indeed, they do little else. Some eat many times their own weight of food per day.

2 A willow tit picking a caterpillar out of the bark of a birch tree. Caterpillars and grubs provide food for a large number of species of birds and animals.

FOOD IS a basic requirement of life. Without it life cannot continue. This is not the inflexible experience of human beings only, but applies equally to all forms of life. Life requires food because all life uses up energy all the time for movement, reproduction, repair and all the internal activities of living matter. Food provides the energy for life in the form of chemical energy. The metabolic processes of the cell break down the food releasing locked-up chemical energy.

The basic types of food for most living matter are *proteins, carbohydrates* and *fats*. These three types of compounds serve different functions in living matter. The proteins, which consist basically of long chains of smaller molecules called *amino acids*, are the fundamental 'building blocks' of the cell. In animals, they are closely involved in the reproduction of the cell and control of its development. Most animals can make protein from its constituent amino acids, but require protein in food to obtain the amino acids from which to manufacture further protein.

## Sources of energy

Carbohydrates, such as sugar and starch, are composed of longer or shorter sugar molecules, in much the same way that proteins are chains of amino acids. The carbohydrates are ready sources of energy for the activities of living cells. They are used by some living matter to provide structural material as protein is used by animals. The cellulose which makes up the cell wall of many plants is a form of carbohydrate.

Fats are another energy source. For human beings, and many other animals, fats are an essential part of the diet because they carry certain vital substances which are required in small quantities if the metabolism of the cell is to proceed normally. These substances, particularly vitamins, form an essential part of food because without them the cell cannot break down other foods to provide energy in the correct way. In other cases, vitamins are required to take part in the construction of the structure of the cell and other organs.

An apparent paradox is suggested by this description of the relationship between life and food. If all living matter is using up energy throughout its life, the sources of energy-containing foods must be rapidly exhausted. How then is life able to continue? All the energy of

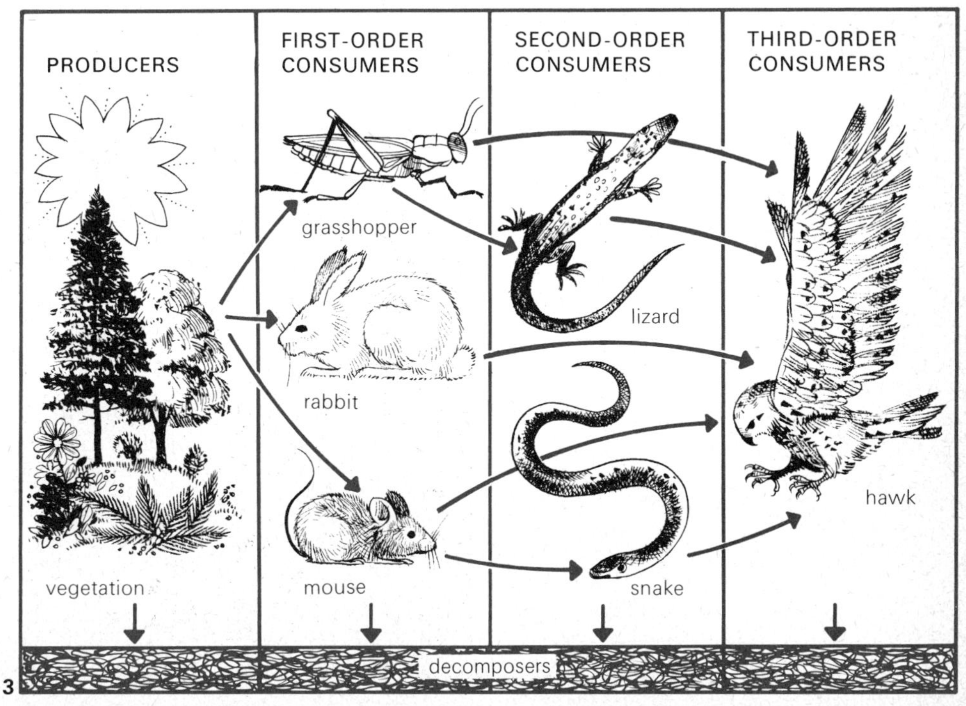


3 Scheme of a typical food-web. The first-order consumers are vegetarians, feeding on the green plants. Second- and third-order consumers are carnivores.

living matter on Earth can be regarded as coming from the sun. Living matter can be divided into two types. The first, which forms the bulk of living matter on Earth, consists of those organisms which are able to make direct use of the sun's energy. This group of organisms is known as the *autotrophs*. The green plants, which are its main constituent members, are machines for turning the sun's energy into complex chemical compounds in which energy is locked up. The basic process involved in the green plants can be summarized as:

carbon dioxide+water+energy
→ sugars+oxygen.

This synthesis or fabrication of energy-containing substances takes place every day on a vast scale. One has only to look at the countryside with acre after acre of green plants stretching as far as the eye can see to understand that the scope of *photosynthesis*, as this process is called, is vast. But of course not all life consists of green plants. The reverse process, the breakdown of energy-containing compounds, also takes place on a very large scale. This is the fundamental equation of the *heterotrophs* – those forms of life which cannot synthesize their own energy requirements:

complex molecules+oxygen
→ energy+carbon dioxide.

## Plants – an energy bottleneck

Animals, which have no means of making use directly of solar energy, depend on the green plants to provide the basic requirements of life. As green plants are the basic source of energy-giving food for other forms of life, there must be a greater quantity of green plant life than any other form of living matter. The autotrophs are the basic source of all foods, but they also form a bottleneck in the process of energy utilization. All the energy available to life on Earth must, as we have seen, flow through them. The rate at which living plants can create new energy by turning the sun's rays into chemical energy is thus a fundamental limitation on the amount of life that the Earth can support. Estimates of how much of the sun's energy is converted by green plants are hard to make, but there is no doubt that the figure is only a small fraction of the energy radiated on to the Earth from the sun. It is almost certainly less than one per cent of the energy falling on the Earth in the form of light.

There is a very much larger mass of green plants than of animals and other organisms living off their products. But in addition to the animals which live directly on green plants, there are others that feed on the plant-eating animals. There may be several links in a chain of this type. Thus, tuna fish from Japan which is canned for human consumption, probably fed on smaller fish, which in turn ate green plants. Man is not the final link in the chain, for human tissues will sooner or later be food for bacteria.

The situation is much more complicated than this simple example would make it appear. One species of plant may provide food for a large number of different types of organisms, and each may be the prey of a number of other animals. Instead of a simple chain there is in fact a web inter-connecting many different species which are thus rendered mutually dependent. It is this fact which has led biologists to the concept of *ecology*.

Ecology is the branch of biology concerned with the interactions of the different species inhabiting the Earth. Ecologists have to pay a great deal of attention to the food chains in the areas they are studying. They see life not merely as the life of the individual or species but as the life of the entire mass of living organisms.

One example of the complicated inter-relationship between food and the life of animals is the tragic story of the Kaibab deer of Arizona.

In an attempt to improve the natural balance in favour of the deer, a campaign of extermination was waged against the pumas, wolves and other animals that preyed on them. The grasslands were unable to support the increase in population of deer and the herd began to starve to death, at the same time permanently damaging their grazing grounds.

This story illustrates the fact that the relationship between the various parts of the food-chain is a complex one, and that

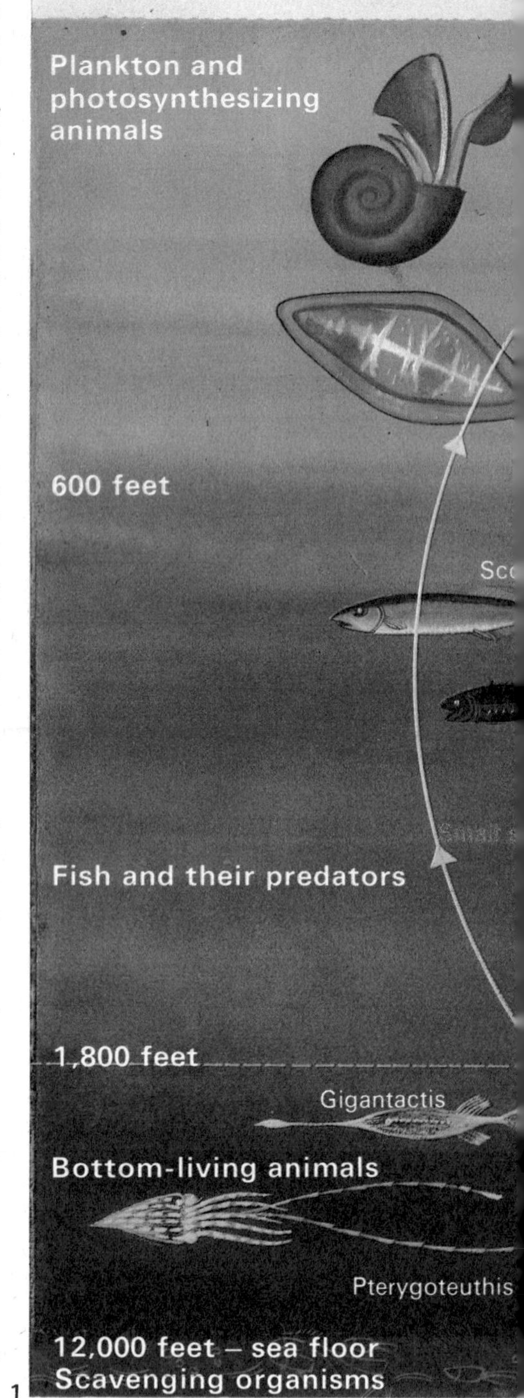

**1** The energy cycle in the ocean. Surface plankton provides the basic source of energy, utilized by whales and fish. Dead plants and animals feed lower-living forms.
**2** An immature kestrel uses its claws and beak to tear apart its prey. The kestrel, a bird of prey, is the summit of a chain involving plants and other animals.
**3** A praying mantis devours a fly. Among the insects, as well as in more developed forms of life, there are complex energy cycles based on food-chains.
**4** A grizzly bear and a puma share the remains of an elk. Both animals are carnivores and are close to the top of their food-chains. They are thus competitors for food.
**5** Two green hydra feeding on water fleas. The short hydra has engulfed its water flea, and is in the process of digesting it, while the longer hydra is paralysing a water flea using the stinging cells in its tentacles.

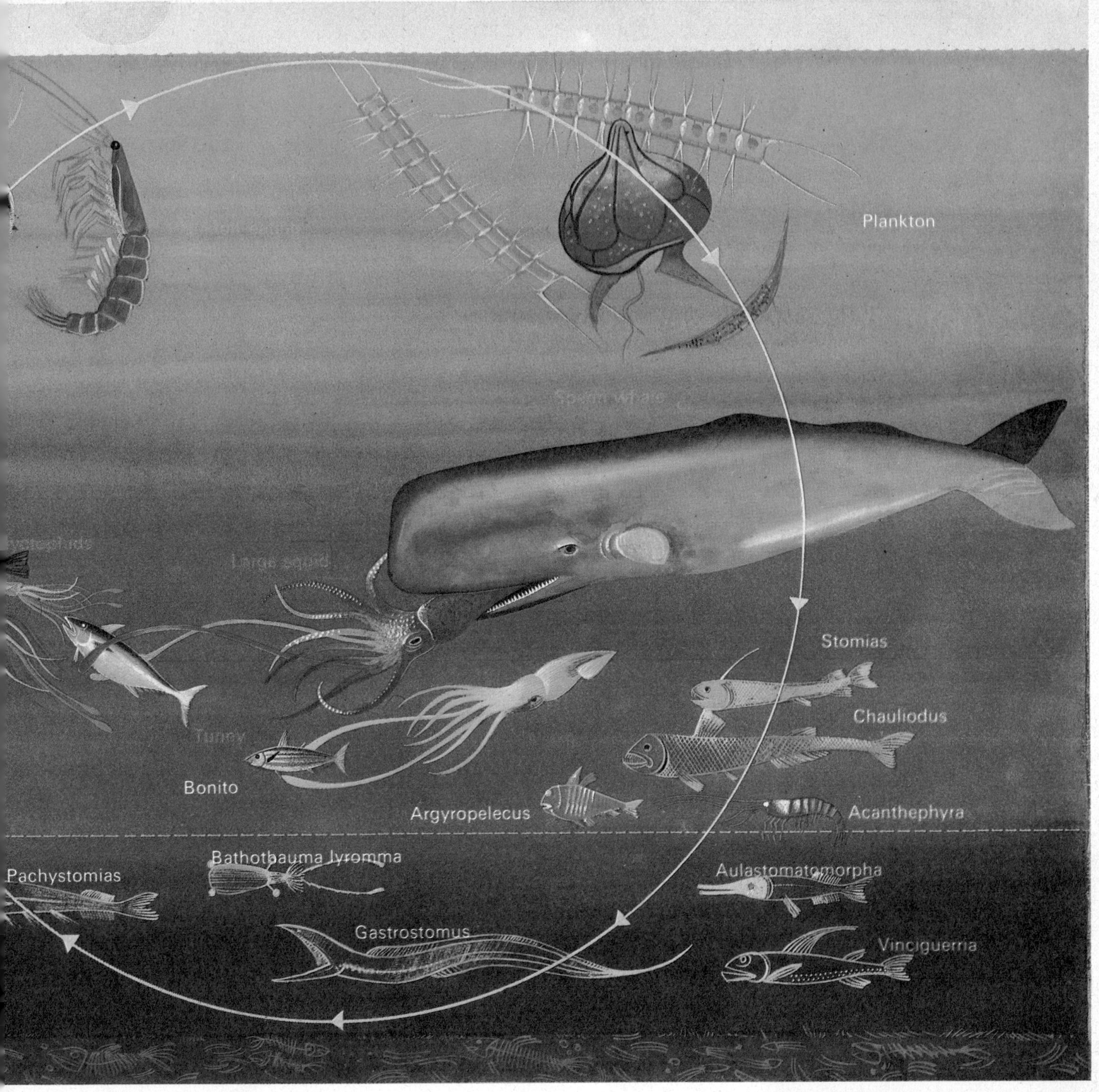
Plankton
Sperm whale
Large squid
Stomias
Chauliodus
Tunny
Bonito
Argyropelecus
Acanthephyra
Bathothauma lyromma
Pachystomias
Aulastomatomorpha
Gastrostomus
Vinciguerria

4

5

it is unwise for human beings to bring about major changes without understanding the links in the chain.

Competition for food shapes the nature of many animal species. The classic example of this is Darwin's study of the finches of the Galapagos Islands. The three main species of Galapagos finches are *Camarhynchus parvulus, C. pauper* and *C. psittacula*. On Chatham Island, where *parvulus* alone is found, the size of its beak, though small, is larger than that found in species of *parvulus* on Charles and Albemarle Islands. The reason for this is that on Chatham Island the species has no competitors, while on the other two islands, *parvulus* has to face competition from *pauper* on Charles and *psittacula* on Chatham. The possession of a shorter beak enables it to eat a slightly different selection of insects from its competitors. Competition for food has shaped the bodies of the animals concerned.

## Devious links

The requirements of two species which live in the same area may be so different that the two species are not in competition. But they may still be linked together by more devious routes. A humorous illustration of this is the story of the origins of roast beef put forward by one of Darwin's early supporters. England's greatness, so the tale went, was based on roast beef from cows nourished on clover. The clover was pollinated by bumblebees, which were attacked in their nests by mice. The mice were kept under control by cats, and the cats were raised by old maids. Thus, went the argument, the greatness of England was due to her old maids. The legend illustrates the links which bind together apparently unrelated, uncompeting species. These links through food-chains show that there is a constant circulation of biological material from plants to animals and thence to other animals.

Investigations of the links in food-chains have shown conclusively that there is a pyramid based on the green plants. The green plants cannot supply food continually to more than a small proportion of their own mass in the form of plant-eating animals. Again, the number of carnivorous animals is limited to a relatively small fraction of the number of herbivores. This explains why the number of eagles in a given area of Scotland is much less than the population of game-birds. Again, in the plains of Africa, there are vast herds of deer, antelope and other plant-eaters, preyed on by a relatively small number of lions and jackals.

A measure of the quantities involved has been made in various specialized habitats. Measurements of the masses of the various levels of producers and consumers in a lake in Wisconsin in the United States have shown that the masses (in kilograms per hectare) of the various levels of food-chains in the lake were: mass of green plants – 1,700; mass of herbivorous animals – 220; and mass of carnivorous animals – 23. The amount of energy at each level was found to vary in a similar way. Since the animals at the top

A nest of blue tits at feeding time. A brood this size requires a small army of caterpillars and grubs to feed it. Birds help in this way to keep down insect pests.

of the food-chain tend to be larger than their prey, the effect is even more striking when we come to consider the numbers involved. In another study, this time of prairie land, the ratio was something of the order of 6,000,000 : 700,000 : 350,000 : 3. Here a more complex structure of four levels was involved.

Large ants clearing up the remains of a dead frog. Dead organic matter provides food for many different species of scavengers, from bacteria to fungi and insects.

The circulation of energy-containing material, of course, involves movement from place to place as well as from animal to animal. A good example of this is found in the oceans. It is obvious that the plants and animals of the great ocean depths cannot obtain energy directly from the sun, for no light penetrates to these areas. But in the oceans, as on land, there is a constant circulation of material which enables the animals at the bottom of the sea to obtain food.

In the illuminated zone below the surface of the water, there is abundant plant and animal life. The diatoms and algae which convert solar energy into food are eaten by the many herbivorous fish at this level. Many of these small animals become very abundant and such animals as the *copepods* (tiny shrimp-like organisms) provide food for the whalebone whales.

Below the illuminated level, the organisms have to rely on the debris of life above. Plankton sinks when it is dead and fish from the upper reaches of the sea may venture further down. The animals at this level tend to be voracious and every animal has some predator. At the bottom of the sea there are many organisms living in permanent darkness and re-using the dead matter that has fallen from above.

## Circulation of energy

Water circulates between the surface of the sea and the ocean depths; the cold water from the sea bottom is raised by currents which return the dissolved nutrients to the photosynthetic zone at the surface. The fertilizing effect of this water gives an impulse to the growth of plankton and restarts the cycle.

The constant circulation of organic matter is not confined to the sea. It is characteristic of all types of community. Life on the Earth has evolved to a constantly changing balance. The green plants synthesize the energy which provides food for the animals. The animals preyed on by other animals become in their turn food for some other species. Man must beware of interfering too much with this natural cycle, for to do so could endanger the whole of life on the Earth.

# Blood-suckers and hangers-on

Parasites obtain nourishment in a multitude of ingenious ways. While some tap the sap of trees or the blood of animals, others wallow in the luxury of digested food in their hosts' intestines.

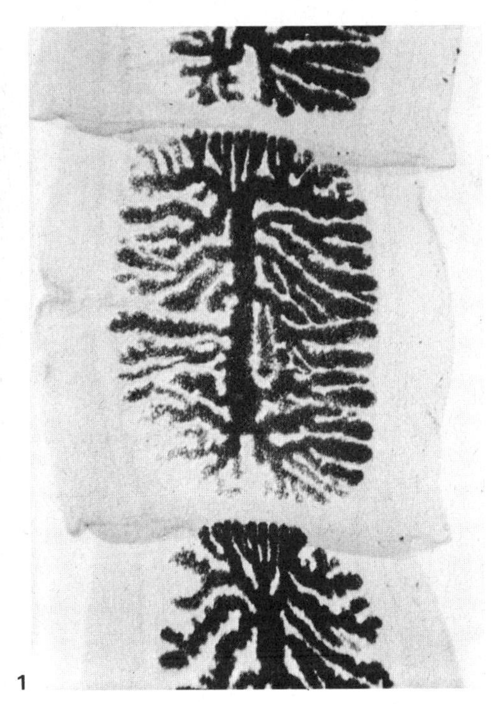

1 By adding new segments to its body, a tapeworm can reach a length of 60 ft or more in the intestine of its host. When ripe each segment contains thousands of eggs.

2 Barnacles are usually associated with rocks and ships. But the sac barnacle parasitizes the shore crab and when mature produces a huge egg mass on the underside of its host.

FOR AS LONG as he can remember Man has come up against parasites which concern him especially because of their attacks upon him and upon his domestic animals. Records of parasites date back very far. Ancient Chinese physicians described malaria in fine detail and the Bible provides other possible references to parasites. The fiery serpent of the Book of Numbers may be none other than the guinea-worm, *Dracunculus medinensis*, a scourge common in Africa and parts of Asia.

In the course of their excavations archaeologists are now finding evidence of human parasites. In 1910 Dr Ruffer discovered the eggs of a type of liver fluke, *Schistosoma haematobium* in Egyptian mummies. This parasite causes bilharzia, a terrible disease which can be fatal and is still widespread in many parts of the world, including Egypt. Close inspection of fossilized human faeces has revealed on occasions the eggs, often extraordinarily well preserved, of intestinal parasites such as the roundworm – Ascaris – and of several types of tapeworm.

Although many of the common parasites have been known and endured for many hundreds of years, until recently very little was known about the parasites themselves. Parasites have a unique and complicated relationship with the organisms they attack as well as with their environment. They are, therefore, difficult to study although they are often a source of morbid fascination.

What do we mean by the term parasite? In nature we find all kinds of associations between animals; when the association is loose and both species are able to live independently of one another – like the association of a sea anemone and a hermit crab with one animal being transported by the other which itself gains protection from predators – this association is described as *commensalism*. When both species are dependent on each other but obtain some mutual benefit – as when certain *unicellular plants* (species of algae) live in animal cells such as those of the coelenterate hydra, and in return for nutrients such as amino acids, photosynthesize and produce carbohydrates which they share with their host – this association is called *symbiosis*. But when one species is highly dependent on the other species and is unable to survive if separated permanently from its host, it is called *parasitism*.

Parasitism is not a freak of nature but a way of life adopted by many different animal types. Indeed almost every major branch of the evolutionary tree in the animal kingdom has some parasitic members, although very few of these are able to infect human beings.

Because parasites have had to evolve a special form and physiology to enable them to lead their special way of life, they have come to look very different from their free-living non-parasitic relatives. For example, a close relative, *Lernaeocera branchialis*, of the crustacean water mites looks quite unlike its near relatives when, as an adult, it is attached to the gills of sea fish that are its natural host. The female has three functions: to remain attached to the gills, to feed on the tissues of the host, and to reproduce.

Whereas *Lernaeocera* cannot move around on its host, fleas are highly mobile. The dog flea, *Ctenocephalides canis*, which also infects cats, does not remain long on Man. It is laterally flattened, enabling it to move about easily amongst the host's hairs. The well-developed jumping legs and the lack of wings are characteristic of all fleas. On the other hand the mite, *Demodex folliculorum* has short, stumpy legs, which it does not use to carry it about for *Demodex*, causing mange in Man, lives in the hair follicles, into which it conveniently fits owing to the elongated shape of the body. The whale louse, *Paracyamus boopis*, has three highly developed pairs of clawed legs, which are used for attachment to the skin. It also has a flattened body and biting mouthparts.

The Lamellibranch molluscs, *Anodonta cygnea*, or swan mussels, common in many streams and lakes move about very little and have evolved a cunning method of dispersing their young. The parasitic larvae are specially adapted for attachment to the gills or skin of the fish with which they come into contact. The larvae remain with the fish for many weeks assimilating tissue which is induced to grow around them. Eventually they drop off and take up a free-living existence as young adults.

Leeches, relatives of the earthworms,

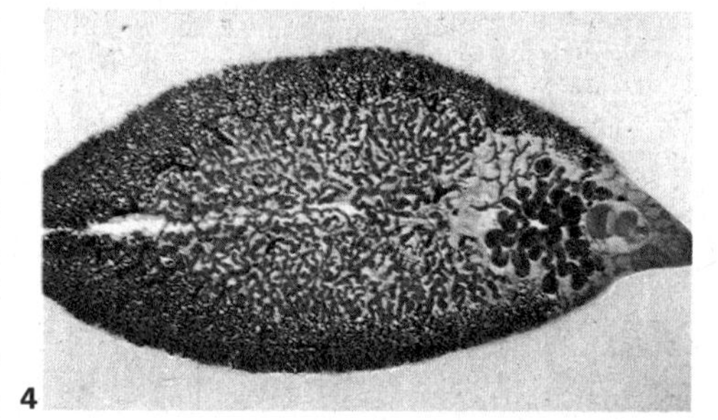

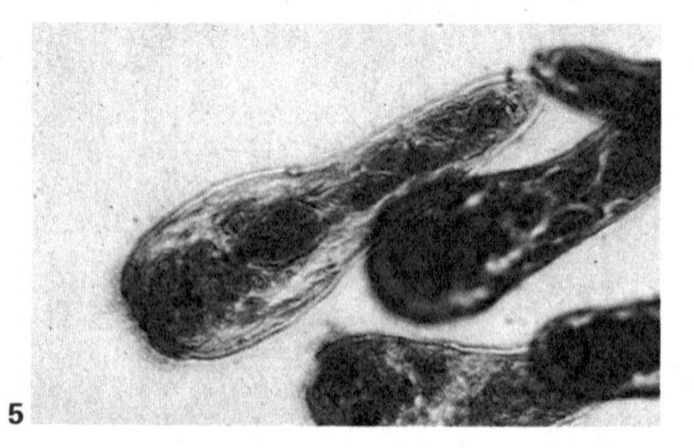

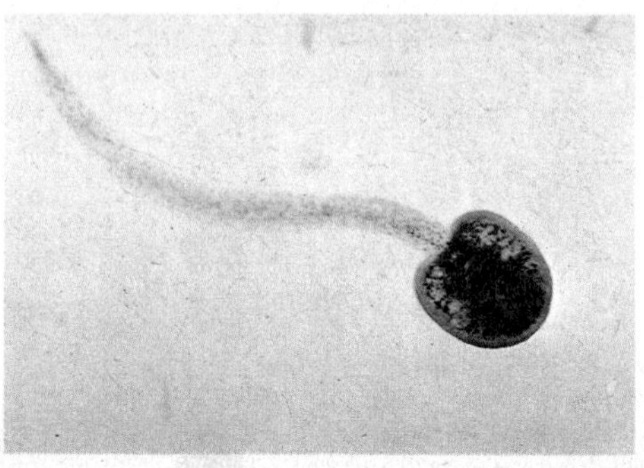

**1** Certain fungi, like *Ganoderma,* grow on the bark of trees. By infiltrating the wood with their roots they may cause considerable damage.
**2** Another fungus, black smut, parasitizes the head of mature barley. When the infestation is severe an entire crop can be ruined.
**3** Mildew is a parasitic fungus that grows like a coat over the surface of its host. These rosebuds will never be able to blossom properly.
**4** The liver fluke, which causes liver rot in sheep and cattle, lives in the large portal veins in the liver of its host. The fluke has a large sucker on its head to prevent it being swept away in a torrent of blood.
**5** Before being able to infect a sheep, the liver fluke must pass through an intermediate host, a snail. The larvae, which infect a snail, reproduce many times into these tiny redia larvae.
**6** The redia larvae also reproduce into mature larvae called cercaria. These then burst out of the snail and swim on to nearby vegetation, where they encyst until ingested by a browsing sheep. The cercaria then matures into a fluke.
**7** Nearly all species of mammal can harbour ticks. These hang on to long grass until an unsuspecting mammal brushes by. Once on the mammal the ticks, like these on a hedgehog, bury their mouthparts into the skin and suck blood.

are common in many waters and are well known for their blood-sucking habits. They are highly developed for blood feeding, with biting jaws and sucking apparatus. The two strong suckers and their slimy nature make them very difficult to remove once on the host.

Parasites which live on the skin and outer tissues, have evolved all kinds of fascinating adaptations. But many of the more economically important parasites live right inside the tissues of the host. The most devastating and important, as far as man is concerned, are the malarial parasites, and *trypanosomes* (the parasites responsible for sleeping sickness). Both are single-celled protozoa, living in the blood, and humans are infected through being bitten by the insects which act as intermediate hosts. As well as being adapted to living in humans, these parasites are adapted to living in mosquitoes and tsetse flies.

The amoeba, *Entamoeba histolytica,* which causes a severe type of dysentery, is a parasite of temperate and tropical areas. It, too, is a protozoan, but has no intermediate host and the infection is maintained by unhygienic conditions. The reproducing form of this amoeba is passed in the faeces. The amoeba can pass unharmed through the intestine of flies and thus get transmitted to food when carried on the feet of flies.

The flukes or *schistosomes* which live in the blood-vessels of Man and other mammals, need to pass through a snail as an intermediate host. A variety of freshwater snails harbour the larval stages. The infective larvae escape from the snails and penetrate the human skin. They then travel to the portal blood-vessels of the liver where they become adult. They are always found in pairs, the female living in a groove formed by folds of the male body. Sophistications of this sort are not uncommon among parasites and are always of some advantage, either for reproduction or transmission, for all parasites have extremely efficient methods of reproduction.

The beef tapeworm, *Taenia saginata,* of Man demonstrates the ultimate in parasite egg production. It can reach a length of 80 ft with 2,000 or more segments, all capable of producing enormous numbers of eggs. The adults live in the intestine, holding on to the gut wall with four strong suckers, and release ripe segments, which pass out with the faeces. Cattle act as the intermediate hosts to the parasite and Man is infected by eating contaminated raw or undercooked beef.

Eelworms are threadworms (nematodes) that parasitize a wide variety of bulbs and other economic crops. Potato rot, for example, is due to *Heterodera rostochiensis,* and once the eggs of this parasite are present in the soil they are very difficult to eliminate. Several diseases of Man are caused by nematodes, like *Wuchereria bancrofti,* which is carried by mosquitoes and manifests itself in Man by the gross enlargement of the lymph nodes, a condition known as elephantiasis. The guinea worm, *Dracunculus medinensis,* uses tiny crustacean copepods living in drinking water as the intermediate hosts. The adult worm may be up to one metre long and can be extracted from under the skin by winding it slowly on to a stick, an unpleasant method, but still the most successful.

If the biology of a parasite is to be understood the zoologist must unravel its fascinating mode of life and especially its passage between one host and another. This transmission is perhaps a parasite's largest hurdle, for failure would prove fatal to any parasite species.

The liver fluke, *Fasciola hepatica,* which causes liver rot in sheep and cattle, is a common parasite in Britain. It is responsible for losses of thousands of pounds to the farmer and thrives in low-lying areas where there is often standing water in which lives the intermediate host, an amphibious snail, *Linnaea trunculata.*

## Multiplication

In sheep, the adult fluke lives in the bile duct of the liver and moves around by the use of two suckers on its ventral surface. Here it feeds, causing extensive liver damage (rendering it totally inedible) and produces many thousands of eggs. These eventually find their way out with the faeces, and if they are deposited in water, the eggs develop and hatch, releasing a very small mobile ciliated larva which swims around in the water, and has a sensory system enabling it to detect chemicals released by the snail. Once the larva finds a suitable snail it penetrates the skin of the snail – the integument – by secreting enzymes.

Then follows two larval stages within the snail, called the *sporocyst* and the *redia,* both of which are purely for the multiplication of individuals. Each sporocyst gives rise to large numbers of redia and each redia in turn produces many other individuals called *cercariae.* These escape from the snail either when it dies or by bursting out into the water. Somehow each cercaria must get back into the sheep to complete the cycle, and it does so by swimming up nearby vegetation, using its tail for propulsion, and encysts there. The cyst is amazingly resistant to water loss and only hatches when a sheep eats it while browsing on the vegetation. The process is extremely wasteful at both stages, for not every larva finds a snail and only some of the cercarial cysts are eaten by sheep.

Most people, at one time or another, have kept a pet cat and watched it meticulously wash and preen itself. Few realize that this habit has helped the tapeworm *Dipylidium caninum* to infect nearly a third of the cats in Britain. The adult worm lives in the intestine of cats and dogs. Although this is an excellent site for readily available food, it tends to be somewhat turbulent, and therefore the tapeworm is armed on its head with four strong suckers and a small protuberance around which is arranged rows of hooklets. The whole apparatus is used to anchor the worm to the gut wall and prevent it from being swept away. Unlike the beef tapeworm, *Dipylidium* is very much shorter and has fewer segments, but they both lay their eggs in a mobile pocket or *proglottid* which breaks away from the end of the worm. This is passed down the intestine and may be expelled with the faeces or crawl out of the anus. As it moves along it leaves a trail of eggs upon which larval fleas feed. These larval fleas become infected with the cysticercoid stage which remains with them through-

7

1 Mistletoe grows as a parasite on the bark of trees. By burying its roots into the bark it can draw the sap of its host.

2 By secreting a special substance the growing gall wasp makes the oak leaf form a protective hump around it.

3 In earlier times physicians made use of the medicinal leech to bleed feverish patients. The leech is endowed with two large suckers, one for hanging on and the other for burying in the skin of its host. The leech also secretes an anti-coagulant to stop the blood clotting.

out their development into adults. Cats and dogs accidentally ingest the fleas while washing themselves and become infected.

In this situation a host has two species of parasites, fleas and tapeworms, in which one, the flea, is acting as host to the larval stages of the tapeworm. Although this is unusual it is not a unique relationship amongst parasites. *Dipylidium* is merely taking advantage of the association between fleas and their cat and dog hosts for its own transmission.

*Dipylidium* only has a brief phase outside a host and the eggs have a thick shell to prevent water loss. Parasites in the aquatic environment do not have to prevent dehydration, and transmission is therefore less hazardous. For this reason fish have many species of ectoparasites living on their skin and gills, such as *Gyrodactylus elegans,* a common parasite of the goldfish in garden ponds.

*Gyrodactylus* is a direct parasite; it relies on bodily contact for its infection and distribution and flourishes under crowded conditions such as an overstocked garden pond. It is able temporarily to attach itself by means of the cement gland, situated at the oral end, which exudes a sticky secretion, but for permanent or semi-permanent attachment it uses the *opisthaptor.* This organ is similar in shape to a feeble sucker, but is armed with a most impressive array of hooks – two large hooks, separated by a bar, near the centre of the opisthaptor and eight pairs of smaller hooks arranged round the edge. The entire organ acts as a most efficient anchoring system. *Gyrodactylus* moves along by a curious looping movement, alternately using the opisthaptor and the oral method of attachment.

*Gyrodactylus* is unique amongst its fellows in that it is mostly *ovoviviparous* (does not lay eggs); the larvae develop within the adult uterus. By the time the larvae are ready to leave the adult they themselves may have a developing larva within their own uterus. The number of *Gyrodactylus* on the fish in winter-time is fairly low, but during the spring larvae are rapidly produced and in overcrowded conditions the numbers may reach a pathogenic level very quickly, resulting in extensive gill damage and sometimes death.

## Ways of reinfection

The nematode *Enterobius vermicularis,* or common pinworm, uses precisely the same crowded conditions for its dispersal, for it is a characteristic parasite of schools and institutions. The adults live in the lower part of the intestine of Man and at night the female partially crawls out of the anus to lay her eggs on the skin. At the same time an acid secretion is produced which causes irritation and induces the host to scratch the area. The eggs are prone to drying out, but at night conditions in a bed are warm and humid and they can survive for some time. They are also very sticky and remain on the fingers and under the nails. People with *Enterobius* often show certain nervous symptoms, such as biting the nails, and in this way reinfection takes place when the eggs are ingested. The sticky eggs may, however, be transferred to doorknobs and railings where they soon dry out and die, unless quickly picked up by the next host.

Despite the multitude of parasites and their successful adaptations we can be cheered by the thought that not all living creatures are weighed down under a heavy burden of worms or festooned from head to tail with ectoparasites. Indeed, it is only under exceptional circumstances that parasites gain the upper hand, for a dead or chronically sick host is no use to a living parasite.

The very nature of parasitism requires the parasite to maintain a finely balanced relationship with its various hosts, for the host must not eliminate it or prevent the continuation of its cycle. We, therefore, have a very effective tool with which to attack the parasite, for by simply looking for the weakest link in the cycle we have some control.

An ever-increasing number of chemicals are being developed for the control of insects, molluscs and the parasites themselves. It is because of this, together with a better understanding of the mechanisms of parasitism and particularly their ecology, that we are now, to a certain extent, able to control and contain infections.

# Predators and prey

Many animals, including ourselves, are predators, hunting and killing other animals for food. Man is the most dangerous of all, because his activities destroy the natural balance of Nature.

THE CONCEPT of ecology has probably been one of the most fruitful developments in biological science over the past 50 years. By taking a broad view of the relations between various animals in an area and by noting how the species interact, the ecologist is able to draw some conclusions about the likely effects of changes in the environment on the intricate links in the life-chain.

Nowhere is this interaction more apparent than in the relations between predator and prey. Human beings are accustomed to see this relationship in moral terms, but this view is of little value. Darwin's famous definition of survival of the fittest is far more applicable than the type of moral considerations often imposed on natural events. What the moral view fails to see is the fact that both predator and prey benefit from the relationship in a balanced ecology, and that the system often operates in the best interests of both species.

## Meat-eaters and plant-eaters

All animal life in one way or another is dependent on plants. Only the plants can make the complex carbon molecules, the sugars and the amino acids, that are required for life. Many animals feed wholly or in part on plants, while other animals eat the plant-eaters. The animals which eat other animals are called *carnivores* (meat-eaters) and unlike the plant-eaters they have to track down and overcome their animal prey, unless they happen to find their meat already dead.

Because of the relationship between plants and animals, the meat-eaters have a much more limited supply of food than the plant-eaters and there are therefore fewer of them. This general rule can be seen in operation in many different types of habitat. Every fisherman knows that while there may be many tiny minnows in a river, there are likely to be few large pike. The same is true of the relative numbers of foxes and rabbits in hunting country, or of the numbers of golden eagles compared with herbivores in the Scottish Highlands. The predators, in other words, tend to come at or near the end of a food-chain, where much of the energy originally taken from the plants eaten by the plant-eating animals has already been spent on keeping the plant-eaters alive. An additional reason is that the predators must not eat all their prey – if the pike were to eat all the minnows no more minnows would be reproduced and the pike would rapidly die of starvation.

These basic considerations, then, condition the relations between predatory animals and their prey. No predator can afford to exterminate the whole of the species it preys on without undermining the condition for its own existence.

At the same time, the predatory animal must be able to catch sufficient of the prey to remain alive, and for this may require certain special attributes to enable it to make sure of catching and eating enough.

For these reasons, predators are generally larger than their prey, although this is not an invariable rule, and they tend to be isolated animals rather than vast flocks or herds. It is estimated, for example, that there is only one grizzly bear to every 40 square miles of the Canadian Rockies. Like many other predators, these animals tend to be solitary in habit and highly jealous of their territory. If another grizzly enters into their domain they are liable to fight it out with the intruder, which will often retreat rapidly over the 'frontier'.

There is therefore a social adaptation among predators which allows them to exploit their prey most efficiently without

**1** A larva of the great diving beetle holds a tadpole clamped between its powerful mandibles. The larva is well built to capture and kill its defenceless prey.
**2** The elongated snout of the giant South American ant-eater equips it for eating the termites which form its staple diet. The ant-eater is itself camouflaged against its predators.
**3** The end of the hunt for an otter. A number of mammals have taken to life in or around water, which contains a plentiful supply of food. The otter's streamlined body aids its swimming.

too great competition between members of the same species.

But predators also need to be specialized in other ways. In many cases, like the predators which feed on the giant herds of antelope in the African veld, their prey is fast-moving and congregates in herds for protection. The predators must be able to stalk their prey so as not to give too much warning of their presence and to be able to catch the prey on the run. For this reason, animals like the lion are capable of considerable turns of speed, at least over short distances, and are well equipped with sharp claws and powerful limbs to strike down and kill their victims once they have caught up with them. The ability to run fast in pursuit of prey is even more highly developed in the cheetah. This animal can run faster than an express train over short distances, and is well equipped to catch an antelope on the run.

Birds of prey also need to be able to make speedy captures. The kestrel is a typical example. This bird feeds mainly on small rodents and insects, and hovers high above them, swooping down with great speed to catch the prey before it has had time to escape. The kestrel's powerful beak and strong talons give it the power to kill and grasp its prey while carrying it off.

### Teeth and jaws

Predators must also be able to eat their food after they have killed it, and for this they require specially adapted teeth and powerful jaws. The dog family of animals have well-developed canine teeth for ripping the flesh of their prey and powerful jaws for cracking its bones.

Not all carnivores are solitary animals; some have evolved the social mechanism of the pack to help them to catch and kill their prey. The dog family is an example, and wolves frequently hunt in packs, enabling them to bring down animals larger than themselves, extending the scope of their predation.

By no means all animals prey on the larger herbivores, however. There are many species specially adapted for eating insects or fish or birds. The various species of ant-eater, for example, are highly specialized for eating ants, and the giant ant-eaters of South America, with their elongated heads and mouths, are virtually incapable of eating anything else. Their success in this activity is testified to by their large size. The termites which form their main food live in huge mounds which tower above the plain, and the ant-eaters can generally find a plentiful supply of ants.

Other animals, both mammals and birds, have made fishing their niche. The otter, like the beaver and the water-rat, will swim underwater in order to catch large fish in their native environment.

The seals have carried this adaptation even further than the otter and spend all their time in the sea, except for a short period before and after breeding.

Other species have become adapted to other forms of predation. The blood-sucking insects provide a good example. There are many different types of blood-sucking insects, and by no means all are adapted to feed on Man. Within the blood-sucking varieties there is considerable specialization, which goes so far that, in the case of the tsetse fly *Glossina*, the insect is unable to ingest blood corpuscles more than 18 microns in diameter. Other blood-suckers, attracted by certain scents or by other forms of chemical attraction, will only drink the blood of a single species.

The blood-sucking bats are highly adapted to take advantage of their prey while it is asleep. Though their activities bear only a tenuous relation to those of the legendary vampire, some blood-sucking bats display remarkable ingenuity in getting at their victim's blood. They attack only at night, while the victim is sleeping, and search out uncovered areas of the body, such as the soles of the feet. There they make small incisions through which the blood seeps out and the bat licks it up rather like a cat lapping up milk. Not all vampires attack human beings – some prey largely on cattle and other large mammals.

How does predation affect the popula-

1

2

3

**1** The genet, a small cat-like carnivore, is found in Africa and southern Europe and feeds mainly on small mammals and birds. It lives in trees and on the banks of streams.

**2** A dead vapourer moth caterpillar surrounded by larvae of the ichneumon fly. The larvae, laid inside the caterpillar, have eaten away its tissues and thus killed it.

**3** A chain snake forms the food for this king snake. Snakes usually eat small reptiles and mammals and devour their prey whole. Their teeth are set backwards to help them swallow.

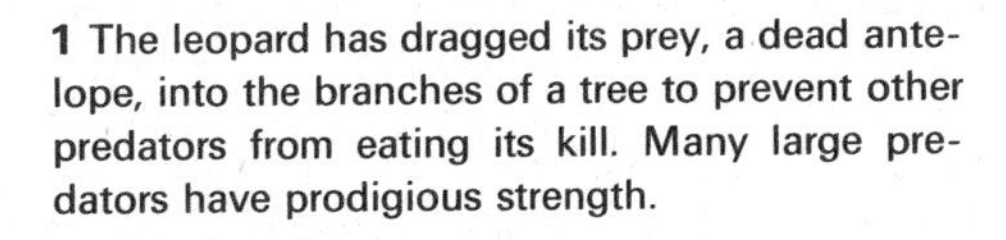

**1** The leopard has dragged its prey, a dead antelope, into the branches of a tree to prevent other predators from eating its kill. Many large predators have prodigious strength.

**2** A crab makes a meal of a lugworm. The sea, like the land, is the arena of sharp struggles between predators and their prey. The armoured crab is well equipped for predation.

**3** The sparrowhawk, a bird of prey, takes the bodies of its victims to a specific spot – the plucking post – where it discards their feathers or hair before eating them.

tion of prey? Naturally, too much predation tends towards the extermination of the prey, and no doubt this happens to some species when the balance of their relationship with their predator is seriously upset. Often the introduction of a new predator into the set-up can menace the survival of a species. Man is easily the most dangerous predator in this respect. The annals of zoology are littered with examples of animals killed off by the activities of human beings. One thinks of the almost-extinct American buffalo, the dodo and the passenger pigeon. But in undisturbed circumstances, the activities of the predators can have a strengthening effect on the population of prey as a whole.

One reason for this is that the very act of predation, particularly on a herd of animals, tends to select the least hardy animals as prey. The old animals, those unable to run as fast as the others, and the animals rejected by the herd are likely to fall prey to the predators first. Indeed, this type of selection occurs all the time in the antelope herds which form the staple reservoir for the predatory activities

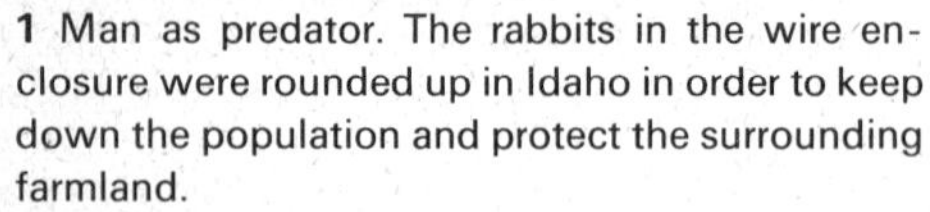

**1** Man as predator. The rabbits in the wire enclosure were rounded up in Idaho in order to keep down the population and protect the surrounding farmland.
**2** A kingfisher with a captured fish. Many types of birds have taken to fishing as a way of life, both in fresh-water rivers and, like the gulls, in ocean waters.
**3** The shrike feeds on small animals and birds, which it kills with a blow of its pointed beak. It bears the bodies off to a thorn tree, where it impales them on thorns until ready to eat.

of the African lion and his family.

Even in cases where this type of mechanism can only operate less directly, predation still has a beneficial effect in maintaining the population of prey within acceptable overall limits. Where a predator is removed altogether, catastrophic effects can result. Lack of the customary predators was probably one of main reasons for the enormous and rapid spread of the rabbit after its introduction into Australia. The animals' formidable breeding system was able to operate without hindrance and within a very few years the whole continent was covered with millions of rabbits, an almost uncontrollable pest. Similar dangers have been found with other species introduced from abroad, particularly with insect pests. One species of ladybirds introduced into America to control cotton pests itself became a serious menace in the absence of its natural predators.

Despite the benefits to the species and to the general balance of nature which predation provides, many animals go to great lengths to avoid falling victim to predators. Among insects many bizarre and often attractive forms have resulted from attempts at protective coloration. Camouflage, like that of the stick insects, provides one obvious type of protection, and hundreds of examples from among the insect community could be found. But less well known are the insects which have developed warning colours to mimic some distasteful or noxious insect which a predator would be likely to avoid.

The various pseudo-wasps have solved some of their problems in this way, matching their colours to those of real wasps in an attempt, often successful, to discourage birds and other insects from tackling them.

A more serious problem is posed for the males of some kinds of spider, which are likely to become the prey of the females if they approach while the females are unreceptive. The male is smaller than the female in many spider species, and has to resort to subterfuge in order to make sure of escaping with his life.

The male spider shakes the web before venturing on to it and judges the female's receptivity by her response. If she comes thundering down the web towards him, he flees, whereas if she gives signs that she is not hungry, he gingerly approaches, mates with her and gets away as best he can.

Cannibalism is not confined to the spiders and is fairly common among animals, and even more common among insects. Sharks are another group of animals noted for their cannibalistic tendencies – they will tear an injured comrade to pieces as readily as they will tear a piece of carrion.

Wolves are noted for the same type of behaviour, and are not averse to a bit of cannibalism when the supply of other food is low.

Many predators change their prey if they are forced to by hunger. Foxes, which usually feed on small mammals, will eat berries and other plant foods if they are faced with starvation. In fact, most predators have fairly catholic tastes, because their food supply is less assured than that of their prey. An over-finnicky predator would not be able to survive for very long.

Many predators are subject to cyclical variations in the availability of their food supply. Many small mammals undergo a cycle of some years duration, during which the population reaches a peak and then declines. The predator population tends to decline with the cycle and rise again as the glut of prey increases.

## Man – the most harmful predator

Human activity is having highly deleterious effects on many of the most important predators, particularly the birds of prey. Some years ago, there were 12 breeding pairs of golden eagles in Wales, but in 1968 there was only one pair. Similar falls in the number of large carnivorous birds have been found in other parts of the world. The reason for this fall is the spread of the use of persistent insecticides. These poisons have a particularly harmful effect on the reproductive system, and eggs with a high concentration of substances like DDT are frequently sterile. The effect on the predators, right at the top of the food-chain, is most marked because the insecticide residues persist for many years in animal fat and are thus passed up the food-chains and retained in the tissues of the animals at the top of the food-chain. The immediate effects are felt among the insects at the bottom of the food-chains, but the effects are in fact far more catastrophic among the few beautiful birds at the top of the chain.

This damage to the most beautiful predators, the birds of prey like the eagles, hawks and owls, is entirely in line with the rest of human disruption of the natural ecology. The plight of many rare animals stems directly from human activities. Whaling has almost exterminated a number of species of whale, while other animals, like the giant panda and the mountain gorilla, are in grave danger of extinction. Man is in fact the most widespread, the most persistent and the most harmful of all predators. His ability to spread death and destruction in the animal kingdom has already had disastrous results in many cases and is likely if continued unchecked, to do still more harm. If there is a moral in predation it is surely in this and not in the activities of other predators.

# How the bee sucks

**Bees, butterflies, mosquitoes and spiders are among the many small creatures which feed on plant or animal juices, extracting them with mouthparts ingeniously evolved for this purpose.**

A WEB of fine threads, beaded with dew, spans the space between a plant's leaves. A fly unwittingly blunders into the sticky meshes. In an instant, it is the victim of a waiting spider. Paralysed by venom injected into it, the fly is quickly wrapped in a cocoon of web filaments. Rather than devour its victim piece by piece, the spider will instead suck the precious body fluids, leaving, in the end, only a dry lifeless husk.

The juices of animals and plants provide one of the best sources of food for other creatures. Plant juices, which are rich in sugars and contain some amino acids, can be easily digested. But whole plant tissues, which contain a high proportion of cellulose, are indigestible to most animals. Animal juices, that is animals' blood, are solutions of proteins with less carbohydrate than a plant's juices, but they are nevertheless a good food supply. In both cases the animal using these liquid foods has to eliminate a great deal of water which it 'eats' with the food. Some animals, such as aphids, which suck up the contents of plant cells, also have to eliminate the large amount of sugars they consume in excess of their nutritional requirements. In aphids, excess sugar is excreted as *honeydew,* which serves as food for ants. Plants also produce special secretions which are attractive to insects, for example *nectar,* the sweet juice to be found in many flowers which must be insect-pollinated if they are to reproduce.

## Crushing, sucking and chewing

The simplest way for an animal to feed on juices is to crush the prey and suck up the juices which exude from it. This is how many *arachnids* (spiders, scorpions and so on) feed. A scorpion, for example, may chew its food, which it holds with large 'pincers' called *pedipalps.* The chewing is not so much to break up the prey into small pieces as to release its fluids. These are sucked in by the scorpion's *sucking pharynx.* This is the fore-part of the gut and has a number of muscles attached to it. When the muscles contract, the pharynx expands and lowers the pressure inside it, drawing the liquid in through the mouth. Spiders suck their prey in a similar way.

But apart from these relatively crude ways of feeding on liquid food, insects, more than any other animal group, have specialized in using liquid sources of food. Insects are a biologically successful group of animals, judging by their wide distribution and the huge variety of their species. No other group has equalled them in diversification, and at least some of their success stems from their ability to adapt and use, thanks to their extremely ingenious mouthparts, food sources which other animals have not exploited.

A honey bee, enlarged until it looks like some terrifying monster, leans forward to drink. Its slender glistening 'tongue' is fully extended as it sucks the sweet liquid up the hollow centre.

In insects, the mouthparts are essentially the paired appendages of the mandibles, and maxillary and labial segments of the head. Although insects are arthropods (which in their original form probably had two pairs of appendages to each segment), they have lost many of these appendages in the course of evolution. But like the appendages of crustacea, for example, which have become modified for many different functions, the insect's mouthparts have similarly evolved into a variety of forms which are perfectly designed to carry out different kinds of highly specialized feeding functions.

The pattern upon which these changes are made can perhaps best be seen in the mouthparts of a chewing insect. The essential parts are the large thickened *mandibles,* the main jaws, with their teeth for biting, the paired *maxillae* (auxiliary jaws), each with a long sensory *palp,* or 'feeler', and the *labium* (lip) formed by the fusion of a pair of appendages. This was the form of the mouthparts of the first insects which appeared in the evolution of life on Earth.

The evolution of flowering plants took place step by step with the evolution of insects and their rapid increase in numbers. Flowers need pollinating, and insects are most important agents for doing this. Indeed, the form of many flowers has evolved in such a way that the insect visitor cannot help but leave pollen behind and carry some to another flower. The colours and scents of flowers have their part in attracting insects, but they could only serve this purpose if insects were 'rewarded' when they visited a flower. It is nectar which is the real attraction and which brings insects to flowers. This is a liquid rich in sugars (mainly sucrose, glucose and fructose – all attractive in themselves).

## The bee's amazing tongue

Bees of all sorts collect nectar and some bees change it into honey, which is stored in the nest for feeding the young. (The main change which takes place when nectar becomes honey is an increase in sugar concentration through the evaporation of water.)

The bees' 'tongues' are specializations of their labial mouthparts. Some species of bumblebee are short-tongued, while other bumblebees and honeybees are long-tongued. The tongue is formed from the *glossa* (lobes) of the labium, which are long and hairy and end in a spoon-shaped *flabellum*. In addition there are two large labial palps. A honeybee's maxillae form blade-like structures called *galeae* on each side; the maxillary palps are very small.

When the bee sucks nectar, it extends its tongue by the pressure of blood forced from the head into the cavity. Under a microscope, it can be seen that the tongue is not flat but has its edges rolled over until they nearly meet in the mid-line to form a tube. The bore of this tube is small enough for liquid to rise up it by capillary action,

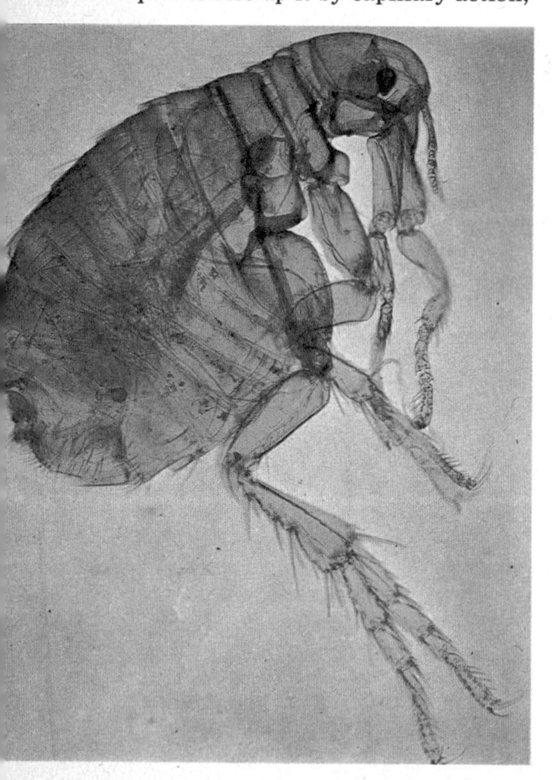

*Above,* the human flea first pierces its victim's skin with razor-sharp mandibles, then injects saliva to stop blood clotting as it feeds.

*Top,* held fast in the spider's fatal grip, a fly has already ceased to struggle. Paralysed and helpless, its body is slowly sucked dry.

Normally, the proboscis of the Tomato Sphinx moth, *above,* is coiled – but at the slightest smell of nectar, it springs into a long probing tongue.

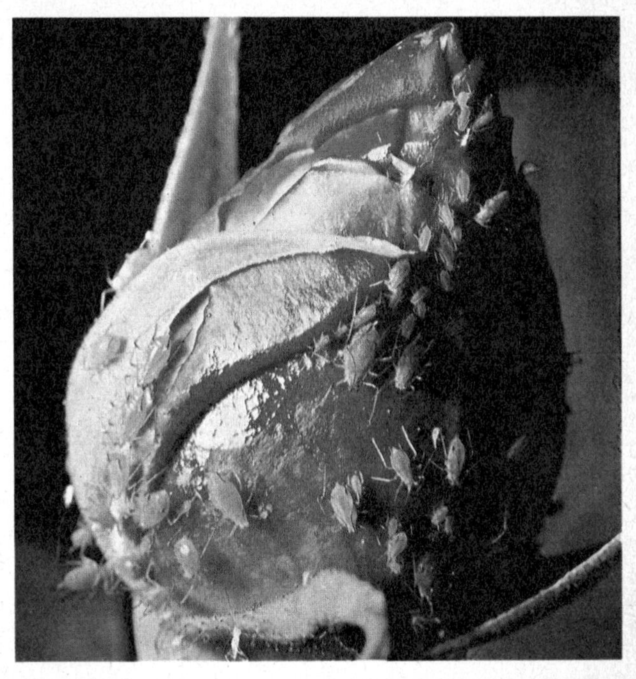

*Top left,* the horse-fly needs its saw-tipped mandibles to puncture tough hide; it then laps up the blood which oozes from the wound. *Top right,* a bee perched on the centre of a daisy is gathering nectar through its dipped proboscis. Its apparatus operates in marked contrast to the fly's searching labella, *left.* The fly is unable to penetrate flowers like the bee, but can liquidize its own food by bathing it in saliva. *Right,* aphids, since they live entirely off plant sap, have mouths specially adapted not only for piercing cellulose, but for penetrating deep inside to gather precious juices.

and the movement of the liquid is aided by a shortening of the tongue which forces liquid higher up. All this is further aided by the sucking action of the pharynx which has special muscles to increase its volume.

When the tongue is in action, it is enclosed by the maxillary *laciniae* (inner lobes) and by the labial palps, so that it is effectively a tube within a tube. Mandibles are still present, although they are small; honeybees use them for moulding wax in building combs. But short-tongued bumblebees use their mandibles to chew their way into flowers from the side in order to reach nectar, when their tongues are too short to reach the nectar through the normal entrance. For this reason, incidentally, the insect does not make any contact with the anther or stigma of the flower it is visiting and so does not contribute to pollination.

Butterflies and moths are almost as efficient at collecting nectar as are bees. Their mouthparts, however, are different in form, for the main part is derived from the maxillae and not from the labium. The galeae are greatly elongated, each forming a half-tube which makes a complete tube when they are locked together. Each galea is also hollow, and so constructed that it tends to coil up into position beneath the head, where the sucking proboscis can generally be seen in butterflies and moths.

## A tube springs into action

The stimulus to extend the proboscis is often the sensing of sugars by hairs on the fore-feet. The signal from these sense cells causes a rise in blood pressure which uncoils the proboscis. As the two halves are held close together by a neat arrangement of overlapping pieces and interlocking hairs the tube is watertight, and the liquid nectar can be sucked up by the action of the pharyngeal pump. The insect probes with the end of the extended proboscis, which suggests that it can use the tip for sensing the right place from which to collect food. Most moths and butterflies have no mandibles, and the labium is no more than a small plate situated on the underside of the mouth.

But there is a great deal more food available to an insect which can pierce through the surface of a plant and penetrate its cells. Each cell is virtually a nutrient-filled bag of liquid which can be tapped. There are many plant bugs of one sort and another which can digest away plant-cell walls to permit their piercing mouthparts to enter, for example, leaf-hoppers, frog-hoppers, scale insects, cochineal insects and cicadas; some of the commonest are the aphids.

All species of this insect feed on the contents of plant cells. Their mouthparts are in the form of fine needles which can be pushed through the outer layers of a leaf, root or stem. When the mouthparts are in the tissue, they make a tube through which the food can be extracted. The two maxillae form the core of the needle, each one being shaped like a letter E in cross-section. The E's face each other and interlock to form two channels. Through the lower one, salivary juices are injected into the plant to digest away the cell walls, and the liquid food is sucked up through the upper channel. The mandibles are half-tubes which enclose and support the maxillae; all four mouthparts are contained in a labial sheath.

Such a delicate, flexible set of mouthparts could not be inserted into tough tissue without buckling, but this is prevented by the sheath, whose tip is held close to the plant's surface, and grasps within itself the mandibles and maxillae. Then one of them is inserted a short distance into the plant, followed by the second for the same distance, then the third, and finally the fourth. The tissue now keeps the tips together so that the process of penetrating a short distance at a time can go on until all four are fully in. The way in which some plant bugs do this is even more remarkable, for their mouthparts are sometimes so long that they are looped or coiled in a sac beneath the head. Yet they can be inserted a long way into plant tissue.

Aphids may carry viruses from one plant to another, as well as taking their juices. Having fed on an infected plant and taken in virus particles with the cell contents, they then pass the viruses into the next plant along with the saliva which they inject to break up the cell walls.

## Blades which pierce

Blood-sucking flies such as mosquitoes and insects such as the bed-bug and 'kissing bug' have similar feeding habits. Not only are their mouthparts superficially similar, but when these insects inject saliva into a wound to prevent coagulation of the blood in their mouthparts, they may transfer various disease organisms. For example, *Anopheles* mosquitoes transmit the malarial parasite in this way, while other species of mosquito carry the organisms of yellow fever and encephalitis. These insects are usually thought of as 'biting', but in fact their mouths are not equipped to do so – they can only pierce.

The mandibles and maxillae resemble fine blades; they are responsible for piercing the flesh and making the wound. But in these flies, the upper lip (which is relatively unimportant in aphids) is as long and almost as fine as the maxillae and mandibles. On its under surface it bears a hollowed channel through which the blood is drawn into the mouth. The open underside of the channel is closed by the long fine *hypopharynx,* through which runs the duct for the anti-coagulant saliva. It is as if the opening of the salivary ducts, generally situated just behind the mouth, had been pulled out to make a long fine tube. All these tubes and blades are wrapped by the labium, which acts as a proboscis sheath. At its tip are two small labella which are used as feelers and enable the mosquito to select the appropriate part of its victim to attack. These mouthparts are fully developed only in the female mosquito, and it is therefore only the females who feed on blood.

This kind of piercing-sucking mouthpart can be found in a less developed form in many other types of 'biting' flies, such as the tsetse flies responsible for transmitting the trypanosome which causes sleeping sickness.

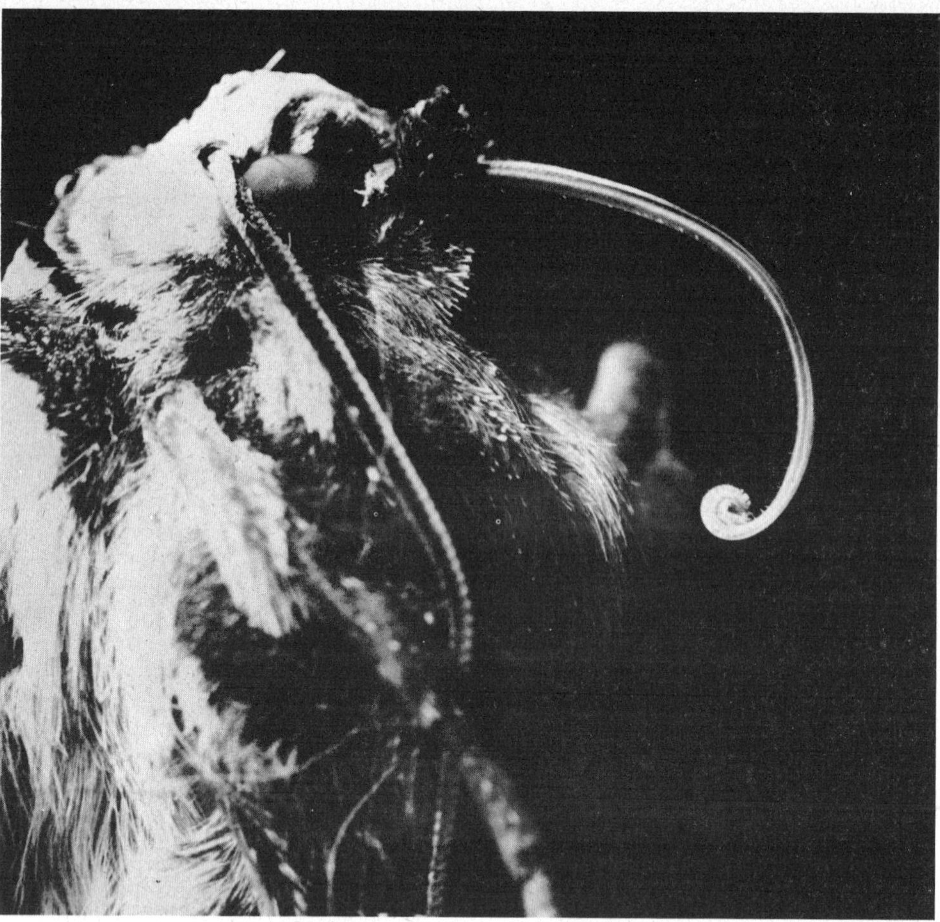

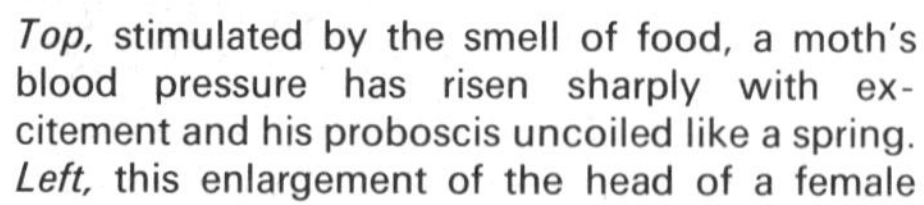

*Top,* stimulated by the smell of food, a moth's blood pressure has risen sharply with excitement and his proboscis uncoiled like a spring. *Left,* this enlargement of the head of a female bluebottle shows clearly her flat, pad-like labella. *Right,* the male mosquito's mouthparts are a study in detail. He is not a bloodsucker; his wife is, carrying diseases from one victim to another.

In other flies such as horse-flies, the maxillae and mandibles are much shorter than those of the tsetse fly or a mosquito; they are flattened and blade-like with a minutely toothed saw tip. The labrum is also sharp and the hypopharynx is long and slender. All these piercing mouthparts are again sheathed by the labium, but the labella are much bigger and more like those of a house-fly. They form pads, the outer surfaces of which contain a series of food-channels passing from the outer edges to the middle. These channels are strengthened and kept open by almost complete rings of cuticle. When the pads are put down into a liquid, this can be sucked up through the walls of the channels into the space within and then passed to the mouth.

The labella of a house-fly are particularly large and this insect lives solely on food which is already liquid or which has been made so by saliva ejected on to it. A house-fly lacks the cutting weapons of the mouthparts of a horse-fly; this uses its labella to lap up the blood which seeps from the wound it makes in its victim.

The detail of the 'engineering' of insect mouthparts is most perfect; the cuticle-covered mouthparts dovetail together or slide smoothly upon one another. They represent the remarkable end-result of evolution, aided by the very great biological advantage to be gained by being able to tap sources of liquid food.

# Teeth, beaks and tentacles

Animals cannot draw sustenance directly from air or soil. They must derive it instead by eating plants or other animals and are therefore equipped with suitably adapted mouthparts.

PLANTS MAKE their own food supply within their tissues; by means of photosynthesis, they convert carbon dioxide and water into sugars. Animals cannot manufacture their own food supply from simple substances within their bodies. They cannot make proteins, carbohydrates or fats directly, but depend on plants to supply the starting materials. In other words, all animals ultimately use plants for food. Some animals, *herbivores,* eat plants directly; others, *carnivores,* eat the flesh of animals that have eaten plants.

The food of animals therefore consists of the flesh and juices of other living things, either plants or animals. For digestion to take place, this food must be in a form in which the enzymes in the animal's digestive system can attack it and break it down into soluble compounds that can be absorbed. Juices are easy to digest, although there are special means for collecting and imbibing them. Large pieces of plant or animal have to be broken up or torn apart before they can be digested. This is one of the functions of the teeth in animals.

## Fish, reptiles and mammals

But structures that can be used for cutting and tearing flesh are equally useful as weapons, and teeth in many animals have the dual purpose of killing the prey and breaking it up. The backward-facing teeth of snakes and the scales which serve as teeth in dogfish and skates aid in swallowing the prey whole as, once grasped, the prey cannot slip out of the mouth again.

The teeth of vertebrate animals are formed mainly by the sub-dermal tissues. The epidermis secretes on to the surface of the teeth a layer of protective enamel. In vertebrates other than mammals, the lower jaw is formed from a number of bones. But the teeth are borne only on the *dentary,* which is the only bone in the lower jaws of mammals. In the upper jaw, it is the *maxilla* and *premaxilla* bones which bear the teeth.

Generally the teeth grow in sockets of bone and they are rarely fused to the bone of the jaw. Some animals, such as amphibians, have teeth in other parts of the mouth – on the *vomer* bones in the roof of the mouth, for example. The teeth in a lizard's jaw are all alike, and this is also the case for most reptiles, all amphibians and all fish. As the teeth in reptiles wear, they are replaced from below.

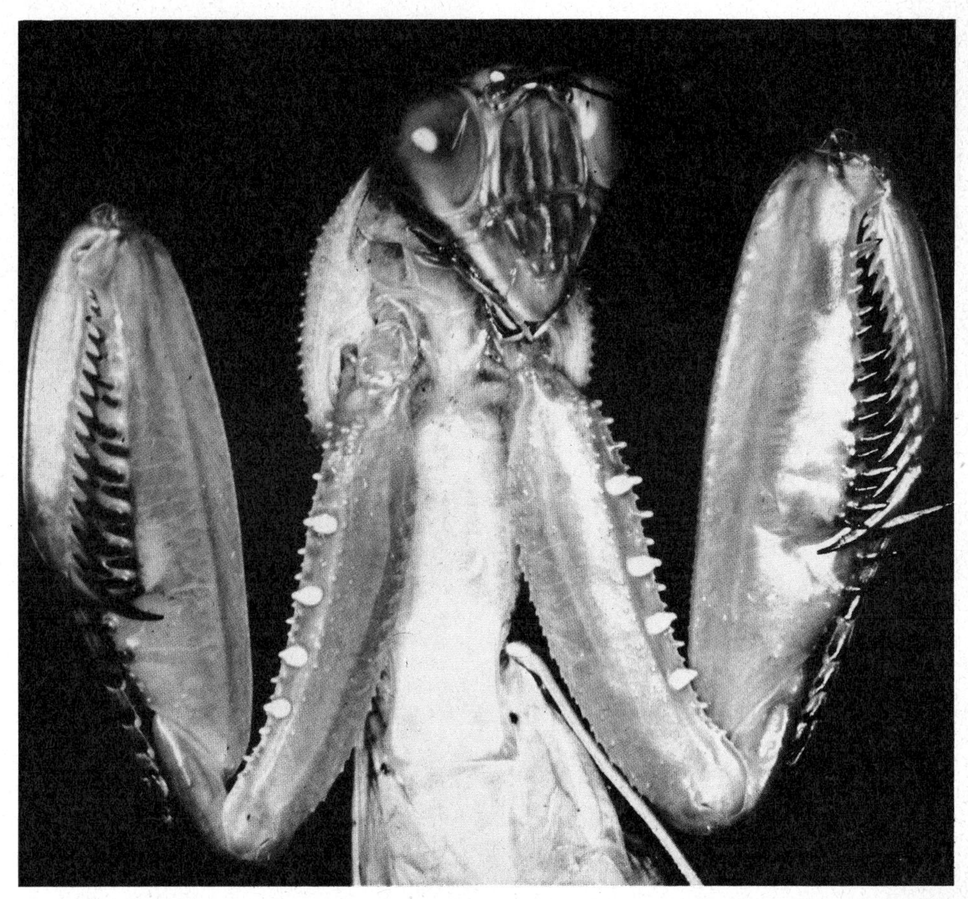

*Above right,* the praying mantis presents a formidable sight as it rears up, displaying the highly modified pincers it uses to grasp its prey. *Right,* because the mandibles of the locust are extremely hard, it can eat almost any kind of plant. A single swarm may need 3,000 tons of food a day.

1

2

The bones of the jaw and palate of snakes such as the boa constrictor are loosely hinged, so that the jaws can gape wide apart to allow the snake to swallow very large prey whole. There are teeth in the *pterygoid* and *palatine* bones which, like those on the maxilla and on the lower jaw, are long and backward-pointing. The hinge of the jaw can be moved forward, allowing the jaws to part very widely, and at the same time thrusting forward the teeth on the palatine and pterygoid. This accounts for the ability of many snakes to swallow whole animals. One example is the boa constrictor, which first crushes its victim to death before swallowing it. Another is the African Egg-eating snake, which is able to open its mouth amazingly wide. Such snakes take one very large meal and then rest somewhere and digest it. In a poisonous snake, such as a rattlesnake, the action of slinging the jaw-hinge forward swings out the fangs on the mandibles. Venom is injected through the fangs into the prey.

In mammals, special kinds of teeth have evolved to function with various diets. The main kinds of teeth are the *incisors* at the front of the mouth (generally chisel-like), the *canines* (pointed and dagger-like), and the *pre-molars* and *molars* (mainly stubby, and used for crushing and grinding).

The original number of teeth in early mammals was three incisors, one canine, four pre-molars and three molars on each side, top and bottom, giving a total of 44 teeth. But this arrangement has altered in the process of evolution of special dentitions. For example, Man has two incisors, one canine, two pre-molars and three molars on each side of each jaw, giving a total of 32 teeth.

## Fangs, grinders and bills

Carnivores have long pointed canine teeth, sometimes called *fangs,* for tearing at their prey. Sabre-toothed tigers, now extinct, used to open their lower jaws until they were almost at right angles to the upper jaws, and use their canines for stabbing. The incisors of flesh-eating cats and dogs, for example, are relatively unspecialized, being small and chisel-shaped; it is in the teeth farther back along the row that real adaptations occur. The upper fourth pre-molar forms a blade-like *carnassial* which, with the first molar of the lower jaw, acts like a pair of scissors, shearing flesh from the prey. These are the real cutting teeth and their position explains why a dog bites at a bone with the back of its mouth. And since these teeth are near the hinge of the jaw, great force can be applied when they are brought together.

If the carnassials were not precisely aligned, they would lose their effectiveness, just as a pair of scissors with loose blades is useless for cutting paper. Alignment is assured by the shape of the hinge of a carnivore's lower jaw. The socket on the skull fits round a protuberance on the lower jaw, restricting movement to a vertical direction.

However, in herbivores, such as cattle and horses, the hinge is looser and the lower jaw can move both up and down and from side to side. This results in a grinding action of the molar and pre-molar teeth of the lower jaw on those of the upper. Each molar tooth in the upper jaw has been squared-up, as it were, by the addition of an extra cusp to the three original ones. In the lower jaw, each tooth has one cusp fewer and so a large grinding surface is formed. The side-to-side movement of tooth on tooth soon tends to wear down the cusps to a level surface. Some cells in grass contain deposits of silica which can act as a strong abrasive. But in grass-eating animals such as a horse, the wear is compensated for by a great elongation of the tooth into a high-crowned form. A thick layer of cement that covers a horse's molar teeth fills in the depressions between the greatly enlarged cusps, and reduces wear. This arrangement is in effect self-sharpening. A horse's grinders will

3

5

6

4

1 The squid normally swims with its long arms withdrawn among its eight tentacles, but throws them out to seize a small fish or shrimp.

2 The tentacles of the Snakelocks sea-anemone twine tightly round a tiny wrasse which is already paralysed by the poison injected into it.

3 With its powerful hooked end, the beak of a bird of prey, such as the eagle, is able to tear away hide and flesh with ease.

4 A deep-sea carnivore swims silently in search of food. Its razor-sharp incisors seize its victims, which are then cut to ribbons by its other teeth.

5 The shape of a bird's beak is often the clue to its diet – the gannet lives entirely off fish, and uses its pointed beak like a spear.

6 The vividly-coloured saffron finch has a short stubby beak – the force it can exert is powerful enough to crack open even the hardest seed.

remain rough, no matter how much grass it chews.

Plant-eating animals have no canines. There is instead a toothless gap in the upper and lower jaws between the premolars and incisors, called the *diastema.* The incisors are used to crop food from the ground or off trees. Many ruminants, such as deer and cows, have evolved without incisors in the upper jaw, their place being taken by a gristly pad. The incisors on the lower jaw act against this in much the same way as a knife on a chopping-board. Plants are grasped between the lower incisors and this pad and torn off by a movement of the head. But horses have retained all their front teeth, which cut off the grass that they eat. An elephant's tusks are greatly enlarged incisors.

The forms of dentition just described are only two examples from a whole range of adaptations among mammals. Man's own teeth are characteristic of an omnivorous creature; his canines are small and his molars have individual cusps. Neither kind of tooth is specialized for a diet of flesh or of plants, so that Man is able to include many different kinds of food in his diet. But in some mammals, all the teeth have become similar, returning to the undifferentiated condition found in reptiles. For example, a sperm whale has teeth that form a row of simple pointed pegs, which are quite adequate for grasping squids, on which it feeds.

One whole group of vertebrates – the birds – is toothless. Many prehistoric birds of the Cretaceous period had teeth, but no modern birds have any. Their function has been taken over by the beak, which is a horny covering on upper and lower jaws. The shapes of birds' beaks are very varied, and give a good indication of the animal's diet.

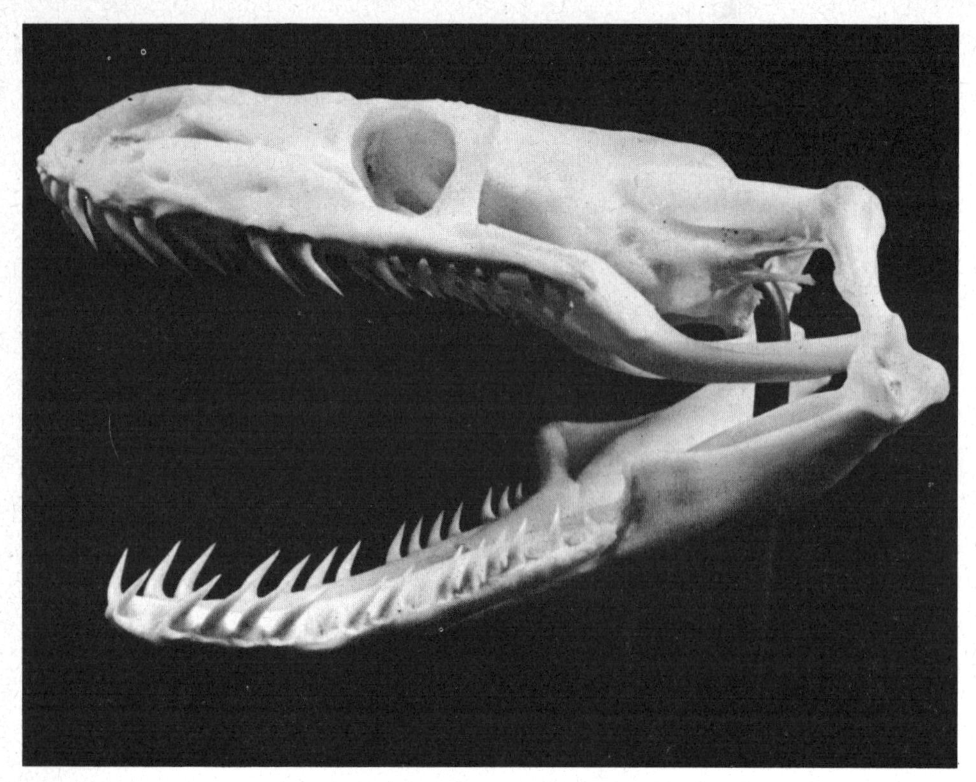

The stubby beak of many common seed-eating birds is strong and short and can bring a great deal of force to bear to break open seeds. A parrot has a beak adapted for manipulating and cracking nuts. The hooked beak of a bird of prey is used to tear pieces of flesh from the bodies of animals they catch or find dead. Insectivorous birds generally have longer beaks better adapted for extracting insects from crevices. A number of wading birds have long bills with which they probe about in mud for their animal food. These are often fringed at the edges to filter out mud and water while retaining small animals and pieces of plant matter.

The earliest insects had jaws with which they chewed solid food. Today, many species still have jaws of this sort, though many modifications of the basic form of insect mouthparts have occurred to enable them to take liquid food from many sources. Insect jaws, called *mandibles,* are pivoted so that they move sideways across the head; they do not move vertically as do the jaws of vertebrates. They are strongly thickened with hardened cuticle, often having the thickest cuticle of the body. The edges of the mandibles have raised teeth in patterns that may be characteristic of the species.

## Insects, crabs and sea-anemones

The mandibles of an insect move in what is almost an open box below the head. The front side of the box is the flap of the upper lip (*labrum*). And behind the jaws lie the *maxillae,* which have appendages called *palps* that are sensitive to chemicals in food and which manipulate the pieces. Behind these, forming the back of the box, is the lower lip (*labium*), which also bears sensory palps. With jaws like these, locusts can lay waste great areas of cultivated ground by eating all the green plants; predatory beetles can feed on other insects; and scavenging beetles can clean the bones of a dead mouse.

Crustacea are remarkable for the many different forms of appendages that they have, often one pair to each segment along their whole body. Some species, such as crabs and lobsters, have mandibles which are used for chewing. The food is carried to the jaws by the great pincers or *chelae* on the first pair of walking legs. The food is also manipulated and passed to the mouth by the *maxillules,* and other appendages on the thorax may also help in dealing with food. Crustacea are arthropods; they have thick exoskeletons and, like the insects, have strong, hard jaws.

Some of the marine bristle-worms, called *polychaetes,* can deal with pieces of food. A rag-worm has a proboscis which it pushes out and at the same time exposes at its end jaws with which it can grasp food. Another worm which lives in the shell of a hermit crab will emerge and take food from beneath the mouthparts of its host crab.

Prey is also captured and dealt with by *coelenterates* (sea-anemones and corals). They possess stinging cells, called *nematocysts,* which form a long pointed needle that can penetrate and immobilize prey. Other kinds of nematocysts are coiled structures that act as lassoes and trap the prey by twisting round its hairs or spines. Mild stimulation of a few tentacles of a sea-anemone by touching them with a straw causes them to bend towards the mouth of the animal. But more vigorous stimulation, such as happens when a prey struggles as it becomes attached to the nematocysts of the tentacles, involves more tentacles, and the whole of one side of the disc of the anemone folds over. This action pushes food into the mouth, which has already been stimulated into opening by tissue fluids from the prey.

Jelly-fish catch their prey in a similar way, and the tentacles hanging round the edge of the bell are also covered with nematocysts, which automatically come into action when touched.

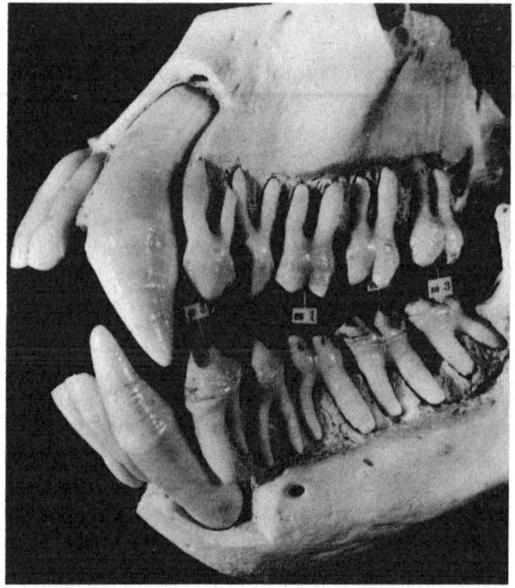

*Top left,* the python illustrates the typical arrangement of teeth in non-poisonous snakes. Since they all point backwards, it is virtually impossible for prey to escape. *Top right,* because Man is omnivorous and eats both meat and plants, his teeth are not specialized in any one direction. *Above,* the gorilla is one of the primates most closely related to Man and his teeth are very similarly arranged. *Below,* the genet has the cat's characteristic pointed canines; the large carnassial teeth act as scissors, shearing flesh from its prey.

# All creatures great and small

Your favourite food is the leaves at the top of the tree. Do you grow a long neck to reach them, or agile limbs to climb to them? Nature tries many ways to fit bodily shapes to basic needs.

A KANGAROO is much bigger than a cat. Yet a new-born kangaroo is much smaller than a new-born kitten. Similarly, an acorn is much smaller than a tulip bulb, and yet a full-grown oak tree is hundreds of times larger than a full-grown tulip. What determines how large a living thing will grow, and how does it 'know' when it has reached that size?

The adult size of an animal is related to the most efficient way for it to survive in its natural environment. Since the young are much smaller than this size they obviously have to grow until they reach it.

Of course, not all animals achieve maturity simply by adding on weight and size to their infant body. A butterfly does not 'grow' at all, because when it emerges from its chrysalis, it is already an adult. Most of the butterfly's growth takes place while it is still a caterpillar grub, which eats almost continuously for several weeks until it is ready to transform itself into its adult form.

But whatever the path from infancy to adulthood, some fail and die before reaching maturity – they have to contend with predators, lack of food, drought and disease. Over a period of millions of years, this has meant that only creatures best suited to their environments – or which can adapt to changes in their environment – have continued to exist.

### What is growth?

Growth, in the biological sense, is difficult to define and measure because it is not necessarily merely equal to an increase in size or weight. For example, when a dog breathes in, its chest expands but we do not say the animal grows. When an elephant drinks a gallon of water its weight immediately increases by ten pounds, but it does not 'grow'.

Biologists overcome these difficulties by defining growth as an increase in the *dry* weight of a plant or animal – that is, an increase in the weight of the tissues after all the water has been removed, generally by heating. Of course, to make such a measurement in practice the plant or animal must be killed and so true dry weight can be found only once. So for most purposes, measurements of live size and weight are used, inaccurate though they may be.

The important thing to remember is that when we say growth has occurred, we mean that the creature concerned has increased the amount of living material in its body. Using this definition, we find that there is nearly always a particular size at which growth ceases, although some fish and a few animals continue growing all their lives. Size varies from species to species, but generally corresponds to the size at which maturity is reached.

Environment greatly affects size and bodily features. The flat face and pug nose of the Alaskan Eskimo may have evolved to minimize heat loss from the body in the frigid arctic climate.

The genetic heritage of an animal sets the limits of growth. A cat is a cat, and nothing it can do will ever change the fact that it is a cat. Cats have a certain range of size within which they may develop. One would be very surprised to see a cat as small as a humming bird, or as big as a horse, because these sizes are out of the cat's range. But cats may vary within their normal range, depending on their environment.

All living cells rely on diffusion to get raw material into and out of them. The oxygen needed for respiration passes through the cells to the places where it is needed. Simple one-celled animals and some more complex ones carry on diffusion directly with their liquid surroundings. In higher animals, special transport systems such as the blood and lymph systems carry gases and foods round the body, right up to the cells. But in the final stages, it is still diffusion that is the essential process.

This reliance on diffusion is one of the chief factors limiting the size of any cell. The extent of 'control' exerted by a nucleus on the cell depends on diffusion and so cells must be small. Of course, not all cells are exactly the same size – they cover a range relatively greater than the difference in size between a mouse and a whale – because cells live under different conditions and perform different functions in various parts of the same body.

Cells have an optimum size in a given situation when they function most efficiently, and so do whole organisms. The most efficient animals are obviously best fitted for survival and, in the long run, all animals evolve hereditary controls which stop the cell growth process when the optimum size is reached. Up to this point, animals generally grow as fast as their food supply allows.

After maturity, some of the food goes towards producing eggs or sperm which are needed for reproduction. So that although growth has stopped, the animal is still using food to build new tissues. These tissues are then released, as sperm, eggs or young animals, and so the building of these particular tissues does not constitute growth in the strict sense although there is no real difference in the cell processes involved.

The most efficient size at which to stop growth depends on many factors. And these are interwoven to such an extent that it is difficult to say which are the main reasons why a particular animal is the size it is. But we can consider some of these factors and see how they contribute to growth.

Many of these controlling factors are part of the natural environment. They include such things as climate, food supply and the medium in which an animal lives. An animal's surrounding medium can play a large part in determining its optimum size. For example, most birds which fly are small whereas those that have given up flying and run on the ground (such as ostriches and emus) can grow much larger and heavier. A similar trend in size is shown by various kinds of plant seeds. Those that are distributed by the wind (such as thistles, dandelions and maple trees) are small and light; those distributed on water (such as coconuts) are large and heavy.

## On land and sea

Land animals are limited in size by the need to support their own bodies, particularly land animals which stand. The legs are on solid ground, but the soft parts of the body 'hang' from the skeleton, because they get little buoyant support from the air.

Animals that live in water grow much larger than their land-bound relatives because of the extra support they get from the water. For this reason, the massive dinosaurs of prehistoric times are believed to have spent much of their life in water. A whale is a modern example of such a creature: if it becomes stranded on a beach, the weight of its own soft parts can crush it to death in quite a short time.

Carnivorous animals (meat eaters) are generally most efficient as killers if they are about the same size as their prey – or even a little smaller and so more agile. Animals that eat plants or insects do not have to kill for food, but their food affects their size in other ways. Tall animals, such as the giraffe, can reach high into a tree to eat the upper leaves – although treetop leaves can also be reached by small animals, such as koalas and some monkeys, climbing up the tree. Climbers cannot be too heavy or they could not cling to small branches, and so most climbing animals are fairly small. Eating plants growing at ground level seems to be one of the ways of feeding which favours large size, because such food is generally plentiful, and reaching it requires no special adaptation. Many of the large land animals feed in this way; for example, the rhinoceros and the bison.

There are also parasitic animals. In fact, there are more of this type than any others, ranging from microscopic protozoa to mosquitoes and ticks. Most kinds of free-living animals have several kinds of parasites which are, of course, much smaller than their hosts.

The temperature of an animal's environment also plays a part in limiting its size. Since heat is lost over an animal's surface, and since surface area increases more slowly than does volume (or weight), animals that live in colder regions tend to be larger than their relatives in more

The fleet-footed ostrich, *top,* clearly demonstrates the compromises an animal must make in adapting its size and structure to meet the demands of its environment. The enormous bulk of its body has stripped the ostrich of the ability to fly. The large size of the camel, *above,* and its one-humped cousin, the dromedary, is made possible by storing water-holding fats inside their humps. Without this reserve, such a large animal would perish in the dry desert heat.

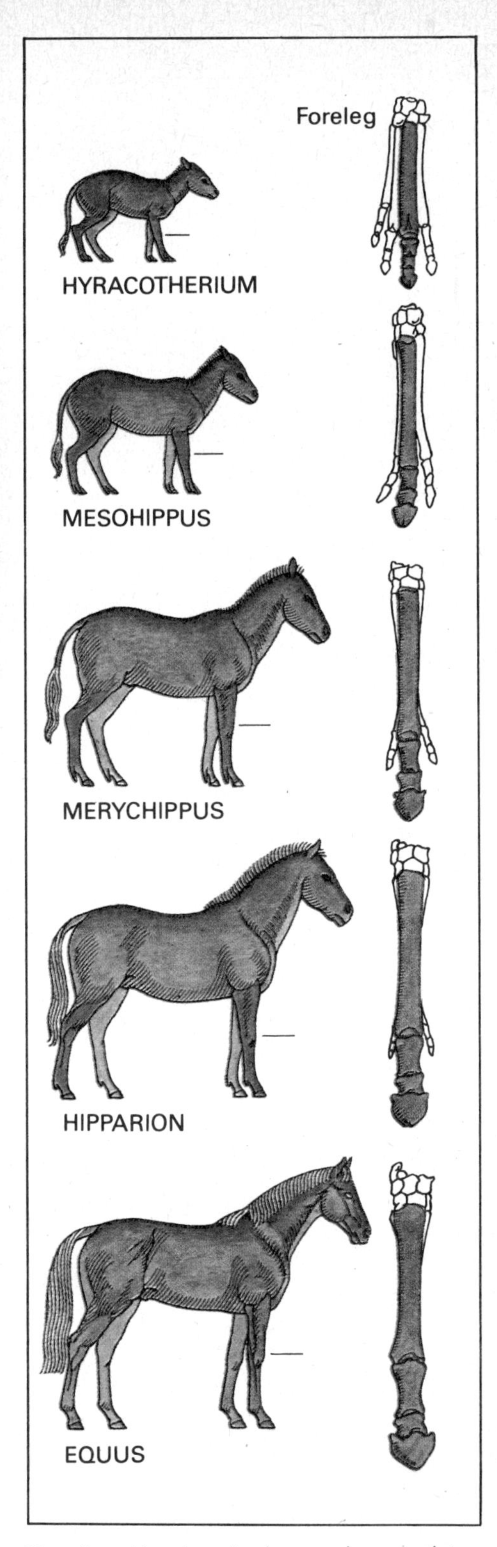

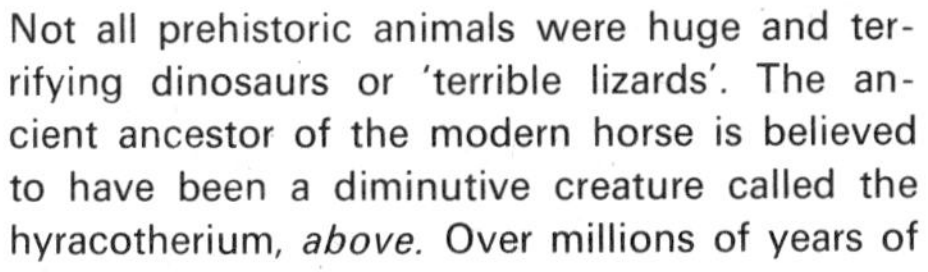

Not all prehistoric animals were huge and terrifying dinosaurs or 'terrible lizards'. The ancient ancestor of the modern horse is believed to have been a diminutive creature called the hyracotherium, *above.* Over millions of years of evolution, it continually altered its size and structure to adapt to its changing environment. 'Twiga', the Swahili word for the African giraffe, suggests its origins. One evolutionary theory states that the giraffe came from an animal with a much shorter neck, as an adaptation for reaching the twigs and leaves high up in trees, *top right.* The little koala bear, native to Australia, solves the problem of nourishment another way; it climbs up after it, *above right.*

temperate climates. For example, polar bears are much larger than the sun bears of Malaysia, because they lose proportionately less heat from their larger bodies. This fact was first noticed by the German zoologist Karl Bergmann more than 100 years ago. The rule named after him states that animals of colder climates are relatively larger and have relatively smaller extremities than do their cousins in warmer climates.

Bergmann's Rule may be used to separate the races of some kinds of birds. In the northern hemisphere, birds from the colder northern regions tend to be larger and have shorter wings and legs than do similar species in warmer regions further south, though there are exceptions, such as the ostrich. Warm-blooded animals that live in the sea also follow the rule. Elephant seals, which live in the polar seas, grow much larger than, say, the common grey seal of Europe.

The way an animal is 'built' also plays a part in limiting size. For example, the size of an insect's body is restricted by the way an insect breathes. The tracheal system used by insects is efficient only for a body up to about an inch across, because it relies on the relatively slow process of diffusion. In a body much larger than an inch, diffusion could not keep up with the demands of the insect's metabolism. Within this maximum limit, the size of insects varies according to the principles we have already described.

In a similar way, the heavy exoskeleton of crustaceans, such as crabs and lobsters, restricts their size – especially on land – because there is a limit to the weight their muscles can support. Even in water, there is a limit to the size and weight which the

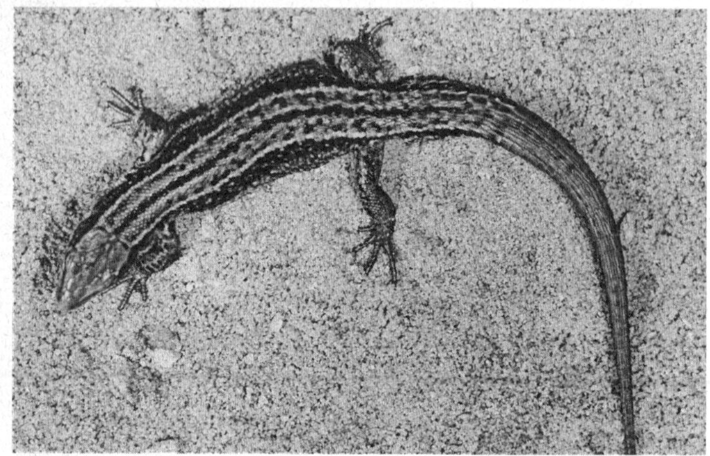

Biologists believe that massive prehistoric animals such as the diplodocus, *top,* spent most of their lives in water, because their flesh was too heavy to be supported on land for long. Some animals, such as the common lizard, can re-generate severed limbs and other parts. The new tail of this lizard, *above left,* looks peculiar because it contains cartilage rather than bone, as in the original tail. The polar bear, which is generally larger than its cousins in warmer regions, illustrates 'Bergmann's Rule' that size is strongly influenced by temperature, *right.*

muscles of these animals can move.

Just as individual cells in a multi-celled animal's body are limited in size, so are the single-celled protozoan animals. When an amoeba grows to a certain size, it splits into two and each half continues to grow as a separate creature.

The actual process of growth is the addition of new living material to the body of an animal or plant. It is not, however, a haphazard form of addition. The various types of body tissue are built as they are required. Using the same basic food materials, an animal's body can repair a wound, produce eggs or sperm, grow hair, or, if it is a developing embryo, form an eye or a heart – all from the same sorts of cells and all from the single cell that was the egg.

Every cell in the body has its own nucleus, and every nucleus is an exact copy of that in the fertilized egg which gave rise to the body. For this reason, each nucleus contains enough information to develop any of the characteristics shown by the cells of the animal. But during the growth of the animal, this information is selectively inhibited so that, as development proceeds, certain cells develop into one kind of tissue while others become a different kind. All cells in a given kind of tissue still retain a faithful copy of the information needed to become any other kind of tissue cell, but this information is somehow 'switched off'. In some cells the switching off is permanent, and in others it is only temporary and cells can modify their function as necessary.

An interesting example of the late growth of new tissues is the phenomenon of *regeneration,* in which an animal or plant grows a new part to replace one which has been lost. All animals can regenerate parts of their body to some extent, but some are much better at it than others. For instance, flatworms (*planarians*) can regenerate a completely new 'head' or 'body', and a starfish can complete its body even if only one arm is left. Crabs and lobsters can regenerate legs and claws when these are lost, and lizards can grow new tails. Higher animals have only feeble powers of regeneration which do not extend much beyond healing wounds, although structures such as tonsils are sometimes regenerated after removal.

## Build up and break down

In some cases, especially with lower animals, the regenerated parts are identical with those replaced; but often they are only similar to them. This is because the conditions which allow a structure to develop the way it does in an embryo obviously cannot be reproduced in an adult. For example, a lizard's regenerated tail looks much the same as the original one but contains no true bone and no notochord tissue. This is because in the embryo, the bones of the back and tail develop around the notochord, which becomes obliterated in the adult. But in the regenerated tail, conditions are not right for the formation of a new notochord and so no true tail-bones can form. Instead, the new tail gets its stiffness from a rod of cartilage.

No matter how complex animals become, the basic processes of life remain amazingly similar from animal to animal. In all animals, cell respiration oxidizes foodstuffs to liberate energy, and the same foodstuffs can be broken down into their basic constituents and used as the building blocks for growth processes. The break down of food for energy is *catabolism,* and the building-up of body tissues from food is *anabolism.* Together these processes make up *metabolism,* which is the total of all the chemical processes occurring in an animal's tissues. When anabolism (building-up) takes place faster than catabolism (breaking-down), growth occurs. When the two are equal, growth stops and there is a state called 'equivalent metabolic turnover'.

When one views growth in terms of the food supply, it soon becomes evident that an animal's social environment – what other animals it lives with – may be just as important as its physical environment. When sheep herders began moving their animals into the American West, cowboys were quick to recognize the danger. Sheep cropped the rangeland grass so close that there was little left for the cattle. In some cases, the sheep and their owners were driven out at gunpoint.

The general study of how an animal relates to its environment is called *ecology.* Since Man is the only creature that can consciously alter his environment, knowledge of ecology is very important. As history has shown, altering the environment without giving due consideration to the consequences can be a very costly business.

# The particle eaters

## The sea is a pasture for many creatures. From great whales to tiny mussels, they graze like animals on land, filtering millions of tiny organisms to provide a continuous intake of food.

THE WATERS of the seas are full of nutrients in the form of chemical substances washed into them by rivers. Animals cannot make direct use of all these substances. But in the upper layers of the sea, there live millions of single-celled plant organisms which can photosynthesise and build the nutrients into proteins, fats and carbohydrates. There are several kinds of these organisms, which are called *phytoplankton,* including *diatoms* with their silica-containing cases, and flagellates such as *dinoflagellates.* There are also enormous numbers of the very tiniest flagellates, called *nannoflagellates,* which are so small that they escape capture in the normal nets used for catching plankton. Despite their small size, these creatures are the main source of food for other larger creatures in the plankton. The phytoplankton is the pasture of the sea.

### Filters and filaments

There are many small animals in the plankton; some of the young creatures which grow to be adults who live elsewhere, feed on the phytoplankton. The whole collection of small animals and tiny plants are an almost limitless source of food for animals that can collect them. But to be able to sieve these forms of food out of the water requires special adaptation quite different from the jaws and teeth of animals that take food in large pieces. For example, the whalebone whales, unlike sperm whales and porpoises, have no teeth. In their place, they have horny strips with frayed edges hanging down the sides of their mouths. After taking a mouthful of sea-water, the whale uses its tongue like a piston to drive water out of its mouth through the whalebone sieve which traps small shrimp-like creatures called *krill* on the inner sides of the strips. Krill occur in swarms in the Antarctic seas and provide the food for these huge mammals. To provide enough energy and proteins, the intake of food must be as continuous as in the feeding habits of many land herbivores.

Filter-feeding involves straining food from large quantities of water, and is found only in aquatic animals. Since most invertebrates live in water, filter-feeding is well developed in many of them. A good example is the peacock worm *(Sabella pavonina).* This worm builds an erect tube which stands six to twelve inches high on the seabed. The worm lives inside the tube, moving to the top to display a fan of tentacular filaments which give the worm its name. Each filament sticks out radially from the head-end of the worm and the worms use them to catch the tiny food particles which swim by or which come raining down on them.

The lovely branching filaments *above* belong to the peacock worm. But not only are they very beautiful; they provide one of the finest examples of a filter-feeding apparatus in an invertebrate. They act as a gill, sifting minute particles from the water, and then passing them on to the mouth.

The filaments of the peacock worm are arranged like a funnel, with the mouth of the worm at its base. Each filament has a row of tiny branches called *pinnules* sticking out on two sides. The rows of pinnules on neighbouring filaments interlock near the bases, but higher up they are free from each other. Hair-like *cilia,* are borne on these pinnules and produce a water current which carries food to the worm. The cilia beat towards the tips of the pinnules, bringing water into the funnel. Other cilia on the upper and lower sides of the pinnules beat cross-ways at right angles to the cilia on the outside. This action creates eddies in the water on the inner side of each pinnule and also deposits food particles inside the worm's 'funnel'. More cilia, beating towards the base of the funnel, convey food particles downwards and towards the mouth.

Notice that this mechanism catches particles and conveys them regardless of their size or of their usefulness as food. Some of the particles may be silt, without any food value at all, and others may be small diatoms and so on which can be used as food. It is typical of filter-feeding that at first the creature makes a random collection of particles. There then follows a period of sorting when some particles are retained and others are rejected. Generally the choice is based on size, and this is the case with the peacock worm which retains only the smaller particles as food. The largest particles are rejected, and those of intermediate size used as building material for the worm's tube. How is this sorting done?

Towards the base of each filament, the pinnules are replaced by two continuous folds that rise from the axis to enclose a space between them. The width of this space is not equal from its base to the upper open side: it tapers towards the bottom. Cilia on the outer surfaces of the folds carry particles upwards to the edges. Cilia inside beat in the same direction and there are two additional tracts down the length of the filament leading to the worm's mouth. There is not enough room for large particles between the folds and they are therefore carried along the top to be rejected at the base of the filament. Intermediate-sized particles travel along one of the tracts and the smallest particles fall to the bottom to be carried to the mouth.

## Selecting particles

The worm's mouth is surrounded by three lips, one dorsal and two lateral. Each has two ciliary tracts on its surface, which coincide with those on the basal folds of the filament. Sorting which has taken place on the filament is maintained by the lips, whose tracts lead the medium and small particles to their appropriate places. The smallest are taken into the mouth as food. The medium particles are also important, although they are not used as food. They pass instead to two expansions of the lateral lips called the *ventral sacs.* Here they are mixed with mucus to form a string which is manipulated by special folds and added to the upper edge of the tube which encloses the worm's body. In this way, the particles collected by the crown of tentacles are used not only for feeding but also for building.

Mucus 'glues' together particles to form larger pieces and sheets which can be moved more easily; the particles for building the tube are held together in this way. The largest particles, due for rejection, are also trapped in mucus on the lips so that they can be discarded more easily. This material, mucus, is found throughout the animal kingdom and is frequently associated with cilia in filter-feeding mechanisms. Its sticky properties, its ability to form sheets and strings, and the ease with which cilia can move it make it ideal for its function. Mucus also poses interesting problems, such as: why the material in which small food particles become stuck does not also tangle the cilia which move it? In a similar way, the mites which inhabit the gills of freshwater mussels move about in mucus without becoming entangled.

Mucus is particularly associated with filter-feeding in molluscs. But it is used in different ways in other worms, such as *Chaetopterus,* which lives in a U-shaped burrow in mud. Its tube is as thick as a finger, and the worm itself has various flaps and appendages on its body with which it creates a current of water through the tube. The circulating water is the worm's source of oxygen and is also its source of food. On its tenth segment, the worm has a pair of appendages which can be held out like arms against the walls of

Attached to each waving, hollow tentacle of the freshwater polyzoa, *top,* are hundreds of little hair-like cilia. These pick up the microscopic specks of organic matter on which the polyzoa feed, before they are carried into their mouths.

*Above,* when submerged again by the incoming tide, each one of these massed gooseneck barnacles will open its hinged shell and start sweeping the water for little plants and animals with its feathery *cirri,* or feeding limbs.

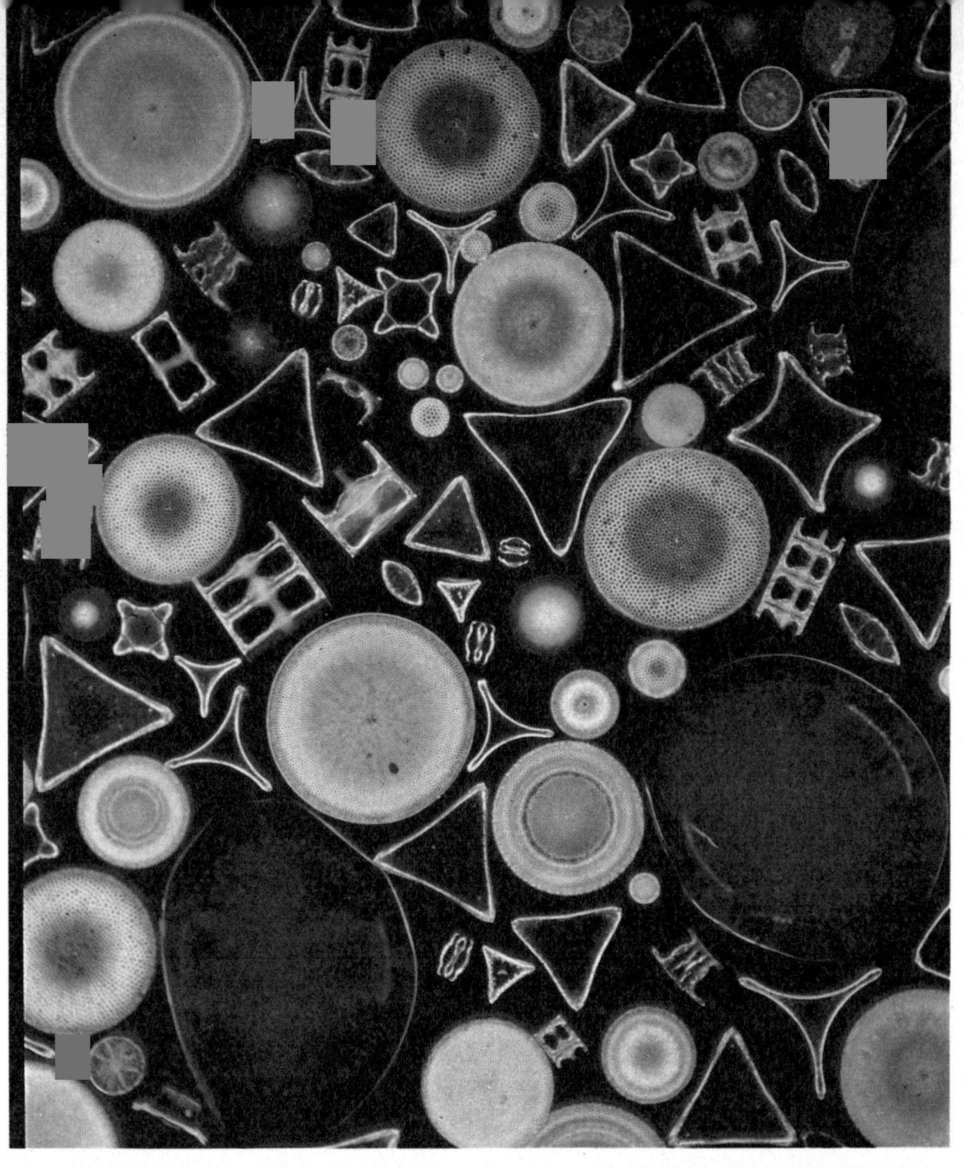

*Left,* a fantastic pattern is made by tiny, unicellular diatoms. They occur in plankton in such numbers they are justly termed the seas' 'pasture'. *Below,* the sponge is virtually a living machine, constantly pumping water in, and out again, while filtering precious food particles *en route.*

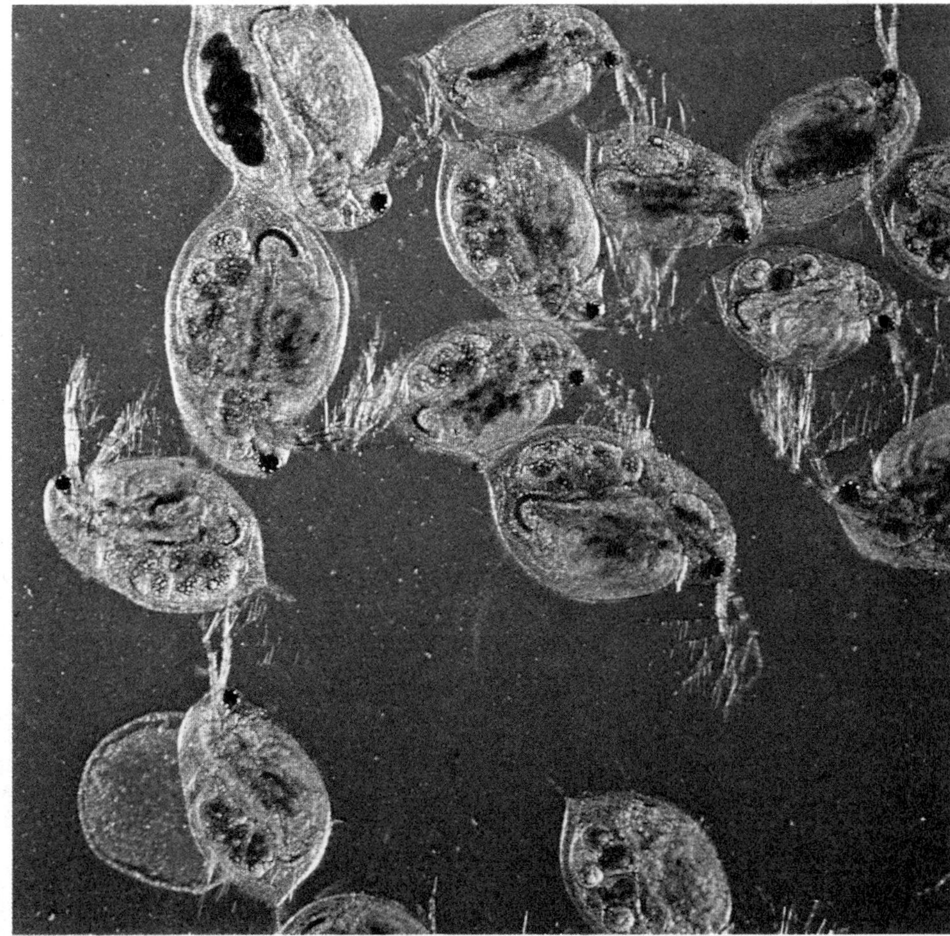

*Above,* although the mussel looks drab and lifeless when exposed, once surrounded again by water it opens up its two shells and displays one of the most elaborate filtering arrangements of all. *Left,* tiny water-fleas—*Daphnia ulex*—dart through the water searching for the minute plants they feed on. These are filtered from the surrounding sea by means of the *Daphnia's* complicated limbs.

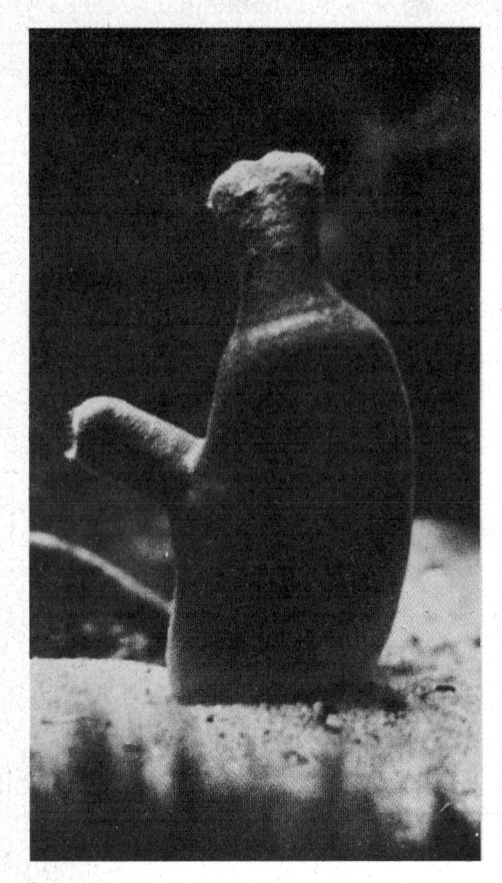

The sea-squirts, *above,* feed by drawing water in through one entrance and then across a large gill chamber where particles become trapped in mucus. The sea-fir, *right,* is made up of thousands of little polyps, each housed in interconnecting tubes, equipped with its own feeding filaments.

the tube. From along their edges, they secrete mucus in a continuous sheet. The bottom edge of the mucus-sheet, next to the body, ends in a small ciliated cup in the middle of the underside of the body (as the worm lies on its back, this appears to be the upper surface). In this way, the sheet of mucus forms a bag which is held open by the 'arms' and which ends in the ciliated cup. The mucus is produced continuously, and the bag is continuously gathered in by the cup. The water current passes through the mucus net and particles are trapped. Then the whole lot, mucus and food, is gathered in and passed forward along the body to the worm's mouth. In this way, food is removed from the water stream as it passes through the tube.

Of all creatures, molluscs have the most elaborate arrangements for sorting and rejecting particles. Most bivalves – the two-shelled molluscs such as oysters, clams and mussels – feed by filtering their food from the surrounding water or from the sediment on the sea bottom beside them. Most of these creatures remain in one place for a long time, often buried in sand or mud. Some of them are capable of moving with ease and speed, but even these remain still for most of the time. The cockle, for example, burrows its way deep into the sand, using its muscular foot as a scoop. Clams, which prefer to lie in mud, are found particularly on the shores of North America, and can weigh up to six or seven pounds. Mussels like to adhere to rocks, between the lines of high and low tide, doing so by means of sticky hairs called the *byssus.*

It is characteristic of these animals that they maintain a stream of water into and out of their shells. The water is impelled by the beat of cilia to enter through the *inhalant* opening of a siphon; after bathing the animal's body within the shells, the water leaves through the *exhalant* opening of the siphon. The shells are hinged along the animal's back. Beneath the animal hangs the muscular foot by which it moves, and at each side of the foot are the gills which are the food-gathering organs of the animal. On the inner side of each shell lies the *mantle,* a thin layer of tissue whose edge forms the shell.

## Fine cilia and mucus sheets

The common shore mussel, for example, has a pair of gills on each side of its body. Each gill is folded back on itself, so that in cross-section the pair resembles a letter W. But the gill is not a continuous sheet of tissue; it is made up a series of filaments which run from the point of attachment to the fold and then to the edge. Each filament is attached to the next by a pad of interlocking stiff cilia, so that the gills are virtually sheets of tissue perforated by many small holes through which water can pass.

The *lateral* cilia on each side of the outer surface of the gill filament draw water into the shells and, by their beating action, pass it between the filaments and into the space within the gills. Just in front of these cilia, standing on the angle of the gills in a perfect position to guard the entrances between the filaments, are the *latero-frontal* cilia which beat towards the outer surfaces of the filaments. In this way, food particles in the water stream are caught by the cilia and thrown on to the surface of the filament. This outer surface has, in turn, a set of cilia called the *frontals* which beat in yet another direction, downwards towards the fold in the filament. These cilia move a sheet of mucus downwards over the gill, and in this sheet the particles become trapped. The mucus from both sides of the gill moves into a food groove along the fold. There, ciliary tracts move the food towards the mouth, where further sorting of particles takes place. This is achieved by a series of overlapping folds. In the gutters between them, ciliary tracts beat outwards while another stream crosses the crests going towards the mouth. Heavier particles tend to drop out of the mucus into the gutters where they are swept away and rejected. But the lighter particles are passed from crest to crest and reach the mouth. This sorting is purely by weight and size; actual food value is not a consideration.

Mucus and cilia are not essentials for filter-feeding. Shrimps, crabs and lobsters characteristically lack both cilia and mucus, and they strain their food from the water by using complicated arrangements of appendages fringed with fine hairs. These sweep the food from the water, and the particles are carried along to the mouth by eddies which form among the moving limbs.

# How nature gets the waste away – I

Death by self-poison, or grotesque growth to enormous size would face a plant or animal unable to rid itself of useless materials. How has nature overcome the vital problem of waste?

ALL LIVING THINGS need a supply of energy in order to survive. They get their energy from various sources: plants generally make use of carbohydrates formed during photosynthesis, and animals use plants or other animals as food. Energy is released from food materials by series of chemical reactions. After the energy has gone, there remain various chemical compounds which, because they are of no further use to the organism, are called waste products. As a result, an essential function found in all living things is that of *excretion,* which is the way in which an organism gets rid of its waste products. And in general, the more highly evolved the organism is, the more complex is its excretory system.

Some waste products are merely a sort of refuse which a plant cannot store or an animal cannot carry around without unnecessarily expanding further energy and growing larger and larger as the useless materials accumulate. (Water is a typical example of such a substance.) Others may be poisonous if present in more than a certain concentration. In either case, the waste products must be removed.

## Loss through the leaves

All plants lose a certain amount of water by *transpiration.* It is purely a physical process similar to evaporation, which takes place whenever a wet surface is in contact with unsaturated air which can take up water vapour. Some water is lost through the walls of cells in the outermost layer of a plant's stems, but most escapes through tiny pores *(stomata)* in the leaves. We can therefore distinguish between *cuticular* transpiration (through the cell walls) and *stomatal* or *normal* transpiration (through the leaves).

Stomata can be opened and closed by a plant, depending on its needs, and so the amount of water lost through them depends on their number and how far they are open. There is a wide variation in the number of stomata in the leaves of different plants. For example, a Spanish oak tree may have as many as 1,200 stomata crowded into each square millimetre of leaf surface, whereas the popular indoor plants known as *Tradescantia* may have as few as 14 stomata per square millimetre. Most plants have about 250 to 350 per square millimetre of leaf surface.

Water moves through stomata by *diffusion,* because each stomatal aperture provides a connection between the saturated air spaces in the leaf tissue and the air outside. As long as the outside air is not already itself saturated, water must pass out of the leaf.

The waste products of one organism are often of value to another. *Right,* a rubber tree is being tapped for its latex, the raw material from which this indispensable product is manufactured.

A simple experiment demonstrates transpiration from a leaf. Certain salts of the metal cobalt are pink when they are wet and blue when they are dry. A piece of absorbent paper soaked in a solution of cobalt chloride and dried in an oven is blue. If this paper is then placed next to a leaf of a growing plant and sealed from the atmosphere by a small piece of glass with its edges covered in grease, the paper slowly turns pink. Since the glass stops any moisture in the air from affecting the paper, the colour change demonstrates that water is escaping from the plant through the surface of the leaf.

Water is not the only waste product lost through stomata. During the night, when photosynthesis stops, carbon dioxide from tissue respiration accumulates. In high concentrations, carbon dioxide is 'poisonous' to a plant's metabolism. So the stomata open and allow carbon dioxide to diffuse out. This has been given as the reason why plants and flowers are removed from hospital wards at night.

## The home-grown weed-killer

Some plants have other ways of getting rid of water. One method, called *guttation*, occurs with plants which grow in conditions favouring rapid uptake of water and slow transpiration. The plants exude droplets of water from the edges of their leaves. Guttation often occurs at night during the summer when the soil is warm and moist, and the air is cool and already saturated. The drops of water are often mistaken for dew, and may be seen on some indoor plants (such as 'water fuchsia') which are heavily watered or actually grown in water.

Guttation involves special structures called *hydathodes*. Active hydathodes are found in runner beans and related plants, and *passive* hydathodes are found in fuchsias and lesser celandine.

Hydathodes are complex structures consisting of colourless, thin-walled, loosely packed cells forming a tissue called *epithem*. This tissue connects with the vascular bundles – the water supply – in

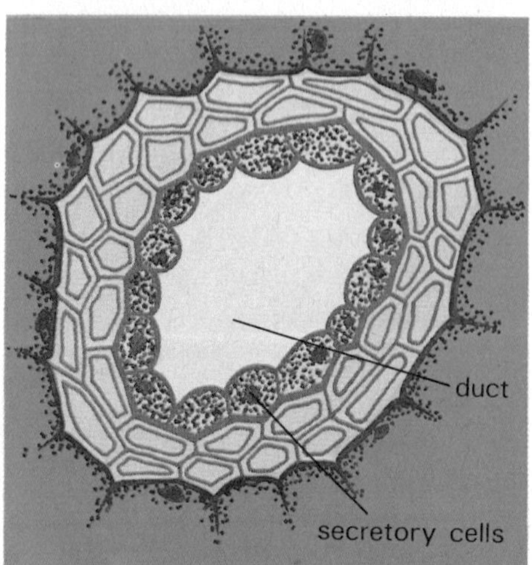


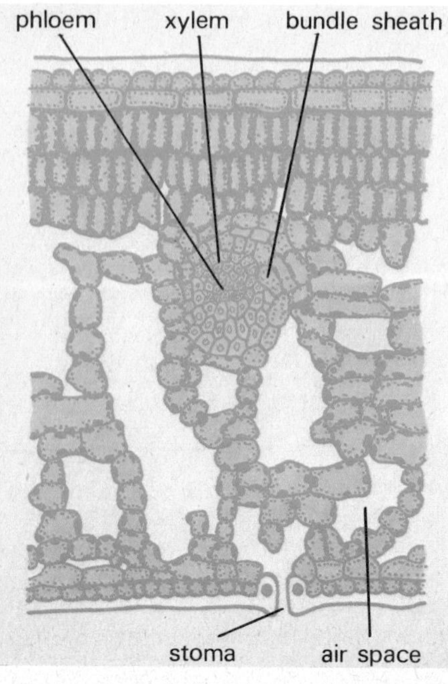


The common garden ant, *top*, spends a good deal of time and energy 'milking' aphids for their excess fluids. Beetles and other insects rid themselves of waste products through numerous Malpighian tubules in a manner quite different from other animals, *left*. The cross-section of a pine tree resin duct, *centre*, shows the cells which secrete the resin, and the duct, or tube, which carries it to the surface. The cross-section of a leaf, *right*, illustrates stomatal transpiration, the loss of gaseous waste such as water vapour through pores called stomata.

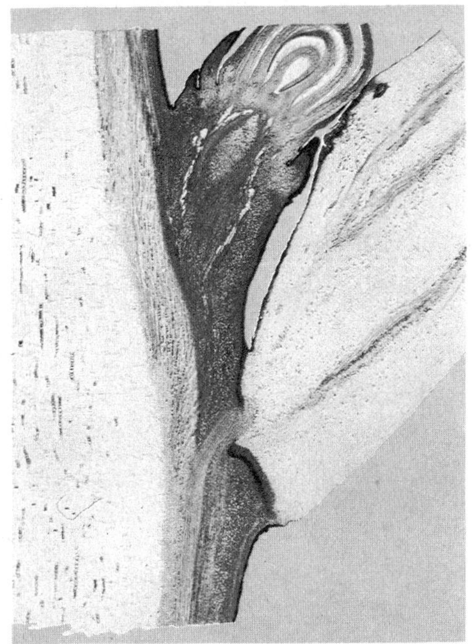

the leaf. Water pores in the outer skin of the epithem resemble stomata, but they are incapable of opening and closing. Water passes through the hydathodes as if it were being pumped out of the vascular system, possibly as a result of root pressure.

Many plants store some of their waste products in insoluble form. These generally take the form of crystals stored in the plant's cells; for instance, salts of oxalic acid are stored in such plants as wood sorrel. (The botanical name for the sorrel family, *oxalis*, gives its name to the acid; potassium oxalate was once known as salt of sorrel.) Silica (chemically identical to sand) is another waste product commonly stored in the walls of plant cells. Grass cuts one's fingers easily because of deposits of hard silica in its leaves, and the silica in the plant called horse-tail (or scouring rush) was once used for scouring pots.

Other by-products of metabolism stored in insoluble form in plants include gums, latex (rubber) and tannin. Some plants give out such substances. For example, many cone-bearing plants such as pines secrete resin, the source of musicians' rosin and turpentine. The oil that can be squeezed from the skin of an orange is a waste product stored in special cavities.

Plants that grow in soils which are rich in minerals (for instance, some grasses which grow on salt marshes) have an interesting mechanism for getting rid of excess salts. They actively excrete salt through the cuticle from special cells or glands. Other plants excrete various organic substances through their roots; for example, plants of the group of the daisy family called *Tagetes* (French and African marigolds) secrete a weed-killing substance and may be cultivated for this purpose.

Towards autumn in deciduous trees, there is a build-up of such unwanted salts as calcium oxalate in the leaves. When the leaves fall, the plant gets rid of these accumulated salts. (This is not the main reason why deciduous plants shed their leaves, but it does have an important excretory function.)

The chief waste products in animals are also carbon dioxide, water and nitrogen-containing compounds. Removal of carbon dioxide takes place during respiration. Water can be lost from several sites (in mammals, for example, through the lungs, sweat glands and kidneys). Nitrogenous wastes are passed out either as solid substances, such as uric acid or guanine, or in solution as ammonia or urea. For these second substances to be in solution, much water must also be lost and so the same organs may control the excretion of nitrogenous wastes and water.

Many nitrogenous excretory products are poisonous and their accumulation within the body could result in death. Insoluble compounds may be crystallized within cells and so prevented from interfering with metabolism. For example, urate crystals are found in many single-celled protozoans and guanine crystals occur in amoebae.

## Flickering flame cells

Soluble compounds must be excreted. Most protozoans do this over their whole body surface. Those that live in the sea have an internal osmotic pressure equal to that of sea-water, and there is therefore no tendency for water to pass through the cell membrane in or out of the animal. But the internal osmotic pressure of those which live in fresh water results in a tendency for water to enter the cell by osmosis. To get rid of excess water, many fresh-water protozoans, such as paramecium, have an organ called a *contractile vacuole* which controls both excretion and the osmotic pressure. Others, such as amoebae, ingest tiny solid food particles by surrounding them with projections called *pseudopodia*. The protoplasm encloses the food within a vacuole and, after digestion has taken place, the solid waste products which remain are expelled.

In simple metazoan animals such as sponges and *coelenterates* (sea anemones and jelly-fish), excretion takes place by diffusion from the tissues to the surrounding water. Starfish and sea urchins *(echinoderms)* also have no excretory organs.

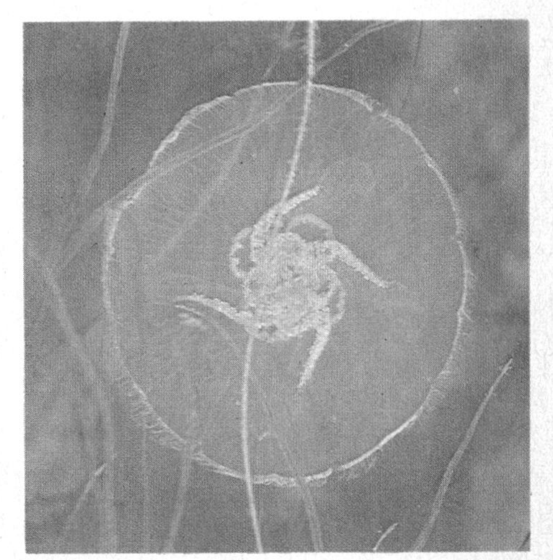

Sometimes a plant is useful because of wastes it stores, rather than excretes. The horse-tail plant, *top left*, was once used for scouring pots because of the hard silica (sand) in its leaves. A rather unusual way of removing solid wastes is to form a corky abscission layer, *middle left*, depriving the leaf of nourishment until it falls off. All leafy plants expel gaseous waste products through pores or stomata, but the extent to which this is done varies widely. A Spanish oak may have up to 1,200 per square millimetre, but the common indoor *Tradescantia*, *left*, has as few as 14 stomata per square millimetre for this purpose. Some simple animals, such as the starfish, *centre*, and the jelly-fish, *right*, have no excretory organs at all. They allow unwanted materials to flow from their bodies to the surrounding sea by the process of diffusion.

Almost all other invertebrate animals have such organs, which may be *nephridia* (as in some worms), *coelomoducts* (as in some molluscs), or *Malpighian tubes* (as in insects).

Nephridia are tubular structures open at the outer end and closed at the inner end or connected with the coelom (body cavity), as in many annelid worms. In the flatworms, this organ takes the form of a closed *flame cell* nephridium which ends internally in a series of tubules which penetrate the cells of the animal. Water and dissolved excretory products pass into the tubules and are wafted along them by the beating action of cilia (hair-like threads). The name flame cell comes from the rhythmic beating of the cilia which resembles a flickering flame.

Some annelid worms and the primitive aquatic chordate creature called *amphioxus* have *solenocyte* nephridia. These resemble the flame cell type but have different terminal cells, which have thin-walled excretory tubules. There are only a few cilia in the solenocyte and the structure lies within the body cavity. Excretory substances in solution pass directly in and flow to the outside along the excretory canal.

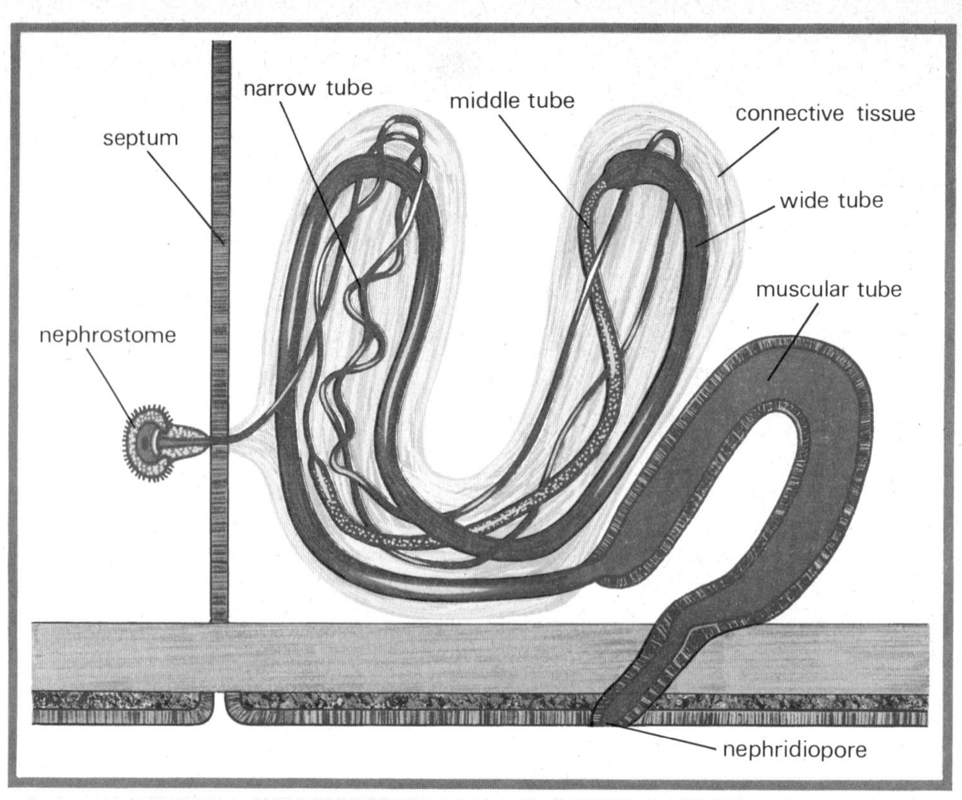


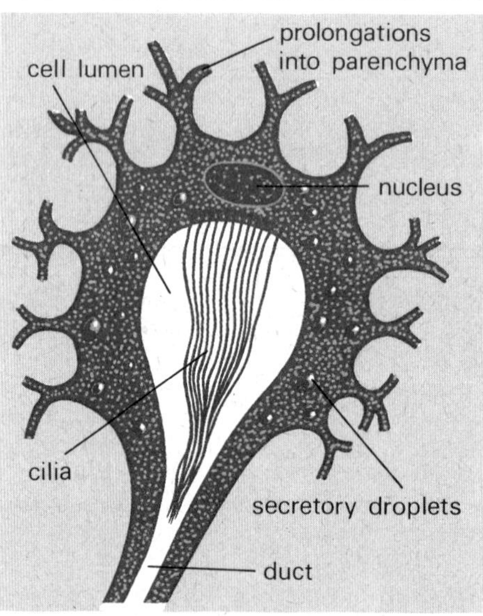


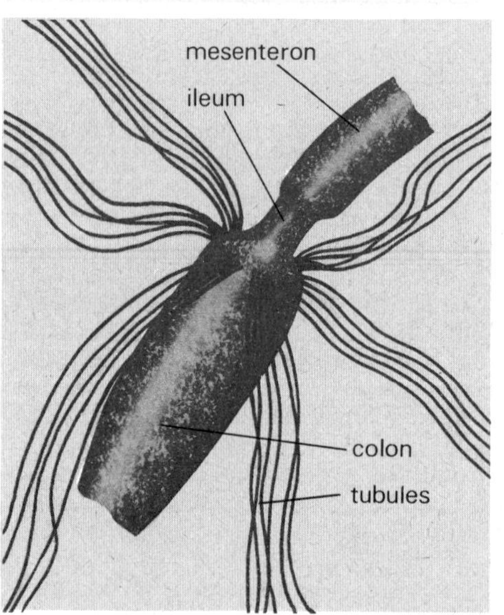


The excretory organ of invertebrates like worms is the nephridium, *top,* which is essentially a tube with an open end at the surface and sealed within the body. In the flatworm, a so-called flame cell, *left,* is added to the structure of the nephridium. Water and dissolved waste products enter into the nephridium tube and are carried to the opening at the surface. Cilia, tiny hairs, help move the liquid along in the flame cell. Malpighian tubules, *right,* used by insects, absorb water, preventing its loss; so insect excretum is generally solid and quite dry. Oxygen is also a waste product. Without plants, animal life would soon suffocate for lack of it.

## Insects are different

Other annelids, including the earthworm, have nephridia which consist of open tubes connecting the body cavity with the body's outside surface, one pair to each segment. At the inner end of each tube, a ciliated funnel (called a *nephrostome*) sucks in fluid which may have other substances secreted into it during its passage along the tube.

Insoluble excretory matter may be stored inside an animal's body, as in the urate cells in fatty tissues of insects. Some animals make use of solid excretory products; for instance, the earthworm has glands which secrete calcium carbonate ('chalk') to help to neutralize acids in the gut.

Some lower coelomate animals have *coelomoducts,* which are outgrowths of the body cavity. These also have ciliated funnels (called *coelomostomes*), often confused with the nephridia which they closely resemble. In the lower forms the ducts play no part in excretion, but carry germ cells (sperm or ova) to the exterior for fertilization. In higher forms, they take over the functions of excretion from the nephridia.

Insects differ from most other animals in practically all their physiological functions, and the excretory system is no exception. The principal organs, the Malpighian tubules, are long, slender tubes with closed inner ends. They lie in the body cavity (called the *haemocoel*) and are freely bathed by the *haemolymph* (insect 'blood'). The closed ends may be attached to the colon or rectum, and the open ends connect with the intestine.

Malpighian tubules occur in groups of two. Beetles have only four to six, whereas some grasshoppers have as many as 120. Waste substances from the surrounding blood accumulate in the outer (epithelial) cells of the tubules, are discharged into the centre, pass into the intestine, and are voided from the anus. The tubules also actively re-absorb water which otherwise would be lost. This function is vital to insects which live in dry environments, such as the meal worm which lives almost entirely on stored grain with hardly any moisture content. This insect retains all the water produced by its metabolism by re-absorbing it as it passes along the Malpighian tubules. The final excretory matter is almost completely dry and consists of uric acid and its salts. A solid insect excretory product useful to man is lac, secreted by some Indian scale insects and made into the resinous substance shellac. Spiders solve the problem of water loss in a similar way; they excrete solid guanine, as do most birds.

Water conservation is less important in insects that can afford to excrete water. Such species include aphids, which feed on plant juices, and their sticky excreta – called honeydew – is used as a source of food and water by other insects such as ants.

The increasingly complex excretory systems of higher plants and animals evolved to aid them in carrying out increasingly more complex activities. Higher plants and animals are not superior to their simpler relatives because they are complex. Rather, they are complex because they are superior; since they can do so many more things, they need more equipment, of a highly specialized kind.

# How nature gets the waste away–2

There are no 'perfect' foods in nature. Much of what an animal eats must be expelled from the body as waste. The more complex the foods ingested, the more complex the disposal system.

AN ANIMAL is very much like a machine. Indeed, many philosophers and theologians from antiquity to the present day have insisted that they *are* machines, because they have no souls. But if they are machines, they are very inefficient ones. Many of the substances taken into the body for 'fuel' are never used, and so animals have had to develop elaborate disposal systems to get rid of this waste.

In higher animals, there are two kinds of waste products: liquids (passed from the kidneys as urine or evaporated from the lungs and skin) and solids (*faeces*). Faeces are composed of those parts of the food which the alimentary canal cannot digest; they pass through the system unchanged. These substances have not entered into any cell reactions and do not need an elaborate disposal system.

The *alimentary canal* is basically a long tube supplemented by a series of specialized organs which extract the useful substances from food and pass on the unused substances as faeces. The process in Man makes an excellent example.

Food is ingested, or taken in, through the mouth and mixed with saliva from glands at the base of the tongue. (Saliva is water containing the enzyme *ptyalin,* which begins the chemical breakdown of carbohydrates into sugars.) From the mouth, the food and saliva is moved down the oesophagus to the stomach by a muscular movement called *peristalsis*. The stomach supplies two further enzymes: *pepsin,* which in the presence of the stomach's hydrochloric acid can start the digestion of proteins; *rennin,* which curdles any milk present to prepare it for digestion.

After some time in the stomach, muscular contractions force the partly digested food into the first part of the small intestine (called the *duodenum*). Then more enzymes, secreted by the pancreas and the walls of the duodenum, begin their work. One of them is lipase, which begins the digestion of fats. However, since these enzymes only work in alkaline solutions, bile must first be introduced to counter the acids introduced in the stomach. Carbohydrates are completely converted into simple sugars, fats to fatty acids and glycerol, and proteins into amino acids.

The food is now fully broken down and as it passes along the small intestine, the function changes from one of secretion to one of absorption. Small, finger-like projections called *villi* stick out from the walls of the small intestine. Each villus has a system of blood capillaries and an extension of the lymphatic fluid system called a *lacteal.* As the digested food passes, amino acids and sugars are absorbed into the blood, and fatty acids and glycerol into the lacteal.

Up to this stage, the food has contained

The faeces of the guano bird, *below,* makes excellent fertilizer. Recovery of guano is aided by the birds' habit of living in large groups.

much water. Now, as it passes into the large intestine (*colon*), most of the water is reabsorbed, leaving the waste products semi-solid. The end of the gut, called the *rectum,* is generally empty. When it fills, a *defaecation reflex* relaxes the sphincter muscles and the faeces are forced out by the muscular action of the colon aided by the abdominal muscles.

This, then, is the system in Man. Other mammals may have slightly different systems depending on their diets, though the purpose is still the same. For instance, a rabbit has a larger appendix (a blind branch of the caecum) containing micro-organisms for digesting the large amounts of cellulose from grass and other plants the animal eats. In Man, whose diet does not normally include much raw plant material, the appendix is small and no longer used. In more primitive vertebrates such as fish and amphibians, the gut is simpler and proportionally shorter than in mammals.

## Less salt than the sea

The liquid wastes of vertebrates consist of by-products of food breakdown not useful to the body. Carbohydrates and fats yield carbon dioxide and water, and proteins yield ammonia. The gases carbon dioxide and ammonia dissolve in the water. An accumulation of ammonia in the tissues would kill an animal, and so the kidney system has evolved to cope with it (and with most of the water). The kidney controls the salt and water balance.

Carbon dioxide is largely excreted by the lungs or gills (or, in the case of amphibians, through the skin). As oxygen diffuses into the blood during respiration, carbon dioxide diffuses out. This is a passive process depending on the relative concentrations of the gases in the blood and in the respiratory organs.

Some of the water formed by metabolism in animals also escapes over the respiratory surface as a vapour – that is why we can see 'steam' in an animal's breath on a cold day. Some water also escapes through the skin as perspiration. But most of it, along with nitrogenous waste products, is excreted by the kidney system.

*Above left,* fresh-water fish are constantly in danger of being bloated by excess water in their bodies and salt-water fish are constantly in danger of dehydration because of the difference in the salt concentrations in their tissues and the surrounding environment. So they have developed various ways of combating this danger. Most animals excrete liquids all over their bodies, but dogs, *above right,* drool at the mouth, because they have no sweat glands in the skin. Rabbits can sweat all over, *right,* especially through the thin tissues of their long ears.

In aquatic animals such as fishes, ammonia (the chief nitrogenous waste product) is easily 'washed' away by water flowing through the gills. But land animals must have a different arrangement. In them, ammonia is generally converted into less poisonous compounds such as urea or uric acid. Animals that form urea, including fish, amphibia, aquatic reptiles and mammals, are called *ureotelic.* Urea is generally extracted from the blood by the kidneys and excreted in the urine, although some animals store it in the blood at high concentrations for uses other than nutrition.

Animals that excrete uric acid as the chief nitrogenous breakdown product, including land reptiles and birds – all animals that develop in a shelled egg – are called *uricotelic.* Uric acid is virtually insoluble and therefore non-poisonous. To be poisonous, a substance must be soluble so that it can diffuse into the cells. As these animals develop within the egg, the excretory product (uric acid) can accumulate harmlessly. (If they excreted ammonia, they would rapidly be poisoned, and a secretion of urea would require a water supply.)

The other function of the kidney, water balance, is of most importance in fish. Sea-water fish have a lower salt concentration in their cells than does the sea surrounding them. Water therefore tends to pass out of the fish into the sea and, if unchecked, would lead to dehydration of the animal. The pores in the tissues of a fish's gills are so small that only water molecules, and not salt, can pass through them, and so the fish cannot achieve a balance of salt between itself and its surroundings this way.

In marine bony fishes, this problem is solved by glands at the base of the gills which permit the fish to keep up their water content by drinking sea-water; the salt passes back into the sea through the glands. Cartilaginous fishes (such as sharks and dog-fish), which also live in the sea, have evolved a totally different solution. They accumulate urea in the blood until the overall concentration of dissolved substances equals that of sea-water. As a result, there is no osmotic pressure tending to drive water either into or out of the fishes' tissues.

## 32 gallons a day

Freshwater fish have the reverse problem. Because the salt concentration within their bodies is very much higher than that of the water around them, there is a tendency for water to flow into their tissues, so they must eliminate large quantities of water from the tissues to prevent swelling. They do this by ex-

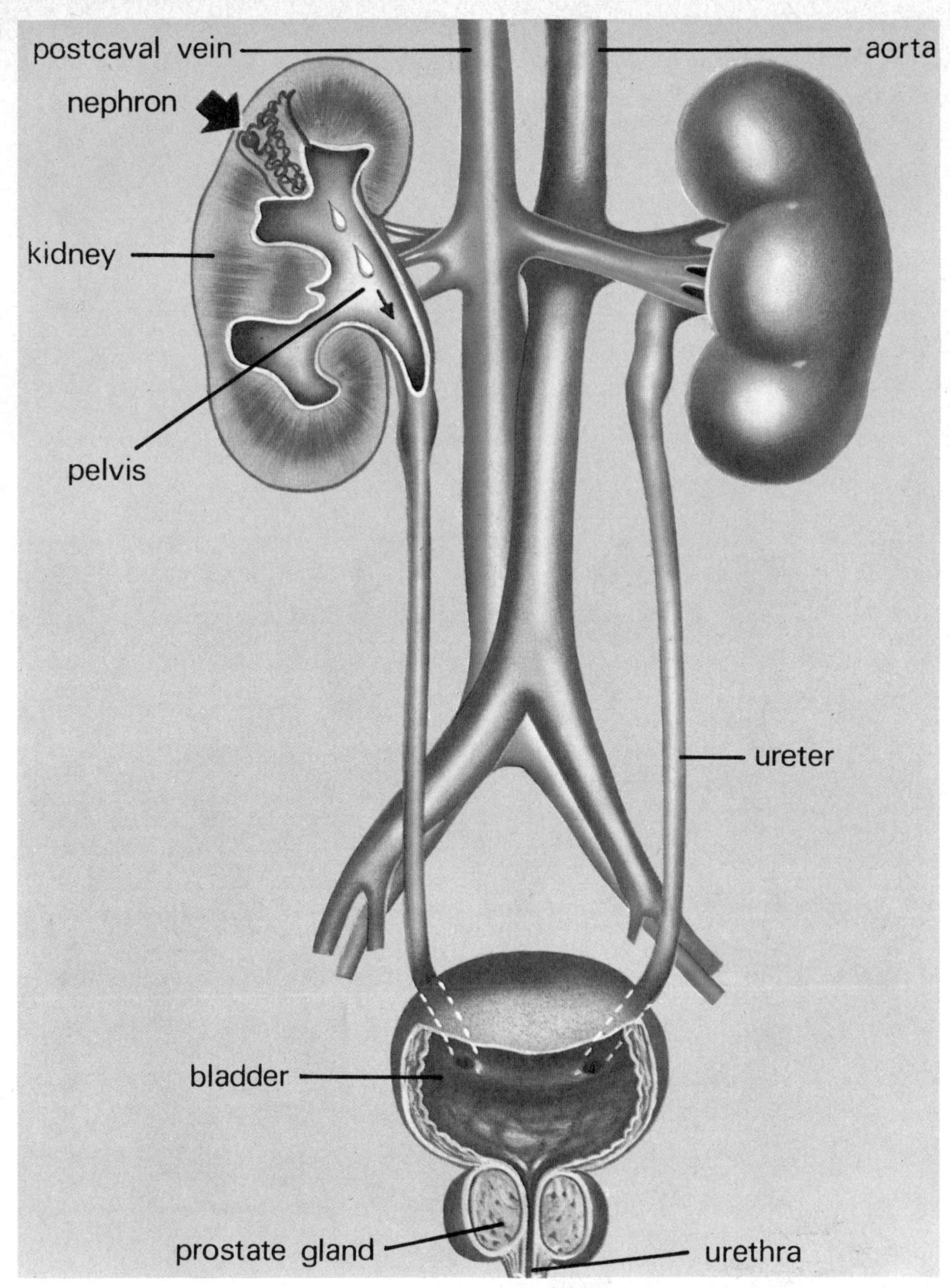


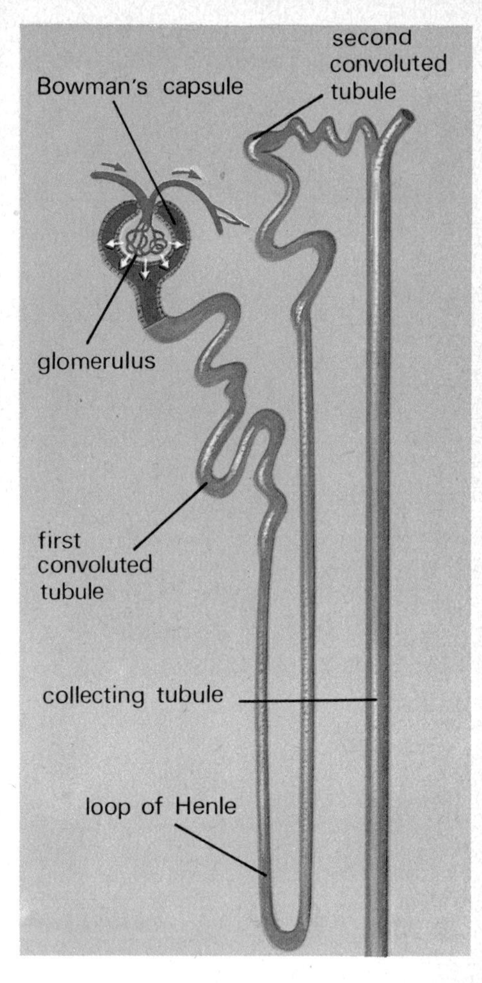


Nephrons, *top,* in the kidneys filter out blood wastes and pass them as urine to the bladder for storage before being expelled from the body, *left.* Most of the water taken out of the blood, up to 98 per cent, is reabsorbed to prevent its loss from the body. *Bottom left,* the close-up of a kidney reveals the cortex layer and the medulla. *Bottom right,* digested foods are taken up by villi extending from the walls of the small intestines, as in this cross-section which has been taken from a frog. Later, water is removed in the large intestines.

creting large amounts of salty urine via the kidneys, and making up the salt deficiency in their food.

Thus, in bony fishes there are two complementary systems to maintain the water-salt balance. In sea-water, water is absorbed through the gut, salt is excreted through the gills, and very little urine is produced. In fresh water, much urine is produced and the lost salt made up in the diet.

In all vertebrates, the main organs of the urinary system are the paired kidneys situated on the dorsal (back) side of the abdomen. Each kidney has many minute tubes called *nephrons,* each capable of excretory activity. (For example, a human kidney is about 4½ inches long and has about a million nephrons.) A nephron has two parts: the *malpighian body* and the *tubule.* The malpighian body consists of a knot of capillaries (*glomerulus*) and a cup (*Bowman's capsule*) into which fluid is filtered.

Nephrons cannot select only waste products from the blood but filter out many useful substances as well. In one day, a man's kidneys filter a total of about 32

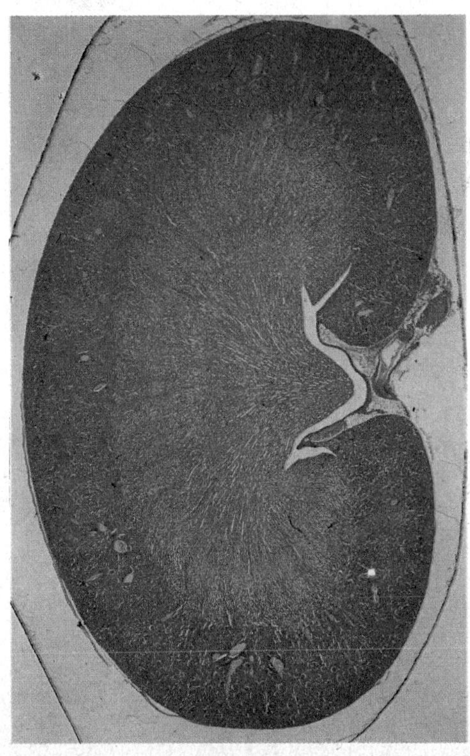

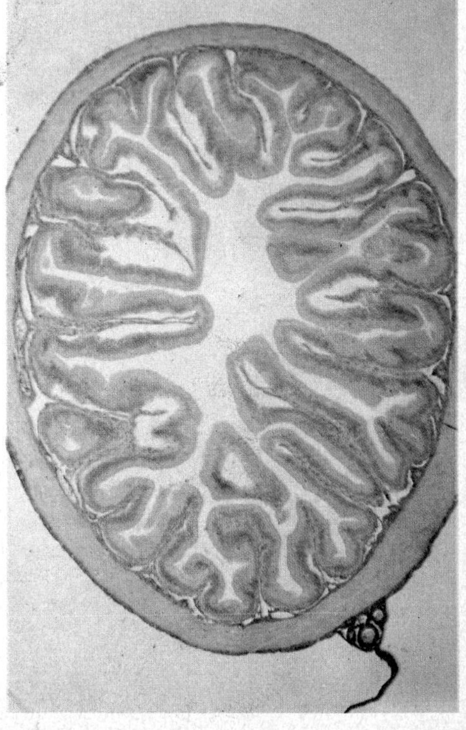

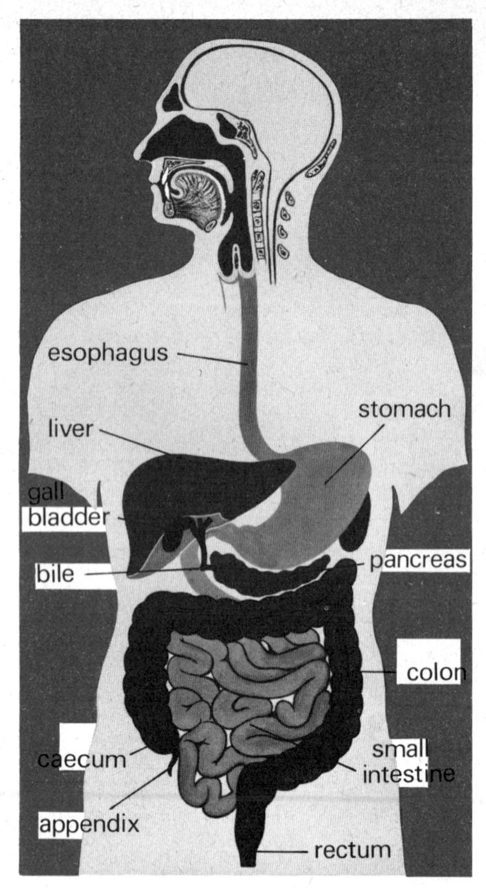


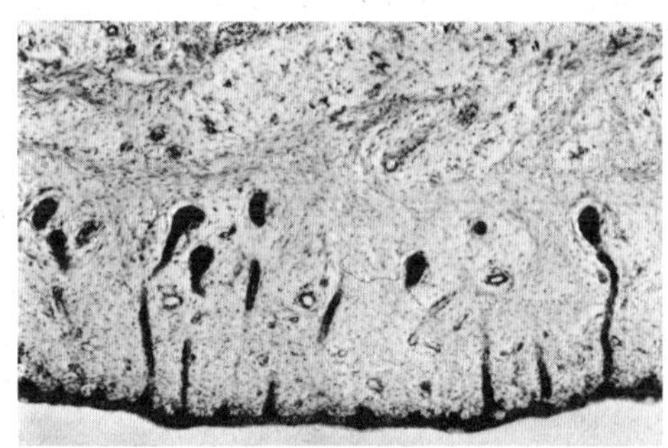

*Left,* the cloud of steam rising from this horse at the end of a race is caused by evaporation of sweat, which cools the animal. Sweat is secreted by sweat glands just under the surface of the skin, *above right.* The alimentary canal, *top right,* begins at the mouth, where food is taken in, and ends at the rectum, where wastes are expelled. Specialized organs assist in digesting the food and extracting useful nutrients.

gallons of fluid. The body obviously cannot and does not lose all this, and so the tubules must reabsorb most of it. In fact, 98 per cent of the liquid is absorbed back into the blood capillaries surrounding the tubules.

In mammals, reabsorption takes place in the following way. There are three regions of the tubule: the *proximal* (or first) *convoluted tubule*, the *loop of Henle*, and the *distal* (or second) *convoluted tubule*. Most of the sugars and vitamins are reabsorbed, along with much water, in the proximal convoluted tubule. The distal convoluted tubule removes most of the remaining water, except for the relatively small amount needed to dissolve the nitrogenous wastes. The loop of Henle 'pumps' salt back into the tissues to prevent it being lost in the urine.

Each nephron connects with a collecting tubule, which carries the urine to a temporary reservoir called the *pelvis* of the kidney. From here, the urine in mammals trickles along a tube from each kidney (the *ureters*) to the bladder for storage. The bladder can stretch if necessary to increase its capacity. When it is full, the sphincter muscle closing the *urethra* relaxes and urine is passed to the exterior via the penis in males or the vulva in females.

In fish, the two ureters join and swell into a small bladder, capable of absorbing some water. Amphibians have a similar bladder, but they have no separate anus and the digestive excretory and urinary systems fuse into a single duct called the *cloaca*. Reptiles and birds have a similar system.

## Fuel and fine leather

In birds, the cloaca is divided into various regions. The urine passes down the ureters into the *urodaeum*, where most of the water is absorbed. It then passes to the *coprodaeum* for further dehydration and mixing with the faeces. The final white excretory product is called *guano*, which is an excellent fertilizer.

The use of animal excreta to nourish crops is not known in some societies, but they have found other uses for these wastes. For instance, in places that have no trees or other readily available fuels, excrement is often dried and burned to defend against the chill of winter. It was also put to use blocking up the air spaces between the wooden poles of simple tribal huts. It is still used for this purpose in some parts of the world. At one time, excrement was even used for tanning leather. Some of the finest, most highly valued leatherbound books of the last century and the early part of the present century were prepared in this fashion.

It must be remembered that some water is also excreted in many animals through the lungs and skin. The skin has many small pores leading to glands which secrete the watery substance sweat. The primary function of sweating is to help to regulate the body temperature, but it also contributes to excretion of water, urea and salt. Although the skin is an active excretory organ, it could never take over completely from the kidneys should they fail.

These then are the reasons why higher animals are fairly inefficient at obtaining the maximum energy from the food they eat. But they have evolved elaborate and efficient systems to eliminate waste products while at the same time conserving vital water and minerals.

# Living world on the move 1

The prey moves innocently into the trap. Suddenly, it is caught and devoured. A lion felling a deer? No, a plant eating an insect. The plant kingdom is more mobile than it may appear.

THE ABILITY to move about is one of the attributes of life we generally assign to higher animals. But some plants and very simple organisms can also move. In fact, all living things show movements of some sort.

In simple organisms, movement is usually associated with the need to find food or to escape from an area no longer suitable for supporting it. How do such creatures move? A typical example is the microscopic single-celled *amoeba,* which consists simply of a nucleus surrounded by jelly-like *cytoplasm.* The outer part of the cytoplasm (called *ectoplasm*) is fairly thick in consistency whereas the inner part, the *endoplasm,* is fairly fluid. When an amoeba moves, the ectoplasm at an area on the surface becomes more fluid and 'flows' forward as a projection of the animal. This projection is called a *pseudopodium,* meaning 'false foot'. The rest of the cell then 'catches up' with the projection and the amoeba effectively moves slowly along.

The speed at which an amoeba can move is governed by the rate at which the viscous cytoplasm will flow. Other single-celled animals have evolved a different, quicker way of moving.

## Paddling the paramecium

One such organism, the slipper-shaped *paramecium,* has a firm membrane (the *pellicle*) round its outside. The pellicle is covered by rectangular dents from which grow short hair-like threads called *cilia.*

By beating its cilia like the oars of a galley, the paramecium propels itself through water. In movement, each cilium stiffens and bends quickly to lie nearly parallel with the animal's body. It then becomes limp and returns slowly to straight-out position. It is the rhythmic beat of the cilia when stiff that provides the movement.

Of course, it takes many cilia beating in step to move the whole animal. Since the cilia move diagonally, rather than backwards and forwards, the paramecium moves along a spiral path while slowly rotating on its axis. To change direction, the animal stops or speeds up one group of its cilia.

Structurally similar to cilia, but much longer, are whip-like hairs called *flagella.* Animals equipped with these structures move in a different way. They flick their flagella – in much the same way as we crack a whip – to produce ripples in the water which propel the animal along.

The *euglena* is an organism which has a flagellum. The euglena is a sort of borderline creature. Since it moves and ingests food, it appears to be an animal. But since it also contains a chloroplast for photosynthesis, it also appears to be a plant. Some biologists classify it as a plant, others classify it as an animal.

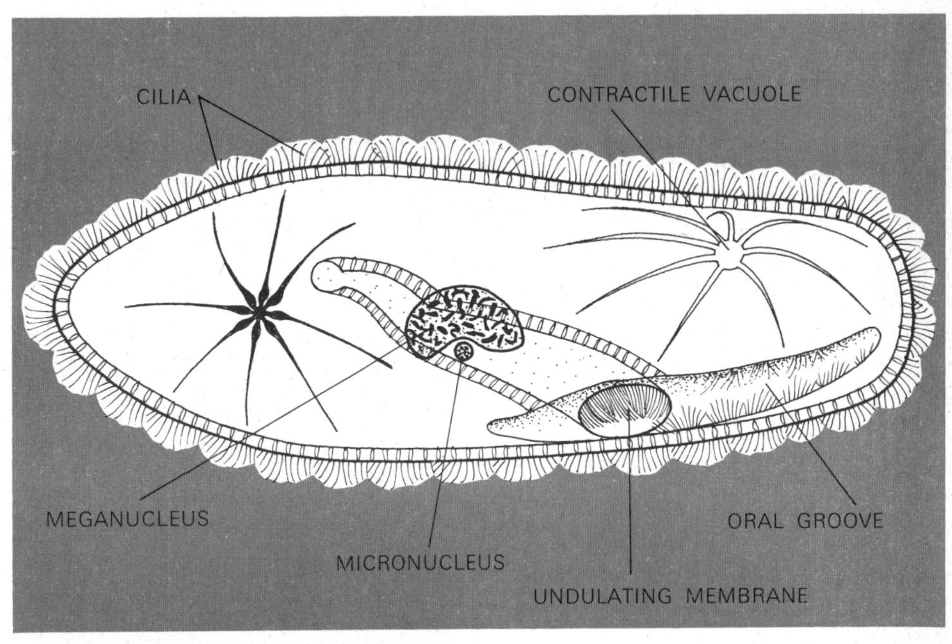


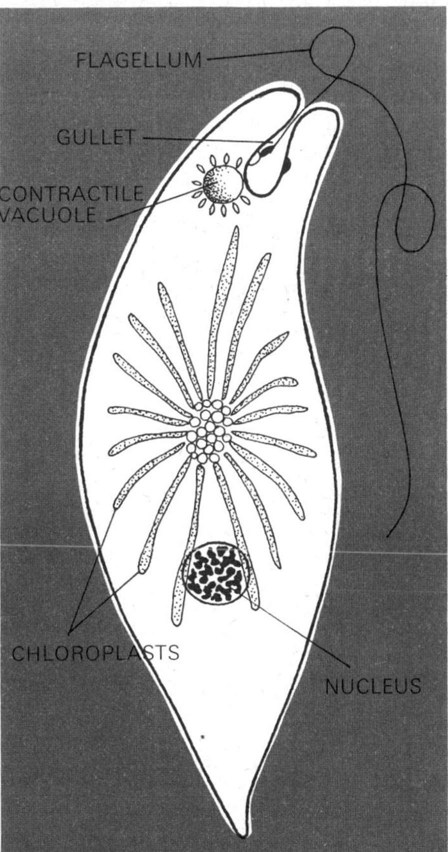


The paramecium and the euglena illustrate two types of simple locomotion. *Top,* the body of the paramecium is circumscribed by hundreds of tiny hair-like threads called cilia, which the animal uses to paddle itself about in water. *Above,* the euglena whiplashes its way through the water with one long thread called a flagellum. The euglena is something of a biological puzzle, because it behaves like an animal, but is equipped for photosynthesis like a plant.

This creature consists of one cell bounded by a pellicle, and it has a short, blind-ended gullet from which grows a long flagellum, which the creature flicks to move along. Euglena can also make wriggling movements by flexing its elastic pellicle. This type of movement is all that can be made by some animals, such as *monocystis.* But this single-celled creature is a parasite which lives in the body of the earthworm, and so its wriggling movements are quite adequate for the very short journeys it makes. Threads of cytoplasm along the length of the animal can contract, causing the wriggling.

## Internal and external stimuli

Passing to many-celled organisms, we find that flagella are still used by the simplest of them. For instance, the alga *volvox* forms spherical colonies consisting of about 50,000 cells, each bearing two flagella. In *astrephomene,* the flagella from a few cells act as a 'rudder' while the remainder propel the organism. This is an example of simple 'division of labour' – a sharing of functions among the colony's cells.

So far, we have considered movements for catching food or for migrating to better feeding grounds. These are movements caused by internal stimuli. In some creatures, external stimuli can cause movement. For instance, the euglena is attracted by light and moves towards it. Such movements are called *tactic.* The euglena needs light because it uses it in photosynthesis. But if the light is too strong, it might damage the cell's delicate mechanism and so a second tactic movement takes place *away* from the light.

A tactic response generally involves

movement of the whole organism and so we should not expect to find it in flowering plants, which are anchored by their roots. Nevertheless, the small oval bodies called chloroplasts, which store the green pigment chlorophyll in the leaves of all plants, do move. They spread out in dim light to catch as much light energy as possible, and bunch together to avoid damage by extremely bright light. Since chloroplasts are free moving, their movement is also called taxis or tactic movement.

## One-side responses

There are other kinds of movements in plants. Anyone who has kept plants in a room knows that they grow towards the light. The side of the stem *furthest* from the light grows more quickly than the side facing it, so causing the stem to curve towards the light. A one-sided response is called *tropism,* and this example of accelerated growth is a *positive* tropism. On the other hand, an avoidance movement or growing away is a *negative* tropism. A tropism towards or away from light is called a *phototropism*.

This movement is believed to be caused by electric currents and auxin hormones. The tip of a stem (or root) produces a hormone substance called auxin which diffuses back and controls the growth process. Roots need much less auxin than do stems – in fact too much slows down root growth. When a plant is placed opposite a window so that only one side of the stem receives light, tiny electric currents are believed to be set up by the action of light. These currents cause the growth-promoting hormone to be carried round to the shady side of the stem. This side grows faster and the lengthening of one side of the stem makes it bend over towards the light.

How do the growing shoots of newly germinated seeds, still buried in the earth, grow towards the light? They cannot be phototropic, because they cannot 'see' the light. Instead, they are sensitive to gravity – a response called *geotropism.* If the shoot starts to grow slightly sideways, the lower side grows faster causing the shoot to curve upwards again. Once more, auxins and electricity are the suspected cause.

Electric currents are induced by gravity and the auxin is carried round to the lower sides of the stem. This side grows faster, and the stem bends away from the gravity stimulus (negative geotropism).

Similar auxin movements occur in roots, but, since they need much less hormone, the accumulation on the lower side *slows* growth and the root curves downwards (positive geotropism). The availability of water also affects the direction in which roots grow. Their first choice is in the direction of water and roots would 'rather' grow sideways towards damp soil than downwards into parched dry soil.

The effect of gravity on the direction of growth of shoots and roots can be demonstrated by an experiment in which the direction of gravity on a growing plant is continuously varied; effectively the plant cannot tell up from down. The experiment is carried out in a constantly lit room, so that phototropism has no influence on the results. If some seeds, such as peas, are planted round the edge of a pot and the pot is laid on its side, the roots still grow downwards and the shoots, once they have broken through the surface of the soil, still grow upwards.

Imagine then rolling the pot through half a turn, so that the shoots point downwards and the roots point upwards. After a short time, the shoots will turn and resume growing upwards, and the roots will turn downwards. But what would happen if we could keep the pot rolling? The direction of the force of gravity on each seedling would apparently keep changing (actually it is the direction in which the growing parts of the plant point which keeps changing, the direction of gravity – downwards – remains constant).

In practice in the laboratory, the continuous rotation of the pot is made by a machine called a *clinostat.* It consists of a

**1** The sundew is a predatory plant and flies are its victims. Attracted by the sticky 'dew', a fly becomes stuck to the plant, which then bends its long pointed tentacles inward towards the centre. When the insect is drained of fluids, the dry body is released to blow away in the wind. **2–3** The *Mimosa pudica,* commonly known as the 'sensitive plant' or the 'touch-me-not', is sensitive to shock. When touched, it immediately folds up its leaves. **4** Some plants move simply by growing to where they wish to go, such as this *Saxifraga arachnoides* overflowing its pot. **5** Positive geotropism causes roots to grow down towards the earth and negative geotropism causes the stem to grow up and away from the earth, even if it must grow horizontally first (**A**). Under normal conditions, this problem does not arise (**B**). But when rotating in a clinostat, the plant cannot always find the earth; it continues horizontal growth (**C**).

vertical turntable, on which the plant pot is mounted (effectively on its side), with its horizontal axis driven by a motor. If the machine is kept running for several days, we find that the plant's shoots grow through the surface of the soil away from the seeds, and the roots grow towards the bottom of the pot. But since the pot is on its side, this means both shoots and roots grow horizontally sideways in defiance of the force of gravity.

## Flowers by night and day

Some plants show a strong sensitivity to the various chemical compounds necessary to their growth and preservation. For example, the roots of the lupin will grow towards concentrations of acids and salts in the soil when those acids and salts are required by the plant to sustain cell division, to aid photosynthesis, or any other need the plant may have. Such a response to chemical substances is called *chemotropism,* and when the response is towards the chemical compounds, it is positive chemotropism. However, should certain substances be harmful to the plant, the roots will tend to avoid them in a negative chemotropic response.

Creeping plants and clinging plants exhibit *haptotropism,* or curvature sensitivity. In this case, when the finger-like tendrils of the plant encounter a solid object, the growth of the cells opposite the point of contact accelerates. As a consequence, the tendrils curve round the object and cling to it. Typical examples of this kind of plant are wisteria, honeysuckle, sweet pea and clinging ivy.

Many flowers close their petals at night, as the air temperature falls, and open them again the following day as the air gets warmer. This movement does not involve growth but does require a stimulus in the plant's environment. Commonly it is called a 'sleep movement'; the scientific term is *nastic* movement. For instance, a response to temperature changes is called *thermonasty.* It is brought about by the loss of water from some of the cells on the inside of the petals. The water loss causes the cells to shrink, and as a result the petals collapse inwards. In the morning, these cells take up water, expand, and force the petals open.

Many plants make nastic movements. For instance, the leaves of the mimosa plant respond rapidly to touch. A collapsing of the leaf-stalk causes the feathery leaves to withdraw from contact. For this reason, mimosa is also called the 'sensitive plant' or the 'touch-me-not'. This sensitivity to shock is called *seismonasty.*

As mentioned earlier, in some cases, the whole organism moves in response to a stimulus, rather than just a part of the

3

5

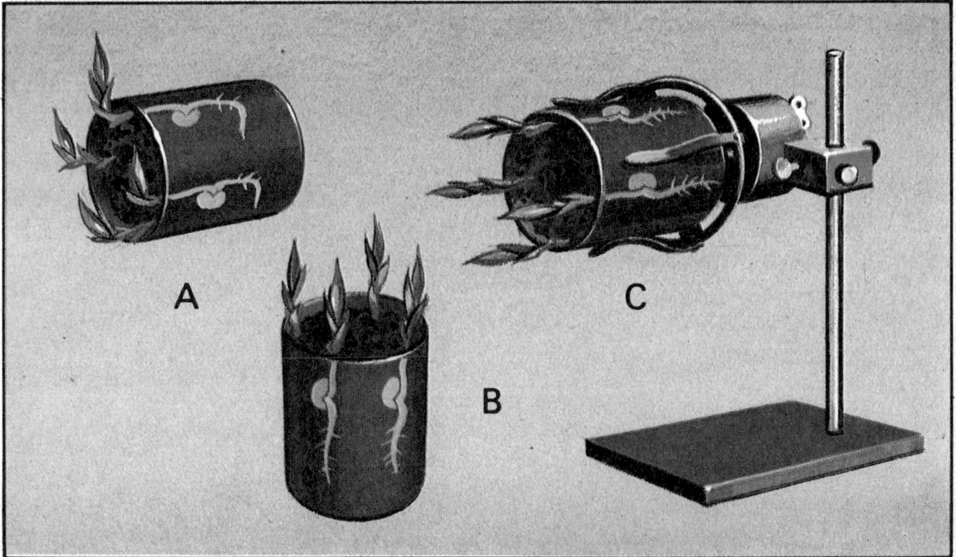

plant, but this is generally confined to the microscopic level. For example, the sperm of a fern is so strongly attracted by malic acid, it will rapidly swim in the direction of any concentration of this substance. It is believed that this kind of *chemotaxis* is used by the sperm in locating the egg for fertilization.

A similar sort of swimming response to the presence of light is called *phototaxis* and may be observed with *chlamydomonas* in a jar placed near a bright window. The green colour intensifies near the light, indicating movement in that direction.

Other plants show very specialized movements peculiar to their ways of life. For example some plants, such as the sundew, devour insects. The upper surfaces of the sundew's leaves are covered with sticky hairs or tentacles. Insects are attracted by the sticky fluid (the 'dew' after which the plant is named) and become attached to it. The edges of the leaf and the long tentacles then bend inwards and envelop the 'victim'. The movement is a rapid form of growth stimulated by secretions from the insect's body.

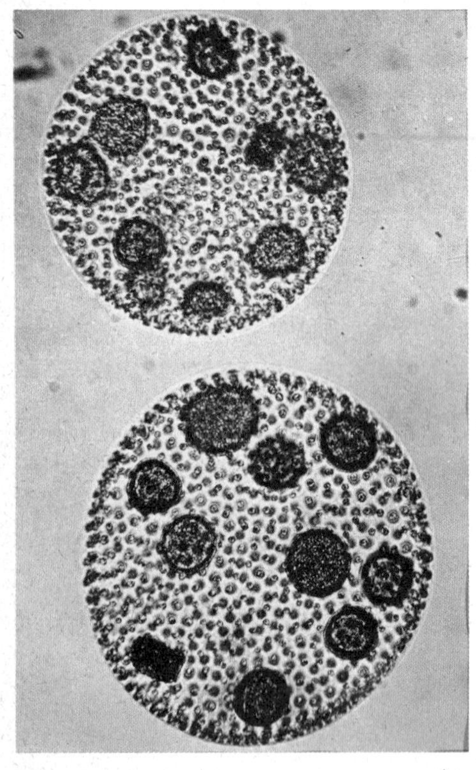

*Above,* a plant's tendency to grow towards light – phototropism – can be demonstrated by experiment. The plant on the left was grown in diffuse light under ordinary conditions; the plant on the right received light from one direction only, and so grew in that direction. The *Volvox* alga, *left,* is a spherical cluster of cells. Each cell has two flagella for propulsion. The dark blotches are new colonies forming. As they become bigger, they burst the parent colony and move off for independent existence. *Below left,* daisies open themselves wide to take up sunshine during daylight hours. *Below right,* at night, they curl up and go to sleep with the rest of the world. Such 'sleep' movements in daisies and other flowers are called nastic movements, and are triggered off by falling air temperature.

Butterwort is another insectivorous (insect-eating) plant that works in the same way (this time the plant is named after the greasy feeling of its leaves). In both cases, after 'devouring' the insect's body fluids, the leaves re-open by growth of the inside of the leaf surface. The dry, dead body blows away and more sticky fluid is secreted ready for the next victim.

Most animals move to find food. Most plants cannot move and must get nutrients from the air and soil near the plant (except, as we have seen, plants that can 'feed' on insects, and some microscopic plants). Eventually the food supply in the soil round the roots will be largely used up. But some plants can take advantage of food further away by growing long creeping stems which take root perhaps many feet from the parent plant – a familiar example is the strawberry. These daughter plantlets then draw on soil better supplied with nutrients. Eventually the parent plant dies off and the plants at the ends of the 'runners' survive. In this way, the plant has effectively moved along the ground. Botanists call this method of spreading *vegetative propagation.*

Among plants and simple animals, there are only a few, limited movements. But they are essential for the survival of the organism. An amoeba must move to feed. In a plant seedling, the stems have to grow upwards and the roots downwards. Some of the earliest experiments in a future orbiting space laboratory – where there will be no gravity and hence no real 'up' and 'down' – will probably involve plants.

# Living world on the move 2

The movement of an animal can be either fast or slow, jerky or smooth, graceful or clumsy; but in all cases it admirably suits the animal for its niche in the world, be it predator or prey.

ONE OF the often-quoted differences between animals and plants is that animals can move from place to place and most plants cannot. Although this is a sweeping generalization and is not strictly true, it does pose an important question: Why *do* animals move? Like so many apparently simple questions in biology, it has no simple, straightforward answer. We can get a long way towards reaching the answer by saying: 'Animals generally move in search of food.'

When food in one place becomes scarce, animals must move on to a region where food is more plentiful. Vast herds of plant-eating animals *(herbivores),* such as deer, antelopes and zebras, roam the plains in search of good pasture and water. Meat-eaters *(carnivores),* such as lions and leopards, follow them and have to be able to move swiftly to hunt and catch their prey. Scavengers, such as hyenas and vultures, move in to finish up what the hunters leave.

Other factors also influence and necessitate movement. The climate may become unfavourable, either by directly affecting an animal or by affecting its food supply. For this reason, every winter large flocks of birds leave northern countries for the warmer climates of southern Europe and Africa. For instance, swallows migrate in the autumn and fly from Britain to Africa.

### Action in earthworms

In the breeding season, animals search for a mate. For many mammals and birds, movement is often required for their complex courtship behaviour. Movement enables a species as a whole to disperse and occupy a wider range of favourable regions.

But whatever the motives, in biological terms, movement in higher animals can be regarded as the conversion of chemical energy into a muscular contraction – which is then transformed into motion.

A contracting muscle must act against something. In the soft-bodied lower metazoan animals, such as worms, shell-fish and starfish, which have no skeletal elements, the muscles act against the body cavity *(coelom).* The coelom here takes on the function of a skeleton. Muscles bring about changes in pressure which are converted into movement. The coelom is said to act as a *hydrostatic skeleton,* and its function can be understood by considering the movements in an earthworm.

Like all worms, the earthworm has a body made up of a chain of segments. Each segment contains a portion of coelom separated from the neighbouring segment by a wall or *septum.* The body wall around the coelom contains muscles running the length of the body. Other circular muscles running around the body control changes

The way an animal moves must be adapted both to the medium through which it moves and its reasons for moving. *Top,* the predatory lion must be swift and agile to catch its prey. The prey, of course, must be even swifter and more agile to avoid becoming the lion's dinner. *Above,* webbed feet and powerful hindlegs are the frog's special adaptations for movement in the water.

in body diameter. The worm anchors itself to the soil by means of small 'hairs' or *chaetae* on its skin.

An earthworm moves forward either in its burrow or along the ground by withdrawing the chaetae of the front segments and by contracting their circular muscles. As the circular muscles contract, the pressure of the coelomic fluid causes the segment to increase in length which, in turn, forces the head end of the worm forward. The segments immediately behind the head now increase in diameter as the circular muscles relax and longitudinal muscles contract. The chaetae on these segments are now stuck out to complete the anchorage of the head end. Chaetae of the rear segments are now retracted and the posterior segments drawn forward by contraction of longitudinal muscles.

The essential features of this type of locomotion are circular and longitudinal muscles working against each other (when one contracts the other relaxes) – these are known as *antagonistic muscles;* the coelomic fluid acts as a hydrostatic skeleton; and there is a means of anchoring the stationary segments to prevent the body from slipping backwards.

Hydrostatic skeletons are found in many other invertebrate animals and are particularly well suited to the act of burrowing. Bivalve shell-fish, such as razor-shells, which burrow in the sea bed rely on antagonistic foot *retractor* and *protractor* muscles acting against the coelom of the foot. The two shell valves are used to anchor the body while the muscular foot probes into the sea bed. The foot is pushed down into the sand and expands at its tip to provide anchorage. The shell closes tightly and is pulled down as the foot muscles contract. As the shell opens to anchor the animal, the foot probes further into the sand, swells at its tip, and the body is again drawn down with the shell closed deeper into the sea bed.

## A skeleton of levers

A starfish crawls by means of hundreds of tiny tube 'feet' on each of its arms. Each tube foot contains a part of the coelom, upon which antagonistic longitudinal and circular muscles act. The end of the foot also acts as a minute suction pad, enabling the starfish to cling to rocks and seaweed.

In animals with a hard skeleton, muscular movements are transmitted into motion by a system of levers. The levers are the bones or plates of the skeleton. In the invertebrates we find animals such as insects, millipedes and crustaceans (crabs and lobsters). These *arthropods* have hard outer skeletons and are characterized by jointed appendages. For example, a typical adult insect has three pairs of legs. Each leg has *flexor* muscles within the joints, and the movement of a land insect is typified by that of the common ground beetle. Of its six legs, only three are in contact with the ground at any one time. The front and back legs of one side are balanced by the middle leg of the other side. In this way, the beetle has a triangle of contact with the ground. A similar but

*Below,* the humming-bird's tiny body and its ability to flap its wings at a dazzling rate give it exceptional manoeuvrability: it can hover, fly backwards, and dart through the air much as a lizard scampers across the ground. *Right,* a lash of its powerful tail launches this hungry fish skyward after an unusual morsel for dinner.

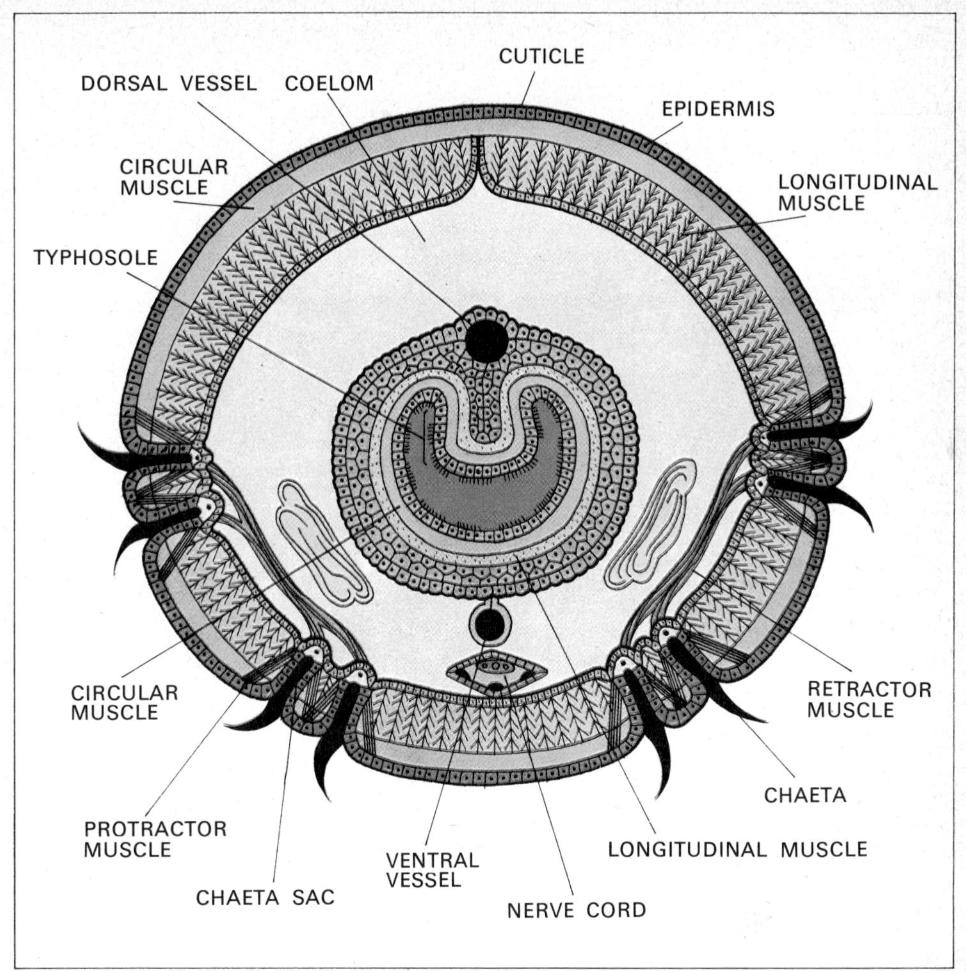


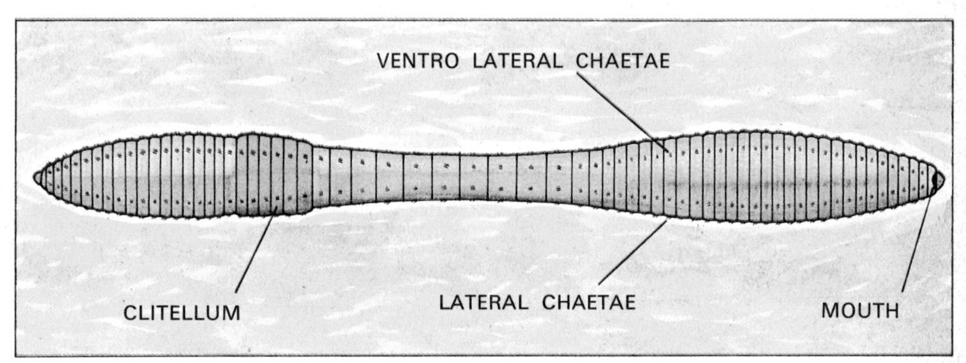


*Above,* birds, fish and aeroplanes in a sense are cousins, because their bodies incorporate similar design elements. The sleek, flowing lines of their shapes minimize friction with air and water as they pass through. The wings of the bird and the aeroplane are essential in keeping them aloft, but they also function to stabilize motion, as do the fins of the fish. *Diagrams*: the earthworm, in cross-section, *top,* shows the muscular structure which allows it to inch along. Contraction of the circular muscles elongates the segments, pushing the head end of the worm forward. *Above,* the diagram shows a worm in the process of motion, the elongation of the middle segments clearly exhibited. The process is slow, but it serves the purpose. The prominent area shown in yellow, the *clitellum,* is for reproduction, not for locomotion.

opposite triangle is made when the other three legs make contact. This quick alternation of a three-point 'undercarriage' produces a zig-zag forward movement, each leg acting as a lever against which muscles are pulling.

Vertebrate animals have an inner skeleton. The backbone, girdles and limbs provide a highly efficient system of levers by which the voluntary muscles act to produce movements. Once again, we find antagonistic muscles involved in the movement of a limb – the bones are the levers, and the joint between them is the pivot. In the human arm for instance, the biceps and triceps are two such antagonistic muscles (lying either side of the humerus bone in the upper arm); the elbow joint is the pivot. When the biceps muscle contracts, the triceps relaxes and the forearm is raised. The opposite applies when the arm is lowered. In this way, the musculo-skeletal system provides a rigid support for the body, while at the same time allowing the jointed bones to remain flexible for movement.

## Streams and streamlining

Water is a relatively dense medium which surrounds some animals and provides support by buoyancy. An animal as large as a whale, for instance, could not live on land – the effort required to lift its weight off the ground would be too great. Even the ancient dinosaurs probably spent much of their time in water in order to 'take the weight off their feet'.

The propulsive forces that move a fish through water are usually produced by the wriggling action of longitudinal muscle fibres along the back. The fins are sometimes used to help forward movement, but more often they act as stabilizers, rudders and brakes. Fast swimmers have streamlined bodies which offer a minimum resistance as the fish pass through water.

Aquatic mammals, such as whales and dolphins, have fish-like forms with an elongated head, no neck, a streamlined body and a powerful tail. Whales have a horizontal tail fin and the swimming mechanism depends on its up and down movement. The fore-limbs have a paddle-like appearance and are used as stabilizers.

Many animals have webbed feet, which increase the swimming efficiency of the limbs. The hind limbs of frogs and toads bear webbed feet, as do the legs of many aquatic birds, and a few mammals such as the beaver whose hind feet are webbed. The uniformity in such animals is well shown by the penguin, a bird which is perfectly adapted to its aquatic environment. Once again, we find a streamlined body with a short neck region. But unlike most water birds, a penguin swims with forelimbs which are modified into flippers; the feet are webbed.

The first prehistoric land animals were confronted with problems very different from those which their ancestors had so successfully overcome in water. Air friction is negligible and so no highly developed streamlining is required.

## Legs for land animals

The main problem is how to overcome gravity and lift the body from the ground with no buoyant water to help. This was accomplished by the evolution of paired limbs, and by fusion of the backbone and limb girdles. The paired limbs of all four-legged animals are thought to derive from the paired fins of an ancient group of fishes represented today by the coelacanth, which has survived for at least 50 million years.

The earliest land-walking amphibians and reptiles were still very fish-like in appearance and relied on undulations of the body assisted by clumsy limbs held outwards. Many modern amphibians such as newts move in this way, and when frightened they seem to 'swim on land' with their bellies on the ground.

Evolutionary trends have led to a more efficient way of locomotion in reptiles and, particularly, in mammals. In mammals, the limbs are tucked in beneath the body, taking the full weight in a less strenuous way. The work required to hold the body up is now switched from what was the front of the animal to the back surface. In mammals which can walk erect, such as apes and men, all the weight is transferred to two limbs.

In the mammals, we find a wide variety of forms and some interesting comparisons. There is the sloth, which hangs upside down in the forests of South America and moves at a rate of 14 feet a minute – when it is in a hurry. On the other hand, a cheetah or an antelope may reach speeds exceeding 50 miles an hour. Nevertheless, the sloth and the antelope are each well adapted for its own way of life. The sloth remains still and inconspicuous to avoid predators; an antelope needs high-speed movement to escape from its predators.

Three types of walking limbs are found in mammals. The first is called *plantigrade,* for the animals which walk with their feet flat on the ground – for example, a polar bear, which pads across the arctic ice. The second is *digitigrade,* for the animals which walk on 'tip-toe' – for example, a dog, which leaves only the imprint of its toes as it walks along. And the third is *unguligrade,* for animals whose limbs become stilt-like with hoofs – for example, a horse, which clops along on what are virtually single toes. The unguligrade condition is also found in all the fleet-footed herbivores, such as deer and antelopes.

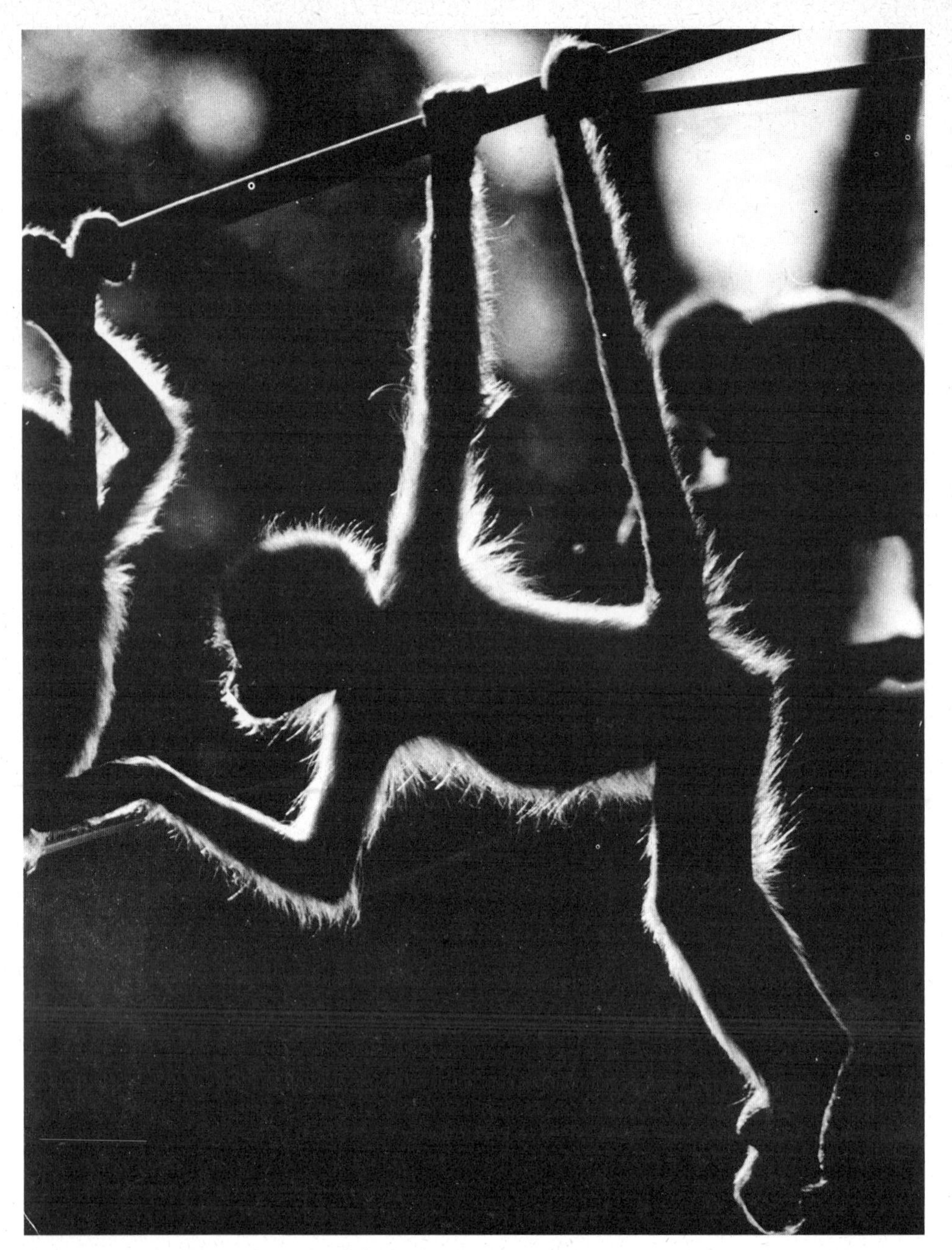

The monkey shows a variety of adaptations for motion. Its four limbs allow it to scamper across the ground; its human-like hands allow it to climb trees; its long, limber tail gives it the ability to swing from branch to branch.

Many animals spend much of their time in tree tops. The gibbon, for instance, is well adapted to this mode of life; it has extremely long forelimbs and digits. The orang-utan is another tree dweller, with special adaptations to allow it to take a firm grip on tree branches.

Bats are a group of mammals that have joined the birds in conquering the air. Bird flight has been studied in great detail. The wing acts as an *aerofoil* – that is, when it moves forwards through the air with its surface slightly inclined, two forces are set up. A *lift* force acts upwards, and a *drag* force acts backwards, tending to oppose the movement. Movement of air over the wing causes the pressure above it to be less than that below. As a result, the wing is pushed upwards into the region of lower pressure by the higher pressure under it.

## Into the wide blue yonder

A small wing area is necessary for efficient flight (to keep drag to a minimum), but has disadvantages since the wings must be flapped continuously to maintain lift. This, in turn, limits the size of the bird. Flapping flight is typical of the pigeon, and is taken to an extreme in the hummingbird where the wings beat back and forth as fast as 200 times a second. Some fast-flying birds, however, have a large wing span, their higher speed giving their wings more lift and compensating for drag. This allows them to glide without losing much height, thereby saving energy. An albatross is an example of such a bird.

Soaring flight, shown by many birds of prey such as the eagles and vultures, makes use of rising hot air currents. These birds can often be seen rising in a spiral fashion with no effort from their wings, soaring like a kite in a breeze. Large broad wings are needed for this type of flight.

From the simple wriggling of worms and tadpoles to the complex movements made by apes and men, creatures have evolved in such a way that they are best suited to surviving in their own particular environments, be it land, sea or air.

# Animal travellers

**Each year hordes of animals migrate from one part of the world to another. Some species seek warmth in winter, some swim oceans to breed, others leave their birthplace in search of new land.**

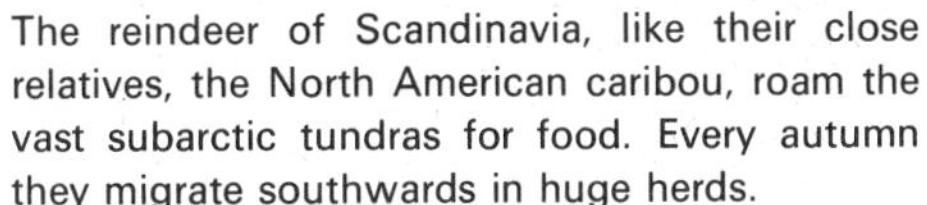

The reindeer of Scandinavia, like their close relatives, the North American caribou, roam the vast subarctic tundras for food. Every autumn they migrate southwards in huge herds.

TO MOST PEOPLE the word 'migration' means the seasonal movements of some species of bird – such as the swallow which in Britain heralds the spring, or the wild goose which flies dramatically across the skies of the United States in its arrow-shaped formations. Comparatively few people are aware that bird movement, although in some ways the most dramatic aspect of migration, is only part of the picture.

Many other creatures, on land and in the sea, behave similarly and do so for similar reasons. They deliberately seek changes of climate and scene in order to achieve better living conditions. This may be designed to protect the adult population, to weed out the old and infirm (by the rigours of the trip), or to provide an environment in which the young have a better chance of survival.

The migration of birds like swallows and geese, implies regular seasonal trips back and forth over roughly the same route in an endless cycle. And indeed, for some zoologists this is the only definition of migration which is acceptable. On the other hand, there are many species of animals which set out to find better conditions and thereby maintain the standing of their kind, yet make no return trip to their point of departure. This may be left to their young, or indeed no return trip may be made at all – the travellers just settle where they land and colonize. Later their offspring may be moved by one circumstance or another to make their own revitalizing journey.

When considering the migrant creatures we find that the regular commuters across the face of the globe – the animals with two addresses, as it were – comprise a comparatively large part of the whole. Of the bird population of the world, nearly half (more than 4,000 species) migrate regularly.

## Following the sun

In the northern hemisphere, this is most likely to be a southerly movement on the outward trip in the autumn, and a return northwards in the spring (although some species, such as wigeon, do travel east-west and vice versa). The reasons for this general similarity are not hard to find. In arctic regions, for instance, the climate is insupportable during winter except for a handful of specially adapted creatures. The rest must leave.

In Greenland of the 64 species common to the island, 36 leave totally for the winter. The rest migrate to its southern edge. When the short Arctic summer begins, the birds return to their former haunts.

In the temperate zone, the picture is similar but the climatic conditions are not so extreme. Yet even so, the winter means difficulties in finding food – the ground is hard, hours of daylight dwindle and there is little fruit. Birds, such as swallows and starlings, leave northern Europe to winter in the south and thus maintain their strength. Then they return for the northern summer to breed.

The autumn has come. No longer living in territories, these martins have forgotten their individual aggressions in preparation for the long flight from Britain to Africa.

Even in the tropics, some seasonal changes takes place. They are likely to be in wet or dry seasons and they, too, may cause migratory movements.

Some bird migrants customarily clock up enormous distances. A case in point is the Arctic tern. Breeding during the short summer of the far north, it leaves in the winter for a marathon journey south – to the southernmost tip of the African continent and sometimes even to the northern edge of Antarctica. One specimen ringed in Greenland in 1951 was retrieved some four months later in Durban, South Africa, having covered a distance of 9,000 miles. But at least one shearwater is known to have bettered this feat. Ringed in Wales, it later turned up in South Australia, a record distance for a marked bird. The sea route is about 12,000 miles.

In the southern hemisphere some species make winter migrations to the north for similar reasons as their cousins in the northern hemisphere. However comparatively few land birds actually cross the Equator; though some sea birds do so in considerable numbers.

At least one southern bird migrates not on the wing, but in the water. Penguins congregate in enormous numbers in Antarctica for breeding purposes during the fine weather. Afterwards they disperse and have been known to make trips of many hundreds of miles entirely by swimming. An emperor penguin killed by members of an American exploration party in 1840 was found to have stones in its gizzard, although there was no known land within 1,000 miles in any direction. The explorers therefore reasoned that there must be some *uncharted* land which was closer. Heartened by the idea, they moved on and discovered Antarctica.

Many marine creatures migrate regularly. Among fish, the tunny of the Mediterranean and Azores follow a well-defined route to the Dogger Bank area and back. Plaice and cod make similar journeys. In these cases the search for optimum breeding conditions, directly or indirectly, give impetus to the movements.

Eel migration is a case which clearly shows the actual effect that migration has on the eel population. Unlike the birds, the eels complete only one migratory cycle in their lifetime. As the eels come to maturity in the rivers and streams of Europe and America, they begin to journey down to the sea. They make for their breeding grounds which are the waters of the Sargasso Sea, a vast area of the Atlantic to the east of the West Indies. In these turgid waters, largely unruffled by wind or current, a great carpet of seaweed thrives and it is thronged with animal life as well. The adult eels reach the Sargasso in the spring, when the summer abundance of food is about to begin.

Breeding takes place and millions of eggs are laid. Within a matter of weeks these have hatched into larvae. The adult eels then die, leaving the larvae to rise to the surface where they become part of the surface life. They spread out towards the edge of the Sargasso Sea until eventually they come into contact with the great ocean current. Then their great journey begins: in the case of the European eel it stretches over 2,000 miles and takes more than two years.

Growing all the time the eels first drift with the currents and later they swim towards the shores from which their parent eels came. On the way this vast horde of immature eels is constantly preyed upon – only the strongest and most agile survive.

The migration of salmon runs in the opposite direction. The salmon are spawned in individual rivers and streams and move down to the salt water where they come to maturity. Then they return, often to the same waterway in which they were born, to continue the breeding cycle.

## Two-way migrants

Examples of two-way migration are extremely common among mammals. They include the springbok of South Africa, the Californian seal, whales and no less than three species of bat in the United States. (Self-protection against the hardships of the winter more usually takes the form of hibernation among bats.)

The caribou of North America move south in the autumn after mating has taken place. Then in the spring they move northwards again, prompted, it has been suggested, by the hordes of mosquitoes which appear in the warmer weather and which harry the caribou unmercifully.

Journeys which are likely to guarantee the survival of many of the young, play havoc with the old. This has been graphically described in relation to the once great herds of American buffalo. When these animals moved to new pastures, as they did in both spring and autumn, they were attacked along the route by hungry wolves. The attack was inevitably launched from behind, and by some natural instinct the older buffalo congregated at the rear of the herd. Likewise any injured beast would take up its position there.

Thus the predators pulled down the beasts which the herd could most afford to lose – the aged and the infirm. That the mechanism of migration worked well for the buffalo is evidenced by the numbers in which they existed at one time on the American plains.

The nomads are the second group of animals within our definition. They are those that are in a state of almost permanent migration, and cover the same ground twice only by accident. The need for fresh sources of food is probably the main triggering factor here.

The army ants of South America move about in very great numbers. They have voracious appetites, and any living creature which cannot get out of their way is trapped and dies in a particularly horrible way. A million tiny but powerful jaws will tear small pieces of flesh from their bodies until nothing is left but the clean, white bones.

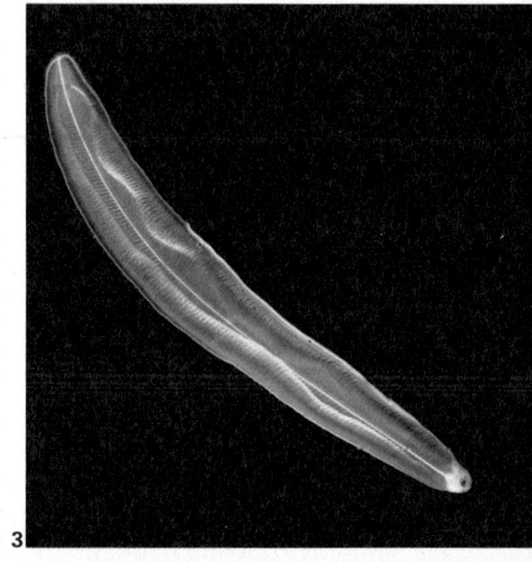
3

1

2

**1** In prehistoric times the nine-banded armadillo was a native of South America. Since then it has migrated north to the United States, where it is now considered a pest.
**2** Whooper swans nest in far northern countries like Greenland and Iceland. As soon as the autumn comes they migrate south in V-shaped formations.
**3** After hatching in the Sargasso Sea, the tiny eel larvae are carried by the ocean currents to the rivers of Europe and America. There they mature before returning to breed.
**4** The rhinoceros is a nomadic migrant constantly searching for good grazing. By travelling with the rhinoceros certain species of bird have an excellent supply of insects.
**5** Caribou crossing a glacial stream in Alaska on their way south in the autumn, after mating. The young are born after the migration.
**6** The common eel makes the journey from the Sargasso Sea and back once in its lifetime. The arctic tern makes its huge migrations every year.
**7** The African buffalo, with its herds of as many as 1,000 animals is a nomadic migrant well adapted to living in forest or savanna.

5

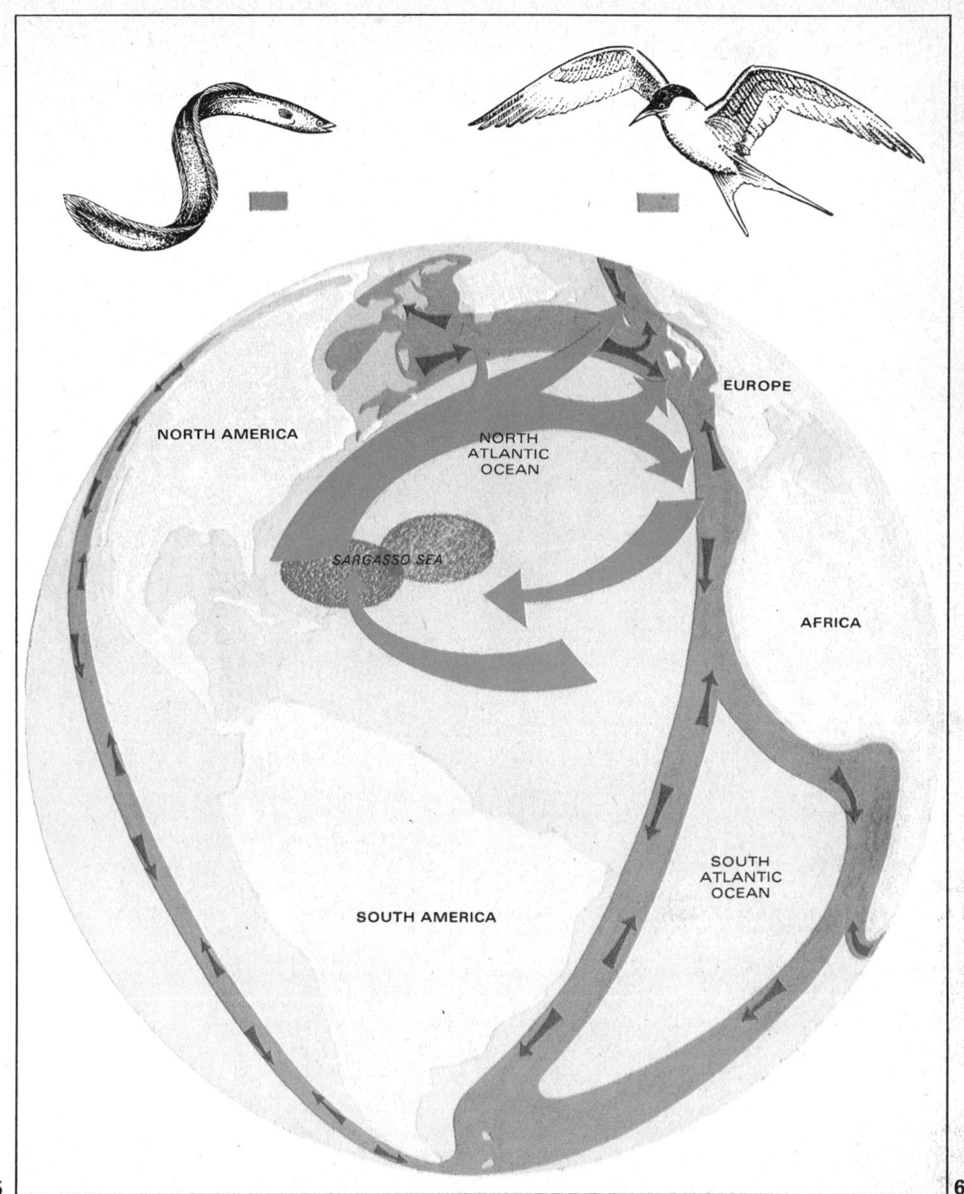


6

7

**1** The Sacramento National Wildlife Refuge in California makes an excellent meeting-point for ducks and geese as they gather in their thousands in preparation to migrate southwards.
**2** The African elephant will migrate far in search of its favourite foods. Early every year herds of elephants move up the slopes of Mount Kenya in search of mukaita berries.

The ant species, *Eciton hamatum,* which thrives in areas of Panama, searches for food on the march for about 17 days and then halts for a further 19 or 20. The respite is for breeding purposes. At this time, the queen lays her eggs and the party waits until the larvae which hatch from them are strong enough to travel. Then each larva is picked up by a worker and carried in its mouth until the next stop. At each stop, the queen lays more eggs, but the larvae carried by mouth from the previous breeding-halt take the opportunity to spin cocoons and emerge before the new start as adult ants. Thus the population level is maintained during the permanent migration.

The elephants of both Africa and India are generally nomadic. But their feeding habits often impart some kind of regularity and pattern to their movements. The elephant eats a vast quantity of vegetation during a day in order to fuel its vast bulk. At the same time it is fastidious, has definite likes and dislikes concerning food and therefore moves about constantly in search of titbits, often returning regularly to the spots where it knows the goodies can be obtained. It was reported by a nineteenth-century zoologist that the elephants of Ceylon were very partial to the taste of the palmyra palm's fruit. When the fruit ripened, the natives kept an expectant eye open for the herds, and they were seldom disappointed. Similarly, in Africa it has been noted during the first two months of the year, that the elephants move up the slopes of Mount Kenya to feed on mukaita berries which ripen at this time.

Very little will deter elephants from reaching food of their choice. Fire and firearms may, but the stoutest fence or stockade will shatter before them, and water, however deep, is no problem. If the latter is deep enough to cover the creatures but they are still able to reach the surface with their trunks, they will walk across the bottom using trunks as natural 'snorkels'. If the water is too deep for this, then they swim.

The gorilla, fierce of feature but gentle by nature unless frightened or attacked, shares at least one of the problems of the elephant. This is its great size – a male can weigh as much as 40 stone – and its need for food in large quantities keeps it on the move. It is a vegetarian like the elephant, subsisting on sugar-cane, fruit and nuts, but it roams over a much smaller area than does the elephant.

## The colonizers

The final group of migrants are those which should be called the colonizers. Their one-way and spasmodic journeys account for the spread of the particular species and its consequent growth in numbers.

The cattle egret, so called because it is found in association with large herds, was originally a native of India and some parts of West Africa. It still exists in these areas, but relatively recently the birds have moved into new areas far removed from the old. By 1930 cattle egrets had turned up in South America; by 1948 they had reached Australia; and 1952 was the year in which they were first spotted in the United States.

The cattle egrets have set up home in large numbers in the areas within these countries which are hot and where cattle exist in quantity. Guyana (formerly British Guiana) must have seemed a particularly attractive spot to the egrets when they arrived. Not only is the climate very similar to that of parts of India, but the country also carries some herds of Brahman cattle.

The arriving birds would, however, have been unable to draw these parallels, even if they were capable of powers of reasoning. They would just find the conditions to their liking. It is very unlikely that the birds which reached Guyana had ever been in India, for colonizing migrations of this kind are much less direct.

In the homeland at the time initial dispersal began, the triggering factor was population pressure. And as a matter of course adult birds drive their young away when the latter reach maturity. Although the treatment may seem harsh, congestion is relieved in this way and it ensures that the colonizing flights are undertaken by the young and strong. They are best suited to make the flight to new grounds and to survive new problems which may arise there. Generation after generation of cattle egrets would be hatched and dispatched by their parents in a slow territorial spread. There is little chance that any colonist actually reached South America direct from India, but came instead from some intermediate colony.

There are several mammals which figure among the colonizers. An interesting example is the nine-banded armadillo. In prehistory the animal is known to have been a native of South America. But the freezing of sea-water to form polar ice-caps caused a drop in the level of the world oceans. What had once been the *island* of South America was now revealed as being joined to the northern land mass by a previously submerged strip of land, the Isthmus of Panama.

The small but tank-like armadillo was one of the first adventurers to cross to the north. But for thousands of years its progress must have been very slow. For example, it was not until the last quarter of the nineteenth century that it was noticed in Texas. But since then, and in particular since the 1930s, it has spread dramatically. In some states it is now even considered a pest.

One reason given for this spread of population has been that intensive agriculture has also spread rapidly across the United States during this period. The armadillo finds it easier to root out the insects upon which it lives, if it is working in cultivated ground.

In short, this is yet another example of the way in which an animal species can maintain or even strengthen its numbers by moving from one location to another. It makes no difference whether the journey is one- or two-directional, regular or irregular. It is to migration of all kinds that we owe the present distribution and multiplicity of wildlife forms.

# Born navigators

**Many animals and insects travel long distances and are able to find their way with remarkable accuracy. How they navigate remains a baffling problem, still the subject of intensive scientific investigation.**

SOME STORIES seem to get into the newspapers time and time again, never losing curiosity value. One such story concerns an individualistic tom-cat which, having been moved with the rest of its owner's belongings to a new home, promptly disappears – only to turn up days or even weeks later at the old address. And it may have travelled over 100 miles in the interim.

Some species of birds migrate, or travel great distances seasonally, in order to enjoy a warmer climate and more plentiful food. Arctic tern, for example, have been known to cover as much as 9,000 miles (Greenland to South Africa) during a migratory trip.

These are among the more spectacular examples of long-distance travel by animals. But it is also true that most animals at some time during their lives accomplish some long trip, although it may be considerable only in relation to their size. Again, like cats and birds, some larger animals seem to be capable of aiming themselves towards a specific geographical location; but among many smaller animals, particularly the invertebrates, the goal is not a specific place but a set of conditions.

These creatures wander aimlessly until they encounter some external stimuli, like a taste or smell which appeals to them, and then they home on to the source. In

1 Salmon leaping a waterfall on their way up the River Conway, Wales, to spawn. Mature salmon navigate hundreds of miles to their birthplaces to lay their eggs.

2 A swarm of locusts on the move. Insect migrations seem to be much more haphazard than those of birds, and the direction of the wind plays an important part in determining where they go.

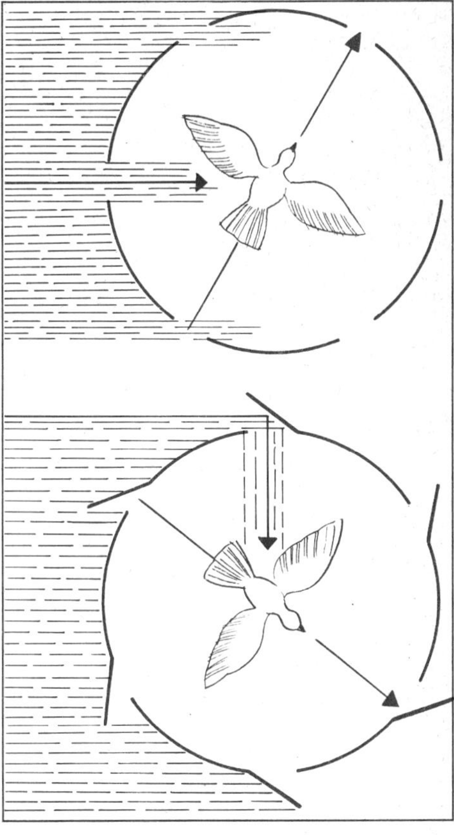

Caged and in direct sunlight, migrating starlings turn to the south. The birds can be made to turn westwards by diverting the sunlight through 90 degrees using a mirror system.

animals of either kind, however, it seems likely that some or all of the senses given to Man, and by which he himself finds his way about, are used. These are the senses of sight, hearing, taste, touch and smell – backed up by memory. Yet these senses are often employed by animals in different degrees and different ways.

The sense of smell is very poorly developed in Man, but is a great deal keener in the dog. To some insects it is as important as sight, and in the blind varieties takes the place of the missing faculty altogether.

## Ant navigation

Some ants can see and some cannot, but all have highly developed senses of smell and of taste. They are needed for navigation within the darkness of the nest, needed to find food sources, needed to make repeated journeys between these and the nest. Thus, the sighted ant on the hunt for food marches out from the nest and locates the food source with its sense of smell. On the way out it notes visually certain landmarks and by these it is able to retrace its steps and so tip off the colony. However, it is *not* able to pass on to the other ants its own memory of the route to be taken.

Nor are others able to smell the food themselves, it is too far away.

So on the way back the forager lays down a chemical trail. This comprises tiny drops of liquid which the ant squeezes from its abdomen from time to time as it hurries along. Like tooth-paste squeezed from a tube which is being moved over a horizontal surface, the ant's trail material is laid down along the line of its march. Each spot has an individual shape.

The next step in feeding the colony is that a column of worker ants back-tracks over the trail left by the food finder. And this is where the ants' sense of taste becomes important. They use tiny chemical-sensitive organs on their antennae to taste the trail material, moving from one drop to the next until they reach their goal. (It has been suggested, but not universally agreed, that they are also able to use their antennae like calipers and so discover the actual shape of the droplet left on the ground, and that this gives them even more directional information.)

As long as the food supply holds out, there is no chance that the trail will lose its chemical magic. For each worker ant, having filled its abdomen with food then heads back towards the nest laying its own trail along the line of the original. When the food source gives out, so does the trail maintenance, and after a couple of hours at most, the potency of the chemical is gone.

Not so the trails left by the army ants of Central America. These marauders are blind and nomadic, wandering at will about the countryside in a great column. They keep their formation by touching, tasting and smelling each other.

Every now and then they decide to bivouac and then a subsidiary column of voracious forager ants is sent out which almost soaks the ground it covers in marker chemical. As the workers at the head of the column pick up the food they have found and work back the way they came through the horde, their places are taken by fresh workers. By following the broad chemical trail which has been laid down, the food-laden worker returns to the main body of the column.

## Underwater scents

Scent is also a potent direction finder for certain animals underwater. Some planarians – small, flat, carnivorous worms – live in streams. Searching for food, they progress in a straight line along the bottom. The food they seek will be diffusing its constituent juices into the water and when the planarian gets close enough, organs on its head scent certain chemicals contained in the juice and carried by the water.

At this point the animal begins to wave its head horizontally, thus sampling the water to either side of its path. Naturally, the amount of attractant chemical on the food side will be greater than on the other, so the worm begins to move slowly in that direction. It continues testing as it goes, continually curving in the direction of the stronger chemical stimuli, until eventually it fastens on to the food.

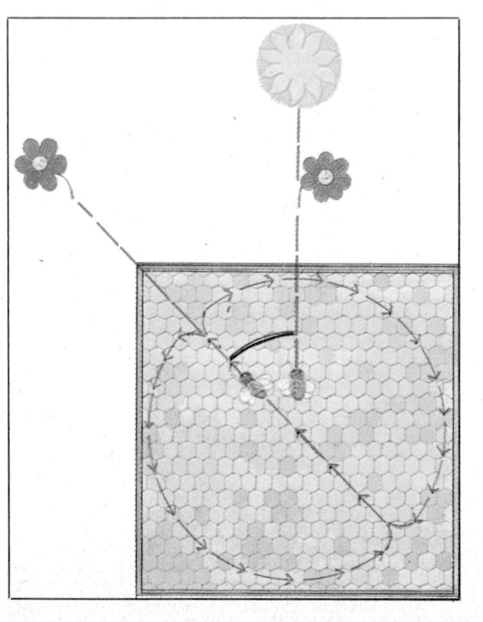

The waggle dance performed by returning bees indicates sources of nectar to other bees in the hive. The bee's dance indicates the angle between the source and the sun's position.

This is a remarkably efficient homing process, but it is nowhere near as spectacular in its scope as that of the salmon. Salmon born in streams and rivers far inland then swim down to the sea to mature. There they feed and grow to full size. After four or five years they return to the fresh waterways of land to spawn so that the cycle of birth, migration and return can begin all over again.

If that was all there was to it, perhaps there would be no great cause for interest. But the fact is that many salmon actually return to the specific water course in which they themselves were hatched, fighting their way up cataracts, waterfalls and even man-made dams to get there.

Now, it is known with certainty that when young salmon descend their particular river to the sea, they do not remain in the vicinity of that river mouth. One marked salmon, for instance, was caught as far as 115 miles from the Vancouver Island creek in which it was hatched; other wanderings on a similar scale have also been recorded. Yet just how these fish are able to navigate over such large distances to return to their birthplace is one of the great unanswered questions in marine biology – and for the time being must be left at that.

However, navigate they do, and we are on safer speculative ground once the salmon has reached the vicinity of its river mouth or stream outlet. Some experimentation with minnows has shown that these fish are capable of differentiating between water taken from two different streams. They will come to the surface of their tank to feed when water of one kind is introduced but shy away when the other is injected in, however subtly this is done.

Water from different sources has a dis-

3

Migration habits of birds are studied by ornithologists through a world-wide correspondence network. Some of the stages in tracking migration routes are shown.

**1** Sandmartins caught in a fine mist net. The mist net allows the capture of birds unharmed which can be recorded and released.

**2** Weighing a willow-warbler after capture in Jordan. The weight is a rough guide to how far the bird has flown since it began migrating.

**3** The metal ring being clamped round the leg of this lesser whitethroat records the place and date of its capture. If caught again, the bird can be identified and its route traced.

**4** Measuring the wing of a lesser whitethroat. This gives some guide to the bird's age.

tinctive chemical signature due to the different organic substances which find their way into each waterway from the soil which it drains. The minnows were aware of this, and it seems likely also that salmon can find their home stream by the smell of the chemical or blend of chemicals peculiar to it.

Indeed, this theory has been put to the test in a small way: in one experiment the nostrils of a small batch of marked salmon were plugged. Subsequently, it was found that these rediscovered their home stream less easily than others in the sample batch which were left untouched.

## Polarized light

While the senses of touch, taste, smell and so on are extremely important to some animals, sight is just as important to others. Bees are one such group and provide a splendid example of the way in which a sense shared by humans is used in a totally different way.

Bees are able to detect polarized light, a very important factor in their ability to navigate between hive and food. But before this is discussed, we should understand what polarized light is.

Ordinary light can be considered to consist of waves which vibrate randomly in relation to the line of travel; that is some are vertical, some are horizontal, the rest are inclined to the path at all angles in between.

Now when ordinary light emanating from the sun strikes the tiny particles which abound in the outer atmosphere of the Earth, some of it is reflected in a way which is said to be *plane polarized*. Simply, this means that only the waves which vibrate in one plane to the direction of the beam (the vertical, say) are reflected.

Not all the sunlight is polarized in this way. The percentage of polarization varies across the sky, as does the angle of the plane of polarization. (In other words, perhaps only the horizontal vibrations are reflected at some points.) The result is that a characteristic pattern of polarized light is beamed continuously down from the sky. It is constant in relation to the sun, and therefore, for eyes that can see it, provides a kind of map of the sky overhead. The bee's eye, and indeed that of a number of other animals and insects, is so constructed that it can detect polarized light. (Most humans cannot do this; a polaroid filter is necessary to do the job.) And such creatures are able to judge the position of the sun from the pattern – even on an overcast day, provided some part of the pattern of polarization is visible.

But before leaving bees entirely, it must also be said that they navigate over short distances by means of visual landmarks and home by means of scent and colour discrimination. Likewise, they apparently measure distances by the amount of effort necessary to cover them. They can also communicate information concerning the direction and distance of a required goal to others of their hive by means of a set of complicated dance routines.

Homing pigeons, for example, are natural navigators. They are trained for a particular event by being removed from the loft and then released at various points along a line between home and start, the distance between release and loft being increased day by day.

Now, like most birds, the homing pigeon has prodigiously developed powers of sight. And over the shorter training flights it is easily understandable that the bird is able to spot familiar landmarks from afar. However, in the later stages of training, the pigeon is moved over distances so great that from the height at which it customarily flies it is geometrically im-

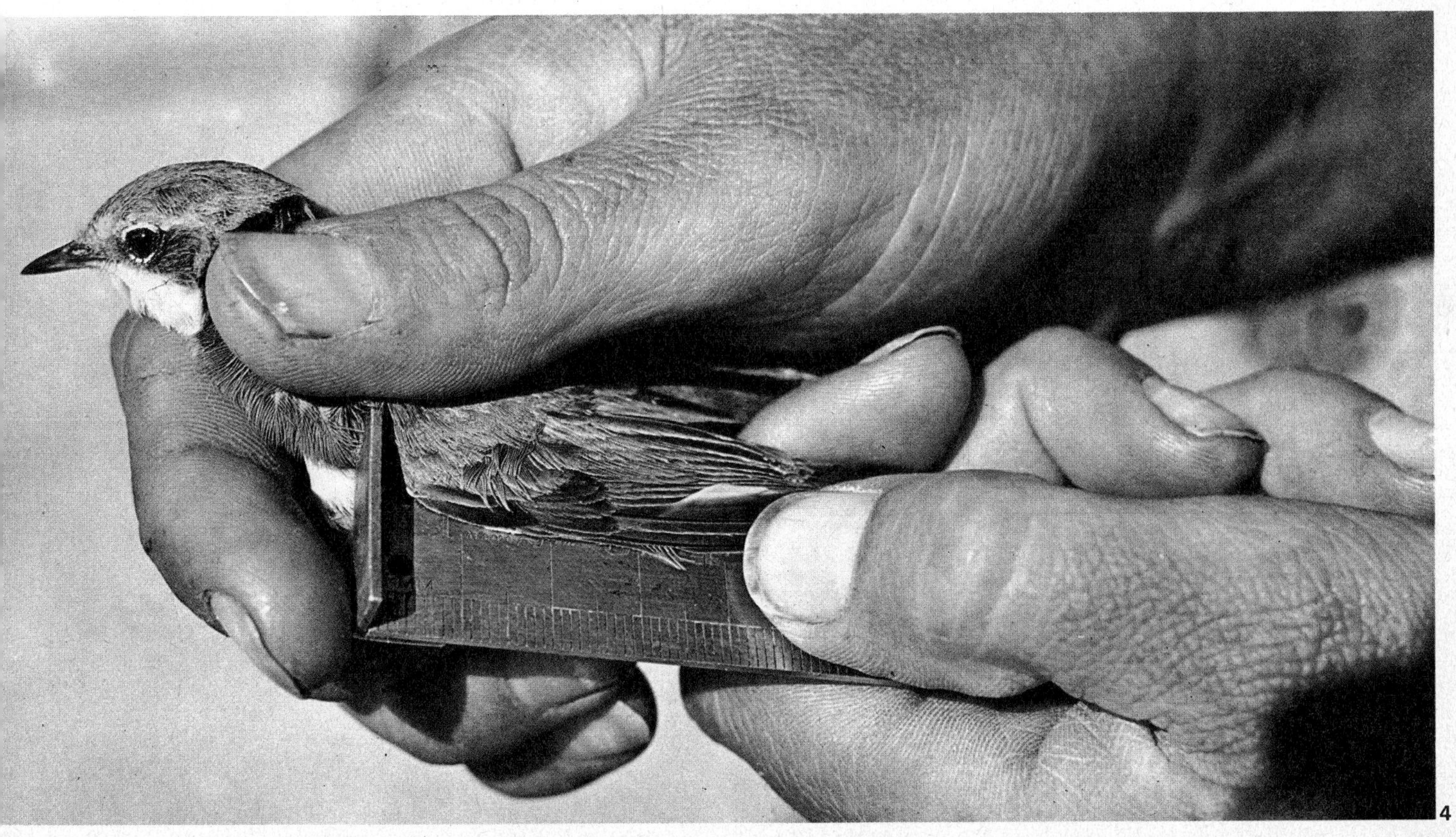

4

Autumn in Michigan. Swallows muster on telegraph wires for their migration, while a flock of Canada geese is already winging its way to the warmth of the south.

possible for it to see landmarks noted on previous days. Obviously then, the birds must navigate by some method of reckoning, and this is where the sun-compass theory comes in.

This is similar to the way in which the sailor can use the sun to establish his location and hence the course he needs to take for home. To start with he requires two basic facts: the position of the sun in the sky above him; and the position of the sun at the same time in relation to some fixed point elsewhere on the face of the Earth – say the Greenwich meridian. Now, provided the sky above him is not clouded he can easily obtain the first piece of information – he can see it. But the human navigator requires chronometers and charts to obtain the second.

Homing pigeons and other birds seem able to *remember* what the position of the sun would be in their home territory at any given time. And just like the sailor, they then compare this with the position of the sun as they see it. Needless to say, they have no chronometer set to their home time, but it seems likely that they do have internal physiological systems which mark time at a steady pace, irrespective of conditions outside the body, and these they use to clock the sun.

By using their internal clock and following the motion of the sun, the homing pigeon, and its cousins, could know where they are in relation to home territory and therefore the direction they must fly in to reach that destination. It is true, also incidentally, that some birds migrate by night, and for this situation similar systems have been postulated in which the moon and the stars are used instead of the sun.

Again, butterflies and locusts migrate in great numbers, regularly, and over considerable distances, but generally navigation here seems to be a much more haphazard affair than with birds. Prevailing winds are known to play a great part in the direction which the swarms take, although over shorter distances sun orientation and the use of visual landmarks may be concerned as well.

## Natural radar

But finally, there is a sense which has yet to be mentioned – that of hearing. An extremely important factor for survival with many animals, it is for one animal at least a vital means of navigation.

Although bats are known to move over long distances, little is known about the way they achieve this. But the mechanisms of short-distance navigation are well understood. What the bat possesses in effect is a natural echo-location system, a built-in radar set. While feeding or moving about at night, it emits certain cries consisting of high-frequency waves – so high in fact that they are outside the range of the human ear – which bounce off objects in the bat's path and are returned to its own ear. In some way the animal is able to judge the time the sound takes to go out and back and relate this to the distance of the object. In other words, the bat is able to 'hear' distance, and it is also possible that the bat can tell something of the nature of the located object by modifications in the returning sound waves.

These then are the ways in which some animals employ the various senses in order to find their way from one point to another. Not only does the usefulness of these senses differ between different animals (including Man), but animals also often use these senses in totally unexpected ways.

Much remains to be learned; and animal navigation remains an area of considerable mystery. It is not surprising then that it is one of the most fascinating areas of study for zoologists and biologists alike.

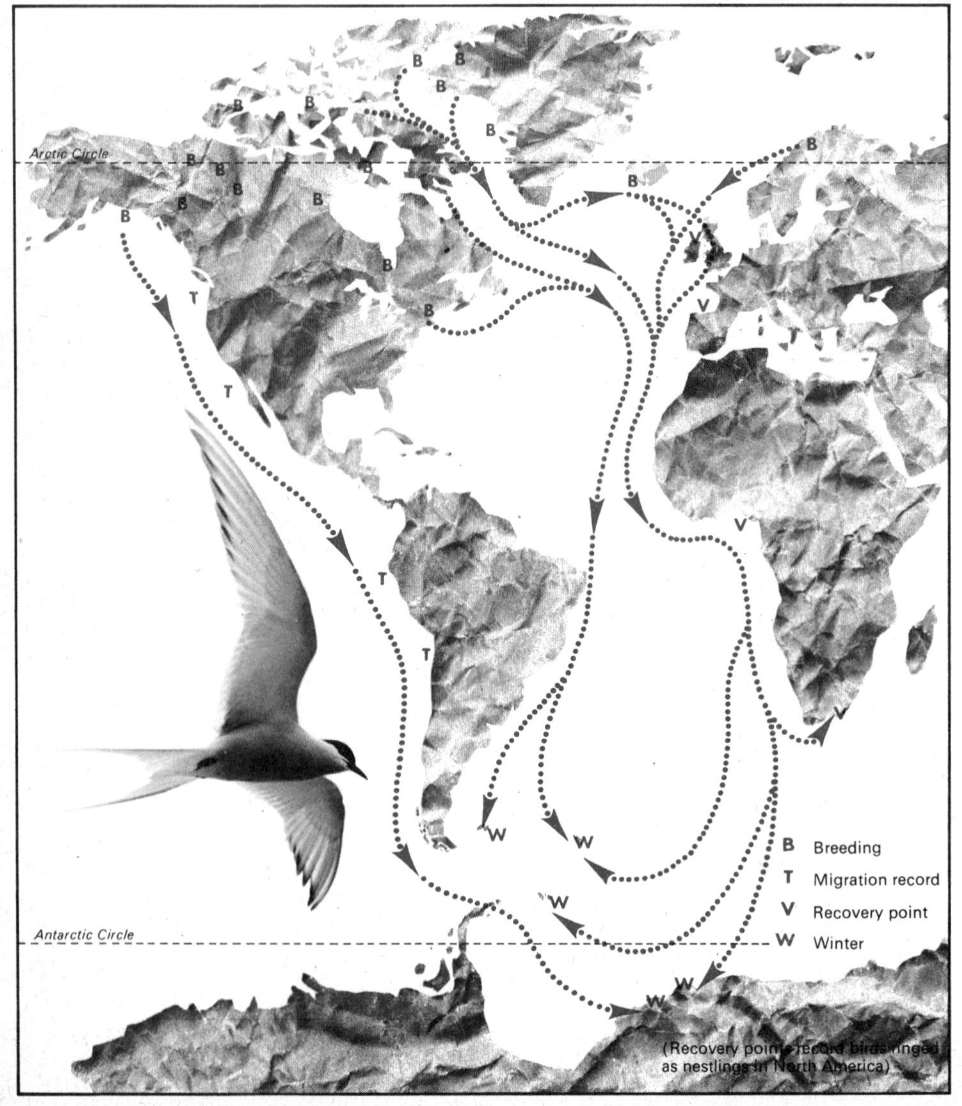


Arctic terns breed in Canada, Greenland and Norway and migrate to the South Atlantic to spend the winter. Note how the tracks of their migrations follow the coastline.

# Habits and habitat

The way animals behave has a strong influence on their geographical distribution. Aggressive territorial behaviour keeps members of the same species apart, while social behaviour brings them closer together.

EVERY SPECIES of animal requires an environment suited to its own bodily requirements. Each has different traits of behaviour which have the effect of bringing it to the place where conditions are right for it. The total effect of all these many different behaviour traits is the distribution of animals across the globe.

Some animals need such special conditions in the place where they live that they are distributed in a very restricted way. The parasitic wasp, *Nemeritis canescens,* will only live naturally in one host, the moth, *Ephestia kuhniella.* Its behaviour is such that it responds only to the smell of that host, even when raised artificially in the laboratory on a different host species. At the other extreme the honey-bee is widely distributed and survives well in many environments from the subarctic regions through the temperate zones to the tropics. The behaviour of these animals helps them to find suitable areas to live in, and thus propagates the species as a whole.

This last point is important. It is no good having too many of the same species in one suitable environment if there is only a limited amount of food available for them. There must be some behaviour mechanisms causing the animals to spread out more and seek other similar places to live.

Darwin first pointed out that food resources are the 'ultimate' factor determining the upper limit of animal population density. Each habitat can support a certain number of animals. This number can vary with the season (the supply of food fluctuates). It can also vary over the years as the climate changes. The number of mouths to be fed is balanced as nearly as possible by the availability of food. As well as behaviour other things, such as the mortality rate, and certain physiological changes, can assist this balance.

Very few complete patterns of behaviour in invertebrates have been analysed properly. Those that have show the complex nature of the stimuli to which the animal reacts. *Lepidiochitona cinera* lives in the upper part of the tidal zone on the sea shore among rocks. When the tide is out the chitons can be found beneath stones, but when the tide comes in and the stones are covered by water the chitons move to the upper surfaces of their stones.

1 Roosting starlings on a television aerial. The birds space themselves along the wire so that they are not quite near enough to peck one another – a tiny version of territorial behaviour.
2 An ichneumon fly lays its eggs inside its caterpillar host. Because of its specialized egg-laying habits, each ichneumon fly species is restricted by the hosts' distribution.
3 Black rats fighting. Like many other animals, rats will fight in defence of territory. Intruders are challenged by the 'home' rats, and are generally fought to the death.

## Gravity and light

These movements are governed by responses to gravity and to light. When the stones are uncovered the chitons react positively to gravity and move downwards. Their response to any light falling on them at this time is a change in speed; bright sunlight makes them move downwards more quickly than duller light. Once they reach the underside of their stones the light is cut off and the chitons stop. As the tide comes in their response to gravity changes and when covered with water the chitons move upwards. The sun's light is more constant underwater and the chitons can move about more freely without having to stop in dark places. In this way simple reactions to stimuli interact to give a much more complicated behaviour pattern. The end result is that the animal's distribution changes with the tides.

Barnacles congregate in places which are suitable for their mode of life by means of an ingenious mechanism. The barnacle larvae have antennules which feel around on hard surfaces for a good place to settle, in order to metamorphose into adult barnacles. They react positively to the presence of other barnacles of their own species, or to the traces of cement left on a rock by other barnacles. These 'clues' are a good enough indication to the larva that its detective work is over – if a spot was good enough for other barnacles it is good enough for a new batch.

There are exceptions to this; barnacle larvae will not settle on glass, even if other barnacles are fixed to it. They prefer a rough surface if one is available nearby. Thus the distribution mechanism seems to be a combination of response to the texture of a surface and a more specialized response to the clues left by other barnacles. The total effect is to keep barnacle colonies only in those areas where conditions for development are good.

1

2

3

Many winged insects are distributed over wide areas by a behaviour pattern which acts on them just after they have emerged from metamorphosis. At once they are impelled by some inner mechanism to fly upwards, or in some particular direction which may be determined by the angle of the light at the moment of departure. In some insects, especially aphids and locusts, this migration is a highly developed dispersal mechanism, and enormous numbers of newly emerged insects swarm in the air. Both of these insects fly upwards and become caught in rising air currents which sweep them away, high into the sky.

Pilots of planes flying at 1,000 to 5,000 feet tell of the masses of insects floating there on a warm day. But in the evening the air cools, and the sky becomes clear again. The insects fall slowly to more normal levels, and there the aphids are attracted by green leaves. They land, and if the leaves are a suitable breeding ground they stay there living out the rest of their lives in a much less exciting way. The drives which make different types of insects fly upwards are varied. Aphids are attracted by the sun's ultra-violet light, and the Scolytid bark-beetle is attracted by the brightness of the sky. But whatever the drive, there is a brief period after emergence when it overcomes all other drives, including sex and feeding drives. In the case of the aphids, the drive is soon replaced by the drive to find green foliage, but the bark-beetle responds to height in a different way. On the way up it swallows air, and the size of the air-bubble in its stomach seems to signal a change in response – it turns from the light, and heads towards pine trunks, which are its breeding grounds.

Behaviour patterns involved in the distribution of the higher animals are usually more varied. The most obvious patterns which govern the number of animals in an area, preventing their numbers from exceeding the limits set by food supplies, are those which cause simple spacing out. Many animals use territories, each territory being held by a single animal, a pair, or a social group. Entry into foreign areas causes fighting, and thus the animals are forced to spread out. As long as each animal can hold on to his own territory, then the total number of animals which can live in a larger area is limited. If there are not enough territories for all the animals in the area, then surplus

**1** Threatening behaviour among fiddler crabs. These males displaying their claws are taking part in a form of aggressive display, which has the effect of maintaining territorial separation.
**2** A swarm of honey-bees on a comb built in the open air. Such combs are very rare. Swarming in social insects is a way of reducing population pressure by expanding to new areas.
**3** Territorial behaviour in the robin. A stuffed robin placed on the territory of a live male provokes a strong reaction. The male displays his red breast in an aggressive way.
**4** Hibernation provides a means of extending the range of mammals into cold regions. This fat dormouse curls up and sleeps through the winter, emerging in the spring.
**5** Masses of aphids find new feeding grounds by flying upwards on warm currents of air during the day, and falling to the ground as the air cools at night. They may reach 5,000 feet.
**6** The chiton, or coat of mail shell, migrates as the tides comes in from under its stone to the top of a rock. Its movements are a response to gravity and light.

animals may be expelled from the area, or may even be allowed to stay on as non-breeders.

There are many kinds of territory-holding in the animal world. In more gregarious animals a personal hierarchy often develops. The dominant animals of a group have the first choice on every occasion. This cuts off the lowest members of the hierarchy from their food, and thus again limits the total population. Ordinary hens exhibit this type of hierarchy: the *pecking order;* each hen knows where all the others lie in the hierarchy and thus it knows whether to expect submission from another hen, or whether it ought to submit.

Sometimes, when there are large groups of animals, such as in a dancing swarm of gnats, or flock of seagulls, such inequalities in status may show up only in adverse conditions, when total numbers must be restricted.

Aggression plays an important part in spacing out animals of a species. It is, in effect, the opposite of herd attraction. Very aggressive animals are not able to live in herds, but moderately aggressive animals can do so as long as they keep a certain distance between each animal. A line of starlings sitting on a telegraph wire are spaced along it so that each bird cannot quite reach out to peck at the next. This space, which each animal needs around it, is, in fact, a tiny version of a territory.

## Aggressive displays

Fighting can be a means of spacing, but it may lead to damage being inflicted on other members of the same species. Because of this, aggressive displays evolved which have the same effect as fighting but none of the dangers. Aggressive displays are usually so effective that they do not end in contact fighting. Many species have even evolved methods of reducing the frequency of aggressive displays in certain social relationships so that they can live together more closely than would otherwise be possible.

Birthrate is clearly a very important factor in controlling the number of animals of one species in an area. Where there is a high density of animals the reproductive rate may drop. But this is a physiological effect. Often, under crowded conditions, adults tend to move elsewhere to reproduce. The main effect of high density is thus to promote movement.

Specialized animals have special problems of distribution. Cryptic moths (which mimic some part of their environment in an attempt not to be seen) need a low population density. If there are too many moths close together this increases the chance that many of them will be eaten by predators at one go, but if they are well spread out this threat is reduced. To help this the adults lay their eggs singly, and scatter them widely.

Migration is a common phenomenon which has evolved where it results in a higher reproductive rate, or a lower death rate, than a static existence would allow. Migration is more common in areas with marked seasonal changes, for example, extremes of heat and cold. These regular seasonal journeys from one area to another and back again are undertaken by many birds, whales, seals, bats, fish and some

4

5

6

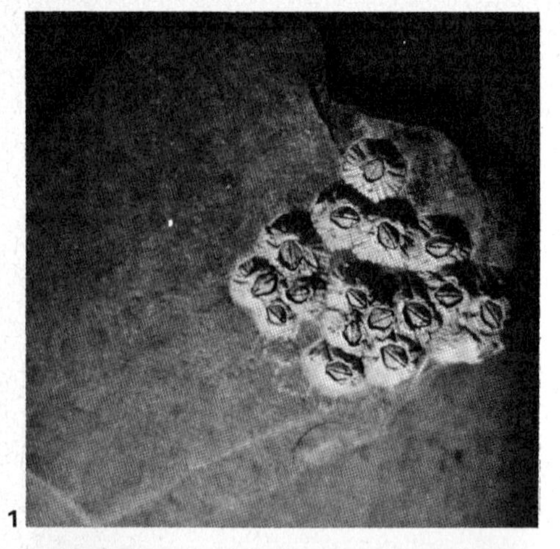

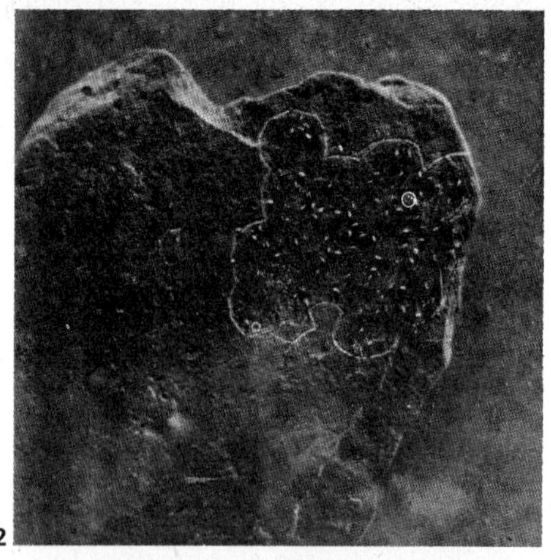

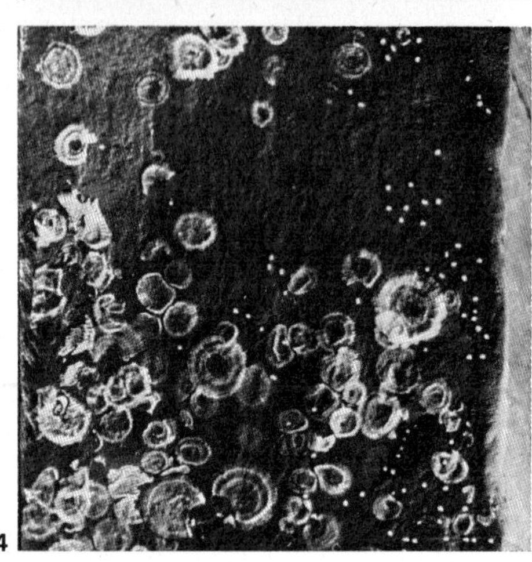

**1** A patch of adult barnacles outlined by a deeply scratched groove. **2** After removal of the adults, barnacle larvae settle in the grooved area, though the whole stone is available to them. **3** Two species of barnacle (*Balanus crenatus*, smooth margins; *B. balanoides*, indented margins). **4** After removal of the adults, *balanoides* larvae will not settle on old *crenatus* bases.

Chickens have a rigid social hierarchy, the pecking order. Chickens low in the pecking order submit to pecking from superior birds, and are able to peck birds lower in the scale.

insects. The longest known migratory journey is that of the Arctic tern which travels some 10,000 miles to its breeding ground, and the same distance back. Sometimes each individual travels each way only once in its life. Eels breed south of Bermuda, and the young larvae journey to Europe where they spend about 20 years maturing. They then swim back to the tropical breeding grounds. In some animals only one such journey is performed, the return trip being made by the next generation.

Migration is a recurring phenomenon occurring in only certain animals. Mass movements can occur which are not at all regular. The number of animals in a given habitat becomes so excessive that something drastic has to happen. Here again the vital factor is food shortage. The suicide pact of the Norwegian lemming, when thousands of animals race westwards, not stopping even for the sea, where most of them drown, is a good example of this. This mass emigration used to be thought senseless, but it is now known that this is not the case. When the lemming population of an area becomes excessive and the lemmings are overcrowded, the animals become very excited. They begin to travel, and sometimes cover great distances, even swimming across fjords. Their aim is to find new habitats suitable for the propagation of a colony. The lemmings just carry on until they find somewhere; those that are unlucky enough to find the sea first are the best known casualties. Not all the lemmings of a colony depart – some are left behind to continue the existing colony.

Perhaps the best known animal which erupts under overcrowding is the locust. It has been shown in the laboratory that crowding will change the locust from a solitary into a highly gregarious insect, and that its structure also changes.

Swarming of bees is a more common type of this eruption. When a colony of bees has grown too big for its hive or nest space, then swarming is likely to occur. In such overcrowded conditions the queen bee is fed less by the workers, and has little space for her eggs, so she lays less. The workers thus have less to do in foraging for food as they have a smaller brood to bring up. This compounds the difficulties; the workers stay in the hive more, and tend to live longer, thus increasing the population in the hive and setting up the swarming mechanisms.

When the colony swarms to relieve this congestion, one or more queens leave the hive, accompanied by workers, and settle in a new home. New queens usually go to the new hive, but honey-bees send the old queen away and the new queens stay and occupy the old hive.

## Battles for food and space

The interaction between different species in an area makes the question of distribution even more complex. If a new animal moves into an area it may easily upset the balance of the original population; animals compete with each other for food and space, prey on each other, and are parasitic on each other. The fox has moved into Australia, and there is a great danger that it will destroy many of the older population. In England the red squirrel was largely ousted by the American grey squirrel, mainly because their requirements in the way of food and shelter were far too similar. One species had to give way.

All these examples, of behaviour which distributes animals, have arisen as a result of natural selection. The species must be propagated, but not so well that it is overcrowded and starved out of existence. Behaviour patterns have thus developed to temper the propagation, by forcing the species to spread out and find other suitable places to live. Only in a completely constant environment populated by animals that breed evenly all the year round can a perfect balance be indefinitely maintained. This static balance may possibly be achieved in some marine habitats, but elsewhere the rough and tumble of natural selection forces animals to develop their specialized safety-valve behaviour patterns which ensure the best possible distribution of the species.

# Instincts in action

Animal behaviour is often explained by zoologists on the basis of built-in 'drives' – the sex-drive, hunger, thirst and maternal instinct. What are these powerful forces and how do they operate?

WHY DOES a bird suddenly begin to make a nest when during the winter it has shown no sign of nest-building? Why does an animal begin to look for food when it has shown no interest in it for some hours? What is it that makes an animal behave in a particular way, often ceasing to do one thing and beginning to do something quite different? What the animal sees or hears will, of course, affect what it is doing but an animal which ignores food when it is well-fed will eagerly eat the same food when it is hungry. What has made it change its responses?

Watching a hungry animal seeking food gives the impression that it is being forced to look for it, ignoring everything else. It looks as if the animal is being 'driven'. This gives rise to the idea of *drive,* of something within the animal which orders its behaviour. When looking for food the animal is under the influence of a feeding drive, when looking for a mate, a mating drive and so forth. The drives must all be present in the animal but remain latent until they are aroused.

The strength of a drive can be measured by seeing what obstruction the animal will overcome to pursue the behaviour. For example, a rat can be confined in a box which connects by a corridor with another box. On the floor of the corridor is a metal grid through which a small electric current can be passed. If the rat is hungry, it may be tested by putting food into the other box. Then it is a question of finding out what strength of current will deter the rat from going down the corridor to the food. It will be a stronger current for a hungry rat than for a rat which has fed recently. In fact the strength of the drive increases steadily with the time from the rat's last meal, and reaches its maximum after four days of starvation. But thirst makes its maximum effect earlier, for it reaches a peak at the end of one day without water.

## Exploration

An interesting discovery in this type of experiment is that a rat will try to run along the corridor even if the box at the other end is empty. There seems, in other words, to be a drive to *explore.* This of course would be useful in nature for it would cause the animal to find new food or nesting places during its searching.

It is easy enough to put forward the idea of drive and it 'explains' the observations, but what is it we are calling 'drive'? Like so much that goes on inside an animal, scientists at present can only get clues about its nature. We can certainly point to changes in an animal's physiology which could account at least in part for the change in behaviour.

An active animal is using up blood sugar to provide energy for its muscular movements and so forth. This blood sugar comes from stores in its liver and directly from the food in its gut. If it has gone unfed for a time, the level of the blood sugar will have dropped, and indeed the reduced level will affect areas in the brain. These are stimulated to produce the

1 The Friesian bull gauges the cow's readiness for mating by resting his chin on her rump. If the cow does not move away, the bull mounts and mates with her.

2 A rabbit's nest is lined with fur plucked from her own body. Sex hormones released during pregnancy loosen the hairs on her chest, making it easier for her to pull them out.

activity which we see as a search for food. If the animal is successful in its search it takes more food into its gut, the blood-sugar level rises once again and the searching behaviour ceases. Incidentally, when the blood sugar is low, nerve impulses pass from the brain to the stomach which contracts in a way which makes itself felt as hunger pangs.

Hormones – the chemical messenger substances produced by ductless glands – play a large part in determining the behaviour of vertebrates; their role in insects and other invertebrates is also beginning to become clear.

The cycle of changes which go on in a female mammal as she comes into season brings about changes in her behaviour. She becomes sexually receptive and accepts the advances of a male which at other times she rejects. This period is known as *oestrus*. Ultimately this leads to mating and, with a fertilized egg in the uterus, further changes take place as she becomes 'maternal'. The end result of these changes is that when the young are born, she is capable of nursing, and nest-building. Her behaviour cycle is controlled by hormones from the ovaries and other glands. She cannot be in oestrus while she is pregnant nor, usually, for a time after birth when she is suckling her young. During these times the particular hormones responsible for sexual behaviour are not being secreted by her glands.

A cow will refuse to let a bull mate with her except when she is in oestrus which occurs for only a few hours every few weeks. The bull can detect a cow that is soon to come into condition, perhaps by her scent or by something in her behaviour that is not obvious to us. At this time he guards her, remaining near and standing parallel to her, nose to tail. When she is in full oestrus the bull becomes greatly excited. He may paw the ground or dig it with his horns, tossing dirt over his back. Then he moves behind the cow and places his chin and throat on her rump. Then if the cow permits he mounts and mates with her.

A female rabbit makes a nest which she lines with fur plucked from her own body. One of the effects of the sex hormones circulating in the blood is to loosen the hairs on her chest, so that they can easily be pulled out. When the young are in the nest, she suckles them, and protects and cleans them. The nest-building is stimulated by the circulating hormones, and not by the presence of embryos, for removal of the embryos (and even of the ovaries) during pregnancy does not stop the nesting behaviour. Indeed, the injection of stilbestrol, progesterone and prolactin (from the pituitary) will bring about nest-building in some rabbits even when they are not pregnant. A rabbit is not very good at nursing on her first pregnancy. She improves during subsequent ones so that

3

1

**1** Hedgehogs emerge at dusk and begin foraging for food. Like many other animals, their activities are closely governed by cycles, some due to external and some to internal influences.

4

2

**2** Pigs breaking through ice on a pond to drink. The drives released by thirst are often even more insistent than those due to hunger, and take far less time to come into operation.

**3** A herd of wildebeeste (better known as gnus) on the march near Lake Manyara, Tanzania. Many animals follow regular routes from waterhole to waterhole or from breeding ground to pasture.

4 A young dove thrusts its beak into its mother's mouth to drink the 'milk' produced in her crop. The crop begins to secrete 'milk' under the stimulus of the sex hormone prolactin.

5 Swans grubbing for food on the river bottom. Much of their time is spent compulsively exploring the river bottom for the larvae and small animals that make up their food.

she builds a better nest rather earlier each time, suckles a greater percentage of the live-born animals, scatters them about less and is less likely to eat her own offspring. So though hormones produce the behaviour, experience shapes it into a more efficient pattern with time.

Doves, though they are birds, feed their young with 'milk', produced not in mammary glands like mammals, but by the walls of the crop. This crop milk is regurgitated into the beaks of the squabs (as the young are called). The crop-milk production is brought about by prolactin, and injection of this hormone into the female doves which are not incubating eggs causes the walls of their crops to thicken ready for crop milk to be secreted. If the injected birds have previously brought up young they will feed a hungry seven-day-old squab as if it were one of their own young ones.

The increase of bird song in spring is so noticeable that it has been recognized as a sign of the change from winter to summer for hundreds of years. It stresses the fact that birds, like a number of other animals, do not breed just at any time of the year; they begin when the temperature is increasing, bringing plants into flower and insects out from their winter hiding places, in other words when food with which to feed the young is beginning to be abundant. Breeding time seems to be brought on by the increase of the hours of daylight which shows itself in early spring and continues steadily until midsummer. It is possible to bring birds into breeding conditions earlier than usual by providing them with increasing periods of artificial light each day during the early part of the year. The greater length of day gives birds a longer time in which to find food for their young, so that spring is the appropriate time for mating to take place.

In both males and females hormones are responsible for the sex drive that brings about courtship. Longer daylight hours are perceived through the eyes; this in turn affects the pituitary at the base of the brain which through its hormones causes the sex glands to increase in size, the eggs to ripen in females, and sperm to be formed in great numbers of males. In tropical countries many species of birds are brought into breeding conditions not by lengthening days but by the rains which waken plant life into greenness, supplying abundant food and pliable nesting materials.

## Marking out territory

The first signs in the male of the change in hormone levels come earlier than the actual nest-building. The flocks which many birds, like reed warblers, form during the winter break up, for the males become aggressive to each other. Instead of feeding with the other birds, each male begins to mark out his territory, taking over a tall tree as a song post from which he sings, loudly advertising his ownership of the area. This song also serves to attract the female to the area; while the territory owner scares off male intruders of his own species, he admits the female. Then courtship can begin.

When hormones were discovered in insects, it was their effect in controlling growth and metamorphosis which attracted attention. Nowadays a great deal is known about the actions of insect hormones in that way but far less is known about their effects on behaviour. There is no doubt that they will prove to have as great an effect as those of a bird or a mammal, but for the moment we have to do with scraps of evidence. One of these pieces is the effect of removing one of the glands, the *corpora allata*, from a female grasshopper, *Gomphocerus rufus*. After

1 A vast herd of gnus driven by the heat to seek water. When water is scarce, many different species congregate at waterholes and river banks and elaborate behaviour rituals take place.
2 Mating among weaver birds involves the drive to build carefully fashioned nests by sewing together two or three leaves and filling the resulting tube with down and fluff.
3 A young cuckoo, having ousted a reed-warblers' brood, already dwarfs its foster-mother. The warbler's instinctive drives give her no rest as she feeds the voracious young monster.

the operation she will not sing in the usual way, nor will she copulate with singing males. However, her normal responses are restored within seven days after the corpora allata from another sexually mature female have been implanted in her.

At the end of the summer, as the days shorten in the autumn, some species of birds begin to gather in flocks which wheel restlessly in the sky. These are species which migrate to spend their winter further south than their breeding places. They and other migratory birds build up considerable stores of fat in their bodies. This will supply the food they require for their journeys. Their restlessness heralds their actual departure. But what brings about this change in behaviour and the accumulation of the fat? There seems little doubt that for birds in the northern hemisphere the cause is the same – activity of the pituitary gland. Unlike the spring burst of secretion this one is brought about by decreasing day length. Experiments by Rowan in the 1920s showed that temperature had no effect and that light was important. He kept juncos in cages in their breeding areas in Canada. Some were kept under normal lighting conditions, others were lit by artificial light which gave them longer and longer days though the autumn real day was decreasing, while others had artificial days which shortened more rapidly than the real day. The ovaries and testes in the birds in the last group regressed faster than the ones under normal conditions, while the longer day-length birds' ovaries and testes increased as they would do in spring. When he released the birds he found that the birds with the reduced gonads migrated south as did the controls a little later, but the other birds hung about. The temperature had been the same for all, so it was the light regime which was controlling the behaviour.

The effect of the change of day length on bird behaviour, acting through hormones, is an example of external events bringing about behaviour. In this way, the reproductive drive is set going in spring and the migratory drive in the autumn. We can explain a great deal of behaviour in this way, but there are some pieces of behaviour which appear not to be connected with what is going on outside the animal, but seem to be initiated from within. This is particularly true of some rhythmic behaviour, when an animal does something repeatedly but at set intervals of time.

If you want to see some animals you have to go out at night. Badgers, for example, come out only in darkness. Other animals can be seen only by day. They have a rhythm of activity on a 24-hour basis. It may be the result of the change from light to dark but sometimes the cycle goes on even if the animal is kept in continuous light or in permanent darkness. Cockroaches begin to be active just before dusk and their activity increases to a peak in the early part of the night. After this they move about less and less, and remain relatively inactive through the remainder of the night and the next day until dusk comes. But if the insects are kept in cages which are lit throughout 24 hours they show peaks of activity which fall at approximately 24-hourly intervals. Under these conditions, of course, there is no dawn and no dusk to trigger off activity. The behaviour is controlled from within the animal.

The cockroaches' behaviour is in fact controlled by the cyclic secretion of hormones from cells in the sub-oesophageal ganglia, the part of the nervous system which lies beneath the insect's gullet. But what makes the glands secrete at these fixed intervals is still a mystery.

## Tidal cycles

Other animals have cycles of different lengths. Many animals on the sea-shore, for instance, follow the tidal cycle. They will continue to show the rhythm in a tank in the laboratory where there is no rise and fall of the tide to stimulate them into activity. Yet others follow a lunar cycle. The Palolo worms of the Pacific swarm in October and November at the third quarter of the moon. The worms break off the ends of their bodies which are by then stuffed with reproductive products. The ends wriggle their way to the surface to discharge the eggs and sperms in clouds, turning the sea milky.

Longer cycles can be detected in birds, for there appears to be an internal cycle of one year which brings the birds into readiness to react to the changes in day length at the beginning of the year. These long cycles are far more difficult to detect than the shorter ones but they are probably equally as free from the environment as the daily cycles.

The word 'drive' is a convenient shorthand, but when it is necessary to explain just what a drive is we are forced to look deeply into the physiology of animals to discover reasons why animals behave one way one minute and another way the next.

# Hives of industry

'Go to the ant, thou sluggard; consider her ways, and be wise.' While King Solomon's advice may not cure idleness, it shows how old is Man's fascination with the busy lives of social insects.

AN INSECT SOCIETY conjures up a ruthlessly efficient organization with all the individuals bent more or less without exception upon some task for the common good. It is a kind of 'brave new world' where the individuals are totally subservient to the state as well as being born to their role in life. A queen bee passes her few years of life laying thousands upon thousands of eggs to keep the hive populated. The worker bees, incapable of reproducing under normal circumstances, keep the hive in order and replenished with food by their tireless and selfless activity. The insect society seems to us, bedevilled as we are by disorder, a paragon of faultless organization, whereas our societies appear to pass through one cycle after another, first of flourishing growth, then of ageing and crumbling decay, the insect society seems to maintain itself over the years, efficient, active and unchanging.

## Evolution

But insect societies, like our own, have had to evolve and, in all instances, their most complex organizations, as for example, the hive of a honey-bee, have had to spring from a far simpler form and way of life. In fact, if we went back far enough in time we should find the ancestor of the honey-bee living a virtually solitary existence, except perhaps for a short period after fertilization and reproduction, when it might care for the helpless growing larvae by providing them with food.

How has the evolution of the multi-individual insect society come about, and what advantages does it bring? As is so often the case in studying the way a species has evolved and the way it has adapted to living, it is necessary to look among the existing species of social insects, especially the ones with primitive societies, for any clues that may indicate evolutionary trends. We must, therefore, take a look at some of the solitary wasps and bees living for inklings of social behaviour and co-operation.

Some of the most successful wasps are the ichneumon flies; these are tiny creatures with a delicate hovering flight, and the females bear a long proboscis-like projection from their tails which is, in fact, a needle-sharp ovipositor. The ichneumon flies parasitize large juicy caterpillars, laying their eggs deep in the caterpillar's tissues by means of their ovipositor. Only one egg is laid in each caterpillar and the female ichneumon flies are somehow able to sense, by smell, whether or not a caterpillar has already been parasitized. The young wasp larva then hatches from the egg and starts living on the tissues of the caterpillar, which it in time kills, but not until it is mature and ready to leave its host.

**1** A honey-bee removing the dead body of one of its comrades from the hive. Keeping the hive clean is one of the first tasks carried out by newly hatched worker bees.

**2** The carpenter ant builds its colonies inside dead trees: the ants' powerful jaws allow them to cut out tunnels through the wood, in which they rear their young.

Apart from finding precisely the right environment for its developing young to grow in, there is nothing particularly social about the ichneumon fly's behaviour. But the digger wasp, *Ammophila adriaansei* takes the care of its young one stage further. This wasp digs a hole in the ground for its young and then, having carefully covered the opening with small stones or pieces of earth, goes off to seek food. Once again the food is a caterpillar, but this time the wasp paralyses the caterpillar completely with a nerve poison that it injects into the tissues of the prey. The wasp now drags the paralysed caterpillar to the nest, removes the stones and hauls the caterpillar in after it. It lays an egg on the caterpillar, climbs out of the nest and replaces the stones to close the entrance. The caterpillar makes ideal food, for by being paralysed and not killed it remains wholesome and does not putrefy. Some species of digger wasp have several nests on the go at once. The female must, therefore, remember exactly where each nest is and, before leaving a nest, she can be seen making an orientation flight in which she looks for special landmarks, like a stone on the ground next to a tree, or a fallen pine cone. Having remembered where each of her nests is, she also seems to know intuitively how much of the food supply is left, and she will keep on replenishing the nests until the larvae are fully grown and about to pupate. The female wasp has now done her duty and she does not survive much longer. After a time the pupae emerge as adult wasps and the cycle is recharged for another season.

Some species of Halictine bee, *Augochloroposis sparsilis,* have developed their society a little more. About ten per cent of the females that emerge in the summer months are, for some inexplicable reason, not disposed to mating. These unmated females become industrious workers, confining their activities to nest-building and foraging for food.

## Bumble-bees

In bumble-bees for the first time we find that division of labour is absolutely essential for the survival of the species. There is now one predominant female, the queen, and she, having been fertilized the season before, passes the winter sheltering in the earth. In the spring she goes off to found a colony of her own, selecting a suitable hole such as a mouse hole for her first brood to develop. She builds a few rounded waxen cells for these and occasionally opens the cells to replenish the food store. The first larvae all develop into females. They are quite distinct from the queen, being much smaller and having underdeveloped ovaries so that they are in fact sterile. From that moment the queen no longer has time for any duties other than laying eggs, and she relies on the first brood of emerged females to do all the other work. They build new cells, fly out to gather food and feed both the queen and her offspring. As in the social wasps, *Vespa,* and the hornets, the bumble-bee society comes to an end in the autumn. Instead of sterile workers emerging from the cells, the newcomers are sexually mature and some of them are now, for the first time that year, males. These sexually mature adults now mate and the large family disintegrates. All except the newly fertilized females die. These, the prospective queens, seek a place to hibernate, and so the cycle is complete.

All societies of insects can be considered as overgrown families, for they have all originated from the egg-laying of one female. Some experts have even called these families 'super-organisms' for in one sense they are like an organism which needs all its parts to survive healthily.

Of these overgrown families the honey-bee community is undoubtedly the best known to Man. It is a staggering thought that the 60,000 to 80,000 worker bees in a flourishing hive are all the offspring of a single female. In the honey-bee the division of labour is carried to an extreme, and the hive may remain in existence for year after year. The queen lives for several seasons, but the males and the remainder of the females, the infertile workers, are relatively short-lived. From time to time new queens are reared and the old queen is forced to leave. She takes with her a large contingent of workers as a swarm and sets out to establish a new hive community. The new queen, a lone dictator so to speak, now embarks on her nuptial flight where she is fertilized by a male drone bee. This one act of fertilization lasts her for the remainder of her life, and the drones having fulfilled their function in life are driven from the hive by the worker bees and destroyed by being stung to death. The sting of the worker bee is a modified ovipositor.

As in bumble-bees, the worker honey-bees have a variety of tasks in the community. Some of them collect nectar from flowers, others pollen. Others again do nothing except build new combs, or specialize in looking after the developing larvae, either by cleaning out their cells or feeding them on special secretions that they regurgitate from their mouth parts. In the

1

2

**1** Wasp colonies last only one season, as the insects make no provision for the winter. Only the young queen wasps survive the rigours of the winter to produce a new spring brood.
**2** A large termitarium in central Africa. Termites are the architects of the insect world, and their colonies often rise to considerable heights above the African plain.
**3** Worker bees lick the 'queen substance' – a pheromone – from their queen's body and circulate it from mouth to mouth. The flow of the pheromone prevents production of new queens.
**4** A bumble-bee nest. The irregular cells on which the insects are standing are used for storing honey and pollen. The worker bumble-bees are all sterile females, smaller than the queen.
**5** An ant queen outside the entrance to her nest. Once she has established a suitable site, the queen is rarely seen again, as she proceeds to full-time reproduction.

3

4

5

honey-bee the exact task of a bee depends largely on its age, although there is a certain built-in flexibility depending on the requirements of the hive.

After emerging from its cell, a worker bee's first task is real drudgery – to clean and sweep the cells from which other workers have recently emerged, in preparation for the cells to be re-used by the queen for laying eggs.

After about three days, the worker matures to feeding the larvae, in particular the older ones, and she gathers pollen and honey from the stores. Her next task, a few days later, is to feed the younger larvae and this she does by giving them, in addition to pollen and honey, a kind of milky food secreted from special glands in her head. Bees of this age also begin to brave the open for the first time and they make short reconnaissance flights. When it is ten days old the worker bee no longer concerns itself with the brood and it takes on jobs like packing pollen into cells, feeding the foraging bees with honey and building new cells. For this it secretes wax from glands in the abdomen. On about its twentieth day the bee takes on guard duties. Every bee that enters the hive has to be inspected, and if the incoming bee does not have the distinct smell of the hive about it, it is immediately recognized as a foreigner and attacked. Finally the bee is mature enough to forage for food in the surrounding countryside.

Bees' foraging behaviour has been the subject of exciting research particularly by Professor von Frisch of Vienna. He discovered some years ago that the bees

The grotesquely distended body of the queen termite is esteemed as a delicacy by African tribesmen. The tiny head and thorax is tacked on to the enormous abdomen.

A flying digger wasp bears a paralysed caterpillar to its solitary nest. The wasp lays its egg on the caterpillar, thus ensuring a supply of fresh, live food for the larvae when they emerge.

are able to convey precise information to each other as to the whereabouts of sources of food, whether nectar or pollen. The bees communicate this information by means of a special dance enacted in the hive. There are two sorts of dance – the *round dance*, which is only used when the source is relatively close to the hive; and the *waggle dance* which is used for longer distances.

The dance on its own is not enough to stimulate foraging bees to activity; they also need to get a taste of the food source. Smell and taste are in fact extremely important to social insects as methods of communication. All the many thousands of bees in a hive, know whether their queen is alive. This comes about because the queen secretes a special *pheromone* substance – oxodecenoic acid – from her mandibular glands. This substance is transmitted from one bee of the hive to the next and prevents any of the worker bees from taking action to raise another queen. Should the queen disappear or die, the worker bees – lacking the queen pheromone – start building large 'queen cells'. At the same time the ovaries of some of the workers begin to ripen, and in time these bees lay eggs in the new cells. The developing larva is fed more or less exclusively on the worker-bee secretion, 'royal jelly', rather than on pollen and honey, and this food seems to possess some factor which stimulates the young larva to develop into a queen rather than another worker.

Two other groups of insect society, the ants and the termites, also depend largely on the exchange of foods and secretions for the integrity of their communities. In termites, all the eggs laid by the queen termite have the genetic potential for developing into any one of a number of castes. There are worker termites, soldier termites with large aggressive-looking mandibles and supplementary reproductives, as well as the primary reproductives – the queen and her mate. In

A single guard at the entrance to a hornet colony. Hornets make their nests of paper by chewing up wood and plant fibres. Usually they nest only for one season, and then move on.

between all these forms is a general factotum termite – the *pseudergate* – and this caste is an intermediate larval form, which unlike the larvae of the *hymenopteran* insects, the bees, wasps and ants, looks more or less like an adult termite. Which caste of termite develops depends, it seems, on these *ectohormonal* substances – the pheromones – which act by controlling which of the genetic blueprints of the cell are going to be switched on and used during the development of the termite.

## Termites

The termite mound is an extraordinary structure, sometimes rising to a height of ten feet or more and containing millions of termites. The mound contains many chambers and passages including a chamber for housing the royal couple and other chambers for growing fungus, on which the colony feeds. Because of the sheer numbers of insects, the oxygen requirements are very high, and the mound has an elaborate system of ventilation built in.

At certain times the pseudergates develop wings and fly away from the colony in huge swarms. There are males and females among the swarm and these settle on the ground in pairs. The paired male and female now lose their wings and start burrowing. They then copulate, the female lays eggs and a new termite colony is in the making.

Although from an entirely different order of insects, the ants show some remarkable similarities to the termites. The ants, too, have a winged sexual pair which loses its wings after settling on the ground to start a new nest. They, too, have castes made up of worker ants and soldiers.

Pheromones play an important part in an ant's life. One type of pheromone, secreted from the underside of the abdomen, is left as a trail by foraging worker ants when they return to the nest laden with food. This pheromone trail attracts other ants from the nest and they find their way to the food. When these ants have also gathered food they leave more trails and the composite trail attracts more and more ants until the food source is drained. Some ants have developed a method of milking aphids of some of the sap sucked from plants via the aphid's sharp stylets. This milking behaviour shows an extraordinary relationship between two species of insect.

Despite its complexity, a social insect's behaviour is based entirely on instinct. Nonetheless insect communities are remarkably flexible in the face of a crisis. Honey-bees, for example, should the hive be running short of water, will all rally round in search of supplies, or should the hive be getting too airless and hot, will begin beating their wings in the hive to generate a current of air. Such a response, however intelligent and reasoned it may seem to the human onlooker, depends on a swift instinctual communication of mood between one bee and another. The result is a highly adaptable and efficient organization.

# Animal behaviour

The complex and sometimes bizarre behaviour patterns found in animals enable them to survive, find food and procreate. How far are these patterns inborn and how do they adapt to environmental changes?

Like many other animals, the oribi, a species of antelope, marks out its territory by means of the secretions from its scent gland. Many forms of behaviour are based on protection of territory.

THE STUDY of behaviour concerns animals in their interaction with the environment, and particularly with the activity of locomotion.

According to Bernard Campbell in *Human Evolution*, 'broadly, it is concerned with how animals come into contact with their environment – how they breathe, how they touch and move on the ground, how they eat the portion of the environment that constitutes food, how they escape from that portion that constitutes predators, and how they communicate with and copulate with the portion that constitutes their own species.' Behaviour describes the way that an animal is related to the environment, and much of the interaction between the phenotype and the environment occurs through the medium of behaviour.

All behaviour is hereditary in the sense that it is an expression of genetic information coded in the genes.

As the nervous system develops in the embryo, definite behaviour patterns are provided for in its structure.

## Nervous organization

Insects and spiders exhibit this nervous organization to a high degree; it is found to be well developed also in fishes, birds and other animals. In some vertebrates (particularly mammals), in some molluscs (soft-bodied unsegmented animals usually having a hard shell) and in various other groups, the structure of the nervous system makes allowance for flexible responses and learning. But this does not mean an animal's behaviour is either completely fixed in pattern or completely flexible: mammals, in addition to intelligence, also possess instincts; perhaps far more than has been suspected: similarly insects, despite their repertory of stereotyped instincts, can learn some things.

Behaviour can be either innate, or, to varying extents, learned. In practice it is difficult to draw a line between innate (inborn) and learned behaviour – the problem is that since innate behaviour develops as a result of the interaction of internal and environmental influences, it is, like learned behaviour, to some extent determined by the environment. For this reason the distinction is not clear-cut, and the term unlearned is often preferred to the terms innate and inborn.

The young cygnets of this mute swan inherit an instinct to follow the first large white object they see after they are born. The inherited behaviour keeps them close to their mother.

The best example of innate behaviour is provided by birds. In fact the discovery of extensive and varied innate behaviour in birds has literally revolutionized the attitude of scientists towards their behaviour. It is now recognized, for example, that hawks, gulls, ducks and most of the familiar passerine birds will defend a certain area shortly before mating and while mated. This territory-defence behaviour appears to be a trait inherited from the lizards, from which birds descended.

The characteristic bird song serves notice to others of the same species that a certain piece of territory is claimed. This is the message conveyed when one male bird, whether wood thrush or barnyard cock, answers another. To a female the song may indicate a male and a possible mate.

The actual song in some species is inherited, and this has been demonstrated by rearing the birds by hand in the complete absence of others of the species. It was also found that male canaries so raised will sing a typical, although somewhat simple, canary song; for the development of the flourishes, apparently, the example of other males is necessary. Female canaries injected with the male sex hormone will sing as long as the hormone lasts.

## Territorial behaviour

Scientists studying the behaviour of birds have found that in defending their territories against intruding males of the same species, male birds respond to definite features that are characteristic of their rivals – even when these features are combined in some object only slightly resembling a rival bird. Thus male bluebirds will attack a ball of blue and reddish feathers. When male birds attack their own images in window panes or mirrors, they are usually trying to defend a breeding territory against intruding males.

The building of nests is also under the control of instinctive responses. Captive birds that have been reared out of nests for several generations will construct the proper kind of nest, which they have never seen, when they mature and are provided with the necessary materials.

There are three different ways of learning: by trial and error, by imitation and by instruction. The trial and error method is found in all animals that can learn and is the sole means of learning in invertebrate animals. Compared with other methods, it takes a long time and can be dangerous. It is the method usually referred to in discussions of learning and in experiments testing learning ability.

For example, rats can learn to find their way through a maze by trial and error so long as a reward is offered. Learning by trial and error, however, reaches its highest development in mammals.

## Learning by imitation

Learning by imitation is a speedier and much more sophisticated means of building up behaviour patterns. In the first place imitation depends on the ability of an animal to recognize and copy another member of its species, usually its mother. A very good example of this is seen in certain species of birds within a few hours of hatching. Normally, young ducklings follow the mother duck, but if they are raised in an incubator and the first large moving object they see is a large ball, then after that they will always follow the ball, and not a female duck, even if the latter is shown to the ducklings later. Imitation is a short cut to learned behaviour, but it introduces a certain inflexibility in the behaviour pattern that is not found in trial and error learning and is therefore more valuable when behaviour is concerned with the more constant features of the environment.

Instruction is, of course, a uniquely human way of creating behaviour patterns, for it involves conscious thought and intent.

In addition, a great deal of behaviour in animals, from jelly-fish to birds and mammals, falls into one of two general categories: *appetitive* behaviour or *consumatory* behaviour. Appetitive behaviour is more or less a series of actions performed at random, often an apparently aimless wandering, which may nevertheless serve to disseminate the species or bring an animal that is hungry into contact with food. Appetitive behaviour is usually, and perhaps always, due to some motivation,

**1** This mass of caterpillars all display marked degrees of appetitive behaviour. As soon as they hatch from the egg, caterpillars are driven by instinct to search out food.
**2** A belted kingfisher about to swoop down on a fish. Despite the difficulties of spotting the exact position of fish underwater, kingfishers are able to track them down.
**3** A sparrow placed in front of a mirror will try to fight its own image. Many birds behave in this way towards real or fancied rivals. Threat behaviour is often well developed.

2

3

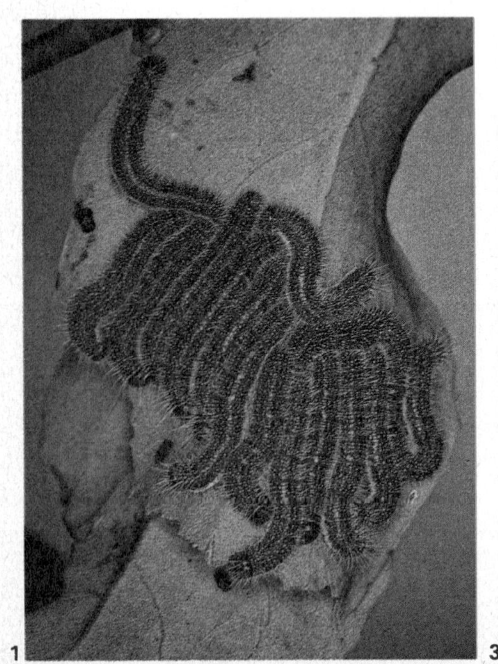

1

**1** A blue tit stealing milk from a milk bottle. This is an example of learned behaviour. The tits learn that milk can be extracted from the bottles by a process of trial and error.
**2** Beavers have a highly developed behaviour pattern, partly inherited and partly learned. Their persistent nibbling at trees in order to build their lodges is an example.
**3** Another example of territorial behaviour. The dog-fox on the log in the photograph is threatening a strange dog which has invaded his territory. In the foreground the vixen waits.

drive, or 'need'.

One usually finds that a large number of caterpillars must spend a certain amount of energy in walking before they will settle down and spin a cocoon. A hawk that is hungry will fly in irregular lazy circles. A male spider that is sexually mature will wander at random until it comes into contact with the web of a female.

Consumatory behaviour is the act or series of acts that end, or at least interrupt, the generalized appetitive phase and results in satisfaction of the drive.

The classic type of primitive response is the so-called trial and error behaviour found in one-celled animals, e.g. the paramecium and other ciliates. When a paramecium collides with a solid object it reverses the beat of its cilia, backs away, turns through a small angle, and moves off in a new direction. A series of such responses will enable the ciliate to avoid the obstacle. At the moment there is no

Even plants can show primitive forms of behaviour. Here, the sticky secretions of a sundew leaf have trapped a gnat, which will eventually serve the plant as food.

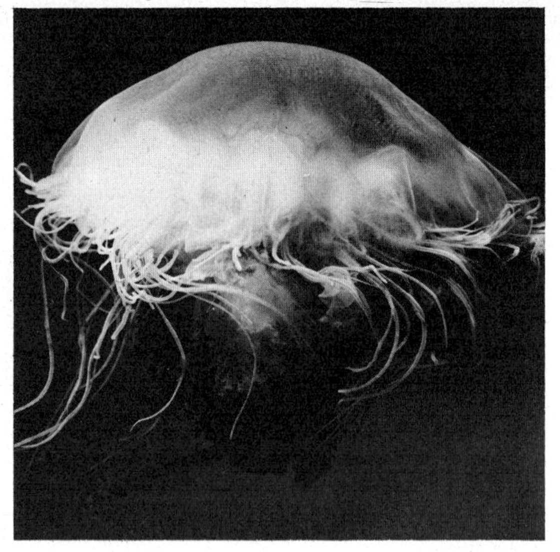

The lion's mane jelly-fish is a stinging variety. Like most of the open-sea jelly-fish, this species floats at a certain depth fairly near the surface catching small marine creatures.

convincing evidence that learning takes place in a paramecium. But the trial and error response does occur in a host of different animals, and the successful trial may result in learning.

A cat or a man making an attempt to get away from a confining puzzle box will resort to random trial and error by pulling, pushing, turning, squeezing, lifting and depressing the door handle until he stumbles on the correct answer and opens the door.

Coelenterates – jelly-fish and sea-anemones – are thought of as having the most primitive type of nervous system – a network of nerve cells. The jelly-fish behaves in an instructive way which shows how the behaviour of animals is characteristic of the species and adapted to the type of environment in which animals live. Jelly-fish also illustrate the continuous state of activity common in many kinds of creatures. *Cassiopea*, a jelly-fish that lives in very shallow water around the Florida Keys in the United States of America, spends its time lying on its 'back', mouth up, while languid pulsations of its bell-shaped body keep a current of water passing over its tentacles. In this way it catches small fish and other animals.

## Sinking jelly-fish

Jelly-fish that act very differently from *Cassiopea* are *Aurelia*, usually studied in laboratories, and *Dactylometra*, the sea nettle, both of which live in coastal waters. These jelly-fish usually swim very slowly to the surface of the water, turn over, and then drift to the bottom, catching any small creatures that become entangled in the tentacles. As soon as the animal gets to the bottom, the muscles begin to contract; these contractions have the effect of sending the jelly-fish up to the surface again, and this is repeated again and again. Jelly-fish of the open sea, for example *Liriope*, behave in marked contrast. They swim very quickly at a fixed depth. If they allowed themselves to sink to the bottom, which in the open sea can often be much more than a mile from the surface, they would be in waters in which there are very few living things small enough for them to capture.

The kind of prefabricated answer to life's problems that instincts provide for their possessors can be profitably studied in the water flea *Daphnia*, the honeybee and birds.

Daphnias are small crustaceans that live in ponds, and instinctively swim to the surface whenever the concentration of carbon dioxide ($CO_2$) in the water increases appreciably. This is a very useful response, because close to the surface the concentration of $CO_2$ is low owing to diffusion into the air, and the concentration of oxygen is relatively high. In the laboratory it is easy to show that this reaction is really a response to light, the response occurring whenever the water becomes sufficiently acid, which it does in nature when the $CO_2$ concentration rises.

The long sticky tongue of the chameleon claims another victim. Though largely instinctive, the chameleon's behaviour requires considerable muscular and eye co-ordination.

As is often the case with instinctive behaviour, no single stimulus is sufficient to elicit or release the response. In the above example, the acidity becomes the 'releasing' stimulus, and the light the 'directing' stimulus.

In their famous 'language' honeybees exhibit a remarkable combination of learned and innate responses. Von Frisch (1950) has shown conclusively that a worker bee that has discovered a new source of food will, on returning to the hive, perform a dance on the face of the honeycomb.

## Flexibility of behaviour

This dance is known as the 'waggle dance'. It is known that if the waggle part of the dance is vertical, the source of the food is directly towards the sun. However, if the waggle is done at an angle of 45 degrees to the left of the vertical, the food source is in a direction of 45 degrees to the left of the direction of the sun. The direction of the waggle taken in relation to the direction of the food source is not learned in any normal sense of the word, because bees do not have to be taught the correct signals to make on their return to the hive. Nor do the bees in the hive have to be taught or have to learn by trial and error what these signals mean.

The purpose of the dance then is to transmit information to other worker bees about the direction, distance and nature of the food source, and is thought a rare example of a descriptive language among animals. This descriptive information is in condensed, coded form and accurately enables other bees to find the flowers described.

This innate behaviour is not flexible, and in an environment that is changing quickly it could be disastrous for the species, since it could be changed only by the slow processes of variation and natural selection.

Learned behaviour, however, is expensive in time and danger but is much more flexible and allows readaptation to occur in every generation.

# Art of survival

**For animals and plants, variety of colour and form is a matter of life and death. Only through its variedness can a species adapt to the stringent conditions imposed by its own environment.**

IN THE YEARS spent sailing around the world in the *Beagle,* Charles Darwin collected thousands of different species of plants and animals and made painstaking observations of them and of the habitat from which they came. Without this voyage and his encounter with such a variety of life and its remarkable adaptations, Darwin would never have had the insight to create his theory that evolution occurs through the agency of natural selection.

But times have changed; many of those researching into the mechanism of evolution base their premises on experiments performed in the laboratory using animal or plant cultures kept under carefully controlled, often unchanging conditions. These modern geneticists very rarely go into the field to study the wild forms of the species they can culture so successfully in the laboratory; they believe that the results of their experiments can be related to conditions in the wild. Some of these 'armchair' theories have a certain plausibility; they often come to be accepted as true both for the laboratory and for the wild.

1 Some species of butterfly and moth, like this moth have vivid 'eye-spots' on their wings which, if mistaken for real eyes, make the animal look very large and fearsome.

2, 3 In contrast to normal red blood cells (left), sickle cells curl up (right) and cannot transport oxygen properly around the body. But they are more resistant than normal blood cells to malaria. Individuals who have half sickle and half normal red cells in their blood are, therefore, better adapted to survive in countries where malaria is endemic.

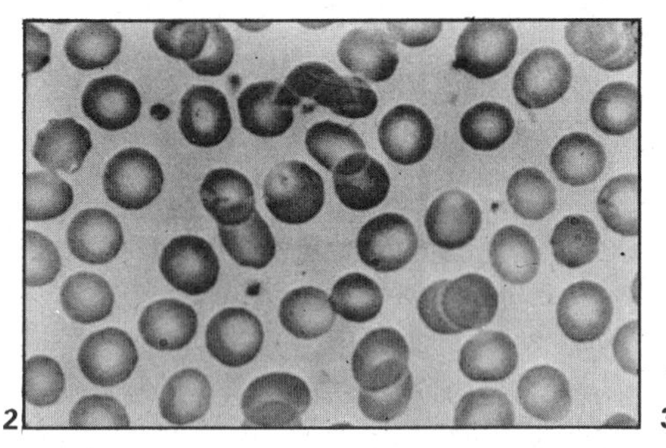

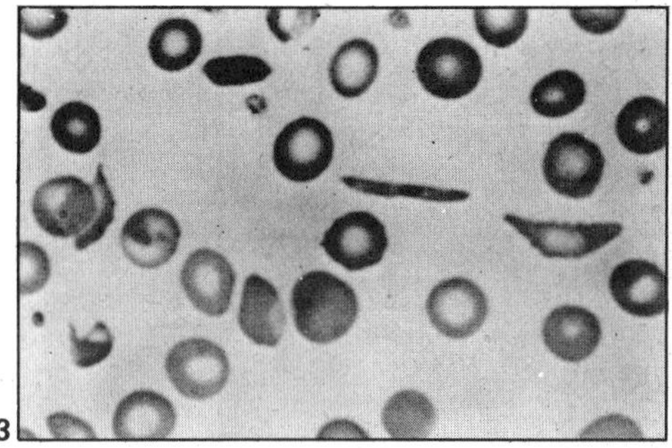

## Field observation

Yet, there are biologists who continue to maintain that evolution can only really be understood by observing species living in their natural habitat. These biologists, known as ecologists, do not dispute that laboratory experiments are useful, nor that time spent thinking over ideas is essential, but if they are to provide an accurate analysis of evolution, they must be combined with meticulous observation in the field.

The difference between wild and cultured populations is often much greater than can ever be imagined. In 1935 an ecologist, C. Gordon, released 36,000 fruit flies into one locality in South Devon. The fruit fly was *Drosophila melanogaster,* a species that is commonly cultured in the laboratory. Gordon used a strain of this species that carried both the gene for *ebony* body colour and its dominant normal *wild type* gene. Although at the beginning of the experiment both these genes were present in equal amounts, after 120 days only 11 per cent of the ebony genes remained in the total population. It had, therefore, taken only five to six generations for the elimination of nearly all fruit flies that carried the ebony gene whether in a double or single dose. Yet in the laboratory ebony is one of the genes that, mixed with the wild type gene, confers greater viability and breeding success than does a double dose of the wild type.

Insects are excellent material for the ecologist. They breed rapidly and their external markings can be used to indicate whether or not they are harbouring a certain gene. In *Drosophila,* for example, genes that have an effect upon the viability, the length of life or upon the fertility of the fly, may also have some other apparently trivial effect. Such genes may, therefore, be responsible for an associated change in eye colour, in the shape of the abdomen, or in the number and form of the bristles on the thorax. Genes with such multiple effects are very common – they are known as *polygenes.*

No one is more aware than the ecologist that external characteristics, like the markings on a butterfly's wings, can be tell-tale indications of some important, yet hidden, physiological adaptation of the animal to its environment. The British scarlet tiger moth, *Panaxia dominula,* for example, has almost tropical colours. The fore-wings are black with a green iridescence and have white spots, except for the two basal ones which are yellowish; the hind-wings are scarlet with black spots and markings. Dr H.B.D. Kettlewell, an English ecologist, tried to breed a line of moths with the lightest possible markings on both wings. After ten years and, therefore, ten generations he had bred moths in which the white and yellowish-white spots had coalesced on the fore-wings, and in which a large amount of the black had been lost from the hind-wings. All who saw his moths after this long period of intensive breeding agreed that they bore little resemblance to the wild type.

In 1948, as he was leaving England for some time, Dr Kettlewell decided to found a colony of these moths in Hertfordshire. The first year after their release the moths produced very few offspring but, by 1951, the adults were fairly common. Ecologists, such as Dr. P. M. Sheppard, who saw these adults were astonished by the speed at which these cultured forms were returning to the ordinary wild English form of the moth. The next year thousands were flying – and the larvae were so numerous that most of them died of starvation. Dr Sheppard and his colleagues collected some of the survivors and bred them. The moths they produced had very nearly returned to the wild type. Dr Sheppard believed this return to the wild type in such a short time could only have happened because the powerful force of natural selection was acting on the hidden physiological effects of the same genes that controlled wing colour.

Ecologists are now realizing that natural selection is a more powerful force than they had first imagined. Instead of giving one gene or set of genes a 1 per cent advantage over another, it can on occasions give a 20 per cent or more advantage. Many evolutionary theorists have based their calculations on natural selection offering little more than a 1 per cent advantage at most. Some of these theorists, like Sewall Wright, have therefore thought up mechanisms of evolution, which according to many ecologists cannot under any circumstances fit the facts.

## Population changes

Sewall Wright proposed the theory of *random genetic drift*. This theory, which some research workers still accept, concerns small populations of animals and plants. The idea is that should a population of a species become very small, a particular gene may show up in the next generation to a greater extent than could ever be expected on the basis of its selective advantage over other genes. This increase in the frequency of a gene, could, suggests Dr Wright, result from chance differences in fertilization and survival. Two opposing genes called *alleles,* present in equal amounts and conferring equal advantages should theoretically be passed on in exactly equal amounts to the next generation. But if in, say, a population of ten individuals, two more of one gene rather than of its opposing gene were passed on to the next generation because of random drift, then in the next generation there would be 12 of one gene and eight of the other – a difference of 20 per cent. Should the same happen again in the following generation, two-fifths of one gene would have vanished from the population – a very significant amount. On the other hand, in a large population such chance deviations would have an almost imperceptible effect and could therefore be discounted as a mechanism of evolution.

Sewall Wright calculated mathematically that evolution would occur most rapidly in a species that was abundant but divided into very small groups. It would be essential that these groups, though predominantly inbreeding, should have some contact, be it occasional, with several of the other groups; under these circumstances both random drift and natural selection would be operating. Thus there would be plenty of 'variety' for natural selection to operate on.

In small and completely isolated populations random drift would virtually operate alone, suggested Dr Sewall Wright, and in time whole sets of genes would be lost. Such a loss would cut down on the survivors' potential to throw up varieties and to adapt, and the population would probably be doomed to extinction. In large

1

2

3

4

6

5

7

**1** By being coloured like a wasp some insects, such as this hoverfly, try to convince their predators that they, too, have an unpleasant sting. in fact they are quite harmless.

**2** The harmless wasp longicorn beetle tries to seek protection by mimicking a wasp. Some insects, however, come to resemble wasps because they, like it, are unpleasant to eat.

**3** To ensure cross-fertilization plants like the primrose have two forms – pin and thrum. The bumble-bee carries pollen from one form to the other when it feeds on the nectar.

**4** Because it looks like barley, wild rye often escapes the attention of the farmer and is not weeded out. This is an example of mimicry aimed especially at confusing Man.

**5** The snail, *Cepaea nemoralis* uses combinations of colour and bands around its shell to camouflage it for different localities. Grass and woods, for example, require different camouflages.

**6** Some forms of camouflage are very effective, as in this stick insect from Java. But, to be effective the insect must stay on bark or else it will be noticed immediately.

**7** The night moth, *Griposa aprilina,* rests on the bark of trees during the day. If it had no camouflage it would soon be eaten by a bird, but, looking like lichen, it escapes attention.

populations the effect of drift would be minimal and that of natural selection all important. Under such circumstances evolution could occur, but more slowly than in the small but not totally isolated populations.

Despite its plausibility the theory of random drift does not seem to fit what actually happens to a small isolated population struggling to survive in the wild. More than 50 years ago Professor E.B. Ford and his father, H.D. Ford, investigated a colony of the marsh fritillary butterfly, *Mellitaea aurinia,* in Cumberland. Records of this colony dated back to 1881 when the butterfly was quite abundant. By 1894 the insect had become very common indeed and then, suddenly, it began to disappear from that site. From 1912 to 1920 the insect was very rare. But, as suddenly as its numbers decreased they began to increase again and by 1925 the numbers of the colony were back at a high, well-established level.

During the first period in the 1890s when the butterfly was abundant, and during the period of declining numbers, all the insects captured had very uniform physical characteristics. Yet from 1920 to 1924, the period of rapidly increasing numbers, Professor Ford and his father caught an extraordinary number of varieties. Some of these insects were so deformed that they could not even fly. Then, after 1924, the colony settled down again to a uniform type – but this uniform type was noticeably different from the uniform type of the first period of abundance.

Professor Ford interprets these findings as follows: when the population is abundant selection pressures are powerful and any butterflies that are the slightest bit deformed or unviable are exterminated in the struggle for survival. When the population is declining, selection pressures are still as great as before, if not greater, and there is no room for experimental varieties. When, however, the population has been drastically reduced and is just beginning to expand again, selection pressures are at their lowest, and varieties can flourish. But, as the colony grows the fight for existence becomes tougher and selection pressures clamp down again on any varieties that are not absolutely viable. When the population is again abundant, variants of the successful uniform type become very rare.

Small populations in isolation tend to isolate themselves further by preventing the interchange of any genetic material between them and other populations. Such isolation can arise through genes that are responsible for a group of interrelated characters binding together in a linear fashion along the chromosomes. Because these associated genes are together they get passed on to following generations as such and they are not split up and fragmented. This mechanism serves, for example, to keep all the genes that govern a set of enzyme reactions together and under one control. Such a unit is known as a *super gene*.

Sometimes a species evolves alternative super genes. When a population contains a balance of several such alternatives, the situation may arise in which the individual that carries two such alternatives – one of them necessarily dominant over the other – is more viable and successful than its fellows which have a double dose of just one of the alternatives. Such a situation gives rise to a *balanced polymorphism* (polymorphism means many forms).

For example, sickle-cell anaemia is an inherited blood disease of humans that is very often fatal. Those with the disease have a double dose of the sickle-cell gene, and their blood cells tend to curl up in the veins where the oxygen tension is low. Yet, those with both a single dose of the sickling gene and a single dose of the normal gene have recently been discovered to have some resistance to malaria, a resistance which those with a double dose of the normal gene do not have. Indeed, the ecologist finds sickle-cell anaemia in countries such as West Africa where malaria is endemic.

Balanced polymorphism can become complicated. The snail, *Cepaea nemoralis,* is adapted to living in a variety of habitats – beechwoods, oakwoods, mixed deciduous woods, hedgerows, rough grass and short grass. Birds, particularly thrushes, go for the snails and break open the shells on a stone, the thrush's anvil. The better hidden or camouflaged the snail, the better its chance of escaping its predators. But each of the different habitats demands a very different camouflage, and the snail has evolved a variety of colours – from a near white right through shades of grey to black and even to red. It also has a series of black bands around its shell. The colour and the number of these bands, up to five, come under supergene control. Some combinations suit one environment better than another.

## Colour adaptation

According to Dr Sheppard the darker the woods and the more uniform the underlying vegetation, for example in beechwoods, the darker the shells and the less banded they are. On the other hand, in grass and hedgerows, a lighter, less uniform habitat, the more yellow the shells and the more banded they are. Snails with other less suited combinations of shell colour and bands will be found in any of these environments, but their numbers will be very small because of predation.

A balanced polymorphism in plants like the primrose, *Primula vulgaris,* promotes outbreeding. There are three forms – pin, thrum and homostyle. In the pin form, the *stigma* (the female part that traps pollen) lies at the top of the corolla-tube, while the anthers (the pollen producers) are half-way down. In the thrum form, the position is reversed and the anthers are at the top of the corolla-tube and the stigma half-way down. In the homostyle form the anthers and the stigma are at the same level, whether at the top of the corolla-tube or half-way down.

Insects such as *Coleoptera* (beetles) and *Lepidoptera* (butterflies and moths) pollinate the thrum and pin forms of the primrose – but the homostyle form is self-pollinating and therefore inbreeding. When the beetle or butterfly thrusts its head into the corolla-tube it comes up against the stigma in the pin form and the anthers in the thrum form. To reach the nectar the insect pushes its proboscis down the tube. The tip of this comes into contact with the anthers in the pin form and the stigma in the thrum. By visiting first one form and then the other the insect carried pollen from one to the other. Cross-fertilization is therefore ensured.

As a result of ecological studies balanced polymorphism is now seen to be far more common among animals and plants than had ever been imagined, even by its most ardent proponents. Many species of insect, for example, carry sets of genes which enable them to mimic other unrelated insects that are immune from predators because they are poisonous or distasteful. By mimicking the vivid colours, the shape and the movement of the unpleasant species, the unprotected species strive to warn any would-be predators that they had best leave them alone.

Of course, if the unprotected species become too abundant their predators will get used to the idea that a great many insects with that distinctive colouring and behaviour are not distasteful after all, and may perhaps start taking 'pot luck'. For this reason some species of insect have a number of different forms so that they can mimic several different unpleasant species. Each of these forms depends on its own set of genes.

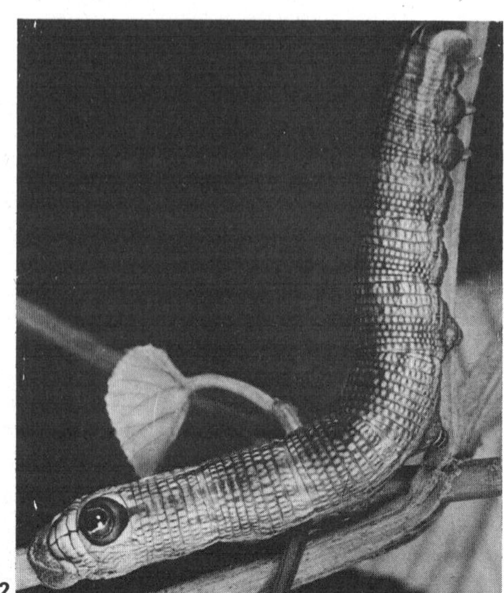

1 Breaking the shells open on its stone 'anvil' the thrush is one of the main predators of the snail. The more the snail can resemble its background the better it is able to avoid predation.

2 The *Thyrous abbotti* caterpillar has a large false eye at the rear of its body. When a bird approaches the insect tries to frighten it off by swaying its rear to and fro in the air.

# Living in communities

**The social life of animals involves a constant tension between individual aggression and the need to associate with others. This conflict underlies the dynamism of all communal life.**

FOR A SPECIES TO SURVIVE it must breed enough young to take the place of its adults when they become aged and die. Broadly speaking, in striving to reproduce, animals can either blanket the environment in a mass of young, in the hope that sufficient numbers will get through the hazards of development; or they can guarantee that most of their progeny survive by carefully nurturing and protecting a small number of young. These two types of sexual reproduction – the profligate and the highly economic – can occur only if there is some sort of co-operation between males and females.

In fish and amphibia the beginnings of social co-operation between the two sexes can often be seen. Mature males seek out females that are about to spawn, and although there may be no physical contact, the male is ready to ejaculate sperm as soon as the female has unloaded her swollen belly of eggs. The female frog has to be physically stimulated by the male, and for this he rides on her back; clinging on tightly with special pads that develop on his front feet during the breeding season.

## Profligate and economic

This is the *profligate* type of reproduction, while in the *economic* type, with its associated 'care of young', there are some extremely complicated behavioural interactions between individuals. During the breeding season some species of animals become territorial, with the result that all sorts of new patterns of behaviour appear; such as aggression against intruders, and the feeding and defence of the young. Very often both male and female parents co-operate closely in defending the territory and young.

Herring gulls behave quite differently at different seasons of the year. In the autumn and winter they live together in flocks, which consist of a homogeneous mass of birds that feed, sleep and fly together. During this period the herring gull does not recognize any individual in the flock, but responds to group behaviour. Thus one gull of the flock may be disturbed while eating and start uttering the rhythmic alarm call – a 'ga-ga-ga'. The other birds all stop to listen and, should the alarmed bird take off, the rest without being at all aware of the cause of danger, will immediately follow.

Then, in the spring, the flock makes for the sand dunes, which are its breeding grounds. There, many of the birds settle on the ground in pairs of opposite sexes and take possession of patches of ground, that they will defend as their territories. At first not all birds have territories and any unmated female has to entice a male. She does this by approaching a lone male in a very special 'appeasing attitude'; for he at this time, in anticipation of having a territory of his own, is becoming quite aggressive. She approaches him with her neck withdrawn, her bill forward and upward and her body held horizontally. This attitude contrasts absolutely with the herring gull's upright threat posture. Should he accept the female's submissive approach, he may either strut around and threaten any males in the vicinity, or he may utter a long-drawn cry and make off with the female. Very often the female then confirms her willingness by begging for food with a curious tossing of her head, to which the male responds by regurgitating a morsel of something.

An eagle – a foreigner and a predator – is driven from their territory by 'dive-bombing' crows. The mobbing eventually induced the eagle to move away from the crows' nests.

Grooming plays an important part in the social lives of baboons: it reflects the relative social standing of groomer and groomed. The groomer is always lower in the social scale.

All this courtship serves to acquaint the two birds with each other and strengthens the bond between them. Once the pair have established themselves they leave the 'unmateds' and select a territory somewhere in the colony. After they have established their territory they become intolerant of any trespasser. Actual attacks on intruders are rare as threatening gestures are generally sufficient to send the stranger away. The mildest form of threat is, as described by Professor Niko Tinbergen, the 'upright threat posture': the male stretches its neck upwards, points its bill down and sometimes raises its wings. If this threat fails to drive the intruder away, the male may resort to 'grass-pulling'. He approaches close to the other gull and all at once bends down and starts pulling up with his bill bits of grass or moss – this movement is an *intention movement*, as if to say 'if you don't go, this is what I will do to you'. Sometimes both the male and female join together in driving strangers away; with their legs bent, their breasts close to the ground, and their beaks lowered, they make a series of incomplete pecking movements at the ground, at the same time emitting a hoarse sort of cooing sound. After copulation and nest-building, the female lays her eggs and both birds begin their long vigil of incubating the eggs and, once the young have hatched, of protecting and feeding them.

This utter transformation of a bird's behaviour from being a homogeneous part of the flock to becoming territorial, having a mate and then caring for the young, depends on entirely new patterns of nervous activity being unleashed in the brain. A sense of the season of the year plays a major part in triggering off this new mode of behaviour, and it seems that the message of the change in the season is carried from the sense organs to other parts of the brain by special hormones. Certainly in birds and mammals the hormone, prolactin, which is secreted in the pituitary gland, plays a major part in bringing out the parents' instinctive reactions to build nests and then care for the young.

Often there is some form of conflict involved. For example, a bird which is territorial during the breeding season will make aggressive threats to any intruders, and yet will protect and care for its young. The young must, therefore, not arouse any aggressive instincts in its parents, and for this reason the young are very often marked in a nondescript, unaggressive way. Furthermore, when the adult birds see the open beaks of the young clamouring for food, they respond by regurgitating a morsel and passing it on to the young. In their turn the young only expose themselves when the parents are present. The herring gull has a red patch on the end of its bill, and only when the young see this do they become active and beg for food. This behavioural response serves to protect the young from the danger of exposing themselves at the wrong time, perhaps when a predator is lurking somewhere in the vicinity. There are innumerable examples of parent-young response in birds, and they all indicate how complicated social life is even at the level of the care of young.

As an animal's life becomes more concerned with other individuals of its species, the more it seems that aggression comes to play an important part. At one level, in, say, the flock behaviour of birds like the house-sparrow, the wagtail or the jackdaw, we can see a sudden communal attack on a predator such as a sparrow-hawk, an owl or a prowling cat. Such an attack usually takes the form of the entire flock 'dive-bombing' the unsuspecting 'foreigner' so that it is forced to flee or take cover. But, as soon as animals exhibit any form of territorial behaviour in combination with social behaviour, aggression becomes more and more prominent. Aggression can be seen in the social insects like the honey-bee which set up their territories in the form of the hive. The honey-bees have bees on 'guard duty' at the hive entrance to prevent any intruders, including bees from other hives, from entering. In fact, the bees of any one hive have a distinctive smell which the guards recognize, and should a foreigner come with a different smell he is immediately set upon and if possible put summarily to death. The situation is analogous to the frontier guards, or the immigration authorities who check passports before they will allow anyone to enter their country. When social animals live in territories their aggression against members of their species serves a very valid purpose; it causes the species to spread out over a much larger area of

**1** A pair of guard bees at the entrance to their hive. The guards distinguish 'alien' bees by their scent and drive them away, or put them to death with their stings.

**2** A crèche of Adélie penguins on Anvos Island, off the coast of Antarctica. The birds have spaced themselves out over the area so that each has its own small patch of ground.

1 Herring gulls courting. The female, her beak pointing upwards, is soliciting scraps of food from the male. This odd behaviour is part of the ritual which overcomes both birds' aggression.
2 Threat behaviour among stags. The stag on the left has intruded on the other's territory. His opponent has lowered his antlers in a threatening gesture to show him he is unwelcome.
3 Different species can sometimes live cheek-by-jowl without friction. Here a goliath heron has built its nest just above that of a long-tailed cormorant.

land than it would perhaps if fraternizing among all members of a species were tolerated. Such aggression rarely harms any of the species through fighting and squabbles; threatening behaviour by the defender of the territory is usually enough to drive away the intruders.

For the most part, animals which set up territories in the breeding season and spend the rest of the year in homogeneous flocks behave instinctively – responding to a way of life that is entirely inborn. There are animals, however, of which human beings are of course a superb example, that depend very much on experience in their behaviour. It is to such animals' advantage to live in complex social groups where the animals all know each other and can learn from each others' experience. In such societies we see the origins of what is called the *peck-order*, or *social status*, or again, the *hierarchy*. And because wisdom and experience is equated with age it is very often the older animals that become the leaders of the group.

## Bird societies

Among birds, members of the *Corvidae* family, such as the jackdaws, live in social groups, and there is always a well-established peck-order. Jackdaws do not instinctively know what their predators are, and it is experience handed on from generation to generation that dictates how the birds react at any given moment. A younger bird, lacking experience, may sometimes show alarm and try to rouse the rest of the social group to activity, but unless the older, supposedly wiser bird, makes a move, the group will remain quiet. Again it is the older birds that keep the social group in order and prevent it drifting into anarchy; birds of high rank will protect birds of low rank from birds of intermediate rank. Konrad Lorenz supposes that a bird of low rank elicits less of an aggressive response in the birds of high rank than do the birds of intermediate rank; the high-ranking birds therefore come out on the side of the 'underdogs' – and peace returns to the group. An interesting situation develops when an unpaired female jackdaw, who automatically ranks low because of her status, gets paired off at some later date to a male of high rank. She now acquires

1 Animals living in a social group observe a strict social order. About to be attacked, the bank vole, on the right, adopts a submissive attitude to a dominant vole.

2 An old bull sea-lion faces inland over the bodies of his populous harem. Frequent fights during the spring months decide which males will acquire harems.

the status commensurate with being paired off with a high-ranking male and can 'lord' it over females that before had been of higher rank. Apart from occurring in jackdaws such behaviour can be seen in primates like the baboon or ourselves, where despite great jealousy a woman of low social class by marrying 'above her' acquires an entirely new status in keeping with her new situation.

In animals which live their entire lives in the social group there are all sorts of behavioural mechanisms to prevent animals of high status attacking and severely wounding animals of low status. We have already seen the appeasement behaviour of the unpaired female herring gull as she solicits an unpaired male who is at that time potentially aggressive.

Although the 'threat' is enough to drive off intruders, in the social group the animals must live in harmony and yet be aware of their status, albeit unconsciously. A new element of behaviour then enters the scene – the *submissive response*. Whenever an animal feels itself about to be attacked by a dominant animal it throws itself into a posture of submission and remains inviolable while it is in that posture. Two dogs, for example, meeting each other on one or the other's territory may well attack each other. Usually one feels its position to be weaker and less tenable and so take up a submissive posture. It stands sideways, cringing to the dominant animal with its head turned away and its neck exposed. The aggressor could very easily grab the submissive dog by the throat and kill him, but some built-in instinctive code of honour prevents this. Then, having assured his dominance he walks off proudly, leaving the other dog to slink off as honourably as he can.

How important the submissive response is to animals living in complicated social groups can be seen from the behaviour of rats living in their large communities based on stable relationships between the males. Two rats encountering each other will, if there is any doubt as to the status of one or the other, sway back and forth between offensive and defensive postures until the one conceding will roll on its back. The other rat now straddles over the submissive rat and somehow this very act is enough to establish dominance. On the next encounter the two rats may act in just the same way, but in time they both get used to each other and the dominance of one is tacitly respected by the other without there being any need for a submissive posture. Mice on the other hand, have no built-in submissive posture and it is significant that, given space, they do not set up large communities.

In their natural surroundings, primates like baboons and rhesus monkeys form well-organized social groups in which the leaders co-operate to protect the females and young from any outside dangers. Not only do the leaders take the group from one feeding ground to the next, but they guard the group and maintain a constant look-out for predators whenever the group stops to feed or rest. Here again there is a new component in the animals' behaviour; for instead of fleeing or trying to avoid a dominant animal, the lower-ranking individual will very often seek out an animal of higher rank. Possibly it feels some kind of protection in the presence of the dominant animal, and it has been pointed out that this turning towards the dominant animal may be based on the young monkey's relationship with its mother. Whenever afraid it flees towards its mother. Then as it grows up it retains this element of infantile behaviour and when afraid projects itself on ever higher-ranking individuals. In this way the threatened animal tends to go towards the centre of society, and when adult to congregate in the region of the dominant males. In the primates the bond uniting the society appears to be the complete suppression of the escape or avoidance reactions. Obviously such a situation is never absolutely easy for the weaker individual and there will be some conflict as to whether to stay or go. One way he has resolved this conflict is by showing his intention to appease the dominant animal. In monkeys the act of grooming is an act of appeasement, and a dominant male will often solicit grooming from a submissive female.

There are few open aggressive attacks in monkey societies in the wild but as soon as monkeys, like the Hamadryas baboon, are held in captivity in their social groups the organization breaks down entirely. Instead of co-operating with each other to protect the group against natural enemies, terrible squabbles develop between the animals, and the dominant males, instead of leading the group, become tyrants that attack and maim or kill the females and infants as well as submissive males. The whole structure of the society in captivity becomes violent and destructive. How relevant this type of behaviour is to our situation of overcrowding and lack of freedom is a matter of conjecture.

# Animal languages

The smile of the chimpanzee, the grasshopper's song and the bright colours of an insect all involve communication. These simple 'languages' are specially adapted to the animal's way of life.

IN THESE DAYS of artificial satellites, very high frequency radio and messages sent by light beams, the word 'communication' conjures up all these advances in the speed and accuracy with which human beings can pass information to each other. Human beings have an elaborate language with which to communicate with other members of their species. So elaborate is the structure of this language that present men can not only tell one another about past and future events, but they can also discuss abstract concepts. Communication in this complex form may not be found among animals but communication itself is not unique to human beings – animals also pass information to each other.

Few, if any, animals exist without contact with fellow members of their species. At some time in the lives of the great majority of animals, the sexual products of the male must find those of the female for reproduction to take place. It is therefore no surprise to find that under these conditions animals of opposite sexes must behave in such a way that the behaviour of the other animal is altered. The special behaviour which is produced is mating. Even relatively inactive animals in the sea, like sea-urchins, are influenced by others; the discharge of sexual products into the water by one stimulates other animals to release their eggs or sperm likewise. This is communication by chemicals.

1 Grasshoppers signal one another by rubbing their hind legs across their wings. Variations in volume give the grasshopper a vocabulary of about 13 different sounds.

2 The Japanese sika deer, now found in America and Europe as well as Japan, displays the white patch on its rump as a reaction to danger, thus warning the other members of the herd.

Courtship shows clearly the kind of information which may be transmitted from one animal to another. The species must first be identified so the signal must preferably be one which is unique to that species; secondly, the sex of the animal has to be signalled. Thirdly, the physiological state of the animal – in this case, its readiness to mate – must be conveyed, and finally, its position given, for if it is to be located by the other animal it needs to indicate where it is. This is a good example of the range of information which can be conveyed by a relatively simple piece of behaviour.

## Mutual behaviour

All kinds of mutual behaviour can be viewed as examples of communication, for in them one animal influences the behaviour of another. The behaviour of the animal which we can call *the sender* is a reflection of its physiological state. If, for example, a male stickleback threatens another male intruding on its territory, its behaviour reflects the aggressive internal state of the fish. Such a posture seen by an intruding fish, one which is off its own territory, causes it to retreat. No consciousness occurs in either fish; both the behaviour of the territory owner and that of the intruder can be considered to be inborn and automatic.

The essence of communication is a signal which bears information. It is sent by a sender and received by a receiver. The signal can be in any form which the receiver can sense. It is not unexpected, therefore, to find that animal signals can be visual, auditory, touch and chemical;

indeed, any kind of stimulus that falls within the spectrum of action of the sense organs. But each of the kinds of signal have their own advantages and disadvantages making one suitable for one way of life and another adapted to some other habitat. It is best, therefore, to look at communication by considering the different kinds of signal.

The bright colours of some insects, fish and birds immediately suggest they have importance in the life of the animals bearing them. Some of them, like the black and yellow stripes of a wasp's abdomen, serve as warning signals marking out distasteful prey to possible predators; birds, for example, learn to avoid cinnabar moth caterpillars with their black and yellow rings round their bodies, after their first unpleasant encounter. Others camouflage the animal. But very many colours are used as parts of displays which make an animal conspicuous to its species mates. The brilliant bluish colours to which a male Siamese fighting fish turns on sighting a rival is a simple example. Among birds, coloured tufts and patches of feathers are displayed in the movements of courtship.

## Birds of paradise

Perhaps some of the most amazing are the feathers and plumes of birds of paradise. The riflebird, for example, throws its head back at one point in its display to show an iridescent blue and purple chest patch; while the ribbon-tailed bird of paradise trails a pair of two-foot long white feathers, tipped with black, from its tail.

But splendid colours and patterns are not the only visual signals which may be employed. The pattern of movement of some part of the body may be important. Different species of fiddler-crab, for instance, can be distinguished by the way in which their enlarged claw is raised and brought down again. In general the path followed is from flexed in front of the eyes – extended out horizontally sideways – flexed vertically upwards – brought down to the starting position. The various parts of the movement may be made quickly or slowly, the downward movement may be jerky or smooth and so forth. These are the gestures of male crabs attempting to lure a female to join them as they stand beside their burrows. So distinctive are the signals that as many as five species of these crabs can live side by side on the same beach apparently without confusion between the species.

Another kind of visual signal is the light flash of fireflies. The light is produced at special places on their abdomens. The males of one common species flash their lights in a short series of 'Morse' dots, and the female responds by showing her light exactly two seconds after the end of the male's signal. He will respond by heading towards the female, but he will only move to lights which show at exactly the right time interval after the end of his. In this way he is attracted only by females of his own species.

Facial expressions play a great part in human communication, for by a look at a person's face we can get some idea at least of whether he is angry, sad and so forth. In monkeys and apes whether a smile is given with the teeth exposed or with them covered by the lips makes a great deal of difference in the information conveyed.

Visual signals are therefore varied. But they all require that the sender and receiver should be in view of each other – which rules out the use of these signals among the leaves and branches of a tropical forest. Furthermore, the sender will be conspicuous as he has to get his message across; he therefore exposes himself to danger from watchful predators. The advantage of visual signals is that they may be visible over a great distance; when they are employed we can guess that their possible disadvantages have been weighed, by natural selection, against the advantages and found wanting.

Sound, however, can be used for communication even among the roots of grass or in the thickest bush. Also sender and receiver can remain hidden from view. The range over which sound will travel is often restricted, so that this kind of signalling is usually over a shorter range than visual signalling.

No animal has as complicated a language as a human being; the vocabulary of a grasshopper, for example, may consist of only 13 different sounds. These insects make the sound by rubbing their hind legs across their wings which are folded along their bodies. On the inside of their legs there is often a row of pegs each of which strikes the wing in turn. This sets the wing into vibration, at the natural vibration

**1** The splendid plumage of New Guinea's birds of paradise has a purpose: it is used in courtship to win the interest of the mate.
**2** Male fiddler-crabs have an elaborate signalling 'language' involving the display of their prominent claws. Some displays attract a mate, while others are for threatening intruders.
**3** Its feathery antennae enable the male emperor moth to detect minute amounts of sex attractants released on to the wind by females. Males follow the sex attractant to its source.
**4** The flickering light of the firefly also has a part to play in courtship. Different species have their own 'codes' of lighting to avoid confusion during courtship.
**5** Chemical communication brings these barnacles together on the same rock. Larvae which are about to settle down are attracted to other barnacles by chemicals they emit.

frequency of the wing material. In a sense this is like the movement of the violinist's bow across the strings – the bow plucks at the strings, setting them into vibrations which produce the sound. Such a sound from a grasshopper does not vary in note, for the sound has the frequency of the natural vibration of the wing. But each time a peg hits the wing the vibration is increased in intensity, for the *amplitude* of vibration is increased. Thus the song of a grasshopper is *amplitude modulated.* It is the pattern of these modulations which renders the song of one species unique. And this pattern can be altered by a change in the rate at which pegs strike the wing. So different species have different patterns of pegs or move their legs at different speeds from others.

The sound signals of grasshoppers are particularly important in courtship. The males, for example, have one song which they sing together, duetting with each other. This makes a group of males conspicuous and attracts females to them. When a male sees an approaching female, he literally changes his tune, to a courtship song. In addition to these two songs he may have a 'triumph' song, a special song made during mating, a rivalry song and a number of others. But the range of possible songs is rather limited as they depend for their variety on amplitude modulation alone.

When frequency changes are introduced songs become far more variable. One only has to compare the songs of birds with those of grasshoppers. Making their songs by the effect of air moving over vocal chords with a range of cavities in the head acting as resonators, birds produce notes joined into distinctive phrases. Even to our ears, bird and grasshopper species can be identified by the noises they make.

The best known bird song is that of the male advertising his presence from a tall tree in his territory. The songs of blackbird, thrush or robin are examples of this advertisement song. It conveys the singer's species, his sex, that he is in reproductive condition, that he wishes to attract a female to his territory and that he defies another male to attempt to enter the territory.

Sound is now known to play a part in what is probably the most remarkable piece of communication behaviour among animals. This is the honeybee's dance by which a successful forager informs her hivemates of the place where she has found food. On her return from a nectar-gathering expedition to flowers within about 80 metres from the hive she dances in a circular pattern on the vertical face of the comb within the hive. This gives much less information than the figure-of-eight dance she will perform after finding food at a more distant place. This dance conveys both direction and distance of the food source. If the line of the middle part of the dance is straight up the comb, the food is in the direction of the sun; if vertically down the food is in the opposite direction to the sun. Thus the direction of the sun is indicated as vertically upwards and a line of dance at an angle to the vertical shows food at the same angle from the sun's direction.

During the dance, the bee makes low-frequency sounds in a series of bursts. The rate at which these bursts are produced seems to bear a relationship to the distance that she has flown and thus indicates the distance of the food. It is difficult to know precisely what information another worker gets from the dance and it may be that the speed with which the dance is performed is also very important in 'describing' the distance of the food. The bees which follow a dancing forager cannot see her movements as we do, from above, as they are in the dark, moving with their antennae lightly touching her body. They must pick up the pattern of the dance in this way.

When animals have acute powers of smell, they may communicate by scent. Moth collectors know that males of a number of species will congregate around a female of their own species, coming to her from thousands of yards away. They will even be attracted by an empty box in which she has been. This is the result of sex-attractant substances produced in the

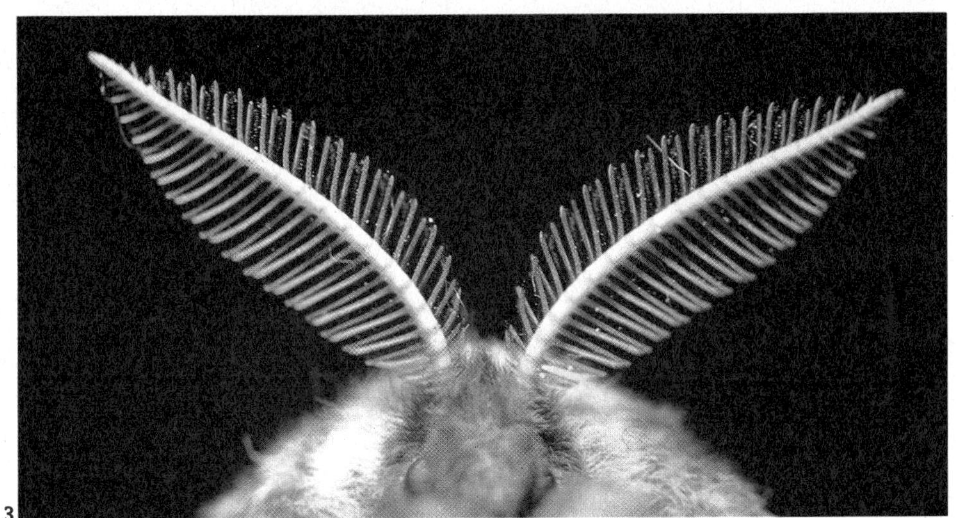
3

4

5

glands on the female moth's body. At least one of these has been isolated and synthesized in the laboratory. Under the name of Gyplure it is used to attract male gipsy moths to insecticides. The scent is picked up by the feathery antennae of the male insects.

In social insects chemicals play a very considerable part in organizing the activities of the thousands of insects which often make up colonies of bees, ants, wasps and termites. The queen honeybee advertises her presence to the hive by the 'queen substance' she produces from glands in her head and which she spreads on her body. The 'queen substance' is licked off her by the workers attending her and passed round the hive as they exchange food with each other. So long as this substance is circling through the hive no queen cells are produced on the comb – without these no larvae will be raised to give queens. But should the queen be removed, or should she fail to produce the substance in sufficient quantity, workers in more distant parts of the hive begin to construct the larger cells in which new queens will be reared.

Ants use chemicals to mark the paths they make back to the nest after finding food. The marks remain attractive for a short time only and new marks are laid only if the food supply is a good one. An unreinforced trail rapidly loses its attraction so that workers are not drawn off along paths which lead to an exhausted source.

1 Angry wolves circle one another, making threatening gestures. The bared fangs and the raised mane are both part of an attempt to intimidate the opponent and indicate anger.
2 Smiling – baring the teeth to indicate pleasure and greeting – is universal among the primates. Monkeys can interpret human facial expressions, just as we can this chimpanzee's.

Scent marking of territory is common among mammals. Dogs use their urine to mark areas and the urine of a bitch in heat is particularly recognizable, advertising her presence to the dogs of the neighbourhood. Many of the ungulates on the African plains mark the bounds of their territory. Some smear the ends of twigs with material from a gland on their faces, others have glands in their split hooves.

The specificity of scent depends upon the chemical structure of the substances which are used. These are many and are sufficient for a large 'vocabulary', but cannot be patterned like a sound or like the pattern of light from a butterfly's wing. If scent is produced in puffs, like the bursts of a grasshopper's song, the pattern is soon lost as small wind movements mix up the odour. Nevertheless, scent has shown itself to be an efficient means of communication.

Human language has a quality that is absent from all the methods of communication used by animals. It is able to convey abstract thought, concepts derived from the development of human society, mathematical expressions, humour, justice, truth. It has what biologists call predictive value, because it can convey not only the present moods and desires of the person involved, but his future intentions. Animal communication, on the other hand, lacks the abstract quality of human speech. The various signals that animals make between themselves are, in many cases, sophisticated but lack this feature.

The distinctive difference in all these signals from those used in human language is that they reflect the animal's present physiological state. Only in that a mammal, for example, which is aggressive and whose fur is standing erect may well attack have these signals the predictive value of human language. But all animal language, simple though it may be, is highly adapted to the life which the animal leads.

# Protective colouring

The colours of animals and insects are not merely decorative. Sometimes they help to conceal the animal from its enemies, whereas in other cases they warn potential predators or frighten them away.

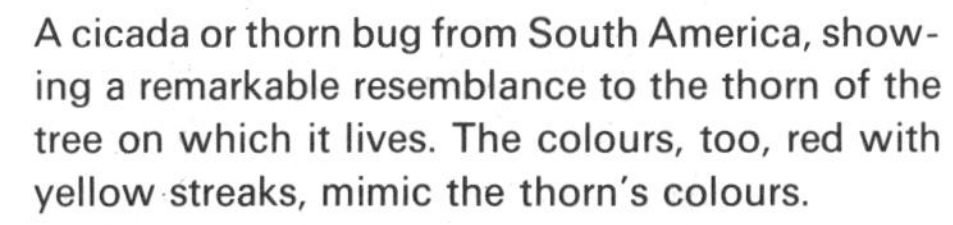

A cicada or thorn bug from South America, showing a remarkable resemblance to the thorn of the tree on which it lives. The colours, too, red with yellow streaks, mimic the thorn's colours.

The skunk's prominent stripes are warning coloration. With its foul-smelling secretions, the skunk has little need to worry about predators, and the colouring reminds them to keep away.

THE COLOURS of many animals help them to avoid unwelcome contact with others. This may be because they cannot easily be distinguished from their surroundings, or because they can give a warning signal that discourages others from approaching. These camouflage colours have been acquired because they are an advantage to their owners in the struggle for survival. It is useful for a predator to be able to conceal itself from the prey it wishes to catch, and of course it is also useful for hunted animals to be able to keep their enemies away, at least some of the time.

A great many predators blend with their natural surroundings so that they can stalk their prey unnoticed. The white coats of polar bears and other Arctic animals blend with the snow and ice, but many other animals that may seem conspicuous in the zoo are not at all easy to distinguish in their native surroundings. The stripes and spots of zebras, tigers, giraffes and leopards blend imperceptibly with the moving patterns of light and dark among the grassy plains and scattered trees of the tropical savanna that they inhabit.

These large animals have acquired their camouflage because it helps them to catch their food, but smaller animals, particularly invertebrates, including insects and small water creatures such as shrimps, are preyed upon by larger animals and need their colours to enable them to avoid capture as often as possible. The caterpillars of many moths closely resemble the twigs of the trees on which they are to be found, and birds are unable to distinguish them. Other insects escape attention because they resemble objects that are not usually a source of food; the caterpillars of the swallow-tail butterfly, for example, have a black and white saddle on their backs and resemble bird-droppings. Birds would have to be very hungry before investigating these as a source of food.

## Variable camouflage

Most insects that gain protection by blending with their background depend for their camouflage on their presence in very particular surroundings. But some animals are less confined because they can change colour to match a new background, sometimes quite spectacularly, as do chameleons. These reptiles can be green, yellow or cream or dark brown, often with darker or lighter spots, to blend with different backgrounds. This helps to conceal them from their snake and bird enemies.

The flounder is another well-known animal that can change colour. This fish will assume a speckled appearance against an unevenly coloured background, or a uniform colouring against a plain background. Many other sea creatures are adept at changing colour, and one of the most versatile is the octopus (*Octopus vulgaris*), which can change its colours and colour patterns to match practically any sort of background. This is possible because the pigments which give the animal its various colours are contained in many special organs called *chromatophores*, which vary in appearance according to their degree of expansion. The octopus has two sets of chromatophores, one varying from black to red-brown, and the other from red to pale orange-yellow. Below the chromatophores is a thin layer of special bodies called iridocytes that break up white light to give green and blue. Thus the octopus has a vast repertoire of colour patterns that it can adopt, to make itself inconspicuous on any sort of marine background.

The shrimp is another sea creature with a striking ability to change colour. At night its whole body becomes a beautiful translucent blue whatever the daytime colour may have been – green, brown or patterned. A crab known as *Uca* has a remarkably constant rhythm of colour change. It is pale at night and dark during the day and these changes are attuned to the tides. The organs which contain the coloured pigments are always at their largest and darkest just before low tide. This is the time when *Uca* is most actively foraging for food and so is also the time when it needs the most concealment.

Crabs in different localities have their own rhythms of colour change synchronized with the different times of low tide. *Uca* obviously has some kind of internal clock that maintains the rhythm of its colour changing, but like most biological clocks its mechanism is still a mystery.

The cuttlefish (*Sepia*) has an elaborate colour-change mechanism for deceiving its enemies. When it needs to make a rapid escape, the cuttlefish ejects the contents of its ink sac – many tiny granules of the dark-brown pigment, melanin. Immediately after sending out this 'smoke-screen' the animal becomes very pale and swims away at right angles to its previous direction. Predators are momentarily confused and attack the cloud of pigment while the cuttlefish makes its escape.

In other cases potential predators are frightened away by some special behaviour combined with the colouring of the animal they would have attacked. Some moths, butterflies and other insects have markings on their wings that closely resemble the eye of a large and much more fearsome animal. The 'eyes' are usually concealed when the animals are at rest but are displayed when they are disturbed, and have been observed to frighten away bird predators. Sometimes the 'eye' affords a different sort of protection. When a butterfly such as the grayling (*Eumenis semele*) comes to rest, predators tend to attack the conspicuous eyespot because the eye is usually on the head, the most vulnerable part of the body. If attacked in this way, however, the grayling will not lose its head but only a part of its wing. It can fly with a large part of its wing missing and so it is likely to survive the attack.

Eyespots are also found on the tails of some fish, where they serve the same purpose of directing attack to the least vulnerable part of the body. Some caterpillars, for example those of several swallowtail butterflies, have small eyespots which direct attention away from the unprotected abdomen towards a part of the body which has a special protection, such as a stinging mechanism. The attention of a predator is, therefore, drawn towards a part of the body which has properties that may well cause the attack to be broken off.

## Warning colours

Another way of confusing observers is by a sudden change from bright colours to inconspicuousness, which is practised by insects such as the large yellow underwing (*Triphaena pronuba*). This is well concealed when at rest, but when it flies away its colours are conspicuous and give a flashing sensation. At the end of a flight the insect usually descends suddenly to the ground and immediately it has landed covers the bright parts of the body and remains very still thus confusing pursuing predators.

Some colour patterns do not actually deceive predators, but merely warn them not to attack animals that are distasteful or dangerous. Conspicuous, easily recognized colour patterns have evolved in many cases to advertise an unpleasant nature. This is an obvious advantage in saving the animal concerned from unnecessary attack. Birds soon learn to avoid the familiar yellow and black stripes of the wasp with its unpleasant sting, and the same goes for the black and orange caterpillars of the cinnabar moth (*Hypocrita jacobaeae*), which are very distasteful.

In summer these caterpillars can be seen in thousands feeding on ragwort, a sure indication that they must be distasteful, for otherwise they would surely be eaten up by birds which tend to concentrate on a particular food while it is available. Because of this tendency, most larvae that live in large groups need to be protected from attack; many of them are hairy and cause irritation when touched. The small tortoiseshell caterpillars (*Aglais urticae*) which gather in large groups are black and yellow, and the caterpillar of the peacock butterfly, which behaves in an equally conspicuous way, is black. Yellow and black are both warning colours and very few birds will eat these caterpillars.

Although the best known cases of warning coloration are among the insects, there are many larger examples, such as the American skunks with their conspicuous stripes advertising the evil-smelling and pervading fluid they can squirt at their enemies. And there is a toad which has glands in its skin that secrete an unpleasant substance, while its underside is bright scarlet. When a potential predator, perhaps a stork, flies over a group of these toads the animals flop on their backs exposing their scarlet bodies. The birds associate the bright red colour with the unpleasant taste and do not try to eat the toads.

Some animals that have no special

**1** The male orange tip butterfly *Euchloë cardamines* is well concealed at rest on orange blossom. The outer covering of the wings blends closely with the blossom, camouflaging the butterfly.
**2** The caterpillar of the giant *Papilio* butterfly looks like a bird-dropping. This makes it unattractive to birds, and ensures the insect's immunity from predators.
**3** The larva of the spice-bush swallowtail butterfly has a large false 'face'. Its ferocious appearance tends to frighten away enemies which might otherwise attack and eat it.
**4** A hen pheasant concealed in brush. The plumage is broken up into areas of markings, breaking down the bird's outline and making it more difficult for predators to see it.

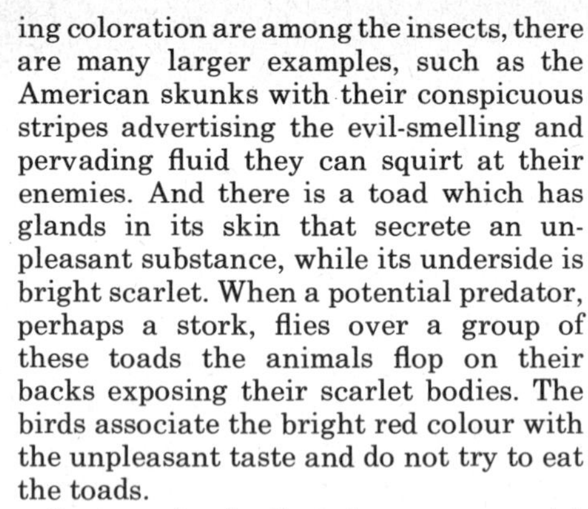
1

2

3

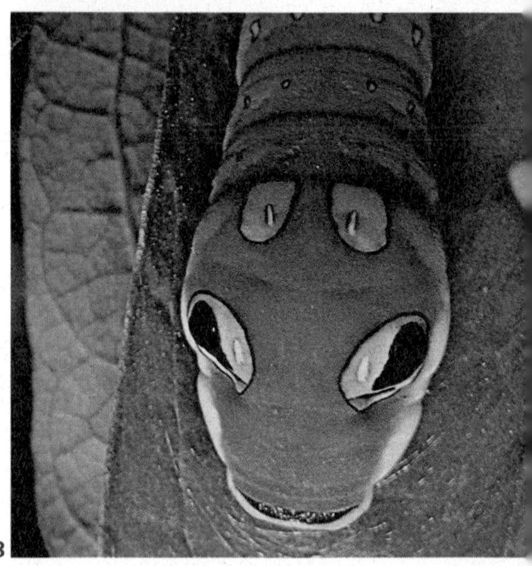

4

means of protection against attack, such as stings or glands, gain protection by closely resembling and mimicking others that are distasteful or in some other way make life unpleasant for their attackers. Predators learn that it is as well to avoid eating anything with the particular colour pattern of the distasteful species. But in avoiding these colour patterns they must avoid the mimics as well as the unpleasant genuine models, without knowing that some of the animals they are avoiding would be quite harmless to eat and even enjoyable. Very familiar examples in temperate countries are flies that have striped bodies and look just like bees or wasps.

The advantage to an edible animal in resembling outwardly a much less edible animal, to which it may not be at all closely related, was first recognized in 1862 by H.W. Bates, and became known as Batesian mimicry.

There will, of course, only be an advantage to the mimic if there are many more models than mimics, so that young predators unused to the warning colours are more likely to try to attack the inedible models than the mimics. If there were more mimics, the predators might soon learn to associate a particular coloration with edibility and attack every time they saw it.

There are many examples of Batesian mimicry in the tropics. Among birds the distasteful and aggressive drongo (*Dicrurus adsimilis*) lives in savanna areas and is often found in company with the very similar black fly-catcher, *Melaenotnis pammalaina*; the second seems to be a mimic of the first. In Southeast Africa there are several types of friar bird which are noisy and aggressive. Their flocks are often accompanied by orioles, which are not close relatives, but always resemble the friar birds they are with. This again seems to be a case of Batesian mimicry, with the friar birds as the models.

More than one species may mimic the same model or models. In West Africa the colourful butterflies *Papilio dardanus* and *Hypolimnas dubius* have three models in common, showing how closely many species have come to resemble each other. Only the females of *Papilio dardanus* are ever mimics, but there are a great many different forms within the species, mimicking various models.

In 1879, F. Muller pointed out a different sort of mimicry. He argued that while young predators are learning to avoid distasteful species, a certain number of animals with warning colours are bound to be killed. But if two species, equally distasteful and warningly coloured, closely resembled each other, fewer of each species would be killed than if the predators had to learn to avoid two separate warning colour patterns. This idea has been proved experimentally, for the black and yellow markings on the caterpillars of the cinnabar moth have been found to save them from attack by a predator not familiar with them, provided that it has already tried to eat wasps. This is Mullerian mimicry, with all the species

**1** The brightly coloured, unpleasant-tasting caterpillars of the cinnabar moth are often found on ragwort in hedgerows and on waste ground. Despite their bright colours, they are rarely attacked.

**2** Like the chameleon, the octopus can vary its pigmentation to blend with the surroundings. It has several different types of pigment cell in its skin which respond to external colours.

concerned not only warningly coloured but also having some special means of protection from attack. Another difference from Batesian mimicry is that all the species involved, being equally distasteful, can be equally numerous.

In tropical Africa are two species of butterfly, *Heliconius melpomene* and *H. erato,* which are found in very many different forms with their own distinct colour patterns. In any one place, however, the patterns of the two species are very similar. Both are known to be extremely distasteful to birds, and provide a good example of Mullerian mimicry.

A further type of mimicry involves the eggs of birds such as cuckoos which are laid in the nests of other birds. These eggs closely resemble the eggs laid by the owners of the nest, who are deceived into brooding the eggs as their own and subsequently bringing up the young birds. This brood parasitism, practised by several groups of birds, is most highly developed among cuckoos. Parasitic species of the European cuckoo, *Cuculus canorus,* lay eggs that are rather smaller than those of their closest non-parasitic relatives – their eggs are about the same size as those of the usual foster parents, such as meadow pipits (*Anthus pratensis*), reed warblers (*Acrocephalus scirpaceus*) and redstarts (*Phoenicurus phoenicurus*). In some areas the cuckoo will lay several distinctly different types of eggs each mimicking the eggs of one species of the unwitting foster parent.

This rather extreme example is typical of animal camouflage in that one animal is deceived by another to the advantage of the deceiver. This does not mean that a camouflaged species will automatically survive while the species it is deceiving dies out. One might ask why the mimics and their distasteful models have not starved their predators out. But camouflage is a form of adaptation to the environment and all successful species, including the predators of mimics, are adapted to their environment or they would not be able to survive. Predators may have another source of food or perhaps, if very hungry, they will eat something relatively distasteful and warningly coloured.

Whatever the exact situation, camouflage is a very fine example of adaptation and shows just what elaborate systems have developed to fit animals to their various ways of life.

**1** The brill, *Scophthalmus rhombus,* matches the sea-floor in an attempt to avoid detection. It is able to vary the pattern of pigmentation to merge with the sea-bed.
**2** Though the stripes of the zebra make it very conspicuous in the zoo, they serve to camouflage it in its native savanna. The animal's outline is broken up against the scrub background.
**3** The morepoke, an Australian bird, is camouflaged to look like a dead branch. The bird's plumage imitates the texture and colour of tree-bark and the head is camouflaged.

# Learning by experience

**Most animals learn something in the course of their lives, though not all learn in the same way. The study of animal learning is still in its infancy, but it may give vital clues to human learning.**

TO SURVIVE, animals need information about their environment. The hydra feeds by stretching its tentacles towards protein-like molecules exuded by the tiny pond creatures on which it feeds. This method of feeding implies that the hydra 'knows' that the protein-like molecules floating past it indicate the presence of potential food. Again a mouse might avoid the marauding owl through its ability to dash back to its hole by the quickest possible route – an ability that depends on the mouse's 'knowledge' of the layout of its immediate environment.

These two examples illustrate the two fundamentally different ways in which animals acquire and store information. The information that nitrogen-containing molecules are exuded by potential prey animals is encoded in the hydra's genes; it stretches towards such molecules because it has inherited the behavioural mechanism that makes it do so. Its knowledge and activity are purely 'instinctive'. But the mouse cannot be born with knowledge of the exact position of its burrow and the objects around it. It acquires this knowledge through the agency of its senses – particularly its eyes and nose – and stores it in its brain. The process of acquiring knowledge in this way, through the agency of the nervous system, is known as learning.

Professor W. H. Thorpe, whose *Learning and Instinct in Animals* is the classic text on this subject, defines learning as '... that process which manifests itself by adaptive changes in individual behaviour as a result of experiences'. The key word in this definition is 'adaptive': the essential point is not merely that the animal's behaviour changes as a result of experience (for example, an animal's behaviour would change following the experience of having half its brain blown away; but this change could hardly be considered the result of learning), but that the animal's behaviour following an experience becomes more appropriate, more apt, more likely to increase the animal's chances of survival.

To analyse the behaviour of the more intelligent animals in the wild is extremely difficult, because their activities are very complicated and subject to changes of mood, just as ours are. But by studying animals under controlled laboratory conditions, and by concentrating a great deal on simple animals whose behaviour tends to be more rigid, experimental psychologists have demonstrated many recognizable systems or patterns of behaviour among animals. Thus they have defined several different kinds of learning, which Professor Thorpe has tentatively classified into six types: habituation; classical conditioning (which depends on the conditioned reflex); instrumental conditioning, otherwise known as trial-and-error learning; latent learning; insight learning; and imprinting. It could be that these are false classifications. Perhaps, for example, imprinting might turn out to be a special case of classical conditioning. Nonetheless, some kind of classification is always needed in science if only to give scientists definable problems to work on, and it is worth examining what each of these terms means.

Habituation is in some ways the simplest manifestation of learning and it is possibly the most primitive. As Aubrey Manning points out in his excellent *Introduction to Animal Behaviour,* habituation involves not the acquisition of new responses, but the loss of old ones. Manning quotes as an example the case of a snail crawling over a sheet of glass. If you tap the glass, the snail instinctively and immediately retracts into its shell. There it stays for a little while and then re-emerges and carries on its way. If you tap the glass

Young lions graduate from playful fighting among themselves to making their first kill. These lions, co-operating to bring down a buffalo, are learning skills they will use as adults.

Play has an important role in learning. These otter cubs rapidly overcome their initial clumsiness through playing together and develop control over their body movements.

Apes are able to tackle problems requiring some degree of insight or reasoning power. This chimpanzee displays obvious concentration in his efforts to darn a sock.

again it will again retract; but this time it stays in its shell for a shorter time before re-emerging. After a few more taps the snail hardly 'bothers' to retract at all and, eventually, it 'ignores' the taps completely. It has, in fact, learnt to ignore a stimulus to which, if untrained, it would instinctively react.

The second form of learning, classical conditioning, is the most elementary example of 'associative learning'. It depends on the conditioned reflex.

## Reflex learning

At the beginning of this century the great English physiologist C.S. Sherrington studied what are now called simple reflexes in so-called spinal animals – that is, animals in which the brain has been removed and only the spinal cord remains. He showed, among other things, that if an electric shock was applied to the foot of a 'spinal' cat then the animal immediately withdraws its foot, even though there is no brain to tell the animal to move. In this experiment the electric shock is called the stimulus and the withdrawal of the foot is called the response; the whole action – the 'automatic' retreat from the noxious stimulus – is called a reflex action.

At about the same time the Russian physiologist I.P. Pavlov was studying reflexes of a slightly different kind in whole animals, with intact brains. It was known that if meat is placed in a dog's mouth, then the dog salivates; this is a reflex response, though it is slightly more complicated than the ones studied by Sherrington. Pavlov found that he could measure the strength of the response by making the ducts from the dog's salivary glands run to the outside of the animal's cheek, instead of the inside of the mouth. Then, after introducing meat to the animal, he could simply count the drips of saliva running out.

In one series of experiments, just before giving the meat, he would sound a bell, or set a metronome ticking. At first, the dogs would ignore this sound; after a time, if the sound *always* preceded the presentation of the meat, the dogs would salivate when sound was made – that is, before the meat was given. The animals had learnt to associate the sound with the meat. In this experiment the meat is known as the unconditioned stimulus and the sound of the bell is called the conditioned stimulus. The point is that the unconditioned stimulus always produces the reflex response, such as salivation; but the conditioned stimulus produces the response only after the animal has been 'conditioned', or trained, to associate the bell sound with the meat. Eventually, conditioned animals would produce as much saliva when they heard a bell as when they were presented with meat; and finally, they would salivate at the sound even if no meat was given. After a time, however, if the experimenter repeatedly sounded the bell without then giving meat, the dogs ceased to salivate at the sound of the bell. In other words, the conditioned reflex was lost, or, as psychologists say, it was 'extinguished'.

The possibilities of learning by conditioned reflexes are limited; all an animal can do through this method is to respond in a very stereotyped way to some new stimulus which it associates with a stimulus to which it would normally respond instinctively. And we know that animals learn things that would be very difficult to explain in terms of this simple conditioning process. For example, the American physiologist B.F. Skinner observed pigeons which he kept in a special cage of the kind that has become known as a 'Skinner box'. The pigeons wandered around pecking at this and that, in purely random fashion, and quite spontaneously, without any encouragement from the experimenter. But the cage was so designed that if they happened to peck at a particular bar, a small amount of food was released. Eventually the pigeons stopped pecking at random and pecked only at the bar that caused the release of food. Skinner proposed that animals could learn to perform particular actions if that action (called a response, though strictly speaking it is not a response since it can be a piece of spontaneous activity) is immediately rewarded.

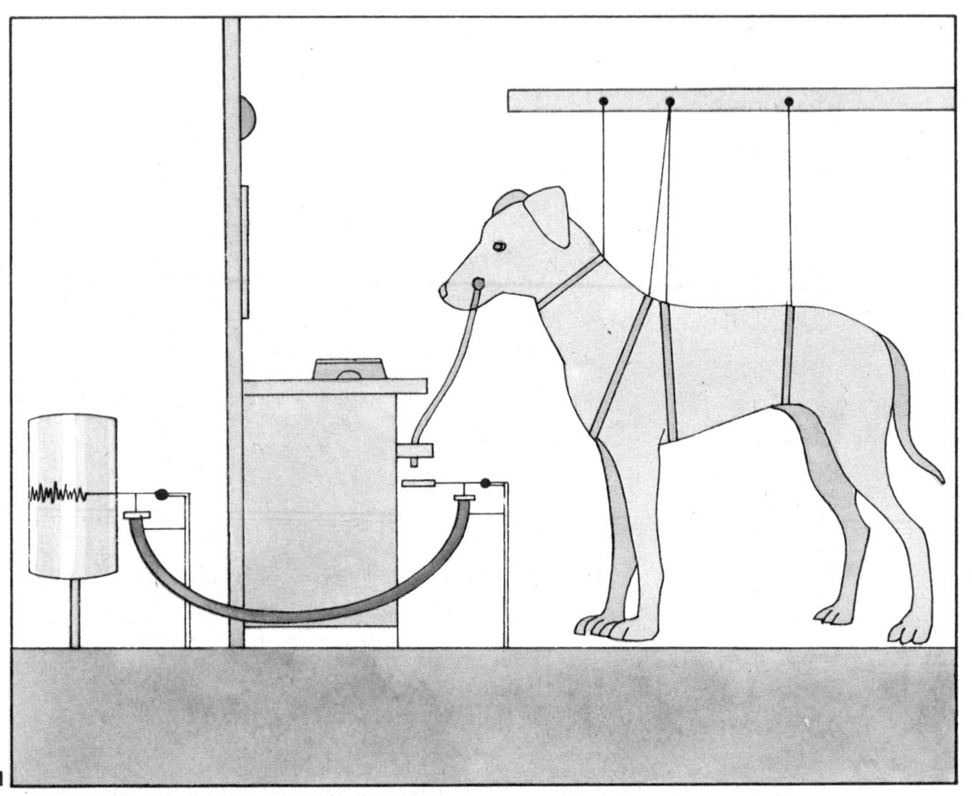

**1** Pavlov's set-up for his famous conditioning experiments. The duct from the dog's salivary gland is diverted to the cheek so that salivary output can be measured.
**2** The Indian elephant *(Elephas maximus)* can be trained to carry out heavy work like logging, and is widely used for this and similar purposes throughout South East Asia.

**1** The squirrel's characteristic posture for nibbling a nut is arrived at by instrumental or trial-and-error learning. Young squirrels rapidly become able to hold nuts and nibble them.
**2** Sheepdogs, like these animals herding a flock in southern Germany, have to be trained by a combination of instrumental learning and classical conditioning.
**3** Dolphins are highly intelligent animals and can be trained with very little difficulty to carry out a wide repertoire of tasks. They undoubtedly possess some ability to reason.

Skinner called this kind of learning 'operant conditioning', and it is also known as 'instrumental conditioning', or sometimes, more simply, as 'trial-and-error learning'.

Many activities of wild animals can be explained in terms of instrumental learning. When kittens or baby otters, for example, play they make all sorts of peculiar and comic movements that achieve nothing more than making the young animal look a fool. But some of the animal's random movements achieve a particular effect; for example, a cuff to the side of a playmate's head will send it spinning. Soon the animal learns which of its movements will achieve a reward (such as tumbling an opponent) and which will merely serve to trip itself up. Very quickly its gambollings become less random and much more streamlined and directional. And this improvement can be explained in terms of instrumental conditioning: the 'good' movements are rewarded and become established; the 'poor' ones are not and are eliminated.

Instrumental learning, like classical conditioning, is an example of associative learning. The third and final type of associative learning, which is much more difficult to explain than the other two, is known as latent learning. Professor Thorpe defines this as '.... the association of indifferent stimuli or situations without patent reward'.

## Exploration

If a bird or a mammal is put into a strange cage the first thing it does, after it has got over its fright, is to explore. And soon it becomes evident that it knows every inch of that cage. Obviously animals in the wild know a great deal about the terrain they inhabit; we already cited the mouse which, in the dark of night, can make an instant dash back from any part of its territory to its hole. Many insects make special 'orientation flights' in which they learn enough of their environment to be able to move around freely in it. They learn a few fixed points in the terrain and the position of those landmarks relative to the position of the sun.

But a conditioned reflex in a dog can be induced only if it is taught to associate an otherwise meaningless stimulus (like a bell sound) with a rewarding stimulus (like the bit of meat). And animals only learn instrumentally if particular actions (like pressing a bar) are followed by rewards (like receiving some food). But what reward does the animal get from learning something about its territory? How can it learn to associate a particular tree with a particular part of its territory when this association is not consolidated (or reinforced as the psychologists say) by any immediate reward?

Followers of the American psychologist C.L. Hull have produced one answer. They argue that all activities by animals are motivated by some kind of 'drive' – a hunger drive, a thirst drive and a sex drive. And, they say, an activity is 'rewarded' when the drive is reduced; thus food rewards foraging activity because it reduces the drive (hunger) that first induced the foraging. And the Hullians propose that animals have an 'exploratory drive', which makes them explore and that this drive is reduced – rewarded – as the animal becomes familiar with its territory. But although it is true that an animal explores less as it becomes more familiar with the terrain, just as an animal forages less when it becomes less hungry, it is not true that an animal can be sated by exploration as it can be by excess of food. If an animal is taken from a cage that it has been vigorously exploring and then put into another cage, it will explore the second cage no less vigorously than the first; it has not become 'tired' of exploring. Thus the analogy between 'exploration drive' and 'hunger drive' does not seem all that helpful and the process of latent learning, whereby an animal learns something that may or may not be useful at a

1 Performing animals in circuses are now trained by rewarding the successful performance of tricks. The reward reinforces the behaviour the trainer wishes to develop.

2 Young geese become imprinted with the first object they see at birth. Professor Konrad Lorenz here demonstrates how a young goose will follow with a dogged fixation the first object it sees.

future date, and may or may not be rewarded, remains a mystery.

Yet another form of learning that is difficult to explain is illustrated by the famous Kohler's apes. In one experiment Kohler placed chimpanzees in cages and put bananas outside the cage, well out of reach. Inside the cage were a number of sticks, which the chimps could join together to make one long stick. The animals learned to attach the sticks together so as to reach the bananas, which they could not reach with their hands or with the aid of only one stick. It appeared that the animal had sat down and arrived at a solution to the problem, just as a human being might. To perform several quite complicated acts in order to achieve a particular end seemed to require an insight into the problem that went beyond any of the mechanisms of learning that have so far been discussed. Insight implies reasoning power: we cannot doubt that apes do reason and it is very possible that other intelligent animals, like dolphins or dogs, can do so as well.

Finally, some animals learn at a particular time of their lives to attach themselves to particular objects and they never lose that sense of attachment. This form of learning, so brilliantly described by Konrad Lorenz, is known as 'imprinting'. This phenomenon is seen most clearly in many birds. Generally, when they hatch, the first thing the young birds see is their mother and from then on they follow the mother around everywhere, with a dogged fixation. This has obvious survival value since it means the young birds are unlikely to get lost. But if the mother is missing and the young birds spot some other object instead, then they will follow that object around as if it was their mother. If young goslings, for example, are reared by hand they will follow a human being. They are particularly impressionable during this period and what they see may affect them for the rest of their lives.

## Courted by a jackdaw

Lorenz relates how a young jackdaw which he reared was convinced that Lorenz was another of his own species, since Lorenz was the first object the jackdaw saw. When the jackdaw grew up, it tried to court Lorenz as a mate. Jackdaws, when courting, perform ritual feeding – the male suitor presents the female with tit-bits. Lorenz's jackdaw, in the mating season, would attempt to thrust chewed-up worms into his ear. The idea that Lorenz was a jackdaw was 'imprinted' in the bird's 'mind'.

The behaviour of animals is the most complicated of their attributes and the most difficult to understand. The classifications of learning described here are no more than crude gropings, the very early beginnings of Man's attempt to comprehend his own behaviour and that of his fellow creatures. But as an intellectual exercise it is interesting to try to classify the behaviour of yourself and friends. Next time you pull on your socks ask yourself whether this is a conditioned reflex or the result of instrumental learning, or a masterly piece of insight.

# Animal courtship

The strange, often colourful, rituals and fierce fights for territory are closely connected; they are vital to the successful mating of animals which preserves the balance and continuity of species.

A pair of garden snails embrace. After circling round one another, getting closer and closer, each fires a 'love dart' at the other. A dart can be seen in the neck of the left-hand snail.

Two male ruffs fight for supremacy while two reeves (females) wait unconcernedly for the outcome of the contest. Note the finer plumage of the male birds.

THE GREAT MAJORITY of animals reproduce sexually, a method which requires two separate sexes. By bringing together the genes from two distinct hereditary lines, this system of reproduction at least ensures that the offspring of a species will differ to some extent from its parents. Since we equate 'variety' in a species with a more flexible approach to survival in the struggle for existence, we have come to think of sexual reproduction as being one of the means whereby the species can best adapt to a changing environment.

But, unless they interact in some way, males and females are incapable of reproducing. There must be some means by which sperm and eggs are brought together when both are ripe, and this event must also be synchronized with other factors, like, for instance, the season of the year; for fertilization that led to the birth of young in the depths of the winter would hardly benefit the future survival of any species.

Some animals, such as the oyster or the sea-anemone, do not come into close physical contact with each other to mate. Nonetheless, when they release their sperm and eggs into the water, it is not a random event taking place at a random time of year in a random place. Instead the eggs and sperm are released more or less simultaneously in established breeding grounds and fertilization can therefore take place readily.

Animals are generally able to respond to set conditions of the environment, such as the length of day or temperature, and for this purpose they have built-in physiological mechanisms linked to a hormonal control system. Strangely enough, it is the moon that influences the oyster, and several other species, like the Palolo worm of the Pacific. The oyster spawns two days after a full or new moon, particularly between 26 June and 10 July. In reality, the oyster is not observing the fullness of the moon, but is responding to movements of the sea as it ebbs and flows more strongly than usual with the tides of that season – the spring tides. Dutch oyster breeders use this response to increase their yield of oysters. The larvae swim in the upper waters ten days after the spring tide and then sink to the bottom where they settle. They flourish much better on a clean, hard sea bed and so the breeders put down roof tiles. The tiles, however, must only be put down at the last moment, otherwise they get covered with other organisms. The breeders can calculate more or less to the day when to put the tiles down.

Hanging from a branch on a thread of mucus, two slugs lock their sex organs together. At this point in copulation, sperm liquid is transferred from one animal to the other.

Nature is always striving for economy, and the shedding of sperm and eggs indiscriminately into the environment, however synchronized, leads to much wastage. If instead males can be induced to stand over females while they spawn, at least the sperm should have more chance of finding the eggs. In fact, the two sexes of many fish, including the salmon, come together in close proximity during spawning, and the male frog goes so far as to mount the female. She may take many hours before she spawns – which she will only do if a male is on her – and the male develops special breeding pads on his front legs which enable him to cling on safely. As soon as the eggs are out of the female he liberates a generous volume of sperm. But the male must first attract a mature female and this he does by croaking in competition with all the rival male frogs. Each species of frog has its own characteristic croak, and a female is only attracted by a male of her own kind.

As nature has devised more intricate methods of mating, including insemination actually inside the female, the relationship between the two sexes becomes more elaborate and difficult. Imagine the problem: two animals which have never seen, let alone encountered each other, have to come together into close, harmonious physical contact. How can the animals recognize each other as being of the same species, and at the same time of the opposite sex, and how can they know that having encountered each other, both are going to be ready and ripe for mating? Each species has developed an

The distended air sac of this male tree frog is a secondary sexual characteristic. It acts as a sounding box for its booming cry, calling the female at night.

extraordinary mode of behaviour that is only put in action during the breeding season. This behaviour, 'courtship', may prelude and release a whole new pattern of behaviour that serves for the care of the young. This then is the final economy: insemination inside the female, the development of the embryo within the female, giving rise to *viviparity,* and then the care of young.

The essence of courtship is therefore to bring males and females together. It is not confined to vertebrates and we can see beautiful examples of it in certain insects, like the Grayling butterfly, and in the molluscs, including the common garden snail and its more sophisticated relative, the squid. Outside the breeding season the Grayling butterfly is not a social animal, and although several butterflies may be seen together in one habitat, this gathering is purely a response to abundant food. Nevertheless, sometime after emerging from their cocoons at the beginning of July, the butterflies develop their reproductive behaviour. The males stop feeding and take up position on the ground, or on the bark of trees. When another butterfly flutters by, the male takes off and pursues it. Should it be a receptive female Grayling butterfly, she reacts to the male's approach by alighting on the ground. The male walks round her until he is in front, facing her. If then she keeps motionless he begins his stately courtship.

## A ritual courtship

First he jerks his wings upward and forward a few times, then keeping them slightly raised to show off the beautiful white-centred spots on his forewings he opens and closes the front part of his wings rhythmically, then comes the most elegant part of the ritual: he raises his forewings and opens them widely with a quivering motion so that it seems he is executing a low bow to the female. Still in this posture, he folds the two forewings together and clasps the female's antennae between them. Now the actual mating takes place. He walks quickly behind the female and placing his abdomen with its copulatory organs against the female's, he remains facing away from her for some 30 to 40 minutes, while he passes sperm. The two animals then break contact and never see each other again. The 'bow' is more than just an elegant behavioural quirk. The male has a number of scent scales on his forewings in a narrow strip at the front, and when he clasps the female's antennae within his wings he is essentially bringing her smell receptors into contact with his scent. Once she has sensed his particular scent, she is ready to copulate.

Many insects rely on scents to bring about mating. Some insects, like the male silkmoths, can attract the females from more than a mile away should the wind be in the right direction. Then again, the female cockroach, when she is ready to mate, releases a particular scent, and this brings the males scurrying to her. A scent of this sort, which influences the behaviour of other members of the species, is known as a *pheromone.*

The garden snail is hermaphrodite; nonetheless for sexual reproduction to occur a mate must be found, and then a sort of cross-fertilization takes place with the sperm from each snail fertilizing the ova of the other. When two reproductively mature snails have found each other, they circle around, coming closer and closer. At the climax each snail fires a calcareous 'love' dart at the other from a special organ peculiar to the species. This 'Cupid's' dart embeds in the tissues of the other snail and is the prelude to copulation.

The final act of the elaborate courtship of the six-spot Burnet moth. Male and female can remain linked together, abdomen to abdomen for an hour or more.

Male scorpions fighting. The darker male has just torn off one of the other's claws, and its opponent is lying on his back, struggling to right himself.

The magnificent plumage of the turkey-cock rivals that of the peacock in splendour. The cock struts and preens during courtship, displaying his finery to his dowdy mate.

A great many species of animals, the majority of birds for example, as well as fish like the stickleback, take to living in territories during the breeding season. These species for the remainder of the year, comprising mainly the autumn and winter, live in flocks (or, in the case of fish, schools) and these flocks consist of an anonymous group of animals that do not recognize each other individually. When the animals become territorial, their behaviour changes drastically. Instead of living in harmony with each other, the animals, in general the males, go off and find territories which they then defend against any intruders. This territorial behaviour serves several purposes. It promotes mating; it provides an area where the young can be cared for and protected against possible predators; it prevents overcrowding and therefore safeguards an adequate supply of food; and finally it effects at least for a season the dispersal of the species.

To defend their territories animals have to become aggressive. This does not mean that any intruders are fought with to the death; instead by a series of stereotyped threats the defender of the territory can make his claims known and clear to any possible rival. The further inside his territory the more intense the defender's aggressive intentions, and the closer to the boundaries of his territory, the less sure he becomes of himself. This doubt can lead to an amusing ding-dong battle. First one male chases the other, but in his enthusiasm he may get carried too far into the other's territory. This latter, finding himself on home ground, swiftly turns and now becomes the aggressor, forcing the original aggressor to flee. Finally, both animals having determined to their own satisfaction where the boundaries lie, leave each other in peace.

Great crested grebes exchange gifts during courtship and nesting. These conciliatory gestures play an important part in maintaining the family unit during the breeding season.

The male stickleback first shows this aggressive behaviour when he leaves the schools of fish and goes off to select a territory. Concurrently with his changing behaviour, he assumes brilliant nuptial colours. The eye changes to a shining blue, the back from a dull brownish becomes greenish, the underparts red. If another fish, particularly a male, should enter the territory, the defendant darts towards the opponent with raised dorsal spines and open mouth, looking as if it were just about to bite. If the newcomer does not flee, instead of gripping it with its teeth, the attacking stickleback points its head down and standing vertically in the water makes a series of jerky movements as if it were about to bore its snout into the ground. This strange display usually drives the intruding stickleback away.

While not concerned with defending his territory, the male stickleback makes a nest. He hollows a pit out of the river bottom and presses pieces of nest material, usually threads of algae, into it, binding these all together with a glue substance secreted from his kidneys. Then, when this part of the work is completed he bores a tunnel by wriggling his body through.

But, now he has to attract a female, and for this to occur he must overcome his innate aggression. The females which have become swollen with eggs, are parading over the territory while still swimming with the school. Being a drab colour they do not elicit much aggression from the male, whose colours are now even more glittering: his back now being a brilliant shiny blue and his belly dark red. The male approaches the stickleback school in a peculiar zig-zag dance. First he swims towards the females with his

A male three-spined stickleback takes up his aggressive display posture, nosing the bed of the river. This territorial defence position also plays a part in courtship.

mouth open then turns and swims away again. The 'zig' part of the dance has the elements of aggression in it, and most, if not all, the females are frightened away. One female, however, may be ready to spawn and she turns towards the male, adopting an upright attitude of appeasement. In the soliciting 'zag' part of the dance, the male swims to the nest and thrusts his snout inside, while turning over on his side. The female now enters the nest, and, because of her swollen abdomen, gets stuck half-way, with her head and tail protruding at either end. The male next prods the base of her tail with his snout and persuades her to spawn. This done, she leaves the nest and he enters and fertilizes the eggs. While his mating urge is on the male may collect eggs in this fashion from other females. After a time his behaviour changes and he spends long periods just outside the nest, fanning it with broad sweeps of his pectoral fins. This motion keeps a steady flow of aerated water over the eggs and is essential for their healthy development. Once the young have hatched – until they are big enough to escape his attentions – the male guards them against all intruders and possible danger.

## Displacement activity

Professor Niko Tinbergen points out that there are some fundamental elements in the stickleback's behaviour that can be applied generally to animal behaviour, particularly courtship and aggression. The whole course of events can only unfold if both animals of the partnership respond precisely to the other's intentions. The zig-zag dance serves to entice only those females that are absolutely ready to mate, the remainder flee; while the male must show the female the nest entrance she must enter before he will prod her with his snout and entice her to spawn; then only after she has left, will he enter and fertilize the eggs. His colour is also very important, especially his red belly, and a model hardly resembling a male stickleback at all, except for a dark red underside, can be used to attract a female to a stickleback's nest, so long as the motions of the model are sufficiently imitative of the male's movements. The female can then be made to spawn by prodding the base of her spine with a rod, just as if it were the snout of a proper male.

The upright threat position of the stickleback has some characteristics in common with its nest-making activities, when it actually buries its snout in the sand to make a depression. Such displacement activities have become highly meaningful signals for other members of the same species, and are a communication of mood. By instantly understanding the intentions of the other animal, a member of the same species will respond correctly. If the movement is one of threat, then bloodshed is averted when the intruder either goes away, or makes some appeasing movement.

Complex rituals like those found in stickleback courtship may appear to be absurd but they are vitally important to the successful mating of the species.

1

2

3

**1** Love-play of the giraffe. These huge animals go through elaborate and touching courtship preliminaries, caressing one another with their long necks and rubbing flanks.

**2** The male lyrebird of Australia dances on a mound during courtship, displaying his superb plumage to his mate. The lyrebird's long tail feathers are brilliantly coloured.

**3** Aggressive behaviour in insects. Two male stag beetles lock mandibles together as they fight. Aggression is not uncommon among insects as well as among higher animals.

# Almost human

Despite obvious differences, many features of human behaviour can be found in animals. In fact, human beings bear comparison in some aspects of their lives even with lowly shellfish and ants.

GO TO any big natural history museum and compare your arm with, for example, a bat's wing and a seal's flipper. Outwardly, they are as different from one another as the functions they perform. But the bones of these 'limbs' reveal such an essential similarity of design as to suggest that Man, the bat and the seal evolved in the course of millions of years from a common ancestor. The similarity of animal skeletons, including that of Man, demonstrates that a basic skeletal structure persists throughout geological time in spite of widely diverging functions of its components.

And just as the skeletons of Man and animals reveal a common origin, so does the behaviour of Man and animals show a close relationship. Indeed, the consensus of scientific opinion is that behind all the many variations in the behaviour of Man and the animals there is a fundamental structure of inherited behaviour common to all. When we remember that other animals inhabited the Earth for millions of years before Man, it is not too fanciful to suggest that Man has inherited his pattern of behaviour from animals.

As Man slowly learned the art of personal adornment it was the male who decorated himself the most fancifully. Indeed, clothes were originally not so much a matter of keeping warm or symbolizing modesty but much more a form of decoration. And when it came to personal adornment, the man invariably outshone the woman. Just as the peacock's magnificent plumage and display dazzles the drably feathered peahen, and the lion's mane distinguishes the male from the lioness, so early Man far outdid the woman in self-decoration. Apart from the effects of human hunting and the taking of grazing lands for agriculture, most animals maintain a remarkably steady population level, decade after decade, and even century after century. It would, therefore, seem that non-human animal population is regulated by some system that keeps it within fairly narrow limits of a set average density.

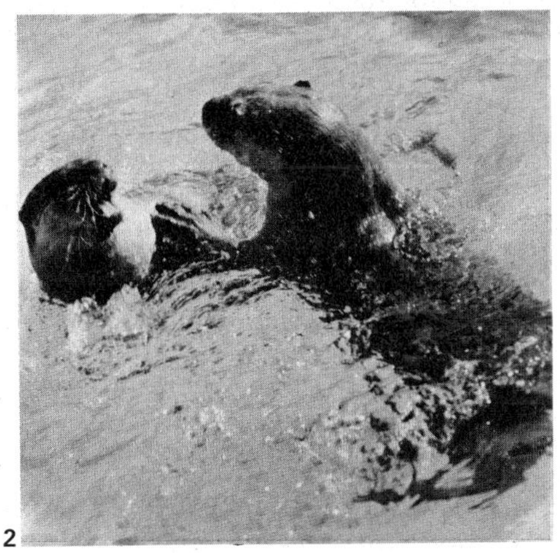

1 Like many human beings, animals show aggression. This whooper swan, angered by the intrusion of a photographer, speeds aggressively across the water's surface.

2 Play is another aspect of behaviour young animals have in common with young human beings. Here, two otters frolic playfully in a rough and tumble which teaches them co-ordination.

Ecologists were for long of the opinion that increase or decrease in population of any particular animal was the result of natural factors over which the species had no control. The chief of these factors were predators on the particular species, accidents, starvation, and infestation by parasites causing disease.

## Animal populations

The idea that disease or predators are essential controllers of animal population has little real scientific basis. There are several animal species that are not readily liable to parasite diseases and seldom fall prey to predators. The lion and the eagle, for example, are remarkably free of disease and have no predators, yet they have a very stable population level.

Shortage of food is not the all-important factor once considered chiefly responsible for limiting animal population. Careful study and observation reveal that starvation is comparatively rare in animal communities. It is very unusual for all the members of a species living in an area not to get enough food to survive. Sometimes severe cold or drought starves animals out, but this is a meteorological 'accident' that does not arise from population density.

One way in which animals artificially restrict their population density is related to their food supply. The practice of certain birds staking out a territory for nesting and hatching and rearing a family is an example. During the breeding season, each cock bird lays claim to an area of a minimum size and drives out all other cocks of his species. By this means a group of cock birds will divide up the available ground as their individual territories and so limit over-population by adjusting itself to the food sources available. Instead of fighting furiously in competition for the food, the members of the group each competes for a piece of ground which becomes the exclusive food preserve of itself and its family. Any cock bird unable to win and hold a feeding territory is obviously a weakling, and without a territory it cannot win a mate and feed a family.

With certain species of mammals, biological reaction keeps animal population at a fairly steady level. At certain times the rate of ovulation in the females is reduced by changes in the output of hormones. Rabbits, foxes and deer will reabsorb embryos in the uterus during times of stress.

The human male is by nature a family man. He prides himself on being the head and protector of a family, and this trait in human behaviour has its counterpart in

1

**1** Some ants, like these red wood ants, carry on a primitive form of 'agriculture'. The ants live together with colonies of aphids, which they 'milk' for their nectar.

**2** Curiosity is a feline characteristic shared with human beings. Here, a cat explores the inside and outside of a glass-sided box. The exploring instinct is strong in many animals.

**3** Biological rhythms, many of them tied to natural cycles like day and night, the tides, and the seasons, play a part in the life of most animals. Human beings are often governed by internal 'clocks' as are these scallops, which open at a predetermined time each day.

**4** A tool-using finch photographed on the Galapagos Islands. Apart from Man, very few animals use tools.

**5** Another bird which uses tools is the Egyptian vulture. It holds sharp stones in its beak and breaks open eggs with them.

3

2

5

4

the behaviour of certain mammals. One of the outstanding examples of family behaviour by animals is provided by the gorilla. Gorillas normally live in large bands or family parties led by a big male. The leader, who is distinguished by the silver-grey hairs on his back, decides when and where the family group goes. Gorillas feed on sugar cane, berries and other vegetation, and they consume such huge quantities of food that they are always searching for fresh feeding grounds.

## Family life

When a family group of gorillas find a place where there is plenty of food, they start with a meal, watched over by the leader. Then the latter feeds, guarded by his older sons. After all have eaten, the adults set to work making living quarters for the night. This they do by twisting together branches in trees and covering the framework with grass and leaves. The beds or nests for the babies of the gorilla family are on the higher branches, where they will be safe from danger, while the females and young males sleep on the lower branches. At nightfall, the father of the family drives his mates and the young gorillas up to bed. Then he settles himself down with his back against the tree and his arms folded across his chest. There he dozes throughout the night, but ever on the alert to protect his family group against any approaching danger.

Many human beings are adept at bluffing their way out of danger or to win a game or personal advantage. It is a trait of behaviour that Man learned or inherited from animals. The gorilla, for instance, is a master of the art of bluffing.

Far from being bellicose creatures that roam the forests spoiling for trouble and ready to attack any creature that crosses their path, gorillas are rather timid and avoid a fight whenever possible. If anyone suddenly comes upon a family of gorillas, the leader sends the others to safety and begins his great bluffing performance. First he starts hooting and snatching branches from the trees. Then he rises on his hind legs and throws branches about. Next he beats his chest with his forepaws, kicks one leg in the air and lets out a mighty roar. If that does not scare off the intruder, he takes a short run sideways, thumps the ground with the palm of his hand and charges. But it is all bluff. Provided the intruder does not attempt to attack him, the gorilla stands still for a moment, then turns and peacefully ambles away. It is only when the bluff fails that the gorilla attacks. Many a foolhardy leopard or lioness has tried to call the gorilla's bluff and been torn to pieces by the great ape's tremendous arms and teeth. The gorilla's great bluff is reflected in the behaviour of small boys in the school playground.

Jealousy is another of the basic behaviour patterns shared by Man with the other animals. Both domestic and wild animals are capable of intense jealousy and, as their emotional behaviour is not bound by the social and moral conventions of human society, animal jealousy is more obvious and less inhibited. The most common cause of jealousy amongst wild animals stems from threats to their basic needs. These include shelter, food and the protection of their young. Probably the most subtle manifestations of jealousy occur amongst domestic animals which form close links with their human owners. A dog, particularly a bitch, displays extreme jealousy towards any human being or animal threatening to interfere with the special relationship between the domestic pet and its owner.

Just as human jealousy can culminate in murder, so animal jealousy may end in violence. This has been demonstrated many times by what is called the 'one-man' dog. Such an animal becomes so possessive and jealous of its love and devotion to its master, that it may attack anyone who appears to threaten its relationship.

Prehistoric Man was comparatively defenceless and vulnerable. He had neither the teeth nor the claws to defend himself against predators, and he survived in a world of stronger animals only because he had the intelligence to realize that, by banding with his fellows, their combined strength could equal that of a strong, hungry enemy. But this realization that unity is strength is a fundamental of behaviour in certain other species of animals.

A solitary goose is an easy and favourite prey for the fox. Yet it is not uncommon for wild geese to form themselves into a phalanx and advance on their predatory enemy, intimidating him with their relentless surge forward and loud honking. No fox thus threatened has ever been known to turn on his tormentors. Normally, a pig is terrified by a farm dog, but if a nervous dog ventures into a piggery the inhabitants will combine to drive him out.

## Time and tide

Much of modern Man's social behaviour is conditioned by the clock. He has fixed hours for sleeping, work, recreation and feeding. Similar arrangements are found in the animal kingdom. Mosquitoes in equatorial Africa bite in seeming obedience to a time-scale inherent in those insects. The 'biting time' is generally restricted to a period of 30 minutes or so every 24 hours. Even more remarkable is the fact that the biting period varies according to the particular type of mosquito. Some bite at dawn, others at midnight and others just as night falls. Similarly with honeybees; the workers stay in the hive until the exact time of day when their favourite flowers are just opening with a new supply of nectar. As the summer advances, the bees adjust their sense of time to the particular plants in bloom.

This sense of time is also possessed by the oyster. Oysters regulate the opening and shutting of their shells according to the times of the tide ebbing and flowing over the beds where they were born and pass their lives. But if live oysters are moved to a marine laboratory hundreds of miles from their home, they continue to open and shut their shells according to the times of the tide in their home waters.

Human behaviour in a fight that ends in surrender is a duplication of animal behaviour in similar circumstances. When surrendering to an opponent, he holds up his hands in token of submission. Much the same thing happens with dogs. If two dogs fight, the vanquished will stand still

Family life among the gorillas. Contrary to popular legend, gorillas are shy and retiring, but if approached too closely, the male will charge an intruder in order to protect his family.

and so long as he remains still the victor will not continue the attack, although he continues to growl and snarl. Then the victor celebrates by urinating, which is, in effect, leaving his trade mark on the battlefield and vindicating his right of possession. And while the victor is celebrating, the vanquished usually slinks off: his surrender accepted.

Wolves also offer and accept surrender. When two wolves fight and one decides that he is having the worst of the contest, he stretches out his neck and adopts a general attitude of 'hang-on' humility. The victor invariably accepts the offer of surrender, and although he may continue to growl and bare his fangs he breaks off the fight.

The almost forgotten coyness of the 'Victorian miss' to her swain was a form of sexual behaviour that has been practised by animals long before Man appeared on the Earth. Some birds, such as the female redshank, will shy and run away at the approach of a cock of the species. But the hen invariably runs around in circles as though anxious to be chased by her wooer. Another example of animal coyness on the part of the female is provided by the spotted turtle. At the approach of a male she starts to lumber away, but all the while she is gazing over her shoulder at her suitor as though fearful that he might not be following her.

Coyness is an essential part of the courtship behaviour of red deer. When a stag approaches the hind of his choice, she stops and waits for him and then licks him. Immediately he attempts to complete his conquest, the hind runs away, then again waits for him to approach. The coy behaviour is repeated until she finally accepts his advances.

Just as children's play behaviour has little relation to preparing them for adult life, so many young animals have play behaviour which is just amusement and has nothing to do with the existence they will lead when they leave their parents and must fend for themselves. Baby otters spend hours sliding down mud banks and young penguins are expert at tobogganing on their stomachs down icy slopes. In the evening baby badgers are often seen playing leap-frog outside their home, while other cubs indulge in games of hide-and-seek.

Even human behaviour when attempting to restrain an outburst of temper has its counterpart amongst animals when they are exasperated. Two men may quarrel and be on the verge of violence when one gives vent to his feelings by banging on a table or smashing some immediate obstacle. So starlings will suddenly stop early in a quarrel and start preening, while a couple of male rats on the verge of a quarrel will stop and groom themselves. It all suggests that they are giving vent to their feelings so that a fight to the death does not develop.

## Subconscious behaviour

Finally, there would seem to be a link between the subconscious behaviour of Man and animals. Man dreams in his sleep and often his dreams are a repetition of his activities when awake. A sleeping dog will jerk its legs, growl and pant; just as it does when chasing a rabbit. Sleeping dogs may dream of food, as is suggested by their drooling in their sleep and champing their jaws.

It is probable too that, as in Man, animal dreams may develop into nightmares. Army horses that have been in battle, often rear up and neigh in terror, in the way they did during the heat of a cavalry charge.

A pride of lions laze during the day in Kenya. Male lions often maintain a 'harem' of mates, a pattern of family life not dissimilar to that found in many human societies.

# Dead and dying species

The history of life on the Earth is punctuated with examples of animals which have become extinct. Extinction remains an imminent threat to many species which may need protection to survive.

'AS DEAD AS THE DODO!' What could be more final than that? Everyone knows that the dodo is an extinct animal, but very little is known about it and the other animals which have disappeared for ever from the face of the Earth. Certain species alive now are also in danger of extinction.

Animals are fitted to survive and prosper in a given set of natural circumstances. As long as these circumstances remain the same the success of the animal group continues. But if the situation changes, perhaps in only a very minor way, the animal comes under pressure from nature. It is then no longer the right kind of machine to deal with its environment.

Unless the animal can adapt to the new circumstances it will perish. Animal groups which are narrowly specialized – those which are designed to deal with one specific type of environment – are particularly prone to extinction.

## The death of the dodo

The dodo is a dramatic example of this theory in practice. This strange bird, which was larger than a turkey, succumbed to the arrival in its environment of a larger and intelligent animal which preyed upon it mercilessly. That new animal was Man.

Until 1598, the dodo existed in considerable numbers on the island of Mauritius. Although it was flightless and therefore particularly vulnerable on the ground, it was able to exist simply because there was no animal large enough to attack it.

At the end of the sixteenth century the island was discovered by Van Neck, a Dutch admiral, and subsequently became a station for merchantmen bound for India and the East Indies. Apart from water and fruit, Mauritius also had a ready supply of meat – the dodo.

1 Cow and calf of the North American bison. Huge herds of these animals once covered the great plains, but they were massacred for their meat during the nineteenth century.
2 Orang-utans are shy retiring animals found in remote jungles of Borneo. They are threatened by the advance of civilization, and the Borneo government is trying to protect them.
3 The trumpeter swan, now rare and threatened with extinction, once ranged over a wide area of North America. It is now limited to a small part of the continent.

In 1644 the Dutch decided to colonize the island completely. The newcomers brought with them their own domestic animals. These included dogs and pigs, and together they finished the job of extermination which Man had begun.

Some dogs and pigs escaped from their owners and took to the forests, living wild. The dogs slaughtered the dodos, while the pigs ate their eggs.

In under 100 years, from the first discovery of the island by Europeans, the dodo had disappeared for ever. The only way that it could have escaped its fate was to have redeveloped the ability to fly; but the onslaught was too great and too fast.

Man has made considerable attacks on the animal kingdom, but they are nothing when compared to the changes wrought by non-human agencies through history.

The great age of extinction was the Cretaceous period, the latter part of the Mesozoic era, which ended about 63 million years ago. This saw the destruction of almost all the reptiles, which had been the dominant creatures of the Earth. The most likely reason for this 'great death' seems to be that climatic conditions gradually became unsuitable for these animals.

The only way that we can form any idea of the nature and variety of these creatures is from fossils left in the ground. Careful research in this direction has revealed an enormous amount of fascinating information about the reptiles, great and small, which trod the Earth, swam in the waters, and even flew in the sky.

The *Brontosaurus* is easily the best known of the extinct large reptiles. It lived its life in and around swamps in the Jurassic period (mid-Mesozoic) and it was easy meat for the carnivorous reptiles which also abounded. It had no body armour and its only defence was to take to the water.

It was extremely large, weighing as much as 5,000 lb and is known to have achieved some 65 ft in length. The *Diplodocus* resembled the Brontosaurus but was often much longer; the bones of the longest specimen found measured 97 ft in length. It fed on aquatic plants in the main, but also preyed on some of the smaller animals – molluscs and crustaceans.

Both of these reptiles moved on all fours. Not so the savage *Tyrannosaurus rex*. As much as 50 ft long, this terrifying beast stalked about on its highly developed back

1

2

3

4

legs and reached a height of 20 ft. Its front legs were comparatively puny, but it was able to dispatch its prey with powerful jaws equipped with a large number of sharp teeth. A specimen of its footprint was discovered in a coalmine. The foot was about 2 ft 6 in. long.

## Long extinct

It was not only the reptiles which suffered extinction during prehistory. Many types of fish were able to adapt to the changing conditions – some developed so far that they were able to leave the water for short periods altogether. But many were unable to adapt.

One of them was the *Xiphactinus*. A fossil discovered in the chalk beds in western Kansas, U.S.A., is truly spectacular. It is 16 ft in length and thus is the largest fossil of a prehistoric bony fish yet discovered. The specimen has the fossilized skeleton of another fish still inside it.

Among the mammals, the list of departed species is great indeed. Mammoths, the contemporaries of early Man, were protected from the rigours of the Ice Age by thick coats which covered even their

5

**1** *Tyrannosaurus rex*, a giant carnivorous dinosaur. Twenty feet high and 50 feet in length, *Tyrannosaurus* became extinct with other dinosaurs in the Cretaceous.

**2** Reconstruction of a Siberian woolly mammoth. A contemporary of early Man, this sub-Arctic elephant is sometimes found buried intact in the frozen soil of Siberia.

**3** Reconstruction, based on fossil evidence of a sabre-tooth tiger. The sabre-tooth may have died out because its canine teeth grew longer as the species developed.

**4** The extinct Irish elk is closely related to the American moose. The elk died out in Ireland only a few thousand years ago, and this illustration shows a reconstruction of its appearance.

**5** Female of the giant Australian stick-insect. This remarkable insect grows to a length of ten inches, and feeds on desert plants. It is now rare and threatened with extinction.

**1** Extinct fish found fossilized in Italy. The three large fish are *Myripristis* (sea bottom fish) and the smaller fish are *Clupea* which are similar to sardines.
**2** The London Zoo s giant panda Chi-Chi. Attempts to mate Chi-Chi with Moscow Zoo's Anan focused attention on the rarity of the giant panda, found only in a small area of China.
**3** Human hunting reduced the Hawaian or néné goose population to a low point of 30 in 1951; since then, breeding of specimens in captivity has raised the number of birds to 400.

trunk. They had comparatively small ears, but closely resembled the modern elephant.

Remains of mammoths have been discovered in Europe, Asia and North America, but the most spectacular finds have been uncovered in the harsh and frozen soil of Siberia. It is not uncommon to find complete skeletons and even bodies in this great natural deep-freeze.

Scientists are able to discover exactly what the mammoths lived on because the contents of the stomachs are often preserved. The animal had a thick layer of fat beneath its skin to supplement the protection afforded by its covering of hair, and a large hump of fat on its back that provided a store of food when the blanketing snow and ice made other food impossible to obtain.

Thanks to the fact that conditions in Siberia have remained so severe, the museum of the Academy of Science in Leningrad is able to boast of a unique specimen. This is nothing less than a *stuffed* mammoth. In fact, the body was discovered in 1907 on the banks of the River Berezovka and an expedition was specially mounted to save it from the depredations of the local population who could sell mammoth tusks at a great price.

It is possible also that Man, or his ancestors, shivered in the night at the roar of the great sabre-toothed cats. These are commonly called sabre-toothed tigers but in fact were not tigers at all, although they did stem from the same root as the modern cats.

The difference can be seen in the now extinct *Machairodus*. It lived in Europe and preyed upon antelopes, gazelles and ancestors of the horse. It was covered in fur and had a short tail; its paws were equipped with razor-like claws. But the most outstanding features of this creature were its teeth.

In the true cat (Felinae) the canines became smaller as the breed evolved, but in the sabre-toothed cats (Felidae) the very opposite happened. Among the last generations of *Machairodus* these teeth grew to 6 in. in length. When the mouth

closed they projected outside and when used for attack they naturally needed strong roots. The roots of each tooth continued right through the upper jaw to the lower rim of the eye socket.

It has been conjectured that the sabre-tooth cats became extinct because, though their teeth may have been excellent for making the kill, they rendered difficult the actual process of eating. But the real truth of the matter is lost in the past.

So far, all of the animals mentioned, with the exception of the dodo, have been extinct for thousands of years. But a number of other animals have become extinct more recently, and an alarming number are threatened with extinction right now.

## Man, the greatest hazard

Today, the greatest hazard to wild life is Man himself. He has exterminated a great many species directly by hunting, and indirectly by industrialization, intensive agriculture and the introduction of particular species to areas of the world in which they were not previously found.

Hunting, for example, has put paid to the great auk, a flightless bird which was once found in the North Atlantic area. The major centre of population was a small group of islets off the coast of Iceland, and there, after the discovery of the birds in 1534, they were killed in great numbers. They were killed not for food, but for their feathers which were highly prized for decoration. Now every single bird of this type has gone.

Food requirements of native workers and the need for hides for various purposes led to the wholesale slaughter of the curiously named quagga in South Africa. Before the Boers arrived, these animals, which were actually a species of zebra, existed in herds numbering many thousands. They, too, are now extinct.

A dramatic example of the dangers inherent in the introduction of species to new areas arose in the late nineteenth century in Jamaica. The crops on the sugar-cane farms were seriously threatened by a plague of rats – themselves accidentally introduced – and somebody came up with the idea of decimating the rat population with mongooses. Consequently, large numbers were imported from breeders in London and released in Jamaica.

1 The Tasmanian wolf or thylacine. This is the only existing photograph of this very rare marsupial carnivore. The thylacine is threatened by more efficient competitors.

2 Until the arrival of Europeans on the island of Mauritius, the dodo, a large flightless bird, was fairly common. Within 100 years of colonization by Man, it was extinct.

The experiment proved a total flop, for the London-born mongooses refused to attack the rats. So the next step was to import the animals from India.

The new variety spread like wildfire and the rats began to disappear. Such was the population pressure that the mongooses were forced to turn elsewhere for food and promptly wiped out a number of reptiles and birds. Now they are firmly established in Jamaica and are only controlled at considerable expense.

## Threatened animals

The list of animals threatened by extinction at present is large, and makes sombre reading. Quite recently the Survival Service Commission of the International Union for Conservation of Nature and Natural Resources and the International Council for Bird Preservation published such a list; it contained 204 mammals and 312 birds.

Choosing almost at random, we find that these species include the mountain gorilla, of which only a few thousand are left in the eastern Congo and Uganda, and the orang-utan, which exists only in some areas of Sumatra and Borneo.

No less than seven species of whale have been sadly depleted by hunters; the North Pacific right whale has almost reached vanishing point and only a few hundred blue whales still exist.

Although whale fishing is now closely controlled by international agreements, many leading zoologists feel that present protection is inadequate. Each country's whaling fleet is allowed a quota of whales, classified according to species, to limit the amount it can catch in any one season. But some species are now so diminished that the fleets can no longer catch their full quotas. The northern seas are now very depleted, and the advent of modern industrial whaling ships, which are more like floating factories than anything else, is opening up the Antarctic to the full effects of exploitation. Relatively little is known about the breeding habits of these mammals and some marine ecologists fear that the depletion of some species is already so far advanced as to set in motion an irreversible process of decline for the whole species.

From the very large underwater to the very large on land: the Ceylon elephant has been greatly reduced in numbers. It is now protected and the population, although small, is stable.

## Breeding rare species

The importance of the breeding attempts made in London and Moscow with the giant pandas Chi-Chi and An-An can be readily understood when it is realized that the species is threatened with extinction. Population estimates are not available but there is little doubt that few remain in the high bamboo forests of central and western Szechuan, China.

Numbers of the Javan rhinoceros, which is a survivor from the Pleistocene era and the rarest large mammal in the world, had dwindled to the desperate level of 24 in 1964. And so the list continues – the African cheetah, the Manchurian tiger, some kinds of seals, and, of course, many species of birds. But why should we care about the disappearance of life forms from the planet Earth? This is perhaps best answered by quoting the words of Professor J.L. Cloudsley-Thompson, a distinguished zoologist. There are, he says, three reasons why Man should care about and therefore conserve wild life. 'The first is to provide material for research purposes, in particular with regard to ascertaining the economic potential of the land. The second is purely economic; because the natural fauna has been selected over such a long period that it is inevitably more productive than introduced, exotic forms. Finally, the conservation of variety is an insurance against ecological imbalance with the attendant risk of pestilence, plagues and soil erosion.'

To this one thing alone could be usefully added. That is the fact that the beauties of wild life can also provide us with great visual stimulation, and that in itself is an enriching experience.

# Change, modification and decay

Four-legged chickens and two-headed sheep are too common to be ignored. What is the mechanism that produces such freaks along with the many other variants which make up the variety of life?

ANYONE WHO LOOKS around him can see changes in the forms and colours of living things. Some changes come about during the course of normal growth and development: a caterpillar changes to a chrysalis which changes to a moth, a seed 'changes' into a tree. Some changes are seasonal: a tree in winter is stripped to bare twigs which bud again the following spring.

Other changes are connected with changes in the environment and are easily changed back: the leaves of a potted avocado pear plant turn yellow as the magnesium in the soil becomes depleted; given a dose of Epsom salts, they are green again within a week.

Other changes are equally due to the environment, but are more permanent. If the grubs of the fruit-fly *(Drosophila melanogaster)* are subjected briefly to a temperature of 40 °C. instead of their usual 25 °C., the adult flies that eventually emerge are sometimes seen to have one of the tiny cross-veins in the wing missing or broken. And once broken, they are never mended.

There are, however, some changes that most people never see or become aware of. This is not because the degree of change is small, or occurs in only a few plants or a few animals. On the contrary, the changes may be either gross or inconspicuous and all living things are subject to them. Their main properties are that they occur only rarely: one must be very familiar with a particular kind of plant or animal and observe many of them before becoming aware of these changes. Their occurrence is usually completely independent of any change in the environment.

## Mutation as an inheritable factor

Their other main property is that they are inherited. If a biologist takes two (a male and a female) of the cross-veinless fruit-flies produced by the temperature shock experiment and allows them to breed, all their offspring are perfect, with not a broken or missing vein among them.

However, one can sometimes – very, very rarely – find cross-veinless flies among stocks kept at a normal temperature all their lives.

Two such spontaneously changed *mutant* flies together produce a brood which are all alike and like their parents – cross-veinless. Cross-veinlessness in these flies is due to *mutation. Mutation* is a change in the form, colour, physiology, habits or any other characteristic of a living organism which is inherited.

Mutations are inherited because they are the consequence of changes in the genetic material. This material is a chemical found in every living thing which determines its form, colour, physiology, habits – every characteristic – and also determines whether they are inherited. The chemical is deoxyribonucleic acid (DNA) which consists of a spirally twisted stack of pairs of molecules called *bases*. There are four kinds of bases: *adenine, guanine, cytosine* and *thymine*. Each is attached to a deoxyribose-phosphate molecule. There are only two kinds of pairs: adenine-thymine (AT) or guanine-cytosine (GC), but each can be turned through 180° or substituted for the other without affecting the shape of the spiral. As a result, four arrangements are possible: AT, TA, GC, and CG. The stacked base pairs are linked through phosphate groups which connect the deoxyribose molecules along the spiral outside edges of the molecule.

The molecule can be of indefinite length, but the phosphate backbones must twist round each other at exactly the right distance apart. Nevertheless, this distance can be achieved regardless of which of the four base pairs is present at any level in the

1 Wings on these fruit-flies are stunted. Their parents were dosed with radioactive phosphorus. Occurrence of the defect in the second generation shows this is a true mutation.

2 Radiation can be used to produce mutations in wheat. Most of these forms are useless to agriculture, but occasional forms are obtained which lead to new usable strains.

stack. Thus the order of the four kinds of base pairs along the molecule can be unrestrictedly varied. The result is that the number of possible DNA molecules differing in their orders of bases is extremely high. If a molecule only three base pairs long is made, there are 64 different orders possible. A molecule ten base pairs long could have one million different arrangements. The DNA of one of the simplest of living organisms, a virus, contains 200,000 base pairs. A bacterium has 50 times as many, and a man has 100 times as many again.

It is also clear that the molecule is *self-determining:* that is, it could be split down the middle through the stacked base pairs so that adenine separates from thymine and guanine splits from cytosine. But, provided the splitting did not break the phosphate-sugar-phosphate backbone, two new molecules could be reconstructed from the halves. Both would be like the original, as each base can take only one of the four possible bases as its partner – the same one that it was paired with before.

## Mechanism of mutation

This process of splitting DNA and reconstructing two daughter molecules identical with each other and with the original occurs in every dividing cell in the living world. It ensures that every daughter cell contains the same amount of DNA as its parent, and that the order of bases in each molecule is the same. Every nucleus in a dividing amoeba, paramecium, or cork-making cell in the bark of a tree contains the same DNA, quality and quantity, as the sister nucleus

**1** Mutations in the garden geranium (Pelargonium) may be caused by changes in DNA in the chloroplasts rather than in the cell. This process is rather uncommon.

**2** This Malayan five-legged bull is a mutation produced by a natural agent, probably radiation. Such oddities are badly adapted to survival, so that they normally disappear in a generation.

**3** Changes in the colour of chrysanthemums are caused by loss of a complete chromosome. Duplication of chromosomes can also cause quite striking changes in physical appearance.

**4** A strain of hybrid corn is produced by interbreeding over two generations. This method is used to produce new varieties with special desirable characteristics.

3

1

2

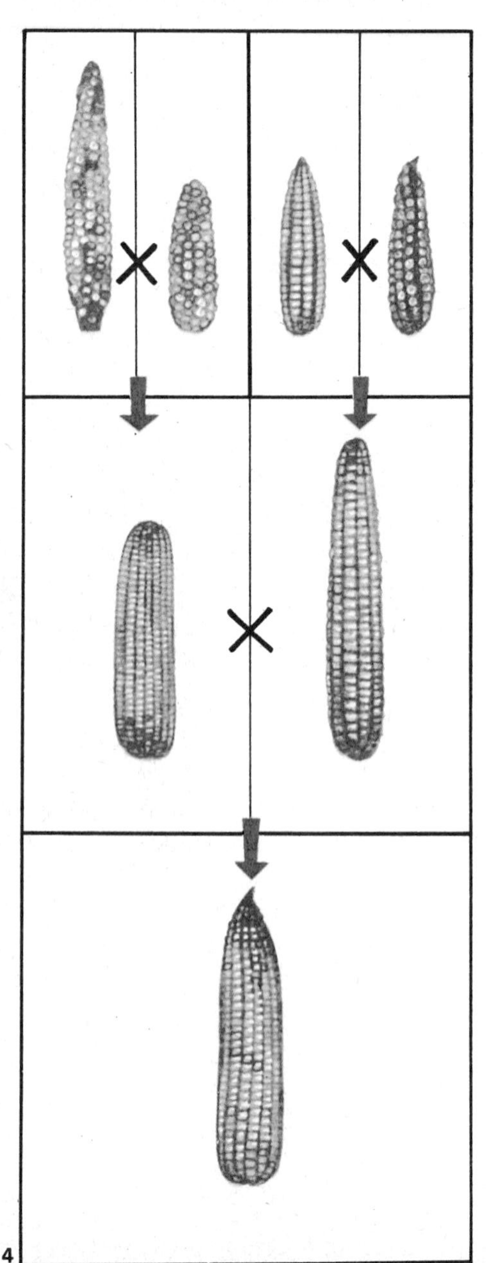

4

Another sort of mutation is when the total number of chromosomes changes. The change can happen in multiples of the characteristic (basic) number for that cell. Thus, a bean plant has two sets of seven chromosomes. Its pollen cells have one set, and plants *(polyploids)* can occur with three, four, five or six sets of the basic seven chromosomes. Alternatively the change may be to have only one extra or one too few chromosomes. Such abnormal cells are said to be *aneuploid*: cells with multiples of complete sets are *euploid*.

## Different numbers

Chromosomal mutations are of two kinds. There are those in which the *balance* of genetic material has been altered. In duplications, deletions, and aneuploids, genes are lost or gained, while the others remain intact. Such changes in balance usually have very bad effects on the organism. An example is Down's syndrome (mongoloid idiocy) in Man, which is due to the presence of one extra copy of one of the smallest chromosomes in the human set of 46.

In the other kind of mutation, no change in balance occurs. In the polyploid series, the number of genes is increased without changing their proportions. Translocations and inversions only rearrange what is there, without necessarily damaging any of it. Balanced chromosome changes seldom have a serious or even noticeable effect on the appearance or character of an organism, although polyploids are sometimes found to be larger than their diploid relatives. They often, however, have a large effect on the cell divisions that lead to gamete formation. Many gametes (sperm or eggs) die as a result of the mechanical difficulties caused by pairing and crossing-over in chromosomes which have suffered inversions or translocations.

No one knows what causes mutations. Their occurrence appears to be spontaneous and unconnected to any physical or chemical happening in the life of the cell. However, a lot is known about what *can* cause mutations. High-energy electromagnetic radiations such as X-rays and gamma-rays were the first mutagenic agents to be discovered and ever since they have been used in laboratories to induce mutations. The increase in mutation rate is proportional to the dose of radiation received. The particles emitted in the decay of radioactive substances such as radium (which emits alpha-particles) or radioactive phosphorus (beta-particles) also cause mutations.

The exact chemistry of mutation by these agents is not known, but they do have one property in common – they can cause atoms to lose electrons and become ionized, thus becoming chemically reactive. Ultraviolet light also causes mutation. This is the kind of light most strongly absorbed by DNA.

The second class of mutagenic agents is a mixed bag of chemicals. The first to be discovered was mustard gas, which reacts with various components of the cell, including DNA. It is not certain how mustard gas causes mutations, but it is

Huia birds show adaptation producing distinctions between the sexes. The male has a short, strong beak for making holes in tree-trunks, while the female's is long and curved for extracting grubs.

from which it divided.

The precision and speed of this process are remarkable. The ten million base pairs of a single bacterial cell are reproduced in exactly the same sequence once every 20 minutes, or 1,000 million times in ten hours. Exactly, that is, except for the mistakes. Now it is unlikely that more than one mistake is made in every ten replications. However, all mistakes once made are faithfully reproduced as such: they are inherited. Because DNA also determines all the characteristics of the cell, some of the mistakes may be detectable as changes in observable characteristics. They can then be described as mutations.

In organisms more complex than bacteria, the exact division of the genetic material is assisted by having it organized into blocks which appear, during cell division, as the chromosomes. The division of the chromosomes, naturally enough, reflects the precise replication of the DNA they contain, so during cell division each chromosome splits into two identical halves. The process is repeated accurately time after time, through countless generations, except for the rare mistakes.

Mistakes can be of any size. A working DNA molecule, like that of a bacterial cell, is functionally subdivided. Every length of 1,000 or so base pairs has a job to do. It determines the structure of one of the tens of thousands of different proteins which perform the cell's chemistry and form its membranes and fibres. Such a length of base pairs is called a *gene*.

It is easy to see that if one such length is lost, then the protein it determines will disappear from the cell: the cell has no information about how to make it. If a gene is changed, the protein it makes may also be made in a changed form. Sometimes, if the biochemists' techniques are good enough, such an altered protein can be detected, or its absence noted. More often, we can only tell that the mutation has occurred because the missing protein affects the characteristics of the cell in some obvious and dramatic way.

The sequence of base pairs in a gene can be changed in a number of ways: in any position, one base pair can be substituted for another; a base pair may be added to the sequence or deleted from it; or whole sections of the DNA chain may be deleted.

Mutants which affect only one base pair, and therefore only one gene, are known as 'point mutations'. But some mutations are large enough to affect the visible structures of chromosomes. There may be *deletions,* when a block of DNA containing several genes is lost; *duplications,* when one or more bits of a chromosome are duplicated; *inversions,* when a block of chromosomes is turned through 180° relative to the other parts of the chromosome; and *translocations,* when a part of one chromosome is moved to another part of the same chromosome or to a different chromosome altogether.

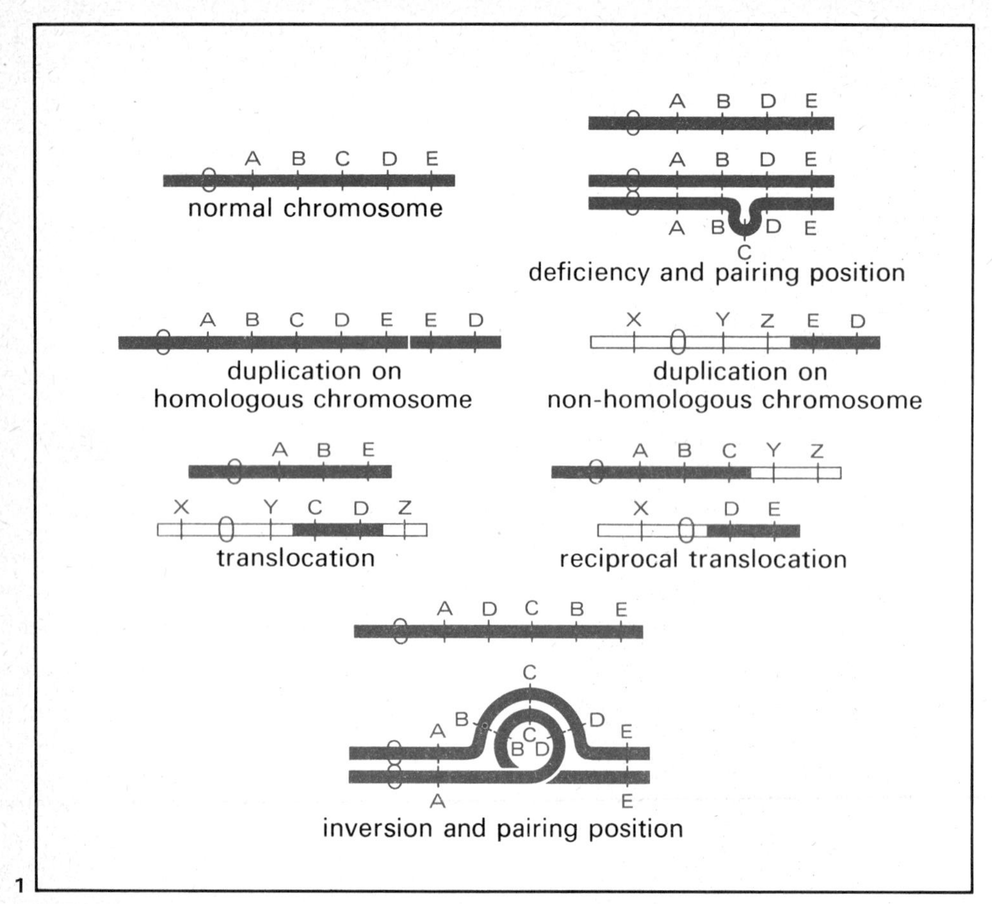

**1** Structural changes in the chromosomes can take place in a number of ways. Any change involves complications in subsequent pairing with a normal chromosome due to the distortion of one of the pair.

**2** Industrial melanism is an example of current evolutionary change. Its environment determines the colour of each moth.

**3** Its colour makes the black moth an easy prey in rural conditions.

able to unite chemically with both strands of a DNA molecule at once. This prevents the DNA strands from separating during replication, and can lead to the formation of gaps or breaks. Breaks can be seen in the chromosomes of cells treated with mustard gas.

The action of other chemicals is better understood. For example, nitrous acid reacts with cytosine, converting it to *uracil,* a base which pairs only with adenine. Thus it can change GC base pairs to AU base pairs, which are subsequently replicated as AT base pairs. Nitrous acid can also react with adenine to convert it to *hypoxanthine.* This then pairs with cytosine, so nitrous acid can also cause AT to change to GC.

Other chemicals, the *base analogues,* act by behaving temporarily as bases, but causing mispairings. For example, the substance *2-aminopurine* is very like adenine, but it can pair with either thymine or cytosine. So if 2-aminopurine is given to a cell, it may become incorporated into the DNA instead of either guanine or adenine. Once in, pairing with either thymine or cytosine during DNA replication will cause base-pair changes at the point where it occurs. As a result, mutations can arise.

As far as one can tell, all mutagens except base analogues cause the same range and kind of mutations as those which occur spontaneously. To produce mutations, all mutagenic agents have to be administered to cells in much higher doses than any cell normally encounters. So it is uncertain whether the mutations that occur spontaneously are genuine accidents or are caused by very low chance doses of mutagens, some of which (for example ionizing radiations) are always with us.

## The logic of survival

Charles Darwin, when he described his theory of organic evolution, showed that it depends on two things. One is a struggle for existence. The other is the occurrence of variation. Because some individuals of a species are different from others in colour, or size, or habits, or physiology, some are bound to get on better in the struggle than are others. The fittest – those better at 'getting on' – survive. Thus the characteristics which make them better and fitter are passed on to their progeny. In other words, evolution occurs because inheritable variations occur. As we have seen, the variations which arise as mutations are inherited: and mutation is their only source. Mutation is the basis of evolution.

Chromosomal mutations also affect evolution, but often in a rather subtle way. Clearly, if they have effects on the characteristics of an organism, these effects are subject to selection. But as we have seen they may not have such effects on cells, only effects on cell division. This is sometimes an advantage. If two groups of plants are growing in different environments, they will come, by evolution, to have different sets of genes. If the two groups of plants are close enough together to pollinate each other, they will constantly be getting genes in their progeny which are of advantage in the other environment, not in their own. If this could be prevented, both plants communities might benefit. The rhododendrons of Tibet and China are an example of plants in which interbreeding is prevented by chromosomal mutation. But there are many others in which chromosomal mutations which have arisen by chance like other mutations have evolved as internal controllers of the variation passing from one generation to another. As a result, they are controllers of the process of evolution itself.

Within a framework laid down by environment and other evolutionary forces, genes and chromosomes provide blueprints, changes in which caused by external factors, will determine the future shape and character of animals and plants.

# Adapting in adversity

**Many living species have to contend with extreme or abnormal environmental conditions. They have evolved special ways of dealing with the problems posed by these circumstances.**

OF THE MILLIONS of different species of plants and animals on Earth, many face special problems in the struggle for existence. Each animal and plant is adapted to carry out certain functions in a particular way. For example, bacteria which are specially able to resist heat are found in the hot springs that exist in volcanic regions. In other bacteria, the cell chemistry is subtly changed so that the bacterium can extract food from petrol. These tiny animals are found in the petrol tanks of motor cars. Such species as these are intensely specialized to live in the unusual conditions they have chosen. Other species are able to live and thrive in severe cold, in the parched deserts, and in other bizarre and extreme environments. What sort of adaptations are necessary for animals and plants to survive in such environments?

The regions around the Poles are extremely inhospitable to life. The animals and plants face intense cold combined with a shortage of sunlight for long periods of the year. Only a few land mammals are able to live near the Poles. The best-known is the Polar bear, which is to be found within the Arctic Circle. The Arctic bears and foxes develop white fur so that they become inconspicuous when hunting in the snow. This has an obvious advantage for animals that have to hunt under snow conditions. The marine mammals, seals and walruses, require no camouflage, for they have few predators apart from Man. They have developed, as a protection against the cold, a heavy layer of fat or blubber around their bodies and are hardly affected by the intense cold.

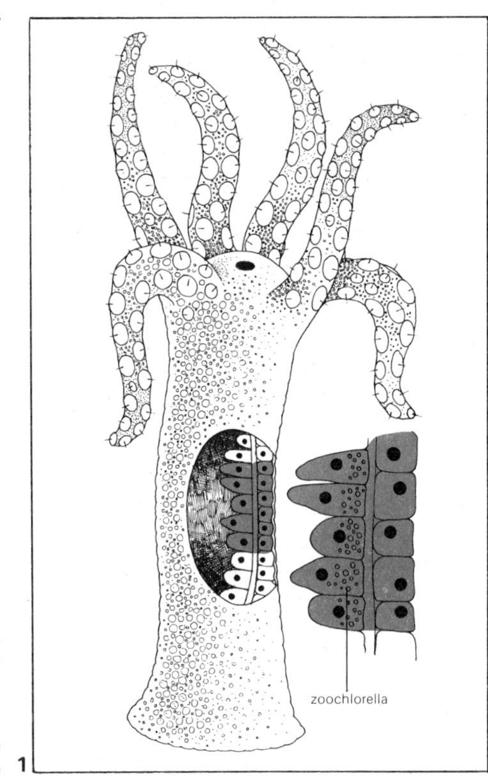


1 Hydra, a freshwater animal, contains a plant, zoochlorella. Each supplies the other's chemical requirements. This is symbiosis.

2 These knots, gathering for their winter migration, avoid the cold Arctic winter by moving south to Africa.

3 The caribou of northern Canada are well adapted for life in the frozen Arctic. They live on moss and can find food in the snow.

The long Polar night poses special problems for both plants and animals. Plants cannot survive long periods of frost, though some of them are remarkably hardy. For this reason, there are no trees above a certain latitude. The plants almost all lie dormant in the ground until roused to frenzied growth by the rays of the summer sun. Arctic species of plants are able to take the maximum advantage of the limited time at their disposal for reproduction and growth.

Many of the bird species of the Polar regions have solved the problem of the Arctic winter by a complicated migratory cycle which brings them to the far north during the summer and far south during the winter. They have evolved a very sophisticated navigational method to enable them to undertake these long journeys.

## Land animals

The land animals have solved the same problem rather differently. Many, like the Polar bear, undergo long hibernations during the worst part of the year. The Polar bear digs out a cave for itself and its family and sleeps through the winter. The animal must accumulate sufficient food in the form of fat deposits during the summer and autumn to last it through hibernation. In addition, it has the ability to slow down its metabolism so that it does not burn up energy at anything like the normal rate. Hibernation is, in fact, typical behaviour

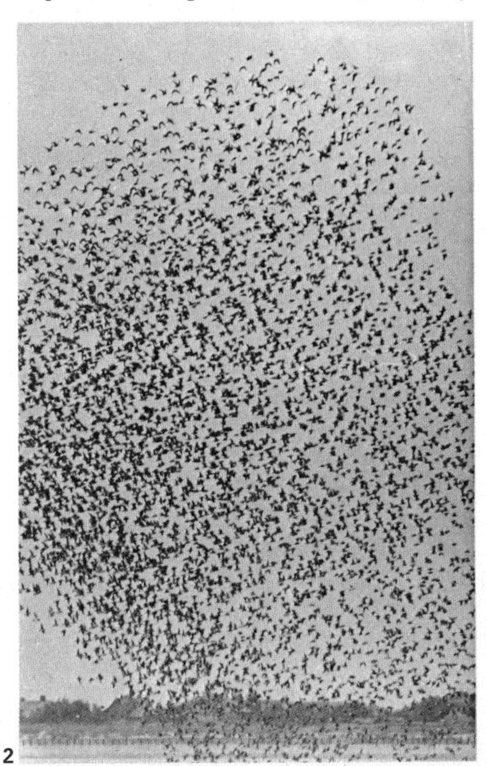

for Polar mammals and even the Eskimos of the far north are far less active during the winter than during the summer. The Eskimos are physically adapted for life in the far north: they are short and stocky in build, a body form which presents the least surface for radiation of heat. Their faces tend to be flattened, with snub noses, again presenting less area to the cold. The physique of the Eskimos is in marked contrast to that of races that live in hot areas. The Dinkas of the Nile, for example, who live in an extremely hot environment, tend to be very tall, thus giving the maximum area for radiation of heat.

An environment that presents very different problems of adaptation for animals and plants is the desert. The main problem is finding and conserving water. There are two types of desert. In one, water is not available in sufficient quantity – the Sahara and the Kalahari deserts of Africa. The second type of desert is one in which the conditions are so cold that the water is in an unobtainable form. Such deserts are found in high plateaux and in the far north. Various plant and animal forms have evolved in a specialized way to live under these conditions. A familiar example is the camel. It can go for long periods without water and it is able to store fat in its 'hump'. The camel is also well adapted to prevent excessive loss of water. It is able to excrete a highly concentrated urine so that very little of its body water is required to rid it of waste materials.

## Special relationships

This ability is shared by a remarkable desert rodent called the kangaroo rat. Its kidney is specially adapted and it can conserve its limited water supply very much longer under waterless conditions than other mammals. Many of the animals that live in the desert have evolved specialized senses – particularly the sense of smell – in such a way as to enable them to find water under adverse conditions. Other animals have become adept at finding food in the sparsely vegetated desert. The Lapland reindeer lives where vegetation is sparse because the ground is frozen for much of the year. It is able to survive on a diet of 'reindeer moss'. This lichen is itself a remarkable adaptation. It is not a moss at all but really consists of two plants, an alga and a fungus, which live together in an extremely close association. This remarkably resilient combination, found in the most exposed sites and spots on mountains and within the Arctic Circle, is an example of a type of adaptation known as *symbiosis*.

Symbiosis is one of the most remarkable adaptations found in Nature. In the case of lichens, the two species cannot live apart because each provides the other with substances necessary for life. Another example of a similar process is provided by the common hydra, a small freshwater plant related to the sea-anemones. Hydra contains inside its body a small freshwater plant called zoochlorella, which produces oxygen and sugar. These substances are necessary to the hydra's development, while the hydra itself produces nitrogen, which is required by zoochlorella. All these adaptations take advantage of the increased resources that two plants have over one.

A similar type of symbiosis is found between human beings and certain bacteria, which live in the intestines and form a necessary part of the process of digestion. But these are not truly in a symbiotic relationship. Man can live without bacteria and the bacteria can, in some cases, live without the man. But they do provide

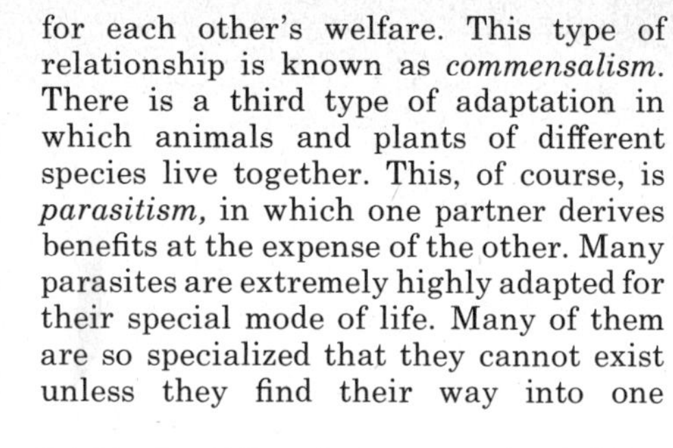

for each other's welfare. This type of relationship is known as *commensalism*. There is a third type of adaptation in which animals and plants of different species live together. This, of course, is *parasitism*, in which one partner derives benefits at the expense of the other. Many parasites are extremely highly adapted for their special mode of life. Many of them are so specialized that they cannot exist unless they find their way into one

**1** The sponge crab is host to a commensal sponge which lives on its back and feeds from the scraps of food left after the crab has eaten. The crab is not inconvenienced by the sponge.

**2** The prickly pear is physiologically adapted to withstand both snow and frost and temperatures above 100 °F. Succulent to survive drought, its spines discourage animals.

**3** A hermit crab just about to enter the shell of a periwinkle. The crab has no shell itself, but makes use of empty shells to provide the protection it needs.

**4** A dwarf mimulus or monkey flower growing in chips of lava in a volcanic crater in Oregon. The dwarf stature of the plant is an adaptation to the poor environment.

1

2

3

particular species of host. A successful parasite does not kill the host, although it may weaken it. Host and parasite may grow together so that they become mutually tolerant.

A very good example of this type of adaptation is found in parts of Africa and Asia where the disease called tertiary malaria, caused by a form of the malarial parasite or *Plasmodium*, is rife. In the areas where this type of disease is common,

**5** The guanaco of the Andes is an animal similar to the camel. It is well adapted to life in the high, dry environment of the mountainous deserts.

**6** An Arctic fox in its winter coat. During the summer, the Arctic fox has a reddish coat, but in winter this is replaced by a white protective coat which acts as camouflage.

4

5

6

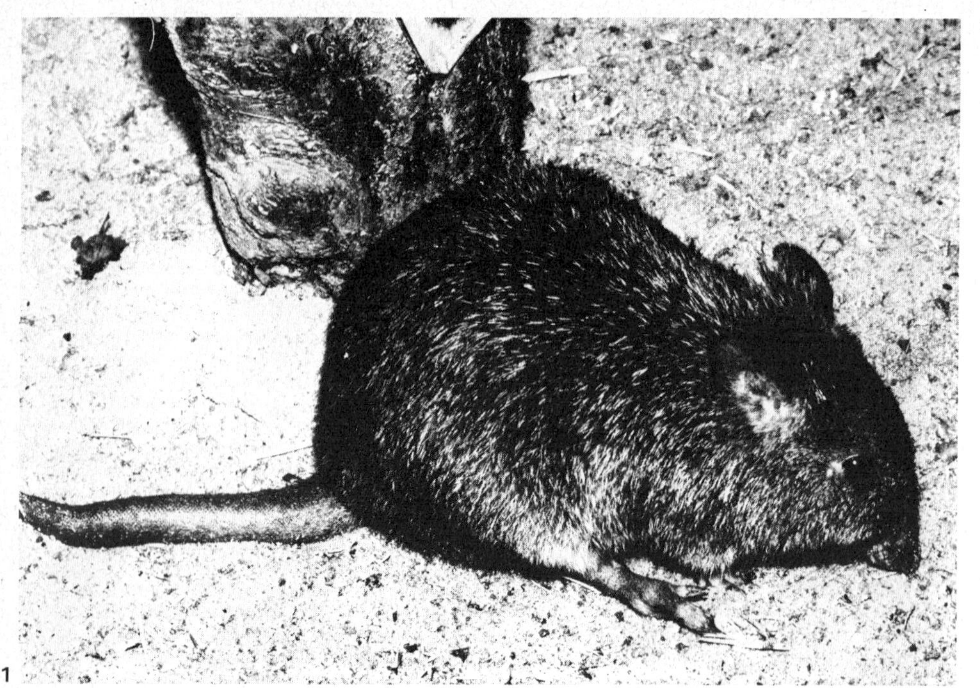

1 The kangaroo rat, so called because it moves by leaping with its strong hind-legs, is well adapted to life in the desert. Its kidneys produce a highly concentrated urine.
2 Mistletoe lodges in the cracked bark of trees and becomes parasitic on its host. This property puzzled the early Britons, who worshipped mistletoe as a sacred plant.

it has been found that many of the people have a particular form of hereditary anaemia called sickle-cell anaemia. This disorder is caused by a gene which is lethal when both chromosomes contain it. However, where a person carries only one gene for the disease, that person is normal except that his blood cells under certain conditions become deformed. He is also highly resistant to tertiary anaemia. The advantage conferred by this adaptation in the human population is an example of the successful ability of the parasite's host to develop ways of neutralizing the parasite. Where tertiary malaria has been eliminated, the gene for sickle-cell anaemia, which now carries only disadvantages for its bearer, is fairly rapidly eliminated from the population.

## Degeneration of parasites

Another example of adaptation in the host-parasite relationship is found in the mite *Demodex folliculorum*. This remarkable little parasite lives in the hair follicles of dogs, where it gives rise to the disease called follicular mange. The rear part of the mite's body is elongated so that it can fit into the follicle.

Some parasites are almost completely degenerate and their mode of life as parasites has left them permanently altered. Such are the pentastomid parasites, like the tongueworms of dogs. Despite their wormlike appearance, these parasites are in fact closely related to the spiders. Their mode of existence makes it easy for them to get food from the tissues of the host, and they do not have to work hard for a living. The parasite *Sacculina* is a parasite of crabs. This animal is, in fact, closely related to the barnacles, but has become so well adapted to its mode of life that it is now little more than a sac containing the sexual organs and feeding on the crab's tissues by means of tubes which spread through the body of the host.

In a sense, of course, these animals are not degenerate at all. They are in many cases extremely well adapted to their way of life. But biologists are not immune to the fallacious reasoning that uses human values to judge the worth of animal species, and parasites are often regarded as rather inferior forms of life.

In human beings there are many adaptations that have fitted us for our unique mode of life. One of the most important of these is the ability of human beings, as opposed to the apes, to bring together their thumb and forefingers to grasp objects. This ability is called 'opposing the thumb'. The upright posture of human beings is not so well developed in any other animal species. The change to bipedal movement involved considerable anatomical changes, particularly in the position of the pelvis. This bone, in human beings, is tilted back, and the spine is curved in such a way that the centre of gravity is brought over the feet.

The advantages of upright posture are numerous. Man is freed from having to walk around on all fours, and can thus use his hands to the full. Standing upright enables Man to increase his range of vision. The most important disadvantage, however, is that the bone structure is not fully adapted to the upright posture, and so tends to become deformed as the man grows older. Back trouble, slipped discs and the like, are the penalty we pay for being able to walk on our hind legs.

Some animals have been able to develop highly specific adaptations for their particular mode of life. Bats provide us with an example. In these highly specialized mammals the vision sense is very poor – they live much of their lives in the dark. But bats are able to 'see' at night because of their ability to sense high-frequency vibrations. In fact, the bats have developed a form of radar.

## Protective adaptation

A remarkable example of protective adaptation has been observed in moths. Certain white moths found in Britain used to produce black offspring sometimes as 'sports' or mutants. Where these moths live in industrial areas, however, the species are now almost entirely black. The moths have adapted to the dark background created by the smoke of the towns and are able to survive fundamental changes in their environment. Those remaining white have stood out against a black background and become easy prey for birds and other predators. A similar but more ancient type of adaptation is found in certain insects which mimic more ferocious or inedible insects in order that their predators will pass them by. The harmless grass snake feigns death to fool its enemies.

The hermit crab is born without the customary hard carapace, or shell, and would undoubtedly offer a juicy morsel to a passing fish or to another crab. However, the hermit crab has found a neat solution to its problem. It finds a winkle shell and pushes its soft body inside it for protection.

One is constantly amazed by the very exact way in which natural selection fits an animal for its environment. This is achieved by a long process of survival of the fittest in which those members of the species which fail to adapt to their environment, which are born less fitted for their particular mode of life, are eliminated by predators or are unable to compete with their fellows for the available living space. This process, which lies at the basis of all adaptation in plants and animals, constantly refines the species so that it is better able to live in the existing conditions.

Adaptation of species to fit them for special ways of life is part of this process of constant refinement. In this way it becomes possible for animals originally fitted for life in one type of environment to change gradually and become able to cope with the extreme conditions encountered, for example, in the Arctic, in hot deserts and on high mountains. This ensures that life extends over the entire planet.

# The frozen deserts

**Although the most inhospitable regions on the Earth, the Poles harbour unique forms of life. Both plants and animals have made special adaptations in order to survive the constantly cold climate.**

THE ARCTIC AND THE ANTARCTIC, the 'Poles' of the world, are perhaps the environments least altered by Man. Here nature, grand and forbidding in its primeval scenery, has reigned unchallenged, at least until recent years. The Poles are the regions of cold, which is the very opposite of life; in fact the Greenland and Antarctic ice-caps are the world's only absolute deserts, the only completely lifeless places. The Poles are not identical: the Arctic is a semi-frozen sea surrounded by *tundra* lands several miles square, the Antarctic is a continent between Europe and North America in size.

Distinct as the polar environment is, its boundaries are not simple to define. Its main characteristics are high latitude, long winters, short cool summers, low rainfall, permanently frozen ground, or permafrost, frozen lakes and sea, absence of trees, winds and varying types of drifting snow-storms or blizzards.

The Antarctic is an enormous dome of ice formed by the snows of ages past. It has about eight times more ice than the Arctic. This is because the Antarctic is a continent, a land mass and a poor heat conserver, whilst the Arctic is primarily ocean, which has a greater capacity for storing summer heat and moderating the cold of the winter. Over the Antarctic as a whole there is perhaps five inches of annual rainfall in the form of snow. The Arctic is much milder and much less hostile to life. In the winter it is very cold, but a brief warming-up phase in the summer gives life the chance it never has in the Antarctic. This summer heat, and the moisture it releases during the thaw make possible a surprising amount of vegetation.

The Finnish word *tundra,* meaning 'barren land' is used to describe the area which separates the sea and ice of the Northern hemisphere from the forests. Its average yearly rainfall is only eight inches, but unlike the deserts, the tundra maintains its water because its cold air cannot easily absorb water vapour, and because permafrost just below the surface acts as a barrier to drainage. This permafrost gradually releases its ancient reserves of ice in the annual surface thaws. Though littered with lakes and swampy ground, only a few sluggish rivers drain the tundra.

A young Emperor penguin is kept warm on its parent's feet. Although the penguin is the most familiar of the animals in the Antarctic, only a few species actually breed there.

This then is the polar environment. Obviously it is one which is hostile to most kinds of animal and plant life. A few, specially adapted, do survive. Here as elsewhere all life, including that of Man, is dependent ultimately on plants, both of the land and the ocean. The latter is surprisingly rich in plant life. Land vegetation is poorer both in quantity and the number of species present.

Arctic plants belong to five main groups: lichens, either on rocks or in mats on the ground; grasses; cushion plants; low shrubs; and mosses. This is the home of small plants, with only a few species growing more than a couple of inches. There are, of course, no upright trees; the ones that are found, including willows, elders and birches, are stunted. Unlike the Antarctic, the Arctic has vast stretches of ice-free land where animals can roam and plants can grow. It also has much sunlight and during the short Arctic summer plants are able to grow almost continuously.

The most obvious difficulties for Arctic plants are the combination of cold winds and a short growing season. Flowering plants, such as the Arctic yellow poppy, will only grow when the climate is mild enough to allow a few weeks of weather each year when day and night temperatures are above freezing. Apart from the cold and wind, the plants have to meet harsh soil conditions. Arctic soils are relatively infertile: although many soil

Yakuts tend their reindeer in the Arctic tundra of Siberia. They are a people accustomed to living in the severe climate and can sleep in the open when the temperature is −50 °C.

Ample insulation is necessary for survival in the Arctic. The willow ptarmigan, coloured white for protection, has feathers on the soles of its feet to keep them warm.

constituents are present in normal quantities they are lacking in nitrogen. Where nitrogen is more abundant the comparative luxuriance of vegetation is startling, as on the well-manured slopes below a cliff-bird colony.

Faced with the limiting factors of wind-chill, low nitrogen concentrations, the disturbance of soil by permafrost and scanty rainfall, Arctic plants have developed many ways of overcoming their difficulties. They have to compete with physical factors, rarely with rival plants as is common in more clement regions. Nearly all the Arctic plants are perennials, climatic conditions providing such a short growing season that the annual's life-cycle cannot be completed. If the plants fail to produce flowers and seeds one summer, they can endure for several years without blossoming – ensuring the continuation of the species.

Very low annual growth rate is the dominant factor of polar vegetation; willows and junipers have been found which are 400 years old. Most species, in fact, take several years from seed germination to their first flowering season. Because of the erratic weather, many plants do not rely on producing seeds in order to propagate but on various means of vegetative reproduction – underground budding from creeping rootstocks for instance. To protect themselves against dryness and drifting snow and soil, many of the cushion plants hide their withering buds under the soil or within a mass of dead leaves. In this way the buds can bloom and mature in one month when summer comes.

## A rich plant life

The waters of the Arctic region are full of plant life; small freshwater lakes which lose their ice-cover early and warm up rapidly in summer have a rich plant life including many vascular forms. In the cold water of the larger lakes and the sea, vascular plants are not often found, being replaced with a rich microflora, algae and diatoms. In the latitudes of the long day photosynthesis can go on continuously, for both land and water plants. This, combined with the low nitrogen concentrations of the soil, means that the sugar level of Arctic plants is high. What scarce vegetation does exist is nutritious and indispensable fare for the Arctic animal life.

The northern polar region, unlike the south, has a considerable amount of land and sea fauna with sometimes large numbers of an individual species, such as the lemming, the caribou or mosquito.

The Arctic land animals have to submit to wide fluctuations of temperature. The reason why the polar animals do not freeze to death is one of evolution's major developments: warm-bloodedness. But warm-bloodedness alone does not ensure survival. It does guarantee that the animal will be alert and active as long as body heat is maintained. The three main ways polar animals deal with fluctuations of temperature are hibernation, migration and insulation by fur covering or feathers. Well-known fur bearers of the Arctic include the polar bears, king of the Arctic.

1

2

This bear has long, oily hairs, and a summer coat of less insulating quality. Not only do northern animals have better winter coats, but these provide better coverage; the ptarmigan, for example, has feathers on the soles of its feet. The hair of the caribou, which is thicker at the tip than at the base, in order to trap more air, is the best clothing material known for its warmth-to-weight ratio.

Some animals, such as lemmings, hibernate during the cold months. Polar bears, however, do not hibernate. Most males are out on the pack-ice all the year round hunting seals, fish, birds' eggs, and sometimes venturing inland for grass and berries. Only the pregnant female lapses into partial sleep while her cubs are born. The only other carnivorous land animal that strays as far north as the polar bear is the Arctic fox, trailing the bear and living off its left-overs. Dormancy is the rule for most of the Arctic invertebrates. Many spend the winter as eggs or larvae providing food for the Arctic birds. Almost all Arctic birds migrate; exceptions are the snowy owl, some ravens and some of the ptarmigan. Other migrators are some marine mammals and land animals like the caribou.

An interesting point concerning the number of certain Arctic animals is the cycle of scarcity and abundance. These cycles are three to four years in length and

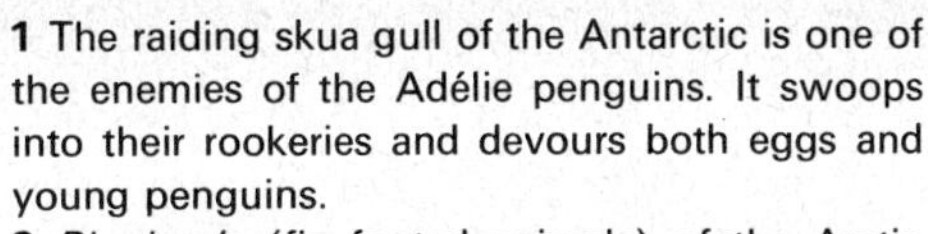

**1** The raiding skua gull of the Antarctic is one of the enemies of the Adélie penguins. It swoops into their rookeries and devours both eggs and young penguins.
**2** *Pinnipeds* (fin-footed animals) of the Arctic are divided into three main groups: eared seals, walruses and true seals. Some, valued for their pelts, are hunted under strict supervision.
**3** The Arctic fox and the polar bear are the only carnivorous animals in the north. The fox follows the bear and helps itself to scraps left over from one of the bear's killings.
**4** Caribou stand on a patch of snow in the thawing tundra near Mount McKinley. They are trying to escape the swarms of flies that infest the area during the summer.
**5** The polar bear can grow to weigh 1,600 lb. The thick, oily hair of the animal allows it to hunt its favourite prey, the seal, across the ice and in freezing waters during the fiercely cold Arctic winter.
**6** The pasque-flower blooms in the Alaskan tundra. Arctic plants have a very short growing season; only in July and August is the temperature usually warm enough for growing.

are based on the number of rodents. Thus the lemming cycle has repercussions in numbers of its predators, particularly the Arctic fox and snowy owl. Exactly why the lemming increases so violently is still not known. The decline is explicable through over-grazing, disease and mass migration in search of new areas during starvation, when it is particularly exposed to predators.

One of the most characteristic Arctic animals, having no relatives in other latitudes, is the musk ox. This animal is defenceless against armed Man and is now only to be found in the virtually uninhabited Canadian and Arctic islands and north and east Greenland. The caribou with its domesticated cousin, the reindeer, is the most important land animal to the Arctic natives. Recently the caribou population has declined alarmingly, a result above all of hunting by rifles. This has completely changed the lives of some of the inhabitants: whole groups of Eskimos have starved or had to move. Legislation has been proposed to prevent the killing of calves and all females from 1 January to 31 July, the use of 0·22 rifles, or the feeding of dogs on caribou.

The Arctic seas are teeming with creatures. All kinds of fish are to be found, including polar char, cod, trout and Greenland shark. It is the larger sea-mammals, however, which are the most conspicuous members of polar wild life and are all of great importance to hunting Man. The biggest group of these is the *pinnipeds*, the fin-footed mammals. There are three families of them: the eared seals, including sea lions and fur seals; walruses which, like them, have back flippers useful for 'walking' on ice or land; and finally earless or true seals, sometimes known as hair-seals. Sea temperatures remain fairly uniform throughout the year and the marine mammals' layer of subcutaneous fat is a sufficient protection against the chill of the icy water. A big danger for the sea mammals is ice forming over their heads. Those mammals which do not migrate, such as the bearded seal, have learnt how to deal with this hazard by using their front limbs to claw breathing holes through the ice.

Seals and walruses have been seriously harried by Man for their skins. In 200 years the walrus population has declined from perhaps half a million to 70,000. The history, legends and economy of both Arctic and Antarctic seas are based on the pursuit of members of the whale family, which include the blue whale, the largest mammal that has ever existed. Whales, however, were never as numerous in the north as in the south, possibly because the Arctic Ocean is only sparsely covered with plankton. In the Arctic remains of about half a dozen whale species survive, notably

the 12 to 14 ft white whale and the long-tusked narwhal, both of which are hunted by Eskimos, their meat being considered a delicacy.

It seems almost incredible that bands of people have settled and survived amidst the Arctic rigours. Over hundreds of years hunters like the Eskimos have lived by killing the big game of the far north's waters while others, like the Lapps, have tamed the reindeer. The Eskimo was, and is, more dependent on animal products than most other primitive peoples. Perhaps the most important of these products is animal fat for fuel, taken mostly from the seal. Sealskins provide the material for boats and clothing, along with the caribou. The diet of the Eskimo is essentially a meat one; apart from seals, he eats white whales, birds including ducks, geese, auks and their eggs, and walrus.

The plant and animal life of the Antarctic does not have to contend with Man, at least not native Man, but other hazards to growth are enormous. There is very little vegetation; outside the Grahamland peninsula flowering plants have yet to be found, only algae, mosses and lichens have taken hold. With so little vegetation it is not surprising that the land fauna are even more limited. In the entire region south of the Antarctic Circle there are fewer than 70 species of animals; 45 of these are insects – an astonishingly small proportion considering that nine out of ten of the world's animal species are insects. There are no land mammals at all in Antarctica and only five kinds of seals inhabit the waters around the continent. Life belongs to the sea. This is crowded with creatures, from the speck-sized zooplankton to the killer whale which feeds on penguins, seals and smaller whales. Despite the presence of predators, the populations of Antarctic birds and animals are relatively large. In fact a general law of polar life seems to be that there is a paucity of species of plants and animals, yet each is represented by many individuals. The opposite situation prevails in warmer areas, where there are many species tending to fewer members.

The most familiar of all Antarctic animals is the penguin. Only a few species, however, breed on the continent; most are found in warmer climates to the north. Antarctic species include the King penguin, on the Grahamland peninsula, the Adélie penguin and the Emperor in occasional colonies. The Emperor is the best adapted to the polar regions. It has a strange breeding cycle. Eggs are laid in April or early May and incubated on the parents' feet under a fold of skin at temperatures of 40 to 60 degrees below zero. The young are looked after until the summer, when they are fully fledged. They are then able to take to the water to fish for themselves. During all this time one parent at least is starving for weeks at a time. The total Emperor population is now estimated at 135,000. All penguins are streamlined for polar life. With their sleek bodies protected by a good deal of fat under the skin they are well prepared and insulated for the cold sea. The Adélie penguin is very agile; to escape from a leopard seal or a killer whale it can propel itself seven feet straight up out of the water to the safety of an ice-floe.

Seals and penguins are especially adapted to endure the severe weather on the world's most barren continent. But, unlike the Arctic, no human being has his natural habitation there. However, both the Arctic and the Antarctic have been charted by the heroic efforts of the great explorers, defying death to conquer the polar wastes. Both Poles are proving to be rewarding areas of study for scientists and both have enormous potential for improving life in more clement parts of the world.

1 A rorqual whale comes up through the Antarctic ice to breathe. Marine mammals in the polar regions run the risk of being trapped under the ice and drowning.

2 These husky puppies will be trained to be invaluable aids to Man in the polar regions. They will help him to hunt and will transport him over the difficult terrain.

# Life in the desert

**The inhospitable desert is not as lifeless as many people think. Animals and plants – and men – have evolved ways of coping with the problems of living in intense heat without a regular water supply.**

THE TWO MAINSPRINGS of life are sun and water. Too much of the former and too little of the latter makes the struggle for survival in the desert an intense one. Yet deserts contain many types of plants and animals which show an amazing adaptability to unique and harsh conditions.

Life in the desert is faced with an environment where there is no permanent flowing water and very little rain. The yearly amount of water may vary – parts of the Sahara may have no rain for over ten years, although the average is five inches annually – but when it does rain, it is in a great downpour. Deserts are very hot during the day but cool at night, an important factor in the survival of plants and animals. The soils are usually heavily impregnated with soluble minerals, unleashed from the Earth's rocky crust by weathering and erosion. In wetter climates rain dissolves these surface minerals which are washed into the ground. Depending on which minerals are present the desert may be fertile as in California's Imperial Valley, or almost barren as in the Atacama.

## Desert belts

Deserts are found in every continent except Europe in two discontinuous strips, one in the Northern and one in the Southern hemisphere, roughly centred along the Tropics of Cáncer and Capricorn. Conditions between the deserts vary according to their geographical position and height above sea-level; the low-lying Sahara near the Equator is the hottest and the Gobi, above sea-level and north of the Tropic of Cancer, is the coldest.

Plants are indispensable for all other forms of life in the desert – animals would not survive without nourishment from them. There are two ways desert plants can survive the long waterless periods and take advantage of the bouts of rain. The annuals avoid the problem by spending most of their lives as seeds which grow quickly after rain, bursting into bloom in a startling spectacle of life and colour after the long brown drought. On the other hand, the perennials or evergreens are thrifty plants which live during the dry periods by developing a special physiology.

The billions of seeds of the annuals prosper better in sand, where they find a warm, moist niche, than on hard surfaces where most of them are washed or blown away. An ideal spot for them is under the shade of a bush or tree where they are sheltered and protected. Not all the seeds flower at once. Some never do, but provide the basic diet of certain desert animals. Others remain in the soil to sprout later if the early crop fails. There are always seeds in the soil, thus ensuring the continuation of the species. The basic problem for the seeds is to bloom on time, a complicated one, because deserts can go for years without substantial rainfall. Also there may be the occasional shower to tempt the seed to sprout but which would not provide enough moisture to sustain the plant. Scientists have concluded that seeds have a built-in device which must be dissolved by a large amount of water before the seeds will sprout. In addition the temperature of the soil indicates to the plant when it should flower, so summer flowers only erupt in rainy summers, while winter ones are dormant.

1 *Welwitchia mirabilis,* which is found in the Mossamedes desert in Angola, has a life span of several hundred years. This 'octopus' has a root system which retains water during dry periods.
2 Rattlesnakes, like this magnificent diamondback, are common in North American deserts. Normally slothful, they are quick to strike at an enemy if they are disturbed.

The perennials or evergreen plants on the other hand have a unique structure. The roots of evergreens compete for the scarce water supply in the soil and so the plants are thinly distributed throughout the desert. The plants must utilize every available drop of water. Plants which can tolerate great dryness are called *xerophytes.* They are xeromorphic – they possess features which both reduce transpiration and protect against too intense heat. The most effective and frequent protection against excessive transpiration is a drastic reduction of the transpiring surface. Many plants have tiny leaves and some shed even these at the beginning of the dry season. The palo verde tree has tiny leaves no more than a millimetre across which it sheds during drought. *Photosynthesis* – the conversion of sunlight, air and moisture into food – can continue even after the leaves have fallen because the chlorophyll which for most plants is found in the leaves, is contained in the stems and twigs of the palo verde. Excessive heating is often prevented by the leaves hanging vertically, as do those of the eucalyptus trees of the Australian desert.

More than half the species of evergreen desert plants produce thorns as a protection against grazing animals. Desert plants can ill afford to lose leaves which can be more readily replaced in wetter climates. Some plants which are generally thorny in their native desert habitat have no thorns when grown in the moist atmosphere of a greenhouse, but botanists have not yet been able to discover the process whereby this happens.

The roots of the evergreens take various forms. Most desert trees grow in the dried-up water courses where the soil is deep and underground water is available. Some trees normally have extremely long roots in order to reach the water. The American mesquite tree can have roots as long as 100 feet. The young trees consist almost entirely of roots until they reach enough water to allow the tree to grow above ground. Other plants have shallow fibrous roots which are very well designed for soaking up moisture; the radius of the roots of the saguaro cactus often equals its height of 50 feet. The cereus, which blooms only at night, has bulbous roots which store water and feed the plant. Particularly remarkable are some of the orchids which consist almost entirely of roots, dispensing with the whole vegetative shoot. Their green aerial roots, besides anchoring the plant and absorbing water also perform some of the functions of leaves. To store food as well as water during drought, thickened roots, bulbs, tubes and nodules of many shapes and sizes have developed. A spindly vine grows in the Kalahari in Africa, springing from a huge underground tuber. The native Bushmen often dig this out when desperate for water, for the tuber can grow as big as a football.

## Plants under challenge

Desert plants generally need the challenge of harsh conditions in order to grow. In softer conditions some of them will not develop to their real potential. The Joshua tree of the Mojave, for example, can live for hundreds of years and grow up to 25 feet. It can only do this, however, if planted at an altitude of 2,500 feet, where the summers are burning and the winters cold. At sea-level or along the Californian coast the seedlings stop growing after two or three years. In order to grow vigorously the Joshua tree needs a period of low temperature, during which it lies dormant. The seeds of other trees of the American deserts – for example, the ironwood and the smoke tree – need to be chipped and bruised before they can germinate. This drastic action allows water to get through their hard coats. Making a virtue of necessity, some desert plants have to be eaten in order to live. The seeds of the mesquite tree are encased in a pod, like peas. They can only grow in any abundance if eaten by cattle, deer or other browsers, and pass through their digestive tracts. The process is a good method of seed dispersal because seeds grow well in manure, and the digestive juices of the animal erode the glassy seed letting water penetrate and germination start. Similarly the sturdy seeds of the enormous baobab tree of the Kalahari grow more readily after being swallowed and excreted by baboons. The most famous of desert plants is, of course, the cactus.

The nature of the vegetation decides the number and kind of animals to be found in the desert regions. Many plants are pollinated by insects, of which the desert contains a great variety – beetles, ants, wasps and moths. Most desert insects live short lives. Insect eggs and pupae – and adults – are the staple diet of many arthropods, birds, reptiles and mammals. Men also eat them; the people of the Middle East desert eat roast locusts when these insects have stripped the desert bare of vegetation.

Harvester ants are practically unique among desert insects because they are in adult form all the year round. They live on seeds which they gather from the ground during the cool periods of the day. These are taken underground, masticated into 'ant-bread' and what is not eaten immediately is stored. The ants vary their diet during the seasons to meet the current crop of plants. Another curious insect is the honey-pot ant. The young have their elastic abdomens pumped with plant juice by other workers and, hung from the ceilings of underground nests, function as living reservoirs of food.

Besides the insects a great variety of arthropods – spiders, scorpions, centipedes – are found in the desert. Their thick body coverings are a sound protection against water loss. Insects are their staple diet and, in turn, they are food for many animals. The elf-owl, for example, eats spiders, which are 80 per cent liquid, and can thus survive a whole season without drinking. Some arthropods need great patience: when the first rain for 25 years

1

2

**1** The girdle-tailed lizard appears to be almost a cross between a lizard and a snake. Its limbs are little more than vestiges and it moves by wriggling its body.
**2** By contrast, the stumpy-tailed lizard of the Australian deserts is short and plump, with prominent large scales on its body. Its stumpy tail serves as a store of fat which enables the animal to survive long periods of drought.
**3** Cactus plants are extremely common in deserts. Their fleshy stems store water, while their thorns deter animals from eating them. This beaver-tail cactus, in the American Joshua Tree National Monument, opens its brilliant flowers in the hottest period of the day, when pollinating insects are at their most active.
**4** Black vultures, in the Mexican desert, congregate round the corpse of a goat. Vultures are found in both Old and New World deserts.
**5** These little elf-owls have solved their problem of survival very neatly. By gouging out a nest in the core of a saguaro cactus, they have ensured not only a ready water-supply, but a place where they can avoid the sun's heat.

3

4

5

came to Bicycle Dry Lake in the Mojave in 1955, the shallow water was soon crowded with fairy shrimp, tadpole shrimp and clam shrimp. Their eggs had lain dormant in the soil for a quarter of a century.

Fish, on the other hand, need permanent water and are found in springs, at water-holes and streams. Amphibians, however, are far more successful in the desert than fish. Frogs, toads and sometimes salamanders collect around the water-holes. The spade-foot toad is one of the best adapted. When the drought comes it digs deep into the ground with its feet which have a thorny projection for this purpose. It can then lie dormant for nine or ten months. It emerges when the rain comes and eggs are laid and fertilized at once. They hatch in a day and a week later are ready to find their own way back into the ground.

Reptiles are generally well adapted to desert conditions. Their scaly skin is very resistant to drying and they usually deposit their eggs in soil where there is enough moisture for them to hatch. Lizards are among the most frequently noted desert creatures. The fringe-toed sand lizard hides from its enemies by swimming under the loose sand. It is able to do this by means of scaly fringes on its toes and a sand trap in its nose which allows it to breathe. A similar device is found in snakes that inhabit sand dunes. Desert reptiles cannot survive when it is very hot and have to find shade. Like birds, reptiles depend almost entirely on respiratory cooling, they pant when they become hot. One kind of reptile, the tortoise, converts some of its food to water, which is stored for the hot season in two sacs under the upper shell.

Birds are numerous in arid lands but compared with most groups of desert animals they are not very different from their cousins in more clement regions. Apart from the burrowing owl they cannot dig into cool holes and many avoid the summer heat by migrating. Vultures are common in deserts. Their large wings and light bodies enable them to ride on rising currents of warm air. Insect-eating birds, like hawks and owls, get water from the flesh of their prey. A defence mechanism used by some birds, like swifts, is *aestivation*. When food is scarce they drop their body temperature and become torpid, reviving when conditions improve.

## Camels and llamas

The camel is the most familiar of desert mammals. Its special physiology is enormously important for the economy of the desert. By storing fat in its 'hump' it is able to go for long periods without water. It does not pant or breathe rapidly and can also pass a highly concentrated urine, so very small amounts of its body water are needed to rid it of waste materials.

The New World counterpart of the camel, the llama, is in many ways remarkably similar, though it has evolved completely independently. The llama, like the camel, is now found mainly as a domesticated animal, having been saved from extinction by the Incas. Its smaller relative, the alpaca, provides wool for the inhabitants of the high Andes and of the semi-desert regions around the Atacama.

Most of the animals of the desert are seed eaters, principally rodents. One of the most remarkable of these is the kangaroo rat, so called because of its hopping gait. It is food for almost all the meat-eating animals of the desert. It can go its whole life without drinking, living off seeds, grasses and cactus pulp. It survives by remaining in its burrow during the heat of the day, catching the moisture it loses in breathing and letting some recirculate into its body. It has no sweat glands and with its specially adapted kidney it excretes almost no urine.

Less numerous than rodents are species that live off foliage, twigs and the storage organs of perennial plants. These animals include deer, antelopes and rabbits. Carnivores like foxes, jackals and badgers are also found. Many of these are paler than their relatives in less arid regions. Some, like the pocket mouse, hibernate in times of extreme heat, drought or cold. Those which cannot retreat in these ways must find other methods of cooling. The centre of life in the desert is the water hole, which, particularly in the evening, becomes crowded with many different species. Animals of the desert have been forced to adopt a wide variety of structural and behavioural devices to meet harsh habitat. Yet unlike the plants, all of these have equivalents elsewhere. It is important to realize the chain of life in the desert: plants provide food for the small animals who in turn give this vital nourishment to the larger ones. Human desert dwellers exploit native flora and fauna to survive, from the Stone Age Bushmen of Kalahari to the sophisticated Arabs of parts of the Sahara. Man is now taming the desert as never before, using advanced technology to reach its rich minerals, to provide bases for armies and build holiday resorts.

The potential now exists to turn large areas of desert into fertile land. This is, of course, done on a small scale through irrigation, but there is now speculation in scientific circles that it may before long be possible to change the climate of desert areas by re-shaping the face of the Earth, diverting ocean currents and similar projects. Human mismanagement has also made deserts like the Dust Bowl of the mid-west of the United States. The seemingly timeless world of the desert plant and animal life will undoubtedly not remain unmolested.

1 Lizards live largely on insects. Here, a bearded dragon lizard is about to swallow a captured rhino beetle. The dragon's horny armour protects it against predators and heat loss.

2 Water – a commodity in short supply – plays a predominant part in the desert economy. A water hole in the Arizona desert of the United States attracts many animals and plants. These deer drink at night to avoid excess heat.

The White Sands of Almogordo, New Mexico, have abundant water a few feet below the surface – too deep for most plants, but not for this cottonwood tree, which hibernates during winter.

# Between the acorn and the oak

**A seed is dropped into the ground and covered with earth. Soon a shoot pushes its way through the soil, reaching for the sun. A new plant is born and the process of growth is under way.**

AN ACORN measures about half an inch long and weighs at most half an ounce. And yet from it may grow an oak tree 40 feet tall weighing several tons. Such phenomenal growth may take nearly 100 years. But no less remarkable is the growth in a few months of, say, a cabbage weighing three pounds from a tiny seed not much bigger than the head of a pin.

All the biological processes taking place within a plant are concerned in some way or another with growth, so no one process can be pin-pointed as the all-important one. However, certain of the more prominent ones can be singled out for special consideration. Growth within a plant, as in any organism, consists of a *synthesis* (build up) of new materials and the incorporation of these materials into the body structure of the plant. This leads to an increase in size, commonly, but not necessarily, accompanied by an increase in dry weight.

## The fertilized egg

In single-celled plants, such as some algae, growth of the individual takes the form of an enlargement of a single cell and therefore the whole plant. But with large, woody plants, increase in size requires the production of new cells and increasing complexity of the plant body. All parts of the plant share in this growth and development.

Initially any complex plant, such as a grass or a tree, starts from a single cell – the fertilized egg. At this stage, growth resembles that of a single-celled plant; each cell enlarges, then divides into two. But in the vascular plants (plants with many cells), the cells remain together rather than going to live as separate individuals and become altered to perform specialized functions, each contributing to the organization of the whole.

Some of the cells become concerned with the synthesis of food materials by photosynthesis (these are mainly the cells of the leaf, though green cells in the stem are capable of the same function). Others perform the function of absorbing water and minerals from the soil (these are located in the roots). Since these cells, each providing what the other needs, are located at the opposite ends of the plant, a third type of cell is needed which is specialized for transporting the food materials from the leaves to the roots, and

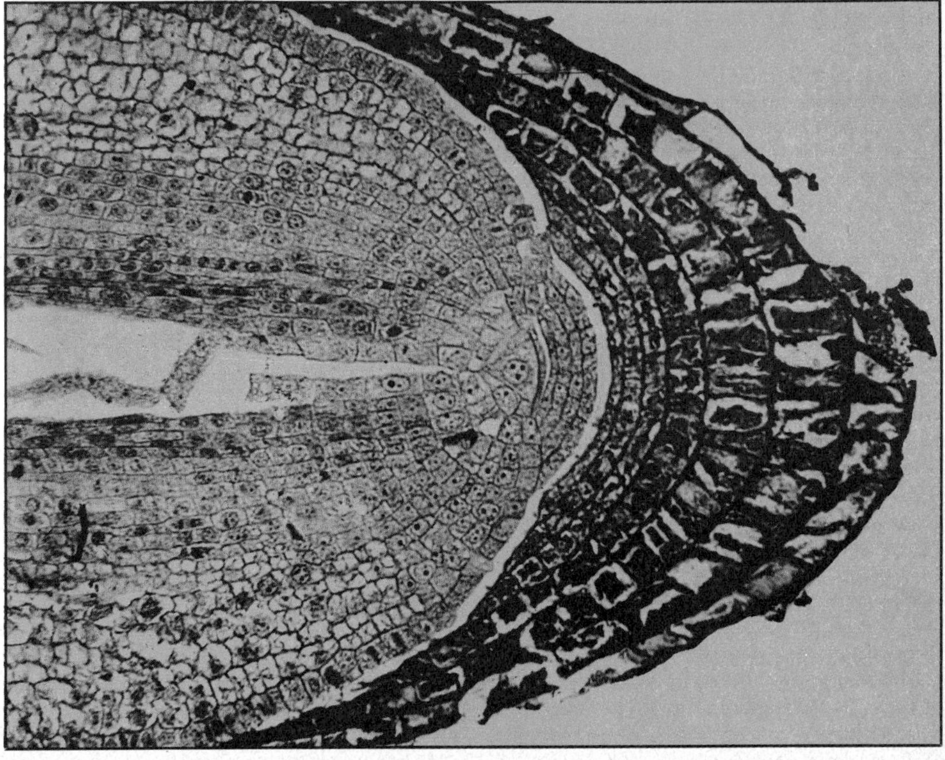

Whatever our palates may tell us, nature did not create sweet, juicy apples solely for the pleasure of human beings, *top*. Instead, the succulent flesh of the fruit was made as nature's protection for the seeds inside before they begin to grow into trees. Plants grow from both ends, top and bottom. *Right*, a cross-section of the apical region of a root.

raw materials from the roots to the leaves.

These transportation cells for food are found in the multi-cellular strands of the *phloem* tissue. Other conducting strands (*xylem* tissue) convey the mineral salts and water from the roots to the leaves. Many other cells are used as packing, protecting the other vitally important parts. In such a complex organism, where the functions are divided between groups of cells (an arrangement which biologists, using a term also employed in economics and sociology, call 'division of labour'), it is not surprising to find that the responsibility for the growth processes of the plant is limited to distinct regions within the plant.

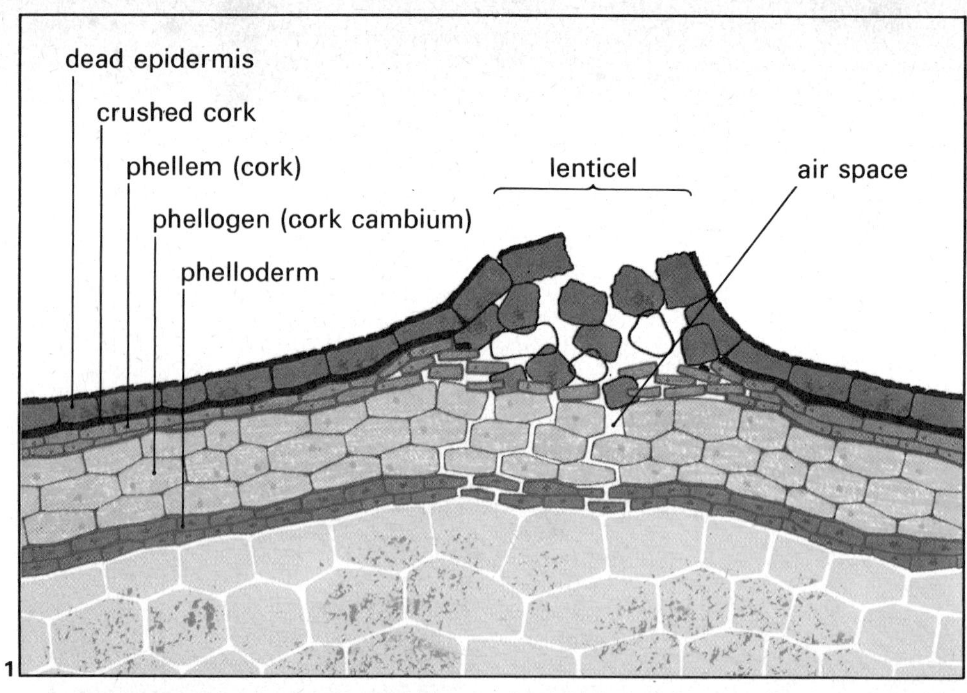


The regions of dividing cells causing growth are called *meristems* and the cells are said to be *meristematic*. When a meristematic cell enlarges and divides, one of the new cells formed retains the ability to enlarge and divide again, while the other ultimately adapts itself to one of the plant's specialized functions.

Often the regions containing meristems are obvious; for example, in the tips *(apices)* of roots and shoots, and in buds. But they also occur in other parts of the plant, contributing to the increase in width which must accompany any increase in height if the plant is to remain stable and not become top-heavy.

## How cells divide

At the tip *(apex)* of the stem, the *primary* meristematic region forms cells which contribute not only to the formation of new stem tissues, but also to the formation of new leaves. The apex is more or less dome-shaped. The outer one to five layers of cells cover the dome, forming the *tunica*. These cells divide mainly at right angles to the surface of the plant; as a result, they increase the surface area. The mass of cells inside them (the *corpus*) divides in all planes, increasing the volume of the plant. Leaves arise directly from the tunica in plants in which the tunica consists of many layers, or from both tunica and corpus in plants in which the tunica consists of only one or two layers.

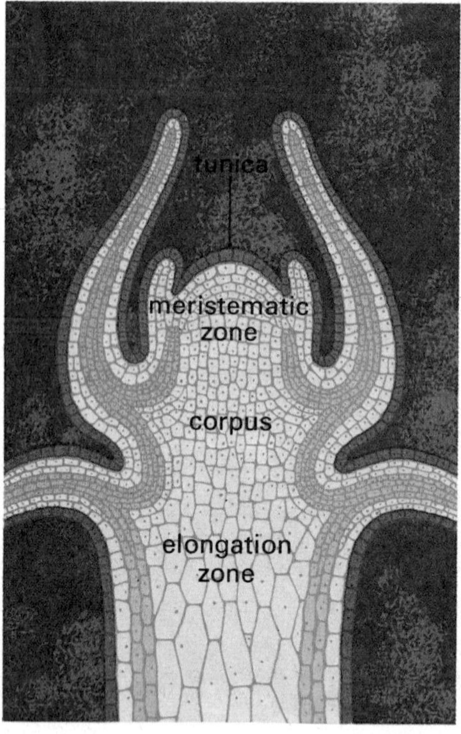

As meristematic cells divide and enlarge, they are effectively added to the top of the plant, in much the same way as a tower is built by adding bricks to the top. Any cell formed at the apex will, as the cell ages, become embedded deeper and deeper inside the plant by the addition of new cells above.

The meristematic cells contain a dense jelly-like material *(cytoplasm)* and a spherical structure (the *nucleus*) which controls the activities of the cell. Around the cytoplasm and nucleus is a membrane (the *plasmalemma*) which prevents the cytoplasm from flowing and oozing out of place. It also allows only selected materials to pass into or out of the cell. Surrounding this is the cell wall, which is a rigid structure and gives the cell a definite shape.

When a meristematic cell divides at the stem apex, it does so by first duplicating the internal structure of the nucleus and then dividing into two separate nuclei. By forming a new wall across the cell, two new cells are created. Each new daughter cell therefore contains the same materials (nucleus and cytoplasm surrounded by a membrane and wall) as before.

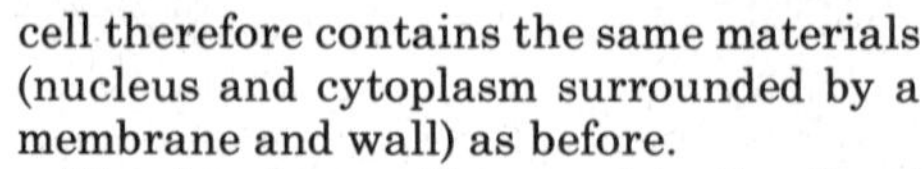

The daughter cell nearest to the tip of the stem is the one which continues to form new cells. The lower daughter cell starts to undergo structural changes. It begins to enlarge and a number of small cavities called *vacuoles* appear in it, which contain sap (water and dissolved salts). The vacuoles get larger as the cell ages, and finally join together to form a large central vacuole with the cytoplasm and nucleus now confined to the outer region of the cell, just inside the cell wall.

From the apex back along the stem, therefore, the cells become progressively larger and more vacuolated. They then start to develop distinctive characteristics for their special jobs. Groups of cells become specialized for conduction of food materials (phloem), others for conduction of water and salts (xylem). A small number

**1** The tough stem covering of plants protects the more delicate interior, but shuts out air. Lenticels, small breaks in the surface cover, remedy the problem. **2** The apex, located at the tip of the stem, is a primary growing region. It is generally dome-shaped and is the source of both new stem cells and new leaves. Disruption of the normal growth processes can produce unusual results. **3** This bonzai maple tree has been considerably dwarfed by confinement and pruning of the roots during its early growth. **4** These abnormally small leaves of the *Malvaviscus penduliflorus* plant are the result of a hormone disturbance. A normal leaf is shown to their left for comparison. **5** The tumours on this *Escheveria gibbosa* are not due to artificial interference with the plant, but to a congenital defect. **6** The imposing *Sequoia gigantea,* popularly known as a California redwood tree, often reaches heights up to 300 feet and an age of 1,000 years or more. **7** It is difficult to imagine that these giants were once seedlings, such as this two-year-old infant.

of cells do not vacuolate but remain small with dense contents. These cells make up the tissue called *cambium,* which is used for width expansion later on.

The phloem, cambium and xylem together make up a *vascular strand,* which extends from near to the apex back down the plant and into the root. There are a number of vascular strands within the stem close to the apex, separated from one another by large vacuolated cells which serve as packing tissue (called collectively *parenchyma*). These cells also exist inside the vascular strands (forming the pith of the stem), between the strands and the outside of the stem (forming a tissue called the *cortex*). Many of the cells of the xylem are long and narrow. As they lengthen, the cell membrane splits and the cell ultimately dies. At the same time, the wall of the cell becomes impregnated with a substance called *lignin* which makes it very hard and rigid.

## Wood and leaves

In this way, xylem cells become long, hollow, hard-walled cells that make up wood. They form a continuous series linking with each other from stem to root, with other xylem cells passing out of the stem as part of a vascular strand into the leaves. Phloem cells also elongate, but not enough to sacrifice themselves. They remain alive even when mature, and form a continuous series just as the xylem cells do.

At the root apex, there is a similar organization but the meristematic cells are located a little farther back from the very tip. A few cells towards the apex form a cap over the root tip to protect the meristematic cells. These are replaced as soil particles wear them away.

This apical development within the plant allows shoots and roots to grow. An increase in the width of the plant must, of course, also occur or the long thin plant would be unable to support its own weight.

The increase in width is achieved by the small cells of the cambium between the xylem and phloem in the vascular strands. Although these cells cease to divide after their formation at the apex, they retain the ability to do so later on. As the stem continues to elongate, they in fact do start to divide again, providing what is called *secondary* growth. Once again one daughter cell remains meristematic and the other develops into a xylem cell (if it is on the inside) or a phloem cell (if it is on the outside).

More xylem cells are formed from cambium than from phloem. The cambium in some plants does occasionally divide at right angles to the surface of the plant so that it spreads sideways between the vascular strands. (This may also be achieved by the parenchymatous cells between strands becoming meristematic.) The cambium in the vascular strand is called *fascicular* cambium and that between the vascular strands is *interfascicular* cambium. The cambium in both positions continues to divide parallel to the surface of the plant, so that ultimately the interior of the stem becomes solid *wood* (xylem) with the original pith crushed and reabsorbed. 'Wood' is an alternative name which biologists can use for xylem tissue.

The cambium continues its activity during the growing season until the autumn, when growth slows down. The xylem cells formed by the cambium do not then enlarge as much as they did earlier in the year. During the winter in cold climates the cambium ceases its activity altogether, as do all the other meristems, because of frost, lack of sufficient sunlight for photosynthesis, etc. In the following spring, the cambial activity restarts and the xylem cells formed grow and enlarge rapidly. The line between the autumn-formed cells of the xylem and the larger spring-formed cells can be seen in the wood as the annual 'rings' (visible when trees are cut through). Such rings may be used to determine the age of the tree.

Since more xylem is formed than phloem, the increase in the diameter of the stem tends to result in a splitting of all the cells outside the cambium, including the outer protective layer (the *epidermis*) with its waxy covering (the *cuticle*). This must be replaced in some way since breaks in the surface layers would lead to excess water loss and allow disease organisms to enter. The plant overcomes this problem by developing *cork* cells to replace the epidermis. Large vacuolated cells of the cortex now begin to become meristematic. They divide, some parallel to the surface of the plant and others at right angles to it. New cells formed by divisions at right angles remain meristematic, forming a ring of *phellogen* around the ever-growing vascular tissue.

## Protected by cork cells

The cells derived from phellogen towards the inside are parenchymatous (packing cells) and form a new tissue, *phellorderm*, almost indistinguishable from the rest of the cortex. The cells formed towards the outside develop thick walls containing fatty material *(suberin)*: these are cork cells *(phellem)*. The fat makes them impervious to water and prevents water loss. They soon die, but the protection they afford against invasion of the plant by bacteria and viruses and against water loss remains. Cells outside the cork (the old epidermis and outer cortical layers) are now cut off from their source of food materials and so they die and quickly wear off the surface of the plant. The cork layers beneath become exposed as the familiar dark brown bark.

Although cork protects the plant, it has the disadvantage that it prevents oxygen from the atmosphere getting to the living cells of the phloem and cambium. At intervals along the stem, therefore, some phellogen cells give rise to living parenchymatous cells. As these increase in numbers, they split the surface cork in places and form small openings through which air can pass to the living cells. These small openings are called *lenticels*.

Plant growth processes are controlled by complex organic compounds called *hormones*. The first hormones discovered were the *auxins*, the most important of which is indole acetic acid (IAA). This hormone is produced in a number of places

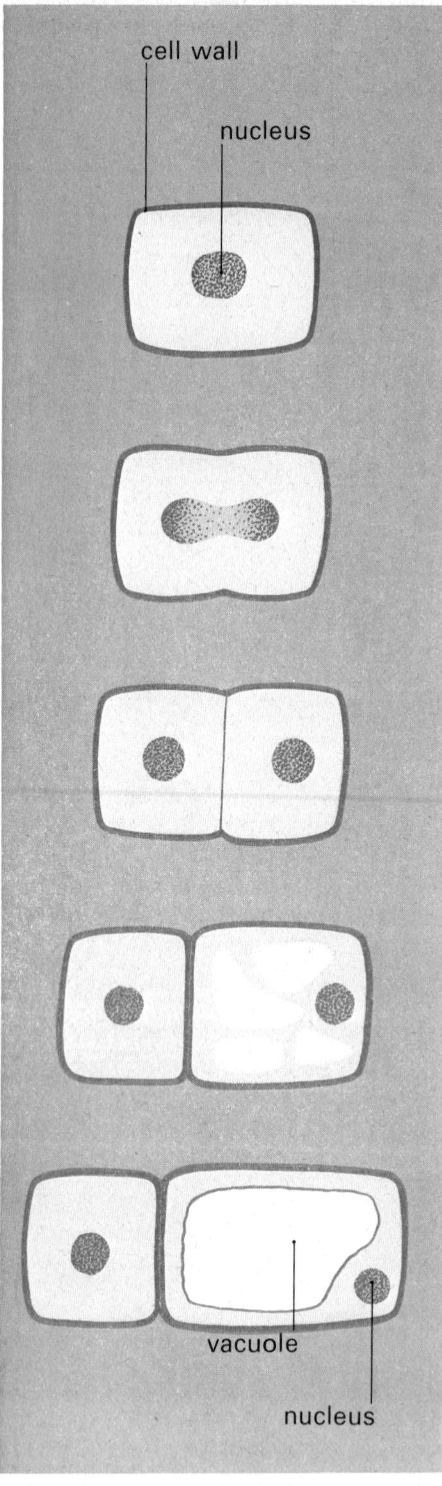


within the plant, particularly at the tips of the roots and shoots from where it passes back into the plant body. As a result, a definite pattern of auxin distribution occurs within the plant. Auxin compounds determine the rate of cell division at the apical meristems, as a simple experiment shows. If the extreme tip of a young grass shoot is removed, growth slows down appreciably. Applying a small block of jelly-like material (agar) containing IAA restores the growth rate to its original level.

Auxins control not only the extension growth of shoots and roots, but are also responsible for the production of new roots, for fruit development, for autumn leaf fall, and for the renewed activity of cambium in the spring.

In many of these processes, the auxins do not act on their own but in conjunction

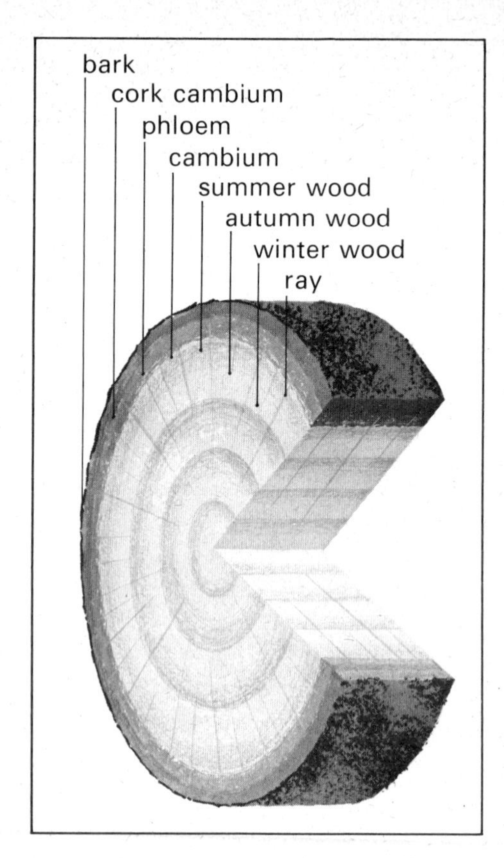


*Left,* a plant cell reproduces when the nucleus splits into separate pieces. A wall develops between the two cells. One of the new cells retains the ability to divide; the other cell vacuolates and adapts its structure to the needs of the plant. *Above,* a section of a plant stem clearly reveals its structure. The rings indicate the plant was four years old when cut down.

with other hormones, such as the family of *gibberellins*. Gibberellins accelerate extension growth in organs such as shoots, but unlike auxins do not stimulate root growth. They are, at least in part, responsible for a wide variety of plant processes such as controlling dormancy of seeds, and possibly inducing the formation of flowers. Both indole auxins and gibberellins separately stimulate some cambial activity, but unless both are present the new cells formed are not normal xylem cells.

A third important group of growth-regulating hormones are the *cytokinins*. Like the other two types of hormones, these have now been isolated from plants in the laboratory. The cytokinins induce cell division and enlargement, but only when in combination with auxins such as IAA.

Though growth in a simple one-celled bacterium and the most advanced tree may appear to be very different, mainly because one is simple and the other complex, the underlying process is the same. The simple plant cell enlarges its body by increasing the amount of material it contains. But at a certain point, the body can no longer expand, so the cell divides into two new individuals, each of which goes its separate way. The same thing is true of more complex plants, but instead of each new cell going off to live as an individual, they cling together in a community, each specialized cell contributing its labour for the benefit of the living whole.

# Sunlight on green leaves

The green leaves of the world add up to form Nature's most amazing chemical factory. Powered by the sun, they withdraw some 40 thousand million tons of carbon dioxide from the air each year.

The elm tree in a well-watered English field and the cactus equipped to flourish without water for six months at a time are both engaged in the world's most important single chemical reaction: photosynthesis. Together, green things take up one five-hundredth of all the light energy that reaches the Earth. Each year they withdraw some 40,000 million tons of carbon dioxide from the Earth's atmosphere.

ALL CREATURES need food – insects, fish, birds and men. And the reason we need food is to provide our bodies with energy. We use energy all the time, even when we are sitting around doing nothing in particular. All animals must eat to stay alive – elephants, mice, caterpillars and men. This picture of all the world's creatures eating away in unison raises a very interesting question: if everyone is taking *in* food, where does it all come from and what is supplying it?

Consider a man about to eat a Sunday lunch of roast beef, Yorkshire pudding, peas and potatoes. The beef probably comes from a specially bred and reared bullock. The Yorkshire pudding is a batter made mainly of flour and eggs; flour from wheat and eggs from chickens. The peas and potatoes are the seeds and tubers of vegetable plants. All the items on the list have one thing in common: all the food comes either directly from plants or from animals that feed on plants or on plant products.

Plants supply the entire world with food, and we should be in a very sorry state without them. The sources of biological energy would dry up and life would soon cease. But what do *plants* eat? They are living things, and they, too, need energy. Plants are remarkably self-sufficient; they make their own food on the spot as they need it. But even they cannot do it on their own. They have to get the energy from somewhere, and they get it from the sun.

Plants could not have a more reliable source of energy. The sun comes up every day and pours a ceaseless torrent of light energy which penetrates the thickest clouds. During the day, plants trap some of the sun's energy and use it to drive chemical reactions in the cells of their leaves and stems. These reactions lead to the manufacture of food – for the plant itself – and eventually for animals and men. The remarkable process in which light energy is used to make food for plants is called *photosynthesis*.

## Sugar from the air

The plant foods formed during photosynthesis are carbohydrates. Plants make all sorts of other things as well, but the first products are always carbohydrates. As their name suggests, carbohydrates are compounds made up of 'hydrated carbon' or carbon and water, giving a basic chemical formula $CH_2O$. In fact, carbohydrates consist of several $CH_2O$ groups linked together to form chains or rings. One of the commonest has six such units and has the formula $(CH_2O)_6$ which, written another way, becomes $C_6H_{12}O_6$. This is the chemical formula of a molecule of the sugar glucose.

Fructose has the same formula, but its atoms are arranged in the molecule in a slightly different way. If a molecule of glucose is joined to a molecule of fructose and a water molecule removed from between them, the remaining carbohydrate is sucrose, or cane sugar. This substance, which in the form of a white powder many people spoon into their morning cup of tea, is common to all plants everywhere. If a lot of glucose molecules are joined together in a particular way they form starch. Starch is abundant in the leaves and seeds of plants as a storage product.

Sugars and starch, then, are carbohydrates, and they are the foods that plants make during photosynthesis. But what are the sugars made from? As they consist of carbon, hydrogen and oxygen, the plant must have a supply of these raw materials. And the plant gets them from the air.

As its source of carbon, a plant uses carbon dioxide. Carbon dioxide is a gas present in small amounts in the atmosphere – only 0·03 per cent, but plants make good use of it. Hydrogen and oxygen come from water, one of the most abundant substances on the Earth. There is plenty of water in the atmosphere and in rain, and plants that happen to live in streams or the oceans have an unlimited supply all around them which they are able to utilize.

But something else is essential to photosynthesis, apart from a supply of light energy and raw materials. This factor is a special pigment, which can trap light and convert it into chemical energy. Without this energy-converter, a plant could not make a single molecule of sugar. The best-known pigment is *chlorophyll,* which is the substance that makes green plants green. Chlorophyll strongly absorbs red and blue light rays from the sun and reflects the rest – the rest being predominantly green light. Some plants rely mainly on other pigments, which absorb light rays from different parts of the spectrum. For example, many seaweeds have additional pigments which make them look brown or red. Whatever the colour of these pigments, however, their function is always the same: to capture light energy and make it available for synthetic reactions.

Chlorophyll is packed away neatly in tiny capsules called *chloroplasts* in the leaves of photosynthesizing plants. But chloroplasts are not just little bags of green powder; their structure is astonishingly complex. And it needs to be because chloroplasts carry out the entire process of photosynthesis. Within their membranes lies all the apparatus needed to make carbohydrates. One of the greatest achievements of biology, and a quite recent one, was the isolation of whole chloroplasts from living plants and the demonstration that these chloroplasts, on their own, were chemically equipped to make starch from carbon dioxide and water, when light shone on them.

## The remarkable chloroplast

The photosynthetic ability of chloroplasts is destroyed if they are damaged or broken. This would seem to indicate that the arrangement of the 'apparatus' is delicate and precise. In recent years, research workers have been able to use electron microscopes to look into the minute architecture of these remarkable bodies.

Chloroplasts are tiny oval sacs of colourless fluid which contain dark-coloured discs arranged in columns. The darker blocks, called *grana,* contain the chlorophyll. The colourless fluid around them is known as *stroma.* The stroma carries all the catalysts and intermediates for making carbohydrates, once the chlorophyll provides the energy to do so.

A single granum looks remarkably like a pile of coins. Imagine we can lift off a single 'coin' (actually called a *lamella*) and look closer. Each lamella consists of several layers; some are made of protein, some of fatty substances called lipids, and some of chlorophyll and other pigments. The whole arrangement looks rather like a multi-decker sandwich, in which the protein and lipid layers correspond to the slices of bread and the pigments are spread thinly over them to provide the fillings.

Now let us consider what happens when light strikes the surface of a leaf. Straight away about one-third of it either bounces off again or passes right through. And most of the remaining two-thirds is converted into heat. Only about 4 per cent of the light actually gets absorbed by the chlorophyll.

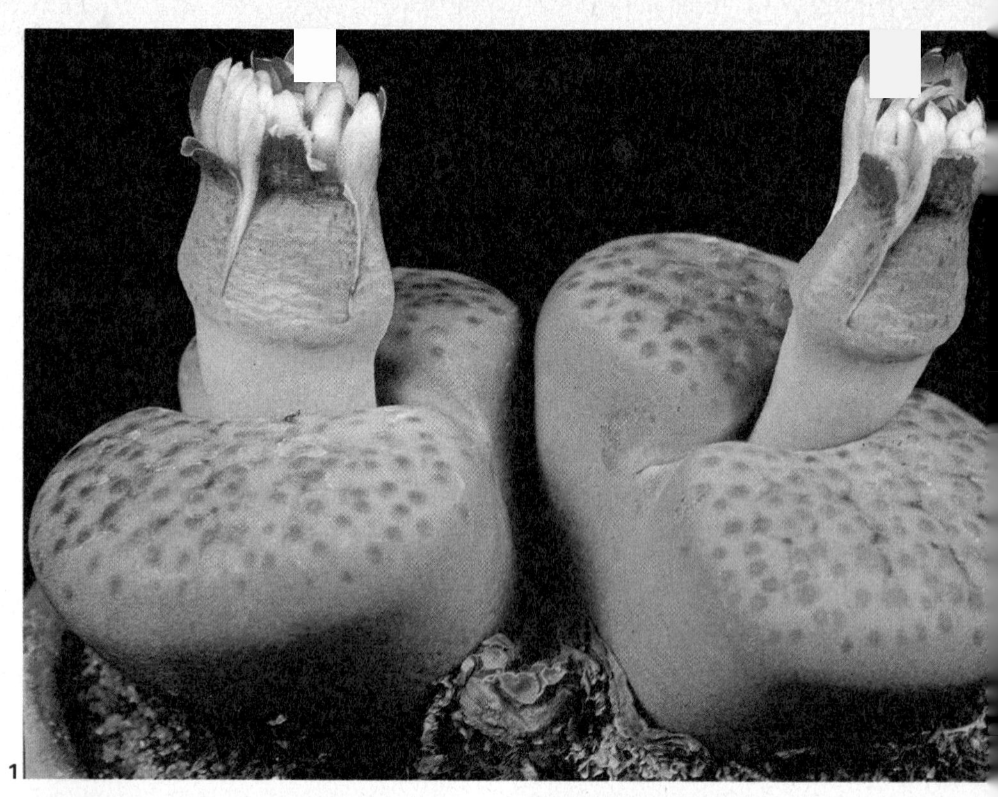

1

2

3

But as soon as light hits the chlorophyll, things start to happen. Certain electrons in the chlorophyll molecules are particularly sensitive to light. They absorb the energy, become 'excited', and leave the chlorophyll molecules. The excited electrons, rich in energy, induce two important reactions: one is the formation of ATP from ADP (ATP is the compound in which living things store energy released by cell reactions), and the other reaction is the splitting of water molecules into hydrogen and oxygen. The oxygen escapes as a by-product. But the hydrogen is valuable to the plant and is rapidly picked up by molecules of a hydrogen acceptor called *triphosphopyridine nucleotide* ($TPN^-$, for short).

The ordered architecture of the chloroplast grana is related to these energy-transfer reactions. Excited electrons would simply fall back into the chlorophyll molecules if there was nothing close at hand to pass on their energy to, and as a result, their energy would be wasted. This leaves us with another question: where does the chlorophyll get its supply of electrons from? If it were not constantly re-stocked, it would soon run out of electrons and photosynthesis would stop. One suggestion is that chlorophyll gets its electrons from ionized water. Water dissociates feebly into $H^+$ ions and $OH^-$ (hydroxyl) ions. Electrons from the $OH^-$ ions are transferred to chlorophyll, and the OH radicals left, then condense to form water and oxygen.

Now that the ATP batteries of the chloroplasts have been re-charged and the plant has plenty of hydrogen on hand (as reduced TPN), they are ready for the next step, which is the reaction with carbon dioxide. Carbon dioxide gas filters into the leaf through small pores, called *stomata,* on its surface. The gas dissolves in water on cell boundaries and diffuses into the cell. Eventually, carbon dioxide enters the chloroplast, diffuses through the stroma and meets its acceptor molecule.

## From gas to sugar

The carbon dioxide acceptor is a substance called *ribulose 1:5 diphosphate.* It is a sugar molecule containing five carbon atoms, with a phosphate group on carbon atoms 1 and 5. In the presence of an

4

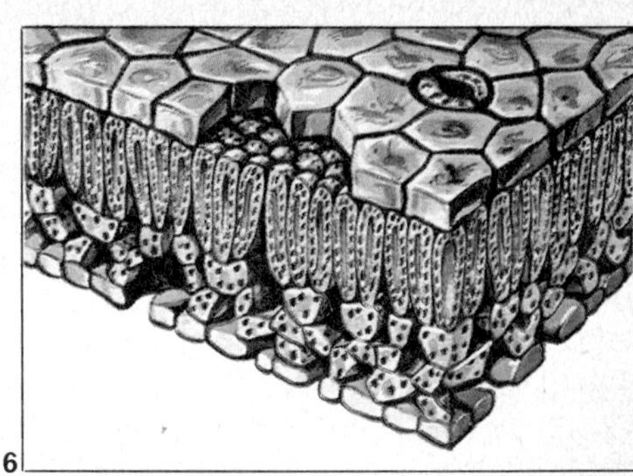

6

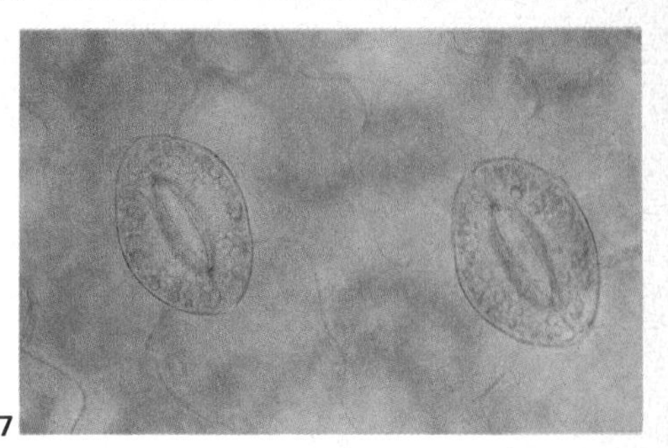

7

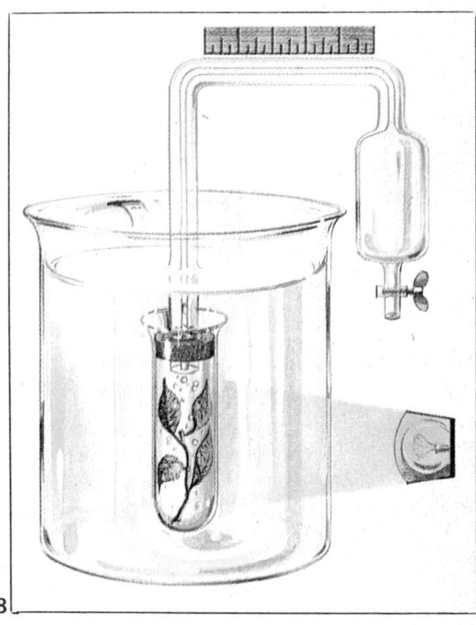

8

5

**1** Invisible among the pebbles in which it grows, this South African succulent plant has developed highly specialized leaves, but they function in the same way as the fronds of a fern, **2**, which have adapted to catch light in the shade of trees. **3** Fungi have no chlorophyll and cannot photosynthesize. They absorb organic matter derived from other living organisms. **4** To show that chlorophyll is necessary for photosynthesis, the leaf of a plant that has chlorophyll only in patches can be treated with iodine. The parts containing chlorophyll turn blue because they contain starch. The presence of starch is accepted as a proof of photosynthesis. **5** In autumn, leaves lose their chlorophyll, and other pigments are revealed. **6** In cross-section, a green leaf reveals four clearly defined layers: below the skin lies the palisade tissue containing many tiny oval sacs of colourless fluid called chloroplasts. These are able to turn within the cell, in order to take as much advantage of the light as they can, and recently scientists have discovered that even an isolated chloroplast can carry out the essential processes of photosynthesis, the making of sugars and release of oxygen. Below the palisade tissue lies spongy chlorophyll tissue. On both the upper and lower surfaces, apertures called 'stomata' allow gases to enter and leave. **7** Stomata of a lily leaf, viewed through a microscope. **8** A simple experiment with lamp and sealed tube demonstrates the release of oxygen that accompanies photosynthesis.

enzyme (catalyst), it reacts simultaneously with a molecule of carbon dioxide and a molecule of water. Some of its atoms undergo a rearrangement during this reaction. The whole molecule also splits in two, giving a two-carbon unit and a three-carbon unit. Carbon dioxide is tacked on to the broken end of the two-carbon piece. This results in two molecules of a three-carbon compound called *3-phosphoglyceric acid*. This acid is then reduced with the aid of an enzyme to *3-phosphoglyceraldehyde* by a reaction that needs a supply of hydrogen and energy to make it work. But the chloroplast is equal to this. It has a supply of ATP and reduced TPN, and the first supplies the energy and the second the hydrogen. One-sixth of the 3-phosphoglyceraldehyde formed is tapped off and converted to starch. The remaining five-sixths undergoes a lot of re-shuffling of its carbon atoms before ending up as ribulose-5-phosphate. Finally, with the help of ATP and the appropriate enzyme, ribulose-5-phosphate becomes ribulose 1:5 diphosphate, which is then again ready to pick up more carbon dioxide. This whole process is a cycle: carbon dioxide enters at one point and sugars come out at another. At the same time, the carbon dioxide acceptor is re-formed.

A few large leaves, or a host of small ones? Nature provides both means to provide her plants with the 'working surface' for photosynthesis.

## Packets of light

All this chemistry may be impressive because of its complexity, but is it particularly efficient? And just how useful is photosynthesis as a method of converting light energy into food energy? To answer these questions we need to know something about the physical nature of light.

Light is a form of radiant energy that travels in waves. Whenever a light wave hits something, however, it can be considered to behave as if it were composed of 'packets' of energy. Each 'packet', called a *quantum*, contains the same amount of energy, which is proportional to the frequency of the light. The important thing to remember is that quanta cannot be split into pieces. So that if a reaction needs a bit more than, say, six quanta, the object has to take in seven whole quanta of light energy even though most of the energy of the extra quantum is not needed.

We can calculate how much energy photosynthesis requires by carrying out the reverse process in the laboratory. If a sugar is burnt in oxygen, it changes completely into carbon dioxide and water. This reaction gives out a certain amount of energy, which can be accurately measured. This amount of energy must equal the amount that has to be put *in* during photosynthesis to make the reverse reaction work completely.

The amount of energy contained in a quantum of light can be calculated quite easily. In laboratory experiments, plants have been found to need between 8 and 12 quanta to make $CH_2O$ from $CO_2$. So although 8 to 12 quanta of light are absorbed, and seem to be necessary for the process, only a third to a quarter of this energy ends up in sugar. If 12 quanta are needed, the efficiency of photosynthesis (the energy appearing in sugars divided by the light energy absorbed) is less than 20 per cent. In more usual conditions, with plants growing in their natural environments, the efficiency may fall below 5 per cent.

All this may sound rather inefficient, but the world has a lot of plants growing in it. Every year, the weight of carbon captured by the world's vegetation totals between two and three hundred thousand million tons!

Green plants decompose water to get their hydrogen; at the same time they release essential oxygen into the atmosphere. A few kinds of bacteria also carry out photosynthesis, but they do not use water as a source of hydrogen. They use hydrogen sulphide, complex alcohols, or even hydrogen itself. In none of these cases is oxygen released. So we can see that before there were green plants carrying out photosynthesis, there was probably little or no free oxygen in the atmosphere. Living things had to rely on the process of fermentation to get their energy from digested foods. But a supply of free oxygen changed all that. It opened the door to the development of aerobic respiration – a major breakthrough in the evolution of living things.

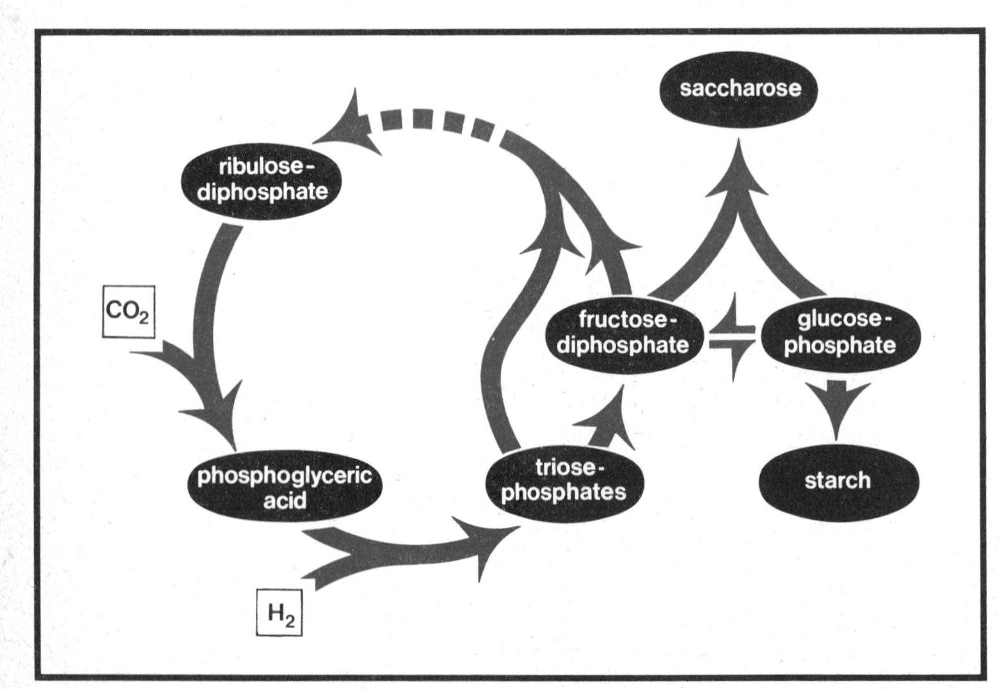


A flash of light energizes the creation of a molecule of glucose – the stages in the cycle of the metabolism of carbon in photosynthesis are rapid. By using radioactive carbon, an American chemist in 1939 found how the cycle worked. Its stages are shown, simplified, *above*.

# Under the greenwood tree

**Mosses and fungi, insects, reptiles, birds and mammals – all have a vital role in maintaining the closely related balance of the forest and woodland communities and ensuring that they continue.**

WOODLANDS CONSTITUTE a quarter of the surface of the Earth and there are over four acres of woodland for every person in the world. There is a wide variety of woodland and forest, from the huge tropical rain forests, which are evergreen and abound in different species, to the scrub-like forests of the cold temperate zone.

Woodlands appear, at first glance, to be static and permanent but they are, in fact, dynamic communities with constant change and turnover. Although the trees dominate in woodland life, they are only a part of an inter-relating community made up of many different organisms. This inter-relating is expressed most clearly in the energy cycles that develop in such communities and are themselves part of the overall energy cycle central to life as a whole on the Earth. Green plants (trees, mosses, ferns, grasses) are the basic organisms in the cycle as they are able to use solar energy. No energy is produced in the cycle without them. They convert the sun's energy by photosynthesis into biochemical energy. Other organisms are consumers that live only by virtue of the activities of the green plants. They form various levels of consumers depending on whether they are herbivores (first-level consumers), predators (second-level consumers) or carnivores (third-level consumers). Other organisms intervene in the cycle as parasites and decomposers (bacteria and fungi).

A badger sow leads her cub from the family den. Their diet of insects and small rodents means that they play an important part in rodent control – essential for forest regeneration.

Within the framework of this general energy cycle, woodlands can be seen to have great advantages for human society. One aspect of this is the enormous timber harvest of about 60,000 million cu. ft of timber. Man has discovered that not only can the forests and woodlands be chopped down for timber but they must also be replaced. As a result, forestry management has become a basic and vital branch of ecology.

Trees are the dominant form of life in woodlands and forests. Both in the energy cycle and the physical make-up of the forests, they provide the centre around which other life forms develop. In forming this centre, they also dictate to a certain extent what other forms of life can exist under their canopy. For example, *vertical stratification* (distinct layers of vegetation and animal life within a specific woodland) is much less complex in temperate than in tropical forests because of the types of trees that dominate and because of the conditions under which they grow.

## Conditions for growing

Trees are able to grow only under certain environmental conditions and this largely determines their general distribution over the Earth's surface. The mean temperature of the warmest month must be above 10 °C. (50 °F.) and the annual rainfall must be more than 10 in., for trees to grow. Within these limits many variations take place and many other factors come into play. Tropical conditions, because of the constant warmth, high rainfall and fertile soil, are abundant in trees of all varieties. Temperate conditions, which are variable within themselves, tend to allow the growth of much less vegetation and particular types of trees that are equipped to deal with the variable conditions. The deciduous woodlands are an example of this type of adaptation resulting in trees that shed their leaves in autumn in preparation for the cold winter.

Some trees are able to establish themselves and survive in very different ecological situations and are therefore very widely spread while others have a very restricted distribution. The effects of climate and soil on the distribution of a single tree can be shown by the example of the Sitka spruce. The species occurs only where there is an oceanic climate with equable temperatures, high rainfall and no extreme cold or excess cloudiness. Its natural range is, therefore, a distinct belt along the Pacific coast of North America, from Alaska to California for 1,800 miles. This belt is never wider than 130 miles. Within this general range, the spruce occupies mainly west-facing slopes and the height (above sea level) at which it grows varies according to latitude. Therefore, in northern Alaska, the Sitka spruce is only found in a narrow coastal strip, in southeastern Alaska it reaches higher altitudes, in British Columbia it is found lower down again (below 1,000 ft) and at its southernmost limit in California it is again confined to a narrow coastal strip. Variations in volume of timber

One of the nocturnal woodland animals is the carnivorous American racoon. Almost as much at home in the trees as the squirrel, it has a curious habit of apparently washing its food.

occur throughout its range, the maximim being where the soil is deep and medium textured, rich in organic material and well drained.

The example of the Sitka spruce shows the general factors which dominate tree distribution. In the temperate woodland, coniferous trees (spruces, *Picea,* pines, *Pinus,* firs, *Abies,* these are evergreens; the larch, *Larix,* is deciduous) with needle-like leaves dominate the northern sector from 45th to the 70th parallels of the northern latitudes. These trees are able to withstand the very cold winters that occur in this sector. The coastal forests of the Pacific coast of North America, are an example of variation within the general conditions of the northern coniferous forest. Here the climate is milder and moist and such giants as the coastal redwood, *Sequoia sempervirens,* the big redwood, *S. wellingtonia,* and the Douglas fir, *Pseudotsuga taxifolia,* grow.

Southwards in the temperate woodland, the trees pass into deciduous forests mainly made up of hardwoods. Rainfall in these areas is fairly even throughout the year (28 to 60 in.), woodlands are fairly simple and few tree species are present. The sessile oaks, *Quercus petraea:* the pedunculate oak, *Q. robur;* the ash, *Fraxinus excelsior;* the beech, *Fagus sylvatica;* and the lime, *Tilia cordata,* are the trees that dominate the deciduous forests of central and western Europe.

Trees within their local community also show differences which are related to their genetics or stock. It has been possible to breed hybrids and particularly strong trees adapted to certain types of environment.

All these many factors affect the dominant type of tree in a particular woodland and have an effect on the rest of the life forms in the woodland community.

Many kinds of flora besides trees occur in woodland communities and they may be present in all woodland strata and take on many life forms. Some of the factors affecting tree growth may equally affect the other flora and the trees themselves dictate certain conditions under which the other plants must live.

## Regional conditions

Broad geographical differences mean that whereas certain types of shrubs thrive in the northern coniferous forests they are unable to grow in the tropical rain forests. Within these broad differences, regional differences occur which result from soil changes, whether or not the trees fully block out the light and other factors. In England, for example, oak woodlands on clay soil have an increasing proportion of ash present as the soil becomes more calcareous. As a result, there is an increase in the number of calcicolous shrubs and herbs such as privet, spindle, wayfaring tree, and wild basil. These shrubs are almost absent in oak woods growing on acid clay.

**1** A brilliantly coloured 'orange-peel elf-cup fungus, growing from the stump of a dead tree. It is typical of the decomposers which help in the disintegration of organic matter.

**2** The male stag beetle, easily identified by its enormous antler-like mandibles. The larvae live in rotting wood and are an important food source for other woodland animals.

**3** The wild boar has been hunted for centuries until it is now a rarity. Such interference with flora and fauna can lead to serious imbalance in the woodland 'cycle'.

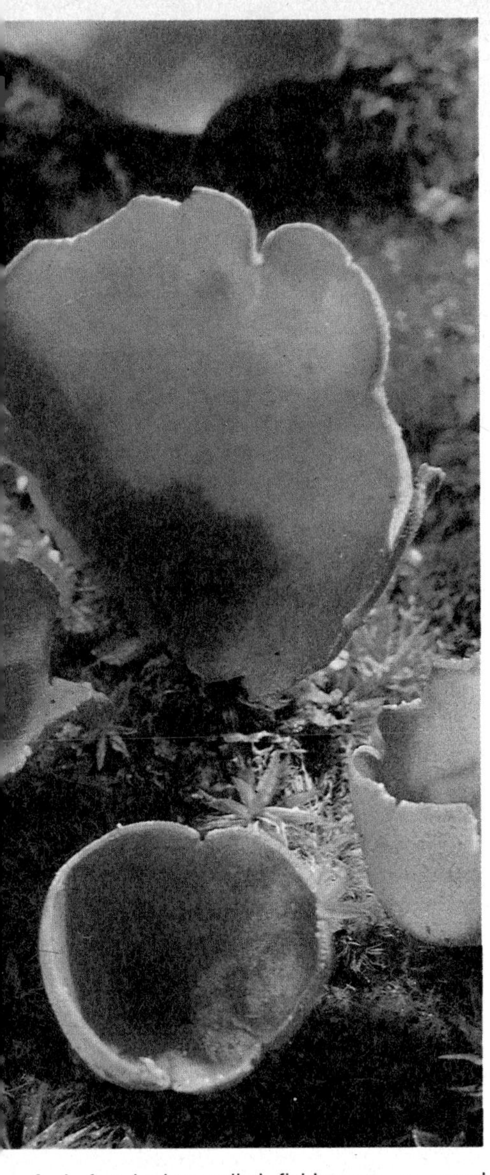

For plant growth under the tree cover to be luxuriant and various, there must be adequate light. Also the species of tree under which different plants will grow seems to be important. For example, in controlled trials at Thetford Chase Forest in England, it was found that under the alder, birch and larch trees, the commonest plants are stinging nettle, *Urtica dioica;* the grasses, *Holcus lanatus, Agrostis tenuis* and *Festuca ovina;* and bracken, *Pteridium aquilinum.* It was found that no field layer grew under the pine and fir trees.

Other factors affecting under-storey plant growth are the area in which the tree is growing and seasonal factors. In the English woodlands, the bluebell is abundant in the early spring before the tree and shrub buds have opened but is present at no other time of the year.

Apart from plants growing in the soil surrounding the trees, many grow on the trees as parasites or grow on aerial parts of the tree but get no sustenance from it as such. Fungi grow mainly on dead trees but can be found on living trees. Spanish moss is not a parasite but is completely dependent on the tree to give it a position in which it can get adequate light. Many different types of climbers occur and they tend to favourite trees. These plants have their own roots but use the trees to get their leaves into favourable positions for photosynthesis. Typical temperate forest climbers are poison ivy in North America and ivy in Europe. Field and shrub layers

1 A female long-tailed fieldmouse, or wood mouse, with her family. It lives in fields, woods or gardens, and burrows and hoards. The long tail is a distinctive feature.

2 The crossbill lives in the coniferous forests of Europe and North America where it picks open cones and eats the seeds. Such birds have an important function as dispersers of seeds.

3 A wood-boring wasp, or greater horntail; the female deposits her eggs in the wood by means of her long ovipositor. Insects can cause havoc to crops and forestation.

of tropical forests are often sparse whilst lianes are abundant, draping around trees and spreading through the forest canopy. There is a huge variety of woodland flora, ranging from shrubs to grasses, mosses, ferns and fungi. They live in conditions dominated by the trees, climate, soil and rainfall.

The woodland habitat with all its variety provides unlimited scope for different kinds of insects to live.

They are dominated by a number of factors in the forest. The climate, the rainfall, the tree types and their distribution are important in determining a particular woodland community. Many insects, however, are extremely adaptable and are consequently found under many different conditions.

There is an extremely complex relationship between plants and insects. While some woodland insects feed on a wide range of plants, others are restricted to plants of a single species. Also some plants, are more resistant to insects than others as a result of many different factors. Weevils feed on many different plants whereas many of the 200 species of insect that are closely associated with the oak tree, only feed on oak. The spruce gall aphids are confined to conifers and have a complicated life cycle which involves five different generations of host trees.

## Insect relationships

There is also a complicated relationship between different species of insect. One species often depends for its survival on the activities of others. As logs or tree stumps rot, different insects invade at different times. One species invades and prepares the decomposing stump for the next species which is likely to be less specialized. Many species may carry on their activities alongside each other.

Insects have an important role in woodland life. They are among the decomposers and, with fungi and the weather, bring about the disintegration of organic matter so that new nutrients come available in the soil for further plant growth. Insects also represent an essential link in the food chain for some woodland birds and mammals depend on insects as their main food supply. Insects assist the pollination of many plants; for example, the lime tree has flowers which are pollinated by insects.

On the other hand, insects can equally play a destructive role. Defoliation, feeding on barks and roots, and boring into living woods, are some of the ways in which insects can create havoc to trees.

Birds play an important role in woodland life and, as with insects, are many and varied in species. Birds function as dispersers of seeds, as controllers of harmful insects and as limiters of rodent damage. Preservation of certain species, such as the kite and goshawk in Britain, has become an important human activity which not only preserves the birds as attractive features of the woodland but as essential parts of the natural balance.

Many factors determine the species of birds present in particular woodlands. The age and species of tree in the forest and the availability of particular kinds of food also affect animal life. Factors which are specific for birds are the size and shape of the woodland in the general landscape, the form of the forest margin and the proportion of open space to dense wood. The presence of adequate under-storey shelter, nesting sites, food supply and the amount of dead wood present are all influential.

In many woods the species which colonize them change as the wood itself matures. This was illustrated in the heaths of Breckland in England which were originally dominated by heath birds such as the skylark, stonechat, wheatear and the yellow wagtail. When the heaths were planted with pines, after seven to ten years the bird population had begun to change and new species, such as the chaffinch, the hedge-sparrow and the song-thrush, moved in. Fifteen years later, the heath birds had completely gone and typical woodland species, the goldcrest, the coal titmouse, the great titmouse, the robin and others, had taken over. Seasonal factors are also important in determining the species present at a given time. Many birds migrate from the temperate climates during the winter, but others are adapted to the conditions and are able to stay and adequately survive.

Mammalian life in the woodlands has been changed more than any other by the intervention of Man. Many of the mammals in forests, particularly the large mammals and the carnivorous ones, have been made extinct by hunting over a period of centuries. This has probably led to many disadvantages. For example, these mammals play an important part in rodent control and this would have led to more abundant natural regeneration if they had been allowed to remain in their natural quantities.

Mammalian life in the forests ranges from the small rodents, such as moles, through monkeys to the huge bears of the coniferous forests of the north. Mammals are noted for their destructive role; tree bark is eaten by rabbits, squirrels, porcupines and moose; trees are debarked by deer rubbing the velvet off their antlers. However, without them, the forest could not function. The main problem is the maintenance of a balance between herbivores and carnivores and between them and the rest of the community.

It can be seen that woodland life is an extremely complex relationship between different living organisms and between them and the environment. From the smallest soil organism to the largest mammal, they all have their role and are important to the natural balance in the forest.

1

2

3

1 The red squirrel lives off seeds, nuts and tree bark. It is often destructive and like most rodents, will hoard far beyond its needs. The thick bushy tail acts as a natural rudder.

2 Although it has been severely hunted the American black bear is now given protection in national parks. Weighing up to 500 lb., he is a born and agile climber.

3 The great spotted woodpecker clings to the tree trunk with its legs, using its stiff tail feathers as extra support. In this position it hammers away at the bark to extract insect larvae.

# Green factories in the ground

On foot or on the wing, the animal world can forage for its prey. Rooted to the spot, how have green plants solved the problem that all living things share – the endless quest for food?

A study in contrast – streamlined fish, able to streak through the water at lightning speed, are backed by a plant firmly anchored to the soil, with leaves spread to catch precious sunlight.

ONE OF the most obvious differences between animals and plants is that nearly all animals can move and plants can not. The basic reason for this lies in their methods of feeding. Most plants can make all their own foods on the spot; animals cannot do this, and so they have to go and find their food.

Once an organism has to move to survive, its body needs all sorts of extra 'apparatus', and it is these extras that make animals so different from plants. Animals need legs, fins or wings. They need muscles to power their bodies and nerves to control their muscles. They need finely-tuned sense organs to locate their food, and streamlined bodies which move quickly once food is in reach.

A typical plant shows none of these features – no legs, no eyes, no muscles. And as for streamlining, a plant is the very opposite to most animals in this respect; bits and pieces stick out in all directions. Think of a tree: above the ground, branches fan out into the air exposing the leaves to the sun. Below the ground, a network of roots pushes through the soil to absorb water, nitrogen salts and a variety of other minerals necessary for healthy growth.

It makes sense for a plant to have many branches – above and below ground. Any organism that relies on raw materials from its immediate surroundings does well to tap as many parts of its environment as it can. So plants are just as well adapted for *their* ways of feeding as animals are for theirs. Let us consider some plants in more detail and find out why they are so successful.

## Manufactured energy

Plants rely on photosynthesis to make foods that are rich in energy. When these foods are broken down chemically, some of the energy they release is used to drive synthetic processes to make such things as proteins, nucleic acids and fats. Photosynthesis takes place almost entirely in a plant's leaves, and it is not surprising to find that a green leaf is very well equipped for the task. (This task is to make carbohydrates from carbon dioxide and water, with the aid of chlorophyll activated by sunlight.)

Consider the leaf of an oak tree or a beech tree: it is broad and flat. Its large surface catches a lot of light, and light is essential for photosynthesis. The upper surface is bright green, whereas the lower surface is paler in colour. This shows that most of the chlorophyll is concentrated near the upper surface – the surface that receives most light. If we turn the leaf over, we see that the leaf stalk (called the *petiole*) extends into a midrib or main vein. The midrib runs the length of the leaf and has a number of branches. Veins are bundles of pipe-lines; some of these pipelines bring water and mineral salts into the leaf, others carry sugars out. In addition, the leaf surface is dotted with tiny pores called *stomata*. They open in the light and close in darkness. Carbon dioxide enters the leaf through these pores whenever they are open.

If we look at a magnified cross-section of a leaf, we will be able to put all these features together and see why a leaf is so good at its job. The whole leaf is wrapped

1

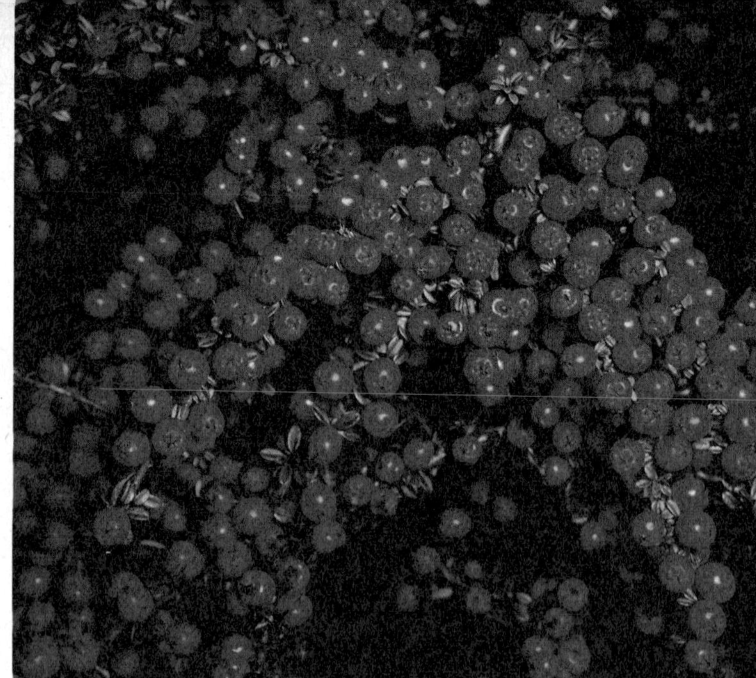

2

3

in a sheet of surface tissue one cell thick. This layer is called the *epidermis*. Usually, a thin continuous coating of a waxy substance called cutin covers the epidermis. Cutin does not let water through and in this way prevents the broad surface of the leaf from losing water at a much faster rate than the tree could afford.

The cutin layer and the epidermis are interrupted here and there by a pair of thick-walled *guard cells* which guard the entrance to the stomatal pores.

Since the pores make up about only one-hundredth of the leaf's surface area, we might wonder how the plant gets sufficient carbon dioxide by this supply route. But it so happens that stomata are very efficient. If it were possible to collect together all the stomata from one leaf and make out of them one large pore, we would find that the single pore would not collect carbon dioxide at anything like the same rate. By having a porous surface spread over a large area, plants have evolved a remarkably efficient method for getting carbon dioxide out of the air.

As well as letting carbon dioxide *into* the leaf, stomata are also efficient at letting water vapour *out*. Water is supplied to the leaf by cells in the veins. The veins pass back through the petiole and down the stem of the plant, almost to the tips of the roots. Water absorbed by the roots is fed into the lower ends of these pipe-lines. When a leaf requires water, it sets up a pressure difference which pulls water up the stem and through the petiole.

## A network of pipe-lines

The main vein of a leaf divides again and again into finer and finer branches, so that a network permeates the leaf tissue. The surfaces of the cells are wet and so the air spaces in the leaf are saturated with water vapour. As a result, water vapour leaks out through the stomata whenever they are open. On a particularly dry and windy day, the rate of loss of water may be so great that the roots cannot supply water fast enough. The leaf continues to lose water until it wilts. Then the guard cells clamp together, shutting off the water escape valves to prevent irreparable damage to the plant. At the same time, of course, carbon dioxide is shut out and photosynthesis stops, but this cannot be avoided. Under more usual conditions, the loss of water is an advantage. It ensures that water continues to pass into the roots, taking with it a constant supply of essential mineral salts.

Making sugars is the job of the chloroplasts, found in two kinds of cells within the leaf. Most of the chloroplasts lie in a group of cells called *palisade cells* set just beneath the upper epidermis. The epidermis is only a protective tissue; it contains no chloroplasts and readily admits light. If we liken a leaf to a food factory run on light energy, the epidermis corresponds to the transparent roof. Palisade cells are oblong in shape and stand upright in two neat rows, one above the other. Chloroplasts are also found, in fewer numbers, in irregularly shaped cells called *mesophyll*

4

**Legs, arms, fins and wings – animals need these to survive, but plants feed on the spot.**

**1** The leaves of this forest giant are all near the top to obtain sufficient light for photosynthesis; for its base is nearly always hidden in shadow. **2** Full to bursting point with rich supplies of food, these scarlet berries could only form from stores already manufactured by the plant. **3** Since the centre of a tree trunk is solid wood, new growth has to take place on the outside. The young growing cells are protected by a layer of dead, corky ones known as the bark or *phellem*. **4** Leaves of the water-lily, *Victoria Amazonica*, float on a pond, the whole of their face devoted to catching the maximum amount of sunlight. **5** Plants like leeks and dandelions must ensure that each one of the developing seeds on their crowded heads has an adequate supply of food to ensure the survival of individual embryos. **6** Even poppy seeds have enough food stored to regenerate successfully after the long dormant periods which can follow their scattering.

5

6

*cells*, which extend from below the palisade cells to the lower epidermis. It is clear then that a leaf is perfectly adapted for making food. Light floods in and bathes the chloroplasts in the palisade and mesophyll cells; carbon dioxide and water enter freely through the stomata and veins.

## From starches to sugars

To prevent sugars accumulating during photosynthesis, the chloroplasts condense them into starch, which takes the form of tiny white grains. Under a powerful microscope, the starch grains can be seen in the chloroplasts of a leaf which has been in the light for some time. Starch is a food for the plant (as it is for many animals) and can be broken down to yield energy. Although a leaf itself needs some energy to make new proteins, to manufacture new cell walls, and to replace worn or damaged tissues, it could never on its own use all the starch it accumulates through photosynthesis. Yet after a period of darkness, all the starch disappears from the leaf. It has been packed off down the pipe-lines to the rest of the plant.

The roots, for example, are in constant darkness and contain no chlorophyll, and they have to be supplied with nourishment. Also the growing points of the stems use up energy at a tremendous rate and they need food all the time. Developing seeds also need a stock of food in them so that their embryos can get a good start in life. And perennial plants, which die down in winter, must have plenty of food for fresh growth the following spring.

Sugars are not carried around in the form of starch. Moving bulky, insoluble grains of starch is a feat that even plants cannot manage. What most plants do is to mobilize the starch by changing it into *sucrose* (cane sugar) and to send the food on its way in this form. When the sucrose gets to its destination, it is either used up to provide energy, or is reconverted into starch and stored.

Roots are just as important for feeding a plant as are the leaves. They absorb water from the soil through a mass of tiny, filamentous root hairs which stick out from the root just behind the tip. In moist soil, there is more water in a given volume of soil outside the root hair than there is in the same volume of cells inside. For this reason, water tends to enter the root hairs to restore the balance. Once inside the root, the water is taken to the pipe-lines and drawn up the stem.

But roots absorb more than water from the soil. They also take up mineral salts in the form of electrically charged particles called *ions*. These ions are dissolved in the water of the soil. Plants need a whole variety of chemical elements for proper growth. They need nitrogen to make protein, calcium for their cell walls, and phosphorus for many of their reactions. They also need other elements such as potassium, sulphur, iron, magnesium, cobalt, boron, copper, zinc, molybdenum and manganese. For example, magnesium is part of the chlorophyll molecule and sulphur is contained in certain proteins.

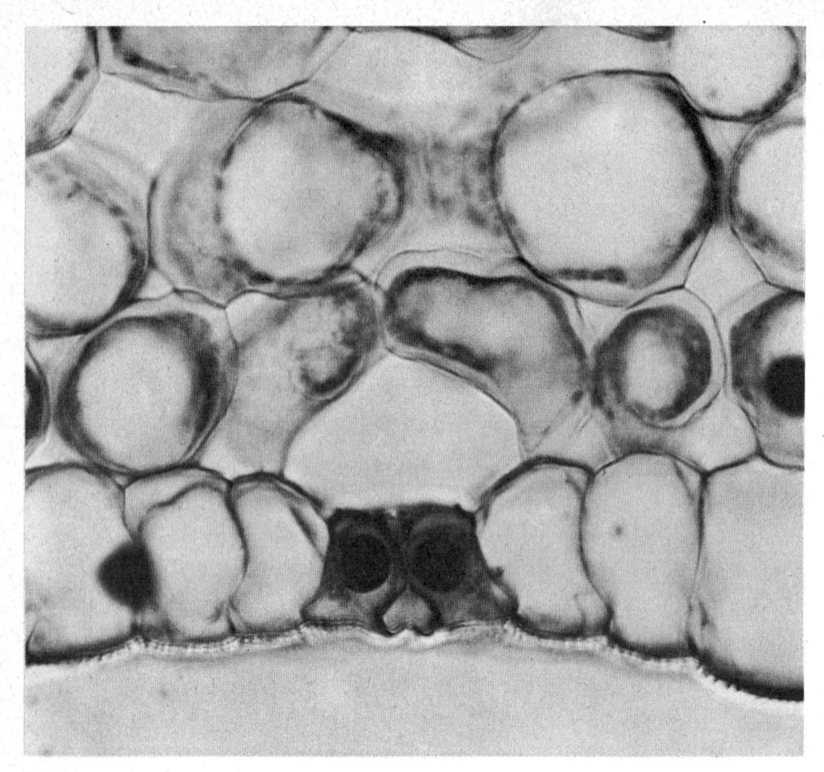

The small, mouth-like opening on the edge of this section through a leaf is a single stoma, which opens in daylight to admit carbon dioxide, *left.* At night, when photosynthesis ceases, the stoma shuts in order to prevent water loss, which in turn slows down the movement of the sap.

Lumpy nodules, clumped together on a lupin's roots, contain millions of bacteria which convert nitrogen into proteins for their host's use, *right.*

Most of the other elements are needed as activators of enzymes – the biological catalysts that speed up reactions in cells.

Elements such as zinc and molybdenum are needed in such minute amounts, that biologists did not recognize their importance until quite recently. In early experiments on plants to find out which elements were essential for healthy growth, the tiny traces of impurities in the chemicals used were enough to supply the plant with all the zinc and molybdenum they needed.

## The fabric of life

Of all the chemical elements needed by a plant, none is more important than nitrogen. Nitrogen is a component atom of all amino acids, which are linked together in long chains to make proteins. And proteins are the fabric of living organisms and life is impossible without them.

Nitrogen is abundant in the air; it makes up 78 per cent of it. Yet very few organisms can capture nitrogen from the air and convert it directly into proteins. The vast majority of the plant kingdom has to find some other way. Green plants solve the problem by capturing nitrogen compounds from the soil through their roots. Nitrogen is available in the soil as nitrates, nitrites and ammonium salts. But before we go any further, we must describe how they get there.

Nitrogen is made available to green plants by the combined actions of various kinds of soil micro-organisms. Certain kinds of soil bacteria and blue-green algae are able to *fix* (incorporate) nitrogen gas into proteins. When these organisms – and any plants and animals – die, other bacteria act on their remains and break them down to release the energy they contain. During this process, the proteins in them are converted into ammonium salts. Ammonium salts are themselves foods for other kinds of bacteria, which oxidize them to nitrites and nitrates.

Plants belonging to the pea family, including such plants as clover, lupin, lucerne grass, beans and vetch, have evolved the very useful device of housing nitrogen-fixing bacteria in their roots. Bacteria in the soil invade the plants through root hairs and penetrate right inside the root. The root reacts to the invasion by swelling up around the region occupied by the bacteria. These little swellings, called *nodules,* can easily be seen on the roots of lucerne grass or clover. The bacteria in the nodules fix nitrogen gas, converting it into simple nitrogen compounds and eventually into proteins, and the plant helps itself to this convenient supply. In exchange, the bacteria are housed and are fed with sugars made by the plant.

Most plants are not so fortunate, however, and have to make their own proteins. They absorb their nitrogen from the soil mainly in the form of nitrate ions. Once inside the roots, the nitrate ions are converted to nitrites and then to ammonia. But how is the nitrogen eventually made into plant proteins?

## How proteins are formed

Proteins are enormous chain-molecules built up from huge numbers of small units called *amino acids.* The properties of a protein – the kinds of things it will do in a cell – depend on the kinds of amino acids it has in its molecule and on the precise order of these acids in the protein chain. A plant cell can make any protein it needs by collecting together the amino acids necessary for its construction. The amino acids are then joined in the exact sequence needed to make a protein with the desired properties.

To produce proteins, the plant must first make the amino acids. It does this by using the products of respiration. During respiration, sugars are degraded in small steps through a long series of complex reactions to carbon dioxide and water. In the course of these reactions, a number of compounds called organic acids are formed. One of these, *alpha-ketoglutaric acid,* is particularly important to plants because it can combine with ammonia. Ammonia gets tacked on to a molecule of alpha-ketoglutaric acid and this changes it into an amino acid called *glutamic acid.* Then the ammonia – or as it now is the amino group ($NH_2$) of glutamic acid – is transferred to the organic acids *oxaloacetic acid* and *pyruvic acid* to form the amino acids *aspartic acid* and *alanine.* At the same time, alpha-ketoglutaric acid is reformed and made available to combine with more ammonia. This mechanism leads biologists to believe that perhaps other amino acids originate from similar transfers of $NH_2$ from glutamic acid to suitable organic acids.

Whatever the exact process, the green plant has developed an excellent system for collecting nitrogen and combining it to make all the amino acids and proteins it needs. Compared to animals, these plants are often considered to be dull and uninteresting. But as frequently happens in nature, simplicity and elegance go hand in hand. Animals are much more impressive because they can move, and hunt or forage for their nourishment. But they do so only because they must in order to keep alive. The ability to synthesize its own nitrogen compounds and to produce its own sugars helps to explain a green plant's unique form and structure, and provides the basic reason for its sedentary way of life. A plant has no need to hunt for food, or to be hunted. There is no reason why it should move – so it doesn't.

# Lifelines of a plant

**From earth and air, the raw materials of a plant's food travel to the leaves for synthesis and out again to nourish the tissues. What transport system carries this essential traffic?**

TO REMAIN ALIVE, any animal or plant organism must have a constant supply of tissue-building and energy-yielding substances. The energy needed for these vital processes is obtained from the oxidative breakdown of various carbon-containing compounds, the most common of which are carbohydrates (such as glucose and starch) and fatty acids.

The oxidation of these food substances takes place in the cell. It is a complicated series of reactions involving enzymes and co-enzymes. The net result is the formation of adenosine triphosphate (ATP). ATP is an energy-storing compound; when energy is needed it is broken down with the aid of enzymes to produce adenosine diphosphate (ADP), liberating phosphate. Most vital processes use up a great amount of ATP and an organism must constantly replace it.

Animals and saprophytic and parasitic plants get their sources of energy by absorbing organic foods from their surroundings. Green plants, some bacteria and a few protozoan animals are able to convert inorganic materials directly into complex organic compounds resembling the foodstuffs of animals by the process of photosynthesis, which utilizes the energy obtainable from the sun.

## Transport system

The raw materials from which the plants manufacture their sugars, fats and proteins are obtained in a variety of ways. Carbon dioxide is obtained from the air through the pores of leaves and occasionally through stems. Water, containing such essential elements as nitrogen, potassium, calcium, magnesium, iron, phosphorus, and sulphur in solution, is obtained through roots.

The synthesis of complex organic compounds from these inorganic substances generally occurs in the leaves of a plant. For it to work, the plant needs a transport system to convey the substances from the roots to the leaves. A transport system is also necessary to distribute the synthesized products from the leaves back to the tissues of the plant where they will be needed.

The most common product of photosynthesis is the sugar glucose. In leaves, glucose is converted into insoluble starch, which the plant uses as a storage product. If glucose formation is rapid, it is almost immediately converted into starch. But at night (when photosynthesis stops), or in other conditions, such as a drought, when sugar synthesis ceases or occurs very slowly, the starch is reconverted with the aid of enzymes into glucose. This glucose is then transported to the various plant tissues.

Many plants are capable of storing large amounts of starch and other food substances. In times of need, this starch is reconverted into glucose.

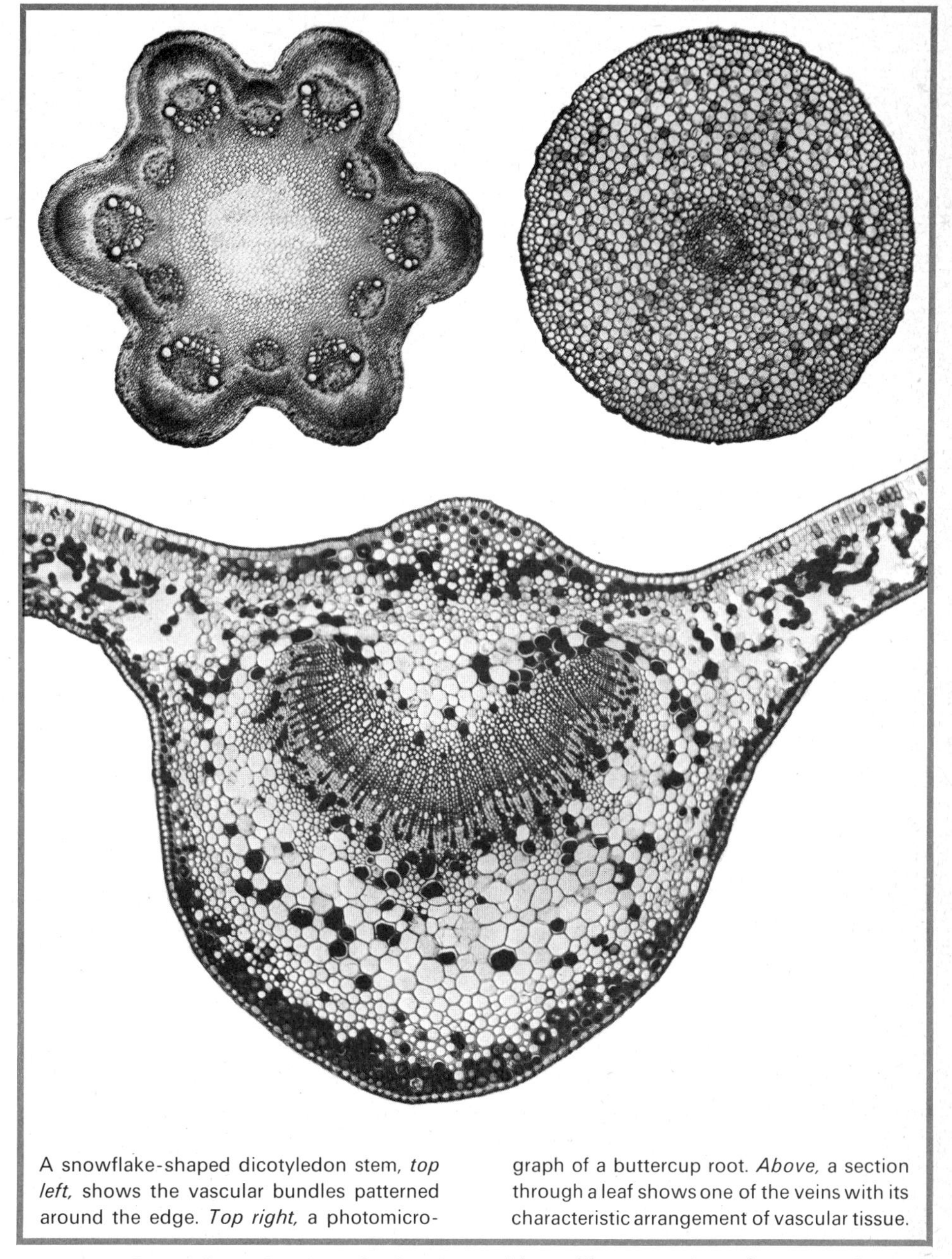

A snowflake-shaped dicotyledon stem, *top left,* shows the vascular bundles patterned around the edge. *Top right,* a photomicrograph of a buttercup root. *Above,* a section through a leaf shows one of the veins with its characteristic arrangement of vascular tissue.

The transport system has, therefore, to connect the various organs of a plant. In this respect it can be compared to the blood transport system in animals.

Not all plants have a transport system. Most seaweeds and other algae, and fungi, have no true transport system. In mosses and liverworts, there is either no transport system, or at best a very simple one.

The transporting system of more complicated plants, known collectively as *tracheophyta*, is also known as the *vascular* system, and the parts of the system as vascular tissue. Vascular tissue is composed of two well-defined structural and functional tissues known as the *xylem* and *phloem*. These run from the roots, through the stem, and into such structures as the buds, branches and leaves. The veins of a leaf are the upper extremities of the vascular system.

The vascular tissue often forms a complete ring of tissue, although there are numerous variations. For example, the ring may be split into a series of separate vascular bundles.

In a young plant, the system is referred to as the primary vascular system. And in many plants, especially the dicotyledons (plants with two seed-leaves), it is augmented by the formation of a secondary vascular system.

Xylem transports sap from the cells. It also gives a certain amount of structural support to the stem. The two most common elements of xylem tissue are cells called the *tracheid* and the *vessel,* which have thick walls and no living protoplasm. Both elements are not necessarily present in all plants.

The mature vessels form a long, open pipe-line. Intervening cross-walls have holes in them, and are referred to as *perforation plates,* which allow water to pass from one vessel to the next. The vessels are connected sideways by pits, which may be regarded as gaps in the cell wall where only a thin membrane remains. Pits nearly always occur in pairs, so that the pit of one cell wall is adjacent to the pit in the neighbouring cell wall. The pit membrane is also permeable to water.

## Sieve cells

The tracheids are more elongated than the vessels. They have tapering edges that dovetail with other tracheids to give intercommunication.

The xylem also has fibres, *scleroids* and parenchyma cells. The fibres and scleroids are elongated cells with thick walls. They are concerned solely with strengthening the plant, and take no part in water conduction. The xylem parenchyma cells can occur singly or in radial strands (called medullary rays), and they do contribute to the conduction of cell sap.

The phloem is also a composite tissue, and is normally associated with the xylem. The basic structure is called a *sieve element,* of which there may be two kinds. Sieve cells occur individually and resemble the tracheids of the xylem, and the more complex sieve-tube elements join together lengthways to form a sieve tube.

The cell wall between the sieve elements is thin and depressed; this is known as the sieve area. It contains a number of pores through which, according to one theory, run strands of cytoplasm known as *plasmodesmata.* In this way, each sieve element is thought to be connected to the next. But there is some controversy regarding these plasmodesmata; many workers have claimed that they do not exist.

Sieve elements possess an outer layer of cytoplasm, but when mature they lack a nucleus. The cell vacuole is composed of a viscous substance called slime, which is believed to consist of protein.

Associated with the sieve tubes (but not the sieve cells) are highly specialized parenchyma cells called *companion* cells. They develop from the same cells as do the sieve-tube members. They contain dense cytoplasm with a nucleus, and communicate with the sieve tubes by means of plasmodesmata. They are not found in all higher plants.

The xylem is concerned with the transport of water and dissolved ions (cell sap) from the roots to the leaves. There is no transport in the opposite direction through the xylem.

Water is obtained both actively and passively through the root hairs. They provide a large surface area for the uptake of water through the root. Rapid root growth is essential to rapid absorption of water. For example, it has been estimated that a growing rye plant develops more than three miles of new roots and 55 miles of root hairs per day.

Passive absorption of water results from transpiration of water out of the leaf surfaces. Water evaporates from the walls of the mesophyll cells, and more water is drawn from the adjacent protoplasm to replace it. This, in turn, takes water from the vacuole and adjoining cells. The movement of water from adjacent cells works back to the xylem vessels in the veins of the leaf. As a result, a column of water is drawn up through the xylem.

The action of lifting water is opposed by its own weight. This brings about a state of tension which is increased by the resistance of the xylem vessels and tracheids, and by the resistance of the cell walls

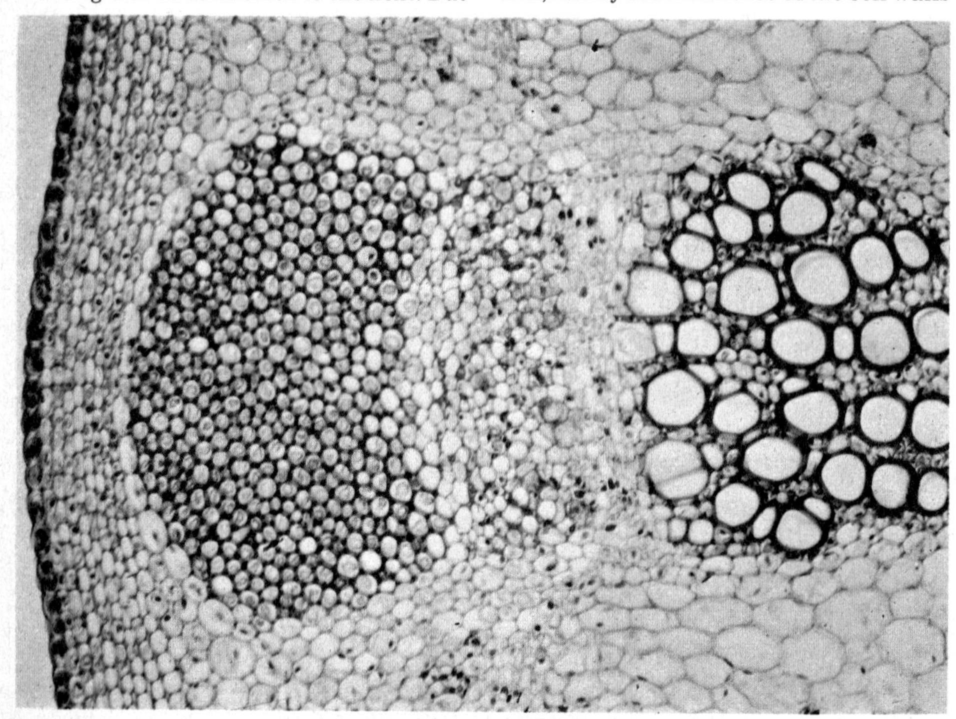

A close-up look at a vascular bundle in a sunflower stem. The large xylem cells, *right,* are part of the water transport system. The phloem cells, *left,* are arranged into elongated sieve-tubes with large vacuoles for the transport of food produced in the leaves by photosynthesis.

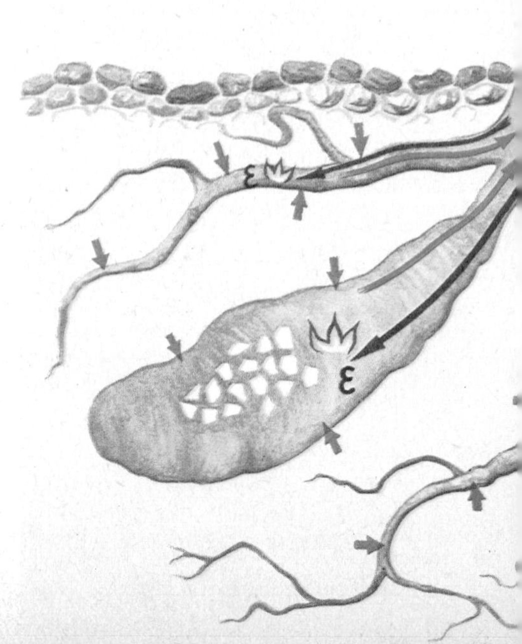

Apparently placid on the outside, inside a plant is a bustle of activity, absorbing water, transporting minerals, exchanging ions, oxidizing glucose, inhaling carbon dioxide, exhaling oxygen, repairing cells, and generally doing a whole host of things needed to keep itself alive and healthy. Arrows show the leaf taking in carbon dioxide from the air for use in photosynthesis and giving out both water vapour and oxygen as by-products. The system of roots plays its part by absorbing water and minerals. The white crystals in the leaf are starch, those in the root are sugar. The flames indicate oxidation, or energy release, the red and green arrows show transportation, the 'E' means enzymes.

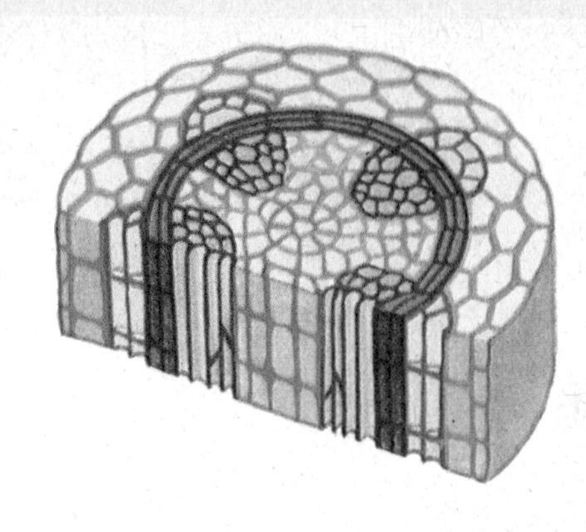

Woody xylem tissue is rare in the stem of fleshy plants. The ring-like arrangement of the vascular bundles provides both flexibility and strength.

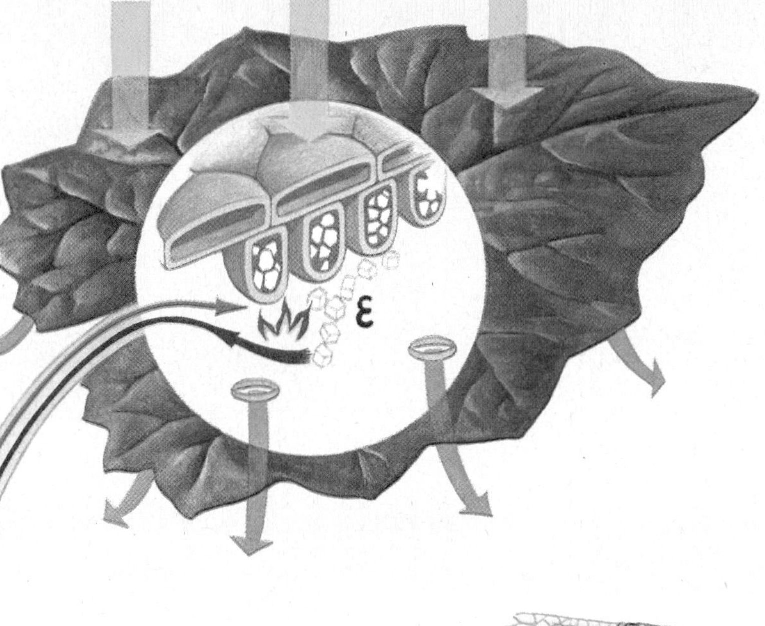

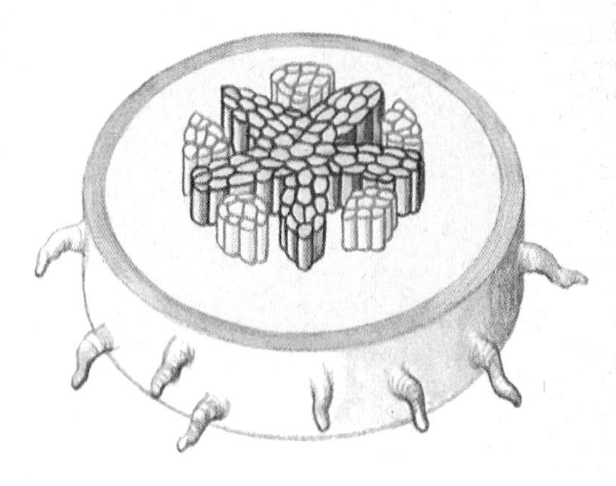

The woody xylem tissue concentrates in the centre of the root, giving the plant cable-like strength ideal for anchorage, as in this buttercup section.

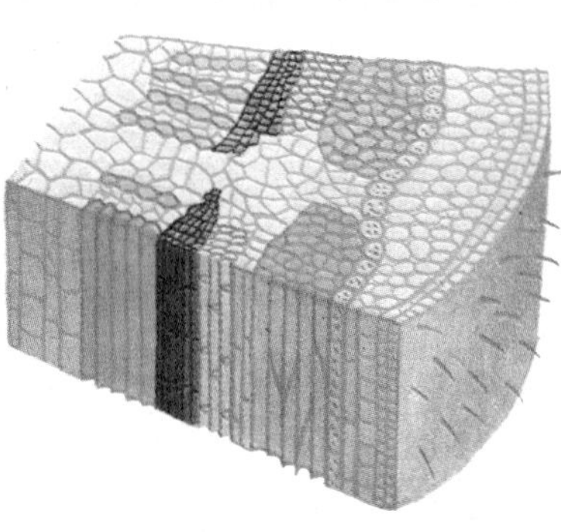

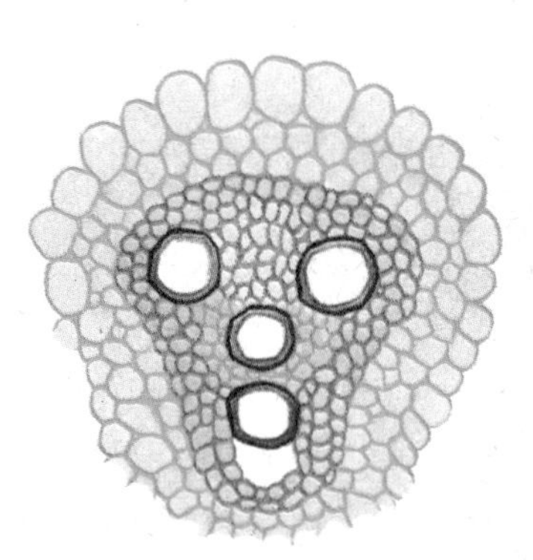

The bundles of dicotyledon plants, *left,* are said to be open because they contain cambium, the name given to an actively dividing type of cell in the centre of the bundle. On the other hand, monocotyledon plants, *right,* are closed because they do not contain any cambium. In addition, monocotyledon bundles are not arranged into any recognizable pattern.

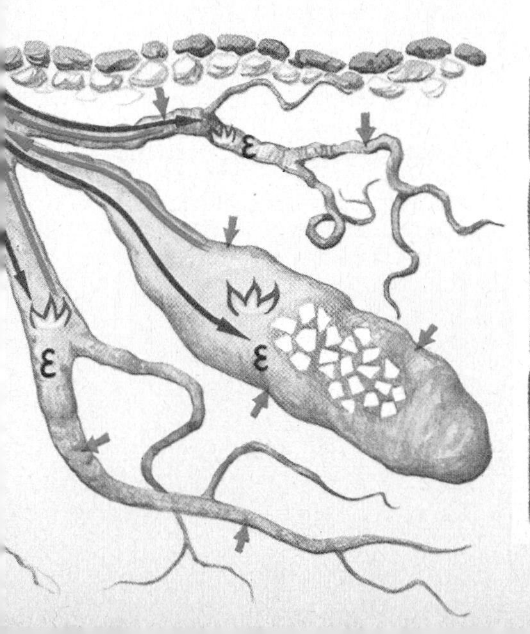

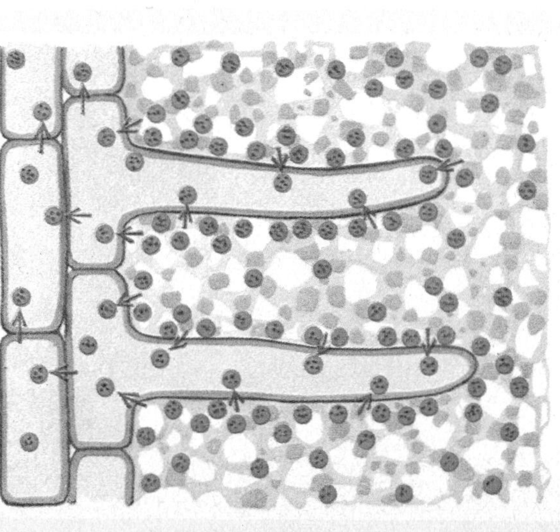

Root hairs are the gateway to the internal transport system of the plant. Water enters the hairs by osmosis, but the method by which minerals gain admittance is still a puzzle. The rate at which plants absorb minerals varies widely. Of greater interest is the fact that concentrations of minerals within the root may be greater than concentrations in the soil, implying that the plant somehow 'sucks' minerals inside. Once taken into the root, minerals are passed from cell to cell, into the transpiration system for distribution to the upper parts of the plant.

and membranes of the root cortex cells. We can think of the water in the plant as being continuous from the cell walls of the mesophyll to those of the root hairs. The resulting flow, of water is called the transpiration stream.

Whereas the passive uptake of water involves the pulling of water through the plant cells and through the root hairs, the active uptake of water can be thought of as a *pushing* of the water through the cells. It is believed to be important only when the transpiration stream has virtually stopped. It is responsible, for example, for replacing during the night water that the plant has lost during the day.

The passive uptake of water is achieved by *osmosis.* The root hairs constitute a semipermeable membrane between water in the soil and water in the protoplasm. This membrane separates the vacuolar sap (which is a watery solution of salts and organic substances) from the water in the soil surrounding the root hairs. This soil water is a much weaker solution of various salts and other substances than is the cell sap, and so water tends to move by osmosis through the semipermeable system of the root hairs into the cell vacuoles. There is no passage of dissolved substances, just of solvent (water) molecules. (The dissolved substances are actively taken up by a completely different metabolic process.) The force of the water being pushed up from the roots in this manner is known as *root pressure.*

## Dye stains the xylem

A simple experiment demonstrates the part played by xylem in the transport of cell sap. If the roots of a small herbaceous plant are dipped into a solution of the red dye eosin and left for several hours, some of the solution is sucked up by the plant. Transverse sections may then be taken of the plant stem and examined under a microscope, when it will be seen that the xylem elements have been stained by eosin. Other parts of the stem, including the phloem, will not have been stained.

The movement of such substances as sugars, amino acids and inorganic materials through the tissues of the plant is known as *translocation.* Biologists have done much experimental work on this subject, and many conflicting results have been obtained. But it is well established that the phloem is intimately connected with translocation, this being its main function.

Experiments with dyes such as eosin show that there is a two-directional flow in the phloem (as opposed to the one-directional flow in the xylem). The rate of movement is sensitive to temperature, suggesting that phloem transport is partly affected by metabolism. Further evidence for this conclusion is the fact that there is a definite oxygen requirement for translocation. In conditions of low oxygen concentration, translocation of sugars, amino acids, etc., slows down and may eventually stop.

One of the first theories about the mechanism of translocation was proposed by de Vries in 1885, who suggested that it was accomplished by simple diffusion. This mechanism would involve the movement of ions and molecules from regions of high concentration to regions of low concentration. But diffusion is an extremely slow process and could not, on its own, account for translocation.

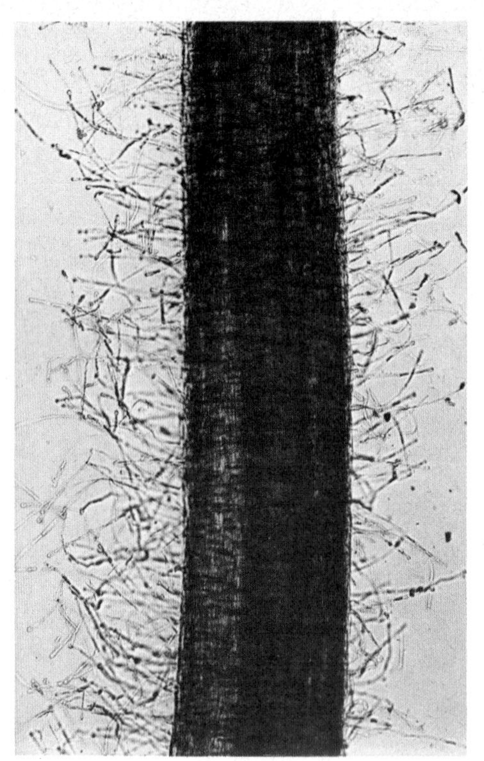

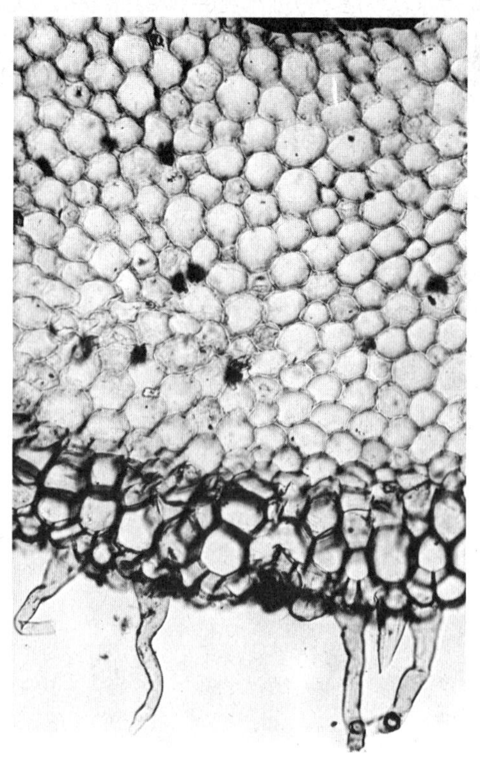

The root gathers nourishment for the plant from the surrounding soil by means of hundreds of root hairs scattered along its side. It then passes raw materials throughout. Water is pushed up the roots by *root pressure. Right,* a cross-section reveals external root hairs.

Another theory (Mass Flow Hypothesis) was put forward in 1930 by Munch, who based his mechanism on osmotic forces. He suggested that the manufacture of sugar in the cells of the leaf increases the osmotic pressure of the cells. This results in their taking in more water, with a corresponding increase in cell pressure. The high pressure then forces water and the dissolved sugars out of these cells into the phloem. In this way, there is supposed to be a mass flow of water and solutes (dissolved substances) from a region of high concentration to a region of lower concentration.

## From one cell to another

This mechanism does not, however, satisfactorily explain all the characteristics of phloem transport. For example, it would not require any metabolic energy, although it is known that phloem transport is affected by metabolism. It implies a one-directional flow, and it is well established that translocation is a two-directional phenomenon. It also implies that the osmotic pressure in the leaf cells must be greater than the osmotic pressure in the root cells for translocation to work. In many tuberous plants, such as potatoes and dahlias, it has been found that this is not so.

It has also been suggested that cytoplasmic streaming could be responsible for translocation. This streaming is a phenomenon that has been observed in both plant and animal cells. The cytoplasm may flow along a definite path, such as up one side of a cell and down the other. It is possible that, as the cytoplasm moves, it carries the various food substances with it – there could be a streaming of cytoplasm from one cell to another. This theory has much to recommend it. It certainly accounts for the two-directional flow. And the speed and direction of flow could be independent of concentration differences. However, it is believed that although cytoplasmic streaming occurs in the phloem cells, it does not occur through the plasmodesmata connecting one phloem cell to another. It has been suggested that some sort of metabolic pump is responsible for the movement of the substances from one cell to another. This could account for the dependence of phloem transport upon metabolism. As yet none of these theories has conclusively been proved or disproved and many problems remain.

In addition to transport through the xylem and phloem, individual plant cells are also capable of achieving transport. It is believed that the lateral transport of solvents occurs either by diffusion or by cytoplasmic streaming. It is known that cytoplasmic streaming occurs between cells (although it is believed not to occur in phloem cells), but it is much more likely that substances move from one cell to another by diffusion through the plasmodesmata. This would involve the movement of these substances from areas of high concentration to areas of low concentration. The membranes of cells are differentially permeable (allowing some substances to pass through them more readily than others). Water is allowed to pass freely from one cell to another, but permeability to sugars, amino acids and inorganic substances varies. It also varies with the age of the cell; young actively growing cells are more permeable to food substances which they need for the process of growth.

# The forest's winter greenery

**Evergreen trees like pine and fir lend a splash of colour to dull northern winter landscapes. These trees are part of the world of gymnosperms, graceful and valuable denizens of our forests.**

MOST PEOPLE are familiar with the story of the *coelacanth,* the 'living fossil' fish found in the Indian Ocean. At the time the first coelacanth was caught, it was pointed out that the fish had survived in a form almost exactly similar to that of its ancestors two or three hundred million years ago. Until the first specimen of a coelacanth was trawled from the sea off the South African coast in 1938, biologists thought that the fish had been extinct for 60 million years. The dramatic story of the coelacanth hit the headlines all over the world. But it is not generally realized that the coelacanth is only a particularly striking example of a 'living fossil'. There are also a number of plants that have changed remarkably little for many millions of years and still retain many of the characteristics of their fossil ancestors.

## Trees for timber

The conifers and the plants similar to them have many claims to be included among the living fossils. They form part of a division of the plant kingdom known as the *gymnosperms* – a name derived from the Greek words for naked seeds. The gymnosperms are the lowest form of seed-bearing plants. They are thought to have evolved from the more primitive spore-bearing plants some time towards the end of the Palaeozoic period of the Earth's history. They were thus the first seed-bearing plants to appear on Earth, and they were the dominant group of plants throughout most of the geological 'Middle Ages'.

All the living gymnosperms are trees or shrubs. Some of these plants are of colossal economic importance. Without the various pines and firs, for example, the newspaper industry would be very restricted. Millions of acres of pine forest are sacrificed every year to satisfy the almost insatiable demand of printing presses all over the world. The pines grow fairly rapidly and their wood is often used for making furniture and for lumber such as pit-props. Conifers are also often planted as ornamental trees.

Resin derived from the various species of conifers is often used in the manufacture of varnishes. Other gymnosperm species are also useful. The sago-palms, or *Cycads,* also included among the gymnosperms, are a source of food in some parts of the world. The gigantic coniferous redwood trees of California are the largest trees in the world. They are also among the oldest, some flourishing specimens dating back before the birth of Christ. These trees have been extensively exploited for their hard and beautiful wood. It is said that a single large redwood tree contains enough wood to build five largish bungalows. Indeed, much of the city of San Francisco, before the great fire of 1906, was built of redwood. The redwood forests are now in danger of extinction, but despite the efforts of conservationists large amounts of timber are still being taken from them.

Among the gymnosperms, trees are economically important for their timber, and many countries carry out extensive programmes of conservation and reafforestation.

Apart from the conifers and the cycads, the order of gymnosperms also contains two very unusual plants. One, *Welwitschia mirabilis,* resembles a large beetroot buried in the ground. It is found only in a small area of South-West Africa. Welwitschia produces only two leaves in its entire life, although it may survive for more than 100 years. The leaves, which may eventually attain a length of ten feet or more, continue to grow from the base of the plant. Despite its long life, Welwitschia appears to retain many of the characteristics of a seedling. It forms part of a division of the gymnosperms called the *gnetales,* which are also represented by a number of tropical and sub-tropical desert shrubs. The gnetales appear to come late on to the scene from a geological standpoint. The few fossil gnetales that can be found come from recent deposits.

The fourth order of gymnosperms now contains only a single species, although the order to which it belongs, the *Ginkgoales,* has an extensive and ancient fossil record. The sole survivor is the *maidenhair tree,* or Ginkgo. Now cultivated in

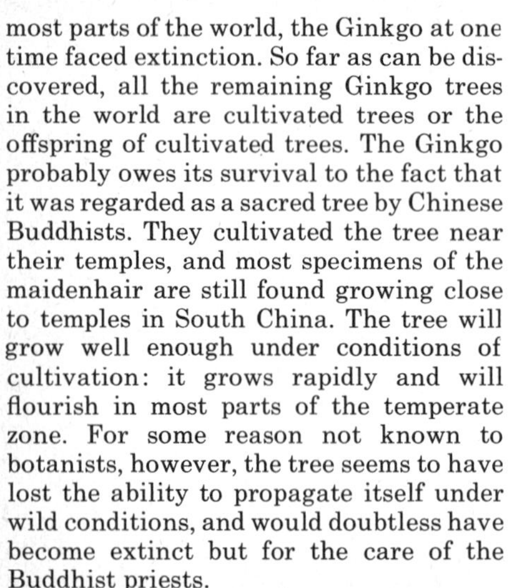

**1** The long-stalked fan-shaped leaves are a distinguishing feature of the maidenhair tree (*Ginkgo biloba*).

**2** Cones of the Atlas cedar grow up to three inches long. When ripe, they disrupt and release their seeds.

**3** The yew (*Taxus baccata*) produces its seeds in bright red berries.

**4** Each *Cupressus* cone bears between two and five seeds, winged for efficient dispersal.

**5** Male (left) and female cones of the Scots pine differ markedly in size and shape. In the United States, this tree is widely cultivated for its timber.

**6** Cycads, common in tropical areas, are fern-like in appearance and habit.

most parts of the world, the Ginkgo at one time faced extinction. So far as can be discovered, all the remaining Ginkgo trees in the world are cultivated trees or the offspring of cultivated trees. The Ginkgo probably owes its survival to the fact that it was regarded as a sacred tree by Chinese Buddhists. They cultivated the tree near their temples, and most specimens of the maidenhair are still found growing close to temples in South China. The tree will grow well enough under conditions of cultivation: it grows rapidly and will flourish in most parts of the temperate zone. For some reason not known to botanists, however, the tree seems to have lost the ability to propagate itself under wild conditions, and would doubtless have become extinct but for the care of the Buddhist priests.

Thus it can be seen that the gymnosperms contain a varied collection of trees and shrubs, some of them most unusual and ancient. They are united chiefly by their common method of reproduction. This method represents a distinct break with the method of reproduction found in more primitive plants, from which the gymnosperms are thought to have developed.

The ferns and mosses, from which the gymnosperms are thought to have developed originally, have a rather primitive method of reproduction. In the ferns, the success of reproduction depends on the availability of moisture in which the sperms can swim to fertilize the ovules. Although the gymnosperms retain many of the characteristics of reproduction in the ferns, their method of reproduction no longer requires a damp environment for its success. Thus, gymnosperm reproduction is more advanced than that of the ferns. This advance has enabled the gymnosperms to colonize areas of the Earth's surface which the ferns cannot reach. Gymnosperms do not require atmospheric moisture in order to reproduce successfully. They are the first plants to be fully emancipated from the consequences of their aquatic ancestry.

## Reaching sexual maturity

Reproduction in the pine *(Pinus)* is generally used as an example to indicate the general lines of the process of reproduction in gymnosperms. While reproduction in the other gymnosperms is not exactly the same as that in the pine, it is sufficiently similar for the pine to serve as an example.

Pine trees do not begin to produce reproductive organs until after a number of years of normal growth. The immediately visible reproductive organs are the cones, which are of two types. At the tip of the growing branches in the spring are developed the male cones which occur in bunches on some of the growing shoots. These cones give rise to the pollen, technically called the microspores; botanists call them *microstrobili.* On the same branch as the male cones will generally be found female cones in various stages of development. Towards the tip of the branch can be seen the developing female cones, still small and green and tightly closed up. Nearer the trunk of the tree are the female cones developed in the previous year. These are woody and well developed, but have not yet opened out. Still closer to the trunk are the female cones which began developing two years before. They have opened out and scattered their seeds, and are now dying on the branch. The female cones are the ones generally called 'pine cones'. Because they bear the egg-cells or megaspores, botanists call them *megastrobili*.

The scales of the male cones have two pollen sacs on their underside. The individual pollen grains are produced inside these sacs from cells called pollen mother cells or *microporocytes*. The pollen mother cells divide to produce pollen cells. They divide in such a way that each pollen cell contains only half the number of genes or chromosomes that the pollen mother cell contained. The pollen grains produced in this way are yellow granules, each with a pair of air bladders to enable it to stay airborne. When mature, each pollen grain contains four cells. When the pollen is ripe, the pollen sacs burst and release the pollen on the wind. Each pine tree produces a vast quantity of pollen in order to make sure that at least some of it falls in the right place. The right place in this case is a young female cone. This type of pollination by wind is obviously extremely wasteful, but so long as the individual trees produce sufficient pollen, it is fairly effective.

Meanwhile, the female cones are preparing to receive the pollen. Under every scale of the female cone are two ovules, one on each side of a central dividing line. The ovules consist of an egg mother cell inside a vase-shaped group of cells called the integument. The integument has a small hole at the upper end so that the egg cells can be reached by the pollen. This hole is called the micropore. As the ovule develops, the egg mother cell divides in a similar way to the pollen mother cell, so that the ovule is finally provided with only half the usual amount of genetic material.

## Growth of the seed

The immature female cones secrete a sticky fluid from the ovules called a pollination droplet. The purpose of this droplet is to trap the pollen grains as they are blown on to the cones. Pollen grains caught in this sticky fluid float through it into a space at the tip of the ovule called the pollination chamber. The pollen cells remain in the pollination chamber, under the protective covering of the scale of the female cone, while both cone and pollen grain complete their development.

During this year, the female germ cells divide and become enlarged, so that finally a number of large egg cells are produced. At the same time, the pollen grain extends a long tube down towards the microspore. The tube eats through the tissues of the female ovule until it comes into contact with the female germ cell. When this contact has been made, sperms from the pollen grain swim down the tube and fertilize the female cells. The fertilized cells are called embryos.

Inside each ovule, a number of embryos may be formed, but only one develops very far. This successful embryo grows by feeding on the surrounding cells and the remains of the dead embryos. At the same time, the walls of the ovum, the integument, grow harder by thickening their cell walls. Several months after beginning their development, the embryos become dormant inside their hardened outer shells. The seeds, as the ovules now are, have extended wings to enable them to fly easily through the air. In this way they may land further from their parent tree than if they had just dropped to the ground.

After about two years from the beginning of the process of fertilization, the cones open and shed their seeds. The seeds

These stages in the development of the ovule and embryo of the pine culminate in the production of a winged seed which develops into a seedling. Female cones are borne at the end of twigs, while male cones are attached to the main branch.

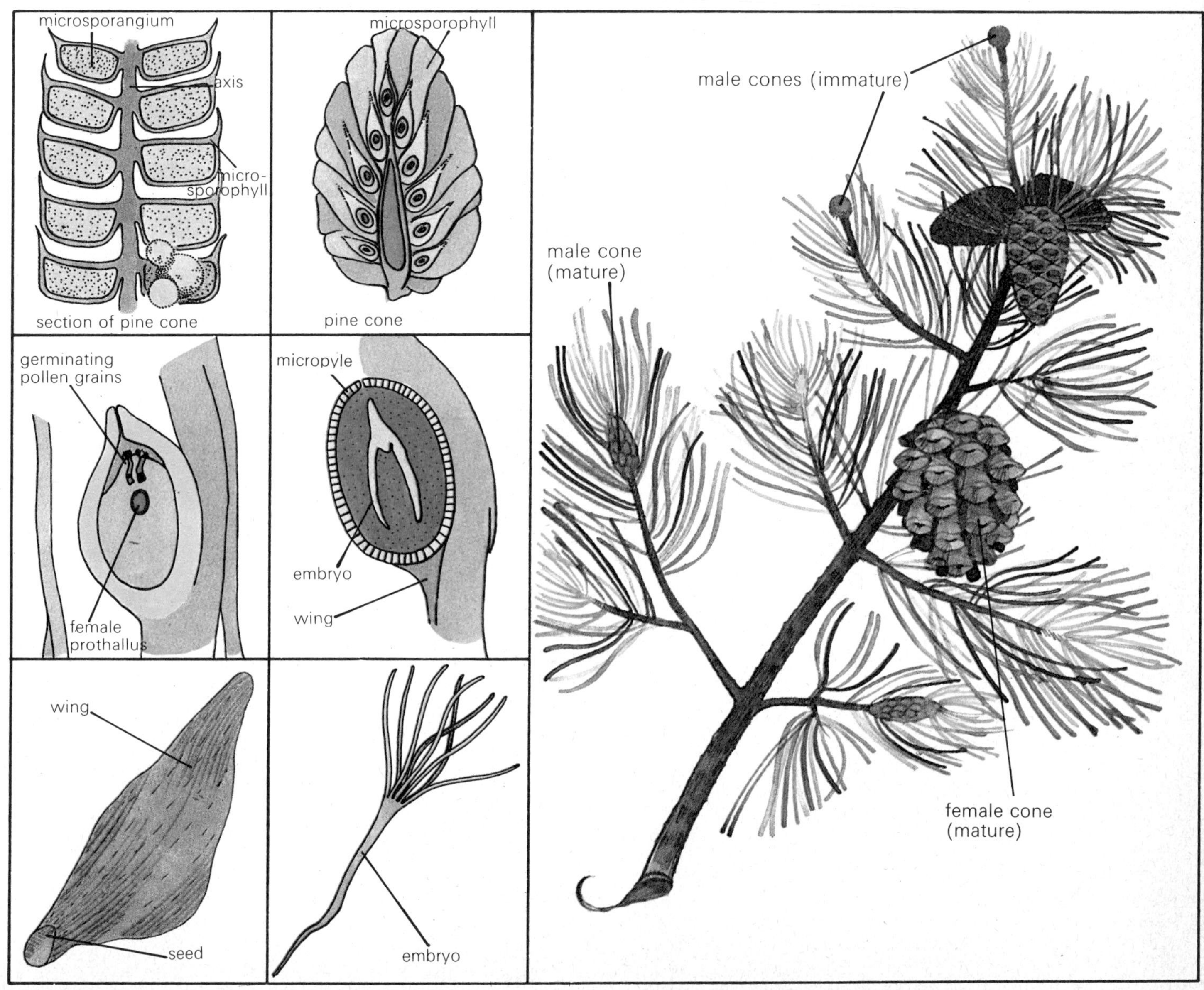

1 The cedar of Lebanon (*Cedrus libani*) takes on a distinctive adult shape with marked horizontal alignment of the foliage.

2 The cone of the Monkey Puzzle, which is up to seven inches long, bears a seed on the upper surface of each scale.

are carried on their wings and come to rest wherever they are carried.

## Distribution by wind

If the windborne seed encounters the right conditions when it lands, that is, if it lands in a fairly warm damp spot, it will begin to develop into a pine tree by a process known as germination. The seed is already partially developed when it is scattered from the tree; it already has miniature roots, a tiny stem and seed-leaves. It only needs to land in a favourable spot to begin its development.

Superficially, it might appear that the process of reproduction in the conifers is completely different from that in the ferns. This is not so. The process of reproduction differs mainly in the mode of transport. In the ferns, it is the sperm itself that requires transport in order to reach the egg-cell. In the conifers, on the other hand, the spore alone requires transport by an external agency, and in this case it is not water but wind that is required. Wind is present all over the Earth's surface, so that the conifer is emancipated from the requirement for surface water.

Apart from their method of reproduction, the conifers have several other peculiar features. Most of them are evergreens, their leaves persisting from year to year. In the case of the monkey-puzzle tree, *Araucaria,* trees have been found with leaves at least 45 years old. Most of the conifers retain their leaves for only two or three years, and the larch sheds its leaves every year.

The leaves themselves in a number of conifers, including the pine, have characteristic and unusual shapes. Indeed, in some types of conifer, there may be as many as three entirely different types of leaf. In the pine, for example, the leaves are needle-shaped, thick and sharp at the ends. At the opposite extreme, *Podocarpus* has leaves seven inches long and two inches broad.

The leaves of Ginkgo, the maidenhair tree, give their name to the plant. They are thought to resemble those of the maidenhair fern, itself named because its leaves are similar in shape to a maiden's pubic hairs. Its seeds are carried completely naked on the tips of its twigs.

The gnetales, in the details of their reproduction, are more advanced than the conifers and the other gymnosperms. Their cones resemble the flowers of angiosperms more closely than those of any other type of gymnosperm. In their internal anatomy, too, they are more highly developed than their allies. Unlike the rest of the gymnosperms, their wood contains true vessels, and lacks the resin canals that are characteristic of conifers and other gymnosperms.

## Odd man out

Some botanists have tried to picture the gnetales as the forerunners of the angiosperms, but lack of specimens of gnetales in the fossil record, except in very recent times, seems a rather compelling argument against this view. It seems best to regard the gnetales as a sort of 'sport' and to consider them as outside the mainstream of plant development.

The gymnosperms, as a group, have shown considerable adaptability and have maintained their position as an important part of the plant kingdom, despite their somewhat primitive make-up. Some of their representatives, like the conifers and the sago-palms, are of great value to Man. They contain some of the most unusual and impressive plants in the world from the giant redwoods, the biggest living things on Earth, to the sacred and unusual maidenhair trees.

Such a diverse and widespread group, displaying as it does a remarkable ability to survive in so many different environments, must represent a striking advance in the evolutionary process. Botanists are agreed that this development of the seed habit marks the gymnosperms off from their lesser fellows in the plant world and gives them their adaptability.

But for the fact that gymnosperms are found all over the globe, it would have been almost impossible for Man to build great cathedrals as monuments of skill and ability. And in modern times, the communications industry, particularly books and newspapers, depends completely on the gymnosperms.

1 Gymnosperms can grow to great thicknesses, as this yew growing in England shows. In this case, the height is below average.

2 The lace-bark is unique among pines in shedding its bark in the same way as do a number of deciduous trees.

# Giants of the past

**Standing on the sidelines of evolution, the ferns remain much as they were millions of years ago. What has caused them to maintain this unique position in the plant kingdom?**

NO CONSERVATORY, the Victorians thought, was worth the name unless it contained a fernery. Fern collectors – or pteridologists, as they preferred to be called – scoured the countryside in search of fresh varieties to stock their rock gardens, and a generation of natural-history writers waxed lyrical about the intricate symmetry of these handsome plants. Since that time, of course, the fern has gone the way of the aspidistra, and the growing of ferns has languished, perhaps in a reaction against the excessive enthusiasms of the Victorians. But the lack of a cult is really no excuse for neglecting these unusual and interesting plants.

During the Paleozoic era, that is about 250 million years ago, the ferns were far more abundant and luxuriant than they are today. The fossilized remains of gigantic tree ferns are frequently found in the coal-measures which are all that remain of the tropical forests that covered the Earth at that time. The ferns were probably the most common type of plant, and they existed on a much grander scale than the ferns we know today. But they gradually lost their dominant place in the plant kingdom, being ousted by more versatile and adaptable plants.

The ferns probably originated from primitive water-borne or aquatic plants. Their ancestors probably resembled the mosses of today. Most present-day ferns still need a moist soil and a humid atmosphere to grow well. Indeed, some species of ferns, such as *Azolla*, grow entirely on the surface of ponds and sluggish streams. And in their structure and method of reproduction the ferns have not entirely lost the signs of their aquatic origin.

## Ubiquitous plants

Ferns are found almost all over the world. Some varieties in the tropics grow to the size of trees, with woody trunks, but ferns found in the temperate parts of the world rarely grow larger than a man. The majority of species of fern are found in the tropics, and a quarter of all known species are present in India. Bracken, one of the hardiest and commonest ferns, has successfully colonized hillsides and waste land all over the country, and the varied colours of its leaves as they wither and die in the autumn have inspired generations of landscape painters. Most ferns, however, grow more readily in damp places, or at least in places where there is plenty of moisture in the atmosphere. Perhaps this preference for moisture is a legacy of the ferns' aquatic origins.

A fern plant consists basically of roots, a stem and leaf-like organs called the fronds. The fronds are so-called because in addition to carrying out the usual functions of leaves – converting carbon dioxide and water into sugars (photosynthesis), and drawing water up from the roots (transpiration) – they also carry the equivalent of seeds which are generally found on the underside of the fronds.

In many of the common ferns the stem is wholly or partially buried in the soil. It is generally short, woody and comparatively thick, although in the tropical tree-ferns, as in their Paleozoic ancestors, the root-stock is extended to form a trunk and the plant is able to grow to a considerable height.

The fronds of the ferns consist of a stalk and an expanded leafy blade called a *lamina*. The shape and structure of the frond provides botanists with the chief means of distinguishing one species of fern from another. Although there are ferns in which the fronds are undivided – a good example is the hart's-tongue fern – in the majority of ferns the fronds are divided into smaller segments called *pinnae*. Frequently, the pinnae themselves are divided into *pinnules*.

The budding fronds of almost all the ferns are arranged in a characteristic and unusual fashion. They are coiled up like watch-springs – a condition known as *circinnate vernation*. The fronds uncoil as they develop, gradually revealing the mature frond. Most British ferns uncoil their fronds rather slowly through-

1

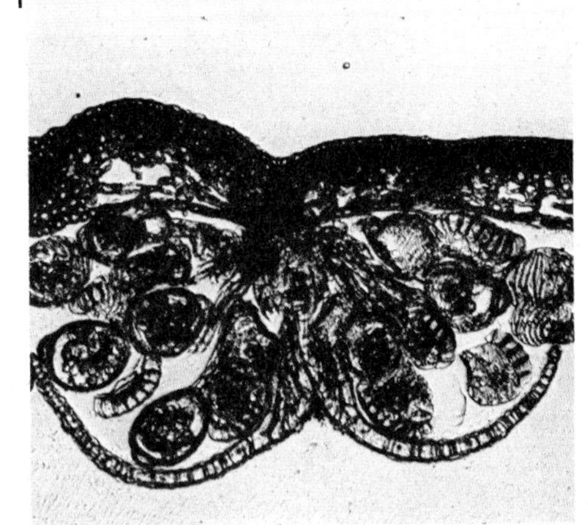

2

3

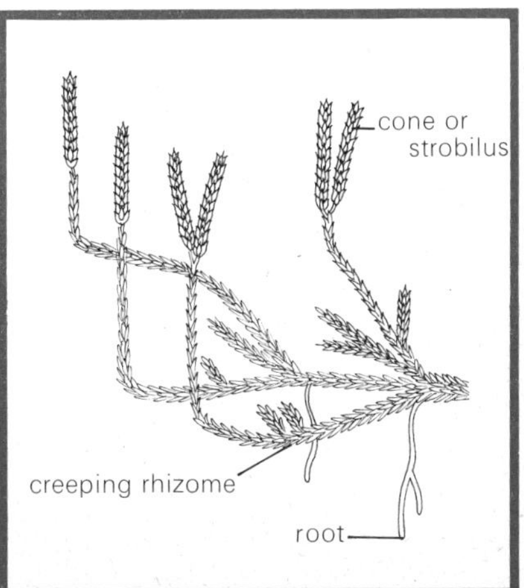


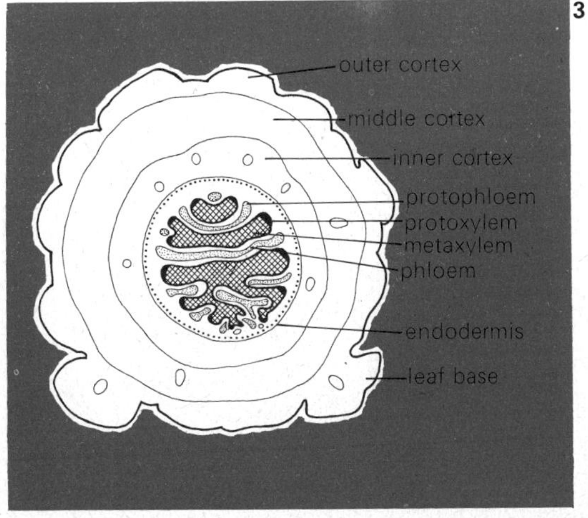


**1** Spore capsules on the underside of fern fronds are often covered by protective flaps.
**2** Although it strongly resembles normal trees, this is a true fern, similar in many ways to the giant ferns of the Paleozoic era.
**3** *Lycopodium* is a fern ally of the creeping variety, with small, simple leaves arranged in four rows. The cross-section of the stem shows the highly-developed food and water transport system, located in the centre of the stem.

out the early months of the summer, and the different stages of this process can be observed as the summer goes on.

The internal structure of the ferns is more primitive than that of the flowering plants. Like the flowering plants, the ferns have a system of *xylem* for transporting water and minerals from the roots to the upper portions of the plant. In this respect, the ferns are more advanced than the mosses and liverworts, the plants immediately below them in the evolutionary scale. But their system of *xylem* in general is less highly developed than that of the flowering plants. In some ferns there is a single *tracheid* at the centre of the stem up which minerals and water are transported. In others, such as the male fern (*Dryopteris*), the *xylem* occur in bundles, although many of the refinements present in the tissues of the flowering plants are not present in the fern. The epidermis or 'skin' of the fern is generally well developed, often consisting of a double layer of cells.

## Specialized spore-chambers

The structure of the fronds is basically similar to that of the leaf of a flowering plant. The fronds are usually thin, and the outermost layer of cells and the cuticle which acts as a protection against loss of water are usually rather poorly developed. Ferns cannot stand up to dry conditions for long periods.

Reproduction in the ferns involves two generations of plants. The spores of the mature plant are carried on the underside of the frond in a capsule called a sporangium. In some ferns, such as the parsley fern (*Cryptogramma*), only certain of the fronds have sporangia. These fronds are called the fertile fronds. In other ferns only part of the frond is adapted for reproduction. The sporangia of a typical fern, such as the male fern, can be seen as distinct brown blotches on the underside of the mature frond. These spots, which are called *sori*, contain the individual sporangia. The sporangia grow out on stalks from the underside of the frond and are covered with a protective roof known as the *indusium*. The shape of the sori is variable, although in each species the sori have a characteristic shape and arrangement. In the male fern, the sori are small and kidney-shaped, while in the hart's-tongue fern the sori are arranged as long thin patches along the veins of the frond.

The sporangia contain the spores themselves, almost always in the multiples of four. In the male fern, each sporangium contains only 48 spores, whereas in other kinds of fern, each sporangium can contain up to 64 spores. The sporangia are capsules which look rather like tiny magnifying glasses, the stalk corresponding to the handle of the magnifying glass, and the sporangium to the lens. The part corresponding to the edge of the lens is almost completely made up of a band of thick-walled cells called the *annulus*. At one point on the edge of the 'lens', however, the annulus is interrupted by a group of larger cells with thinner walls called the *stomium* (from the Greek word for 'mouth'). During the summer, the action of the sun and wind dries out the sporangium, and increases the tension in the annulus. Eventually, the tension becomes so great that the stomium cells, the weakest point in the sporangium, give way and the spores fly out.

During the course of a single summer a fern plant will release hundreds of thousands of spores. This represents an enormous number of possible offspring, but it is as well to bear in mind that most or even all the spores may meet with adverse circumstances and be prevented by drought or other unfavourable events from ever developing. Even the plants that do develop are not guaranteed survival. The fern plant cannot ensure that its spores will land in a favourable place. But it can take advantage of the laws of chance and release so many spores that it becomes almost a certainty that one spore at least will find favourable conditions. In any event, even the failure of an entire season's output of spores would not be fatal to the race of ferns. They would still be able to put out another crop the following year.

## Second generation reproduction

The new generation produced from the spore is called a *prothallus*. The prothallus is quite unlike the parent plant. The exact nature of the prothallus varies from species to species, but in most cases it is a small leaf-like organ, which anchors itself to the ground by means of root-like growths called *rhizoids*. The mature prothallus of most ferns is no bigger than a thumb-nail. Given moist conditions, the prothallus can continue to live for some time, perhaps two or three years. On the underside of the mature prothallus, male and female sexual organs develop. These grow out among the rhizoids. The male organs, the *antheridia*, develop on the outer portions of the prothallus, and the female organs, the *archegonia*, grow closer to the centre of the plant. Each prothallus produces several male and several female organs, each one developed from a single cell.

The antheridia are very small, and as they develop, take the form of a pouch of cells containing the sperms. The sperms are capable of movement, being provided with tiny hair-like projections which enable them to 'swim' in water. Each antheridium produces about 20 sperms.

The archegonia are slightly larger than the male organs and are partially buried in the leaf of the plant. They grow out as blind tubes, originally closed at both ends. The tube tip protrudes from the prothallus, and when the archegonium is ripe for

1 Tree ferns of the type which formed coal deposits still flourish in tropical areas. Although tree-like, they are classed as ferns because of their method of reproduction.

2 The hart's-tongue fern (*Phyllitis*) is distinguished by the numerous rows of fruit dots carried on the thick, glossy fronds, which grow to lengths of 18 inches.

3 The fronds of ferns are coiled rather like watch springs and uncoil as the plant reaches maturity. A good example of this development is seen in bracken (*Pteridium*).

4 The field horsetail produces two different stems at different seasons. The green shoot on the left is sterile, while the brown shoot is fertile.

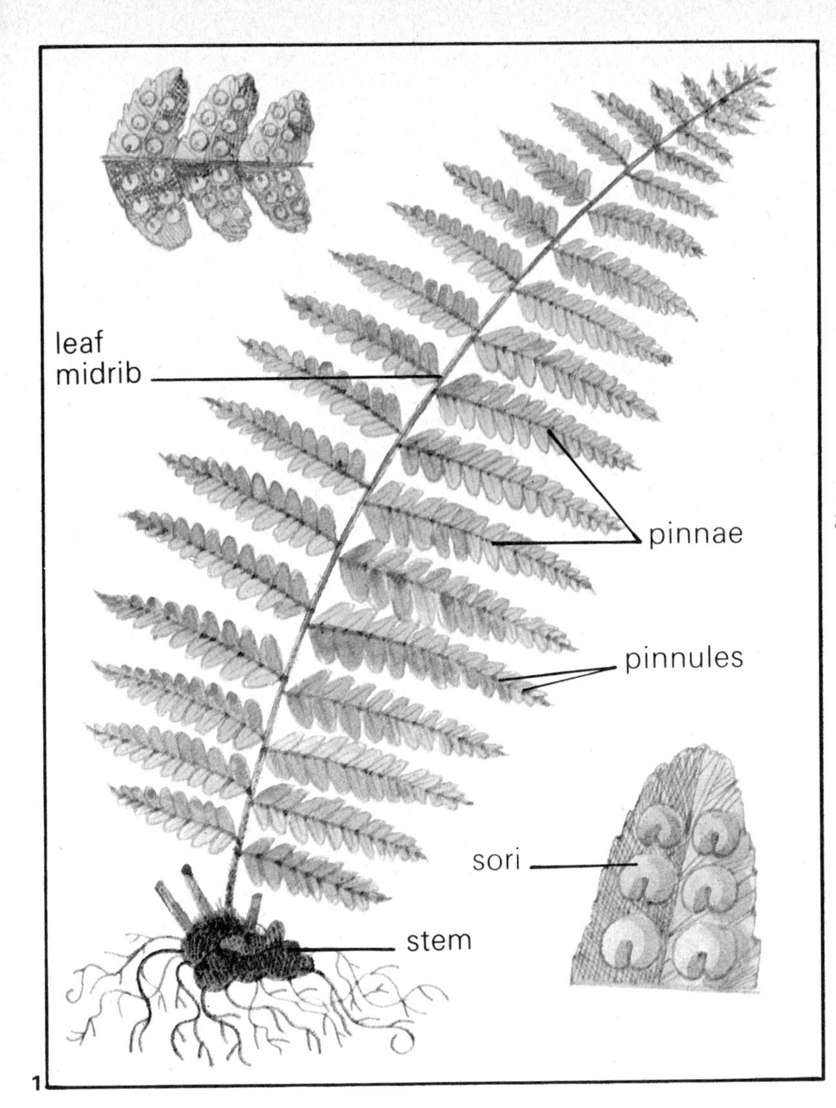


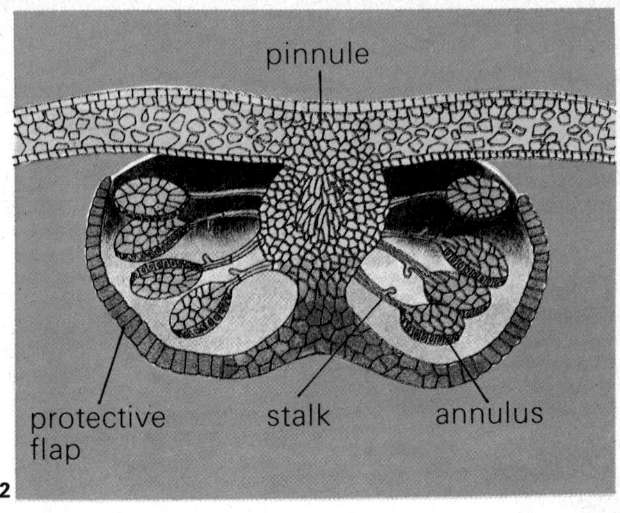


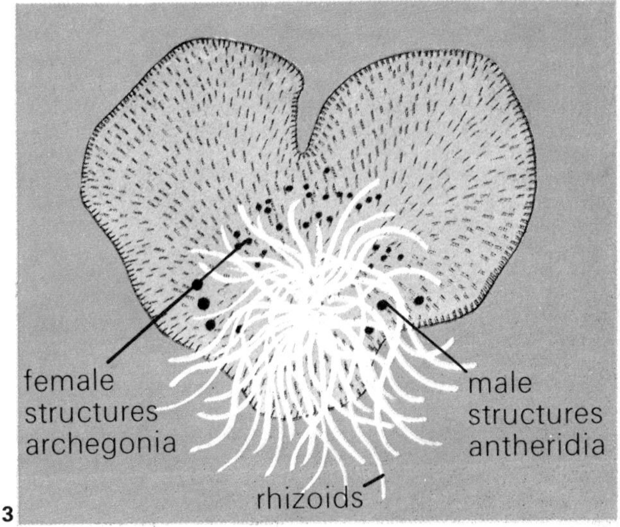


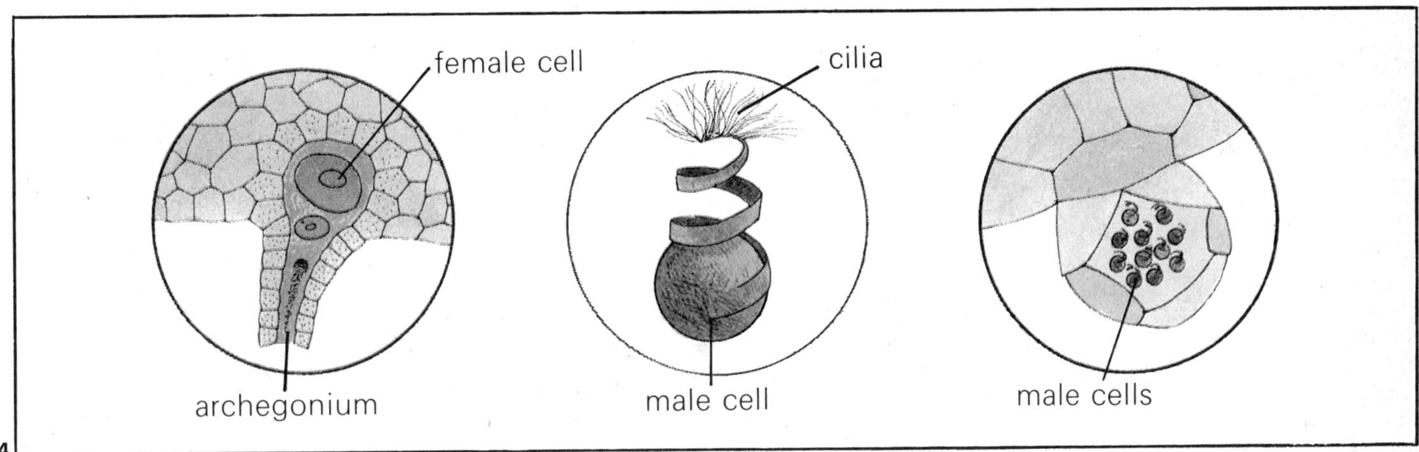


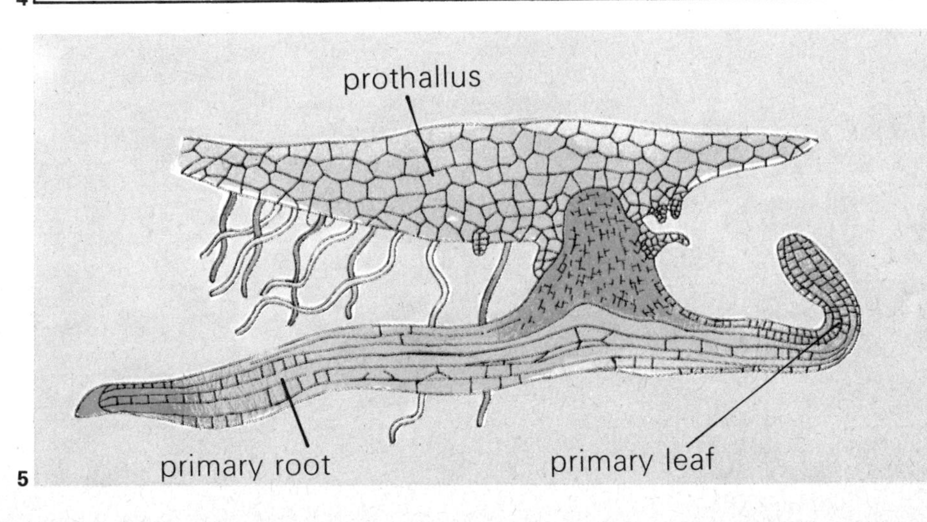


**1** The *pinnae* branching from the frond midrib are divided into *pinnules.* When fully developed, these carry specialized reproductive structures (*sori* of *sporangia*) on their undersides.
**2** The protective flaps of the *sori* wither and the spore capsules within split when the spores are ripe. They are thus released to the atmosphere.
**3** A view of the underside of the prothallus shows the hairy 'roots', among which the sexual structures develop.
**4** The female cell, contained in its flask-shaped chamber, is fertilized by the mobile, spirally-shaped male cell which is released in wet conditions from the male structure on the right.
**5** This section through the fern prothallus shows the young sporophyte still attached to it by its 'foot'.

for fertilization the outside end of the tube opens and exudes a liquid. This liquid contains a substance called malic acid, which is attractive to the sperms. Indeed, the sperms can be 'fooled' experimentally into swimming into a glass tube full of malic acid and water.

About the same time as the archegonia ripen and open their tubes, the antheridia burst and release their stock of sperms. The sperms, attracted by the malic acid, swim towards the archegonia across the moist underside of the prothallus. When they reach the tubes of the archegonia, they disappear inside. Inside each archegonium is a single *oosphere* or egg-cell. One of the sperms fertilizes the oosphere, which immediately begins to divide into an embryo. The embryo rapidly becomes a tiny but recognizable fern. At first it draws its nutrition from the prothallus, but soon puts down roots into the soil and absorbs its own nutrients. Eventually this embryo will develop and become a fully grown fern.

## A limit to adaptation

Thus, reproduction in the ferns requires two generations, one of which is dominant and long-lived, while the other exists simply to provide a platform for sexual reproduction. This is not really a very flexible method of reproduction. It confines the ferns largely to places where there is sufficient moisture for the prothallus to develop and for fertilization to take place. This type of reproduction was ideally suited to the humid moistness of the Paleozoic forests, but less well adapted to conditions existing over most parts of the world today. It has the additional disadvantage that it allows little scope for cross-fertilization between different species.

The possibility of frequent cross-fertilization between different plants of the same or related species is the main driving force of the evolution of new species which may be better adapted to changing conditions. A plant produced by cross-fertilization between two different plants has some of the features of both, just as a child has some of the features of both his parents. The best of these slight changes in the character or make-up of the plant are continued into the next generation and enable the plant to adapt gradually to change in its environment. In the ferns, the mode of reproduction limits these possibilities. Cross-fertilization can take place only if two prothalli grow up close together so that the sperms of one can swim across and fertilize the oospheres of another.

Compare this with the wealth of opportunities for cross-fertilization in the flowering plant, where the pollen from the male organs of one plant can be carried for miles by insects or by the wind before meeting the female organ of another plant. This arrangement in the flowering plants gives them great ability to adapt to changes in their environment, and undoubtedly explains why they are now dominant over almost the entire Earth. It also explains why, even after more than 250 million years of evolution, the ferns still retain the characteristics which their remote ancestors had. In a sense, then, the ferns can be regarded as living fossils – compared with the flowering plants, their evolution is halted or proceeds very slowly because their method of reproduction allows for so little variation.

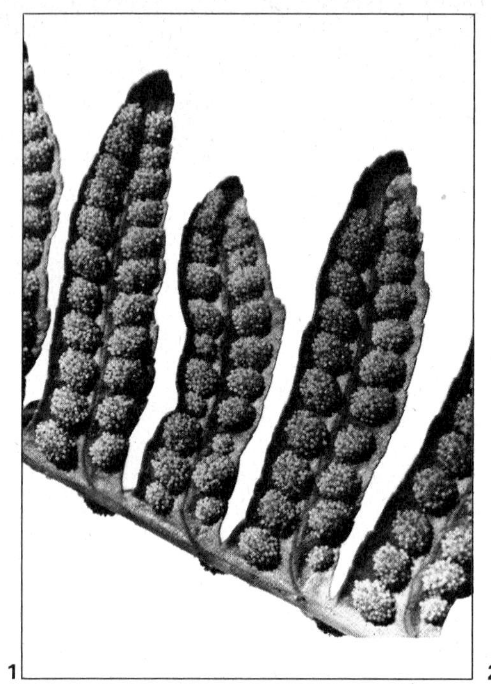
1

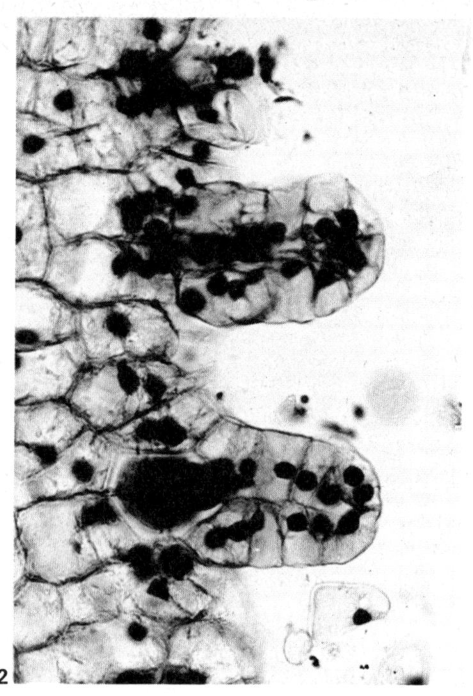
2

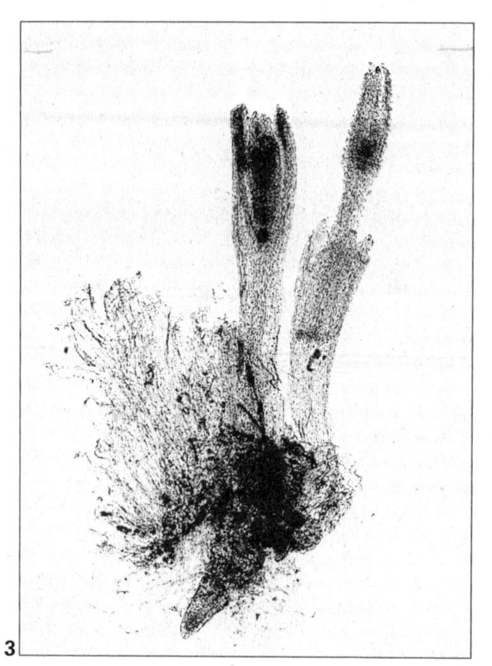
3

1 The *sori* bearing ripe sporangia are prominent on the fronds of *Polypodium vulgare*. Their number indicates the vast number of sporangia which are released from a single plant.
2 This vertical section through a fern prothallus shows nearly mature female sex organs (*archegonia*). The stained areas are the female cells.
3 The fertilized egg develops into a sporophyte within the female chamber. When mature, it detaches itself and eventually develops into a new horsetail plant.

There are several other plants which are usually classed with the ferns. These plants – the horsetails and the Lycopods – are also descended from magnificent tree-like plants found fossilized in coal seams. In many respects, the horsetails and the Lycopods closely resemble the ferns, although they do not appear at first glance to be related. In the horsetails, the leaves are merely small scales arranged in circular way around the stem. The horsetails share with the ferns the method of reproduction by prothalli.

The Lycopods (the name means wolf's foot) are often called clubmosses. The name is really a misnomer: although the Lycopods look more like mosses than ferns, they are really closely allied to the fern family. Internally, they are fairly highly developed, with a distinct system of tracheids for transport of water and minerals. Like the ferns and the horsetails, the Lycopods produce spores which develop into prothalli. The spores of some species of Lycopods are highly prized by scientists. Lycopodium powder, as the spores are called, is a very finely divided powder and the individual spores have little tendency to stick together. The powder also floats on water. It is frequently used in physics experiments to indicate vibrations or the fine movements of molecules on the surface of liquids or solid bodies.

## Relics of a past age

The ferns and their allies have a long history. From the heights of their sway in the primitive forests of the Paleozoic, they have gradually been reduced to the almost insignificant part they play in the plant world today. The decline of the ferns is a startling verification of the Darwinian theory of natural selection. The ferns were not equipped to adapt to new conditions. As the Paleozoic forests died away, the ferns were gradually reduced in size, unable to maintain their once massive and luxuriant trunks. Now they are forced to hide away along the banks of streams and in damp hedgerows, victims of their own requirement for abundant moisture. The flowering plants are so adaptable that they are able to fill almost every crevice and nook on Earth. The ferns cannot – and they suffer a natural revenge for their inability to adapt.

# Life in the rain forest

Stinging trees and strangling figs, robber-flies and birds of paradise – all are inhabitants of a shadowy, self-contained world which has provided invaluable information for scientists.

A RAIN FOREST is the most complex combination of living things occurring on land, and is comparable with its counterpart of the ocean – the coral reef. In both communities the lush quantity of living material is only equalled by the astonishing variety of forms.

A typical rain forest takes hundreds of years to grow to maturity – a coral reef takes much longer. But the individual species of plants and animals in a rain forest are the product of many millions of years of the evolution process; many species have survived over such a period with little change in the subdued forest environment. Examples of the latter are the caterpillar-like peripatus of the damp forest floor and the fern-like *Tmesipteris* which grows on the trunks of the more highly evolved tree-ferns.

Although the forest provides shelter from some rigours of the climate, there is the struggle of the seedling on the ground to reach the light without which it would starve, the struggle for living space, food, and the struggle to avoid being eaten. Add to this the stress of Man's steady destruction of the great forests and the age-old struggle seems destined to end in tragedy; rain-forest plants and animals cannot continue to reproduce once the forest is gone.

The evergreen forests of wet tropical (sometimes subtropical) areas such as Malaya are most typical. The term rain forest is frequently also applied to the much simpler wet, broad-leaved, evergreen forests of temperate latitudes, such as the myrtle-beech forests of Tasmania with their wealth of tree-ferns.

## Tree nightmare

Tropical rain forests are populated by a bewildering number of tree species which provide a nightmare for the botanist who must often try to identify them from ground level. Leaves and branches form a continuous covering called the *canopy*, which greatly reduces the sunlight reaching the ground. Certain trees have characteristics which are not shared by those of cooler climates. Where the annual weather cycle provides no well-defined springtime, a regular once-a-year flowering does not necessarily take place. Some trees do not flower and fruit more than once in ten years; some flower twice a year or continuously throughout the year. Instead of producing flowers and fruit from the new shoots near the tips of the branches, other trees flower out of the old rough bark of the main trunk or older branches. Buttress roots are commonly seen in rain-forest trees. These form woody walls standing out from the base of the trunk. They help to support tall trees where the soil, softened by frequent tropical downpours, might not otherwise provide sufficient anchorage for the roots.

1 The tapir, found in the dense forests of South East Asia, is typical of the small mammals which live below the rain-forest canopy. Its distinctive markings serve it as camouflage.

2 The pitcher plant supplements its diet by digesting the protein of insects trapped inside its 'bell'. Some pitcher plants are epiphytic, growing on the branches of trees.

The stinging trees *(Laportea)* of South East Asia and eastern Australia have large, soft, pale green leaves which are covered with fine, sharply pointed 'hairs'. These break off in the skin when touched, producing a violent burning sensation. Despite their venomous properties the leaves are usually riddled from the activities of a green beetle, whose hard, horny covering is evidently not penetrated by the hairs.

In the same part of the world are the spectacular trees known as strangling figs. Birds deposit the sticky seeds of the figs on the trunks or branches of other trees where the seed germinates and sends long roots down to the ground. Gradually the roots of the fig increase, envelop and kill the host tree. The fig plant has by now formed its own trunk and becomes an independent tree with the rotting remains of its host within. Strangling figs, of which the banyan is one species, acquire a grotesque appearance because their manner of reaching the ground may produce a number of trunks, each consisting of fused interlaced roots, while younger roots growing towards the earth form a curtain or lattice. Such plants are ideally adapted to life in thick forests; by starting their growth within reach of the light, they have an obvious advantage over plants which start at ground level.

Palms are common in tropical rain forests. Most have straight, erect trunks,

1

2

3

but differ from typical trees in the absence of branches. One group of palms, the rattans or lawyer-vines *(Calamus)*, takes on a very different form. Rattans are one of many kinds of *lianes* or climbing plants which give rain forests their peculiar tangled eeriness. Lianes depend on trees for support in their struggle to the light; they grow rapidly to the light because they have no need to use their resources in building a solid trunk. Lianes climb by twining their stems round trees, or by producing slender twining tendrils or roots which cling to bark. Rattans also have hard, sharp-pointed, curved spines which catch in the bark or branches of trees, and bite in deeply so that the plant is lodged firmly on its support. The spines occur on the backs of the midribs of the leaves and along the long fine tendrils. The tendrils frequently dangle from the forest canopy almost to ground level so that the unwary pedestrian may become entangled or have his skin or clothing severely torn.

*Epiphytes* grow upon other plants without themselves reaching the ground. All take advantage of generous quantities of sunlight available in the canopy without having to climb for it. They range from the microscopic single-celled algae to the massive orchids of the genus *Grammatophyllum* which produce clumps of stems ten feet long. Mistletoes are parasitic epiphytes, and many grow on rain-forest trees. Their tissues penetrate the host tree so that they can draw directly on their host's sap. Trees heavily infested with mistletoe are often sickly and may die prematurely. Other epiphytes usually grow with the roots attached to the outside of the bark of the host only, and are thus not parasitic. As the bark has very little ability to retain water, these plants are faced with the possibility of drying out between falls of rain. It is probably for this reason that epiphytes attain their greatest density in the cloud forests or moss forests of high mountains where evaporation is minimal.

## Pineapple family

The *bromeliad* or pineapple family is an American group which includes a vast number of epiphytic species in the tropical forests of that region. Many of these have a rain-catching reservoir formed by the tightly cupped rosette of terminal leaves. Most of the enormous variety of rain-forest orchids are epiphytes. They generally have thickened fleshy stems or thickened leaves (or both) which store water. It was once supposed that these orchids were 'air plants' obtaining all their food requirements from the air. In fact they feed on waste substances deposited in the bark of the host tree and generally die after the host dies.

Contrary to popular belief the vegetation nearer the ground is rather sparse in an undisturbed rain forest, so that one can walk easily where the ground is level. The explanation for this is the dimness of the light below the canopy. Ferns may grow on the ground and mosses on fallen logs and rocks. Both of these are adapted to low light intensity, though they make use of such light as is available. The fungi, on the other hand, can grow here because they have no need of light and use the substances already present in living or decaying plants and animals.

Animal life is inconspicuous within the rain forest for several reasons. The mammals are shy and frequently nocturnal. The larger ones, such as leopards and elephants in particular, have been heavily hunted by man and are rarely seen. Birds, though abundant, keep mainly to the treetops. Insects – the most plentiful of all non-microscopic animals – congregate in

small clearings or live in concealed situations.

The canopy contains a profusion of birds, which include tiny but brilliant humming-birds (South and Central America) which take nectar from flowers; the fantastic birds of paradise, mainly fruit-eating and living in New Guinea; the hornbills of Asia and Africa which eat fruit and sometimes the young of other birds; and everywhere the brilliantly coloured tropical parrots. Also in the canopy live fruit-eating mammals – monkeys and the large fruit-bats or 'flying-foxes'.

A tree in blossom attracts many insects – bees, flies, moths, butterflies, which take its nectar or pollen. Other insects prey on these in turn – mantises, robber-flies and an unbelievable number of parasitic and predatory wasps. Spiders also are abundant. If one species of insect multiplies unchecked, its combined numbers can have a devastating effect. Large populations of caterpillars or stick-insects may destroy whole trees. On the other hand most trees and other flowering plants depend on insects to fertilize their flowers. Undoubtedly insects are, next to Man, the most destructive force in the rain forest. On the other hand the continued existence of the rain forest would be impossible without insects; although it would be quite possible without Man.

On the ground live a large number of rodents, like the giant African pouched rats, concealing themselves in nests or burrows by day and feeding at night on fruit, seeds and herbage. In some places there are also larger ground animals. In South East Asia elephants may feed in rain forest, tearing whole branches from trees with their trunks. Formerly in this area the forests also contained rhinoceros and the Malayan tapir, which has relatives in Central and South America. The cassowary lives in the rain forests of New Guinea and tropical Australia. It is a massive flightless bird standing more than four feet high but its apparent clumsiness is deceptive. Of the large rain-forest carnivores, those of the cat family are the best known: the tiger (Asia), the leopard (Asia and Africa), and the jaguar (South America).

A number of the insects of the forest floor live in rotting wood – stag-beetles and their larvae and many others. The

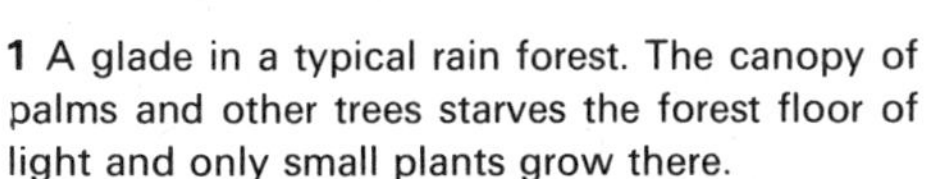

5

6

**1** A glade in a typical rain forest. The canopy of palms and other trees starves the forest floor of light and only small plants grow there.
**2** Roussette bats are found in the rain forests of Asia, where they feed on a diet of fruits.
**3** Brightly coloured butterflies are common in rain forests, which support an enormous variety of insect life.
**4** The cassowary is a flightless bird found in the forests of New Guinea and northern Australia. Standing more than four feet high, it is surprisingly fleet-footed for a bird of its size.
**5** The pineapple is a typical rain-forest species, though it can also be grown on plantations in areas where the climatic conditions are right. This one has a Malayan tree frog perched on its leaf.
**6** The Boyd's rain-forest dragon is a rare Australian lizard found in the forests of New South Wales. Its bright coloration and delicate structure have led collectors to hunt it down.

Lawes's six-wired bird of paradise, shown here, is very rarely photographed. Like most of its brightly coloured relatives, *Parotia lawesi* inhabits the forests of New Guinea.

larger fungi serve as homes and food sources for the larvae of countless kinds of flies and beetles. Under fallen leaves and logs may be found the fast-moving carnivorous ground-beetles and various cricket-like insects which emerge at night to scavenge for dead or helpless insects. Snails and slugs, always faced with the danger of their moist bodies drying out, are only active in the cool humidity of night or during showers of rain.

Although often surprisingly inconspicuous, the huge variety of insects which live on the ground have a role to play in the organization of the forest. Without this army of scavengers, the dead leaves, branches and animal debris raining down from the trees would pile up in suffocating proportions. The termites in the rain forests of Africa, for example, carry leaves and other material underground. Many of their activities are hidden but millions of driver ants may suddenly march in ordered formation through the forest in search of food.

Under the ground earthworms perform a useful task by constantly bringing fresh soil to the surface. The *nymphs* or young cicadas spend several years burrowing among tree roots from which they suck the sap, eventually breaking the surface and taking on the winged adult form. The shrill, resonant notes of myriads of adult male cicadas calling from the canopy is a familiar sound.

## Destructive impact

Though the impact of Man on the forest has been, and in some countries still is, essentially destructive, in some countries there is a new awareness of the importance of preserving the remaining forests. In Australia most existing rain forest, except in very remote localities, is either state-owned or is reserved for recreational or scientific purposes.

Because of the multitude of different plant and animal species it supports, the rain forest is uniquely suited to studies of the subtle differences between the environmental requirements of different species. These factors determine whether they can co-exist or even continue to survive at all. The co-existence of many closely similar species of animals and plants provides ideal conditions for studying the evolutionary processes by which numbers of distinct species are produced from a single ancestral one. The large number of plants and animals also enables important studies in population ecology and population genetics to be carried out on an adequate statistical basis. Rain-forest flora is proving of special interest to biochemists because the diverse plant species continuously yield new and often useful substances.

The tree kangaroo is a marsupial tree-living species found in Australia. Its long tail serves it as a balancing limb while it climbs in the forest canopy.

# Parasites and scavengers of the plant world

**Differing from other plants in that they cannot make their own food, the fungi must live on dead, decaying matter, or as parasites on plants, animals, or even on human beings themselves.**

WHEN THE GREAT WAVES of Irish immigrants arrived on the shores of the United States in the 1840s they were driven, not by tyranny or oppression, not by religious persecution, but by a fungus. This particular fungus, known popularly as potato blight, caused almost complete failure of the potato crop in Ireland in the years 1846 and 1847. And as the potato formed the staple food of the Irish peasantry, millions crossed the Atlantic to begin a new life, seeing this as the only practicable alternative to starvation.

But not all fungi are destructive. They include the species which makes penicillin, and the yeasts which are necessary for both bread and wine-making. They are the source of many drugs, and species found in different parts of the world, notably in Mexico and South America, yield a drug which produces hallucinations. This particular fungus, a type of mushroom, played a large part in the religious ceremonies of the tribes in these areas.

## Feeding without chlorophyll

Fungi number about 100,000 species, and belong to a group of primitive plants called *Eumycophyta,* which is a subdivision of the *Thallophyta,* or plants not differentiated into stem or root, and constitute the largest group of non-flowering plants. Fungi range in size from the microscopic yeasts to the biggest mushrooms and puffballs, and all are distinguished by lacking the green pigment chlorophyll, which enables self-feeding plants to obtain nutrient from the air and soil.

Consequently, fungi must obtain their food ready-made from other sources: some, the *saprophytic* forms, get it from dead organic matter, while *parasitic* fungi get it from living organisms. Besides the essentially parasitic and saprophytic fungi there are intermediary species which alter their method of nutrition according to environment.

Other species of fungi establish a *symbiotic* relationship with another organism so that the two organisms derive mutual benefit, forming a plant structure called *mycorrhiza.* An example of this are the lichens, which are composed of a fungus and a green or blue-green alga.

Fungi feed by releasing enzymes which change their organic food into liquids. The liquids are then absorbed into the fungus and are broken down to supply energy for growth.

One very strange thing about parasitic fungi that attack plants is that many are highly selective. Potato mildew, for instance, is caused by one species of fungus, rose mildew by another, and grape mildew by yet another species.

The *thallus* or vegetative plant body of

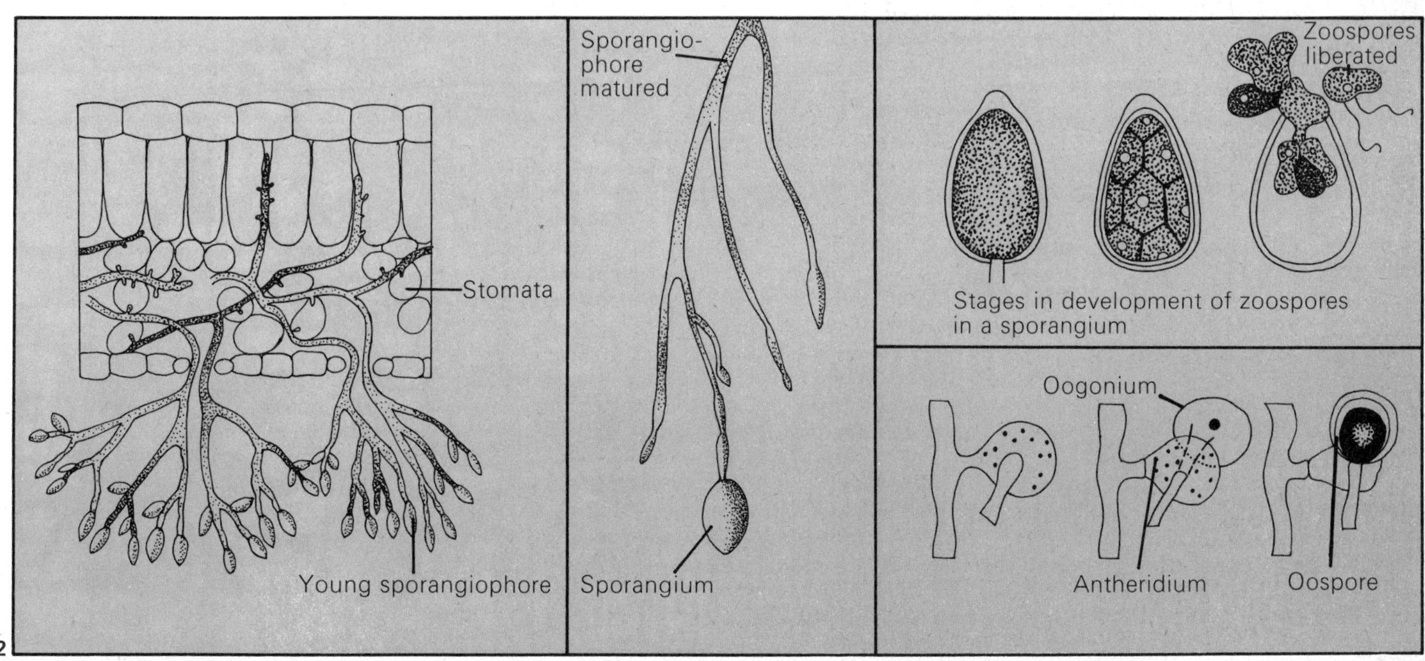


1 Dry rot fungus (*Merulius lacrymans)* can cause severe and extensive damage to badly ventilated timbers, such as those used in buildings.
2 Potato blight (*Phytophthora infestans*) attacks the leaves of potato plants (left). The sporangia (centre) contain the zoospores (top right) used in asexual reproduction. Development of oospores for sexual reproduction is shown bottom right.

most fungi is called the *mycelium* and consists of a tangled mass of colourless branching *hyphae* or filaments. Within the protoplasm of the hyphae are numerous tiny nuclei, similar in structure to the nuclei of the cells of other plants and animals. A few species have a much more complicated thallus, while there are some with a more primitive structure enclosed in a tiny membrane.

Fungi reproduce by spores, of which there are many kinds, but each is a cell containing protoplasm and surrounded by a protective wall. Spores are so light that they can be carried by the slightest breeze to any part of the Earth's surface; they are found even in the air over the North Pole. They remain alive for a considerable time after release from the parent plant and develop only when they alight on a damp substance. Some are so resistant that they have germinated after being kept in storage for over 30 years.

Germination of the spores of most fungi is normally induced by the presence of moisture, which releases the *amoeboid body*. This evolves into two or more cells capable of movement by means of flagellae.

Mushrooms and toadstools 'bloom' in damp woods and fields in the autumn, when conditions are right for the production of spores. A ripe mushroom or toadstool produces up to 40 million spores an hour, while a puffball the size of a football can release as many as 7,000 million spores. Therefore it is not surprising that fungus spores are present in the air in vast numbers and that a piece of fungus-free soil exposed to the air can develop a growth of fungi in a matter of minutes.

Much of our knowledge of fungus physiology is derived from the study of the *Mucor* genus, responsible for moulds on bread and jams.

When growing on the surface of jam, *Mucor* absorbs glucose in solution, together with oxygen from the air. While doing so, it has normal respiration, so releasing carbon dioxide, water and free energy. In the deeper layers of the jam the mycelium of some species may respire *anaerobically* (without air), thereby converting the glucose into alcohol and carbon dioxide. This probably accounts for the alcoholic smell and taste in jams that are being fermented by the respiratory activities of Mucor growth.

Research into the life of *Aspergillus*, another fungoid mould, shows that when growth is suspended or limited, the amount of carbon dioxide released is such that it is reasonable to suppose that practically all the glucose absorbed is completely broken down to carbon dioxide and water, and that the free energy is being dissipated as heat. But when the mould is

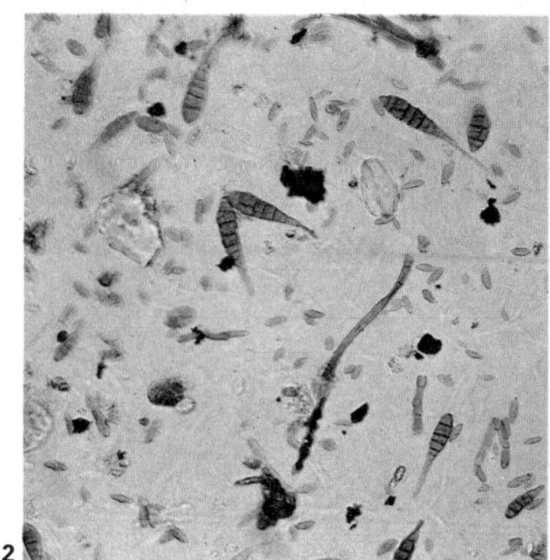

**1** Lichens, a mutually beneficial partnership of an alga and a fungus, are the most widely distributed of all plants. They are able to live clinging to bare rock in cold, exposed positions.
**2** Air contains a wide variety of fungus spores. This sample was trapped on a fly paper.
**3** Some fungi can devastate crops and cause famine. The best known of these in the Western world is the potato blight, which was responsible for the famine in Ireland in the nineteenth century.
**4** Bread mould (*Mucor mucedo*) thrives on damp bread, where its sexual reproductive cycle can be observed. Two progametangia from separate growths unite to form a single gametangium. When mature, this breaks away from the supporting side branches, and after a period of rest germinates rapidly to form a new growth when it finds a suitable base material.

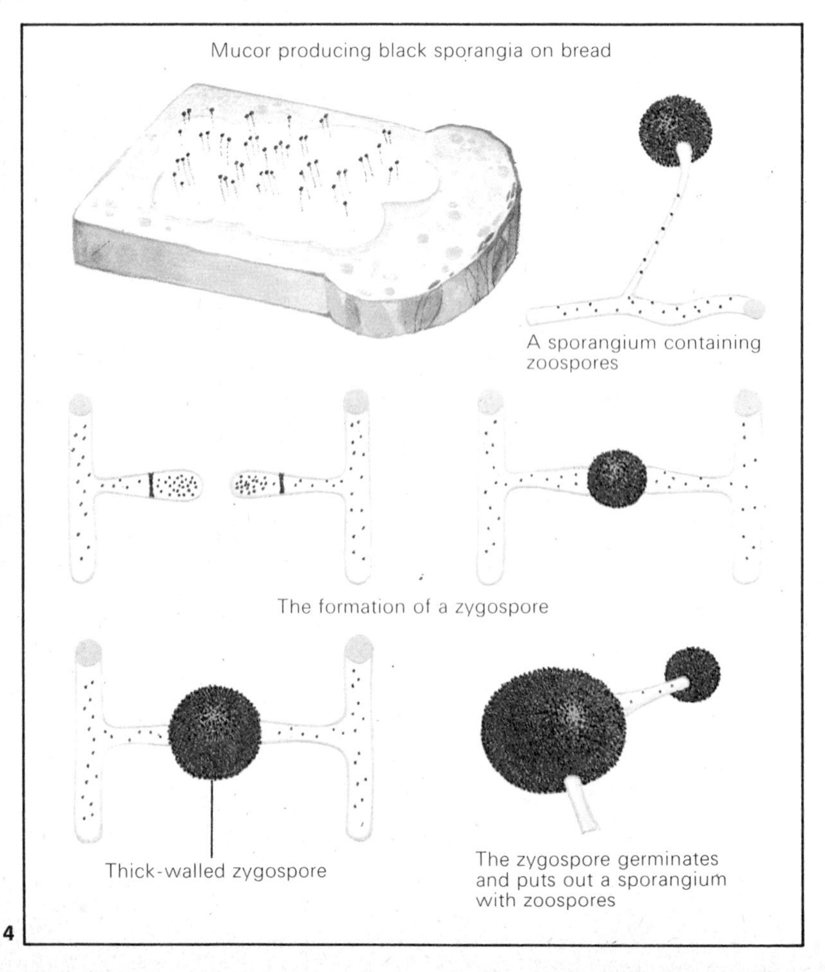

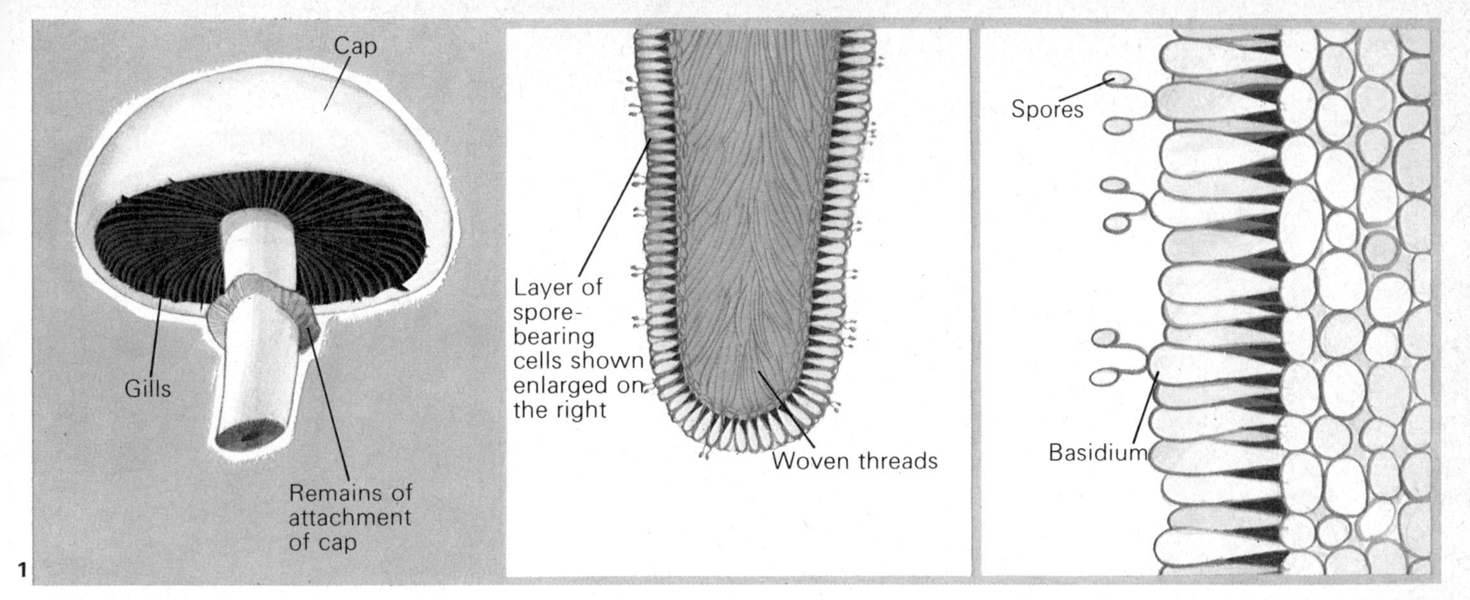

1 Mushrooms reproduce asexually by spores on the gills beneath the cap, or *sporophore.* As the section of gill shows, each basidium produces only two spores, which mature and fall away from the parent plant.

2 *Calocera viscosa,* commonly known as the Beautiful Horn, is common in pine woods in Scotland, where it grows on dead trees.

3 Earth stars (*Gaestrum bryantii*) derive their star shape from splitting of the thick outer layer.

4 Many fungi, such as mushrooms, are edible, but others are extremely poisonous. Very often, the poisonous varieties can be distinguished by their brilliant colouring, which acts as a danger signal.

growing normally, the heat released is much greater than might be expected from the amount of carbon dioxide liberated. Also, the amount released under these conditions is apparently less than would be expected from a complete conversion of all the glucose absorbed by the mycelium. Careful interpretation of these phenomena suggests that respiration in fungi results in the formation of compounds intermediate between sugar and the final products of respiration. It is these compounds that are responsible for the growth of the fungus.

## Fungal reproduction

That fungi release an appreciable amount of heat is proved by the fact that the leaves of plants attacked by certain parasitic fungi have a higher surface temperature than do unaffected leaves. In other words, fungoid disease may be a form of vegetable fever which gives diseased leaves a 'temperature'.

Fungi are sub-divided into three main classes: *Phycomycetes, Ascomycetes,* and *Basidiomycetes.* This classification is based on their reproductive systems.

Phycomycetes are algae-like fungi and include a variety of species ranging from the saprophytic common green mould that forms on stale bread to the parasitic *Peronospora* which infests vines. Other Phycomycetes are *Pythium,* which causes 'damping off' of seedlings, and the notorious *Phytophthora,* which caused the potato blight responsible for the disastrous Irish famine.

Ascomycetes or sac fungi commonly reproduce asexually by means of a reproductive body in which eight spores arise in a slim sac or capsule called the *ascus.* One of the best known Ascomycetes is the blue or green mould *Penicillin,* which is a common parasite of citrus fruits and is the source of the antibiotic named after it. Included in the Ascomycetes classification are the fungi responsible for brown rot on peaches, rye ergot, Dutch elm disease, apple scab and chestnut blight. The yeasts are classed as Ascomycetes, though they rarely produce sacs. Truffles and morels are edible species of Ascomycetes.

Basidiomycetes, or club fungi, produce their own spores on short, blunt 'stems' or clubs, often on the surface of the vertical pores or gill-like plates under the caps of mushrooms. They range in size from the microscopic species that cause smut on cereals to puffballs and cap fungi. Death cap, hairy ring, Jew's ear and shaggy parasols are all club fungi, as are those responsible for rust on wheat.

*Myxomycetes,* or slime moulds, are rather border-line cases for fungi classification. They go through a stage of life-cycle in which they resemble amoeba, a very elementary form of animal life in which shape is subject to constant alteration. Myxomycetes are found in damp woodlands and in their amoeba stage have many nuclei. Their tiny, erect spore cases are marvels of delicate design.

## Disease in plants and animals

Then there are the so-called 'imperfect' fungi. These lack sexual reproductive parts and are as yet unclassified. Imperfect fungi include those responsible for ringworm and athlete's foot. Their life history is not fully understood, but as mycologists establish the life-cycle of individual species they assign them to a recognized classification.

Parasitic fungi do such enormous damage to farm, garden and forest vegetation that it is worth examining how they induce

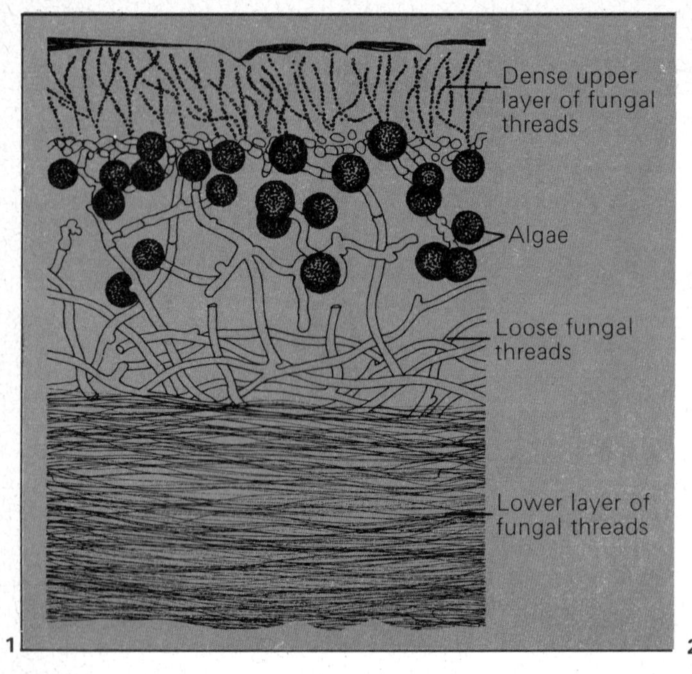


**1** A sectional drawing of the thallus of a lichen shows the intimate relationship between the spherical algal cells and the dense fungal hyphae which attach the plant to the substrate.

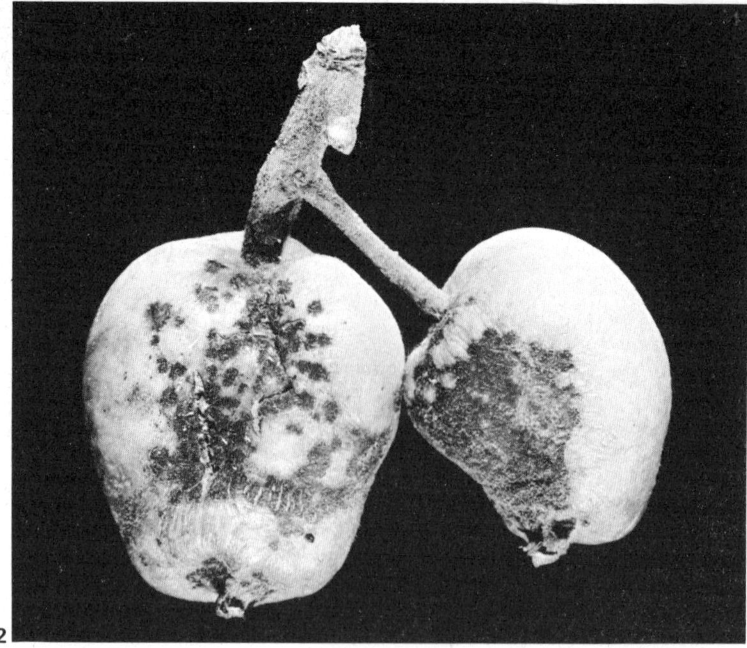

**2** Apple scab, caused by the fungus *Venturia inaequalis,* is the most widespread of apple diseases. It attacks both the leaves and the fruit of the tree.

the diseases for which they are responsible. They do this in a variety of ways, all of which provide valuable pictures of fungi life-cycles.

*Pythium* fungus, the cause of 'damping off' of seedlings, attacks its victim at ground level, where it softens the young plant tissues so that the seedlings fall over. The fungus sinks its mycelium into the seedling and produces sporangia, spherical swellings, in which the spores, called zoospores, are formed. The zoospores possess two minute cilia, hair-like organs which enable them to swim in a drop of water.

Pythium activity is encouraged by excessive moisture, but in very dry conditions the sporangia can germinate directly into new mycelia without the formation of zoospores.

## A common pest

A particularly common saprophytic fungus is *Rhizopus nigricans.* It is familiar to housewives as the common bread mould, but also attacks fresh fruit, besides being able to multiply on decaying vegetation. It flourishes in normal temperatures on damp bread, pastes, rotting potatoes, preserved fruits or any substances containing starch or sugar.

The leaves of some plants, particularly hop, strawberry and gooseberry, are subject to attack by the species of fungi which cause white powder mildew. A notorious example is *Sphaerotheca,* which is responsible for a very destructive infestation called American gooseberry mildew. When a spore germinates, it forms a white, web-like coating over the leaf and sinks a disc called a *holdfast* or *hepteron* into the leaf's epidermal cells.

Throughout summer, infection of the leaf is spread by liberation of *conidia,* the oval spores produced along the external hyphae of the mycelium. In late summer sex organs form on the mycelium and after fertilization, there the asci, the spherical fruit bodies with thick walls make their appearance. When mature, the asci are black or dark brown and can be seen on the infected leaves. Within them are the spores which spread the infection in spring.

Rust fungi are among the 14,000 species classed as Basidiomycetes. They induce destructive diseases of cereals and grasses and derive their name from the rust-red streaks made on the stem and leaves of their host plants. Reproduction is simple, without normal fusion of male and female elements. The spores, called *basidiospores,* are produced externally on stalks from the *basidium* or mother cell.

Black rust is a fungus disease of wheat. The mycelium grows within the host plant's tissues and in summer produces blister-like prominences containing *Uredospores,* which are rust-red. These spores are blown off their stalks by the wind and infect other plants.

Yeasts are species of Ascomycetes that Man has domesticated for use in the brewing of beer and the making of bread. Yeasts are simple types of fungi and do not have well-developed mycelia, but occur as single ovoid cells. The cells, or yeast 'plants', reproduce by budding, when the cell develops a small protuberance which grows until it is as big as the parent, from which it then separates.

Certain fungi are *pathogenic* to Man and are responsible for a number of diseases, including skin infections such as ringworm and athlete's foot. The skin infections are due to species of fungi which have the property of being able to derive nutrient from *karatin,* a component of the skin. Scalp ringworm in children is caused by a fungus called *Microsporum audouni. Actinomycis bovis* is a fungus often present on the teeth and in the tonsils of healthy people, but with unhealthy persons the fungus rapidly multiplies and manifests itself as a disease called *actinomycosis.* This begins with swellings which eventually discharge colonies of the fungus which then attack the jaw, the subcutaneous tissues of the face and, in very serious cases, the liver and lungs. One of the most serious fungoid diseases is *torulosis,* which can develop into meningitis.

Man is always exposed to the threat of airborne fungi, particularly the spores of the saprophytes. A serious source of fungoid infection is the eating of unwashed fruit and vegetables.

Nevertheless, it would be a mistake to dismiss fungi as destructive pests. Mushrooms and truffles are a valuable food, while penicillin and aureomycin derive from fungi and constitute one of the most important weapons used by medicine in the fight against disease and infection. There are also fungi which are a source of such vital products as citric acid and vitamins.

## Benevolent parasites

Although fungi destroy plant life they are sometimes necessary to its reproduction and healthy growth. Certain orchids and plants of the heath family indicate infection by fungi, yet if the plants are treated to rid them of the fungi they do not develop healthy seedlings. Others do not even germinate their seeds unless fungi have been present on the plant at some stage.

Saprophytic fungi are essential to Man's very existence by feeding on dead organic material and accelerating the release of nitrates, potash and sulphates. These minerals are then taken up by new and growing plants, many of which are eaten by Man or consumed by animals which Man then eats.

Directly or indirectly, fungi are important to Man and his nutrition. Despite their lack of chlorophyll, which puts them in an inferior category of plant life, they nevertheless constitute a class of plants of particular biological significance, as a food, as food for his animals, and as a source of drugs and chemicals.

# The diversity of flowering plants

The flowers in our gardens, the fruit in our homes and the corn in the field are all the products of the angiosperms, the diverse, beautiful and useful world of flowering plants.

**1** Barley, one of the grasses, is an extremely important angiosperm, economically. Both seed and stalk provide food for human beings and animals.
**2** Weeds like burdock often have seeds with hooked bristles which attach themselves to the coats of animals. In this way, the seeds are distributed over a wide area.

| | Dicotyledons | Monocotyledons |
|---|---|---|
| **Cotyledons** | Two | One |
| **Stems** | Vascular bundle in a ring. Secondary thickening common. | Vascular bundles scattered. Secondary thickening very rare. |
| **Leaves** | Venation net-formed with branches ending freely. | Venation usually parallel. No free ends to veins. |
| **Flowers** | Flower parts in fours or fives. | Flower parts in threes. |

BOTANISTS IN THE EARLY YEARS of the science were faced with very great problems. They looked at the vast diversity of the plant world, and tried in various ways to group plants into families and orders so as to bring out the relationships between different species. First attempts to do this were inevitably confused by the limited state of knowledge, particularly by the lack of knowledge of the internal and microscopic structure of the plants and by the lack of understanding of their life-cycles. The first of these attempts in the modern period was that made by Paul Hermann at the end of the seventeenth century. Hermann grouped the plants according to the form of their seeds.

The names he used in his classification are still used today, although they are not applied in the same way. Hermann divided the flowering plants into two groups: the *gymnosperms,* plants with only one seed to each fruit; and *angiosperms,* plants with more than one seed to each fruit.

## Dominating the plant world

The great Swedish botanist Linnaeus continued the use of these names in a similar way, though in a slightly more restricted sense. It was not until 1851 that Wilhelm Hofmeister discovered the basic differences in the reproduction of the gymnosperms and angiosperms. Since Hofmeister's discovery, botanists have used these two names in a different way from Hermann and Linnaeus. Nowadays, angiosperms embrace all true flowering plants, while the term gymnosperms is restricted to the true 'naked seeded' plants.

Like all other living things plants are subject to the laws of evolution. In general, the trend of plant evolution has been to develop plants able to live on land and less dependent on water for reproduction and the continuation of the species. The angiosperms or flowering plants are at present the highest point in this development. They are also the most recent of the various types of plants to develop. They are now the dominant form of vegetation on the Earth's surface; that is to say, most of the plants we see around us are angiosperms. Directly or indirectly, they provide us with nearly all our food, and most of the economically important plants are angiosperms. Among them are all the grasses and grains, most of the trees and shrubs, and all the flowering plants.

The angiosperms are the most diverse of all types of plants. Included in the division are more than 300 families and over a quarter of a million species. They range from the tiny duckweed, with its simple floating leaves, its simple shoot and its rudimentary vertical root, to great forest trees with vast root systems and branches reaching 100 or more feet from the ground. The angiospermous trees are an important source of lumber and fuel. Other angiosperms provide textiles, like cotton; drugs, like quinine; and vegetable oils, like ground-nut oil. The grasses support cattle – a major source of protein – and also provide us with bread, rice and other grain foods. The roots and tubers of several angiosperm plants are valuable sources of food; examples are potatoes, beets, carrots, turnips and parsnips. In other plants, the leaves are sources of food. The lettuce, spinach and cabbage are examples. Examples of flowers, fruits and seeds of angiosperms used as food are even more numerous. The flowers of the cauliflower and broccoli, the seeds of corn and rice, and the fruits of oranges, apples, tomatoes and grapes provide a substantial part of our diet. From the human point of view, the angiosperms are by far the most important plants on Earth.

The angiosperms divide naturally into two groups. These two groups differ markedly in their internal anatomy and in their history. They take their names from the fact that one of the groups, the *monocotyledons,* has only one seed leaf *(cotyledon)* while the other group, the *dicotyledons,* has two. The dicotyledons form by far the larger of the two groups. They have the faculty of being able to grow in thickness by depositing a tissue called cambium in their stem throughout life. This faculty is absent in the monocotyledons, and where they do grow in thickness, it is by some other mechanism. Most of the monocotyledons are small plants, and the

Pollination by insects is very common among angiosperms. Butterflies play a large part, and often the morphology of the flower dictates which insect is able to carry out the operation.
**2** The distinctive foetid smell from the arum lily encourages insects to crawl down inside the flower, depositing pollen already gathered from other plants.
**3** The torch lily (*Kniphofia uvaria*) has distinct colouring which helps attract particular insects during pollination.
**4** The wind-borne tufts of 'old man's beard' are a familiar sight in the country hedgerows of Britain. The red berries are of the Black Bryony, *(Tamus communis)*.
**5** Grasses normally use wind dispersal of seeds, which are carried to favourable growing positions when they are ripe. In the case of commercial crops, this dispersal is done artificially.

group contains only one great tree family – the palms. The two groups also differ in the structure of their leaves. The leaves of most monocotyledons are narrow, and veins in the leaves run parallel.

Many dicotyledons have broad leaves in which the veins form a network. In monocotyledons, the parts of the flowers are usually found in threes, while in the dicotyledons the flowers usually have four or five of each part. Clearly, these two groups are quite distinct, and the fossil evidence indicates that they separated from each other and evolved in different ways from an early date.

Among the important monocotyledons are the plants belonging to the lily family, which includes the tulips and the hyacinths. The arum lily, which belongs to a different family, is also a monocotyledon. Rushes, snowdrops, irises and sedges are widespread families of monocotyledons. The two most important groups, from an economic point of view, are the *Palmeae*, the palms, and the *Gramineae*, the grasses, which include the bamboos and most of the economically important grain-bearing plants.

The dicotyledons include such varied

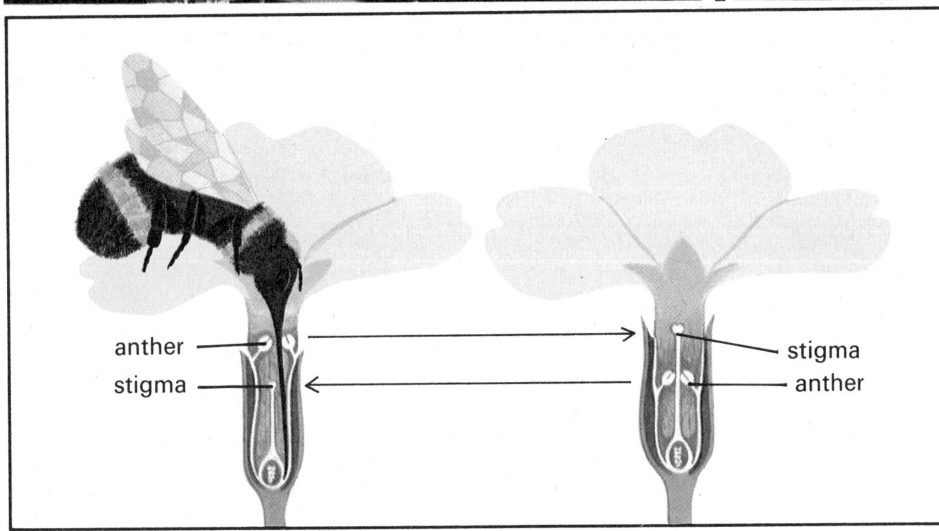

**1, 2** Fruit and vegetables are among the many commercially useful angiosperms, which provide food for Man and also for his domesticated animals which are secondary food sources.
**3** Some angiosperms are anatomically adapted so that pollen grains from the anther are deposited on the right part of the insect's proboscis for deposition on the stigma of another flower, thus excluding self-pollination.
**4** Pin-eyed and thrum-eyed primroses show the anatomical differences involved in the prevention of self-pollination.

plants as oaks, beeches and chestnuts, all of which belong to the family of *Fagaceae*. The alders and birches belong to a similar family. Roses, carnations, sycamores, peas and cactuses are all representatives of various families of dicotyledons. The buttercup family, the *Ranunculaceae,* is a very ancient one, and is thought by many botanists to be the oldest existing family of flowering plants. Certainly, magnolias and laurels are found in fossil form in cretaceous rocks, and these plants are closely related to the buttercup.

The main feature distinguishing angiosperms from the other main types of plant is their mode of reproduction. This is sufficiently similar in all angiosperms to mark them off from the other types of plant. On the other hand, the mode of reproduction varies in detail so greatly from one flowering plant to another as to make it impossible to give more than a sketch of the variety of methods used by flowering plants. Most people are familiar with the outlines of the reproductive process in flowering plants – the transfer of pollen from the male stamen to the female stigma, the fertilization of the female germ cells and the development of a fruit containing the seeds. The details of the process vary very widely.

The means of transfer of pollen, the type of insect involved, the adaptation of the flower to attract a particular type of insect, the detailed structure of the stamen and stigma, the type of fruit – all these factors differ greatly from family to family and even within the same family. There are many examples of plants adapted in the most precise fashion to fit into a particular environment. An interesting tropical example is the very beautiful *Yucca* lily. This plant is totally dependent on a particular species of moth, the yucca-moth. The female yucca-moth lays its eggs in the seed-box of the lily, and deposits with the egg a laboriously collected ball of pollen. The pollen fertilizes the flower and the seeds develop and swell, providing food for the caterpillars when they emerge. Although the caterpillars eat some of the seeds they do not eat all of them, and the lily is thus able to reproduce alongside the moth. This is only one example of the remarkably close relationships that exist between many flowers and the insects that pollinate them.

The process of reproduction in angiosperms can be divided into five stages. These are: sporogenesis, the production of flowers; the development of the pollen and ovaries; pollination; fertilization; and the development of the embryos into seeds and fruit.

In the case of the buttercup, the yellow petals are overlaid by *sepals,* the green, leaf-like structures which originally protected the budding flower. Inside the petals, of which the buttercup has five, lie a number of fine stalks with bulbous ends surrounding a central cluster of small spiky organs which individually are similar in shape to tear-drops. The stalks with

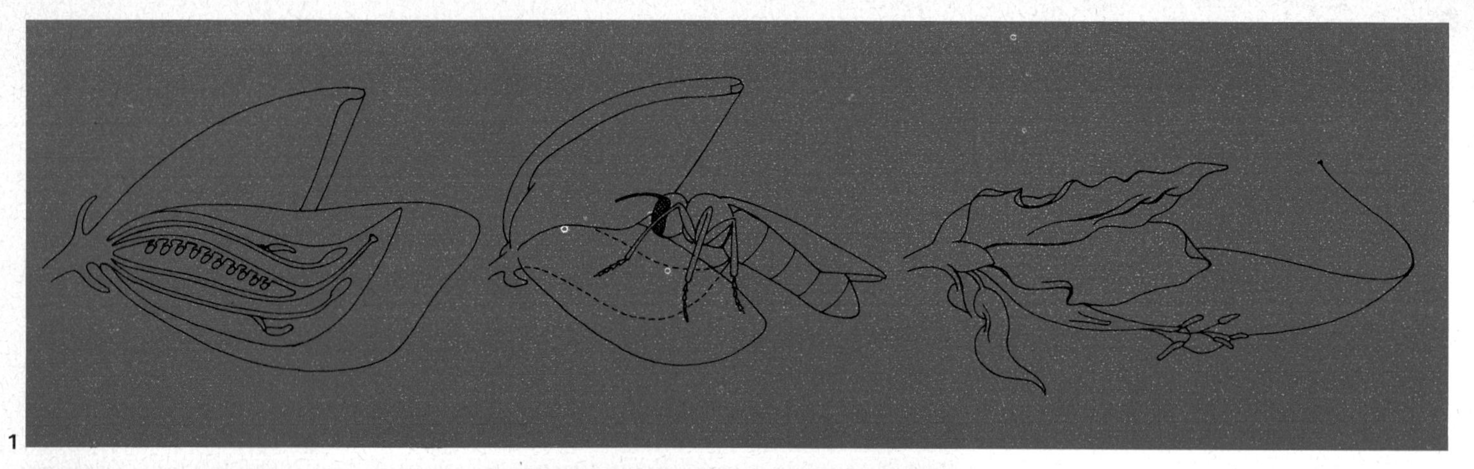

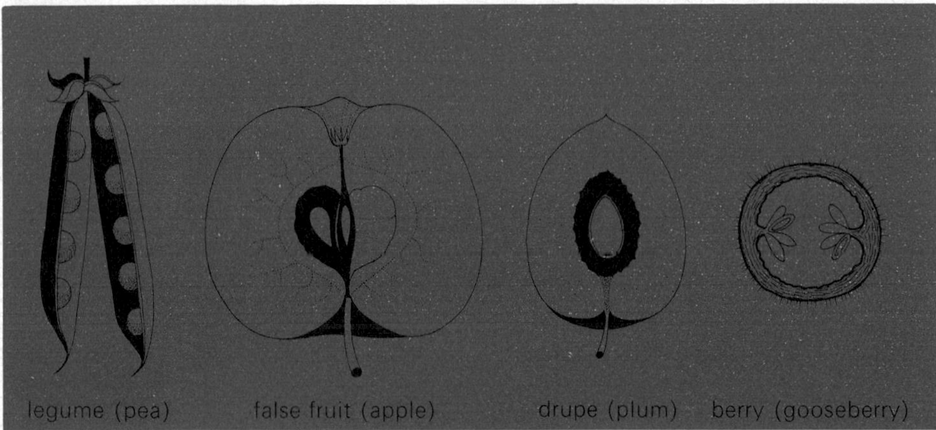


**1** The petals which attract insects by their scent and colour during pollination wither and die when the process has been completed and the seed is ready for distribution.
**2** Fruits are a means of encouraging seed distribution by animals, and of protecting the seed from damage. Some fruits contain only one seed, while others have several.

bulbous ends are the male organs – the stalks are called *filaments* and the bulbous ends are called *anthers* and carry the pollen. The central cluster is called the *calyx,* and each of the spike-shaped organs are individual *carpels,* containing ovaries.

Sporogenesis is the preparation of the flower, and particularly the anthers and the ovaries, for reproduction. Inside the anther are a number of germ cells which are responsible for the production of pollen. This they do by dividing into four to produce a group of cells called a *tetrad.* The cells of the tetrad contain only one of each pair of chromosomes. The cells of the tetrad rapidly become fully fledged pollen cells, complete with the distinctive markings characteristic of their species. Inside the budding flower, the ovaries undergo a parallel process of development. Each ovule produces a single mother cell which divides into four cells with only half the normal complement of genetic material. Three of these cells rapidly degenerate, although they may remain in the mature ovary as remnants called antipodal cells. Thus, each ovary contains one cell capable of being fertilized by a male cell. The ovule is inside the ovary, and in the case of the buttercup is surmounted by a small, thick, protruding part called the *style.* At the top of the style is a specialized surface for receiving the pollen grains known as the *stigma.*

In many plants, the development of the flower is so arranged that the pollen and the ovaries ripen at slightly different times. The purpose of this arrangement is to ensure that the flower does not pollinate itself. Cross-pollination is a great advantage in reproduction, as it means that the genetic material of the offspring is constantly interchanged with material from other plants of the same or related species. This makes sure that the race will develop and makes variation possible. It is undoubtedly this characteristic feature of the flowering plants that is responsible for their great diversity. Many plants have an elaborate mechanism to ensure cross-pollination.

The ripening of the anthers leads them to open and shed their pollen. This pollen is transferred, by one means or another, by gravity, wind, insects, animals or water, to the surface of the stigma.

*Palynology,* a specialized branch of botany, deals with the identification of the source of pollen grains by the markings on their surface.

## The process of pollination

Once on the surface of the stigma, which may be sticky or in some other way adapted to trap and hold the grains of pollen, the pollen grains rapidly develop long outgrowths called pollen tubes, which grow into the tissue of the stigma and style. Provided a sufficient number of pollen grains have landed on the surface of the stigma, one at least will grow a pollen tube towards the opening of the ovary, the *micropyle.* The favoured pollen tube grows through the micropyle and makes contact with the female ovule. Once the contact has been made, the pollen tube bursts, releasing the male cells into contact with the female cells. In the case of flowering plants, each pollen cell releases two nuclei. One of these fertilizes the female cell and the other combines with the residual nuclei left over from the process of division by which the female cell was developed. This process – double fertilization – is a characteristic of angiosperms.

Fertilization stimulates the growth and enlargement of the tissues surrounding the fertilized female cell. The development of these tissues eventually forms the fruit. At the same time, the fertilized female cell divides and forms a rudimentary plant. This plant is the germ of the seed. At a certain point, the plant stops developing and becomes dormant.

## Broadcasting the seeds

The embryo plant is contained inside a number of enveloping tissues which form the seed coats. In addition, the ovary of the flower may become a fleshy container for the seeds. In this case, it is called a fruit. There are a wide variety of ways of distributing the seeds once they become ripe or ready for distribution. In some plants, like the vetches, the fruits burst violently, releasing the seeds over a wide area. In others, like the dandelion, the seeds are provided with tiny parachutes of fine hairs to enable them to travel with the wind. In others, the seeds are designed to be carried by water or to tangle in the coats of animals. If the seed is carried to a favourable spot, it germinates and develops into a new plant.

This process is called sexual reproduction, since it involves the bringing together of male and female cells. Many angiosperms, however, have well-developed methods of asexual or vegetative reproduction. The strawberry, for example, can spread over a wide area by putting out shoots, called runners, the tips of which take root and give rise to fresh strawberry plants. There are a number of variations on this method of reproduction. A typical example of asexual propagation is the ability of cut shoots to take root and develop – an ability often exploited by gardeners.

The amazing variety and adaptability of the angiosperms have made them the most widespread and successful of all the different groups of plants. They are a remarkable illustration of the adaptability of living tissue to their widely varying environmental circumstances.

# Next year's flowers

Higher animals may be either male or female. Plants may also be male or female – or more often both. But despite differences, sexuality in plants and animals serves the same basic purpose.

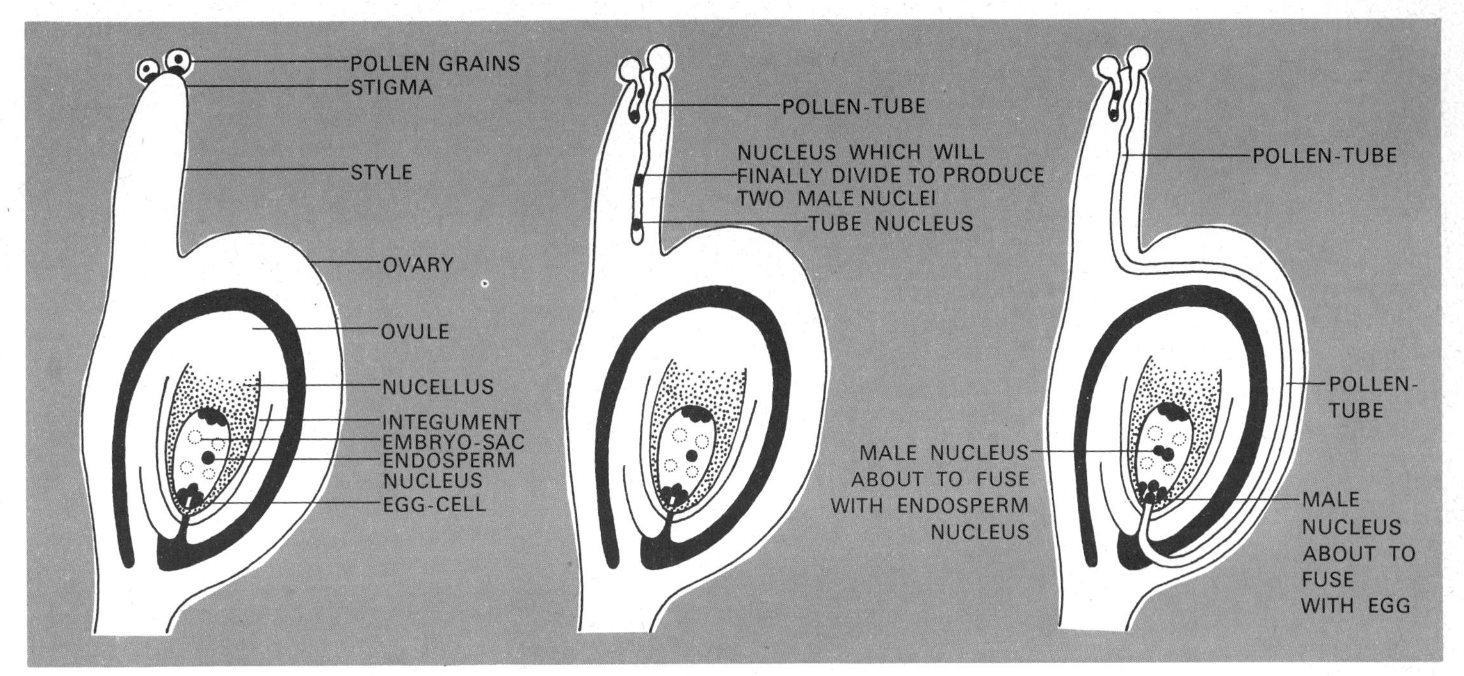


MOST PEOPLE associate the idea of sex exclusively with the world of animals, and particularly those animals which show distinct separations into males and females. But 'sexuality' is known throughout the living world, including plants. Of course, sexuality in plants is not exactly like that in animals, but there are close parallels.

The discovery of sexual reproduction in flowering plants is usually attributed to Rudolf Camerarius who noted in 1694 that in certain plant species not all individuals were capable of producing seeds. Yet these 'unproductive' plants were necessary, because the others which were capable of producing seeds would not do so in their absence. He found that for seed to be formed on potentially seed-bearing plants, it was necessary for *pollen* to be carried to them from the 'unproductive' plants.

## Similar functions

Camerarius transferred the pollen by hand; he recognized that, in nature, wind and insects would transfer the pollen from one type of plant to the other. He thought of pollen as a 'fertilizing agent', that is, a substance ensuring fertility, similar in function to the semen of animals which is also essential for the production of offspring. For the same reason he thought of the two types of plants as male (pollen-bearing) and female (seed-bearing).

But while Camerarius may have 'discovered' sexuality in plants in the scientific sense, he was by no means the first to notice that in certain species of plants some individuals are apparently either male or female. The Arabs knew that *pollen* from 'male' date-palms had to be transferred to seed-bearing 'female' date-palms or no fruit would be produced. Since 'male' trees are economically unproductive (they do not yield fruit) but occupy the same amount of space and need the same amount of water as the 'females', very few 'males' were grown. The pollen from these 'male' plants was collected and later used to *pollinate* the flowers of the 'female' plants to ensure a maximum yield of dates.

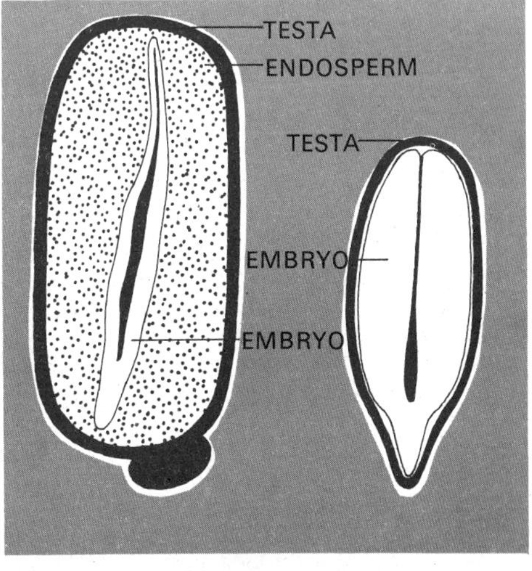


*Above left,* the first phase of fertilization occurs when a pollen grain successfully lands on the pistil. *Above centre,* a pollen-tube begins to grow down through the pistil in search of the ovule. *Above right,* fertilization is completed when a male nucleus fuses with an egg. *Left,* some mature seeds carry food (endosperm) within them; in others, the embryo fills the whole seed.

Though some species of plants produce distinct 'male' and 'female' individuals, such as date-palms, it is more usual for a plant to be bi-sexual, i.e. both 'male' and 'female' at the same time. The pollen is produced in the *stamens,* which are arranged round the central *pistil* of the flowers from which the new generation will subsequently develop.

Without pollination, there is no sexual reproduction. Many plants pollinate themselves: in some, pollen from the stamens is shed directly on to the pistil of the same flower, or is commonly taken by insects to other flowers of the same plant. However, some plants cannot pollinate themselves; the pollen from a stamen is not effective if transferred to the pistil of the same or another flower of the same plant.

For these species, the pollen from one plant must be transferred to an entirely separate plant for pollination to be effective and for seeds to set. This operation in nature is hazardous at best, and the structure of the stamens and pistil have evolved to make this vital transfer as efficient as possible. When the flower is mature, it opens and the stamens release the pollen which has been formed.

## Insect pollination

At about the same time, the pistils develop a receptive surface called *stigma* to receive the pollen. The receptive stigma surface is generally raised above the other parts of the flower on a long, stalk-like structure called the *style.*

The majority of plant species rely on insects to effect the transfer of pollen. The insects are attracted by coloured floral parts, by pollen or nectar as food, by the odour of the flowers (scented or foetid). In travelling from flower to flower and from plant to plant, the insect deposits pollen and so effects pollination.

Many plants are wind-pollinated; these produce vast quantities of dust-like pollen which, being almost weightless, is suspended in the atmosphere. The stigmas of flowers which are wind-pollinated are generally feathery or covered with large projections. Wind-blown pollen is 'filtered' from the air on these exposed and specialized stigmatic surfaces. The transference of pollen by wind is characteristic of catkin-bearing trees and of grasses; it distresses some humans who are allergic to pollen, by causing the symptoms of 'hay-fever'. The flowers of these plants are not conspicuous and generally consist of little more than the essential organs. A few other specialized methods of pollen-transfer are known; the agencies responsible include water-currents, bats and birds, and perhaps strangest of all, snails! There are also a number of species in which 'pollen-transfer' cannot be said to occur: their pollen is shed directly from the stamens on to the stigma soon after the flower opens. In the most extreme cases, the pollination is effected even before the flowers open.

## Fertilization

The next stage of the reproductive process is invisible to the naked eye as it takes place inside the tissues of the pistil, and to understand it one must know something of the structure of that organ. The base of the pistil is expanded into the *ovary*, on the inner surface of which the *ovules* are formed. Each ovule contains at maturity a large central cell, the *embryo-sac*. There are several nuclei within the mature embryo-sac; one is the functional gamete, the *ovum*. Two other nuclei (the *polar* nuclei) are often closely associated together, or even united into a single secondary nucleus. Both the ovum and the polar nuclei are involved in the formation of viable seed.

Pollen grains, when transferred to a receptive stigma, each put out a long, slender tube which grows down inside the tissues of the pistil towards the ovary. When it reaches the ovary, the tip of the pollen-tube grows into an ovule and discharges its two nuclei into the embryo-sac. One of these male gametes fertilizes the ovum and from the resulting *zygote* an embryo develops. The other male gamete fuses with the polar nuclei; the *endosperm* is the tissue which is formed from this union. The endosperm develops first, utilizing food supplied by the parent plant. The

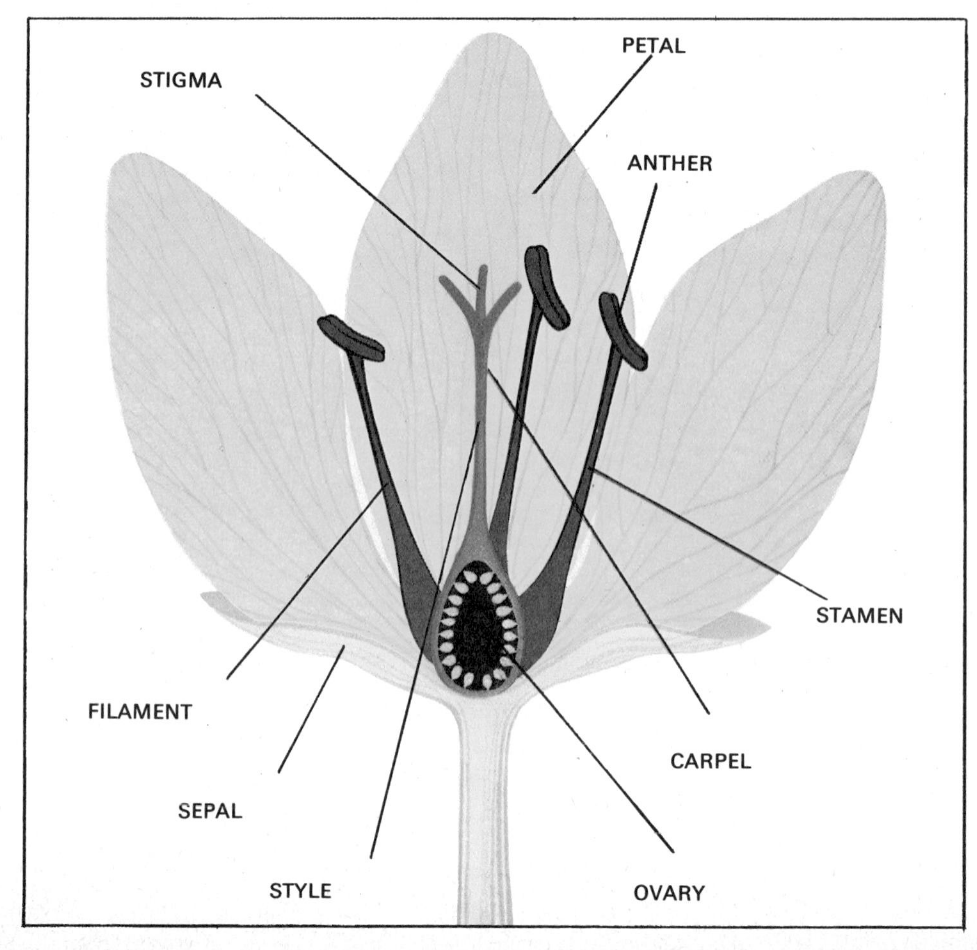


*Top,* some flowering plants can be 'male' (left) and 'female' (right) at different times. This helps to prevent self-pollination. *Above right,* the hazel tree ensures cross-pollination with hanging male catkins which shed pollen on the red stigmas of female flowers when jostled by a breeze. *Above left,* a dissection of a magnolia reveals its basic structure. The long barrel-like structure in the centre is the pistil, and the surrounding red filaments are the stamens. The stamens are shorter than the pistil as a physical safeguard against self-pollination. *Right,* though varying widely from species to species, the essential parts of a flower are the same. The stamens are 'male', the pistil is 'female', and the ultimate goal is fertilization.

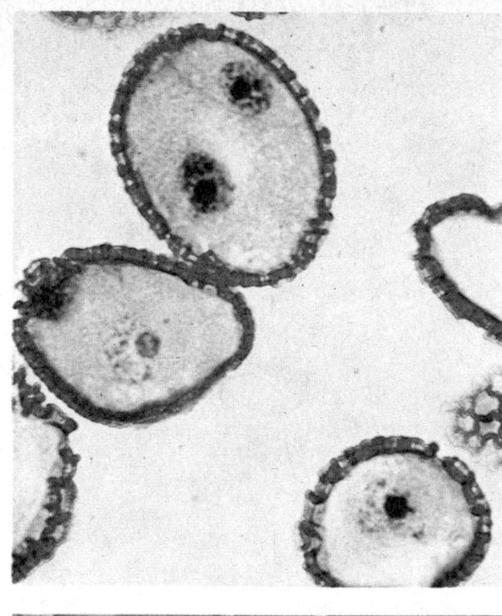

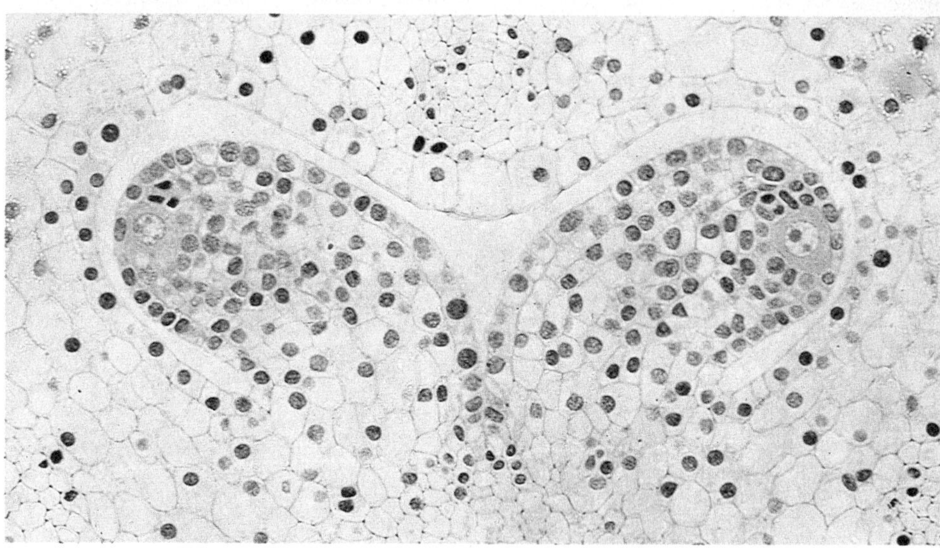

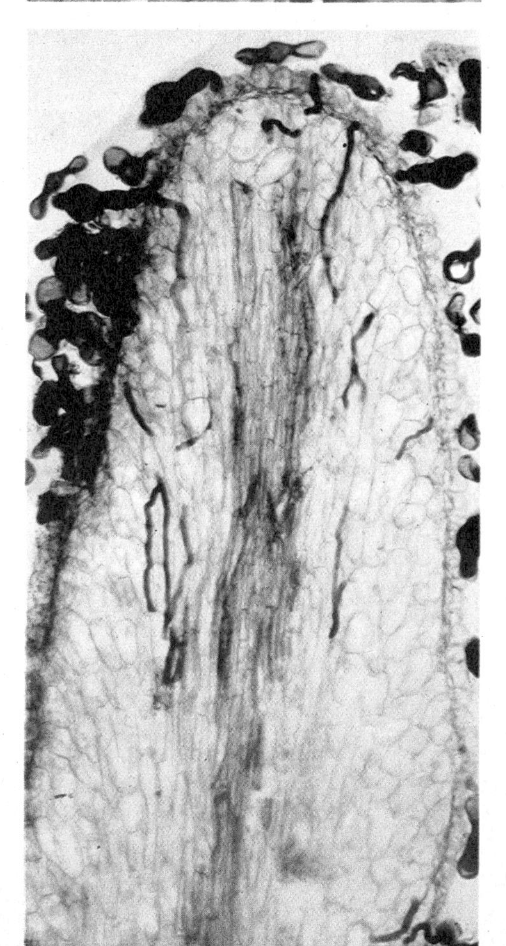

*Top left,* cross-section of pollen grains, magnified more than 300 times, clearly reveals the two nuclei inside. *Top right,* bees and other insects pick up pollen from the stamens of one flower and carry it to the pistil of another, aiding in cross-fertilization; although the insect can also pollinate the pistil of the same flower, thereby aiding self-fertilization. *Above left,* most flowers attract insects by their colour and/or smell, but the fly orchid attracts pollen-carriers by disguising its flowers as other insects ready for mating. *Above right,* a cross-section of an ovule-megaspore mother cell from which female nuclei will be produced. *Left,* a stigma with numerous pollen grains, some growing into the pistil.

embryo-sac is enlarged as a consequence and becomes filled with nutritive material. Initially, the zygote lies at one end of the embryo-sac but by transverse divisions, a row of cells is formed towards the centre of the embryo-sac; the innermost cell of the row begins to divide in other planes. The resulting sphere of cells is the beginning of the embryo proper. It enlarges, comes to occupy a more central position, becomes more elongated, and differentiates one or two embryonic leaves at one end. All this development takes place at the expense of the endosperm, and ultimately utilizing food supplied from the parent plant.

At the conclusion of this growth, the ovule has increased considerably in size; its outer layers harden, and a progressive desiccation of its tissues takes place. The ovule becomes a *seed.* The structure of seeds at maturity depends upon the developmental sequence: if all the endosperm is utilized by the developing embryo, the seed coat encloses only a tightly folded embryo; if the embryo does not absorb all of the endosperm, the seed is found to contain a small, often straight embryo, enclosed in a starchy or oily endosperm at maturity.

It is at this stage that the seed is dispersed, either on its own, or enclosed by structures adapted to some particular agent of dispersal. The seed is often *dormant*: a plant will not develop from it immediately even when the seed is in ideal conditions. Such dormant seeds may need a cold treatment, a prolonged leaching by water or the rotting of the outer layers of the seed, before germination will take place. Other seeds develop immediately after they encounter favourable conditions. Germination involves the resumption of growth by the embryo, and a continuation of its development using the food stored within the embryo or endosperm until the new plant has developed enough to be able to photosynthesize and support itself. The plant which develops from the seed is a new individual essentially the same as its parent plant or plants. The cycle of sexual reproduction

*Top left,* insects are often drawn to flowers in search of nectar. This moth, unravelling a tongue longer than its body, is determined to get the nectar, no matter how well it is hidden. *Left,* many plants disperse their seeds by wind, so the seeds must be adapted to this mode of transport, as demonstrated by this wild clematis. *Above,* a wind-dispersed dandelion seed.

has finally reached its ultimate goal.

It remains to ask: 'Why does this complicated sequence of events take place at all when, for example, small detachable buds produced in a simple manner would serve better to reproduce the species?' This question requires two answers: a historical explanation and a genetical interpretation. Let's take the genetical aspect first. There are two fundamentally different types of breeding-system in all living organisms: *out-breeding,* where fertilization takes place between gametes from genetically different individuals, and *in-breeding,* where self-fertilization occurs. Out-breeding in plants is effected by cross-pollination, and in-breeding by self-pollination. Cross-pollination ensures that the genetic variability of a population is maintained, and multitudes of slightly differing genetic types are continually undergoing *natural selection,* which is the basis of evolutionary change. Thus, out-breeding species will always be able to adapt genetically to their environment; it is hardly surprising to find that most species of higher plants are at least partially out-bred.

In contrast, in-breeding reduces the formation of novel types and through the action of natural selection the total variability of a species may be drastically reduced. If the bewildering diversity of floral mechanisms is examined with this in mind, it will be noted that they predominantly favour the transfer of pollen between different flowers and therefore often between individual plants. In many cases cross-pollination is obligate. Species which have flowers producing pollen on separate plants from those bearing ovules (the willows and campions for example), are necessarily cross-pollinated. So are those which are *'self-sterile',* whose pollen will not develop on the stigmas of the plant from which it originated.

Other species rely on subtleties of the floral mechanism to favour out-breeding, though in-breeding is equally possible. In one common type, the pollen is shed at one phase of floral development, and the stigma is receptive at another period; such a flower is effectively 'male' or 'female' to visiting insects at different times.

## Natural deceit

We have already remarked upon the widespread dispersal of pollen in wind-pollinated species; this also favours out-breeding. On occasion, the degrees of adaptation and specialization to effect cross-pollination which has been achieved by natural selection is almost beyond belief. Some orchid flowers so closely resemble species of insects that they are pollinated by male insects attempting to mate with them; flowers of some stapeliads which smell like putrescent meat, and closely resemble it in colour, are pollinated by blow-flies; deceit abounds in nature too!

The other explanation for sexual reproduction lies in the distant past. The aquatic ancestors of land plants probably had *two* parts in their life cycle. One generation reproduced by spores; the next generation reproduced by gametes. For a complete life cycle, *both* generations had to be passed through in an *alternation of generations.*

As the land plants evolved, the water-requiring *gametophyte* (gamete-bearing) generation decreased in importance. Eventually this generation scarcely escaped from the spores; however, the spores became differentiated into a large one, which contained the female gametophyte generation which gave rise to the ovum, and a small one containing the male gametophyte. The large spores were never shed: together with surrounding structures they became seeds. The small spores were liberated: they became pollen. On reaching the ovules, the pollen now developed tubes down which the male gametes passed to reach the ovum: the conifers are at this stage of evolution. The flowering plants have their ovules enclosed in an ovary so that the pollen-tube must now make an even longer journey to reach the ovum. The pollen-tube and embryo-sac are all that remain of the male and female gametophytes respectively. A long evolutionary history underlies the structural complexity of sexual reproduction in flowering plants.

# The biologist in industry

By seeing how Nature can be put to work, biologists have been a great boon to industry. They have shown how to control fermentation, what drugs to make and how to synthesize nutritious food.

BY FAR the great majority of people if asked what place they thought the biologist had in industry would reply, as far as they could see none, because biological research has little to do with industry. It is perhaps easy enough to get this superficial impression; certainly most biological research seems irrelevant to industrial requirements, at least in the short term. Nevertheless, the biologist has long played a major role in several industries; and the scope for industrial biologists is continually expanding. Indeed, so long as industry continues to use increasing amounts of large organic molecules and polymers as raw materials the greater that scope will become. The food, brewing, petro-chemical and organic chemical, pharmaceutical industrial fermentation, pesticide and fertilizer industries, not to mention agriculture and fisheries, all, to varying extents, depend for their future success on the work of industrial biologists.

The population of the world is currently growing at 1·3 millions a week or by 2·2 persons every second. Undoubtedly the two most important problems the world will have to face in the next few decades are how to cut back this explosive rate of population growth and how to feed the people. Biologists will have to play a central role in solving both these problems. As far as feeding the population is concerned, they will have to devise more efficient ways of exploiting existing plant and animal food crops and discover completely new foods.

## Food processing

Breeding improved strains of plants and animals is the most obvious contribution that applied biologists can make, but they are increasingly becoming involved in the food-processing industry. The British food industry – one of the country's largest – employs about a million people and about a third of the nation's expenditure goes on food. In all the industrialized countries, food technology is becoming increasingly sophisticated; a vast amount of biochemical and biological research lies behind the well stocked supermarket shelves.

Every chemical added to food, to colour, flavour or help preserve it, has to be tested by industrial biologists in prolonged feeding trials that can involve thousands of animals and years of work to ensure that the compound has no toxic side effects. And once an additive has been accepted, its production has continually to be checked to maintain strict quality control. At the same time the food industry employs teams researching into the fundamental biology of the microbes that cause food to rot, working on new processing techniques and measuring the nutritional value of its products. The industry is always on the look-out for ways of making its products more appealing. The meat industry, to cite just one example, finances research into the properties of cuts of meat, to try to find out why some are tenderer than others; it is also experimenting with ways of partially digesting meat with tenderizers, enzymes which partially digest protein before it reaches the housewife.

Chicks fed on yeasts cultured on petroleum grow as well as chicks raised on more conventional foods. Because of a high protein and mineral content, the yeasts are very nutritious.

The demand for this sort of applied biological research is bound to increase, but even more important, and certainly more exciting, biologists have to discover completely new and untapped sources of food. The oceans represent a huge reservoir of food and the world's catch of fish rose about 6 per cent a year during the 1960s, but this rise cannot continue unless biologists devise ways of managing commercial fish stocks. Thus a great deal of research is needed to discover the biology of commercially valuable fish, their reproductive habits, what makes them congregate in huge shoals at certain places and times, and so on. At the same time marine biologists are trying to discover what lesser known varieties of fish and other marine creatures are acceptable as human food and present in numbers large enough to support commercial fisheries. But until fish can be farmed this form of life will never satisfy the world's demand for protein. The most likely way of doing that is developing protein foods from micro-organisms grown in fermentation plants.

Many of the world's major oil companies are now financing research on the large-scale production of food from bacteria, fungi, yeast and protozoans which will feed on oil, enriched with minerals. Their microbiologists are searching for the best strains of micro-organisms to use and, with chemical engineers, are designing fermentation plants. The idea is to inoculate a suspension of oil and water, continuously aerated and enriched with minerals, with micro-organisms that can use the oil as a source of energy to grow and manufacture their proteins. The micro-organisms can be continuously removed from the fermentation vats, washed and then processed to form food.

This may seem a far cry from conventional food but single-cell protein could either be fed to domestic animals or eaten mixed with conventional food. In the Sahara, near Lake Chad, the local people have for years been doing what the oil companies of the industrialized world are trying to do in their fermentation plants. The people of Chad and Niger scrape a green slime from the lake, let it dry in the sun, and eat the 'cake' that results. Biologists have discovered that this 'cake' is simply a fibrous mass of dried microscopic algae. The oil companies' search for exactly the right micro-organisms to grow on oil in fermentation plants has only just begun, but it seems certain that in the next few decades all the major problems will be overcome. It will then be necessary

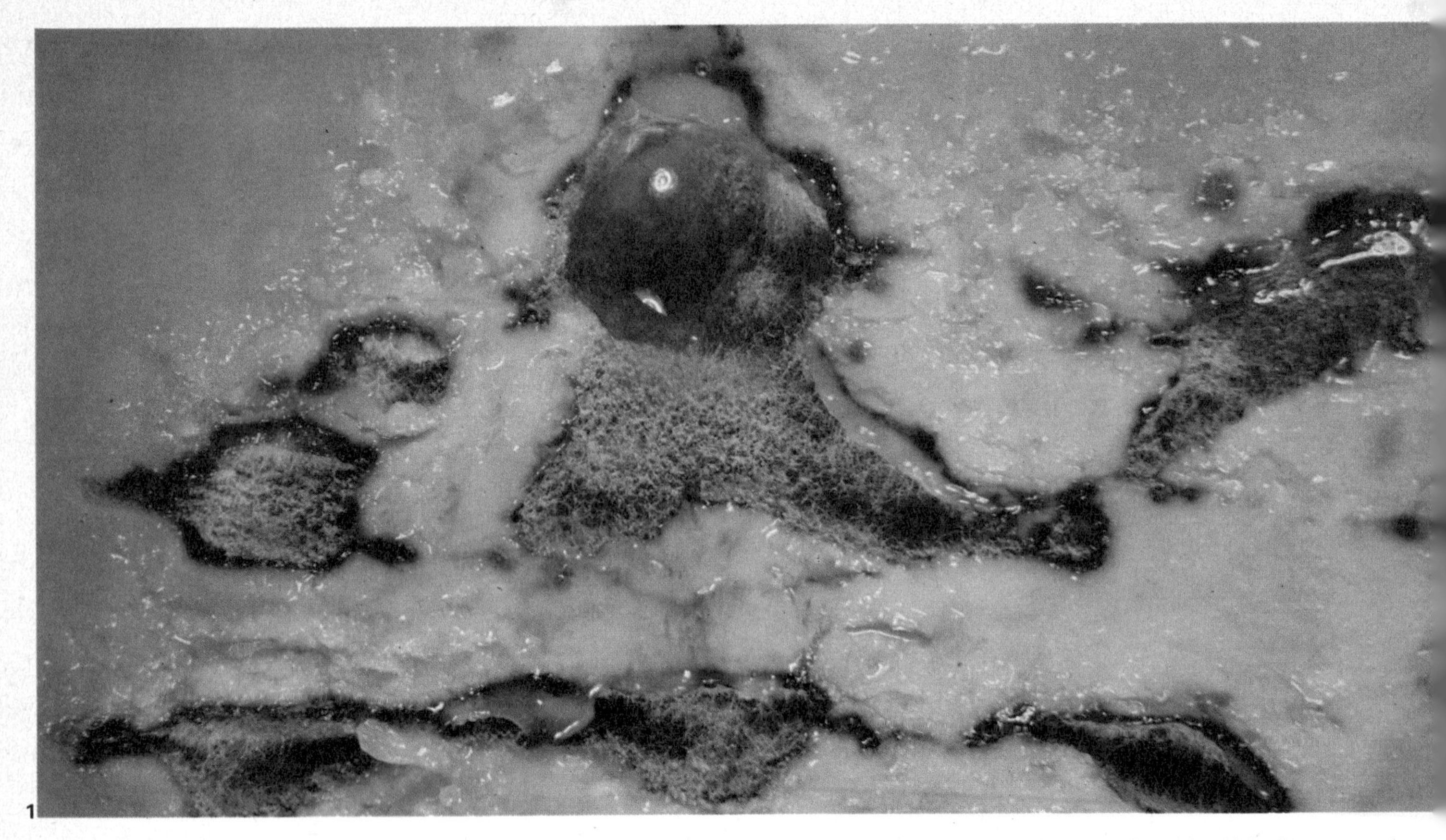

1 A blue cheese, such as Roquefort, obtains its distinctive flavour from a mould which grows down through the veins in the cheese.
2 New drugs are tested in a laboratory on specially bred animals, such as rats. The reactions and side effects can then be measured and the amount of each compound that can be used with safety established.
3 To ensure that food, such as mincemeat, is not contaminated with organisms that might cause food poisoning, microbiologists constantly check its bacterial content.
4 Many different preservatives are now used by manufacturers to keep food in good condition. Here a biologist tests one to check its effective-

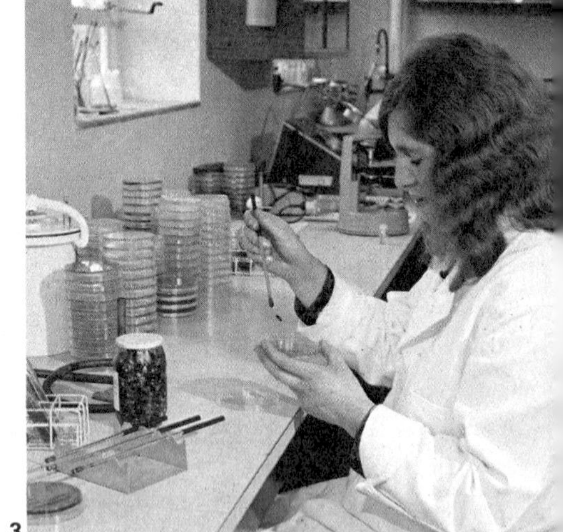

to persuade people that these new single-cell protein foods are really as acceptable and nutritious as a beef steak.

The production of single-cell protein is the most recent industrial exploitation of the metabolism of microbes. Another kind of microbe metabolism leads to fermentation. The fermentation of sugar solutions to give alcohol is as old as civilization itself. It had become an enormously skilled craft long before it was discovered in the last century that micro-organisms are responsible for fermentation. Since then brewing has become as much a science as an art; microbiologists are continually looking for ways of standardizing the conditions of fermentation, so each batch of beer or wine is at its best, and for new strains of yeast more efficient at producing alcohol or more easy to handle.

Cheese is another food that involves fermentation and the microbiologist is now as familiar a figure in the creamery as the brewery. Cheese is made from the curds of milk by the action of a variety of strains of bacteria called *lactic streptococci*. They demand exactly the right conditions for growth and they produce

ness in preventing bacterial growth in certain types of tinned meat.

**5** In the last century it was discovered that the fermentation of grape juice during wine-making is caused by yeasts. Now special cultures are grown to control and maintain the quality of the wine.

**6** These micro-organisms, growing on mineral-enriched petroleum, manufacture proteins which can be processed into food.

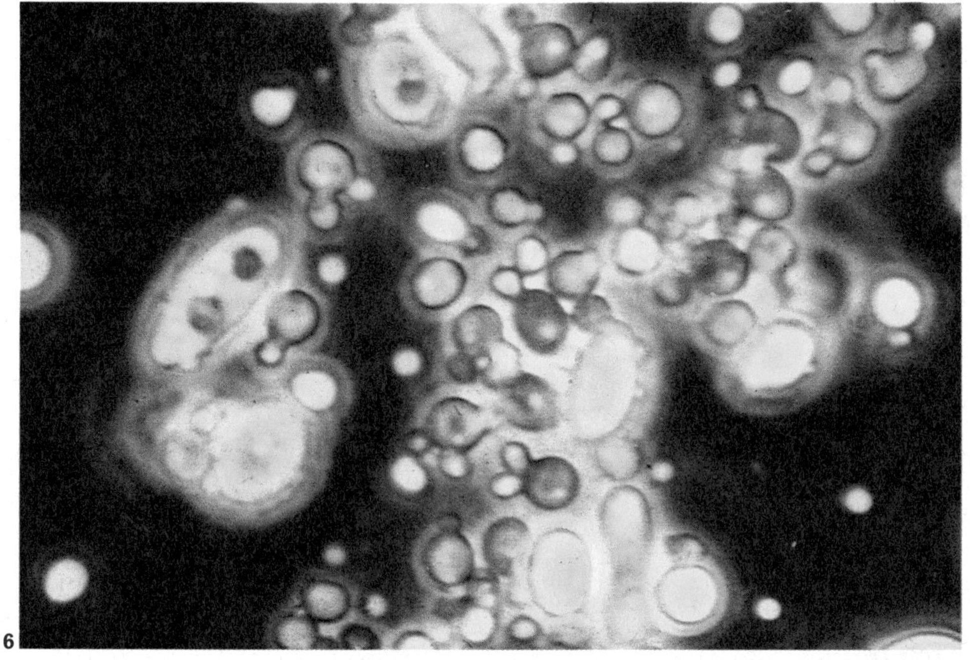

the acids which give each variety of cheese its distinctive flavour. Dairy microbiologists are striving to put cheese making, which is still very much an art, on a scientific basis. They are trying to find the factors which control the growth and survival of the lactic streptococci, how to control the viruses, called bacteriophages, which kill the bacteria, and they are looking for new bacterial strains which may even lead to a new type of cheese.

Apart from making foods, microbiologists have harnessed micro-organisms for the large-scale production of organic chemicals. Some micro-organisms burn up sugar to yield energy but instead of completely breaking up the sugar to carbon dioxide and water, they only partially oxidize it to alcohol acetic, lactic or citric acids or the solvent acetone. Other species will convert starch into simple sugars, and fermentation has long been an industrial process for the production of all these chemicals. It has, or used to have, several advantages over chemical synthesis: the raw materials, usually molasses or starch, are cheap; the plant needed is easier to build and to run than chemical synthesis plant; and often the micro-organisms can complete in one step a reaction that would take the synthetic chemist several steps.

Since the early 1960s, however, the emphasis of commercial fermentation has shifted from the production of simple organic molecules, such as acetic acid and acetone, to the production of more complex molecules. There are two chief reasons for this: first the chemists have learnt how to make simple organic molecules more efficiently and, secondly, microbiologists now understand the process of fermentation more fully and have been able to exploit it for the production of far more valuable large organic molecules. Furthermore, the discovery of the genetic material DNA, and the basic research into the process of mutation that has resulted, means that the microbiologists can now select mutant strains of micro-organisms tailor-made for a specific fermentation process.

With increasingly sophisticated techniques for separating the components of cells, it is now possible to isolate in commercial quantities vitamins and proteins from micro-organisms. At present the organic chemists cannot hope to compete with fermentation when it comes to producing the enzymes which, for example, are now appearing even in washing detergents. As the industrialists find more and more uses for enzymes the fermentation industry is bound to flourish. But undoubtedly the most important development in industrial fermentation since 1945 has been the expansion of the pharmaceutical industry for the production of antibiotics.

## Fungi and bacteria

Antibiotics have completely changed the face of medicine and made the world a very much safer place to live in. Most of them are products of the metabolism of micro-organisms, chiefly fungi.

The modern antibiotics industry stems from Sir Alexander Fleming's chance discovery that strains of the mould *penicillium* secrete an organic acid penicillin which kills bacteria. Since the 1940s intensive research has led to the discovery of a host of other antibiotic compounds, manufactured by various species of fungi and even bacteria themselves, including streptomycin, kanomycin, erythromycin, gramicidin and many others. But the search goes on for more because bacterial populations exposed to an antibiotic tend to mutate so that they become resistant to it.

The biologists of the pharmaceutical companies, therefore, have continually to try to keep one step, indeed one antibiotic, ahead of the pathogenic organisms. The industry has to produce new antibiotics before the old are rendered useless. Nowadays the production of a new antibiotic involves an enormous co-operative research programme. First microbiologists have to screen hundreds of potentially useful compounds. When one shows promise chemists have to determine its physical and chemical structure. Geneticists examine various strains of the parent mould or bacteria to see which produces the compound most efficiently.

At a Japanese research station, a protein-rich alga, *Chlorella,* is grown on small artificial ponds. It is a potentially useful plant for feeding human beings and animals.

Molecular biologists try to find out exactly how it acts, whether it stops protein synthesis or interferes with the permeability of a cell or its synthesis of nucleic acids.

Biologists and toxicologists start preliminary evaluation trials with animals to see if the compound will cure infections without causing toxic side effects. They also have to determine the spectrum of pathogens that are killed by the compound. If it passes all these tests it is subjected to long-term pre-clinical trials to determine the effective dose. Perhaps years later the first clinical trials with a few human beings are performed. After they are evaluated large-scale clinical trials are started and eventually the compound finds its way on to the doctor's prescription and into the chemist's dispensary.

Clearly the pharmaceutical industry is more dependent on biological research than any other. In 1966 the United States pharmaceutical industry claims to have spent over 410 million dollars on research. Not all of that went on antibiotics; the industry also works on new vaccines, new chemically synthesized drugs, new tranquillizers and sedatives and so on. But all of these products have to go through the same rigorous testing. And once a compound has been licensed its production has to be rigorously monitored to ensure each batch is up to standard and safe.

Drugs for human medicine are naturally the industry's chief concern but drugs for animals and veterinary science are also important. Increasingly antibiotics are being used in farming and in the food-processing industry because they are effective preservatives for processed food – so the drug industry finds markets in agriculture as well as medicine.

Even before Gregor Mendel discovered the science of genetics and Charles Darwin had propounded his theory of natural selection, agriculture biologists had practised breeding of improved strains by selection. Nowadays this has become a vast research-oriented industry which should in theory go a long way to solving the world's food shortages. For example, new rice strains and wheat strains bred since the 1950s are being used by Asian farmers in the hope that they will become increasingly productive. But many of these new high-yield strains need heavy doses of fertilizers. The industrial biologist has to evaluate and formulate new inorganic fertilizers so that the chemists can set to work and produce them in the vast quantities that are needed.

## Testing pesticides

Much the same is true of the pesticide industry. Organic chemists and physiologists can, between them, make chemicals that are highly toxic to insects and other pests. The biologists then have the job of evaluating the compounds just as antibiotics are evaluated. Are they active against a large range of pests or just a few? Are they likely to contaminate the crops or animals on which they are used and render them dangerous to Man or wild animals? What concentrations kill the pests without harming the host or Man? Those are just a few of the crucial questions that have to be answered before a pesticide can be sold. The banning of DDT and other organo-chloride pesticides in Sweden, Denmark and some states in America proves that, as biologists learn more about the accumulation of toxic amounts of pesticides in the food chains leading from plants to Man and the mammals, governments will demand ever stricter testing of new agricultural chemicals. And like the drug industry the pesticide industry has to keep on discovering new compounds because insects develop resistance to pesticides just as pathogens develop resistance to antibiotics. Over 80 species of insects are now resistant to DDT.

Clearly the biologist has a place in industry and many industries will depend for their future success on biological research and development. No doubt new biologically oriented industries will be developed because it seems inevitable that industry should exploit the discoveries of the biochemist, who has shown the way to isolate and handle *enzymes* – the protein molecules which act as incredibly efficient catalysts and sustain life. The present-day chemical industry grew out of the work of the nineteenth-century inorganic and organic chemists. Tomorrow's chemical industry will be one of the fruits of current biochemical and molecular biological research. Already enzymes are appearing on the kitchen shelf as meat tenderizers and in the wash tub in enzyme detergents. These two examples are just the comparatively trivial tip of a huge iceberg. The use of enzymes and the idea of making biodegradable materials, that is, materials that are comparatively easily digested by the enzymes of micro-organisms, with a built-in biological obsolescence, will mean that industry's need for biologists will be greater than ever.

Marine biologists on an American research ship study samples of ocean life collected from the middle level of the sea in an attempt to find varieties acceptable as human food.

# Living off the Earth

**During his long history, Man has learned how to put the vast resources of the Earth to his own use. In particular he has increased the soil's productivity by tilling and irrigating the land.**

IT HAS BEEN SAID that if the citizens of the United States were destined for the slaughterhouse and, eventually, the dinner table, they would be declared unfit for human consumption by the medical authorities. This macabre, and not very funny joke, contains a grain of truth. The high level of vegetable food production in the advanced countries is made possible to a large extent by the application of chemical substances, such as DDT, to the crops. These kill great numbers of insect pests but their effect does not finish there.

The pesticide is also taken up by the animals which feed on the crops and by those which eat the animals. Such chemicals are stored up in the animal tissues and when certain concentrations are reached, some suffer serious physical damage. One example is the reduced fertility and reproductive capability of many predatory birds in areas where such pesticides are used.

The American citizen, living in a country where pesticides are used more intensively than anywhere else in the world, probably already harbours enough in the way of chemicals to provide at least a threat to the well-being of any animal which might make a meal of him. And the effect of this gradually amassed chemical cargo on the citizen himself is unknown.

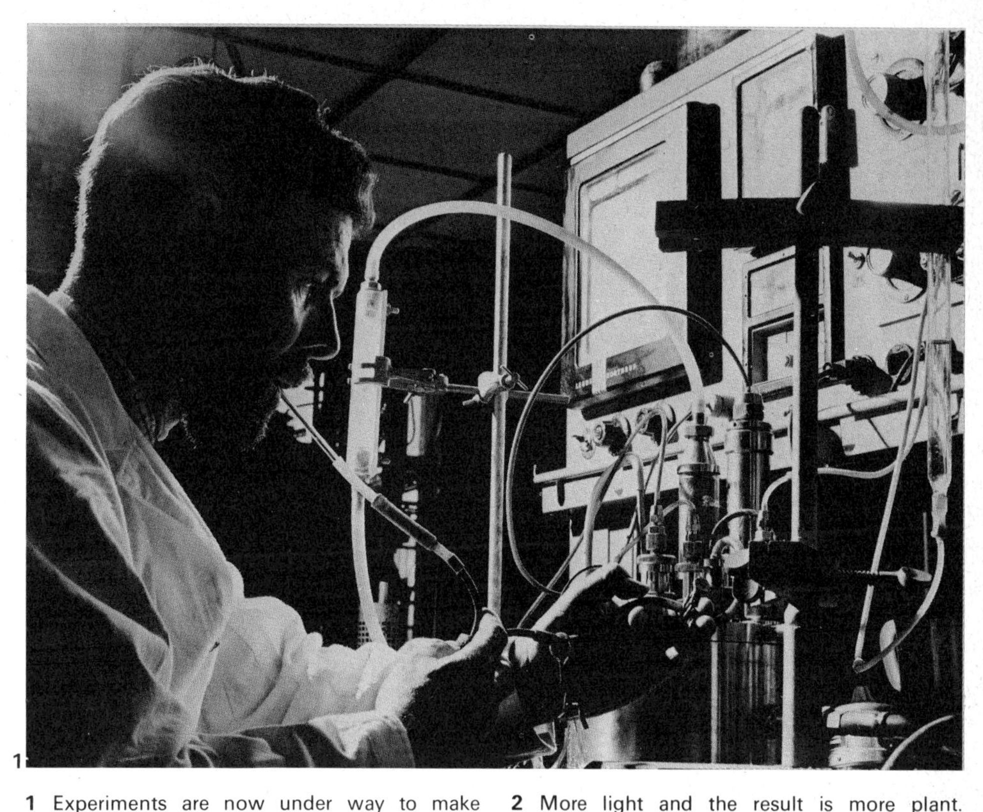

1 Experiments are now under way to make proteins from hydrocarbons such as petroleum oils and natural gases. Here a research worker takes a sample of synthetic protein for analysis.

## Animal, vegetable, mineral

The natural resources of the Earth which are of use to Man are the energy of the sun, the soil, vegetation, animal life, minerals and water. The soil is the first subdivision. Physically, the soil of any particular area consists, in part, of finely ground minerals, either relatively loose or tightly packed as in clay. This material is produced by the disintegration of rock structures or is carried in from elsewhere by wind or water.

The biologists and soil scientists have analysed various types of soil, revealed the minerals which are present and have related these to the well-being of plants. But just as important is the system of living organisms which the biologists have shown to exist in the soil. One calculation, for example, puts the number of bacteria in a cubic inch of soil as being about six million. Further, the scientists have demonstrated that these bacteria break down organic material – such as plant debris, animal bodies and droppings – which are deposited on or in the soil. In doing so the bacteria converts this once-living material into its chemical constituents which in turn promote further plant growth.

The general shape of all this had been known over hundreds of years by human beings who make their living from the land. The ancient farmers knew that if a single crop was grown repeatedly on the same piece of ground, then the yield would ultimately fall off, however fertile that ground had been to begin with. They also discovered that if the crops on the ground involved were changed regularly, then the soil would remain fertile longer. They probably discovered by accident that soil which had received largish quantities of organic matter – say of animal dung – also benefited in terms of fertility.

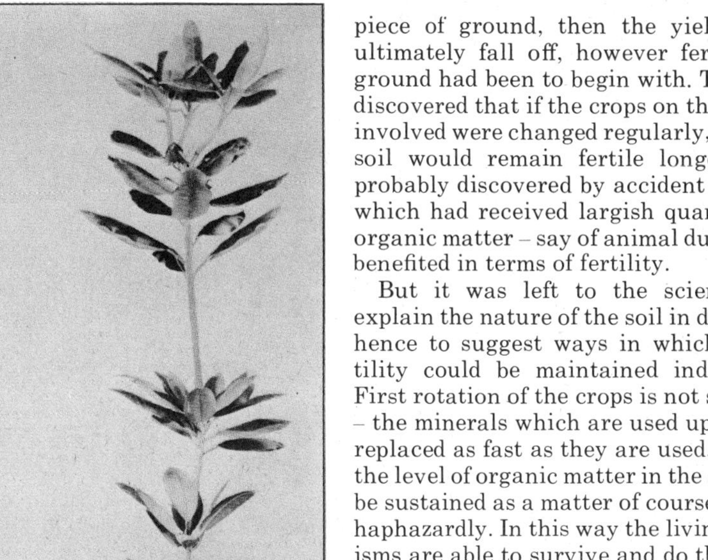

2 More light and the result is more plant. Scientists grew the plant on the left on eight hours of light daily and the one of the right on an additional four hours of incandescent light.

But it was left to the scientists to explain the nature of the soil in detail and hence to suggest ways in which its fertility could be maintained indefinitely. First rotation of the crops is not sufficient – the minerals which are used up must be replaced as fast as they are used. Second, the level of organic matter in the soil must be sustained as a matter of course and not haphazardly. In this way the living organisms are able to survive and do their job.

As a consequence, the rotation of crops and the ploughing in of corn stubble are still practised as of old, but at the same time agricultural chemical industries of considerable size have grown up in the highly developed countries. Their products are applied to the soil by the farmers, in accordance with the prescriptions of the agricultural biologists, in order to keep the land in good heart and produce the kind of crop the farmers want.

The use of the soil is, therefore, very

closely linked with the use of another natural resource, vegetation. In the main, the aim has been to provide food plants in ever-increasing quantities. This can be done, in part, by making sure that the soils in which crops are grown contain the right constituents in the right quantities. It can also be done by protection – that is, the destruction of insects and other animal pests by chemical means – although it is estimated that the pests still devour about 30 million tons of cereals alone in any given year.

However, biologists have discovered other ways of crop improvement which influence the structure and growth processes of the plants. For instance, the biochemical study of plant hormones early in this century showed that plants produce natural substances called *auxins* which act upon the plant cells causing them to lengthen and, hence, cause the plant to grow.

Further biochemical research discovered chemical substances which could be made artificially, called *hetero auxins* and which had the same effect. This form of growth stimulant can be usefully applied to plants and, in particular, has been used to help cuttings to root effectively and quickly. But large doses of the hetero auxins produce such explosive growth in the plant recipient that it weakens and soon dies. The outcome of this has been a whole new race of weed-killers which kill by overstimulation.

In the middle of the nineteenth century certain pioneer wheat-growers in Canada noted that some seeds seemed to thrive better in the harsh conditions of the Canadian north – better than others of the same strain. They, therefore, isolated the seed from the more successful plants and a new strain, called Red Fife, was produced. This was even further refined until the very hardy strain, Marquis, resulted. It proved extremely suitable for the cold, dry areas of the north and, during the early years of this century, was sown in vast areas of Alberta, Manitoba and Saskatchewan. It would grow where crops had never grown before and was extremely productive.

But in 1916 disaster struck, in the shape of a fungus disease called stem rust. In that year alone, 100 million bushels of wheat were destroyed. Similar epidemics followed regularly until in 1935, it was estimated that some 4,000 million bushels were lost. Combating this kind of destruction demanded the concerted attention of the plant geneticists and plant pathologists.

About 200 different species of rust

1

2

3

4

5

6

7

**1** By irrigating a fertile area the natural resources of a soil can sometimes be extended remarkably. On this plot in Majorca three crops of beans and potatoes are grown each year.
**2** Scientists at Loch Sween, Scotland, study the best method for cultivating mussels. The young mussels cling to eight-foot-long ropes dangling from floats.
**3** To find out which variety of wheat is best suited to the harsh environment of India, scientists at Jabalpur are growing different varieties in experimental plots.
**4** A research worker at the Poultry Research Centre in Edinburgh studies the pecking and fighting behaviour of poultry. He hopes to find out how this behaviour affects mating and fertility.
**5** After a century of continual logging more than half of Washington State in the United States is still covered in evergreen forests. Here loggers float the wood to sawmills for pulping.
**6** Seaweed contains some valuable ingredients, including iodine, an element essential for the proper growth of animals. For centuries farmers in Majorca have raked seaweed from the shore.
**7** The high productivity of modern agriculture depends largely on chemical fertilizers. In England fertilizer is usually spread in the spring to boost the growth of the young crop.

fungus were discovered, and the task was to find seed which contained genes conferring resistance to all or most of the fungi. (The genes are complex molecules found in all living cells which contain the 'instructions' which ensure that a living organism grows into the same kind of plant or animal as its parents.)

Success came first in 1924 but it was short-lived. For while the geneticists were selecting suitable strains of wheat and breeding from them, and so artificially improving the ability of the wheat to survive, Nature was doing the same job for the rust fungi. The war has, therefore, been waged by the biologists almost continuously ever since, not only in Canada, but in Australia and elsewhere. Proof of their success lies in the steady growth of world supplies of wheat.

## Healthy forests

Food plants are not the only important constituents of the vegetation section of natural resources. Trees have for long been important providers of building materials for mankind, as shelter for animals, and as protection for the topsoil against the depleting actions of wind and water. Plant biologists have also turned their skills to the preservation of healthy forests.

Once again, however, a great deal of damage was done by Man before he realized fully the effect of his actions. The forest lands which once covered most of Europe and vast areas of North America have been removed. The trees were cut to make homes and implements, or destroyed by domestic animals. The latter have had a particularly damaging effect around the Mediterranean and in parts of Africa. In Tanzania, for example, the cattle which are so important to the status of the Masai tribesmen, contribute much to the progress of erosion of the area.

The third aspect of natural resources is animal life. The selection within a species

– sheep, goat, or cow – of particularly sturdy individual animals from which to breed has been practised for a considerable time. But it is only in the last hundred years or so that science has been brought to bear on improving the quality of the animal stock upon which we partly live.

The process was begun by the chemist Justus von Liebig who studied animal nutrition and suggested that different combinations of food material could be designed to promote growth, or increase milk, wool or egg production. The discovery of vitamins in the twentieth century gave added force to Liebig's ideas.

Then the Cambridge scientist, John Hammond, discovered in the years before the outbreak of the Second World War that growth in food animals followed a definite mode of progress. A new-born lamb, for example, consists mostly of head and legs, with very little meat. Later on the body thickens and the bony head and legs comprise a smaller proportion of the whole. Then a secondary phase of growth begins, the legs themselves put on weight and lengthen.

Hammond reasoned that the various areas of growth, and the amount of meat carried by the animal, could be controlled by varying the amount or quality of food which the particular animal was given during these phases. At the same time the geneticists showed that some strains of animal respond to this feeding régime better than others. These were selected for breeding. The result has been increased yields of various commodities and the building in of desired characteristics in particular animals. The Ancon variety of sheep, for example, has emerged as a very short-legged species, although the bodies carry the amount of meat which the farmer requires. The short legs have the advantage of making sure that the sheep cannot leap the fences enclosing their pastures.

## Wild meat

In many parts of the world wild animals provide the staple meat diet. With growing populations many of these species have been greatly reduced in numbers and, in some cases, wiped out altogether. Biologists, realizing the delicate balance between soil health and the well-being of plant and animal populations, have suggested that the wild animals should be cropped – instead of introducing domestic animals, which can be destructive.

Such a course demands the setting aside of particular areas for the use of the animals involved and the enforcement of the game laws necessary for their protection. In a great many cases this has been extremely successful and the game reserves have become a means whereby not only the local inhabitants benefit but the survival of certain species of animals has also been ensured.

The last great natural resource with which the biologist is concerned is water. Here his interest has been in the main, the plants and animals which the water supports. But the difficulties encountered in the watery medium have until recently severely limited the biologists' effect upon the tapping of this resource. But the migratory paths of certain kinds of fish, for example, have been successfully traced, which has been of great use to fishermen. But the really adventurous ideas, like farming the sea, wait upon the development of suitable underwater vehicles and diving techniques before the scientists can become truly at home in the sea and carry out the large amount of basic observation and measurement.

The biologist has been and is, however, engaged in the battle to protect natural resources in the shape of fresh water. As cities grow, industries mushroom, intensive agriculture spreads, so the amount of damaging effluents produced by these increase and eventually seep into the rivers, streams and lakes. Often protection is a matter for the civil engineer, who must design and build effective filters and methods of sewage disposal.

1 Irrigation can cause a transformation. In this arid part of Arizona as seen in the picture above the dry, dusty soil has changed into a luxurious growth of useful crops.

2 Without water and with excessive grazing the land soon becomes parched and unyielding. The few cattle that do survive are of little value to the farm either for milk or meat.

## Algae as a cleaning agent

But the biologists are hard at work to discover organisms which will do the cleaning job better, which might live upon sewage and waste materials and take their place in the natural food chain. It has been suggested, for example, that certain algae can be used to remove phosphorus – an important constituent of both fertilizers and detergents – from supplies of drinking water.

The search is also going on for organisms which will live on one substance and will turn it into another substance. An example is the work which the biologists of the major oil companies are doing in seeking edible protein from natural gas and oil. Bacteria have been found which live on methane. In doing so they produce organic material, nearly half of which is protein. Other micro-organisms have been found to operate in the same way when fed on oil.

It is hoped that the protein produced – one ton from three tons of methane – will be suitable for enriching the diets of food animals. But exhaustive tests must be carried out first to make sure there are no harmful side-effects.

Although modern Man leads a far more comfortable life than his primitive ancestors, he is still just as dependent on natural resources. His food is still plant and animal life and his shelter is still largely built of wood, stone and clay. Even the more up-to-date materials of steel, concrete and glass are derived from minerals and gravel, sand and stone. His future existence depends on careful and skilful use of the main natural resources: water, air, soil, minerals, plants and animals.

# The search for better harvests

By studying the basic requirements of plants and animals, biologists have discovered subtle ways by which farmers all over the world can increase the production of food for human consumption.

1 The insect breeding room of an agricultural research laboratory. The insects are used to test the effectiveness and toxicity of newly prepared insecticides.

2 Instead of spraying the leaves with pesticides, an insecticide is injected into the sap which carries it throughout the tree to the branches, leaves and fruit.

THE AIM of agricultural research is to increase the fruitfulness of the land by improving agricultural practices. The agricultural biologist who undertakes this research may be involved in devising better diets for farm animals, in breeding stock which are better converters of feed into food for human consumption, or mature faster or are more resistant to disease; he may be helping with the prevention of destruction of crops by pests or with the control of ripening of a harvest of fruit in storage. The list is endless because new problems are continually arising which need to be answered by new research.

Some of the most dramatic advances in increasing agricultural productivity have arisen from fundamental research. Plant physiologists have shown, for example, that the proportions of oxygen, carbon dioxide and nitrogen in the atmosphere, together with temperature, are the major factors which influence the changes which occur when fruit ripens. Thus, knowing how ripening can be delayed, fruit farmers have constructed storage chambers in which the atmospheric composition and temperature are controlled in such a way as to enable them to market apples for most of the year.

Atmospheric carbon dioxide is the raw material which green plants convert by photosynthesis into sugar, using energy from the sun. Plant physiologists now know that by increasing the amount of carbon dioxide in a glasshouse it is possible to increase the yield and accelerate maturation of certain crops grown in them. Yields of glasshouse crops, such as lettuce, tomato and cucumber, can be nearly doubled when the atmosphere in the glasshouse is enriched with extra amounts of carbon dioxide.

The glasshouse is an attempt to control the environment in which plants live. However, the optimum environmental conditions change fundamentally at different stages of a plant. Scientists have been experimenting with a system where small plants in containers are carried on a conveyor belt through chambers which provide the best conditions for each stage of growth from seed to harvest. Engineers and biologists have also collaborated successfully in the area of mechanical harvesting. For instance, machines have been designed to gather field-grown tomatoes. This has only been possible through selecting and breeding varieties of tomatoes in which the fruit ripen all at once and where the oblong shape and tough skin allow mechanical harvesting without excessive damage to the fruit.

Dieticians are concerned not only with the food we eat but with the fodder of domestic animals. One of the most extraordinary of farming operations – the broiler industry – has developed to its present vast size partly because of what is now known about nutrition. Most animals require sunlight so that their bodies may synthesize vitamin D. By discovering how this vitamin affects the animals and what it consists of, scientists have made poultry production independent of sunshine. And by rearing broilers indoors they can exercise far greater control over the birds' environment and, therefore, their growth and development.

Broilers can be sold cheaply in the supermarket because soya-bean meal is used as a source of protein. However, it must be supplemented with vitamins and minerals to provide a balanced diet.

## Animal converters

The chicken and the cow are two of the most efficient converters of feed into human food among domestic animals. This efficiency is measured by comparing the protein in the eggs, milk or flesh of the growing animal to the protein in their diet. The process of converting plant protein into protein for human consumption is, however, always to some extent wasteful. Experiments have been carried out in which the vegetable protein of a cow's diet is entirely replaced by urea (the simple nitrogen-containing chemical of urine) and some ammonium salts. Cows fed such a protein-free diet can grow and produce milk the amount and quality of which are similar to cows fed a normal diet.

What is remarkable about this is that all the amino acids of the milk proteins, and of the enzymes and structural proteins formed in growth are derived from a non-protein nitrogen source. Mammals normally require certain so-called 'essential amino acids' in their diet; they can synthesize all the amino acids required to build proteins except these. The cow and other ruminants overcome this requirement by an elaborate stomach or *rumen* which houses vast numbers of micro-organisms. These micro-organisms convert urea into the essential, as well as the non-essential, amino acids which the cow digests and absorbs in another part of its gut. Even the taste of milk from these experimental cows does not differ from ordinary milk.

By collaborating with chemists, agricultural biologists have achieved some of their most rewarding breakthroughs. Thus chemists elucidated the structure of certain plant hormones and then synthesized *analogues* (structurally similar materials) which the biologist used to fool the plant and make it think it was the natural substance. These substances are used as selective weedkillers and because of their hormone-like action, very little need be used. Another use of these hormone analogues is to induce tomatoes and other crops to develop without being pollinated. They are also used to induce good root formation in cuttings taken from plants.

## Useful chemicals

In view of the present preoccupation over certain insecticides polluting the environment, it is worth remembering that not all the products of the agricultural chemical industry are used as pesticides. Apple growers are exceptionally committed to the use of chemicals; as well as spraying chemicals on to the trees in winter and summer to control a host of injurious insects and fungi, they also use various chemicals during the blooming period to reduce the amount of fruit set, so obviating the need for thinning out the fruit by hand, and at a later stage other chemicals to prevent the young apples from dropping. Then more chemicals are applied to prevent the growth of fungi and bacteria during storage.

Chemists and biologists must first screen the synthetic products to see if they will fit the required purpose. The screen is a test designed to select which chemicals are effective; whether to inhibit the growth of a fungus or to kill a pest such as greenfly. When a biologist has found a promis-

1

2

3

ing 'lead' he passes it to a chemist to synthesize closely related chemicals so as to find a product with optimum activity for the purpose required. Ultimately, a chemical which has shown outstanding activity in a laboratory screen is tested exhaustively under natural conditions in various parts of the world. Often a chemical does not behave as was hoped in these trials and its development has to be dropped. The chemicals that are finally marketed have been tested very thoroughly and sometimes new applications are realized during this research. They are also carefully tested for any harmful effects that they might have before they are used commercially.

## Controlling insects

Insects, it is said, outnumber men by 50 million to one; this is probably a conservative estimate. There is certainly room for more control of insects and there are many ways of doing this without using chemical insecticides in the conventional way. The female of many insects, especially moths, lures the male of the species by releasing scent from the glands in her abdomen. Males are sensitive to tiny amounts of this airborne scent and fly towards its source.

Biologists and chemists have managed to identify a number of these moth scents. The chemicals can then be synthesized in the laboratory and used in the field as remarkably efficient lures for traps which are baited with conventional insecticides. Once the males are captured, the females

**1** Locust swarms in Ethiopia where it was estimated that in 1958 they destroyed enough food to feed a million people for a year. In an attempt to control them, biologists study their behaviour and movements.
**2** The mechanical handling of seed when it is sown and reaped is likely to damage it and so reduce yields. Scientists are now engaged in finding a 'handling resistant' strain of rice.
**3** In Libya an 'agricultural guide' shows a farmer how to use an insecticide spray on his bean crop. As agriculture becomes more scientific there is a greater need for expertise.
**4** By measuring the nutritious content of cattle and other livestock feeds, the biologist has helped farmers select the best products, and so increase productivity.
**5** Carbon dioxide is a raw material of a plant's growth. By increasing the amount in glasshouses a nurseryman can enlarge the yields of his crops and make them mature earlier.
**6** To keep a check on apple mildew infection in an orchard, scientists have set up a 'spore tray' which captures mildew spores in the air.
**7** In Zambia, at the Kalichero station, experimental plots of tobacco are grown so that the local farmers can see for themselves the best methods of growing a crop.

can, at worst, lay sterile eggs. This technique has been used against the Gipsy moth whose larvae defoliate deciduous trees of all kinds in the forests of the northeastern United States from New England to the Ozarks. This species was accidentally introduced from Europe in the late nineteenth century and so its eradication from its new home would hardly be a great loss. The use of these 'sex attractants' shows how fundamental research on insect physiology and behaviour can lead to a practical control measure.

One insecticide already being used is composed of the spores of a bacterium pathogenic to the larval stage of moths and butterflies. It is highly specific, being without activity even towards other insects. The activity of this bacterium is generally thought to reside in a protein crystal which can be seen in the bacterial cell in close proximity to the spore. The crystal is converted to a toxic material within the gut of the caterpillar, and the specificity of the bacterium is thought to depend on the especially alkaline conditions in the gut of caterpillars. This type of insect control has been used, with considerable success, against the spruce budworm in Canada. Its specificity is an attractive feature; it is not a hazard to other organisms in the environment in which it is used.

## Sterile populations

Animals occur in naturally breeding populations. The population may be limited to a single field or cover hundreds of square miles. But the population is always limited by conditions such as the distribution of a food plant or geographical feature. Insect control with insecticides is most efficient when there is a local high density of insects. In other words, the least amount of insecticide is used to kill the greatest number of insects. However, although insecticides will drastically reduce the numbers of insects in a population, there will always be a few which survive and breed the future generations.

Biologists, however, have developed methods to eradicate certain insects in their entirety. They achieve this by interfering with the fertility of the breeding population. In this way it is possible to attack the most dangerous characteristic of insects, that is, their ability for rapid multiplication. If a large number of the pest insect is reared in the laboratory and the males can be sterilized and then released into a natural population, it is possible, under certain conditions, to eradicate the natural population. The following conditions have to be fulfilled. The sterilized males must compete successfully with the wild unsterilized males and mate with the wild females in a normal way, but the eggs which result will, of course, be sterile. The size of the wild population must be known and the sterile males released into the population must be sufficient to outnumber the wild males.

Consider the arithmetic of what might happen in a population of sexually reproducing insects, whose numbers are not increasing. For simplicity we will assume that a male only mates once with a female. This is, in fact, the case with many insects. If sterile males are released into a population of two million wild insects, so that the fertile males are outnumbered by sterile males in the ratio nine to one, then only one-tenth, or 100,000 of the wild males, will mate successfully.

Now, if the size of the wild population is not increasing, then there will be only 100,000 wild males in the second generation. If a further nine million sterile males are released, the ratio of sterile to fertile males will be 90 to one. One thousand and ninety nine males will mate successfully. In the third generation there will be this same number of fertile males. If another nine million sterile males are released, the ratio of sterile to fertile will be 8,000 to one. In this generation biologists would, therefore, not expect a single successful mating. The original population of two million insects would have been eradicated in three generations by the sequential liberation of sterile males.

From this example it can be seen that a control operation using the release of sterile males will be costly. But since it achieves eradication, it should only be necessary to mount it once for every population. The cost of the operation is less if the size of the population is first lowered by using conventional insecticides. Then the number of sterile males which must be released is considerably reduced. It must also be clear that an operation such as this requires the collaboration of a team of scientists working both in the laboratory and in the field.

An unpleasant pest of cattle in the Caribbean and southern United States, called the screw-worm fly, has been eradicated in certain areas by the sterile-male technique. The eggs are laid in open wounds caused by barbed wire or by the attack of other flies. The maggots, which hatch out of the eggs, begin to eat the flesh around the wound and their activities can lead to death of cattle in ten days. The damage done by screw-worms is out of all proportion to the numbers of this insect in the environment.

The first successful operation against this pest was performed on the island of Curaçao. Island populations are ideal for an eradication programme if they are sufficiently far from neighbouring land to prevent re-colonization by the pest. Screw-worm males were bred in the laboratory and sterilized by exposure to ionizing radiation. It is, however, possible to sterilize insects by exposure to certain chemicals. A further method of sterilization has been developed by geneticists and consists of breeding insects with a genetic constitution different from wild insects. It is only necessary that the mating of laboratory-reared insects with wild insects should result in sterile eggs or offspring.

Agriculture and medicine are the two largest areas of applied biological research. Medical science is concerned with saving and prolonging human lives and easing pain; the results of medical research in one country may be applicable all over the world. But because of the nature of agricultural problems it is generally necessary to conduct agricultural research locally in each country. It is therefore an essential activity of the developing, as well as developed, countries. The results of research can, however, be applied to different areas which have such common problems as plant and animal diseases. By cross-breeding with imported food animals, such as cows and sheep, local breeds can be improved as meat producers and their resistance to disease increased, while the selective breeding of plants, such as the grains, can dramatically increase yields. Since biological research usually requires smaller funds than research in engineering, physics or chemistry, it might be argued that employment of biologists is a wise investment of agriculture. Yet, many agricultural problems are most successfully answered by the teamwork of scientists from different disciplines.

1 Both sets of these bean plants were sprayed with the same pesticide compound but the formulation was different. Plants on the left show little deposit compared with those on the right.

2 The growth of this bean plant is completely controlled – the light, temperature, humidity and the nutrients. The results of all these variables can then be analysed one by one.

# Breeding better harvests

Since Man first domesticated crops and livestock he has improved them for his own needs. Chance selection led to better yields but was later overtaken by the science of plant and animal breeding.

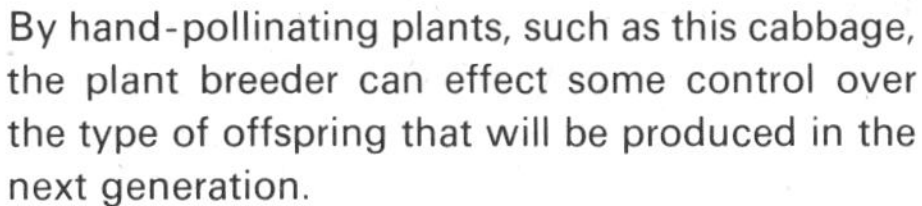

By hand-pollinating plants, such as this cabbage, the plant breeder can effect some control over the type of offspring that will be produced in the next generation.

Cantaloup vines protected from the glaring sun by paper bonnets grow healthily in Imperial Valley. This irrigated land was once a salt-encrusted desert north of the Mexican border.

IN 1968 the Indian government issued a postage stamp in honour of wheat, a rare event in the life of that humble, uncolourful plant. But the honour is well deserved; a new high-yielding strain developed in Mexico a few years earlier has revolutionized agricultural practice in Mexico, India, Pakistan and Turkey. In 1966 the Indian government imported 18,000 tons of seed of the Mexico strain and planted it over great tracts of land. The wheat grew well, and in the following year it was planted even more widely. It gave a harvest of 17 million tons, a dramatic improvement on the 12 million tons that was the record crop with the old strains of wheat. Events in Pakistan have run a similar course, and in the 1970s both countries expect to become exporters of wheat – a situation that seemed previously impossible.

Rice has also been in the headlines. In 1966 the International Rice Research Institute of the Philippines produced a new, short, stiff-strawed strain with which the Philippines have achieved self-sufficiency in rice production for the first time in decades. The same, or similar strains, are also giving high yields in Pakistan, Ceylon and several other Asian countries.

Before Man made his beginnings in agriculture he lived by hunting and gathering; an extremely inefficient mode of nutrition. It is thought that 50,000 years ago there were about 2,000 people living in the British Isles, and that this number was about the maximum the island could support.

But around 15,000 years ago Man began to live in definite settlements, made possible because he had learned to depend on more reliable sources of food – fish, shellfish and planted tubers. He also began to clear the ground round these early hamlets for agricultural purposes, and rear pigs, fowl, ducks and geese, as well as food plants such as date, olive, fig, apple and grape.

Over the next 5,000 years Man's exploitation of the world around him reached a decisive new stage when he learned systematically to gather and plant the seeds of certain grasses. Seeds are concentrated sources of nutrition for the embryo plants they contain, and it can be argued that in learning to cultivate the seed-bearing, swiftly growing and compact grasses Man made possible the development of stable and settled communities. It is not known for certain where the cultivation of the grasses which we now recognize as cereal crops first took place. The earliest occurrence of bread wheat yet recorded is at Knossos, Crete, dated by radioactive carbon as 8,000 years old. Barley, and some other cereals no longer cultivated, also made an appearance about this time at various places throughout eastern Europe and the coastal areas of western Asia, but it seems likely that wheat was the critical crop.

## Fertility rites

The domestication of herd animals – the ox, the sheep, the ass and the horse – seems to be of roughly the same vintage, and these animals brought with them vast improvements in pulling power, transport and the availability of edible protein. It has been suggested that Man's original interest in these animals may have lain in their use for fertility rites and magic sacrifices. The use of manure to fertilize the ground is likely to have ritual origins.

Even at this early stage of agriculture, Man was already improving plants and animals. The dog, for instance, was presumably attracted to early human settlements by the scraps of food there – primitive Man was by all accounts a very untidy animal. As generations of dogs succeeded each other, Man let the more domesticable animals survive, and these, through the process of heredity must have given rise to offspring that were also domesticable.

As with dogs, so with pigs, oxen and horses and with plants. The grasses that became our cereals became established on the cleared stretches of ground near human settlements. Their rapid growth would give them a head start over some of their rivals and their need for a rich, well-manured soil would favour their flourishing around human dwellings. Where Man had scattered his debris, so, in a real sense, the grasses met Man halfway.

In the next stage Man learnt to plant these seeds year after year and to tend the young crops. The history of this process is not known in detail, but it is known that when sowing was established, Man had unconsciously and quite rapidly effected improvements in his cereal crops. The seed-bearing stem of wild grasses is very brittle, with the result that efficient harvesting is impossible. But as Man collected the seed from his crops, probably armed with a primitive sickle, he would tend to gather the seed from plants with a more pliant stem. Such seeds would themselves carry the characteristic of a tougher stem in their chromosomes, and over thousands of years tiny changes in this direction would accumulate, giving Man easily harvested cereals.

The Ancient Egyptians of 5,000 years ago tilled the land and sowed crops, such as barley, flax and a kind of wheat. Basically, methods of farming have not changed over the centuries.

A parallel change was for the grain to weaken its attachment to the stem. This change makes the ripe grain easier to separate from chaff when threshed. The conditions of harvesting, therefore, automatically led to two important improvements in cereal crops. But equally the conditions of sowing led to the selection of forms with even and rapid germination, and the conditions of growth led to the selection of larger, more robust forms.

Wheat is one of the best examples of Man's unconscious selection for growth and robustness. Most plants and animals – including Man himself – are *diploid*, they have two sets of chromosomes in the nucleus of each of their cells. But modern cultivated wheat is *hexaploid*, it has six sets of chromosomes in each cell. Chromosomes carry the genes which convey hereditary information from parent to offspring and also carry out the manufacture of protein molecules, the key constituent of life. The hexaploid forms, with a superabundance of protein molecules in their cells, are usually bigger and more robust than the diploid forms from which they derive. The genetic history of wheat has been reconstructed fairly recently. It turns out that wheat derived from accidental crosses between three diploid grasses still growing wild in Asia Minor. It

1

2

Different types of sheep serve different uses. The Lincoln, **1**, provides a long fine wool, while the Suffolk, **2**, and the Hampshire, **3**, have a compact, heavy coat. Some sheep, like the Dorset Horn, **4**, have now been bred to produce three offspring at once, rather than just one.

3

4

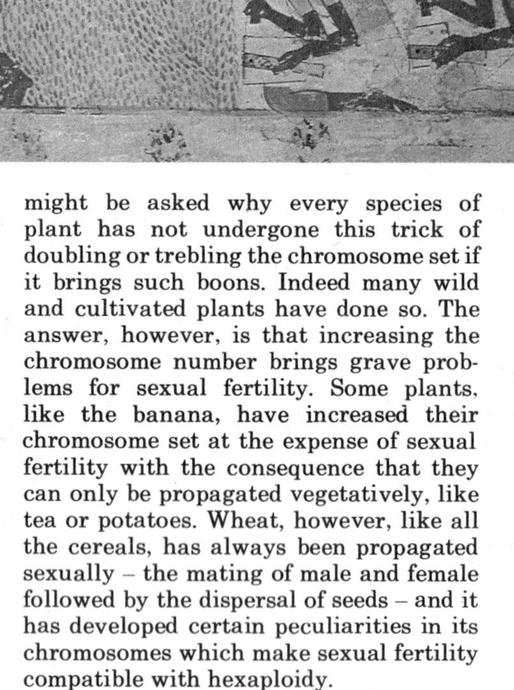

might be asked why every species of plant has not undergone this trick of doubling or trebling the chromosome set if it brings such boons. Indeed many wild and cultivated plants have done so. The answer, however, is that increasing the chromosome number brings grave problems for sexual fertility. Some plants, like the banana, have increased their chromosome set at the expense of sexual fertility with the consequence that they can only be propagated vegetatively, like tea or potatoes. Wheat, however, like all the cereals, has always been propagated sexually – the mating of male and female followed by the dispersal of seeds – and it has developed certain peculiarities in its chromosomes which make sexual fertility compatible with hexaploidy.

Modern maize is also diploid but it has not evolved with the chromosomal finesse of wheat; it is the plant which has changed most in result of Man's unconscious selection. It has no surviving wild progenitor, nor is there any wild plant classified in the same genus. The crop plant may have destroyed its wild relatives by cross-pollinating with them, and making them unfit for survival in the wild. But some botanists feel it more likely that maize arose by selection under cultivation from plants very like teosinte, which still grows as a weed and a forage crop in America. If this is so, then the transformation has been acute. Teosinte has a meagre corn pod and a brittle stem, while its ears are small and enclosed in leaf structures. Maize has a pod a hundred times heavier, with many-rowed ears and

Cattle are bred for meat, milk or a combination of both. The French Charollais, **1**, is good for beef and milk; the Jersey, **2**, famous for its cream, is primarily a dairy breed; the Highland cattle of Scotland, **3**, are hardy and flourish well in a cold, rigorous climate.

large uncovered grains. It readily forms fertile hybrids with teosinte; strong evidence that beneath the skin the two plants are closely related.

Human migration has also affected the unconscious selection of crops. Imperial ambition fired the movement of whole peoples and, as they moved, they took with them the mobile among their crops. The Persians, Greeks and Romans carried fruit and vegetables into Europe, while Islam introduced new crops and livestock into Africa. Imperial conquest not only shifted crops, it changed them. As the cultivated crops travelled, they met many new habitats, sometimes yielding fruitful new variants, and also met and formed

hybrids with the wild plants from which they sprang; hybrids sometimes more suitable to local conditions. Plants, such as lettuces, rhubarb, carrots, turnips and cherries diversified and improved as they moved across Europe.

Man has in all these ways been improving his stock and crops for ten millennia now, although natural selection and genetics, the processes underlying any biological improvement, were only recognized a century ago. There is no sharp distinction between primitive unconscious selection and the rational selection which we now practise. A farmer will tend to breed his livestock from his most useful or perfect animals, but he may be far from having a conscious intention to improve the breed.

Consciously controlled plant and animal breeding is of an older vintage than our theories of natural selection. In Europe, in the seventeenth and eighteenth centuries, there were three developments that together amounted to a revolution in agricultural practice. First, selection became persistent and unremitting instead of casual or unconscious. Secondly, there was movement of new species on a global scale. Thirdly, there was the recognition that pollen, the male principle, contributed something to plant heredity as well as the ovules. This was the beginning of rational plant hybridization experiments. It was also the end of a debate that flourished at the beginning of the eighteenth century: the debate whether all new varieties arose from the variability of the soil in which they grew.

Dutch bulb breeders led the way in this revolution, beginning with tulips and hyacinths from the East, and continuing with all kinds of ornamental plants. But it was the firm and family of Vilmorin, established in 1727, which applied the same methods to crop plants. What, in essence, they did was to replace the complicated mixtures of types of the time with standardized, inbred varieties of known and stable characteristics. Later the sexual hybridization of different varieties became a standard method of the breeder and the two techniques, controlled selection and hybridization, have run hand in hand ever since.

The new methods gave rapid improvements. In 1745 the best strain of sugar beet had 6·2 per cent of sugar. It was introduced into France in 1775. Extensive selection by Pierre Philippe de Vilmorin soon raised its sugar content to 16 and even 20 per cent, producing the beet which relieved the sugar shortage in France during the Napoleonic wars.

Selection and hybridization have disadvantages when pursued independently. Straightforward selection of, say, a field of wheat cannot go far because it is limited to the genetic variability pre-existing in the field of wheat. Once a slightly improved pure-breeding strain has emerged selection can do no more. Plant breeders in England

**4** The two rows of tomatoes flourishing on the left were made resistant to stem-rot disease by breeding from a wild species. The row on the right, a standard susceptible variety, has died.

**5** An animal breeder's dream of the 1790s, this pig was raised on a farm in Berkshire, England. At this time breeding was just beginning to become a science.

of finding new species of potato to hybridize with the domestic crop.

The livestock breeder aims at the same balance of selection and hybridization, in a sense, although he has to deal with smaller numbers of slower growing individuals than the plant breeder, and his selection methods cannot be so rigorous. John Ellman (1753–1832), one of the first important British stockbreeders, prefaced his work by a visit to butchers' shops to find out which joints were the most popular and which the most expensive. The visits were evidently instructive for Ellman went on to create large improvements in a variety of sheep.

Farm animals are much more complicated than crop plants and the stock breeder has had to go about his task more slowly than his plant colleagues. Nonetheless, the common stock animals have been improved enormously over the last two centuries and breeders have strived to balance in particular strains the competing requirements that a farmer may expect of his stock: beef quality, growth rate, milk output and disease resistance, or in the case of sheep quality and length of fleece and meat output.

1 By interbreeding between four pure inbred lines, American agriculturists have produced a variety of millet that gives an increased yield of seed and of growth.

2 Brahman cattle, originally from India, have been exported all over the world to countries with a hot, arid climate. Because of their humps they can survive long periods without water.

reached this situation with wheat, barley and oats a long time ago. Hybridization on the other hand, is haphazard and often fruitless. The results of mating of dissimilar strains are always unpredictable. But hybridization is a more reliable source of improvement if the two parent stocks are well known and it is for this reason that successful strains of oats and wheat carry pedigrees as elaborate as any royal lineage.

Despite its various drawbacks, hybridization has been very important in plant breeding over the last century. It provides an endless source of new genetic constitutions on which selection can do its work and, for the deeper reason, that pure-bred lines – the inevitable outcome of intensive selection – can in a sense become too pure. Pure strains may yield a bountiful crop, but they very easily succumb to disease and parasites. They do not possess the genetic variety out of which resistance to the disease or pest might emerge.

So the plant breeder's job is never finished. When he has selected a satisfactory new strain, he then has to maintain the genetic variety within the strain by continued acts of calculated hybridization. This necessity has had some colourful repercussions: expeditions have been sent to South America with the express purpose

## Fat, lean and bone

Nor is the animal breeder standing still. Artificial insemination is now widely used as a means of bringing about rapid changes in a breed, and the transplantation of fertilized ova to foster-mothers sometimes helps to speed up selection. Methods are available for measuring the fat, lean and bone on animals while they are still alive – an aid in choosing animals for mating – and efforts are being made to introduce useful new hybrids between different animal species. Scientists in Britain are trying to form a fertile hybrid between sheep and goats.

A new venture for plant breeders has been an attempt to speed up nature by exposing crops to chemicals or radiations that cause mutations in the plant cell chromosomes. The method is very much hit or miss, but it has produced new strains of bacteria for fermentation industries, and a strain of wheat that was released in 1968 to farmers in Italy. For some important world crops, like rubber, palm nuts, tea and cocoa, there is still great room for improvement by basic selection techniques. Other crops, however, like the cereals, coffee, citrus fruits and cotton, have perhaps passed this stage.

As for the future, one thing only is sure: that the awesome experiments currently under way in biological laboratories will one day be applied to agriculture. Already chromosome surgery – the direct transfer of chromosomes from one nucleus to another – has been used in plant breeding, and the Japanese have made 'steaks' of a sort out of micro-organisms. Beyond this lies the factory culture of pure lines of living cells, and perhaps the manufacture of radically new kinds of organism out of the viruses and nucleic acids by the molecular biologist. These developments, as they arrive, will force Man to ponder even deeper what he means by an 'improvement' of nature.

# Food for the future

Man's rapidly expanding population is putting increasing pressure on the land to supply him with food. Can agriculture cater for the future or must the coming generations face starvation?

THREE THOUSAND, FIVE HUNDRED MILLION human beings live in the world at the present time and, if the experts are right, this number will have doubled by the end of the century. While not many more than 10 per cent of those now living enjoy as much food as they want, the rest of the world in varying degrees feeds on a diet which is, at best, adequate. Sometimes the margin between subsistence and starvation is very close: a war, drought, excessive frost, disease or a combination of any of these factors can generate disaster for a large population.

If people in certain parts of the world are short of food now, how much shorter they will be in the years to come when their population has doubled or even trebled. Man must therefore find ways of producing enough food and seeing that it is distributed properly – that is unless he can control his growing numbers.

One of the fallacies of the present time is that the world is short of food because not enough is produced. In fact more than enough is produced but a substantial amount is lost through poor storage. Perhaps Man has spent too much of his time producing food and too little trying to preserve it once he has it. Funguses, insects and rodents take a savage toll of stored food. The rat is, undoubtedly, one of the worst offenders; the United States federal authorities estimate that each of the 120 million rats in their country eats about 40 lb a year of food produced for human consumption and contaminates about twice that amount. The cost runs to over 1,000 million dollars annually.

**1** When small quantities of penicillin are fed to poultry they put on more weight. But such use of antibiotics may have to be restricted because it leads to strains of drug-resistant bacteria.

**2** In intensive farming the animals are fed concentrated feedstuffs. A farmer can therefore raise many more animals than he could if he had to support them from his own crops.

**3** Wild animals are often hardier and more disease resistant than domesticated ones. The Russians have begun breeding the indigenous Saiga antelope as a possible source of protein.

Nonetheless, while he is trying to overcome the problems of preserving and distributing food, Man is still very much concerned with food production, especially as he is aware that the pressures on the food available are increasing all the time, as for example in India where there are one million more mouths to feed every month.

Taken as a whole, not more than 46 per cent of the world's land masses can be tilled for growing food. The remaining 54 per cent is made up of deserts, wasteland, built-on land and forest and mountains. Already all but 2·9 per cent of the total 46 per cent is under cultivation, which leaves a scant 950 million acres for development. And, since the last century, the soils that have been cultivated have been increasingly poor and the yields accordingly less. All too often the poor soil has been stretched beyond its limits and erosion has set in. As a result Man has lost more than he has gained: in 1880 the area of deserts and wasteland amounted to some 9 per cent of the total land mass; this area has now risen alarmingly to near 25 per cent.

The felling of trees for fuel, pulp for paper, and to open up the way for the plough has probably contributed more to the loss of soil through erosion than any other single factor. In spite of these implications, vast acreages of trees are still being cut down. Sometimes a government intervenes before the destruction goes too far. Some 100 years ago the forests of Japan were being decimated to make way for industries and agriculture. In

no time the country was in the grip of devastating floods that destroyed crops, cattle and carried down to the sea vast quantities of good topsoil. Because of this bitter experience, Japan introduced forest protection laws which are still in force.

If he is wise, Man will leave the remaining forests intact, except for those areas which are being re-forested. Besides catching water and preventing erosion, forests can have other uses. Modern Man can learn to copy some of the techniques that primitive peoples like the Amerindians of the Amazon and the Pygmies of the Congo have found so successful. These peoples are mainly nomadic, obtaining their food by hunting and by cultivating small clearings in the forest which, after several years of use, are allowed to grow wild again. By growing a variety of indigenous plants together, these peoples produce a kind of forest in miniature with the tallest plants protecting those in the shade.

Many plants now used as the staple diet of peoples living in the West and in Asia had their origins in the jungles where they were, and are, being cultivated by primitive people. The Amazon Indian has contributed manioc – one of the basic foods of Asia and Africa – the potato, cocoa, different species of nuts, as well as many medicines, such as quinine, cocaine and curare.

1 Thousands of birds can be kept in a modern broiler house. If, however, the poultry – which are automatically fed and watered – are overcrowded, disease and stress take their toll.

2 Re-forestation has become increasingly vital throughout the world. At a tree nursery in Scotland, a Forestry Commission officer tends young conifers which will later be transplanted.

3 By growing a wide variety of crops in strips and terraces, farmers in Minnesota, the United States, have been able to prevent soil erosion on the shores of Oak Lake.

Forests in other parts of the world have also been used in the past to provide food. For centuries people living in Europe collected acorns from the oak forests to make flour and raised their pigs on beech nuts. Chestnuts form part of the diet of Spaniards and Italians, and in Siberia the cones of a cembra pine are harvested. In the future Man may have to make greater use of forest for food. As in the cultivation of other crops, there is no reason why the plant breeder and geneticist will not be able to bring out varieties of trees that will give quicker return than the natural trees.

The future of forests depends to a large extent on paper production. It is a sobering thought that the United States, with less that 6 per cent of the world's population, uses some 40 per cent of the paper pulp produced throughout the world. This high percentage would not matter if the United States could grow adequate supplies, but it cannot – it has to import each year the equivalent of two acres of forest for every American. If the future billions of human beings on this Earth are to be literate they will certainly have to study from something other than books made of paper.

The law of diminishing returns applies to agriculture as much as it does to any other activity of Man. Agriculturists can dream of better yields of a crop per acre and of livestock that, fed on basic nutrients, grows faster and more tastily than ever before, but each progression costs more and more. One of the great problems is that, as farming is intensified, so greater care has to be taken to protect the produce from pests and diseases. Undoubtedly plant and animal breeding of disease-resistant strains, the use of chemical sprays and of fertilizers have all contributed enormously to the high productivity of farms, but there are signs that the soil itself cannot withstand such perpetual use of its minerals.

Although the right kind of fertilizers applied to the soil should, in theory, be able to make good any deficiency, in practice there is no such simple solution. At present, while 600 million people of the world depend on artificial fertilizers to make the soil on which they feed productive, the other five-sixths have to manage more or less without. In other words, India, a country of more than 500 million people, uses the same amount of fertilizer as Sweden with only 7·5 million people, and the entire continent of Africa is using no more fertilizer than is Italy. To make up its fertilizer shortage, India would have to invest about 20,000 million dollars in building chemical factories and then it would have to find additional sources of water to dilute the fertilizer in the soil.

6

4 By using different concentrations of certain plant hormones, called cytokinins, the breeder can retard the upward growth of the plant and obtain far better yields of brussel sprouts.
5 In Roman times this land on the Italian island Lampedusa was fertile and was used for growing corn. Since then over-use of the soil has led to erosion and aridity.
6 At a research laboratory in Britain, a scientist tests a proposed lay-out for a plantation of coniferous trees, using model trees in a wind tunnel.

## Caring for the soil

The technologically advanced West is also having problems. Until now farmers have used fertilizers to replace nitrogen, phosphorus, potassium and calcium. But the soil contains at least 20 other elements, including boron, manganese and iron, which are mined from the soil by plants and are essential for their proper growth. To maintain high yields the soil must be replenished with these elements; yet too often it is not replenished and the soils gradually get poorer. Other drawbacks can result from the intensive use of artificial fertilizers; for example, nitrates added to the soil are washed away in ever increasing quantities and are poisoning the rivers upon which Man depends for his water.

The Western farmer, who has been pushed by competition and demand into seeking higher and higher returns from the soil, may have to change tack. He may be forced to revert to a system more akin to a proper crop rotation which gives the soil time to recover from the harvesting of a particular crop before that crop is grown again. By growing leguminous plants, such as peas or beans as one of the basic crops, the farmer can replenish naturally the nitrogen content of the soil. For, through bacteria contained in the nodules of their roots, the plants fix nitrogen from the atmosphere. Some of this remains in the soil after the harvest and, combined with the nitrates formed from the decomposition of manure by bacteria, comprises a good source of nitrates for the next crop.

The rice-growing countries, such as China and Japan, rely on a similar natural fixing of nitrogen to recycle nitrogen lost from the soil in the rice. Instead of bacteria, blue-green algæ grows on the surface of the soil around the bases of the rice stem. Besides fixing nitrogen, the algæ also aerate the soil and provide essential oxygen for the roots of the rice.

The Japanese have started cultivating blue-green algæ in small containers operating on water from hot springs or on natural gas. Each container produces sufficient algæ to spread over 750 acres at least twice a year. The result is a natural and safe replenishing of the soil. Such techniques could become more generally applied in the future.

Except for radiation from the sun and outer space the Earth is a closed system. Whatever the soil produces is recycled back again in the excretion of animals and plants and in their decaying when they die. However, a large percentage of the human population now lives in big cities and the sewage and waste is discharged into rivers, lakes and the sea. Inordinate quantities of rich organic matter are, therefore, lost from the land; the water benefits to some extent but the discharge into them is so great that, instead of being enriched by this decomposing matter, the water becomes choked and loses its oxygen; without oxygen fish and other aquatic organisms die. An alternative to losing the sewage in this way is to direct it to sewage farms where it can be decomposed under controlled conditions into useful products. Some of these can then be applied to the land, or to fish farms.

Because they seek quick returns, farmers in the West have tended to dump all the manure from their livestock and instead use artificial fertilizers. It is becoming more and more apparent that Man cannot afford to lose either animal manure or human sewage.

It seems that intensive animal breeding will not be the order of the day in the future. It is not generally realized that many Western countries are dependent for their high standard of living on the developing countries selling them food products for livestock in exchange for manufactured goods. These food products include fish meal and oilseed cakes, soyabean, peanuts, sunflower seeds, copra, sugar and meat. For example, nearly 95 per cent of world trade in oilseed cakes goes to Western Europe. This is a very significant amount when one realizes that this constitutes more protein than the world's total catch of fish, and is enough protein to double the protein consumption of the underdeveloped countries.

What will happen when the populations of the developing countries would rather feed themselves than export these foodstuffs, especially now that scientists are devising ways of making these various products palatable to human beings? Surely intensive animal breeding will have to come to an end?

## Dangerous cures

To obtain the best animal growth, the modern factory-farm breeder feeds them antibiotics mixed with their foodstuffs. Although it is not known why antibiotics should increase growth production, it is possible that they counteract the stress imposed upon the animals by being confined in a small space and crowded together. Antibiotics are also used to prevent disease when animals, such as calves, are being transported around a country under conditions of filth and close confinement. There is a growing fear that unless the uncontrolled use of antibiotics to increase growth production and prevent disease is banned, strains of pathogenic organisms will emerge that are resistant to some of the antibiotics currently being used against human pathogens. If he cannot use antibiotics so indiscriminately the animal breeder may have to modify his methods of animal husbandry.

One fact is often forgotten. Ruminants, such as cattle, sheep, goats, camels and the many species found living wild in Africa, can make far better use of plants as food than can most other animals. They can do this because bacteria in their rumen break down such constituents of plants as cellulose and lignin, both of which are indigestible to Man. The same bacteria can also synthesize amino acids – the building blocks of proteins – from inorganic nitrates. Ruminants are, therefore, important producers of protein in return for the amount of vegetable matter eaten; by feeding manufactured products to cattle the farmer is losing the potential of these animals to convert grass to flesh.

In East Africa where the soil is poor, wild ruminants, such as antelope and buffalo, by grazing in different habitats, exploit the environment to the full. Traditional farming does not seem to succeed in these regions and Man should, suggest some experts, rear these wild animals in their own natural environment for his own use.

The picture that emerges when looking at agriculture of the future is rather a conservative one. A farmer may do better if he rotates his crops, if he uses as much manure as possible and if he tries to support any livestock on his farm from his own produce. By varying his crops he may find it easier to combat diseases and pests, for these concentrate their attacks when any one species of plant or animal is grown to the exclusion of others.

There are obvious limitations to how much more Man can increase the productivity of his crops and livestock. The most crucial limitation of all, perhaps, is that imposed by fresh water.

Temperate countries have always seemed to have had more than adequate rainfalls to support a good yield of crops; irrigation on the scale that has occurred for centuries in China and India has never seemed at all necessary. Now, for the first time, the Western powers are beginning to find themselves short of fresh water. With industry growing apace – often in direct competition with agriculture for land – so the demands have increased, and hand in hand with this has been a growing, hygienically aware population. The water returned to the land in rain is no longer enough and resources of ground water being tapped at an accelerating pace. All in all the world is slowly, inexorably, running short of water.

Desalination of sea water has been suggested but on the scale required, the amount of fresh water produced can hardly be adequate. Since industrial goods and agriculture for feeding the swelling populations are in competition for water, there may be a time when one or other has to reduce its demands. Let us hope that Man will not choose to starve in order to drive his car up a motorway.

Rats are one of the main destroyers and contaminators of stored human food. It is estimated that in the United States, each of the 120 million rats eats about 40 lb of food a year.

Two varieties of wheat respond to a fungus infection in very different ways. The crop standing erect is resistant to the otherwise devastating effect of eyespot infection.

# Shaping Nature to need

**Biologists can now study the mechanisms of living cells and are learning how to modify them. Control and heredity, exact copies of animals, plants and human beings are all future possibilities.**

TO ATTEMPT to outline the future of biology is like attempting to forecast, at the relevant point in history, the impact of the discovery of firemaking or of the wheel. Everyone has seen something of the effect of these two discoveries; they add up to a complex, bewildering and, sometimes, terrifying pattern of cause and effect. But it would have been impossible to predict their future at the time of discovery.

The situation is the same when it comes to considering the future of biology, but biology is a much more complicated matter. It is not one discipline but many. The physics, the chemistry, the shape and the structure of living processes – not to mention the relationships between them – are all the concern of the biologist. Progress in most of these is going on at an unprecedented rate and is likely to accelerate even more as wider appreciation of the great importance of biology prompts bigger research budgets.

Prediction at this time can only take the form of extrapolation from current knowledge, and here lies another problem. The very speed and scope of biological progress increases the possibility of some breakthrough – possibly achieved by accident – which will invalidate many of our key assumptions and, by extension, invalidate present predictions as well. Even so, it is already clear that the new biology is going to affect our lives. Prediction is useful, therefore; it is better to be half-prepared than not at all.

Undoubtedly the cell will continue to be of major interest to the biologists, for its functioning underlies everything else in the living organism. Some organisms – like amoeba – consist of only one cell, others – like Man – consist of billions of them. In the latter case, the cells of different parts of the body vary according to the tissue which they form. In general, however, each cell takes in food, uses its energy, voids waste products, and reproduces itself. The nucleus of the cell contains the nucleic acids (DNA and RNA) which themselves contain the genetic information which dictate the character of the 'daughter' cells.

## Essential microscopes

Without the microscope very little of the structure of the cell could have been elucidated. Of particular importance has been the electron microscope. The conventional optical type is limited in its usefulness because it cannot resolve objects smaller than about half the wavelength of visible light (the length of a light wave is less than one fifty-thousandth of an inch). The electron microscope uses an electron beam of very short wavelength indeed and objects as tiny as single molecules can be seen and, in certain circumstances, even individual atoms are revealed.

The use of ultra-violet and infra-red reflecting microscopes has made possible the study of the actual chemical composition of cell components. There is no doubt that such apparatus, and what comes after, will continue to play a major part in investigating cell structure and chemistry.

One certain line of attack will be research into a group of cell substances known as *enzymes*. These are produced by the cells of plants and animals and are at work both inside and outside them; they are the catalysts which trigger the many chemical reactions in the organism.

As yet little is known about the workings of enzymes and, particularly, how it is they can cause so many reactions to occur in a split second. It is clear, then, that a great deal of effort will be put into piercing the mysteries of enzymatic functioning. One way of achieving this is to obtain enzymes in pure crystalline form and then, by using all kinds of methods including microscopy, to unravel their chemical and physical structure. Nucleic acids have been very important in recent years as more has been discovered about their structure and functioning. Enzymes also play a part in the synthesis of these substances. DNA has been shown to consist of two long molecular chains twisted together. Each chain consists of an arrangement of four different units called *nucleotides*, the precise sequence being unique to any individual (except identical twins which both stem from the same original egg). It is enzymes which cause the nucleic acid to form from the nucleotides.

The discoverer of this highly significant piece of information was the American biologist, Dr Arthur Kornberg, who actually synthesized DNA by bringing together the relevant enzymes and nucleotides, so that they assembled themselves into a DNA molecule. For this work he received the Nobel Prize. Nevertheless, the

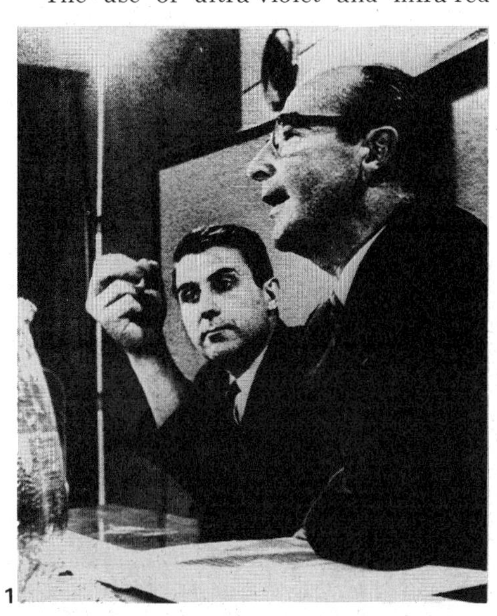

**1** DNA is the basic substance of the genes. Dr Arthur Kornberg, Nobel prize winner, and his colleagues were the first to synthesize biologically active DNA in the test tube.

**2, 3** Even such complicated tissues as limbs will regenerate under certain conditions. The Russian biologist Lev Polezhaev amputated the hind legs of a larval salamander and then irradiated them with x-rays to prevent healing. Yet, three months later he could get the limbs to regenerate by injecting RNA – a gene information-carrying substance related to DNA.

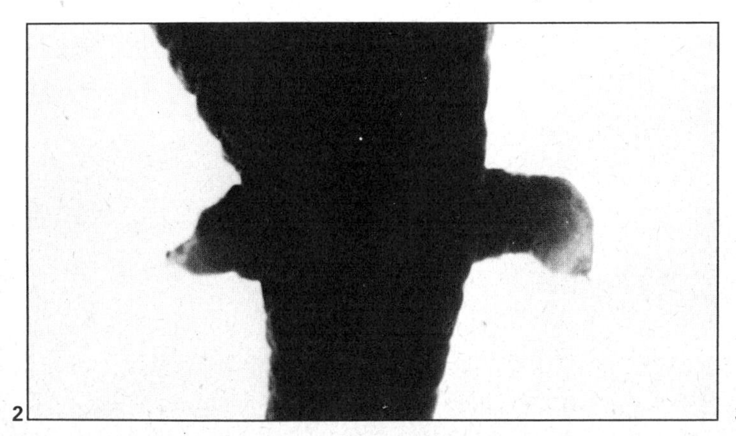

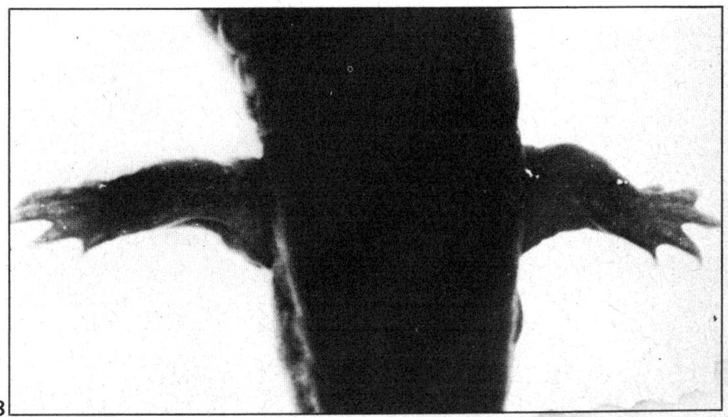

**1** Nobel prize winners, John Kendrew, Max Perutz and Francis Crick with the outcome of their research – unravelling structure of macromolecules such as DNA and myoglobin.
**2** Nobel prize winner Maurice Wilkins helped to decipher the structure of DNA. This genetic molecule has since become a key substance in much biological research.
**3** Getting replicas of any one individual and so making a 'clone' is all in the realms of possibility. It can already be done with plants and may eventually be possible with human beings.

DNA he produced remained biologically inactive, in that it did not cause any reaction when injected into living organisms.

Since then, however, Kornberg and his associates have achieved even greater success. They took the DNA from a virus known as Phi X174, added an enzyme (DNA polymerase) and nucleotides, and in this way got a new DNA chain which was complementary in form to the original.

Working with the complementary form as a template, they produced more DNA, which was found to be an identical copy of the original and not merely complementary. The new product was then introduced in the bacterium, *Escherichia coli*, where it was found to reproduce viruses identical to the natural kind. In other words, the necessary genetic information for a living organism had been assembled artificially and passed from the parent to its offspring.

Work of this kind – a similarly brilliant series of experiments had also been carried out at the University of Illinois by a team led by Professor Sol Spiegelman – is of inestimable value in understanding the reproductive workings of the cell and the origin of life itself.

Indeed some biologists now believe that life can be created from the basic raw materials. In the future a great deal of thought and work will be expended on developing this new-found knowledge.

If, for example, the production of active DNA proves relatively simple, the biologists will have a ready and convenient means of investigating the replication of DNA and the way in which the genes do their work. (Genes are the actual stretches of the DNA chain molecule which carry the instructions for new cell formation.) It may also be possible to modify the chemical arrangement of the DNA in experimental systems so as to alter at will the kind of genetic instruction which is passed on.

## The genetic breakthrough

In parallel with this work, there has also been an important breakthrough concerning genes themselves. At Harvard, researchers have succeeded in isolating a specific gene from DNA. The Harvard team turned their attention to the bacterium, *Escherichia coli* which contains a group of enzymes whose function it is to produce the sugar lactose. Now, some bacteriophages (a type of virus), when they invade the *E. coli* bacterium, integrate themselves into the chromosome next to the section of DNA responsible for this enzymatic control. When they leave they sometimes take this DNA with them to the next host. It was this control section or gene which the Harvard University workers managed to isolate from the phage and render visible under the electron microscope.

All this brings much closer the possi-

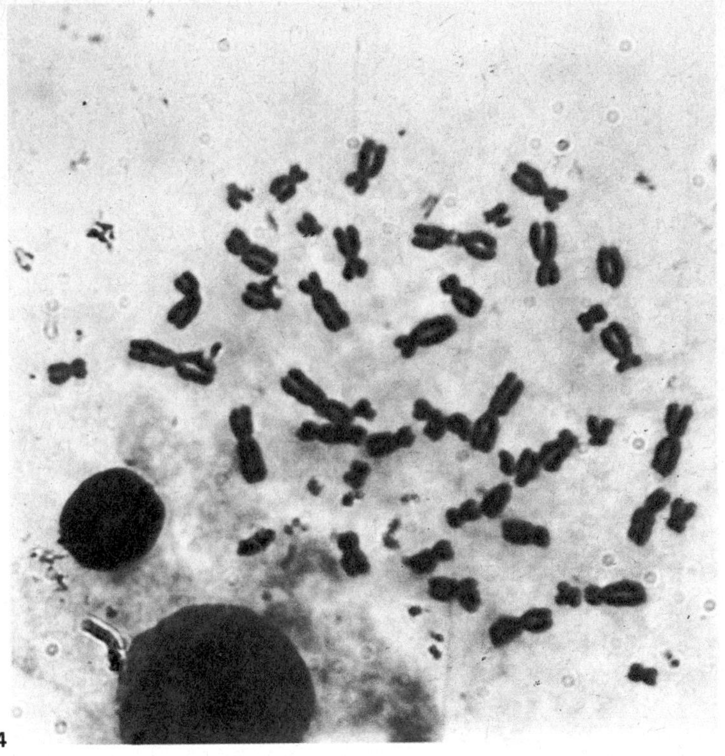

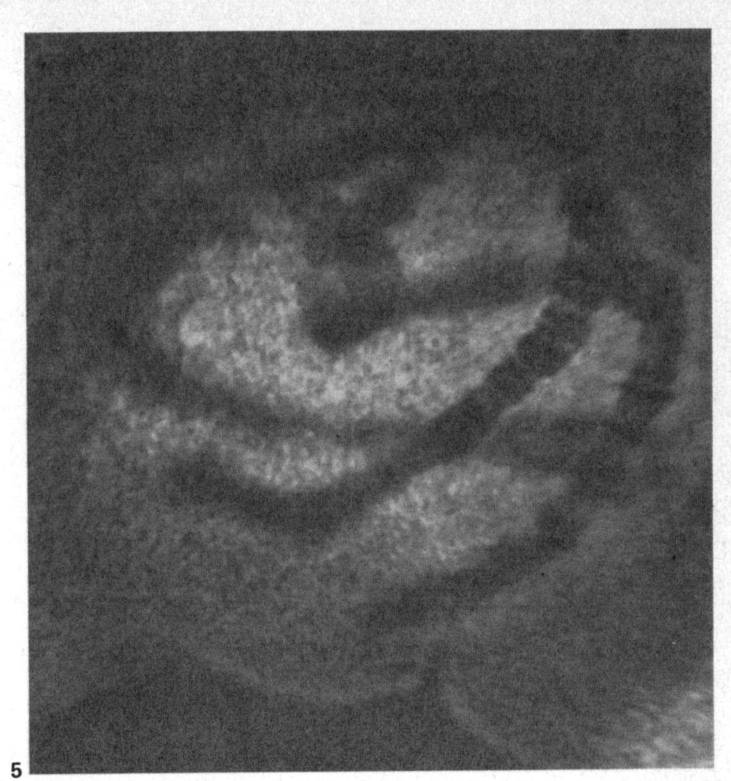

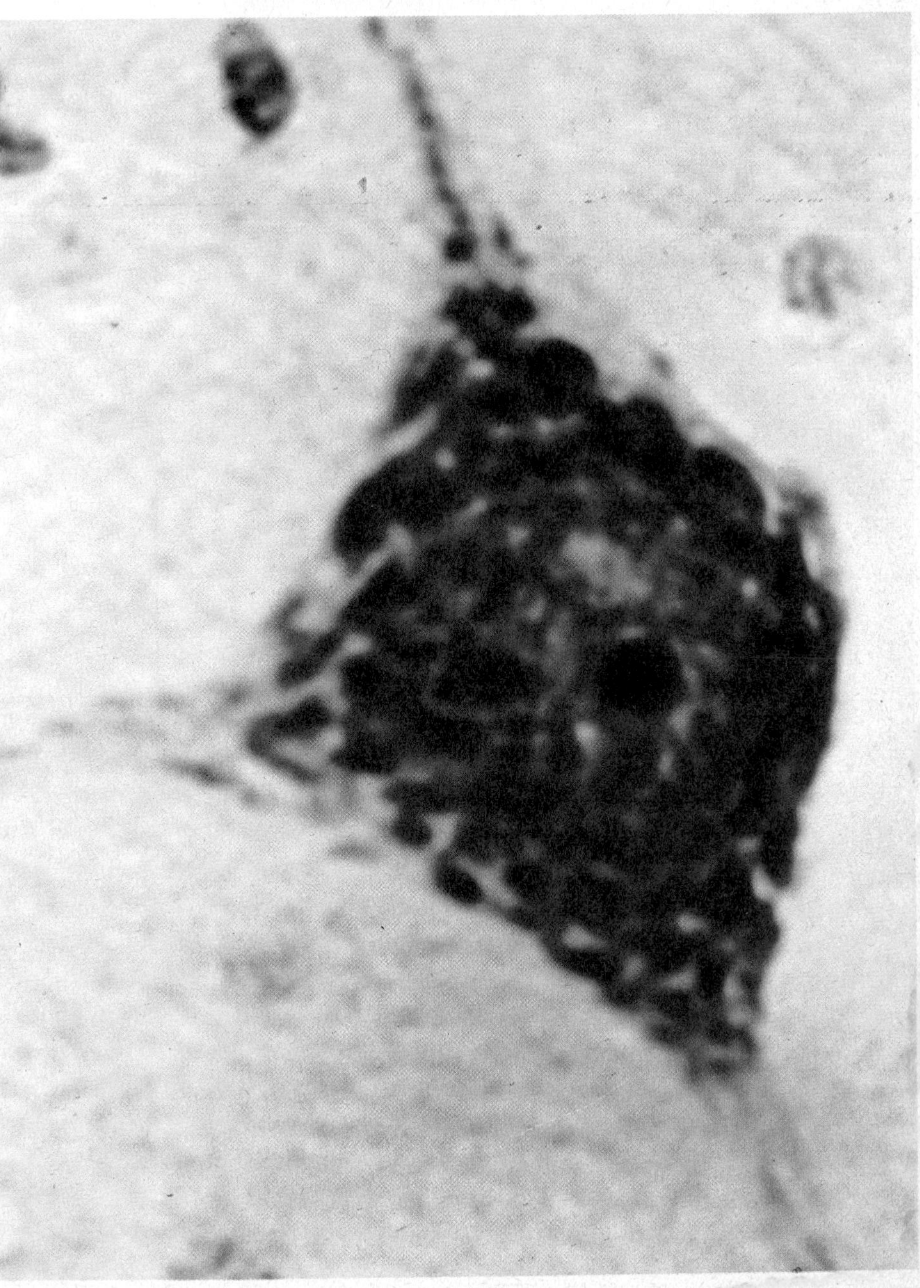

**4** New methods of preparation enable cell-researchers to look at all the chromosomes of the human cell. They can then see any aberrations as well as the factors which determine sex.
**5** The giant chromosomes of the insect, the ironomid larva, are easily seen under the microscope. Scientists have learned much about the genes from studying these chromosomes.
**6** The large pyramidal cell of the brain is involved in such functions as 'thought'. Scientists hope to manipulate these processes by adding specifically acting drugs.

bility of tampering with heredity. It suggests that, in the future, hereditary disease – which occurs when instructions causing defects are passed on from parental nucleic acid to that of the child – may be treated by modifying that substance in the cells of the afflicted individual either before or after birth.

By the same token, resistance, or even immunity, to other kinds of disease could be inbuilt – the transference of drug resistance from one mouse cell line to another has already been effected by the introduction of foreign DNA. Some viruses, called 'passenger' viruses, may be useful in this context. These infect healthy cells, but do them no harm – and in certain conditions it is just possible that they might do some good.

## Making up a deficiency

A number of diseases are caused by the deficiency of certain substances in the sufferer's make-up. If a virus can be found which contains the genetic instructions for the manufacture of the component which is lacking, then the condition will be cured. Thus sufferers from the skin disease, *Xeroderma pigmentosa,* are deficient in a particular nuclease. Kornberg and his team are hunting for a virus which will induce this nuclease.

Finally, there is the possibility of the made-to-measure man or animal, creatures in which the required characteristics are produced by treatment of the genes.

The implications in relation to bodily function are no more fascinating than those for the brain. A team of Californian biologists extracted the nucleic acid, RNA, from the brains of rats which had been taught to respond to certain stimuli and then injected it into the brains of other rats. They found that the second batch of animals needed a distinctly shorter training time before they, too, learned to respond to the stimuli. It seems at least possible, therefore, that in the future Man might be able to train animals by injecting them with information-carrying RNA taken from other, trained animals.

A great deal of investigation has been carried out into the processes of sexual reproduction and this is likely to continue. But recent work has also suggested that it may be possible to do away with the normal processes altogether. One example is the technique of mass reproduction called cloning (the word 'clone' comes from a Greek word meaning 'throng').

The technique was discovered by the British biologist F. C. Steward while working in the United States. He took some cells from the root of the carrot and placed them in a nutrient medium containing coconut milk. There they began to multiply rapidly, and as the culturing process was continued, the cells were seen to develop in a number of interesting ways – the most important of which was that some clumped and began to throw roots. Transferred to a solid nutrient, these developed shoots, and when finally moved to soil, they matured to become entirely normal carrots.

The important thing here, apart from the fact that the usual reproductive processes played no part, was that the new carrots were genetically identical. The significance of this was not lost on the agriculturists. It meant that a prize strain of carrot could be duplicated many times over, exact in every detail, and without any weakening of the strain.

Several types of vegetable are now produced in this way and the biologist will, in the future, turn his attention to elucidating exactly how the process takes place. In this way he will be able to extend the list of plants it is possible to clone. And who knows? He may also discover the means of performing the same trick with animals and even human beings. Culturing animal cells to produce tissues is well established as a laboratory technique, although as yet there has been no success in getting them to group together as organs.

Clues to an answer to this particular problem may be found in work which has been carried out in several research centres, including Britain and Russia, on the regeneration of organs in amphibia and planarians (a group of worms). The Russian biologist Professor Lev Polezhaev has been investigating regeneration in amphibia for more than 20 years. And more recently he has applied some of his knowledge to engendering the same process in certain mammals, including rats and dogs.

## 'Recipe' for a new limb

In his early work he experimented with a salamander. He cut a hind leg from the creature, leaving only a 'cuff' of skin. The bones and flesh of the amputated leg were then pounded up and the resultant mix of cells were sown into the cuff and left. A fortnight later it was opened and a new limb began to grow.

This suggested two things. First, it demonstrated that the component parts of a regenerated limb did not have to grow from corresponding surviving tissues – skin from skin, bone from bone, and so on – because the leg had been totally destroyed and there was no surviving tissue. Second, it looked very much as if it was the cell mix which stimulated growth, much like the effect of an agricultural fertilizer.

Since then, Professor Polezhaev has promoted the regeneration of bone in the head of a dog by filling a hole cut in the cranium with bone dust soaked in the animal's blood. Even more spectacular, he was partly successful in regenerating muscle in the heart of another dog. In this case new growth took place after the injection of a protein extract taken from another heart muscle. The Russians were attempting to heal a wound in the heart, but the drawback was that scar tissue also formed and prevented a complete link-up between old and new muscle. After two months the young muscle dissolved.

As Polezhaev says, 'The work is still not completed, but even now one can say that the problem of restoring lost or damaged tissues or organs in higher animals . . . should be solved not in the distant but in the foreseeable future.'

As the biologists of the future learn more and more about the internal workings of living organisms, they will also look closely at the relationships between such organisms, at their ecological situation. The ecology of micro-organisms, in particular, is likely to become a flourishing field of study in the immediate future.

Classical microbiology has concerned itself mainly with the isolation and culture of various kinds of microbe for study in the laboratory. Yet it has been found that the laboratory microbes, such as the tubercle bacilli, exhibit rather different properties from those taken from infected animals. This demonstrates that the ecological niche in which the bacterium exists has considerable effect on its functioning. Exactly what and how is not known, and it is to finding answers to these kinds of questions that the microbial ecologist will turn his attention. His findings will have great agricultural, medical and social importance.

Reproducing life in the laboratory and understanding the ecology which will support it, are some of the more important lines of study likely to be followed by the biologists of the future. Success will revolutionize our knowledge of the living world and hence our ability to control and modify it. The quality of our lives is likely to be drastically changed.

**1** American researchers have isolated a complete gene – the thread-like portion of DNA – from a bacterium. This research opens up the possibility of genetic engineering.

**2** The 3-D structure of a large molecule of the muscle protein myoglobin has been determined by using x-rays to show the exact position of atoms and the contours of the molecule's shape.

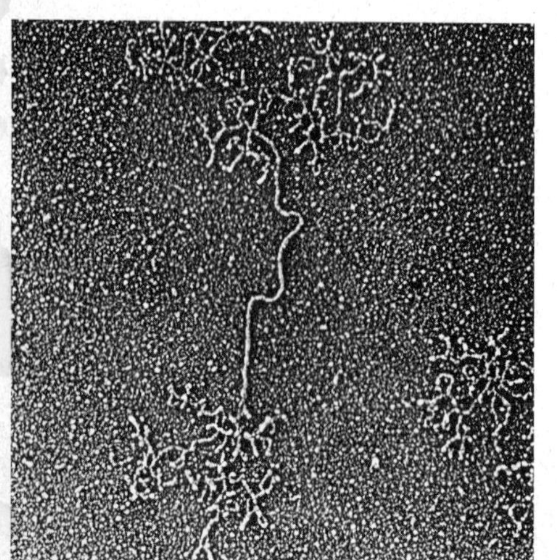
1

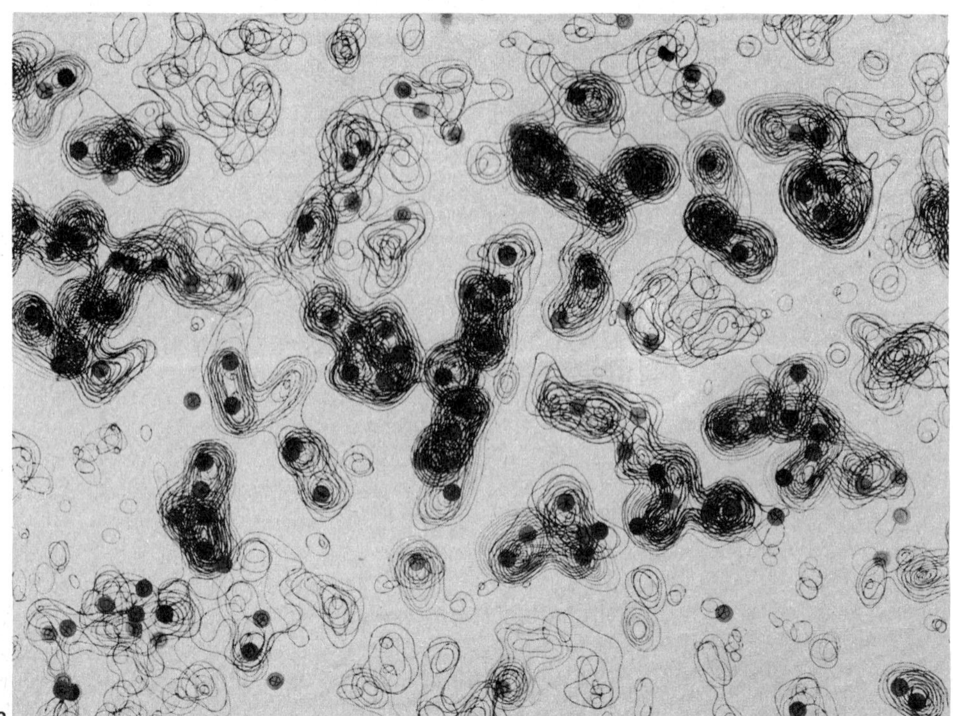
2

# Dangers of domestication

When Man breeds animals for his own use, he tends to lower the resistance to disease that is inbred in the wild. To protect his animals, he has to take drastic and sometimes extreme measures.

ANIMALS IN THE WILD are normally healthy, and it is not difficult to see why. They do not, for example, suffer the diseases of old age – rheumatism and heart disease – for the simple reason that they do not live long enough. Only Man tacks a couple of decades on to his life after he has passed his physical and mental peak: animals reach maturity, grow a little in wisdom, and then die. And wild herds do not usually suffer the effects of hereditary diseases – such as mongolism – because any animal born deformed is actively driven out by the herd, and any population of animals that is sufficiently genetically unstable to produce more than its fair share of defective offspring, dies out.

## Helpful and harmful parasites

Wild animals do, of course, carry a host of infections: their guts are packed with bacteria, some of which are essential to proper digestion. And their guts, and sometimes their blood, may harbour whole ecosystems of flatworms, roundworms and protozoa while insects, ticks and lice browse on and sometimes under their skin. However, through millions of years of evolution, parasite and host have become adapted to each other. Although the parasites take what they want, they do not generally kill their hosts; if they did, they, too, would die.

But animals do suffer from disease when domesticated, and zoo animals – particularly intelligent beasts such as monkeys and apes, as well as extremely active creatures like otters – become neurotic. 'Tail-biting', a form of self mutilation that develops to offset boredom, is common among caged monkeys.

Domesticated animals can show the effects of inherited defects: for example, by breeding animals for particular purposes, Man has often upset the animals' genetic balance. St Bernard dogs have been bred for size: but their great bulk

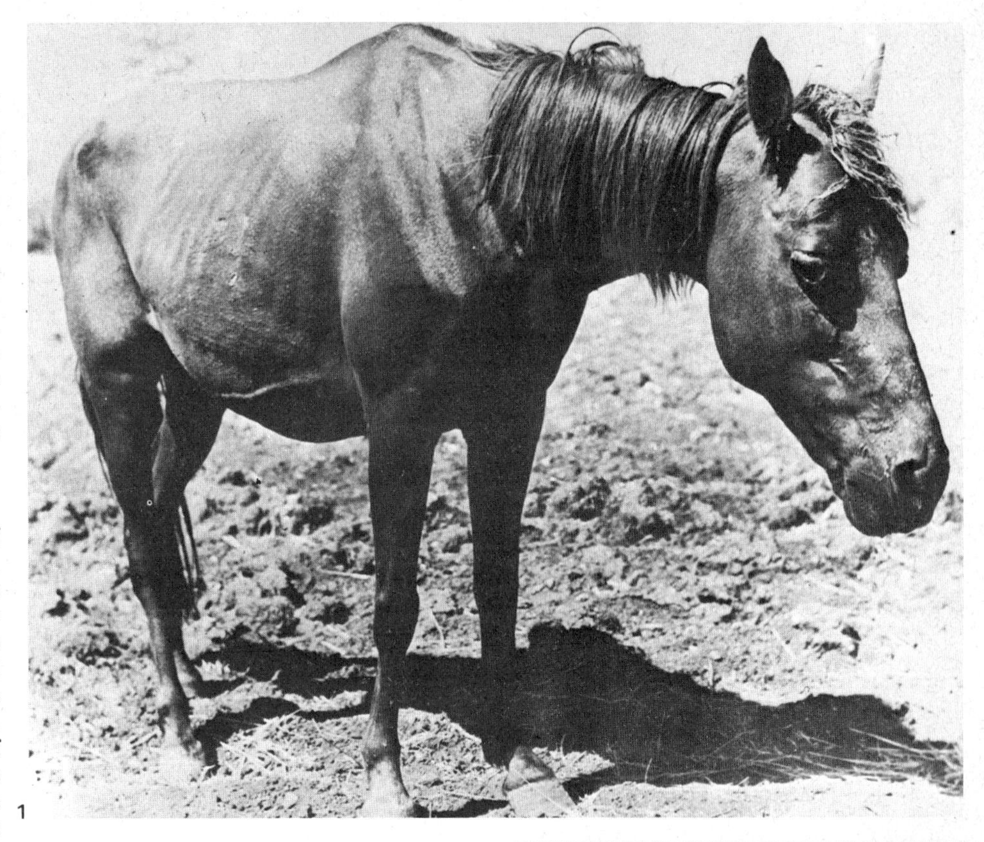

1 Suffering from 'horse fever', this animal is weak, emaciated and barely able to move. Caused by a virus, the disease killed thousands of horses throughout Europe and the Middle East in 1960.

2 At a research institute at Rangoon, Burma, vaccines are produced for use against livestock-killing diseases. Saving livestock is vital in a country short of protein foods.

3 After an outbreak of rabies in Britain in October 1969, a shoot was organized to kill foxes, hares, rabbits and other small wild animals capable of spreading the lethal disease. Since the 1920s, all cases of rabies amongst Man, dogs and animals have been contracted outside Britain.

results from over-production of growth hormone by the pituitary gland. The result – pituitary gigantism – is exactly analagous to a disease in Man known as acromegaly. And St Bernards, like acromegalics, die young, largely because their hearts are too weak for their large bodies. Similar examples are seen among all highly inbred creatures: cows of the Dexter breed frequently produce 'bull-dog' calves – dead foetuses born prematurely, with short head and legs, and a split upper lip. The ease with which genetic balance is upset, producing unviable creatures, slows up all animal breeding programmes.

1

## Hazards of domestication

But the most important result of domestication is to lay animals open to disease from infection. Although some 'parasites' – like the rabies virus – can infect a whole range of different species, most prefer only one species. The great difficulty facing a parasite, living in an animal's blood, or in a plant's cells, is moving from one host to the other. This problem is made much easier when large numbers of the same species live close together.

Secondly, the armistice that exists between parasite and host under natural conditions is not inviolate: if the parasite is strengthened or the host weakened, then the balance is tipped in favour of the parasite, and disease results.

One way of strengthening parasite attack is to increase the numbers of parasites. Keeping farm animals in fields or pens increases their exposure to parasite infection. Parasites frequently pass from one host to another via the dung; this is true of such diverse creatures as the flatworm that causes liver fluke in sheep and cattle, and the *Salmonella typhi* which causes typhoid in man. Wild animals do not live on top of their own dung; herds of cattle and deer are naturally nomadic – the place where they excrete one day they possibly will not visit again for weeks or even years. Monkeys, living in the trees, excrete on to the forest floor, to which they rarely descend. But animals in cages do stay in the same place all the time; unless their excreta are efficiently removed by daily cleaning, then the level of dung-living parasites rapidly mounts. In the Middle Ages, the great epidemics – such as plague, typhoid and cholera – scourged the cities, not the rural country.

2

One way an animal is weakened is by a reduction in its level of 'general fitness'. Calves – in common with most animals – carry the bacterium known as *Escherichia coli* in their guts. Normally this bacterium does no harm. But if the calf becomes 'stressed' – as happens when very young calves are taken from their mothers and packed into cattle-trucks – then the *E. coli* cause disease – a disease characterized by inflammation of the gut, and known as scours.

Another way in which the host-parasite relationship is upset is by an alteration in the genetic make-up of the animal. This, however, works both ways: many varieties of wheat, for example, were bred almost specifically for their ability to resist infection by the rust fungus. But just as frequently genetic alteration of the host favours the parasite. Thus one of the most serious infections among domestic cattle in Britain is brucellosis, which can cause cows to give birth to premature calves that are often dead, and can drastically reduce milk yield and fertility. Yet this disease is unknown among the Wild White cattle of Chillingham, in Northumberland, which are direct descendants of the wild cattle that roamed Britain 2,000 years ago. These Wild Whites are not necessarily 'tougher' than, say, Frisians or Herefords: they are better adapted to cattle diseases.

Disease is best controlled in two ways: firstly by keeping animals 'fit' – well-fed, for example – so that they are more able to ward off infection; and secondly, by reducing the amount of contact between animal and parasite. But the modern trend in farming is to keep more and more animals in a more and more confined space. This reduces their 'fitness', by depriving them of exercise and upsetting them psychologically (a very important consideration in cows); and it increases their chances of contact with disease. Many of the great scourges of domestic animals have been eliminated in Britain – sheep pox in 1850, cattle plague in 1877, glanders of horses in 1920, sheep scab in 1950, and, most significant of all, rabies in

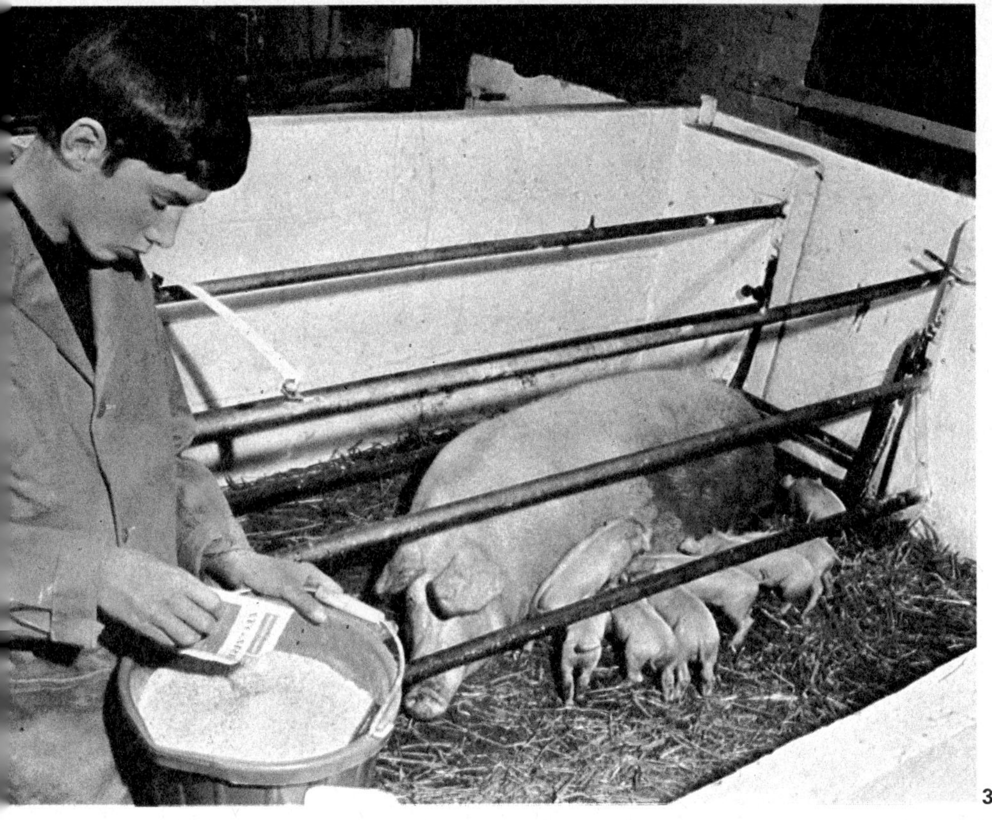

**1** Students at a farm institute in Britain are taught to give sheep a seven-in-one injection to protect them against disease.
**2** Low-lying pasture in Ireland is treated with an experimental spray to destroy liver fluke. During its life cycle, this parasite forms a cyst on grass which, when eaten by a sheep, matures into a fluke and causes liver rot.

**3** To promote health, this pig and her piglets are given a de-worming treatment mixed with the feed. Such treatment prevents parasites from being passed on by infected animals.
**4** Birds imported into Britain are required by law to remain in quarantine for a fixed period. Any infection they may carry can then be detected and prevented from spreading.

1922. But although vets have more legal and medical control over domestic animals than ever before, the problem posed by some diseases of animals is increasing.

Reducing contact between animals and disease organisms is the most important way of avoiding disease. This is done in many ways. Hygiene in animal houses is the most obvious one, but this is not always easy. For example, when the animal hospital was built at the London Zoo it was difficult to decide on the material for the walls. A smooth shiny surface that was easy to wash and disinfect was needed. But the smooth materials then available – plastic and ceramics – were not suitable, because some of the animals were quite capable of smashing such surfaces. Concrete was no good because it was porous and could harbour germs. In the end, concrete was used – but its surface was fired to make it glassy-smooth. Farmers face similar, but lesser problems; modern milking parlours are tiled and shiny like operating theatres.

When animals are kept out of doors they should be kept on the move. For example, sheep should not continuously graze the same fields if liver fluke is present. This prevents the liver fluke from completing its life cycle. The same principle applies in crop rotation; the same vegetable or grain is not grown continually on the same piece of land because its particular parasites build up in the soil and hedgerows, waiting to attack. But if an unsuitable crop is grown instead, the parasites die.

The final way of reducing contact between animal and disease is to limit the movement of animals carrying the disease – or to destroy the diseased animals. Two main examples are rabies and foot-and-mouth disease.

## Rabies

Rabies is an exceedingly nasty disease which is caused by a virus. It can infect every warm-blooded creature, and in most of the world it is carried by the wild animals. But in most wild animals it is not a killer disease as wild animals usually adapt to infections. But rabies is usually lethal in dogs and in man: before it kills, it infects the brain and drives man or dog mad.

The only way to catch rabies is to be bitten by an infected (rabid) animal; the virus is extremely short-lived outside its host. Symptoms of the disease do not appear for some weeks after being bitten; dogs usually show signs of the disease within two months of a bite, and most dogs appear rabid within four months of becoming infected. But sometimes signs do not appear for a year after the animal is infected.

Britain is exceedingly fortunate to be free of rabies. The disease has now reached epidemic proportions amongst wild animals in Northern Europe and North America. Before 1922 rabies occurred in Britain but it never became established among the wild life. It was eliminated by destroying all rabid dogs. The steady trickle of cases since the 1920s, among Man, dogs and some animals were all contracted outside Britain. The British government

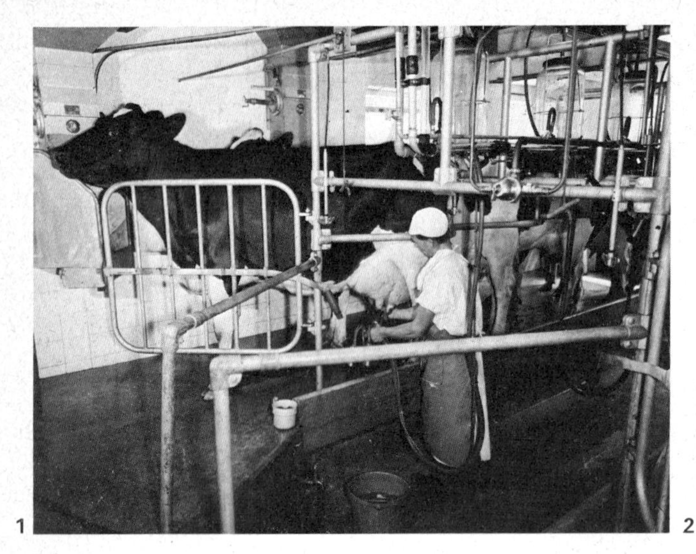

prevents rabies being brought in by ordering all imported dogs and cats to be quarantined for eight months; in that time, the vast majority of animals carrying rabies will show symptoms and can be destroyed. There is no other way to detect a carrier. But because the incubation period can be up to a year, some rabid dogs can and do go undetected.

## Infectious disease

Foot-and-mouth is a disease of cloven-hooved animals: cows, sheep and pigs. Its symptoms include blisters on the tongue and between the toes. It is not usually a killer, but it does reduce an animal's productivity by up to 25 per cent. Because of this, and because the disease is so easily spread, animals with the disease must be destroyed. This points to the fundamental difference between veterinary and human medicine; sick human beings receive treatment for their illnesses whatever the cost; sick farm animals are treated only if the cost of treatment is less than the value of the animal, or less than the risk of keeping an infected animal alive. Unlike the rabies virus, the foot-and-mouth virus can live outside the host for a long time, and is easily carried by human beings, animals, on straw, or in bones from infected animals.

About half the cases of foot-and-mouth in Britain are imported. In the winter of 1967 a sheepdog at a farm in Oswestry, Shropshire, was given a bone from a joint of meat imported from the Argentine. The bone was infected with foot-and-mouth virus: it was picked up by some pigs, and – so it is thought – began one of the worst outbreaks of the disease ever experienced in Britain. Within five weeks almost 250,000 animals that either showed signs of the disease or were in contact with diseased animals, had been slaughtered.

Whenever foot-and-mouth or rabies find their way into Britain, it is asked: 'Why are not animals vaccinated against these diseases?' The general answer is that, although vaccines have proved invaluable against a whole host of diseases – brucellosis in cattle, for example, or distemper in dogs – to vaccinate at all is to admit defeat: it is to admit that the disease is present in the country in such amounts that the risk of an animal catching it is greater than the risk – and the cost – of vaccinating.

1 Cows are milked by electricity in a modern milking parlour in Britain. Cleanliness prevents cross-infection between the animals and contamination of the milk.
2 The Wild White cattle of Chillingham, Northumberland, direct descendants of the wild cattle which once roamed Britain and Europe, are resistant to many domestic cattle diseases.
3 This cow in Uganda is suffering from sleeping sickness. Transmitted by the tsetse fly, the disease has limited the keeping of domestic livestock in many parts of Africa.

What is 'the risk of vaccinating'? In the first place, some vaccines are more effective than others. Present rabies vaccines are not very good: a vaccinated dog can still contract, carry and pass on the disease, although, because it has been vaccinated, it does not show symptoms. The same objection applies to foot-and-mouth vaccine – but with an added complication: foot-and-mouth is caused by seven different virus types, which between them have 53 different sub-types. A vaccine effective against all of them would be very difficult to produce.

Because vaccinated animals can carry foot-and-mouth without showing symptoms of disease, all other animals in contact with them must also be vaccinated – in case they pick up disease from the vaccinated animal. And when a new generation of young animals are born they, too, must be vaccinated to prevent them catching the disease from the animals already vaccinated. Once vaccination is begun, it is difficult to stop. The foot-and-mouth epidemic of 1967–8 probably cost Britain around £100 million, but the cost of vaccinating all the cattle could well have been nearly half that – and that cost would have to be repeated with each new cattle generation.

Disease, therefore, should be prevented. But when a disease does occur, it is often considered better to destroy the animal than cure it. One way of curing animal diseases is to add antibiotics to the animals' feed. If only a few animals in the flock or herd are affected, then all the animals in the group might be treated, in order to forestall infection in the others. When healthy-looking animals are treated to prevent disease, this is known as *prophylaxis*.

Used in this way, for cure and necessary prophylaxis, antibiotics fill a vital role in modern agriculture. But many farmers abuse antibiotics. Animals seem to be more susceptible to disease when under stress: the answer to this is to treat the animals well, so they do not become stressed. But some farmers treat animals badly because it is often cheaper and more convenient to do so, and then try to prevent them becoming diseased by feeding them with low levels of antibiotics (this use of antibiotics is quite separate from their use as growth-promoters). The danger is that when bacteria are exposed to low doses of antibiotics they become resistant to them – so that an antibiotic used in low doses to counteract stress rapidly becomes useless for treating a full-blown disease. Also, some bacteria that become resistant to antibiotics can actually transfer their resistance to other bacteria which have not been exposed to the drug. Since the late 1950s, several strains of disease-causing bacteria have developed that are totally resistant to many important antibiotics.

In general, the best answer to animal disease is good husbandry, and if that fails, the veterinary surgeon must vaccinate or treat. That veterinary medicine is concerned with treating domestic animals is obvious: what is less obvious, is that its main function is to counter the effects of domestication.

# Using Nature's own controls

**Insects, animals and plants destroy huge quantities of human food and damage farming land. Successful attempts to control these pests are now being made by using their own natural enemies.**

Australian rabbits are capable of denuding vast areas (left). The erection of a rabbit-proof fence to protect the land demonstrates what could be available for grazing.

In 1787 the American prickly pear was introduced to Australia as a garden plant. It multiplied so rapidly that 48 species of cactus-preying insect had to be imported to destroy it.

EVERY ORGANISM has an unlimited capacity for reproduction, and given the food and space, will multiply without restraint. But on this crowded planet plant species competes against plant species for water, light and soil nutrients; animal species competes against animal species for food and territory; and both plant and animal species are beset by predators and parasites. But besides these competitive and combative relationships there are many co-operative ones. Bacteria aid plants by converting nitrogen from the air into nutrient salts, animals pollinate many plants, and enrich the soil with their excretions and their own bodies when they die, and many predators are kept in check by predation.

Over the ages this complex web of natural relationships has evolved some measure of stability. If, for example, an animal species multiplies rapidly it will soon deplete the numbers of the species on which it feeds. So the total food supply will diminish, and the burgeoning animal species will be faced with starvation which will last until its population has thinned out enough for the food species to start multiplying again. In this way, the equilibrium is, at least temporarily, re-established.

This interrelatedness of the elements in a living landscape forms a backcloth to biological control, which is the use of biological methods to attack the pests and weeds which threaten Man's crops. The biological controller aims to manipulate the pattern of living relationships in an environment for his own ends. His most important technique is to encourage or introduce natural enemies of the unwanted pest, although other approaches are increasingly being tried. For instance, he can interfere with the pest's reproductive cycle by releasing sterilized but potent adults of the same species, or releasing adults of an incompatible strain.

Although many crops have been successfully bred for disease and pest resistance, the economic importance of crop protection remains colossal. It has been estimated that in the United States, where the most sophisticated control methods are in use, pests and weeds cost the nation about one-quarter of its agricultural production. The methods of modern agriculture themselves contribute to the continuing need for crop protection, and they do so in two principal ways.

## Botanical traffic

First, plants have in the last few centuries been taken from their natural homes and introduced to new areas on a huge scale. The United States Office of Plant Introduction alone has imported nearly 200,000 species and varieties of plants from elsewhere in the world. This botanical traffic is harmless enough in itself, but it is rarely just botanical. It has been estimated that about half the major insect enemies of plants in the United States were introduced accidentally with imported plants. Such pests often wreak more havoc in the new territory than they did in the old by escaping from the natural enemies that restrained them in their native land.

The long migration of the Colorado beetle is a classic example of this. Before 1850 this small beetle was an insignificant insect feeding on tuberous plants in the Rocky Mountains. The spread of the cultivated potato gave the beetle not only an abundant supply of food but a means of transport. By 1859 it had reached Nebraska, by 1870 Ontario, and by 1874 the Atlantic Coast. Before the First World War, the pest made only occasional appearances in Europe and each time it was eradicated before it could spread far. But in the 1920s it became widespread in France, probably crossing the Atlantic with food supplies for the American army, and by 1946 it was established throughout Western Europe.

The second main way in which modern agriculture has intensified its own pest problem is its tendency towards single-crop farming. Whenever Man brings land under cultivation he simplifies the living community of species based upon it. There are fewer plants and the number of animal species is reduced. In a forested area of Malaya, 49 species of rodents and insectivores were counted, but in an adjacent cleared area there were 15, five of which had been introduced by Man.

This simplification of natural communities has been occurring ever since Man first tilled the land, but it has now reached a dangerous extreme, in such places as the American prairies where millions of acres are devoted to wheat, and California where millions of acres are devoted to citrus fruits. The animals that remain suffer less competition, have fewer natural enemies, have a lavish food supply, and are therefore more liable to build up their populations to catastrophic levels than they would be on uncultivated territory.

The farmer's main weapon against pests and weeds has so far been chemistry. Sulphur was used to treat the powdery mildew of the vine in the early part of the nineteenth century, and arsenic compounds were introduced to the battle against the Colorado beetle in 1867. But the modern pesticide industry effectively began in the Second World War with the discovery of the insecticidal properties of DDT (dichlorodiphenyltrichloroethane) and BHC (benzene hexachloride). These materials quickly came into use on an enormous scale against the insect carriers of malaria and trench fever.

Since then the chemistry laboratories of the world have provided farmers with a stream of powerful insect poisons, most of them either *organochlorines* (like DDT and BHC) or *organophosphates*, very toxic compounds related to the nerve gases. A host of specific herbicides has appeared, too. These compounds have been of great value to Man in protecting his crops and controlling insect carriers of disease, but since the late 1950s they have been shown to have some alarming side-effects.

Because many of these laboratory creations are so unlike any natural molecules of life, they escape attack by soil bacteria, and so accumulate in the soil, with unpredicted and indiscriminate effects on the local animal life. But a second, and in some ways more serious problem, is pesticide resistance. In any pest population some individuals will be less susceptible to a particular pesticide than their fellows. Natural selection will ensure that they and their descendants come to predominate in the population, with the eventual production of a completely resistant stock. Once resistance has been acquired, it is not lost, so the pesticide in question has to be replaced by another, and probably more toxic one. In 1958 the World Health Organization listed 26 resistant insect species of importance to public health, including carriers of malaria, yellow fever, plague and filariasis. By 1968, the list had grown to nearly 100.

It is this accidental transport of pests, the simplification of environments by agriculture, and the shortcomings of chemical pest control that explains the increasing interest amongst agriculturalists in biological control. Biological principles of pest control are implicit in such ancient farming practices as crop rotation and the cultivation of mixed forests, but the first conscious application of these principles took place in California.

In 1868 an insect called the cottony cushion scale was introduced to California from Australia, on imported citrus plants. The insect is not an important pest in Australia but in California, unchecked by its natural enemies, it multiplied with such speed that, by 1886, it was threatening the entire citrus industry of the Pacific coast. The United States Department of Agriculture sent an employee to Australia to look for natural predators of the pest, and he came back with a beetle, *Rodolia cardinalis*. Established in California, the beetle quickly brought the cottony cushion scale under control and it has since had equal success in many other citrus-growing areas of the world. The factors behind *Rodolia*'s success are probably its high rate of reproduction, its lack of hyperparasites, and its great activity both as larva and adult.

But not many biological control programmes are as straightforward as this. One of the difficulties that can arise is illustrated by the story of the hispid beetle, *Promecotheca reichei*, a pest of the coconut palm in Fiji. The beetle was not a

2

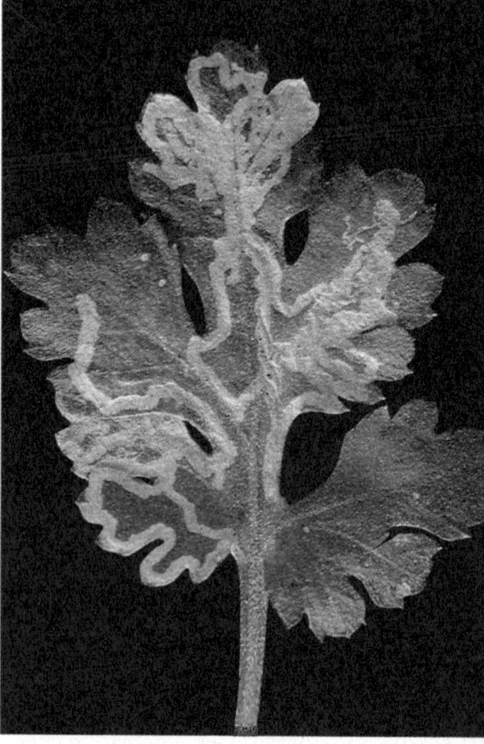
3

1

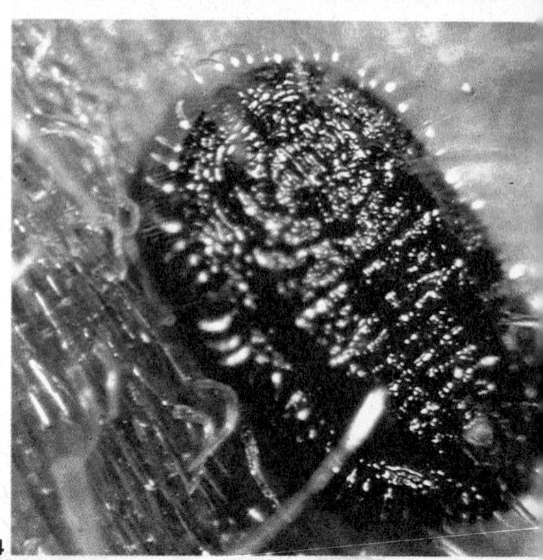
4

5

**1** When introduced to other countries, the Venezuelan water hyacinth grows in such profusion that it chokes rivers and canals. Biologists are still searching for methods of control.
**2** The peach-potato aphid *Myzus persicae* is a common pest of greenhouse plants. In order to destroy it, use is made of a parasite wasp *Aphidius matricariae* which lays an egg in the greenfly. The golden 'mummy' stage shown here represents the pupa of the parasite within the shell of the greenfly.
**3** The larva of the whitefly *Trialeurodes vaporariorum* is a pest of many glasshouse plants, especially cucumbers and tomatoes. It is parasitized by the minute wasp *Encarsia formosa.*
**4** The adult parasite *Aphidius matricariae.*
**5** *Cycloneda sanguinea,* a sub-tropical ladybird, is an excellent predator of greenfly.
**6** A rabbit with myxomatosis dies by the roadside. Disease-bearing micro-organisms are increasingly used in biological control. The myxoma virus has had spectacular success in reducing Australia's rabbits, but the animals are gradually developing a resistance to the disease.

serious nuisance, because its generations overlapped, so that its developmental stages of larva, pupa and adult were all present at any one time, and each of the stages was checked by a different natural parasite. But in 1921 a mite turned up in Fiji attacking all the beetle's developmental stages so successfully that the beetle was almost wiped out. The beetle population began to rise again afterwards, but this time its generations were more or less synchronized: larva turned into pupa and then into adult at about the same time over the whole island. The beetle's native parasites could not handle this situation, and it rapidly became a troublesome pest. The beetle was eventually brought under control by the importation of a parasite of a related Javan beetle. Biological control can founder when a particular relation between predator and prey life cycles is lost.

Both these examples concern the pitting of insect against insect, but insects have also had some spectacular successes in controlling weeds. In the mid-nineteenth century a thorny shrub called lantana was introduced to Hawaii from Mexico as an ornamental plant. It spread rapidly and soon it was menacing pastures. In 1898 several insects that fed on the plant in its native land were introduced to Hawaii, with such successful results that further measures to control the plant were unnecessary.

The prickly pear provides a more spectacular success story. It was established in Australia in 1787 as a garden plant, but it multiplied explosively and by 1925 was occupying about 60 million acres of grazing country. Forty-eight species of cactus-preying insect were brought to Australia from the plant's native America, and 13 of them became so effectively established in their new home that by 1938, 25 million acres of agricultural land had been reclaimed.

Another unwanted plant that has yielded to insect predation is St John's Wort. This hardy perennial, a native of Eurasia, has accompanied European Man on his western travels. It first appeared in the United States in 1793, and by 1900 it reached California. By 1940 it had invaded millions of acres there, displacing the local plants and harming the livestock which fed on it. The plant is not a problem in Europe because it is kept in check by numerous insect predators, and two species of these, natives of southern France, were shipped to California in 1944. By 1948 both were so well established that further importations were unnecessary, and by 1959 the weed had been reduced to 1 per cent of its former abundance. From the point of view of biological control this is an ideal result: if the weed had succumbed totally the imported insects, which eat nothing else, would have died out, too, so robbing California of its protection against future infestation.

Climate is a very important factor in the planning of any biological control programme. In Canada St John's Wort has been subdued by a beetle from the cooler lands of northern Europe. Satisfactory control has not yet been established in Australia, for the insects that have been introduced did not thrive in the climate there. But St John's Wort grows in many climatic conditions in its native Eurasia, and it is probable that an extended search would yield an insect predator of the weed suited to Australian conditions.

6

## Enormous numbers

Pests and weeds are beset by infectious disease and an increasing amount of attention is being given to the use of disease-bearing micro-organisms in biological control. In principle micro-organisms offer several advantages. They reproduce extremely fast and can easily be transported in enormous numbers. They are usually very specific to their target species and threaten no other animal or plant. Often they form resistant spores which can be stored for years until needed to deal with pest outbreaks. In spite of this, their record so far has been disappointing. Probably the biggest single reason for their lack of success is that, unlike insect predators, they cannot actively seek out their prey. They are often only transmitted by contact between members of their target species, and so rapidly lose effectiveness as the target population drops below a certain level.

But there are a few success stories. A bacterium called *Bacillus thuringiensis* has been usefully brought to bear against various harmful caterpillars, but in most cases it has not established itself as a self-propagating disease, and repeated doses have been necessary. In some Canadian forests the polyhedrosis virus has proved an effective control of the pine sawfly, a

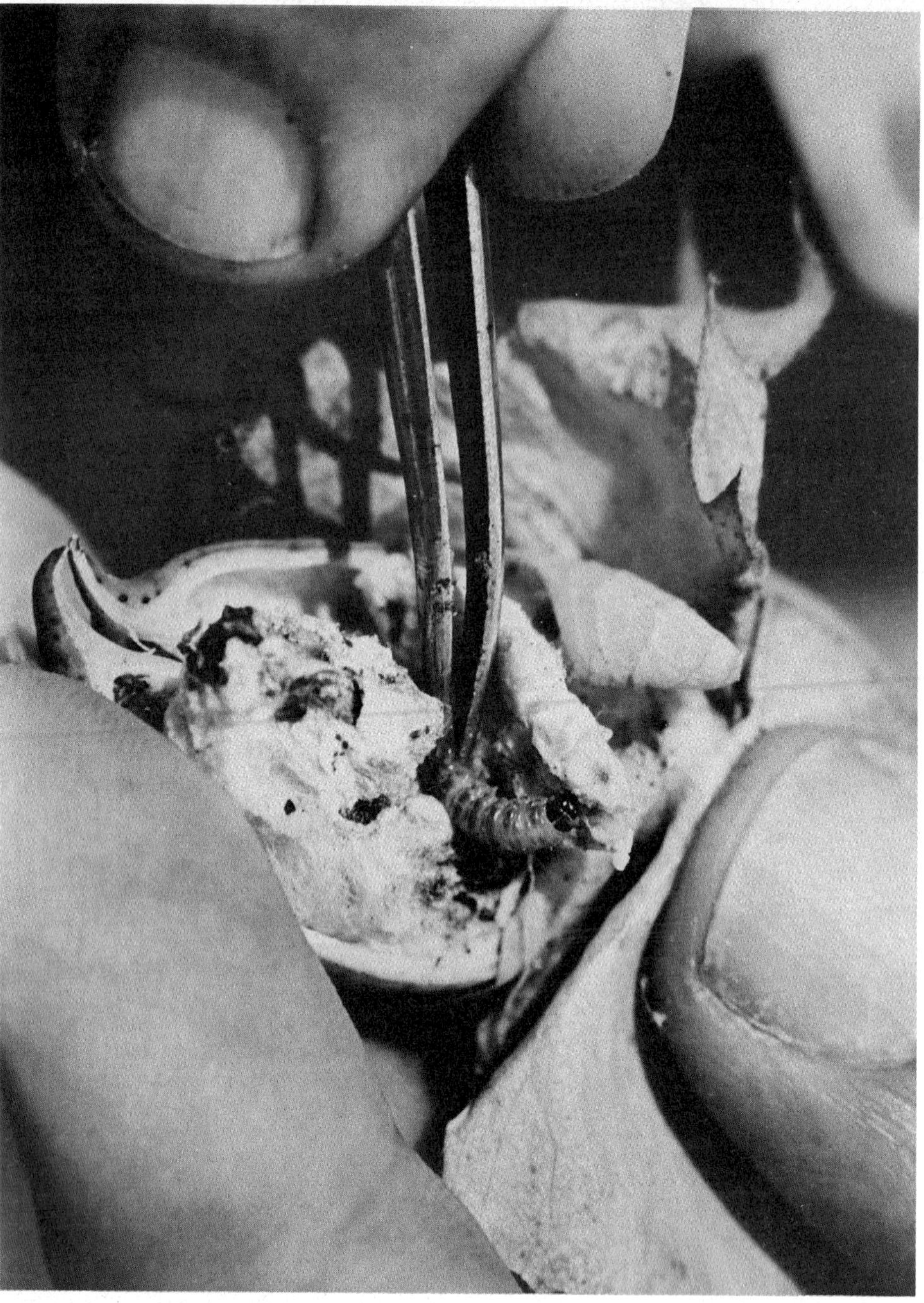

pest of European origin, and experiments in France indicate that the same virus may be useful in controlling the pine processionary caterpillar. The myxoma virus has been spectacularly successful in cutting down Australia's rabbit population, but rabbits are developing resistance to the virus disease.

Higher animals are unlikely ever to be important agents of control. They breed too slowly, and their food preferences are too wide. Weasels were introduced to New Zealand in an attempt to control rabbits, but apparently they preferred to eat poultry. Insects by contrast are often highly adapted for one particular food source, and this is the main reason why they have been used successfully for biological control. California and Australia feature largely in these success stories because intensive agriculture and its associated pest problems have arrived in these areas fairly recently.

An alternative approach to biological control is the release of sterilized males into the pest population. The sterile males compete with intact males and cut down the rate of reproduction of the pest. It has been calculated that a population of insects can be eradicated completely in three generations if enough sterile males are released for each generation. The screw-worm, a parasite of livestock, was exterminated from the island of Curaçao in this way in 1954. A variant of this approach is the mass release of males of an incompatible strain.

Besides overcoming the pollution and resistance problems associated with chemical pest control, biological methods are very cheap and self-maintaining. In favourable cases there is no extra cost once the introduced beneficial species has established itself. Chemical poisons, by contrast, have to be regularly reapplied. Biological control rarely eradicates pests, but the survival of small numbers of the pest species is not a hazard in many situations, and in fact acts as a safeguard against massive re-invasions by the same species.

But biological control should not be regarded as an alternative to pesticides. There are probably not enough pest predators in existence to handle every pest-control situation. Very promising results are being obtained with integrated crop-control schemes which combine biology and chemistry: in Nova Scotia apple orchards, California alfalfa fields and many forests round the world, the native beneficial species are nurtured, a spectrum of carefully chosen pest enemies has been introduced, and pesticides are applied sparsely and reluctantly only when biological control appears to be losing.

**1** An 80-year-old elm near the Jefferson Memorial in Washington D.C. is a victim of fungus carried by the elm bark beetle. A tiny parasitic wasp from Europe is being used against the beetle.
**2** Larvae of *Cactoblastis* moths feeding on a prickly pear. In the 1920s the Australian Prickly Pear Board imported eggs of the moth from South America to control the menace.
**3** Pink cotton boll weevil can destroy whole fields of cotton. A pilot programme launched in Texas in 1968 introduced large numbers of sterile moths to reduce mating between fertile moths.

# Industry–the great destroyer?

Industry is now the mainstay of the modern technological world and few would choose to live without its material benefits. But the price is often devastation of the natural environment.

BY APPLYING his scientific and technological discoveries and inventions to industry, Man, alone amongst the animals, is able to control and exploit his environment to a large extent. And it is the products of industry that enable men to colonize the most inhospitable regions of the Earth and even set foot on the moon. But the list of examples where industries are destroying the environment grows longer every day.

In 1968, when the oil tanker *Torrey Canyon* went aground on rocks of the Scilly Isles, the sea and beaches in the English Channel were polluted with thick oil which killed thousands of sea birds and threatened the sea food industry. In 1969 pollution of the River Rhine by a very toxic pesticide killed millions of fish and made the water undrinkable for several days. Even animals and birds in Antarctica, which is remote from agricultural activity, are now contaminated with pesticide residues. Many of the world's lakes and inland seas, such as the Great Lakes in America and Lake Erie in particular, have been depleted of oxygen, and consequently fish, because vast amounts of inorganic fertilizers have been washed into them from farmland.

## A growing threat

The thousands of acres of derelict land surrounding mines and abandoned industrial sites in many of the industrialized countries of the world are eloquent testimony of the way in which industry has squandered land and life. And now the testing of atomic bombs pollutes the atmosphere, plants, animals and our food with radioactive elements. Even such peaceful applications of atomic energy as nuclear power stations present a subtle threat to our environment. The waste heat from power stations, if it is dissipated in river water, can raise the temperature of the water and cause the death of fish and other aquatic life. Hardly a river in Britain, for example, is free from industrial pollution somewhere along its course.

As these examples show, through errors or misuse of industry Man can, and often does, ruin or degrade his own environment and that of other creatures. Accidents apart, the pollution of our environment stems from lack of knowledge, greed and lack of thought. In the short term it is easier and cheaper to dump an old car on the road side, pour untreated sewage or industrial waste into a river or the sea and for a government to turn a blind eye to what is going on, than to control such destructive activities.

In most people's minds pollution conjures up pictures of grimy industrial towns belching forth smoke and poisonous effluents into the air and rivers. But agriculture causes pollution of a different and more intractable kind – the pollution of plants and animals by pesticides and the pollution of lakes and rivers by fertilizers. Most herbicides are quickly broken down in the soil and present no long-term threat of pollution, but many insecticides, especially the organochlorine compounds such as DDT, BHC, aldrin, dieldrin and endrin, are persistent, remaining active for many years. Moreover, they are accumulated in living organisms and, as a result, they build up in the food chains leading from plants to animals and to Man and can cause sterility and even death.

About 1·5 million tons of DDT, for example, have been used throughout the world and nowhere is free of the substance; it even contaminates the fat of penguins in Antarctica. The average American has 11 parts per million of DDT in his fat, the Briton 2·2 p.p.m. and the Indian 12·8 to 31·0 p.p.m. The prospect of poisoning the world with organochlorine pesticides has led Sweden, Denmark, West Germany and Holland to ban the use of them and Britain to introduce curbs.

This ban, although a beginning, will only have a small effect on this particular

An unprecedented number of seals died off the coast of Cornwall in the winter of 1969. The cause of death is unknown but chemical pollution is suspected as a contributing factor.

type of pollution. Many countries depend enormously on pesticides for their food production, and the organochlorine pesticides, such as DDT, are amongst the cheapest to manufacture.

The problem can be solved to some extent. Effective replacements of those pesticides which do not persist in the soil but break down quickly can be used. The snag to the use of organophosphorous pesticides instead of organochlorine ones, is the cost. At present the farmers do not feel they can afford them.

Fertilizers also cause pollution by over use. In parts of the United States mothers have been told to give their babies only pure spring water, bottled at the spring, because the local water supply contains so much nitrate as to be dangerous to their babies. And quite apart from immediate health risks, fertilizers are causing rivers and lakes to become stagnant. What happens is simple enough. Excess fertilizer eventually washes off land into streams and lakes causing the algae in the water to multiply explosively, forming what is called a bloom. When the algae ultimately die, they sink to the bottom of the river or lake and are decayed by bacteria – a process which uses up all the oxygen in the water. Once this process of *eutrophication* has started the river or lake becomes progressively more depleted of oxygen, bringing about the death of fish and other organisms. To prevent such stagnation from becoming more widespread the amount of fertilizers used must be controlled.

It is not only fertilizers that precipitate eutrophication. Urban sewage pumped untreated into lakes accumulates in just the same way as dead algae and results in deoxygenation of the water. To give some idea of the scale of the problem it can be stated that 115 grams of oxygen are required to oxidize one man's daily sewage output, an amount of oxygen normally dissolved in over 2,000 gallons of river water. The River Thames, for example, flowing at 200 million gallons a day, would be completely deoxygenated by the raw sewage of a town with a population of only 100,000 inhabitants.

In addition to the organic matter in sewage, inorganic chemicals can precipitate eutrophication. Detergents contain large amounts of phosphates which eventually get into rivers. These phosphates can often provide the small extra stimulus to algae, which are already receiving washed-off nitrate fertilizers. Clearly if Man is to live in huge conurbations, sewage treatment must be improved. It costs an enormous amount of money to build and run sewage plants to cope with the sewage of a large town but unless that is done the long-term result will be increasing river and sea pollution.

The Cuyahoga River, one of the rivers which flows through the iron and steel town of Cleveland in the United States and empties into one of the Great Lakes, Lake

**1** Aeroplanes are increasingly disrupting the environment. Their exhausts cause clouds to form, weather to change, and they make an intolerable noise over populated areas.
**2** Industry, which needs enormous quantities of water, tends to grow up along the banks of rivers and lakes. As its growth continues unchecked nothing remains of the original land.
**3** Smoke is one of the major pollutants of industry and if allowed to belch impure and unfiltered from factory chimneys leads inevitably to a spoiling of the atmosphere.
**4** The benefits of industry also create a problem of disposal. These rusting cars have been dumped on the edge of one of the Great Lakes in the United States.
**5** Firemen pour detergent on to oil washed on to the English south coast from the wrecked oil tanker *Torrey Canyon*. As shipping grows in volume, so do the dangers of such pollution.

Erie, has been classed 'the only body of water in the world that is a fire risk'. Unfortunately, the gibe is true. The surface of the river is covered by a thin film of oil poured into it by industrial plants, and sewage lines the bed of the river. Sometimes as the sewage decays it produces noxious gases which spontaneously ignite as they reach the surface and set the oil alight. Lake Erie, the smallest and shallowest of the Great Lakes, is also the most polluted. A thick mat of algae covers several hundred square miles of the lake's surface. It has been estimated that if no more sewage was put into the lake, natural purification would take ten years.

In Britain, although none of the rivers are so strikingly polluted, some 6 per cent of its 2,000 miles of rivers are completely unusable as fresh water and another 20 per cent are badly in need of attention. One observer reported that as many as 177 pipes discharge raw sewage into the first 17 miles of the River Tyne which then flows into the sea. Almost every large industrial town is sited on a river because water was used for power and for transport, and local industries used these rivers to dispose of their waste. The course of pollution can, however, be reversed. Strict control on effluent discharged into the River Thames is having an effect and fish are now found as far downstream as the upper reaches in London.

Air pollution by industry and motorcars presents much the same problems. In Los Angeles the action of the sun on the partially burnt petrol fumes of cars produces what is known as photochemical smog: a mixture of poisonous gases which not only kill plants and trees but are harmful to breathe. Britain discharges about 6·5 million tons of sulphur in fumes and chimney smokes each year and during the London smog in 1952, which lasted four days, thousands of people died. A check of the air in a main shopping street in London one day in 1966 showed that it held so much carbon monoxide at some some times during the day that it would kill people who breathed it continuously for longer than about five hours.

## The need for control

All these facts point to only one thing: the tighter control of the composition of smokes and fumes. Industries will have either to clean up their smoke before discharging it or use fuels with lower sulphur contents. Householders will have to use more smokeless fuels. Cars will have to go completely or be replaced by electric cars. Air pollution could become a thing of the past if certain measures are taken. For example, the Clean Air Act has done much to clean London's air, and similar legislation has transformed the air in the city of Pittsburgh in Pennsylvania. In Sweden only light oils comparatively free of sulphur must be used in oil burners or else sulphur must be extracted from the exhaust of factories. All of these measures cost money at first but all in the long run pay handsome dividends, not only by making air healthier to breathe but by cutting cleaning costs and reducing the amount of corrosion of metals by the air.

4

5

Industry allowed to run riot not only poisons the air, the land and the waters both for Man and animals but also makes land derelict. Anyone who has travelled by train in a heavily industrialized country must have wondered at the derelict abandoned land, the old disused buildings and track, the rubbish dumps, the spoil heaps of mines, the subsiding ground, the holes and quarry pits. In Britain there are, according to official estimates, 127,000 acres of derelict land. At the normal density that is land enough for about a million homes and yet towns are still overspilling on to productive farmland. In a highly industrialized, densely populated country, like Britain, this squandering of a most precious commodity – farmland – seems to be accepted as being inevitable.

In Britain most derelict land is the spoil heaps of mines of one sort or another. To allow such dereliction in the first place and then to balk at the cost of reclamation, which one expert has estimated as a shilling a year per person for ten years, is eloquent testimony of the short-sighted greed of society. The answer yet again is to control all future exploitation of land and pay the shilling a head.

The sea has traditionally been the world's greatest and cheapest rubbish dump. Everything from obsolete nerve gases and radioactive waste to sewage of seaside towns has been dumped in the sea at one time or another. Dumping nerve gas has brought such a storm of protest in America that the United States Army has had to give up the plan, or at least postpone it. But there is still no such strong protest at the dangers of transporting oil around the world, but oil pollution is becoming almost a daily occurrence. It renders beaches unusable for holidaymakers, but far worse, it poisons the fish, animals and birds. Clearly a great deal more research is needed to provide ways of dealing with oil pollution – but the real answer is to stop the source.

## Oil pollution

The wrecking of the *Torrey Canyon* was an accident but on the high seas there are few laws regulating navigation and behaviour. If shipping, especially in such crowded sea lanes as the English Channel, was subjected to the same stringent international control as motor traffic and air traffic, many of the accidents which result in oil pollution might never happen. But even granting that some accidents will always happen, most oil pollution is done wilfully by ships' masters eager to save time and therefore money by discharging waste at sea instead of spending time in port and discharging waste oil harmlessly.

Man's industry inevitably alters the environment if only because it relies on raw materials that constitute the environment. If the same factors that have been allowed to work since the Industrial Revolution are allowed to continue, industry could well end up poisoning the Earth beyond redemption. But the public, industries and governments are at last waking up to the potential dangers to the environment of misused industry. There is every hope that although our environment will inevitably be continually changed as it is exploited, these changes need not automatically be equated with destruction. In the long term it should be possible to feed and give a comfortable life to the world's growing population without converting the Earth into one enormous industrial slum. The ways of preventing pollution are clear and people are now beginning to realize that money spent on such preventative methods is money well spent. They are also beginning to realize that time is not unlimited and that immediate action is a vital necessity.

1 

1 Oil slicks at sea and along the shore take a devastating toll of marine life. Sea birds in particular are often the worst hit. The oil clogs their feathers and causes them to drown.

2 Traffic congestion, like this in Sydney, Australia, has become a problem in many major cities. The action of sunlight on partially burnt petrol fumes produces a type of smog.

3 Years of continual industrial pollution of the River Tyne near Newcastle have led to this scene of desolation. Man still takes far too little care to clean up after himself.

4 The countryside has to take its share of industrial pollution. The plant and fish life in this English river are threatened by detergents carried downstream from factories.

2 

3 

4 

# The struggle for numbers

**Animal populations are generally controlled by predators, disease and lack of food. When these restraints are lacking the numbers of a species may reach plague proportions, with severe repercussions.**

ONE OF THE major tourist attractions offered by Queensland, Australia, is the Great Barrier Reef. Visitors to this extensive belt of coral are fascinated by its colour and the teeming underwater life which makes it its home. Yet, it is possible that future generations of visitors to Queensland will be disappointed; the Great Barrier Reef may be doomed.

Along with many other stretches of coral in the Pacific ocean, this reef is suffering a plague of starfish. The particular species involved is listed in the textbooks as *Acanthaster planci*; more commonly it is known as the crown-of-thorns starfish, a label which refers to its spiny skin and its many arms (between 13 and 17).

The starfish feeds on the tiny creatures (polyps) which secrete the calcium carbonate forming the coral itself. Normally – that is, when the starfishes exist in small numbers only – their feeding habits do not present much of a hazard to the reef; predation of this kind is part of the natural wastage suffered by the population of coral builders. But since 1963, when the crown-of-thorns starfish was still considered a relative rarity, a population explosion has taken place in the species.

## Crumbling reefs

Now they exist in thousands on reefs in Malaysia, Borneo, Fiji and Guam – as well as Queensland. They eat the coral builders and leave the skeletal material to be smashed by the action of the sea. If the starfish maintain their concentration, there will inevitably come a time when there will not be enough coral builders to maintain the reefs, which will be gradually eroded. This will have repercussions on fishing industries in the affected areas; since the crumbling reefs would soon cease to be the kind of magnet to fish and other creatures that they are at present.

Nevertheless, the crown-of-thorns population explosion provides a graphic example of one of the major facts of life. That is: the size of animal populations can suddenly expand enormously; perhaps later to be reduced to very low numbers. Few of these fluctuations are noted by the general public – apart from the dramatic ones, like plagues of locusts in Africa, or like the swarms of rats which overran Hamelin in 1284 and have passed into folk history, Pied Piper and all. But the fact remains that sooner or later animal populations of all kinds expand or contract. And the factors which are responsible for this are complex and mixed.

In general, the size of a population is dependent on the carrying capacity of a particular environment. For instance, there will be food for an optimum number; there will be sufficient materials or the right kind of locations for building nests, lairs and homes for that number; and the climate will usually have a range which will allow the species in question to survive. Nor will the numbers of predators be overpowering, and disease will necessarily have only a low incidence.

If for any reason the carrying capacity is extended, then the population dependent on it will increase as well; in other words the optimum number will increase. Very simply, the improved conditions will allow more of the newborn young to survive, and eventually the increase may reach such proportions that other animal populations – even Man – may be affected, possibly adversely.

In the case of the crown-of-thorns starfish the factor which has increased the carrying capacity of the Pacific shorelines may well be Man himself. Scientists have suggested that coastal clearing schemes, for the building of harbours and so on, may well have provided ideal breeding conditions for the starfish.

If so, then this has been an artificial boost to the environmental carrying capacity. An example from nature occurs regularly in India. Here there are certain bamboos which, for some reason, flower only at very long intervals, and then do so simultaneously over large areas of the countryside. The result is an enormous quantity of seed, which supplements the more regular diet of certain rodents and they in turn experience their own population explosion. Cause and effect are

**1** While some species are abundant others, like the Andean condor, are threatened with extinction. This male is in the San Diego Zoo; sometimes captivity is the only way of preserving a species.
**2** Overcrowding has caused these barnacles to grow upwards instead of outwards as normal. Because they cannot grip the rock so well, many have been washed away in heavy seas.
**3** The osprey lives exclusively on fish. It is now becoming rare because the waters in which it fishes are often polluted. Like other birds of prey, it is susceptible to DDT poisoning.

1

relatively easy to see in such a situation. But occasional freakish changes in natural conditions can have equally freakish and quite unexpected results.

Drought, due to hot sunshine and little rain, can be easily recognized as a great threat to wildlife and sometimes to Man. Yet during a number of irregularly recurring hot, dry summers in Holland over the past century, a falling water level in the canals and waterways has proved beneficial for at least one underwater pest. This is the shipworm, *Teredo navalis,* which bores its way into wooden craft or even piling, and then eats away steadily – sometimes eventually causing collapse of the structure which houses it and its fellows. The shipworm can live only in salt water, and it appears that when the rate of evaporation is high in the Dutch inland waters, it has the effect of raising the salt content sufficiently for the shipworm.

These examples of expansion of population depend upon the improvement of one or more qualities which a particular animal needs in an environment. Just as dramatic population explosions have taken place as a result of the introduction, by accident or design, of a species to an area which is new to it.

Such cases are frequent and sometimes the results have been disastrous. The introduction of rabbits to Australia and New Zealand is well documented. Less well known is the introduction during the 1950s of the giant toad, *Bufo marinus,* into Florida. Originally intended to help keep down the numbers of native insects for the benefit both of the local tourist industry and the many fruit farmers in the Miami area, the Bufo has been found to be all too effective. It not only does its job, but has increased in the process to such a degree that now it supplements its diet on the young of local varieties of toad, and even attacks dogs. Its attacks on dogs are not for food but for defence. Unfortunately for the dog the Bufo has a venomous bite; the bitten dog, unless it is particularly strong or lucky, will die.

The factors which produce rises in population size – increased food, particularly favourable climatic conditions, absence of predators – can also bring its decline whether gently or dramatically. First and most obviously the animals may starve. The numbers of mouths to feed may disastrously reduce the food source. Indeed, the supply may dry up all together. It is more or less inevitable, for instance, that when the glut of crown-of-thorns starfish has reduced the coral building animals to a certain level, the starfish will begin to decline in numbers.

Then there are climatic variations. The occasional hard winters experienced in Britain result in widespread deaths among the smaller varieties of bird – blackbirds, thrushes and tits. The cold does not kill them directly, but it prevents them obtaining food because the ground is frozen. And although drought can be useful to certain animals under exceptional circumstances,

2

for others the lack of water is disastrous. They are not equipped to deal with high rates of salinity or even with the rise in temperature.

Predators exert a measurable control over the numbers of a particular species. Very occasionally, however, the rate of rise in numbers of prey exceeds the ability of the available predators to control them. Such a glut of food may produce a population explosion of a kind in the predator. But the gestation period of a fox is much longer than that of a rabbit, so that while the foxes may be living well during a sudden rise in the number of rabbits, they will not achieve sufficient number… selves to keep down the ra…

The control which … …ates is likely to be disease. The very close proximity of individuals in a particular animal species means that bacteria, viruses and parasites are more easily passed from

3

**1** Man's population explosion has taken its toll of many species. Buffalo and other 'big game' in Africa survive only in national parks.
**2** Every four or five years lemmings are driven to migrate because of severe overcrowding. Although most of the population perishes on the journey there are always a few survivors.
**3** A plague of this crown-of-thorns starfish has now hit the Pacific Ocean and is threatening to destroy entire coral reefs. The starfish lives on the tiny animals that make the coral.
**4** Because of their high reproduction rate rodents are prone to overcrowding. One way their numbers are controlled is by predators: here a weasel is making off with a vole.
**5** The giant toad *Bufo marinus* was introduced into Florida to keep down insects. It has been so successful that as well as killing off all other species of toad, it is now a pest.
**6** The British wild cat is now restricted entirely to Scotland. It is very fierce and untameable and keeps well away from Man.

The European beaver is now very rare, being found mainly in Scandinavia. Man has been the beaver's worst enemy by trapping it for its fur, and by destroying its dams.

Wherever Man goes he destroys the trees as well as the animals and plants that shelter under the foliage. These Dyaks of Borneo have cut down the trees to grow pepper.

one beast to the rest. Once an epidemic has started it will spread like wildfire through the animal community. For example, in Africa individual herds of zebra sometimes number thousands but they are then decimated by outbreaks of disease, which are brought about by an unpleasant parasite called lungworm.

The African buffalo provides another example. In 1890, this animal lived in herds of enormous abundance on the open grassland, but it was suddenly struck down by a disease called rinderpest and the numbers were drastically reduced. It then took 35 years for the African buffalo to recover its former numerical strength.

The lemmings of Scandinavia also experience sudden onslaughts when periodically their numbers exceed the carrying capacity of their environment. But in this case the disease would seem to be psychological. When a certain density of population is achieved – about every four or five years – the lemming communities erupt. The majority pour out of their breeding grounds in the mountains and, moving mainly at night, march down the mountainsides until they reach the sea. They then plunge in and swim until they are exhausted. Ultimately they drown, and do so in such numbers that their bodies end as drifts on the sea-shore.

This is the phenomenon known as the lemming 'rush'. In sixteenth-century Scandinavia, it was thought that the sudden appearance of lemmings in great numbers was due to their having fallen from the sky. Now, of course, it is known that the outpouring is due to population pressures in the lemmings' mountain breeding grounds. Exactly what sends them on their suicide march is not known, but it has been noted in experimental work on rodents and other species that overcrowding produces great psychological stresses (shown by increased nervousness, fighting, lack of appetite and so on) and can engender suicidal tendencies.

These then are the major factors producing population fluctuations among animals. They operate within a general population framework consisting of many thousands of species of animal, in which the species themselves may consist of relatively few to many millions of individuals.

On the face of it, animal life seems to be present in great and apparently permanent abundance – whatever the periodic rise and fall in individual numbers. But looking deeper, it appears that the situation is not really so happy. The numbers of the larger wild animals to be found on the face of the Earth have been drastically reduced over the last few hundred years. While it is still possible to see acres of breeding Adélie penguins in Antarctica or a herd of zebra numbering 25,000 moving across the plains of Africa, the once mighty bison herds of North America are now reduced to a protected few, the whale has almost completely disappeared from Arctic waters and its survival is threatened in the south. And so on, through a depressingly large list of species.

The reason for these sad happenings is simply the remarkable expansion which has taken place in another species in relatively recent times. The species is Man himself.

## The population explosion

Two thousand years ago there were something like 250 million people on the Earth. In the next 17 centuries this figure doubled. By 1820 it had doubled again to 1,000 million and by 1970 it is expected to stand at something like 4,000 million.

Such a remarkable increase in numbers stems from the fact that Man, alone among animals, is able to increase the carrying capacity of his environment by his own efforts. It is an ability which has increased markedly over the last two centuries, with the onset of the Industrial Revolution, and the dawning of the present age of science.

What is more, it is an ability which is still growing apace. Already Man is able to protect large numbers of his kind from disease, predation, starvation and the hostile elements. Even the death of old people can be staved off medically in ways unthinkable to our ancestors. Only war, the predation of human upon human, remains as a seemingly undiminished threat to the continued rise in numbers of human beings, although warning notes are repeatedly sounded about the possibility of future starvation or disastrous pollution of the Earth environment. Yet, as things stand, more people than ever are being born, and are successfully surviving the crucial period of infancy.

It is inevitable that such a dramatic mushrooming in one species should have serious effects on the size of others. In the Pacific area increased harbour building (itself a product of growing numbers of human beings and increased trade between them) may be linked with an increase in the number of crown-of-thorns starfish. What is certain is that if this process begun by Man continues unabated it will have serious repercussions on both him and other species.

Unfortunately the interests of Man are now clashing seriously with those of wildlife. Increasing numbers of human beings are trying to grab all the living space they can regardless of other considerations than their own. Some of the clashes which have upset the balance of animal populations have no excuse at all – the decimation of the American bison, for instance, simply so that the fashionable at the turn of the century could boast a 'genuine Wild West buffalo robe', or the indiscriminate killing of whales in the pursuit of quick, short-term profits.

Thus, Man now emerges clearly as the world's most powerful predator, and one which is fast becoming the most important factor in the survival or otherwise of wildlife. Indeed, in allowing his own numbers to increase almost unchecked, Man poses a threat to almost all other creatures.

# Where the buffalo roamed

**Before the white explorers reached the North American prairies, it was the home of millions of buffalo. Since then Man has turned these vast grasslands to his own use and few have survived.**

MANY NATURAL and geographical phenomena have inspired Man's imagination but none has been so thoroughly exploited for its legendary associations in the twentieth century as the North American prairie. The setting of countless 'western' films, these vast grasslands were named by the French explorers in the seventeenth century who called them 'prairies' from the French word meaning 'extensive meadow'.

The prairies are huge, fertile plains which extend from southern Michigan, across the states of Iowa, Kansas, Nebraska, North and South Dakota including the southern regions of Wisconsin and Minnesota. To the north they stretch far into the Canadian wheat-growing territories of Manitoba, Saskatchewan and Alberta. From the eastern forest line, the prairies extend westwards to the Great Plains into which they merge. To the south they merge with the cotton belt or 'black prairie' so called because of the richness of the black alluvial soil.

The soil of the prairies is usually dark in colour and rich in organic matter. It is composed of very fine particles, which when dried after wetting become very hard. It contains much finely divided sand, and is generally somewhat deficient in clay. Often very rich and of great depth, it is by no means inexhaustible and farmers often find it profitable to add fertilizers from time to time.

1 Two puma cubs squint into the sun; also known as cougars, catamounts or mountain lions, pumas are equally at home in the forested regions or on the open prairie.

2 The North American burrowing owl, so called because it makes its home in old rabbit burrows. It is practically flightless and when disturbed, flattens itself against the ground.

## Rolling grasslands

Climatic conditions are more severe than those of the forest regions, mainly on account of the exposure to the winds in winter and to the heat in summer. The prairies are in the middle of a large land mass and the climate tends to that of a continental climate of extreme differences in temperature. The annual rainfall is at an average of 30 in. diminishing towards the west. The great part of this rain falls in summer and the spring.

These vast plains are mainly flat, but in places they roll like the long swells of the ocean, and rise in gradual elevation from 1,000 to 5,000 ft above sea level at the foothills of the Rocky Mountains. Across the prairies rivers drain down to the Missouri and the 'Gallery' forests extend along these valleys. The prairies are not entirely treeless for the smaller rivers and streams are always fringed with trees. The treeless areas extend over the higher lands from stream to stream. Often these forest fringes are confined to deep, narrow valleys through which the streams flow and are barely noticeable across the plains.

The vegetation naturally divides itself into that of open country and that of the woodlands. In the open country the grasses constitute the dominant vegetation as they are mostly perennial and extremely tenacious forms of vegetable life.

In the more fertile, humid conditions of the east, the grass is richer, more abundant, but towards the west the grasses become sparser and tougher. Altogether 150 native species of grasses have been recognized and regions afford fine pasturage and hay for stock. Where the rainfall is abundant the grasses constitute a continuous sod which completely covers the surface of the earth, but where there is less rainfall the grasses are in isolated clumps called 'birch grasses'. In the open prairie there are other plants which grow intermingled with the grasses. The most conspicuous of these are the 'golden rods'. Other plants include asters, bright sunflowers and occasional shrubs.

The woodlands bordering the watercourses often constitute broad areas extending for many miles of each side of the streams whilst others only form narrow belts a few yards wide. The trees of the prairies are of all species, many of which

**1** A herd of mustang, the semi-wild horses of the prairies. They were imported by the Spaniards in the sixteenth century but their numbers are now seriously depleted.
**2** In the open prairie flowering plants mingle with over 150 recognized grasses. One of the brightest plants is the prairie orchid.
**3** At one time, 45 to 60 million bison roamed the prairie, but with the coming of the white man and his guns, their numbers were reduced almost to the point of extinction. Limited numbers now survive in national parks.
**4** The original 'cowboys' brought with them their cattle which now constitute the main livestock. The rich grasslands provide grazing for vast herds.
**5** Clumps of 'golden rod' dot the prairie with patches of brilliant colour. Other prairie plants include asters, sunflowers and shrubs.
**6** Swiftest of all the prairie animals is the pronghorn. When alarmed, the white hairs on its rump suddenly stand erect and 'flash' to warn others of danger.
**7** The coyote, or prairie wolf. Its omnivorous diet and extraordinary stamina have enabled it to resist attempts at extermination.
**8** A ground squirrel, or 'prairie dog', sits up on its hind legs to feed on seeds of foxtail grass. These animals live together in huge underground colonies which are known as 'towns'.

originated in the great forests. The most common species are oak, hickories, walnut, willows, cottonwood, elms, maples and ashes. As a general rule, the trees are not as tall as those of the thick forest regions of the east and they tend to grow with more spreading tops because of their exposure to the elements. Occasionally some of these trees reach gigantic proportions when they are situated in sheltered positions. Careful observation and research has shown that where trees are protected from fires, stock and adverse influences, they generally reproduce so rapidly that they have gradually extended the forest regions. Since new techniques of fire-fighting stop prairie fires, a natural spreading and widening of the river belts has taken place so that areas which were grasslands when first visited by Europeans are now areas of woodland.

Where agriculture has been developed, changes have taken place. Animal life has also been dramatically affected by Man's presence. Three centuries ago, the prairies and the Great Plains were the haunt of antelope, elk, bison, prairie dogs, ground squirrels, coyotes, cougar and wolves. Now many of these species are greatly reduced in number and some are protected and nurtured in the hope that they may avoid extinction. The fortunes of the men who inhabited these plains, the Red Indians, have been similarly adversely affected. The explorer, the settler and the trader brought horses, whisky, metal wares and guns and this new, more advanced culture became dominant. The new American also brought cattle and sheep, new methods of husbandry, barbed wire, the plough, tools for drilling artesian wells and, of course, the gun. After the 'golden age of the cowboy' up to the 1870s, open range land was converted into crop lands and ranches into fields. Resistance to these developments by the Indians was ruthlessly and systematically swept aside. By the end of the nineteenth century the Indians had almost disappeared (and also incidentally had many of the cowboys) and vast areas were cultivated to create the enormous agricultural industry which produced grass, wheat and stock to maintain the thousands of workers in rapidly expanding industrial centres.

## Death of the buffalo

Inevitably, a great deal of the natural life has been destroyed or sacrificed for modern technology. Perhaps the most striking example of this process is that of the buffalo or the bison. This large, ox-like creature has become a symbol of the American 'Western' era. There are still bison in existence but they are strictly protected. It has been estimated that the primeval population numbered between 45 and 60 million and that by 1865 15 million still survived. These enormous animals, the average male weighs about 1,800 lb, are well known for their ferocious appearance, their enormous hump behind the neck and their shaggy mane. A grazing animal, it moved in great herds from Texas to the Canadian Prairies, but was reduced by drastic overhunting, both for skins and for mere pleasure. By 1907 their numbers had been reduced to only 800.

Another animal that has suffered from overhunting is the pronghorn. Remarkably adapted to life on the grasslands, this antelope-like animal can run at speeds of 40 miles an hour with spurts of 55 miles an hour. Its eyes are unusually large for the size of its head and it has good vision for long distances and over a wide field. Its speed and sight are its main defences against its enemy, the coyote, but are no protection against the modern rifle. From an estimated population of over 50 million in the seventeenth century, it was reduced to 19,000 by 1908. Now protected, the pronghorns have increased in number to the point where limited hunting is possible in some states.

The birds of the plains and prairies are adapted to live on the grasslands. Their food is on the ground so there is little reason for them to fly except to escape predators or to migrate. Although many are strong flyers they are also good runners and walkers and some may cover many miles in a day. Because of the lack of trees, the birds nest in holes, like the burrowing owl, or on the ground, like the prairie chicken.

The prairie chicken has similarities to the grouse; the plumage is plain, the colours being various browns and yellows with white and black mottled patterns. The distinctive feature which characterizes the bird is a patch of yellow skin on each side of the neck, usually concealed by a tuft of narrow pointed feathers attached to the skin at its anterior border. Beneath this patch is an air-sac connected to the respiratory system which can be inflated until the skin is distended to the size of an orange. The head crest is small, the tail is rather short, and the legs are incompletely and lightly feathered to the toes. A full-grown bird is 18 in. long.

Formerly the prairie chicken ranged

3

4

5

6

7

8

1 The North American wapiti, or elk, is a larger relative of the European red deer. Although a number of species have been exterminated, they still exist, chiefly in Canada.

2 The Eastern chipmunk, a small terrestrial squirrel, distinguished by the stripes on its back. It usually remains underground in winter, living on its stores of nuts, seeds and berries.

throughout the open country between the Appalachian and Rocky Mountains, from Manitoba to the Gulf Coast, but there has been a change in population since human settlement and these changes are still in progress. At the same time the clearing of the forests has provided much new open country which it has been prompt to occupy, replacing other species of grouse less adapted to life on the open prairies. They have also become abundant in Minnesota where the land is cultivated in long tracks.

The bird is gregarious and lives in flocks which are now becoming very large. Throughout its wide range this species is not fully migratory, but a definite northward and southward movement takes place in the upper part of the Central Mississippi Valley – and this movement is limited to the female of the species.

The prairie chicken is monogamous and nests in grass and tends to lay from 12 to 20 eggs of a greyish or buff colour which hatch within 20 days. The courtship rituals are quite spectacular; during the spring, the males blow up their sacs quickly to create a loud booming noise to attract a mate.

Another animal of the prairie is the prairie dog or marmot. It is a genus of ground squirrel and, therefore, a rodent. There are two species which range from northern Mexico into Saskatchewan, southern Canada. They are a foot long, of a reddish-brown colour and are social, gregarious animals who live in large communities. They live in burrows under the ground and their presence is betrayed by the fact that each burrow has a hillock at the entrance. The shafts are about 12 ft long and lead to a series of chambers where they spend the winter in comfort. Often these colonies extend for several acres and are frequented by their natural enemies, weasels, wolves, badgers, snakes and birds of prey such as the hawk. They live on a diet of stems, sunflowers and seeds. With the spread of more cultivated and irrigated lands these creatures threaten to become pests and farmers usually dispose of them by suffocation. Bisulphide of carbon is introduced into their burrows and they are killed in large numbers.

## The coyote

Other animals have been greatly reduced in numbers in campaigns against them. With the arrival of cattle and sheep on the grasslands, the farmers declared war on two efficient predators, the wolf and coyote. Although enormous numbers of coyotes have been killed, they still inhabit many parts of the prairies and have even extended their range. Noted for their mournful night howl, they have extraordinary stamina and feed on hares, rabbits, deer, mice and occasionally sheep.

Considered by explorers and settlers to be a featureless sea of grasses and holding little promise of riches, the North American plains and grasslands are now the most important agricultural area on the continent, producing huge yields of corn and wheat, and providing grazing for vast herds of cattle.

# The natural economy

Animals and plants in their natural habitat are closely linked in many subtle ways. Human interference with the environment can wreak havoc with the balance of Nature.

ANIMALS SURVIVE only if they can adapt to their environment, and 'adapting' means either putting up with whatever the environment has to offer, or changing the environment to suit the animal's own ends. In practice, all animals do both. Land animals put up with large fluctuations in temperature and humidity, but most – with the exception of beasts like the great nomadic herds of deer, cattle and antelopes – construct a lair to protect them from the extremes of climate. In general, the more intelligent the animal, the less it will endure, and the more it seeks to change the environment to suit itself. Man, the most intelligent animal of all, is not prepared to put up with any hardship. Engineers seek to control the atmosphere of buildings at the flick of a switch. Farmers, equipped with 'artificial' fertilizers, supply urban dwellers with abundant food – if necessary, produced in multi-storey factory farms, quick frozen and pre-packaged.

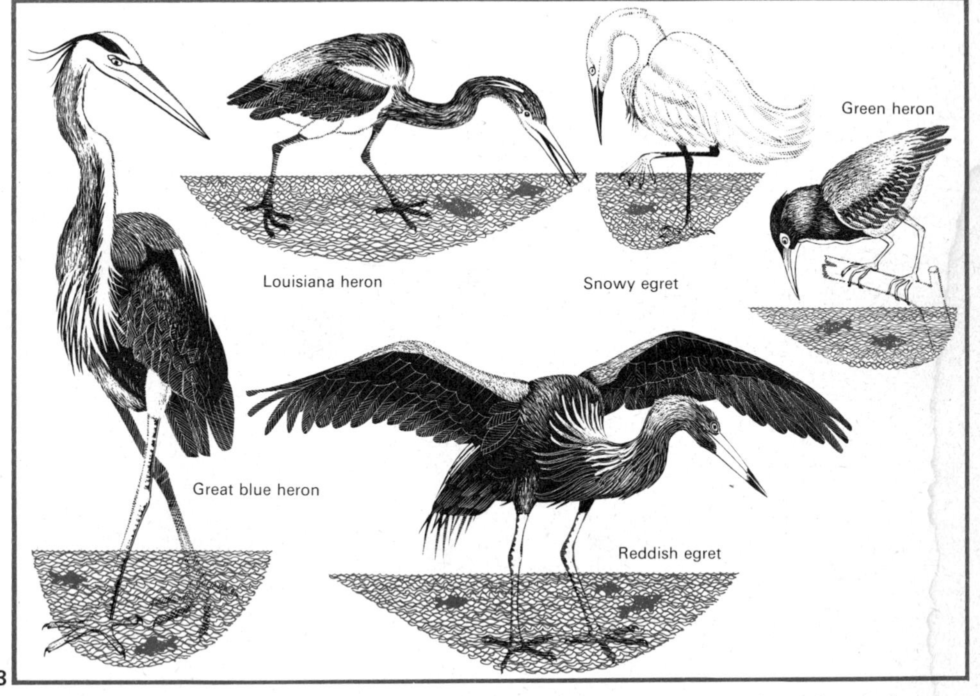


**1** The black rhinoceros, shown here in the Tsavo National Park, Kenya, makes use of its mobile, pointed upper lip to feed by browsing on a thorn bush.
**2** The white rhinoceros, related to the black species, has different feeding habits. Its square lip allows it to feed, as here, by grazing on low-lying vegetation.
**3** The different species of herons found in the swamps of southern Florida all have different ways of feeding. In this way, they avoid competing with one another for food.

## Mere romanticizing?

City Man may get the illusion of being aloof from the rest of Nature. The proper study of Mankind, he thinks, is Man: Man's only pressing problem is how to live with other men. The natural environment can be exploited, bartered with, or ignored, at will. Until a few years ago the only howls of protest caused by such ideas were written off as mere romanticizing. But within the last few years more and more scientists have joined the ranks of the aesthetes who deplore Man's abnegation of his environment. The scientist's main argument is that to exploit the land's resources efficiently it is not enough simply to clear an area of forest and graze a few cows on the newly formed meadow. A cow needs a peculiar variety of dietary supplements to grass hitherto supplied by wild flowers which are now being killed off by weed-killers. Those flowers need a variety of insects, bees, butterflies and moths which are also destroyed by insecticides intended for insect pests.

In short, the scientist argues that Man and the few beasts he has chosen to domesticate are strands in a great fabric of interactions between animals, plants, bacteria and the physical environment. Unless we begin to understand these inter-actions better so that we can *use* Nature's subtleties instead of replacing them with our own artefacts, and unless we stop using the environment as a dumping ground for industrial waste, be it slag, radioactive fall-out, or detergent, then we will destroy other living creatures, and in destroying them destroy ourselves. Thus the study of the way that living things inter-act – the science of *ecology* – has in recent years been

The vegetation in this bluebell wood in Surrey is able to make intensive use of the sun's light. Under the trees are shrubs, and below this level many plants grow on the ground.

The stumps of drowned trees are still visible protruding from the water of Lake Thekkady, India. Artificial lakes like this one can upset the ecology of large areas.

raised from the level of arm-chair natural history to the most important of sciences.

All living things are constructed from materials that are derived from the fabric of the Earth – the rocks, the water and the air. But living things differ from rocks, water and air in that they can grow, reproduce and react to changes in the environment in a way that furthers their survival. The chemistry of living things is very intricate – it depends on extremely complex and relatively unstable molecules of protein, nucleic acids, carbohydrates and lipids. These complicated unstable molecules can be prevented from disintegration only by the continuous use of energy, just as houses can be prevented from falling down only by continual maintenance.

## Limits on life

Any natural stretch of land or sea can support only a limited mass of living things. The limit is imposed by the amount of suitable material the land contains, and the amount of energy available to enable the living things to utilize those materials. The general trend in evolution has been for living things to exploit their environment more and more efficiently – to utilize more and more of the natural materials and more and more of the available energy needed to put the materials together. The increase in the efficiency of exploitation has been a joint effort between plants, animals and bacteria. Plants extract carbon from the air, and simple substances from the soil or sea, and lock these together in complex molecules, using energy from the sun (the sun is the ultimate provider of energy for life on Earth). Herbivorous animals eat plants and break down the complex molecules formed by the plants to furnish material and energy for their own ends. Carnivorous animals then, perhaps, eat the herbivores. This succession of animals which feed on other animals that in their turn eat plants is known as a *food-chain.*

When the animals die, their tissues are broken down by bacteria into simple substances again, and can again be used by plants. Thus the cycle begins again. Animals contribute nothing to the sum total of energy available in an environment but by eating and excreting provide a complex milieu for plants to grow in. Though the world could theoretically be populated by plants alone, though obviously not by plants that require animals for population and seed dispersal, the energy and materials available in any environment can be efficiently exploited only if both plants and animals are present.

But why are there so many different *kinds* of animals and plants? Obviously, the sea demands different animals from the land, and perhaps cold areas require different animals from warm areas; but why should not a limited area just have one 'ideal' plant, one 'ideal' animal to feed off it, and one sort of bacterium to break down the animal's tissues when it dies? This may seem an absurd question, but this is the thinking behind much of today's agriculture. The natural, complex vegetation is being replaced by a few food crops; the natural wealth of animal life is replaced by one or two herbivores, and the natural predators by one predator – Man.

The answer is that even seemingly simple environments can be exploited in hundreds of different ways; no living thing can exploit more than a few – and usually only one – way successfully; and living things are opportunists, they will find their way into any niche not already occupied. In fact, if an area of land is to be used efficiently, enormous complexity is inevitable.

Suppose, for example, you cleared an area of land and planted just oak trees. The trees alone would apparently make a pretty good job of exploiting their environment. The vast canopy of leaves picks up a fair proportion of the sun's energy. The roots probe deep and wide for moisture and minerals. Yet one species alone like this would be extremely wasteful. What of the dim light that filters through the leaves – or floods the wood in spring, before the leaves have formed? Why waste that? It would not be wasted under natural conditions – it would supply wood anemones, aconites, bluebells, violets, bracken to mop up this surplus light energy. This undergrowth does no harm to the trees – if anything it helps them, by slowing water evaporation at root level. And why waste all the dead leaves on the forest floor? Why not have insects, arachnids, molluscs and worms to eat them and break them down so that bacteria can release the materials locked in them? Why not shrews, mice, birds to eat the insects; and owls, hawks, foxes to eat the small birds and mammals? Why not parasites, fungi, bacteria, worms, insects to scratch a living from all the other living matter?

## Efficient energy use

In short, a forest of oaks with nothing else around might appear to exploit the available energy and nutriment fairly effectively, but a well organized conglomeration of many different species of animals and plants – that is, an organized *ecosystem* – will exploit the available energy much more effectively. Thus ecological complexity is necessary for the supreme efficiency found in Nature.

The point about this complex family of different creatures is that in a stable system the different species do not generally compete with each other since all are specialized to exploit slightly different niches. A fine example of this is provided by the herons that hunt in the mangrove shallows of southern Florida. As many as nine different species can be found in the same feeding area. The little green herons sit on the exposed mangrove roots, and dive on passing fish. The common egret prefers a more direct approach – it stalks its prey very slowly, and lunges at the last second. The great blue heron is even more impatient; as it stalks it flicks its wings, so as to startle potential prey into showing itself. The Louisiana heron startles its

A product of the enormous complexity of even simple-looking ecosystems is the extent to which animals and plants have come to rely on each other. The simplest such reliance is the predator for its prey, or the parasite for its host. More complex are the relationships – known as symbiotic relationship – in which two different species benefit from co-operation. Thus algae and fungus fuse together to their mutual benefit to form lichens – the algae provide energy from photosynthesis; the fungus provides energy from breakdown of organic matter and food materials. Hermit crabs sometimes plant anemones on the shells in which they make their homes: the anemone protects the crab by camouflaging it and deterring predators, and the crab benefits the anemone by supplying it (albeit inadvertently) with food. But those few associations that Man has chosen to call 'symbiotic' are not the only ones where association between

**1** Burchell's zebra, one of Africa's many herbivores. The herds of herbivores provide food for numerous predators.
**2** A lion devouring the remains of a buffalo. The lion population helps to maintain the natural balance between different species.
**3** The spotted hyena feeds on carrion and is another of the carnivores of the African veld. It is shown here feeding on a dead elephant.
**4** Vultures are also carrion eaters. Thousands of these birds circle the skies on the look-out for dead and dying animals.

prey into activity by leaping and pirouetting through the water and then suddenly stopping. Most cunning of all is the reddish egret, which first disturbs aquatic creatures by churning up the water, and then spreads its wings so that they rush to shelter under the shade provided by them. The reddish egret then eats his catch. The different heron species rarely appear to compete for the same food – indeed, their feeding methods are apparently complementary.

different species is mutually beneficial. Predators have become part of the environment for prey animals, and the prey animals have adjusted to them. Paradoxically, you cannot remove the predators from a stable environment without – ultimately – doing severe harm to the prey animals.

The reason for this is that nothing destroys an animal population more quickly than overpopulation. Whereas different animal species sharing a stable environment avoid competing with each other – as in the case of the Florida herons – animals of the same species in the same environment are competing directly for the same food and same breeding space.

Overpopulation affects different species in different ways, depending on the circumstances. Though the white rhinoceros of Africa has become extremely rare, it is nonetheless overcrowded in the few valleys in which it lives, and from which it cannot escape. Rhinos have no natural enemies, and the effect of overpopulation in this case is that the limited territory is becoming overgrazed, and unless some of the animals are removed (as is now being done) all will die of starvation. If animals are kept overcrowded in cages their behaviour becomes very changed. The effect is to reduce the population; mice kept extremely overcrowded may become torpid, not bothering to feed or breed; rats fight; monkeys lose their sense of family, fight amongst themselves, and become obsessed with sex. All this behaviour is 'abnormal', and ultimately self-destructive. In the natural state, such overcrowding could not happen; the populations would be kept stable – largely because they would be constantly kept in check by their predators.

At the other end of the scale, no animal population can survive if its numbers fall below a certain critical level. There are many reasons for this. Gannets, for example, breed in very close-packed colonies on rocky islets. If the population is small and sparse, the breeding season is relatively long; if the colony is large and densely packed, the breeding season is much shorter. This is because gannets will breed only if stimulated to do so by other breeding pairs. The more pairs, the more the stimulation, and the quicker the breeding. The advantage of the very short breeding period is that all the young birds are extant at the same time. The various predators – gulls, hawks, skuas – can eat only a limited number of young birds and eggs in a given time. Thus they eat a smaller proportion of the young gannets in a short season than they would in a long one. And if the gannet population fell, so that there were not enough birds around to provide sufficient stimulation to make a short breeding season possible, the gannets would rapidly be exterminated by the predators.

One place where ignorance of ecology could spell disaster both for Man and beast is Africa. His mistake there has been to assume that he can re-create the rich, productive agriculture of Hereford or the Polders – an agriculture that incidentally depends heavily on support from heavy industry – in the totally alien conditions of Africa.

The survival of Africa's extraordinary wildlife rests on a knife edge. It depends, for example, on the existence of a great many plants – trees and herbs – of the *Leguminosae* family. These plants – peas, beans and laburnum trees are familiar examples – have root nodules that contain bacteria capable of taking up nitrogen from the air and making it available to plants in the form of nitrates. Thus the Leguminosae can thrive in the nitrogen-poor soil. Many other African plants – trees, shrubs, grasses – can survive with virtually no water. Some conserve water in fleshy stems, others trap dew in hairy leaves, others send down extraordinarily deep roots.

This unpromising vegetation supports more than 30 species of antelope, together with elephants, rhinoceroses, hippopotami, giraffe, okapi, buffalo and zebra. Each herbivore does a different job. Even the two rhinoceroses have different feeding habits – the white rhino, with its square lip, grazes, while the black, with its highly mobile, pointed, top lip, browses. The tiniest antelopes – the duikers – nibble in the undergrowth like rabbits. The larger ones graze in the plains. Elephants browse among the lower branches, giraffe seek their food among the higher ones.

## Herbivores and predators

Culling the herbivores are a host of predators – each again with different feeding habits. The lions ambush big game on the plains, the leopard takes smaller animals in the forest. Jackals clean up after the lions and hyenas have eaten, and the vultures clean up after them. The maribou storks take what is left.

For these reasons, many scientists have suggested that the only way Africa can support its growing population is by controlling and husbanding the native fauna – not, for example, by replacing the thriving elephant herds with sad-looking cattle, but by shooting and eating the excess elephants. If Man learns to live with and off animals, he and they might fare very well. To do this he must understand the ways of the animals much better than he does at the moment.

A sable antelope with tick birds on its back. The tick birds feed on parasites infesting the animal's coat, while the antelope is relieved to be rid of them.

Gannets are stimulated to breed by other breeding pairs. If the colony is large, the breeding seasons will be shorter. More young birds will survive if they are born together.

# Changing patterns of life

Land laid bare down to the rock does not remain barren for long. Life returns, simple at first but gradually changing, as the soil becomes more fertile, into a complex community of animals and plants.

LAND SELDOM STAYS BARE for very long in most climates and life never stands still. When a garden, a field, a railway track or a building site in the centre of a city, is left for any length of time wild plants start springing up. First come the mosses, followed quickly by annual and perennial herbs; then, after a few years shrubs and bushes – plants with longer life histories – become established. Then tree seedlings and saplings get a hold and the site becomes a tangled wilderness of weeds, bushes and trees. In most parts of Britain and many parts of the world if this process of succession is allowed to continue unchecked the first communities of plants to establish themselves on the site will give way in the end to trees. In this way woods arise.

To anyone who has only glanced at an abandoned garden or field, the process whereby one group of plant species or a community succeeds another seems very haphazard and random. And because birds and animals are always on the move, and micro-organisms such as fungi, algae and bacteria are too small to be seen with the naked eye, it is far from obvious that they too colonize a site in successive waves. Biologists, if they know the major environmental factors, the various aspects of the climate and the type of soil, can predict with surprising accuracy the various species of plants and animals that will make up the distinct communities succeeding each other at any particular site. They can also predict how this succession will culminate in what is called the *climax community*. That is to say the community of plants and animals which is in a relatively stable equilibrium with its environment, best adapted to it and there able to survive unchanged in overall composition throughout the timespan of many generations of the longest lived species present.

To give an example, botanists can say that if Man left Britain for good the successive communities that colonized the light soils of the country would culminate in birchwoods that would give way to the climax of oak forests, whereas on the chalk lands of the southeast, oakwoods or mixed oak and ash wood would give way to a climax of beechwoods. These climax forests would then perpetuate themselves until some drastic change in the climate occurred.

1 With its rich silt the water's edge of Lake Titicaca, situated 13,000 ft high on the Altiplano of Bolivia, provides an ideal environment for rushes and certain species of moss.

2 Trees, such as palms, make up the climax community of tropical forests. Yet the sunlight is so intense that it can penetrate the thick tree foliage and support plant life on the ground.

What are the grounds on which ecologists, the biologists who study the interaction of plants and animals with their environment, base these surprisingly accurate predictions? The basis of all true replacements of one species by another, one community by another, in succession, is first that plants and animals do not live in isolation but on and off one another. Second, every plant or animal alters its environment and during succession each species alters the environment in such a way as to make it less suitable for itself but more suitable for a successor. The climax community emerges because it is the one community that does not alter the environment against itself but keeps it stable so the species can live there indefinitely.

## Dominant trees

Obviously in different parts of the world the species composition of the climax communities differs a great deal. But by studying the composition of climax and sub-climax communities at various stages of succession, the ecologist can get a shrewd idea of which way any change will occur. As a general rule the tendency in all successions is to lead to a climax dominated by the largest plants, usually trees, suitable to the particular climate in question. The reasons why trees are so dominant are simple. Being perennials they are well protected with bark and leaves against the rigours of the climate. Their vast root systems are better able to compete for limited amounts of water than the roots of other plants. Their canopy of leaves, covering a large area above ground, catches most of the sunlight and literally puts smaller plants in the shade, preventing them from photosynthesizing.

In a country like Britain, except in the highlands of the north and west, the wet fens and marshes in the east and along the coast, the natural climax for several thousand years has been deciduous summer forests of oak, beech, birch and ash. But little, if any, virgin forest remains; it has been cleared for timber, agriculture and cities. Almost all the natural development of vegetation is not the colonization of new ground but modification or recolonization of existing communities whose composition has been affected by Man's activities. In other words it is secondary succession.

*Primary succession* is the colonization of new land, the establishment of the first pioneer communities and the natural changes that culminate in the natural climax community. Sometimes the conditions of secondary succession are very similar to some of the stages of a primary succession, as when abandoned quarries or burnt forest are recolonized, but in general secondary succession begins by modification of an existing community.

## Making new soils

Completely new soils are formed in a surprising variety of ways. Rivers lay down tracts of shingle or mud when they flood; very high tides in estuaries deposit layers of salt mud above the level of all but the highest tides; winds can blow sand inland from the sea shore; when glaciers retreat they expose new rocky ground; the rocks that fall from a mountain or cliff accumulate at the foot as virgin land; volcanoes can suddenly throw up new islands from the sea floor as happened at Surtsey in Iceland; volcanoes can erupt lava; earthquakes can bring buried rocks to the surface and lakes and swamps can silt up.

The species of plants that form the successive communities that colonize such new ground during primary succession depend to a large extent on the geology of the land; species that flourish in a silted lake will differ from those that colonize bare rock. But two other factors, as important as they are obvious, control the composition of the colonizing community. First, only species within a comparatively short distance from the new land will be able to colonize it. Rhododendrons, for example, grow well in many parts of Britain but being natives of the Himalayas they could never have reached Britain without Man's intervention. This brings one to the second point: the seed and spores must be transported to the new land by such agents as wind, birds, animals and streams.

The first or pioneer species to colonize dry, bare, volcanic rock are invariably lichens, algae, bacteria and some mosses, because the spores of these plants are extremely light and easily carried long distances by air currents. Moreover, these species can attach to bare rock, survive droughts and do not need soil to grow. As generations of the pioneer colonizers die their bodies decay, and this decay provides a suitable substitute for bacteria and fungi. In time the decayed plant remains, together with fragments of rock, form a thin film of soil. Other mosses are able to colonize this small amount of soil just as they colonize garden walls; as the cycle of their growth and death continues, more soil slowly builds up until eventually it is deep enough to provide a root hold for a few annual and perennial herbs; snapdragons, for example, will grow out of tiny pockets of soil in walls. Over hundreds of generations the cycle of growth, decomposition and regrowth builds up more soil and humus; stunted trees and bushes get a hold and eventually trees appear if

**1** Stonecrop and pennywort can be found growing on dry rocky or stony ground in temperate countries. These plants have succulent, fleshy leaves in which they can store water.
**2** Beech trees form the backbone of the climax community on chalk soils in temperate zones. Now, because of Man's interference, beech trees tend to exist only in isolated groups.
**3** Birches are often the first trees to colonize light loam soils in temperate climates. Gradually birches are superseded by oak trees, although, as seen here, the two species may co-exist.
**4** Lava from an erupting volcano destroys all life; once cooled, however, it provides virgin soil for plants and later animals. Here life begins again where a chance seed has fallen.
**5** Wood ash makes a soil very fertile and the land is very quickly colonized by vegetation after a forest fire. Grass soon returns, followed by flowers, shrubs and in time trees.
**6** Jervaulx Abbey in Yorkshire was destroyed in the sixteenth century during the Reformation. Since then grasses, willow-herb and shrubs have slowly and inexorably taken over.

the climatic conditions favour tree growth. In any case the climax community will be dominated by the largest plants that can grow in the particular climate. Where the environment to start with, the bare rock, is so dry the succession is called a *xerosere*.

By contrast, the succession that colonizes a moist environment like a silted-up pond or estuary is called a *hydrosere*. Naturally enough the climax community emerges more quickly on the site of a silted lake than on new volcanic lava and the composition of the succeeding communities is very different. However, the climax may be the same as the climax of a nearby xerosere. The colonization of lakes

6

usually begins with the accumulation of submerged aquatic plants, plants with floating leaves and reeds. As these die and rot, the floor of the pond slowly rises until it reaches water surface level. Fen or marsh plants then take over from the aquatic plants; rushes, sedges and mosses establish themselves, and as the soil level continues to rise trees that can tolerate their roots being submerged in water, willows, alders and birch, for example, begin to take over the new soil. The process of raising the soil progresses as more and more plants die and rot, so that trees which need well drained and aerated soil find a place in the community and eventually dominate it.

## National communities

In all parts of the world where the climate is favourable for trees, they eventually dominate the environment; thus the tropics have their rain and monsoon forests, the Mediterranean its laurel evergreen forests, temperate countries their deciduous forests, and countries further north have conifer forests. In arctic regions, tundra is the climax community and in deserts large cacti dominate, but everywhere the dominant species of the climax is the largest species that can grow. Another characteristic of the succeeding communities is the tendency for them to become more closed as the succession moves to the climax. Pioneer communities are open, with individuals scattered here and there separated by stretches of bare soil. As the environment becomes richer in humus it can support more plants; the number of individuals and the number of species increase and the community becomes richer. But then one or a few species become dominant in each particular niche of the environment so that it becomes structured and closed. In other words, once the final climax has been established it becomes very difficult for a new species to enter the closed community.

The colonization of land by plant communities is the most easily observed example of succession, but the same principles pertain to the decomposition of plant and animal remains in the soil by micro-organisms and also to the colonization of the land by animals. The decomposition of leaf litter or pine needles provides a classic example of succession in miniature. Freshly fallen pine needles make a difficult habitat for micro-organisms because the water content and temperature fluctuate very dramatically. The pioneer micro-organisms have therefore to be very tolerant of environmental changes.

As the needles pack down and decomposition proceeds, the environment becomes gentler, insulated from large changes in temperature and much more humid. The dead bodies of the pioneer organisms and the waste products of their metabolism then provide rich food for new species which can enter the community. Chemists have shown, for example, that in composts the amount of vitamin B increases by up to 300 per cent in the first few weeks. Organisms that are dependent on an external supply of such vitamins enter the compost and begin digesting the proteins and starch sugars of the plant cells until they are depleted. As the more fastidious micro-organisms run out of rich pickings, other organisms which can break down the cellulose and lignin of the plant cells then take over. Eventually they deplete the cellulose and lignin and all that is left of the pine needles is organic humus and the remains of the micro-organisms which themselves decay. No climax is reached because none of the micro-organisms can regenerate the cycle by synthesizing sugars from carbon dioxide and water.

The decomposition of animal bodies follows a similar pattern. During the first phase insects, such as ants, feed on blood and other body fluids while bacteria within the corpse rot the tissues. Other insects then colonize the body and their maggots eat away at it as it becomes bloated through the gases given off by decomposition. In the third stage the bloated carcase deflates like a punctured balloon as insect larvae bore holes in it. Fluids escape which are colonized by bacteria. Once the maggots have removed most of the tissue, mites, earwigs and millipedes arrive. These eat the hair, skin and remaining tissue fragments leaving the skeleton picked bare.

All flesh is grass, meaning that all animals rely ultimately on plants for a supply of chemical energy. Plants trap the radiant energy of the sun and convert it into chemical energy on which all living organisms are dependent. Clearly, therefore, as the vegetation changes during succession so must the animal communities living off the vegetation change. In the southeastern states of America, ornithologists have followed the changes in populations of various species of birds as a secondary plant succession converts abandoned grassland over a period of 100 years to deciduous forest by way of shrub land and conifer forest. At the start sparrows and meadow larks in the grasslands are common but quickly disappear as soon as the grassland is colonized by shrubs. These species of birds are replaced by warblers, chats and thrushes. Once the conifers have taken hold, gnatcatchers, wrens and nuthatches arrive, only to be replaced in their turn by warblers, woodpeckers and flycatchers as the deciduous forest community establishes itself as the climax. As this example proves, the successive changes in the plant communities dictate the species composition of the dependent communities of animals.

Succession occurs even in an artificial environment, the species of insects that infest the granaries in the United States, for example, show a regular and predictable succession, despite their never becoming a climax community. All plants and animals living simultaneously in any environment are, in effect, one massive community, each species impinging on one or more of the others in a complex chain of reactions. The plants, ranging from unicellular algae to giant trees, are the primary food producers, while the animals that feed on the plants are the food consumers. Nevertheless, activities of the animals make the environment either more or less suitable for the plants. All organisms are linked by the complex web of food chains. The biologist who knows the species in a community and their part in each food chain can predict the direction in which the community is changing if it has not already reached its climax. Perhaps more important, he can begin to predict the likely consequences of removing or adding species to the community either by accident, as for example, when an environment is polluted, or by design, as for example, when a particular predator is introduced into the environment as a means of controlling the numbers of some species that conflict with Man's particular interests.

A dead animal or plant is quickly torn to bits and decomposed by many different organisms, including insects and bacteria. Here ants drag the carcase of a locust back to their nest.

The locomotive in the Amazon jungle is a silent reminder of the time when these forests were a principal source of rubber. A few more years and the jungle will have reached its climax.

# In the name of progress

**Man deludes himself that anything he does to his world in the name of progress is justified. But this 'progress' is inexorably destroying the environment and paving the way to Man's destruction.**

UNTIL THE 1960s, conservation has been regarded as the concern of slightly eccentric people who, for sentimental reasons, or out of an exaggerated love of the picturesque, wish to conserve old buildings, exotic vegetation, rare wildlife or primitive tribes, all of which have become irrelevant to the modern world and are condemned to extinction by the inexorable march of progress.

Now people are beginning to change their attitudes. They are becoming increasingly aware that we are undergoing an appreciable reduction in the quality of life, and that the tendencies we have so far regarded as 'progress' might well be leading us in the very opposite direction. This is being substantiated by the findings of what used to be an obscure academic discipline called *ecology,* but which has now come into the limelight.

Both these developments – one theoretical and the other empirical – lead to the same conclusion: conservation is not an eccentricity but an absolute necessity, so much so that it should occupy the highest possible priority in the thoughts and actions of governments, educators and the public at large.

What are the principal features of an eco-system? Why and in what way is ours being threatened? And what hope have we of conserving it?

First of all, an eco-system must be regarded as having developed by the process of differentiation. This means that each part has a specific role to fulfil and all are closely dependent on each other. It also means that none is superfluous and none can be destroyed without affecting all the others. Without plants to provide animals with oxygen and herbivores with food, no animals could exist. For their part, animals provide plants with carbon dioxide, nitrates, phosphates and with other nutrients on which the latter feed. Herbivores provide food for predators and they, in turn, keep the population of herbivores in check and weed out the unadaptative ones. Even 'pests', parasites and pathogenic organisms have their place and if they are eliminated, the eco-system can be thrown dangerously out of balance.

## Keeping a balance

In other words, to wipe out an insect, such as the mosquito which transmits malaria, or the tsetse fly which transmits sleeping sickness, may seem necessary for the benefit of the human beings living in areas where the diseases occur, but it is no solution if no account is taken of the increasing numbers of mouths to feed within a few generations.

This is easily understood if it is realized that an eco-system has an optimum structure; there is a correct ratio which must be maintained between its different parts. This means that the size of one part cannot be modified without also changing that of the others. A sudden increase in the number of predators would lead to a reduction in the number of herbivores which, in turn, would lead to a proliferation of the vegetation they feed on, upsetting in this manner the balanced structure of the eco-system. Such accidents are normally avoided in a stable eco-system by a complex set of controls. Thus the numbers of herbivores are kept down, not only by predators but also by a variety of different internal and external parasites, disease-carrying insects as well as by the availability of food and water.

These controls must be just right – they must not be too harsh nor too weak. There must, for instance, be just the right number of predators, no more and no less. The latter must also be kept in check – and the set of controls achieving this is likely to be equally complex, and will itself be dependent on a further set of equally complex controls. In this way, all the parts of an

**1** To clean up its atmosphere Britain has been building taller factory chimneys. This policy has had unfortunate repercussions in Sweden where the factory discharge sometimes falls.
**2** When the *Torrey Canyon* tanker sank the British government used detergent to clear the oil. The detergent proved far more lethal to marine life than the oil itself.

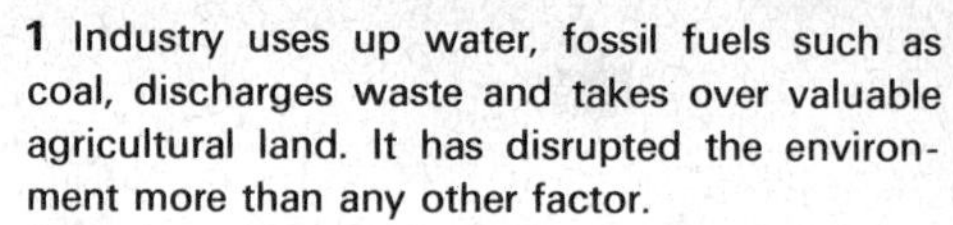

**1** Industry uses up water, fossil fuels such as coal, discharges waste and takes over valuable agricultural land. It has disrupted the environment more than any other factor.
**2** The beautiful Mediterranean has been changed by pollution. Much of the surface of its limpid blue waters is now covered with a thin layer of dirty viscous oil.
**3** In the heat of a summer's day the American city of St Louis, Missouri, is totally enshrouded in a choking smog. Factory smoke and car fumes are the principal culprits.

eco-system are involved in maintaining the other parts at their correct level. From the point of view of the eco-system, the function of each part is to exert some form of control on the others, thereby contributing to the maintenance of the eco-system's balanced structure.

Another feature of an eco-system is that it does not develop in a random manner. Its behaviour is directive in the sense that it tends towards increasing its stability in the face of change; a quality often referred to as *homeostasis*. It tends to achieve this by increasing its complexity and in so doing the parts become more and more specialized. By the same token, their roles become less critical to the eco-system as a whole. If one of the parts is destroyed, or alternatively, if it grows beyond its optimum size, the resulting damage to the eco-system will be correspondingly reduced.

A further characteristic of an eco-system is that its growth, like any other form of growth, involves energy conversion which gives rise to waste. This waste, however, is minimized, mainly because it is *re-cycled* – the waste products of one such process serve as the raw material for another. In this way, what constitutes waste for the eco-system as a whole is but a small percentage of the total energy involved. The oxygen, for instance, which is a waste product of photosynthesis in plants, serves as an essential raw material in the life process of animals.

## Coping with accidents

Finally, an eco-system, like everything else, is subject to accidents. Some of these it can take in its stride; others, if sufficiently unpredictable and of a sufficiently radical nature, can so seriously upset its delicately adjusted balance as to lead to its total breakdown. The eco-system, however, will eventually reconstitute itself but at a much lower level of organization. It will be much simpler and, therefore, capable of supporting a much smaller amount of life and, at the same time, will be far more vulnerable to further changes.

4 Primitive peoples – threatened with extermination – have learnt to live in harmony with their environment. Camiura Indians of Mato Grosso, Brazil, build a dam in the River Xingu to trap fish.
5 Man depends on oil to run industries and to make fertilizers for agriculture. Yet the resources of oil are limited and in the foreseeable future Man will find himself bankrupt.
6 On a single flight a jet airliner burns up huge quantities of oxygen and discharges carbon dioxide. Air travel, with industry and cars, is causing irreparable damage to the environment.

Undoubtedly, the greatest accident of this sort that has ever occurred in the ecosystem that is our world (which is sometimes conveniently referred to as the *ecosphere*) has been the expansion of the human population in recent times, to the detriment of other forms of life. It has been said that Man is Nature's first mistake. He is undoubtedly its most serious one. The extent of this accident is apparent if one considers that it has taken several million years for the human population to attain the figure of 3,500 million but it will take a mere 30 years for another 3,500 million to come into being – for the total population to reach 7,000 million. It is, therefore, evident that the ecological mechanisms that normally control the size of human populations have totally broken down.

Why is this? To answer this question it would probably be necessary to trace the long sequence of events that led up to the agricultural revolution about 11,000 years ago, and undoubtedly those that gave rise to the Industrial Revolution less than two centuries ago. Clearly a most important factor is the development of medicine which has enabled Man to control most of the infectious diseases which once took a very considerable toll among human populations. Another is our growing capacity to produce more food and our ever-greater ability, as a result of the development of industry, to pay for this food.

In addition, this accident has been rendered much more serious by the development of technology. In countries where this has occurred, the depredations made by human populations on their environment have increased in a phenomenal way. The United States, for instance, the most highly industrialized country in the world, which has a little over 6 per cent of the world's population, consumes among other things about three-quarters of the world's softwood, and over a third of the world's energy. It is evident that industry is a great extravagance and can be supported only so long as it is a purely local phenomenon.

It is equally evident that as simple and so-called 'underdeveloped societies' are forced by the 'developed societies' to abandon their ecologically far sounder way of life in order to acquire the 'benefits' of 'civilization' – as they become industrialized – the consequent strains on the already greatly overtaxed ecosphere will be more than it could possibly be expected to support and its very rapid breakdown will be assured.

How is the expanding human population and increased industry affecting the environment? Firstly it is using a very considerable amount of natural resources. Why is this so significant? The answer is that the stock of natural resources is very definitely limited, and rather than living off interest we are rapidly using up our precious capital. Fossil fuels (coal, oil and natural gas), for example, probably accumulated as a result of the death of the vast forests that covered the Earth during the Carboniferous Period 250 million years ago. Now we are simply living off our reserves and we are doing so at an ever-increasing rate. So much so that within the next century, we will probably have exhausted our entire capital.

What is true of fossil fuel is also true of such resources as oxygen. We depend for our supply of this essential commodity on trees and plankton, but forests are being cut down and plankton is being seriously threatened by the pollutants that are being poured into the seas: oil, radioactive

waste, detergents, and, possibly worst of all, DDT. Once more, we are forced to live off our reserves and at the present rate they will probably suffice for but another two centuries.

Much the same can be said of the world's stock of fresh water, top soil and agricultural land, all of which is being seriously overtaxed. We are in fact consuming our environment, of which we are but an integral part and on which we depend for our very survival. But this is not all. The process involved, like all processes, generates waste. When human populations were of a reasonable size, waste products, such as sewage, could be pumped into rivers without their being adversely affected, but once the quantity of sewage becomes greater than the river can absorb, then the whole ecology of the river is seriously modified. Surplus nitrate and phosphate build up, which leads to a proliferation of algae. When these die and putrify, they use up all available oxygen and the river becomes choked, deteriorating into a marsh incapable of supporting complex forms of life. It appears that, at the present rate, every main waterway in North America will become totally polluted in this manner by the late 1980s.

This problem becomes much worse when the waste products of industry are added to those of human life processes. Detergents, noxious man-made chemical substances of all types, add to the water pollution, rendering it even less suitable for the maintenance of life. What is happening to the rivers is also happening to the seas, the land and the air. Worse still, we are introducing new types of pollutant, such as insecticides, the purpose of which is to compensate for the breakdown of the natural mechanisms which, in a balanced eco-system, would control the growth of insects and which, as a result of human intervention, have ceased to be effective. These indiscriminate killers reduce photosynthesis in plants, destroy all sorts of insects and birds that fulfil essential ecological functions and, as experiments are revealing, probably also induce malignant tumours in Man.

We are also affecting our environment in another way: by simplifying it, and hence not only reducing the amount of life it can support but also making it less and less stable in the face of change.

This we are doing in many ways, for instance by extending *monoculture* – the practice of putting vast areas under a single crop – and by substituting cattle for complex populations of grazers, by replacing the natural mechanisms designed to control insect populations by the use of insecticides and in countless other ways.

## No 'new' environment

In spite of all this, some people continue to maintain that the destruction of our environment is of no great consequence, since technology will enable us to build a new and 'controlled' environment, far more adapted to the needs of modern Man. Unfortunately, this is a vain illusion, as there are insuperable theoretical reasons why technology cannot effectively replace the ecosphere that we are destroying.

Firstly, the natural resources are not available. Secondly, technological processes are less efficient than 'natural' ones, and generate much more waste. Thirdly, 'controlled' environment would be vastly simpler than a natural one and correspondingly more vulnerable to unexpected change.

Thus, once we depend on factories to produce our oxygen, to filter out carbon dioxide from our polluted air, and to transform the sea into drinking water, the slightest technical hitch or industrial dispute might well spell the end of life on our planet.

Are we to conclude from this depressing picture that mankind is doomed and that within a few decades the human species will have disappeared from the face of the Earth? According to many of the foremost ecologists, such as Barry Commoner and Paul Ehrlich, this is a distinct possibility. Daniel Moynahon, President Nixon's adviser on urban affairs, has said that he considered Man had no more than a fifty-fifty chance of surviving until the middle of the 1990s.

Whether he survives or not depends on a number of factors. Firstly, it depends on the ability of scientists to develop a unified science so that it becomes possible to build a model of the ecosphere as a whole, including the human societies that it contains, permitting the precise prediction of any local change on the ecosphere as a whole.

At the moment, scientists are each concerned with tiny specialized sections of the ecosphere. Since this constitutes an integrated whole whose parts are all interrelated, by examining them in isolation scientists are inevitably obtaining a distorted view of them.

Even more important, a radical change is required in the set of values that makes up the culture of our industrial society. We must, among other things, develop a goal-structure which in itself does not lead to the destruction and pollution of the environment. This clearly involves recognizing that Man is not the centre of all things, that the world was not simply created to satisfy his cravings for more and more short-term satisfactions, and that the conservation of the environment is essential for his survival.

Is such a set of values likely to develop? It is undoubtedly the case that our culture is breaking down and, in the accompanying social disorder, our alienated youth is frenziedly seeking a set of values which will provide it with a cause to which it can wholeheartedly devote itself. The adoption of most of those they are at present toying with would do little to solve our present plight. However, there are growing signs that the conservation of the environment might well form the basis of a new and perhaps successful movement. Many governments are now concerned about the problems of controlling industrial pollutants, the indiscriminate use of fertilizers and pesticides and the long-term effects on human populations, and are instigating research for remedies and alternatives. If these are effective, and if a new set of cultural values underlying such a movement gives rise to a behaviour pattern on the part of human societies corresponding to their modest but essential function within a balanced ecosphere – then Man might well indeed survive.

1 By forcing a passage through polar ice the *Manhattan* proves the feasibility of shipping oil from Alaska. Should such a tanker be holed, the oil pollution would be disastrous.

2 Nuclear reactors, like this complex at Dungeness, Kent, use huge amounts of seawater for cooling. When the warm water is returned, it causes changes to the life in the sea.

1

2

# Animals sacred and divine

Man has regarded many animals with superstition and awe. Some were treated with honour to gain control over them, while others were worshipped for the gods believed to be incarnate in them.

THE OLDEST KNOWN PAINTINGS are the cave paintings of southern France and Spain. The Palaeolithic, or Old Stone Age artists, who so exquisitely decorated the walls of their cave homes at such places as Lascaux and Altamira, almost exclusively painted animals. They seem to have concentrated either on food animals, reindeer, bison, mammoth, fish and the occasional bird or reptile, or else on dangerous animals, such as lions and bears. Human figures are rarely portrayed; when they are, the human figures are much more crudely drawn than the animals and sometimes even partially disguised as animals as, for example, in the cave of Les Trois Frères at Ariège in France where a sorcerer is depicted with antler heads.

Why were Old Stone Age artists so preoccupied with drawing animals? The answer is certainly not because the artists lacked the technique necessary for human portraiture or landscape painting. More likely they were painting the things most important to their lives. Living entirely at the mercy of their environment, more often than not a hostile one, the cave painters may have had some vague idea that by painting animals they somehow obtained some control over them. By painting a bison, perhaps, the Stone Age artist thought he was ensuring his next meal.

The cave paintings, the clay models of animals and the engravings of animals, such as bison on spear heads, suggest that Stone Age Man believed in sympathetic magic, just as Australian aborigines, still living in a Stone Age culture, believe in it. Moreover, some of the cave mural art suggests that Stone Age Man in Europe, like many contemporary primitive societies, believed in totems. It is not too far-fetched to suggest, therefore, that Stone Age cave art is the first example of sacred art.

Nothing can be sacred without a religion but religions, as we now understand them, are very sophisticated systems of ideas. In the broadest terms, religion means the acceptance and worship of powers superior to Man's, beyond Man's control, which control all nature. Such sophisticated ideas must have evolved slowly in Man's mind and most anthropologists believe religion was preceded by, and grew out of, sympathetic magic. Contemporary primitive people, such as Australian aborigines, believe in magic but have no concept of religion in the sense defined here.

What do we mean by sympathetic magic; for it certainly has nothing to do with conjuring rabbits out of a hat? Sympathetic magic is the belief that either things which resemble each other are each other, or that once things have been in contact they remain forever in contact. For example, the magic of similarity maintains that a model or painting of an animal or person is that animal or person, and control over a model or painting is equivalent to control over the real object or creature. On the other hand, in the magic of contact part of a person, his hair or teeth, for example, remain part of that person forever, even when they have been cut off or extracted. Any harm to cut hair results in harm to the person to whom the hair once belonged. It seems that both religion and the worship of animals arose from these magical beliefs.

The aim of sympathetic magic is to obtain control over the environment. Nootka Indians in British Columbia used, for example, to put a model of a fish into a river or the sea firmly believing that this would bring the real fish to that spot. It cannot have taken long, however, for the more intelligent members of such a culture to realize that sympathetic magic was really a fraud in that it gave no real control over the environment. Such people had come face to face with the awful realization that powers beyond their

1 A Hindu temple in Benares is dedicated to Hanuman – a monkey god renowned for faithfully serving the god Rama. Real monkeys have invaded the temple from nearby trees.

2 Many Hindu tribes are pastoral and they came to revere the cow because it supplied them with milk. The Hindus still hold the cow sacred and they will not harm or kill one.

3 The Romans sacrificed bulls and all kinds of animals to their gods to appease them. The priest performing the rites also looked at the intestines for signs of the god's favour.

understanding and their control governed nature. The only road to survival, let alone salvation, was to worship these superhuman powers in whatever form they seemed to assume and, in many cases, that must have been in animal form. The annual spawning of salmon, the migration of game animals and the like were outside the control of sympathetic magic; the only thing to do was worship those animals to ensure they came each year or each day.

Stone Age cave painters were preoccupied with food animals and dangerous animals of prey. To the primitive mind a soul is something common to all creation and is not unique to Man. Animals have souls and even plants can have souls in the mind of an Australian aborigine, for example. But if animals have a soul, how can Man justify hunting and killing them for food? He is killing a soul which may fly off and warn all the other animals that Man is a danger to be avoided. Primitive Man's answer to these problems is to worship both the animals he feeds off and the animals of which he is frightened. In one case he worships his food animals almost as an apology to them for having to kill them; in the other case he worships animals he is frightened of to buy off their predations on him.

1

### Honouring the corpse

Many tribes of North American Indians used to worship their game. When the Nootka Indians, for example, killed a bear they brought it before their chief, dressing the bear in a chief's head-dress, covering it with down and treating it with great reverence before eating it. When some tribes in Africa kill a lion, they honour the corpse; the chief grovels before it, rubs his face against its muzzle and so on, before the feast begins. In America, Blackfoot Indians, when they caught an eagle, took its body to a special enclosure and stuck pieces of meat in its beak. They hoped the eagle's spirit would fly off and tell all the other eagles how well Man treated the species.

These examples show primitive Man's common belief in and worship of the souls of his dead food. In all cases Man is saying: 'We are sorry we have to kill you, but look we treat you with honour.' And often primitive Man treated the bones of his game with great respect. American Plains Indians never burnt or threw the bones of game to dogs lest the souls of the dead animals saw the desecration and warned their still living fellows. The Kwatiutl Indians in British Columbia even went to the lengths of throwing the offal and bones of salmon they caught back into the sea so that they would be ready at the resurrection of the salmon. The idea that bones of animals might eventually be reclothed in flesh gave the hunter a good reason for preserving them.

In some cultures, amongst the Aino, for example, the idea of propitiating the food animals has resulted in rearing a few members of the species in luxurious captivity. The Aino rear bears in this way, treating them with the utmost honour and killing them when they grow too old with great marks of sorrow and devotion, in a religious ceremony.

Worshipping animals of prey is the other side of the coin. The idea is to appease the frightening animal and, perhaps, try and capture some of its powers. People who worship the lion may expect not only to be free from attacks by lions but also perhaps to gain some of the animals' strength and courage. In general primitive Man makes it a rule to spare the life of animals that are of no great use to him or frighten him. He gives the animals no cause to exact a bloody vengeance and may even go to the lengths of sacrificing a food animal or something else he treasures to the fierce animal.

These two sorts of animal worship, propitiating food animals and buying off animals of prey, were probably the earliest forms of animal worship. But a more sophisticated form involves regarding as sacred a certain species of animal and yet periodically killing specimens with great ritual and pomp. Many peoples have wor-

2

3

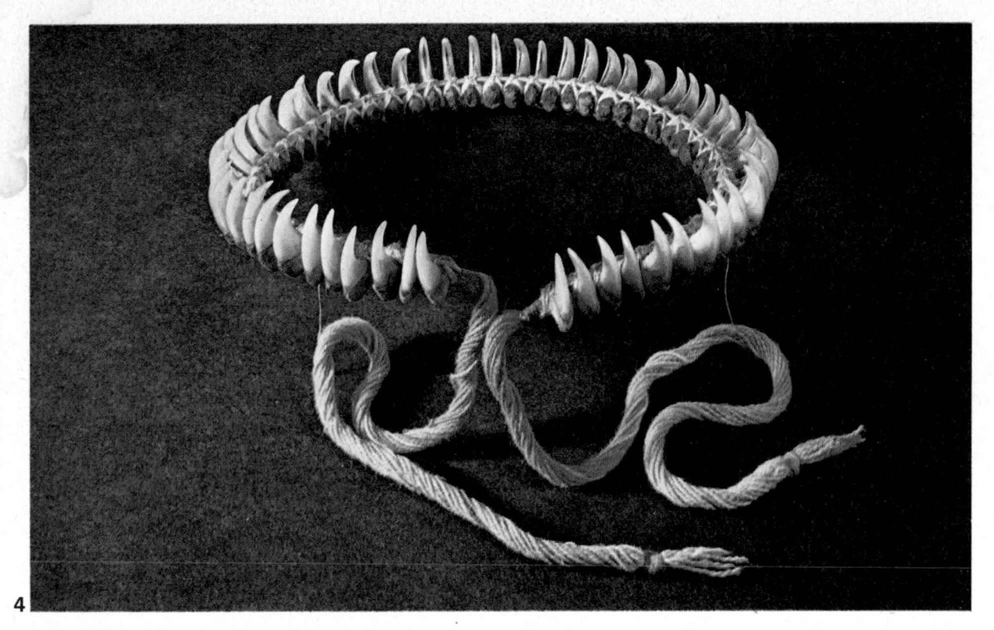

1 'Lung-Ma', a Chinese dragon-horse beautifully carved in jade. In China the dragon was regarded as a good spirit of the sky, dwelling either in the clouds or in the waters.
2 The North American Mandan Indians worshipped the rattlesnake because of its fearsome qualities. By making themselves resemble a rattlesnake they hoped to capture its spirit.
3 With a lion's head on his bronze shield a Celtic warrior hopes to imbue himself with the lion's fierceness and prowess.
4 Jaguars' claws are more than a symbol of strength and ferocity; they are believed to embody the spirit of the animal. The South American Indian wearing them is protected from harm.
5 The Hindu god Vishnu has many different incarnations – or *avatars*. Many of these were in animal form, such as the three represented here: bull, fish and boar.

shipped a particular animal, not because of its food value or its fierceness, but for some other quality they greatly admire. The Acagcheman Indians in California, for example, adored the great buzzard. It is easy enough to see why a primitive people should deify a powerful bird of prey that controls the skies – an element they cannot enter. Yet once a year these Indians ritualistically slaughtered a buzzard.

In ancient Egypt, people at a much higher level of civilization sacrificed a sacred animal once a year. The Thebans, who worshipped Ammon, held rams sacred to the god and would not eat them, but once a year rams were slaughtered and statues of the god clothed in their fleeces. In much the same way, West African Negroes on the island of Fernando Po worshipped the capella cobra but made a yearly sacrifice. Incidentally, snakes have been more widely worshipped than any other animal.

Whatever significance such ceremonies may have acquired in more advanced cultures their origins must be in the primitive fear that, without the sacrifice of an individual, the sacred animal species would somehow go into a decline. To keep the species young, to rejuvenate it each year, a member of the species must be killed. The soul of the slaughtered animal, or animals, can then migrate into a young

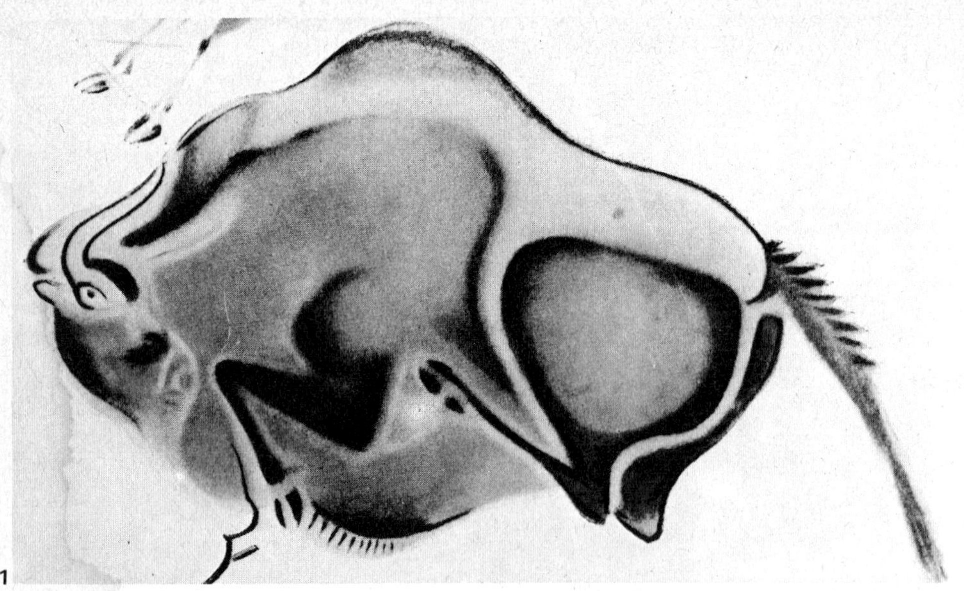

1 By painting in his caves the animals he preyed upon, such as bison, Stone Age Man believed that he in some way had gained control over them and they would be easier to capture.

2 The mandrake is a plant with special narcotic properties. The roots resemble human forms when split and it was believed that it screamed when pulled from the ground.

animal and so ensure perpetuation of the species for another year.

Apart from the worship of food animals and animals of prey the other chief fountainhead of animal worship is *totemism.* Few peoples still believe in totems but in the past totemism was certainly practised in parts of all the continents; according to some authorities, the French and Spanish cave artists of the Stone Age probably had totems and the great pantheon of animal gods in ancient Egypt probably had its roots in totemism.

What is a totem? The word itself comes from the American Ojibway Indian word *ototeman* which literally means 'his brother sister kin'. In practice totems were often a species of animals with which primitive Man believed he had an intimate and altogether special relationship. The belief in totems seems to stem from the idea that a man's soul can temporarily leave his body, without causing death, and reside in some other object, plant or animal. So long as the man's soul is safe in its new receptacle, he is safe. If the animal with his soul is not harmed he cannot be harmed but when the animal or totem is killed, for example, he will suffer and perhaps die. Totemism is a way of safeguarding the soul, almost a route to immortality. In practice it results in a man, a family, a group of families or a clan regarding a particular species of animal, their totem, as sacred. The aborigines on the Murray River in Australia, for example, believed that bats were the totem of men and owls the totem of women. The men would never kill owls; the women would never kill bats. In India the Bhil peoples had as a totem the peacock; they offered grain to the birds, never put their own feet on the footprints of a peacock and never allowed the women to look at the birds.

A taboo on killing the totem animal usually meant that the animal was never eaten; other ceremonies often developed around the totem, including depicting the totem in art, magical ceremonies to gain control over it, sacrifices to it and sometimes sacrifice of the totem species itself accompanied by elaborate ceremonies and mourning. Often peoples who believed in totems subjected boys, and sometimes girls, when they reached puberty to initiation rites. The boy would pretend to be dead, go into a trance, presumably signifying the flight of his soul to the sacred totem animal. He would then slowly come back to life, presumably signifying the drawing of fresh life from the totem.

Although totemism sounds primitive, it probably served the useful purpose of preventing inbreeding. A member of one totem clan was often prohibited from marrying someone of the same totem. And totemism is probably the roots of the animal cults in more civilized societies.

## Changing gods

The pantheon of the ancient Egypt of the Pharaohs is outstanding for the confusion of animal gods and animal cults it contained. It seems that as successive waves of peoples moved from the Near East into Egypt they brought their primitive totemic beliefs with them. The history of Osiris and Isis, the two most famous Egyptian gods, is as good an example as any of this process. Osiris, the father god, and Isis, the mother god, probably originated in Syria where they were worshipped and depicted as superhuman, and were, no doubt, mainly agricultural deities. When introduced into Egypt they became associated with a whole series of locally worshipped animal gods. Osiris seems first to have been associated with the goat and then with two native Egyptian gods, Sakri the hawk and Hapi or Api the bull, and finally Osiris ended up associated with an Egyptian god of the dead ruling the underworld.

Isis went through much the same sort of process. In the pantheon of ancient Egypt the animal gods Thoth, Hathor, Hapi and so on were all indigenous to the Nilotic region, probably vestiges of totemism. And in most cases the connection between the animal god and the faculty he represented is clear enough. Thoth, for example, was god of intelligence whose animals were the ape and the ibis. What could be more appropriate? The ape can parody human behaviour and the ibis is a bird with a long bill which it inquisitively pokes around searching for food. Similarly one of the animals of Horus, god of the skies, was the hawk or falcon, and the cat goddess, Bastet, was the god of love, fashion and feminine matters. Having decided to worship such things as the skies, intelligence and love, it is easy to see how people associated animals which appear to have these properties with the god, so that the god became incarnate in the animal, which is therefore sacred. Animal worship was not restricted to Egypt. In India the pious Hindu worships the cow. Siva, another Hindu deity, is incarnate in the monkey, and the wise Ganesh in the elephant. Just as totemism holds that Man can put his soul in an animal, these animal cults reveal belief that gods can become incarnate as animals.

Now, especially in Christian countries, animal worship may seem a primitive form of religion, but a surprising number of vestiges of animal as well as plant worship survive. One example is the Christmas mistletoe. The raven, Woden's bird, so the story goes, was once white but turned black at the Crucifixion, and the wren was especially reverenced in much of Europe as the king of the birds. Hunting the wren on Christmas Day or Boxing Day, as late as the nineteenth century, was common in parts of Britain. The bird, which was never touched for the rest of the year for fear of bad luck, was hunted at Christmas and its dead body paraded around the village. This ceremony, no doubt, harked back to pagan days. The robin became sacred for having taken a thorn from Christ's brow which dripped blood and turned the robin's breast red. Such ancient beliefs as animism are a long time dying.

# INDEX

# A

# B



# C

# F



# G

# H



# I

# J



# K



# L

# M

# N



# O



# P

# R

# S

# T



# U



# V